Your steps to success.

STEP 1: Register

All you need to get started is a valid email address and the access code below. To register, simply:

1. Go to www.campbellbiology.com
2. Click the appropriate book cover.
   Cover must match the textbook edition being used for your class.
3. Click **"Register"** under **"First-Time User?"**
4. Leave **"No, I Am a New User"** selected.
5. Using a coin, scratch off the silver coating below to reveal your access code.
   Do not use a knife or other sharp object, which can damage the code.
6. Enter your access code in lowercase or uppercase, without the dashes.
7. Follow the on-screen instructions to complete registration.
   During registration, you will establish a personal login name and password to use for logging into the website. You will also be sent a registration confirmation email that contains your login name and password.

Your Access Code is:

USCABI-PRANK-KEVEL-FRIED-RUGBY-HIKES

Note: If there is no silver foil covering the access code, it may already have been redeemed, and therefore may no longer be valid. In that case, you can purchase access online using a major credit card. To do so, go to www.campbellbiology.com, click the cover of your textbook, click **"Buy Now"**, and follow the on-screen instructions.

STEP 2: Log in

1. Go to www.campbellbiology.com and click the appropriate book cover.
2. Under **"Established User?"** enter the login name and password that you created during registration. *If unsure of this information, refer to your registration confirmation email.*
3. Click **"Log In"**.

STEP 3: (Optional) Join a class

Instructors have the option of creating an online class for you to use with this website. If your instructor decides to do this, you'll need to complete the following steps using the Class ID your instructor provides you. By "joining a class," you enable your instructor to view the scored results of your work on the website in his or her online gradebook.

To join a class:

1. Log into the website. For instructions, see "STEP 2: Log in."
2. Click **"Join a Class"** near the top left.
3. Enter your instructor's **"Class ID"** and then click **"Next"**.
4. At the Confirm Class page you will see your instructor's name and class information. If this information is correct, click Next.
5. Click **"Enter Class Now"** from the Class Confirmation page.

• *To confirm your enrollment in the class, check for your instructor and class name at the top right of the page. You will be sent a class enrollment confirmation email.*

• *As you complete activities on the website from now through the class end date, your results will post to your instructor's gradebook, in addition to appearing in your personal view of the Results Reporter.*

To log into the class later, follow the instructions under "STEP 2: Log in."

Got technical questions?

Visit http://247.aw.com. Email technical support is available 24/7.

SITE REQUIREMENTS

For the latest updates on Site Requirements, go to www.campbellbiology.com, choose your text cover, and click Site Reqs.

WINDOWS
366 MHz CPU
Windows 98/2000/XP
64 MB RAM
800 x 600 screen resolution, thousands of colors
Browser: Internet Explorer 5.0/5.5/6.0; Netscape 6.2.3 and 7.0
Plug-Ins: Shockwave Player 8, Flash Player 7, QuickTime 5
Internet Connection: 56k modem minimum

MACINTOSH
266 MHz PowerPC
OS 9.2/10.2.4/10.3.2
64 MB RAM
800 x 600 screen resolution, thousands of colors
Browsers: Internet Explorer 5.1/5.2; Netscape 6.2.3; Safari 1.2*
Plug-Ins: Shockwave Player 8, Flash Player 6, QuickTime 5
Internet Connection: 56k modem minimum

* The gradebook and class manager features of this website have been partially tested on Mac OS X 10.3.2 with Safari 1.2. A future update will fully support this configuration.

Register and log in

Join a class

Important: Please read the Subscription and End-User License agreement, accessible from the book website's login page, before using the Campbell Biology website and CD-ROM. By using the website or CD-ROM, you indicate that you have read, understood, and accepted the terms of this agreement.

Cover image courtesy of Susan Bishop/Papilio/Corbis Images.

Taken from:

Biology, Seventh Edition
by Neil A. Campbell and Jane B. Reece
Copyright © 2005 by Pearson Education, Inc.
Published by Benjamin Cummings
San Francisco, California 94111

This special edition published in cooperation with Pearson Custom Publishing.

Printed in the United States of America

10 9 8 7 6 5 4 3 2 1

ISBN 0-536-94656-6

2005140236

LW/CS

Please visit our web site at *www.pearsoncustom.com*

PEARSON CUSTOM PUBLISHING
75 Arlington Street, Suite 300, Boston, MA 02116
A Pearson Education Company

BIOLOGY

Custom Edition for University of Missouri – Kansas City

CAMPBELL • REECE

Volume 1

Taken from:
Biology, Seventh Edition
by Neil A. Campbell and Jane B. Reece

PEARSON
Custom Publishing

PEARSON
Benjamin
Cummings

This special edition published in cooperation with Pearson Custom Publishing.

Printed in the United States of America

10 9 8 7 6 5 4 3 2 1

ISBN 0-536-94656-6

2005140236

LW/CS

Please visit our web site at *www.pearsoncustom.com*

PEARSON CUSTOM PUBLISHING
75 Arlington Street, Suite 300, Boston, MA 02116
A Pearson Education Company

About the Authors

Neil A. Campbell combined the investigative nature of a research scientist with the soul of an experienced and caring teacher. He earned his M.A. in Zoology from UCLA and his Ph.D. in Plant Biology from the University of California, Riverside, where he received the Distinguished Alumnus Award in 2001. Dr. Campbell published numerous research articles on how certain desert and coastal plants thrive in salty soil and how the sensitive plant (*Mimosa*) and other legumes move their leaves. His 30 years of teaching in diverse environments included general biology courses at Cornell University, Pomona College, and San Bernardino Valley College, where he received the college's first Outstanding Professor Award in 1986. Most recently Dr. Campbell was a visiting scholar in the Department of Botany and Plant Sciences at the University of California, Riverside. In addition to his authorship of this book, he coauthored *Biology: Concepts and Connections* and *Essential Biology* with Jane Reece. Each year, over 600,000 students worldwide use Campbell/Reece biology textbooks.

Jane B. Reece has worked in biology publishing since 1978, when she joined the editorial staff of Benjamin Cummings. Her education includes an A.B. in Biology from Harvard University, an M.S. in Microbiology from Rutgers University, and a Ph.D. in Bacteriology from the University of California, Berkeley. At UC Berkeley, and later as a postdoctoral fellow in genetics at Stanford University, her research focused on genetic recombination in bacteria. She taught biology at Middlesex County College (New Jersey) and Queensborough Community College (New York). As an editor at Benjamin Cummings, Dr. Reece played major roles in a number of successful textbooks. In addition to being a coauthor with Neil Campbell on *BIOLOGY*, *Biology: Concepts and Connections*, and *Essential Biology*, she coauthored *The World of the Cell*, Third Edition, with W. M. Becker and M. F. Poenie.

To Rochelle and Allison, with love

—N.A.C.

To Paul and Daniel, with love

—J.B.R.

NEIL A. CAMPBELL
died October 21, 2004 after finishing work on this revision.
He is deeply mourned by his many friends and colleagues
at Benjamin Cummings and
throughout the biology community.

Preface

Charles Darwin described evolution as a process of "descent with modification." It is a phrase that also fits the continuing evolution of *BIOLOGY*. This Seventh Edition is our most ambitious revision of the book since its origin—a new textbook "species" with several evolutionary adaptations shaped by the changing environment of biology courses and by the astonishing progress of biological research. But these adaptive modifications are still true to the two complementary teaching values at the core of every edition of *BIOLOGY*. First, we are dedicated to crafting each chapter from a framework of key concepts that will help students keep the details in place. Second, we are committed to engaging students in scientific inquiry through a combination of diverse examples of biologists' research and opportunities for students to practice inquiry themselves.

These dual emphases on concept building and scientific inquiry emerged from our decades of classroom experience. It is obviously gratifying that our approach has had such broad appeal to the thousands of instructors and millions of students who have made *BIOLOGY* the most widely used college science textbook. But with this privilege of sharing biology with so many students comes the responsibility to continue improving the book to serve the biology community even better. As we planned this new edition, we visited dozens of campuses to hear what students and their instructors had to say about their biology courses and textbooks. What we learned from those conversations about new directions in biology courses and the changing needs of students informed the many improvements you'll find in this Seventh Edition of *BIOLOGY*.

We have restructured each chapter to bring its key concepts into even sharper focus

The discovery explosion that makes modern biology so exciting also threatens to suffocate students under an avalanche of information. The past few editions of *BIOLOGY* set the details in a context of key concepts, typically ten to twenty per chapter. In this new edition, we have taken the next evolutionary step of restructuring each chapter to help students focus on fewer, even bigger ideas—typically just five or six key concepts per chapter. A new Overview section at the beginning of each chapter sets an even broader context for the key concepts that follow. And at the end of each of the concept sections, a Concept Check with two or three questions enables students to assess whether they understand that concept before going on to the next. Answers to the Concept Check questions are located in Appendix A, as are the answers to the Self-Quizzes from the Chapter Review at the end of each chapter.

In our ongoing interactions with students and instructors, they have responded enthusiastically to our new organization and pedagogy. Compared to other textbooks, including earlier editions of our own, students have found the new chapter structure and design of *BIOLOGY*, Seventh Edition, to be more inviting, more accessible, and much more efficient to use. But in achieving these goals, we have not compromised the depth and scientific accuracy the biology community has come to expect from us.

Key Concepts keep the supporting details in context.

The **Overview** sets the stage for the rest of the chapter.

Figure references in color help students move easily between text and figures.

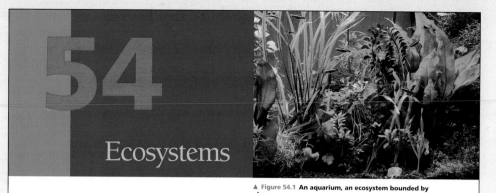

54

Ecosystems

▲ Figure 54.1 **An aquarium, an ecosystem bounded by glass.**

Key Concepts

54.1 Ecosystem ecology emphasizes energy flow and chemical cycling

54.2 Physical and chemical factors limit primary production in ecosystems

54.3 Energy transfer between trophic levels is usually less than 20% efficient

54.4 Biological and geochemical processes move nutrients between organic and inorganic parts of the ecosystem

54.5 The human population is disrupting chemical cycles throughout the biosphere

Overview

Ecosystems, Energy, and Matter

An **ecosystem** consists of all the organisms living in a community as well as all the abiotic factors with which they interact. Ecosystems can range from a microcosm, such as the aquarium in **Figure 54.1**, to a large area such as a lake or forest. As with populations and communities, the boundaries of ecosystems are usually not discrete. Cities and farms are examples of human-dominated ecosystems. Many ecologists regard the entire biosphere as a global ecosystem, a composite of all the local ecosystems on Earth.

Regardless of an ecosystem's size, its dynamics involve two processes that cannot be fully described by population or community processes and phenomena: energy flow and chemical cycling. Energy enters most ecosystems in the form of sunlight. It is then converted to chemical energy by au-

among abiotic and biotic components of the ecosystem. Photosynthetic organisms assimilate these elements in inorganic form from the air, soil, and water and incorporate them into organic molecules, some of which are consumed by animals. The elements are returned in inorganic form to the air, soil, and water by the metabolism of plants and animals and by other organisms, such as bacteria and fungi, that break down organic wastes and dead organisms.

Both energy and matter move through ecosystems via the transfer of substances during photosynthesis and feeding relationships. However, because energy, unlike matter, cannot be recycled, an ecosystem must be powered by a continuous influx of energy from an external source—in most cases, the sun. Energy flows through ecosystems, while matter cycles within them.

Resources critical to human survival and welfare, ranging from the food we eat to the oxygen we breathe, are products of ecosystem processes. In this chapter, we will explore the dynamics of energy flow and chemical cycling in ecosystems and consider some of the impacts of human activities on these processes.

Concept 54.1

Ecosystem ecology emphasizes energy flow and chemical cycling

Ecosystem ecologists view ecosystems as transformers of energy and processors of matter. By grouping the species in a community into trophic levels of feeding relationships (see ... transformation of energy in ... ments of chemical elements

Each numbered **Concept Head** announces the beginning of a new concept section.

Concept Check 54.1

1. Why is the transfer of energy in an ecosystem referred to as energy flow, not energy cycling?
2. How does the second law of thermodynamics explain why an ecosystem's energy supply must be continually replenished?
3. How are detritivores essential to sustaining ecosystems?

For suggested answers, see Appendix A.

Concept Check Questions at the end of each concept section encourage students to assess their mastery of the concept.

Concept 54.2

Physical and chemical factors limit primary production in ecosystems

The amount of light energy converted to chemical energy (organic compounds) by autotrophs during a given time period is an ecosystem's **primary production**. This photosynthetic product is the starting point for studies of ecosystem metabolism and energy flow.

Ecosystem Energy Budgets

Most primary producers use light energy to synthesize energy-rich organic molecules, which can subsequently be broken down to generate ATP (see Chapter 10). Consumers acquire their organic fuels secondhand (or even third- or fourthhand) through food webs such as that in Figure 53.13. Therefore, the extent of photosynthetic production sets the spending limit for the energy budget of the entire ecosystem.

▲ Figure 54.3 **Fungi decomposing a dead tree.**

consumers in an ecosystem. In a forest, for example, birds might feed on earthworms that have been feeding on leaf litter and its associated prokaryotes and fungi. But even more important than this channeling of resources from producers to consumers is the role that detritivores play in making vital chemical ele... available to producers.

D... the organic material in an e... ...ents in inor... ...bombarded...

Global Energy Budget

New "Exploring Figures" provide efficient access to many complex topics

Biology is a visual science. Thus we have always authored *BIOLOGY's* graphics and narrative side by side to coordinate their message. In the Seventh Edition, this text-art integration reaches its next evolutionary level with a new feature called "Exploring Figures." Each of these large figures is a learning unit that brings together a set of related illustrations and the text that describes them. The Exploring Figures enable students to access dozens of complex topics much more efficiently, now that the textual and visual components have merged.

The Exploring Figures represent core chapter content, not to be confused with some textbooks' "boxes," which feature content that is peripheral to the flow of a chapter. Modern biology is challenging enough without diverting students' attention from a chapter's conceptual storyline. Thus, each Exploring Figure is referenced in the main text body where it fits into the development of a concept, just as the text points students to all the other supporting figures at the appropriate places in the narrative.

In **Exploring Figures**, art, photos, and text are fully integrated.

Figure 6.31

Exploring **Intercellular Junctions in Animal Tissues**

Tight junction

Tight junctions prevent fluid from moving across a layer of cells

Tight junctions

Intermediate filaments

Desmosome

Gap junctions

Space between cells

Plasma membranes of adjacent cells

Extracellular matrix

Gap junction

0.5 μm

1 μm

0.1 μm

TIGHT JUNCTIONS

At **tight junctions**, the membranes of neighboring cells are very tightly pressed against each other, bound together by specific proteins (purple). Forming continuous seals around the cells, tight junctions prevent leakage of extracellular fluid across a layer of epithelial cells.

DESMOSOMES

Desmosomes (also called *anchoring junctions*) function like rivets, fastening cells together into strong sheets. Intermediate filaments made of sturdy keratin proteins anchor desmosomes in the cytoplasm.

GAP JUNCTIONS

Gap junctions (also called *communicating junctions*) provide cytoplasmic channels from one cell to an adjacent cell. Gap junctions consist of special membrane proteins that surround a pore through which ions, sugars, amino acids, and other small molecules may pass. Gap junctions are necessary for communication between cells in many types of tissues, including heart muscle and animal embryos.

Scientific inquiry is more prominent than ever in *BIOLOGY* and its supplements

One objective for many biology instructors is for students to learn to think as scientists. In both the lecture hall and laboratory, colleagues are experimenting with diverse approaches for involving students in scientific inquiry, in which questions about nature focus strategic investigation and analysis of data. New textbook features and new inquiry-based supplements make this edition of *BIOLOGY* more effective than ever as a partner to instructors who emphasize the process of science.

Modeling Inquiry by Example

Scientific inquiry has always been one of *BIOLOGY*'s unifying themes. Each edition has traced the history of many research questions and scientific debates to help students appreciate not just "what we know," but "how we know," and "what we do not yet know." In *BIOLOGY*, Seventh Edition, we have strengthened this theme by making examples of scientific inquiry much more prominent throughout the book.

The increased emphasis on inquiry begins in Chapter 1, where we have thoroughly revised the introduction to the many ways that scientists explore biological questions. Chapter 1 also introduces a new feature called "Inquiry Figures," which showcase outstanding examples of experiments and field studies in a format that is consistent throughout the book. Complementing the Inquiry Figures are the new "Research Method Figures," which walk students through the techniques and tools of modern biology. You can find a list of the Inquiry and Research Method Figures on pages xx-xxi. These new features, like the Exploring Figures, are integral to chapter flow rather than being appended as boxed asides.

New **Inquiry Figures** and **Research Method Figures** help students learn to think like scientists.

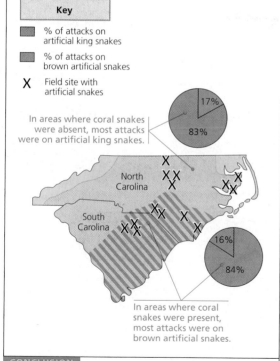

Figure 1.29

Inquiry **Does the presence of poisonous coral snakes affect predation rates on their mimics, king snakes?**

EXPERIMENT David Pfennig and his colleagues made artificial snakes to test a prediction of the mimicry hypothesis: that king snakes benefit from mimicking the warning coloration of coral snakes *only* in regions where poisonous coral snakes are present. The Xs on the map below are field sites where the researchers placed equal numbers of artificial king snakes (experimental group) and brown artificial snakes (control group). The researchers recovered the artificial snakes after four weeks and tabulated predation data based on teeth and claw marks on the snakes (see Figure 1.28).

RESULTS In field sites where coral snakes were present, predators attacked far fewer artificial king snakes than brown artificial snakes. The warning coloration of the "king snakes" afforded no such protection where coral snakes were absent. In fact, at those field sites, the artificial king snakes were *more* likely to be attacked than the brown artificial snakes, perhaps because the bright pattern is particularly easy to spot against the background.

Key

% of attacks on artificial king snakes

% of attacks on brown artificial snakes

X Field site with artificial snakes

In areas where coral snakes were absent, most attacks were on artificial king snakes.

17%
83%

North Carolina

South Carolina

16%
84%

In areas where coral snakes were present, most attacks were on brown artificial snakes.

CONCLUSION The field experiments support the mimicry hypothesis by not falsifying the key prediction that imitation of coral snakes is only effective where coral snakes are present. The experiments also tested an alternative hypothesis that predators generally avoid all snakes with brightly colored rings, whether or not poisonous snakes with that coloration live in the environment. That alternative hypothesis was falsified by the data showing that the ringed coloration failed to repel predators where coral snakes were absent.

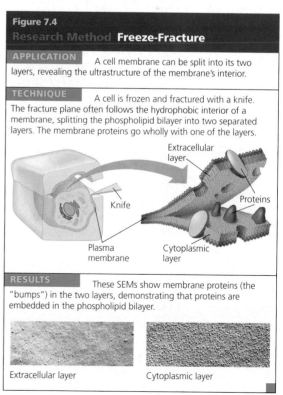

Figure 7.4

Research Method **Freeze-Fracture**

APPLICATION A cell membrane can be split into its two layers, revealing the ultrastructure of the membrane's interior.

TECHNIQUE A cell is frozen and fractured with a knife. The fracture plane often follows the hydrophobic interior of a membrane, splitting the phospholipid bilayer into two separated layers. The membrane proteins go wholly with one of the layers.

Extracellular layer

Knife

Proteins

Plasma membrane

Cytoplasmic layer

RESULTS These SEMs show membrane proteins (the "bumps") in the two layers, demonstrating that proteins are embedded in the phospholipid bilayer.

Extracellular layer

Cytoplasmic layer

Learning Inquiry by Practice

Modeling scientific inquiry by example has only ephemeral impact unless students have an opportunity to apply what they have learned by asking their own biological questions and conducting their own investigations. On a small scale, *BIOLOGY*, Seventh Edition, encourages students to practice thinking as scientists by responding to "Scientific Inquiry" questions in the Chapter Review at the ends of chapters.

On a much bigger scale, new supplements build on the textbook to provide diverse opportunities for students to practice scientific inquiry. One example is *Biological Inquiry: A Workbook of Investigative Cases*, by Margaret Waterman of Southeast Missouri State University and Ethel Stanley of Beloit College, which is available without cost to students whose instructors request it as a supplement to the textbook. This innovative new workbook offers eight case studies, coordinated with the eight units of chapters in *BIOLOGY*. In each case, a realistic scenario sets up a series of inquiry-based activities. The cases work well either as class-discussion projects or as take-home assignments for students working alone, or better, in small groups.

Another student-centered supplement is *Practicing Biology*, by Jean Heitz, University of Wisconsin, Madison, which is also available without additional cost upon request of instructors using *BIOLOGY*, Seventh Edition. This workbook supports various learning styles with a variety of activities—including modeling, drawing, and concept-mapping—that help students construct an understanding of biological concepts.

Students will find still more opportunities for active learning at *www.campbellbiology.com* and the CD-ROM that is included with each book. And the excellent *Student Study Guide*, by Martha Taylor of Cornell University, continues to be a proven learning tool for students.

The Campbell/Reece Interviews: A Continuing Tradition

Scientific inquiry is a social process catalyzed by communication among people who share a curiosity about nature. One of the many joys of authoring *BIOLOGY* has been the privilege to humanize science by interviewing some of the world's most influential biologists. Eight new interviews that introduce the eight units of the textbook provide students with windows to inquisitive minds that are driving progress in biology and connecting science to society. The interviewees for this edition are listed on page xxiii.

Scientific Inquiry

When bacteria infect an animal, the number of bacteria in the body increases in an exponential fashion (graph A). After infection by a virulent animal virus with a lytic reproductive cycle, there is no evidence of infection for a while. Then, the number of viruses rises suddenly and subsequently increases in a series of steps (graph B). Explain the difference in the growth curves.

Biological Inquiry: A Workbook of Investigative Cases Explore *West Nile virus in the case "The Donor's Dilemma."*
Investigation *What Causes Infections in AIDS Patients?*
Investigation *Why Do AIDS Rates Differ Across the U.S.?*
Investigation *What Are the Patterns of Antibiotic Resistance?*

Inquiry Questions, Media Investigations, and the new **Biological Inquiry Workbook** help students practice scientific inquiry.

Balancing Inquiry with a Conceptual Foundation

Although this new edition of *BIOLOGY* showcases the process of science more prominently than ever, there are two good reasons to avoid overstating the power of inquiry-based content in any biology textbook.

First, those of us who advocate more inquiry in biology courses mainly have student-centered inquiry in mind, not textbook-centered inquiry. As a mostly passive experience, reading about inquiry in a textbook should be merely an entryway to a variety of active experiences that are promoted by inquiry-based supplements, by investigative labs, and by activities that instructors create to support student-centered inquiry.

Second, the most important way a textbook can support student inquiry is by providing context with clear, accurate explanation of the key biological concepts. Just as biologists generally study the scientific literature as background for their own inquiry, students will be much more successful in their personal inquiry if it emerges from a basic understanding of the relevant biology. Thus, *BIOLOGY*, Seventh Edition, is *not* a "reform textbook" of the genre that replaces a careful unfolding of conceptual content with a stream of relatively unconnected research examples, requiring beginning students to put it all together for themselves. We believe that such an unbalanced reaction to the call for inquiry-based reform is likely to leave most students frustrated and ill-equipped to practice active inquiry in their labs, course projects, class discussions, and Socratic lecture environments. In *BIOLOGY*, Seventh Edition, we have carefully integrated the inquiry-based content into the development of each chapter's main ideas so that the research examples reinforce rather than obscure the conceptual framework.

BIOLOGY supports a diversity of courses and serves students throughout their biology education

Even by limiting our scope to a few key concepts per chapter, *BIOLOGY* spans more biological territory than most introductory courses could or should attempt to cover. But given the great diversity of course syllabi, we have opted for a survey broad enough and deep enough to support each instructor's special emphases. Students also seem to appreciate *BIOLOGY*'s breadth and depth; in this era when students sell many of their textbooks back to the bookstore, more than 75% of students who have used *BIOLOGY* have kept it after their introductory course. In fact, we are delighted to receive numerous letters and emails from upper-division students and graduate students, including medical students, expressing their appreciation for the long-term value of *BIOLOGY* as a general resource for their continuing education.

Just as we recognize that few courses will cover all 55 chapters of *BIOLOGY*, we also realize that there is no one "correct" sequence of topics for a general biology course. Though a biology textbook's table of contents must be linear, biology itself is more like a web of related concepts without a fixed starting point or a prescribed path. Diverse courses can navigate this network of concepts starting with molecules and cells, with evolution and the diversity of organisms, or with the big-picture ideas of ecology. We have built *BIOLOGY* to be versatile enough to support various syllabi. The eight units of the book are largely self-contained, and most of the chapters within each unit can be assigned in a different sequence. For example, instructors who integrate plant and animal physiology can merge chapters from Unit Six (Plant Form and Function) and Unit Seven (Animal Form and Function). Instructors who begin their course with ecology and continue with this "top-down" approach can assign Unit Eight (Ecology) right after Chapter 1, which introduces the unifying themes that provide students with a panoramic view of biology no matter what the topic order of the course syllabus.

Evolution and *BIOLOGY*'s other themes connect the concepts and integrate the whole book

The first chapter articulates 11 themes that provide touchstones for students throughout the book and distinguish our approach in *BIOLOGY* from an encyclopedic topical approach. In this Seventh Edition, we have added the theme of "biological systems" to integrate a variety of research initiatives based on high-throughput data collection and readily available computing power. But as in all previous editions, the central theme is evolution, which unifies all of biology by accounting for both the unity and diversity of life. The evolutionary theme is woven into every chapter of *BIOLOGY*. Evolution and the other whole-book themes work with the chapter-level concepts to help students construct a coherent view of life that will serve them long after they have forgotten the details fossilized in any biology textbook.

Neil Campbell and Jane Reece

Acknowledgments

One of the eminent scientists interviewed in this new edition pointed out that much of the fun of doing biology comes from working with a diversity of talented people. The same can be said for making a biology textbook. Fortunately for us, this Seventh Edition of *BIOLOGY* is the product of the talents, dedication, and enthusiasm of a large and varied group of people. The authors wish to express their deepest thanks to the numerous instructors, researchers, students, publishing professionals, and artists who have contributed to this edition.

As authors of both past and present editions of this text, we are mindful of the daunting challenge of keeping up to date in all areas of our rapidly expanding subject. We are particularly grateful to the seven Contributors and Advisers listed on the title page, whose expertise has ensured that the book is current and enlivened with fresh examples. We worked especially closely with developmental biologist Lisa Urry, who had major responsibility for updating content and implementing our new format and features for Units 1–3 and Chapter 47. Her rigorous scholarship and attention to detail in the areas of biological chemistry, cell and molecular biology, genetics, and developmental biology were a great boon. We thank her for her commitment and enthusiasm, relentless hard work, punctuality, and good cheer throughout the process. Equally helpful was ecologist Manuel Molles, who brought his scientific and teaching expertise to the revision of Unit 8, enhancing the structure of the unit and its verbal and visual presentation of ecology; he played a major role rewriting the behavioral ecology chapter, which is essentially new. He also helped provide a more ecological perspective to Chapters 40, 42, and 44, in the unit on animal form and function. Science writer Carl Zimmer contributed many improvements and new perspectives to Unit 5, the diversity unit. Evolutionary biologist Christopher Wills helped us tackle the challenge of improving and updating Unit 4, the evolution unit, and Chapter 26. Plant biologist Peter Minorsky helped bring Unit 6 up to date. And neurobiologist Antony Stretton advised us on the revision of Chapters 48 and 49. As in earlier editions, immunologist Mary Jane Niles organized and implemented the significant revision of Chapter 43.

Thanks also to the instructors who suggested revised or new Concept Check and Chapter Review questions. These include (in alphabetical order) Bruce Byers, Jean Heitz, William Hoese, Tom Owens, Mark Lyford, Randy Phillis (special thanks), Mitch Price, Fred Sack, Richard Showman, and Elspeth Walker. It's not easy to write good questions, and we appreciate the time and effort these dedicated educators contributed to enhancing the effectiveness of our book's questions.

Further helping us improve *BIOLOGY's* scientific accuracy and pedagogy, about 240 biologists and teachers, cited on the list that follows these Acknowledgements, provided detailed reviews of one or more chapters for this edition. Special thanks to Lawrence Brewer, Richard Brusca, Anne Clark, Douglas Eernisse, Mark Kirk, Walter Judd, Mike Levine, Diane Marshall, Nick Money, Tom Owens, Kevin Padian, Daniel Papaj, Mitch Price, Bruce Reid, and Alistair Simpson for their guidance.

Thanks also to the numerous other professors and their students, from all over the world, who offered suggestions by writing directly to the authors. In addition, we appreciate the candid and specific feedback we received from the students and faculty who participated in group discussions held at Skyline College, Mills College, and Indiana University. Last but not least, we thank our coauthors on our nonmajors texts, Eric Simon and Marty Taylor, for providing rigorous feedback on a number of chapters. Of course, we alone bear the responsibility for any errors that remain in the text, but the dedication of our contributors, advisers, reviewers, and correspondents makes us especially confident in the accuracy of this edition.

Many scientists have also helped shape this Seventh Edition by discussing their research fields with us, answering specific questions in their areas of expertise, and, often, sharing their ideas about biology education. Neil Campbell thanks the many University of California, Riverside, colleagues who have influenced this book, including Ring Carde, Richard Cardullo, Mark Chappell, Darleen DeMason, Norman Ellstrand, Anthony Huang, Bradley Hyman, Tracy Kahn, Elizabeth Lord, Carol Lovatt, Eugene Nothnagel, John Oross, Timothy Paine, David Reznick, Rodolfo Ruibal, Clay Sassaman, William Thomson, John Trumble, Rick Redack, Mike Adams, and the late John Moore (whose "Science as a Way of Knowing" essays have had such an important influence on the evolution of *BIOLOGY*). Jane Reece thanks members of the Mills College Biology and Chemistry/Physics Departments, especially Elisabeth Wade, as well as Fred Wilt, John Gerhart and Kris Niyogi from the University of California, Berkeley, for their assistance to contributor Lisa Urry.

Interviews with prominent scientists have been a hallmark of *BIOLOGY* since its inception, and conducting these interviews was again one of the great pleasures of revising the text. To open the eight units of this Seventh Edition, we are proud to include interviews with Lydia Makhubu, Peter Agre, Eric Lander, Kenneth Kaneshiro, Linda Graham, Natasha Raikhel, Erich Jarvis, and Gene Likens.

The value of *BIOLOGY* as a learning tool is greatly enhanced by the supplementary materials that have been created for instructors and students. We recognize that the dedicated authors of these materials are essentially writing mini (and not so mini) books. We much appreciate the hard work and creativity of the following: Margaret Waterman and Ethel Stanley (authors of the new *Biological Inquiry: A Workbook of Investigative Cases*); Jean Heitz (*Practicing Biology*, 2nd edition); Joan Sharp (*Instructor's Guide*); Janet Lanza (*New Designs for Bio-Explorations*); Chris Romero (PowerPoint Lectures); Laura Zanello (*Spanish Glossary*); and Judith Morgan and Eloise Brown Carter (*Investigating Biology Lab Manual*, 5th Edition). We thank Bill Barstow for heading up the test bank team, and we wish to acknowledge the test bank contributors: Jean DeSaix, Michael Dini, Conrad Firling, Peter Follette, Mark Hens, Janice Moore, Tom Owens, Marshall Sundberg, Robert Yost, and Ed Zalisko. Thanks also to Bill Wischusen, who compiled our Active Learning Questions and wrote discussion points. Once again, we thank our long-time colleague Marty Taylor for her excellent and student-focused work on the *Student Study Guide;* she has now completed seven editions of this popular student aid. In addition, we are grateful to the many other people—biology instructors, editors, artists, production experts, and narrators—who are listed in the credits for the impressive electronic media that accompany the book.

BIOLOGY, Seventh Edition, results from an unusually strong synergy between a team of scientists and a team of publishing professionals. An all-new design, the comprehensive revision of the illustration program as well as the text, the addition of major new pedagogical features, and a rich package of supplements, both printed and electronic, combined with a tight schedule to create unprecedented challenges for the publishing team.

The members of the core book team at Benjamin Cummings brought extraordinary talents and extraordinarily hard work to this project. Our leader, Editor-in-Chief Beth Wilbur, is a full colleague in the book's creation and a respected advocate for biology education in general and our book in particular in the academic community. Enthusiastic, creative, endlessly supportive of us and the other members of the team, Beth is a wonderful person and a pleasure to work with. Unflappable under pressure, she navigates difficult situations gracefully—a major asset in a project of this complexity.

The incomparable Deborah Gale, Director of Development, managed the entire project on a day-by-day basis. Deborah coproduced the first and second editions of the book, along with the developmental editing of the second edition, and we have been delighted with her return. Amazingly, Deborah is able to combine a totally professional, no-nonsense management style and a willingness to dig into the nitty-gritty with a sense of humor that kept the rest of us happily slaving away at her direction.

Supervising editors Pat Burner and Beth Winickoff had the awesome responsibility of overseeing in detail the work of the contributors, developmental editors, and developmental artists. Together, Pat and Beth carefully read every single chapter and checked every illustration, doing whatever was necessary to make this edition the most effective biology textbook available—and, we think, exceeding the high standards established in previous editions. We are immensely grateful to Pat, the multitalented and tireless Developmental Manager for Biology who has been our colleague for many years, for her incredible dedication, sound editorial judgment, and extraordinary attention to detail. The exceptionally talented Beth Winickoff, new to this Seventh Edition, was the originator of our new process of book development and production. Beth brought fresh perspectives on process, pedagogy, and editorial approach—in addition to her superb hands-on editing of six chapters. We look forward to working again with Pat and Beth on subsequent editions (after they recover from this one, of course!).

The responsibilities of the developmental editors for this edition were especially challenging. Almost all the chapters were heavily revised, requiring intensive editorial involvement from initial planning through production. We were fortunate to have on our team some of college publishing's top developmental editors. In alphabetical order, they were John Burner (Units 5–7), Alice Fugate (Units 4 and 7), Sarah Jensen (Units 2, 3, and 7), Matt Lee (Units 5 and 7), Suzanne Olivier (Units 1 and 2), Ruth Steyn (Units 3 and 7), and Susan Weisberg (Units 7 and 8). In addition to their other tasks, John Burner, Matt Lee, and Ruth Steyn brought their specific content expertise to bear on their chapters' revisions.

The support of our bright, efficient, and good-natured Publishing Assistants, Trinh Bui and Julia Khait, is much appreciated. What would we all have done without them?

We also want to thank someone who doesn't fit neatly into any of our publishing categories: our colleague, former editor, and friend Robin Heyden. Robin brought her imaginative energy and dedication to biology education to the Seventh Edition in several ways. These include early planning for the development of the media for this edition and the conception and developmental management of the new case study workbook by Margaret Waterman and Ethel Stanley. Robin also organized the first Benjamin Cummings Biology Leadership Conference, which brought us a fresh supply of creative teaching ideas from outstanding biology educators.

Once again the book has benefited greatly from the work of Russell Chun, our Senior Producer, Art and Media. Russell established a vibrant new art style for this edition that met the requirements of the content and exceeded our expectations for pedagogical and aesthetic excellence. Under his direction were the developmental artists, who developed all the new figures and redesigned many of the older ones to make them clearer and more appealing. These skilled and creative illustrators were Hilair Chism (Units 1–3 and 7), Blakeley Kim (Unit 8), Kenneth Probst (Units 4 and 5), and Laura Southworth (Units 3 and 7). Carla Simmons (Units 5 and 6) has contributed her artistic and pedagogical talents to every edition of this textbook. Final rendering of the hundreds of new and revised illustrations was carried out by Russell, Phil Guzy, Steve McEntee, and the artists of Precision Graphics. Meanwhile, Photo Editor Travis Amos led a team of photo researchers in finding hundreds of new photos for this edition. The photo researchers were Brian Donnelly, Donna Kalal, Ira Kleinberg, Robin Samper, and Maureen Spuhler. The efficient Donna Kalal also coordinated the ordering of photos from a multitude of sources. We are indebted to the entire art and photo team and to the book's talented text and cover designer, Mark Ong, for the most beautiful and visually effective edition ever. In addition to creating the stunning design, Mark was involved in laying out every chapter, and his artistic sensibility reinforced all of our goals for this revision.

The book production team had the crucial responsibility of converting the text manuscript and illustrations to pages ready for the printer. Many thanks to Managing Editor Erin Gregg, who was responsible for overseeing the complex design and production process, including the management of both in-house and freelance employees. At GTS Companies (the compositor), we particularly want to thank Rob Hansen, Brendan Short, Morgan Floyd, and Sherrill Redd, who provided expertise and solutions to complicated production challenges with good humor, and designer Kirsten Sims, who helped us improve the appearance and pedagogical utility of the Exploring Figures. Finally, we thank Manufacturing Manager Pam Augspurger, without whose work you would not be holding a physical copy of the book in your hands.

We are pleased to thank the topnotch publishing professionals who worked on the book's printed supplements. Amy Austin, Robin Heyden, Ginnie Simione Jutson, and Joan Keyes developed these supplements, and Vivian McDougal and Jane Brundage were responsible for their production.

In regard to the excellent package of electronic media that accompanies the book, we offer special thanks to Brienn Buchanan, who creatively pulled together all the elements of the student CD-ROM and website, and Christopher Delgado, who produced all of the instructor media resources, as well as the Art Notebook.

Linda Davis, President of Benjamin Cummings Publishing, has shared our commitment to excellence and provided strong support for three editions now, and we are happy to thank her once again. We also want to thank the Addison Wesley/Benjamin Cummings President, Jim Behnke (who was the editor of the first edition of this book), for his support of our new developmental process, and Editorial Director Frank Ruggirello for his vigorous commitment to the book's success.

Both before and after publication, we are fortunate to have experienced Benjamin Cummings marketing professionals on our book team. Senior Marketing Manager Josh Frost and Director of Marketing Stacy Treco provided consistent support and useful input throughout the entire development of this edition. Thanks, also, to Jeff Hester, who has recently joined the marketing team. We much appreciate the work of the talented Lillian Carr and her marketing communications team, who have created stunning brochures, posters, and other materials that have helped get the word out about this new edition. And thanks to Mansour Bethany for developing the ebrochure and other assistance.

The Addison Wesley/Benjamin Cummings field staff, which represents *BIOLOGY* on campus, is our living link to the students and professors who use the text. The field representatives tell us what you like and don't like about the book, and they provide prompt service to biology departments. The field reps are good allies in science education,

and we thank them for their professionalism in communicating the features of our book.

Finally, we wish to thank our families and friends for their encouragement and for enduring our continuing obsession with *BIOLOGY*.

Neil Campbell and Jane Reece
October 2004

Reviewers of the Seventh Edition

Thomas Adams, *Michigan State University*
Shylaja Akkaraju, *Bronx Community College of CUNY*
Bonnie Amos, *Angelo State University*
Jeff Appling, *Clemson University*
J. David Archibald, *San Diego State University*
David Armstrong, *University of Colorado at Boulder*
Mary Ashley, *University of Illinois at Chicago*
Karl Aufderheide, *Texas A&M University*
Ellen Baker, *Santa Monica College*
Susan Barman, *Michigan State University*
Andrew Barton, *University of Maine, Farmington*
David Bass, *University of Central Oklahoma*
Bonnie Baxter, *Hobart & William Smith*
Tim Beagley, *Salt Lake Community College*
Margaret E. Beard, *College of the Holy Cross*
Chris Beck, *Emory University*
Patricia Bedinger, *Colorado State University*
Tania Beliz, *College of San Mateo*
Robert Blanchard, *University of New Hampshire*
Andrew Blaustein, *Oregon State University*
Allan Bornstein, *Southeast Missouri State University*
Lisa Boucher, *University of Nebraska-Omaha*
Robert Bowker, *Glendale Community College (Arizona)*
Barbara Bowman, *Mills College*
Sunny Boyd, *University of Notre Dame*
Lawrence Brewer, *University of Kentucky*
Paul Broady, *University of Canterbury*
Carole Browne, *Wake Forest University*
David Bruck, *San Jose State University*
Rick Brusca, *Arizona-Sonora Desert Museum*
Howard Buhse, *University of Illinois at Chicago*
Arthur Buikema, *Virginia Tech*
Al Burchsted, *College of Staten Island*
Alison Campbell, *University of Waikato*
Frank Cantelmo, *St John's University*
John Capeheart, *University of Houston-Downtown*
Robert Carroll, *East Carolina University*
David Champlin, *University of Southern Maine*
Giovina Chinchar, *Tougaloo College*
Anne Clark, *Binghamton University*
Greg Clark, *University of Texas, Austin*
Randy Cohen, *California State University, Northridge*
Jim Colbert, *Iowa State University*
Robert Colvin, *Ohio University*
Elizabeth Connor, *University of Massachusetts*
Joanne Conover, *University of Connecticut*
Greg Crowther, *University of Washington*
Karen Curto, *University of Pittsburgh*
Anne Cusic, *University of Alabama at Birmingham*
Larry Davenport, *Samford University*
Teresa DeGolier, *Bethel College*
Roger Del Moral, *University of Washington*
Veronique Delesalle, *Gettysburg College*
Daniel Dervartanian, *University of Georgia*
Jean DeSaix, *University of North Carolina at Chapel Hill*
Biao Ding, *Ohio State University*

Stanley Dodson, *University of Wisconsin-Madison*
Mark Drapeau, *University of California, Irvine*
Gary Dudley, *University of Georgia*
Douglas Eernisse, *California State University, Fullerton*
Brad Elder, *University of Oklahoma*
Norman Ellstrand, *University of California, Riverside*
Dennis Emery, *Iowa State University*
John Endler, *University of California, Santa Barbara*
Gerald Esch, *Wake Forest University*
Frederick B. Essig, *University of South Florida*
Mary Eubanks, *Duke University*
Paul Farnsworth, *University of Texas, at San Antonio*
Kim Finer, *Kent State University*
Frank Fish, *West Chester University*
Steven Fisher, *University of California, Santa Barbara*
Lloyd Fitzpatrick, *University of North Texas*
Bill Fixsen, *Harvard University*
James Franzen, *University of Pittsburgh*
Frank Frisch, *Chapman University*
Bernard Frye, *University of Texas at Arlington*
Chandler Fulton, *Brandeis University*
Michael Gaines, *University of Miami*
J. Whitfield Gibbons, *University of Georgia*
J. Phil Gibson, *Agnes Scott College*
Simon Gilroy, *Pennsylvania State University*
Alan Gishlick, *National Center for Science Education*
John Glendinning, *Barnard College*
Sandra Gollnick, *State University of New York at Buffalo*
Robert Goodman, *University of Wisconsin-Madison*
Phyllis Griffard, *University of Houston-Downtown*
Joel Hage, *Radford University*
Jody Hall, *Brown University*
Douglas Hallett, *Northern Arizona University*
Sam Hammer, *Boston University*
Laszlo Hanzely, *Northern Illinois University*
Jeff Hardin, *University of Wisconsin-Madison*
Carla Hass, *Pennsylvania State University*
Chris Haufler, *University of Kansas*
Chris Haynes, *Shelton State Community College*
Blair Hedges, *Pennsylvania State*
David Hein, *Tulane University*
Michelle Henricks, *University of California, Los Angeles*
John D. Helmann, *Cornell University*
Scott Herrick, *Missouri Western State College*
David Hibbett, *Clark University*
William Hillenius, *College of Charleston*
Robert Hinrichsen, *Indiana University of Pennsylvania*
A. Scott Holaday, *Texas Tech University*
Karl Holte, *Idaho State University*
Nancy Hopkins, *Tulane University*
Sandra Horikami, *Daytona Beach Community College*
Sandra Hsu, *Skyline College*
Cheryl Ingram-Smith, *Clemson University*
Stephen Johnson, *William Penn University*
Walter Judd, *University of Florida*
Thomas Kane, *University of Cincinnati*

Tamos Kapros, *University of Missouri*
Jennifer Katcher, *Pima Community College*
Norm Kenkel, *University of Manitoba*
Mark Kirk, *University of Missouri-Columbia*
Daniel Klionsky, *University of Michigan*
Ned Knight, *Linfield College*
David Kohl, *University of California, Santa Barbara*
David Kurijaka, *Ohio University*
Elaine La, *Brandeis University*
William L' Amoreaux, *College of Staten Island*
Dominic Lannutti, *El Paso Community College*
John Lepri, *University of North Carolina at Greensboro*
Donald Levin, *University of Texas, Austin*
Mike Levine, *University of California, Berkeley*
Clark Lindgren, *Grinnell College*
Steven Lynch, *Louisiana State University at Shreveport*
Philip M. Meneely, *Haverford College*
Richard Machemer Jr., *St. John Fisher College*
Elizabeth Machunis-Masuoka, *University of Virginia*
Linda Maier, *University of Alabama in Huntsville*
Jose Maldonado, *El Paso Community College*
Richard Malkin, *University of California, Berkeley*
William Margolin, *University of Texas Medical School*
Diane Marshall, *University of New Mexico*
Linda Martin-Morris, *University of Washington*
Lee McClenaghan, *San Diego State University*
Kerry McDonald, *University of Missouri-Columbia*
Neal McReynolds, *Texas A&M International*
Lisa Meffert, *Rice University*
Michael Meighan, *University of California, Berkeley*
Scott Meissner, *Cornell University*
John Merrill, *Michigan State University*
James Mickle, *North Carolina State University*
Alan Molumby, *University of Illinois at Chicago*
Nicholas Money, *Miami University*
Alex Motten, *Duke University*
Rita Moyes, *Texas A&M College Station*
Greg Nishiyama, *College of the Canyons*
Jane Noble-Harvey, *Delaware University*
Richard Norman, *University of Michigan-Dearborn*
Steven Norris, *California State, Channel Islands*
Steve Nowicki, *Duke University*
Linda Ogren, *University of California, Santa Cruz*
Jeanette Oliver, *St. Louis Community College, Florissant Valley*
Laura J. Olsen, *University of Michigan*
Catherine Ortega, *Fort Lewis College*
Charissa Osborne, *Butler University*
Thomas Owens, *Cornell University*
Penny Padgett, *University of North Carolina at Chapel Hill*
Kevin Padian, *University of California, Berkeley*
Dianna Padilla, *State University of New York, Stony Brook*
Daniel Papaj, *University of Arizona*
Ronald Patterson, *Michigan State University*
Debra Pearce, *Northern Kentucky University*
Beverly Perry, *Houston Community College*
David Pfennig, *University of North Carolina at Chapel Hill*
Daniel Potter, *University of California, Davis*
Andy Pratt, *University of Canterbury*
Mitch Price, *Pennsylvania State*
Val Raghavan, *Ohio State University*
Talitha Rajah, *Indiana University Southeast*
Thomas Rand, *Saint Mary's University*
Ahnya Redman, *Pennsylvania State*
Bruce Reid, *Kean University*
Douglas Rhoads, *University of Arkansas*
Carol Rivin, *Oregon State University*
Laurel Roberts, *University of Pittsburgh*
William Roosenburg, *Ohio University*
Neil Sabine, *Indiana University East*

Tyson Sacco, *Cornell University*
Rowan Sage, *University of Toronto*
K. Sathasivan, *University of Texas, Austin*
Gary Saunders, *University of New Brunswick*
David Schimpf, *University of Minnesota Duluth*
Robert Schorr, *Colorado State University*
David Schwartz, *Houston Community College*
Christa Schwintzer, *University of Maine, Orono*
Shukdeb Sen, *Bethune-Cookman College*
Wendy Sera, *Seton Hill University*
Timothy Shannon, *Francis Marion University*
Joan Sharp, *Simon Fraser University*
Victoria C. Sharpe, *Blinn College*
Richard Sherwin, *University of Pittsburgh*
James Shinkle, *Trinity University*
Richard Showman, *University of South Carolina*
Anne Simon, *University of Maryland*
Alastair Simpson, *Dalhousie University*
Roger Sloboda, *Dartmouth University*
John Smarrelli, *Le Moyne College*
Kelly Smith, *University of North Florida*
Nancy Smith-Huerta, *Miami Ohio University*
Amanda Starnes, *Emory University*
Margery Stinson, *Southwestern College*
James Stockand, *University of Texas Health Science Center, San Antonio*
Antony Stretton, *University of Wisconsin-Madison*
Mark Sturtevant, *University of Michigan-Flint*
Judith Sumner, *Assumption College*
Rong Sun Pu, *Kean University*
Marshall Sundberg, *Emporia State University*
Lucinda Swatzell, *Southeast Missouri State University*
Janice Swenson, *University of North Florida*
David Tauck, *Santa Clara University*
John Taylor, *University of California, Berkeley*
Thomas Terry, *University of Connecticut*
Cyril Thong, *Simon Fraser University*
Robert Thornton, *University of California, Davis*
Stephen Timme, *Pittsburg State University*
Leslie Towill, *Arizona State University*
James Traniello, *Boston University*
Constantine Tsoukas, *San Diego State University*
Marsha Turell, *Houston Community College*
Catherine Uekert, *Northern Arizona University*
Gerald Van Dyke, *North Carolina State University*
Brandi Van Roo, *Framingham State College*
Moira Van Staaden, *Bowling Green State*
Neal Voelz, *St. Cloud State University*
Jyoti Wagle, *Houston Community College*
Edward Wagner, *University of California, Irvine*
D. Alexander Wait, *Southwest Missouri State University*
Beth Wee, *Tulane University*
Matt White, *Ohio University*
Elizabeth Willott, *University of Arizona*
Bill Wischusen, *Louisiana State University*
Clarence Wolfe, *Northern Virginia Community College*
Linda Yasui, *Northern Illinois University*
Zai Ming Zhao, *University of Texas, Austin*

Reviewers of Previous Editions

Kenneth Able (State University of New York, Albany), Martin Adamson (University of British Columbia), John Alcock (Arizona State University), Richard Almon (State University of New York, Buffalo), Katherine Anderson (University of California, Berkeley), Richard J. Andren (Montgomery County Community College), Estry Ang (University of Pittsburgh at Greensburg), J. David Archibald (Yale University),

Howard J. Arnott (University of Texas at Arlington), Robert Atherton (University of Wyoming), Leigh Auleb (San Francisco State University), P. Stephen Baenziger (University of Nebraska), Katherine Baker (Millersville University), William Barklow (Framingham State College), Steven Barnhart (Santa Rosa Junior College), Ron Basmajian (Merced College), Tom Beatty (University of British Columbia), Wayne Becker (University of Wisconsin, Madison), Jane Beiswenger (University of Wyoming), Anne Bekoff (University of Colorado, Boulder), Marc Bekoff (University of Colorado, Boulder), Tania Beliz (College of San Mateo), Adrianne Bendich (Hoffman-La Roche, Inc.), Barbara Bentley (State University of New York, Stony Brook), Darwin Berg (University of California, San Diego), Werner Bergen (Michigan State University), Gerald Bergstrom (University of Wisconsin, Milwaukee), Anna W. Berkovitz (Purdue University), Dorothy Berner (Temple University), Annalisa Berta (San Diego State University), Paulette Bierzychudek (Pomona College), Charles Biggers (Memphis State University), Andrew R. Blaustein (Oregon State University), Judy Bluemer (Morton College), Robert Blystone (Trinity University), Robert Boley (University of Texas, Arlington), Eric Bonde (University of Colorado, Boulder), Richard Boohar (University of Nebraska, Omaha), Carey L. Booth (Reed College), James L. Botsford (New Mexico State University), J. Michael Bowes (Humboldt State University), Richard Bowker (Alma College), Barry Bowman (University of California, Santa Cruz), Deric Bownds (University of Wisconsin, Madison), Robert Boyd (Auburn University), Jerry Brand (University of Texas, Austin), Theodore A. Bremner (Howard University), James Brenneman (University of Evansville), Charles H. Brenner (Berkeley, California), Donald P. Briskin (University of Illinois, Urbana), Paul Broady (University of Canterbury), Danny Brower (University of Arizona), Carole Browne (Wake Forest University), Mark Browning (Purdue University), Herbert Bruneau (Oklahoma State University), Gary Brusca (Humboldt State University), Alan H. Brush (University of Connecticut, Storrs), Meg Burke (University of North Dakota), Edwin Burling (De Anza College), William Busa (Johns Hopkins University), John Bushnell (University of Colorado), Linda Butler (University of Texas, Austin), David Byres (Florida Community College, Jacksonville), Iain Campbell (University of Pittsburgh), Robert E. Cannon (University of North Carolina at Greensboro), Deborah Canington (University of California, Davis), Gregory Capelli (College of William and Mary), Richard Cardullo (University of California, Riverside), Nina Caris (Texas A & M University), Bruce Chase (University of Nebraska, Omaha), Doug Cheeseman (De Anza College), Shepley Chen (University of Illinois, Chicago), Joseph P. Chinnici (Virginia Commonwealth University), Henry Claman (University of Colorado Health Science Center), Ross C. Clark (Eastern Kentucky University), Lynwood Clemens (Michigan State University), William P. Coffman (University of Pittsburgh), J. John Cohen (University of Colorado Health Science Center), David Cone (Saint Mary's University), John Corliss (University of Maryland), James T. Costa (Western Carolina University), Stuart J. Coward (University of Georgia), Charles Creutz (University of Toledo), Bruce Criley (Illinois Wesleyan University), Norma Criley (Illinois Wesleyan University), Joe W. Crim (University of Georgia), Richard Cyr (Pennsylvania State University), W. Marshall Darley (University of Georgia), Marianne Dauwalder (University of Texas, Austin), Bonnie J. Davis (San Francisco State University), Jerry Davis (University of Wisconsin, La Crosse), Thomas Davis (University of New Hampshire), John Dearn (University of Canberra), James Dekloe (University of California, Santa Cruz), T. Delevoryas (University of Texas, Austin), Diane C. DeNagel (Northwestern University), Jean DeSaix (University of North Carolina), Michael Dini (Texas Tech University), Andrew Dobson (Princeton University), John Drees (Temple University School of Medicine), Charles Drewes (Iowa State University), Marvin Druger (Syracuse University), Susan Dunford (University of Cincinnati), Betsey Dyer (Wheaton College), Robert Eaton (University of Colorado), Robert S. Edgar (University of California, Santa Cruz), Betty J. Eidemiller (Lamar University), William D. Eldred (Boston University), Margaret T. Erskine (Lansing Community College), David Evans (University of Florida), Robert C. Evans (Rutgers University, Camden), Sharon Eversman (Montana State University), Lincoln Fairchild (Ohio State University), Peter Fajer (Florida State University), Bruce Fall (University of Minnesota), Lynn Fancher (College of DuPage), Larry Farrell (Idaho State University), Jerry F. Feldman (University of California, Santa Cruz), Eugene Fenster (Longview Community College), Russell Fernald (University of Oregon), Milton Fingerman (Tulane University), Barbara Finney (Regis College), David Fisher (University of Hawaii, Manoa), William Fixsen (Harvard University), Abraham Flexer (Manuscript Consultant, Boulder, Colorado), Kerry Foresman (University of Montana), Norma Fowler (University of Texas, Austin), Robert G. Fowler (San Jose State University), David Fox (University of Tennessee, Knoxville), Carl Frankel (Pennsylvania State University, Hazleton), Bill Freedman (Dalhousie University), Otto Friesen (University of Virginia), Virginia Fry (Monterey Peninsula College), Alice Fulton (University of Iowa), Sara Fultz (Stanford University), Berdell Funke (North Dakota State University), Anne Funkhouser (University of the Pacific), Arthur W. Galston (Yale University), Carl Gans (University of Michigan), John Gapter (University of Northern Colorado), Reginald Garrett (University of Virginia), Patricia Gensel (University of North Carolina), Chris George (California Polytechnic State University, San Luis Obispo), Robert George (University of Wyoming), Frank Gilliam (Marshall University), Simon Gilroy (Pennsylvania State University), Todd Gleeson (University of Colorado), David Glenn-Lewin (Wichita State University), William Glider (University of Nebraska), Elizabeth A. Godrick (Boston University), Lynda Goff (University of California, Santa Cruz), Elliott Goldstein (Arizona State University), Paul Goldstein (University of Texas, El Paso), Anne Good (University of California, Berkeley), Judith Goodenough (University of Massachusetts, Amherst), Wayne Goodey (University of British Columbia), Ester Goudsmit (Oakland University), Linda Graham (University of Wisconsin, Madison), Robert Grammer (Belmont University), Joseph Graves (Arizona State University), A. J. F. Griffiths (University of British Columbia), William Grimes (University of Arizona), Mark Gromko (Bowling Green State University), Serine Gropper (Auburn University), Katherine L. Gross (Ohio State University), Gary Gussin (University of Iowa), Mark Guyer (National Human Genome Research Institute), Ruth Levy Guyer(Bethesda, Maryland), R. Wayne Habermehl (Montgomery County Community College), Mac Hadley (University of Arizona), Jack P. Hailman (University of Wisconsin), Leah Haimo (University of California, Riverside), Rebecca Halyard (Clayton State College), Penny Hanchey-Bauer (Colorado State University), Laszlo Hanzely (Northern Illinois University), Jeff Hardin (University of Wisconsin, Madison), Richard Harrison (Cornell University), H. D. Heath (California State University, Hayward), George Hechtel (State University of New York, Stony Brook), Jean Heitz-Johnson (University of Wisconsin, Madison), Colin Henderson (University of Montana), Caroll Henry (Chicago State University), Frank Heppner (University of Rhode Island), Ira Herskowitz (University of California, San Francisco), Paul E. Hertz (Barnard College), R. James Hickey (Miami University), Ralph Hinegardner (University of California, Santa Cruz), William Hines (Foothill College), Helmut Hirsch (State University of New York, Albany), Tuanhua David Ho (Washington University), Carl Hoagstrom (Ohio Northern University), James Hoffman (University of Vermont), James Holland (Indiana State University, Bloomington), Charles Holliday (Lafayette College), Laura Hoopes (Occidental College), Nancy Hopkins (Massachusetts Institute of Technology), Kathy Hornberger (Widener University), Pius F. Horner (San Bernardino Valley College), Margaret Houk (Ripon College), Ronald R. Hoy (Cornell University), Donald Humphrey (Emory University School of Medicine), Robert J. Huskey (University of Virginia), Steven Hutcheson (University of Maryland, College Park), Bradley Hyman (University of California, Riverside), Mark Iked (San Bernardino Valley College), Alice Jacklet (State University of New York, Albany), John Jackson (North Hennepin Community College), John C. Jahoda (Bridgewater State College), Dan Johnson (East Tennessee State University), Randall Johnson (University of California, San Diego), Wayne Johnson (Ohio State University), Kenneth C. Jones (California State University, Northridge), Russell Jones (University of California, Berkeley), Alan Journet (Southeast Missouri State University), Thomas C. Kane (University of Cincinnati), E. L. Karlstrom (University of Puget Sound), George Khoury (National Cancer Institute), Robert Kitchin (University of

Wyoming), Attila O. Klein (Brandeis University), Greg Kopf (University of Pennsylvania School of Medicine), Thomas Koppenheffer (Trinity University), Janis Kuby (San Francisco State University), J. A. Lackey (State University of New York, Oswego), Lynn Lamoreux (Texas A & M University), Carmine A. Lanciani (University of Florida), Kenneth Lang (Humboldt State University), Allan Larson (Washington University), Diane K. Lavett (State University of New York, Cortland, and Emory University), Charles Leavell (Fullerton College), C. S. Lee (University of Texas), Robert Leonard (University of California, Riverside), Joseph Levine (Boston College), Bill Lewis (Shoreline Community College), John Lewis (Loma Linda University), Lorraine Lica (California State University, Hayward), Harvey Liftin (Broward Community College), Harvey Lillywhite (University of Florida, Gainesville), Sam Loker (University of New Mexico), Jane Lubchenco (Oregon State University), Margaret A. Lynch (Tufts University), James MacMahon (Utah State University), Charles Mallery (University of Miami), Lynn Margulis (Boston University), Edith Marsh (Angelo State University), Karl Mattox (Miami University of Ohio), Joyce Maxwell (California State University, Northridge), Jeffrey D. May (Marshall University), Richard McCracken (Purdue University), Jacqueline McLaughlin (Pennsylvania State University, Lehigh Valley), Paul Melchior (North Hennepin Community College), Phillip Meneely (Haverford College), John Merrill (University of Washington), Brian Metscher (University of California, Irvine), Ralph Meyer (University of Cincinnati), Roger Milkman (University of Iowa), Helen Miller (Oklahoma State University), John Miller (University of California, Berkeley), Kenneth R. Miller (Brown University), John E. Minnich (University of Wisconsin, Milwaukee), Michael Misamore (Louisiana State University), Kenneth Mitchell (Tulane University School of Medicine), Russell Monson (University of Colorado, Boulder), Frank Moore (Oregon State University), Randy Moore (Wright State University), William Moore (Wayne State University), Carl Moos (Veterans Administration Hospital, Albany, New York), Michael Mote (Temple University), Deborah Mowshowitz (Columbia University), Darrel L. Murray (University of Illinois at Chicago), John Mutchmor (Iowa State University), Elliot Myerowitz (California Institute of Technology), Gavin Naylor (Iowa State University), John Neess (University of Wisconsin, Madison), Raymond Neubauer (University of Texas, Austin), Todd Newbury (University of California, Santa Cruz), Harvey Nichols (University of Colorado, Boulder), Deborah Nickerson (University of South Florida), Bette Nicotri (University of Washington), Caroline Niederman (Tomball College), Maria Nieto (California State University, Hayward), Charles R. Noback (College of Physicians and Surgeons, Columbia University), Mary C. Nolan (Irvine Valley College), Peter Nonacs (University of California, Los Angeles), David O. Norris (University of Colorado, Boulder), Cynthia Norton (University of Maine, Augusta), Steve Norton (East Carolina University), Bette H. Nybakken (Hartnell College), Brian O'Conner (University of Massachusetts, Amherst), Gerard O'Donovan (University of North Texas), Eugene Odum (University of Georgia), Patricia O'Hern (Emory University), Gary P. Olivetti (University of Vermont), John Olsen (Rhodes College), Sharman O'Neill (University of California, Davis), Wan Ooi (Houston Community College), Gay Ostarello (Diablo Valley College), Barry Palevitz (University of Georgia), Peter Pappas (County College of Morris), Bulah Parker (North Carolina State University), Stanton Parmeter (Chemeketa Community College), Robert Patterson (San Francisco State University), Crellin Pauling (San Francisco State University), Kay Pauling (Foothill Community College), Daniel Pavuk (Bowling Green State University), Debra Pearce (Northern Kentucky University), Patricia Pearson (Western Kentucky University), Shelley Penrod (North Harris College), Bob Pittman (Michigan State University), James Platt (University of Denver), Martin Poenie (University of Texas, Austin), Scott Poethig (University of Pennsylvania), Jeffrey Pommerville (Texas A & M University), Warren Porter (University of Wisconsin), Donald Potts (University of California, Santa Cruz), David Pratt (University of California, Davis), Halina Presley (University of Illinois, Chicago), Rebecca Pyles (East Tennessee State University), Scott Quackenbush (Florida International University), Ralph Quatrano (Oregon State University), Deanna Raineri (University of Illinois, Champaign-Urbana), Charles Ralph (Colorado State University), Kurt Redborg (Coe College), Brian Reeder (Morehead State University), C. Gary Reiness (Lewis & Clark College), Charles Remington (Yale University), David Reznick (University of California, Riverside), Fred Rhoades (Western Washington State University), David Reid (Blackburn College), Christopher Riegle (Irvine Valley College), Donna Ritch (Pennsylvania State University), Thomas Rodella (Merced College), Rodney Rogers (Drake University), Wayne Rosing (Middle Tennessee State University), Thomas Rost (University of California, Davis), Stephen I. Rothstein (University of California, Santa Barbara), John Ruben (Oregon State University), Albert Ruesink (Indiana University), Don Sakaguchi (Iowa State University), Walter Sakai (Santa Monica College), Mark F. Sanders (University of California, Davis), Ted Sargent (University of Massachusetts, Amherst), Gary Saunders (University of New Brunswick), Carl Schaefer (University of Connecticut), Lisa Shimeld (Crafton Hills College), David Schimpf (University of Minnesota, Duluth), William H. Schlesinger (Duke University), Erik P. Scully (Towson State University), Edna Seaman (Northeastern University), Elaine Shea (Loyola College, Maryland), Stephen Sheckler (Virginia Polytechnic Institute and State University), James Shinkle (Trinity University), Barbara Shipes (Hampton University), Peter Shugarman (University of Southern California), Alice Shuttey (DeKalb Community College), James Sidie (Ursinus College), Daniel Simberloff (Florida State University), Susan Singer (Carleton College), John Smarrelli (Loyola University), Andrew T. Smith (Arizona State University), John Smol (Queen's University), Andrew J. Snope (Essex Community College), Mitchell Sogin (Woods Hole Marine Biological Laboratory), Susan Sovonick-Dunford (University of Cincinnati), Frederick W. Spiegel (University of Arkansas), Karen Steudel (University of Wisconsin), Barbara Stewart (Swarthmore College), Cecil Still (Rutgers University, New Brunswick), John Stolz (California Institute of Technology), Richard D. Storey (Colorado College), Stephen Strand (University of California, Los Angeles), Eric Strauss (University of Massachusetts, Boston), Russell Stullken (Augusta College), John Sullivan (Southern Oregon State University), Gerald Summers (University of Missouri), Marshall D. Sundberg (Emporia State University), Daryl Sweeney (University of Illinois, Champaign-Urbana), Samuel S. Sweet (University of California, Santa Barbara), Lincoln Taiz (University of California, Santa Cruz), Samuel Tarsitano (Southwest Texas State University), David Tauck (Santa Clara University), James Taylor (University of New Hampshire), Martha R. Taylor (Cornell University), Roger Thibault (Bowling Green State University), William Thomas (Colby-Sawyer College), John Thornton (Oklahoma State University), Robert Thornton (University of California, Davis), James Traniello (Boston University), Robert Tuveson (University of Illinois, Urbana), Maura G. Tyrrell (Stonehill College), Gordon Uno (University of Oklahoma), Lisa A. Urry (Mills College), James W. Valentine (University of California, Santa Barbara), Joseph Vanable (Purdue University), Theodore Van Bruggen (University of South Dakota), Kathryn VandenBosch (Texas A & M University), Frank Visco (Orange Coast College), Laurie Vitt (University of California, Los Angeles), Thomas J. Volk (University of Wisconsin, La Crosse), Susan D. Waaland (University of Washington), William Wade (Dartmouth Medical College), John Waggoner (Loyola Marymount University), Dan Walker (San Jose State University), Robert L. Wallace (Ripon College), Jeffrey Walters (North Carolina State University), Margaret Waterman (University of Pittsburgh), Charles Webber (Loyola University of Chicago), Peter Webster (University of Massachusetts, Amherst), Terry Webster (University of Connecticut, Storrs), Peter Wejksnora (University of Wisconsin, Milwaukee), Kentwood Wells (University of Connecticut), David J. Westenberg (University of Missouri, Rolla), Stephen Williams (Glendale Community College), Christopher Wills (University of California, San Diego), Fred Wilt (University of California, Berkeley), Robert T. Woodland (University of Massachusetts Medical School), Joseph Woodring (Louisiana State University), Patrick Woolley (East Central College), Philip Yant (University of Michigan), Hideo Yonenaka (San Francisco State University), Edward Zalisko (Blackburn College), John Zimmerman (Kansas State University), Uko Zylstra (Calvin College).

Supplements

Supplements for the Student

Campbell BIOLOGY Student CD-ROM and Website (www.campbellbiology.com)

The CD-ROM and website that accompany each book include 230 interactive Activities, 85 Videos, and 55 Investigations. In addition, new graphing exercises (Graph It!) help students learn how to build and interpret graphs.

The CD-ROM and website are fully integrated with the text, reinforcing students' focus on the big ideas. The media organization mirrors that of the textbook, with all the Activities, Videos, and Investigations for a given chapter correlated to the key concepts in the book.

There are three separate quizzes per chapter: a Pre-Test, a Chapter Quiz, and an Activities Quiz. A new electronic Gradebook automatically records students' quiz scores. Another new feature of the Seventh Edition, Cumulative Test, allows students to build a self-test with questions from more than one chapter. Feedback is provided to students on all quizzes and tests in the media, which have been upgraded in level of difficulty.

New Flashcards, Word Roots, and Key Terms linked to the Glossary help students master terminology. Students can also access Art from the book with and without labels, the Glossary with audio pronunciations, the Campbell *BIOLOGY* Interviews from previous editions, an E-Book, the Biology Tutor Center, Web Links, News, and Further Readings.

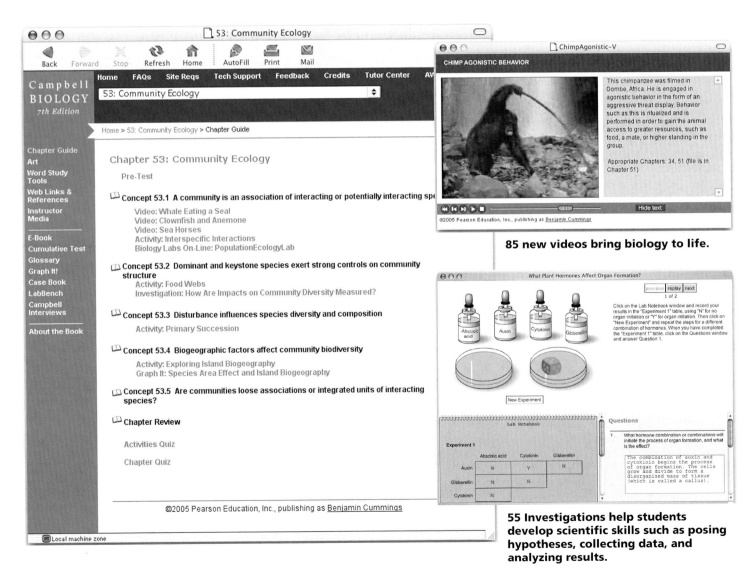

85 new videos bring biology to life.

55 Investigations help students develop scientific skills such as posing hypotheses, collecting data, and analyzing results.

NEW! Biological Inquiry: A Workbook of Investigative Cases (0-8053-7176-1)

Margaret Waterman, Southeast Missouri State University, and Ethel Stanley, Beloit College

This new workbook offers eight investigative cases, one for each unit of the textbook. In order to understand the science in each case, students will pose questions, analyze data, think critically, examine the relationship between evidence and conclusions, construct hypotheses, investigate options, graph data, interpret results, and communicate scientific arguments. Students will actively engage in the experimental nature of science as they gain new insight into how we know what we know. For example, in "The Donor's Dilemma" (the Unit 3 case) students explore the concepts of protein synthesis, viral genomes, and transmission pathways while investigating the case of a blood donor who may have been exposed to the West Nile virus. Web links and other online resources referred to in the investigative cases are provided on the Campbell *BIOLOGY* website.

Student Study Guide (0-8053-7155-9)

Martha R. Taylor, Cornell University

This popular study guide offers an interactive approach to learning, providing framework sections to orient students to the overall picture, concept maps to complete or create for most chapters, chapter summaries, word roots, chapter tests, and a variety of questions, including multiple choice, short-answer essay, art labeling, and interpreting graphs.

Practicing Biology: A Student Workbook, Second Edition (0-8053-8184-2)

Jean Heitz, University of Wisconsin, Madison

This workbook's hands-on activities emphasize key ideas, principles, and concepts that are basic to understanding biology. Suitable for group work in lecture, discussion sections, and/or lab, the workbook includes class-tested Process of Science activities, concept map development, drawing exercises, and modeling activities.

NEW! Test Preparation Guide to MCAT/GRE for Campbell BIOLOGY, 7e (0-8053-7178-8)

Exclusively available with *BIOLOGY*, Seventh Edition, this new guide includes sample questions and answers from the Kaplan test preparation guides, correlated to specific pages in this edition of *BIOLOGY*.

Art Notebook (0-8053-7183-4)

This resource contains all the art from the text without labels, with plenty of room for students to take notes.

BIOLOGY—Basic Concepts Study Card (0-8053-7175-3)

Useful as a quick reference guide, this fold-out card summarizes the basic concepts and content covered in *BIOLOGY*, Seventh Edition.

Biology Tutor Center (www.aw.com/tutorcenter)

This center provides one-to-one tutoring for college students via phone, fax, and email during evening hours and on weekends. Qualified college instructors are available to answer questions and provide instruction regarding self-quizzes and other content found in *BIOLOGY*, Seventh Edition. Visit the website for more information.

The Benjamin Cummings Special Topics Booklets

- **Understanding the Human Genome Project (0-8053-6774-8)**
- **Stem Cells and Cloning (0-8053-4864-6)**
- **Biological Terrorism (0-8053-4868-9)**
- **The Biology of Cancer (0-8053-4867-0)**

The Chemistry of Life CD-ROM, Second Edition (0-8053-3063-1)

Robert M. Thornton, University of California, Davis

This CD-ROM helps biology students grasp the essentials of chemistry with animations, interactive exercises, and quizzes with feedback.

An Introduction to Chemistry for Biology Students, Eighth Edition (0-8053-3970-1)

George I. Sackheim, University of Illinois, Chicago

This printed workbook helps students master all the basic facts, concepts, and terminology of chemistry that they need for their life science course.

Biomath: Problem Solving for Biology Students (0-805306524-9)

Robert W. Keck and Richard R. Patterson

A Short Guide to Writing about Biology, Fourth Edition (0-321-07843-8)

Jan A. Pechenik, Tufts University

Spanish Glossary (0-8053-7182-6)

Laura P. Zanello

Supplements for the Instructor

Campbell Media Manager (set of 8 CD-ROMs) (0-8053-7153-7)

The Campbell Media Manager combines all the instructor and student media for Campbell/Reece *BIOLOGY* into one chapter-by-chapter resource. It includes eight CD-ROMs, one for each unit in the text. Instructor media includes Power-Point Lectures, PowerPoint TextEdit Art, PowerPoint Active Lecture Questions, and the Image Library—1,600 photos, all art from the book with and without labels, selected art layered for step-by-step presentation, tables, 85 videos, and more than 100 animations. Also included are Lecture Outlines in Word format for each chapter. (These resources are also available in the Instructor Resources section at *www.campbell-biology.com*.) The Campbell Media Manager also includes printed thumbnail-sized images for easy viewing of all the resources in the Image Library and a convenient fold-out Quick Reference Guide.

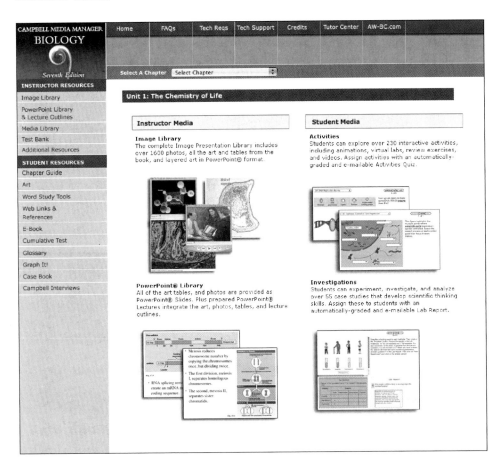

Instructor's Guide to Text and Media (0-8053-7148-6)

Joan Sharp, Simon Fraser University

This reference tool includes a chapter-by-chapter listing of all the text and media resources available to instructors and students organized by key concepts. It also includes objectives, key terms, and word roots. New to this edition are de-scriptions of frequent student misconceptions for each chapter and suggestions for how to address these concerns. The Instructor's Guide is available in print and in Word format.

Lecture Outlines

Joan Sharp, Simon Fraser University

Chapter lecture outlines are available in Word format in the Instructor Resources section at *www.campbellbiology.com*.

Transparency Acetates (0-8053-7149-4)

Approximately 1,000 acetates include all full-color illustrations and tables from the text, many of which incorporate photos. In addition, selected figures illustrating key concepts are broken down into layers for step-by-step lecture presentation.

Printed Test Bank (0-8053-7154-0)
Computerized Test Bank (0-8053-7153-2)

Edited by William Barstow, University of Georgia

Thoroughly revised and updated, the Seventh Edition test bank also includes optional questions from the book's Self-Quizzes and questions related to the media to encourage students to use these resources. Available in print, on a cross-platform CD-ROM, and in the instructor section of CourseCompass™, Blackboard, and WebCT.

PowerPoint Lectures

Chris C. Romero, Front Range Community College, Larimer Campus

PowerPoint Lectures are provided for each chapter and include the art, photos, tables, and an editable lecture outline. The PowerPoint Lectures can be used as is or customized for your course with your own images and text and/or additional photos, videos, and animations from the Campbell Media Manager.

PowerPoint TextEdit Art

All the art, photos, and tables are provided in PowerPoint on the Campbell Media Manager. Selected figures are layered for step-by-step presentation. The PowerPoint TextEdit Art can be used as is or labels can be edited in PowerPoint.

NEW! Biological Inquiry: A Workbook of Investigative Cases, Instructor Version (0-8053-7177-X)

The Instructor Version provides specific and detailed suggestions on how to use each case study effectively, outlining links to specific content in *BIOLOGY*, Seventh Edition, and other supplements, providing direction on how to facilitate problem-based learning, and listing suggested answers and opportunities for extended investigations.

Practicing Biology, Instructor's Edition, Second Edition (0-8053-8184-2)

The instructor's version is available online at: *http://suppscentral.aw.com.*

Course Management Systems

The content from the Campbell *BIOLOGY* website is also available in these popular course management systems: CourseCompass, Blackboard, and WebCT. For more information, visit *http://cms.aw.com.*

Classroom Response Systems

Invigorate lectures with Active Lecture Questions. These multiple-choice questions are adapted from various sources, including the end-of-chapter questions, *Student Study Guide, Test Bank,* and *Biomath: Problem Solving for Biology* by Robert W. Keck and Richard R. Patterson. The questions are available in PowerPoint format via Supplements Central *(http://supps_central.aw.com)* or preloaded on H-ITT and PRS. Sources and answers are located in the PowerPoint Notes field. Selected questions in each chapter include additional Discussion Points added as suggestions for the instructor.

Supplements for the Lab

Investigating Biology, Fifth Edition (0-8053-7196-6)

Judith Giles Morgan, Emory University, and M. Eloise Brown Carter, Oxford College of Emory University

With its distinctive investigative approach to learning, this laboratory manual encourages students to practice science. Students are invited to pose hypotheses, make predictions, conduct open-ended experiments, collect data, and then apply the results to new problems.

Investigating Biology, Annotated Instructor's Edition, Fifth Edition (0-8053-7180-X)

Teaching information, added to the original Student Edition text, includes margin notes with hints on lab procedures, additional art, and answers to in-text and end-of-chapter questions from the Student Edition. Also featured is a detailed Teaching Plan at the end of each lab with specific suggestions for organizing labs, including estimated time allotments and suggestions for encouraging independent thinking and collaborative discussion.

Preparation Guide for Investigating Biology, Fifth Edition (0-8053-7181-8)

Guides lab coordinators in ordering materials as well as in planning, setting up, and running labs.

NEW! Designs for Bio-Explorations (0-8053-7229-6)

Janet Lanza, University of Arkansas at Little Rock

Eight inquiry-based laboratory exercises offer students creative control over the projects they undertake. Students are provided background information that enables them to design and conduct their own experiments.

NEW! Designs for Bio-Explorations, Instructor's Version (0-8053-7228-8)

The instructor's version is available online at: *http://suppscentral.aw.com.*

Symbiosis Book Building Kit—Customized Lab Manuals (0-201-72142-2)

Build a customized lab manual, choosing the labs you want, importing artwork from our graphics library, and even adding your own material, and get a made-to-order black and white lab manual. Visit *http://www.pearsoncustom.com/database/symbiosis.html* for more information.

Biology Labs On-Line (www.biologylabsonline.com)

Twelve on-line labs enable students to expand their scientific horizons beyond the traditional wet lab setting and perform potentially dangerous, lengthy, or expensive experiments in an electronic environment. Each experiment can be repeated as often as necessary, employing a different set of variables each time. The labs are available for purchase individually or in a 12-pack with the printed Student Lab Manual.

Student Lab Manual for Biology Labs On-Line (0-8053-7017-X)

Instructor's Lab Manual for Biology Labs On-Line (0-8053-7018-8)

Featured Figures

Exploring Figures

1.3 Exploring Levels of Biological Organization *4*

1.14 Exploring Life's Three Domains *14*

4.10 Exploring the Functional Groups of Organic Compounds *64*

5.20 Exploring Levels of Protein Structure *82*

6.9 Exploring Animal and Plant Cells *100*

6.30 Exploring Intercellular Junctions in Animal Tissues *121*

7.20 Exploring Endocytosis in Animal Cells *138*

11.7 Exploring Membrane Receptors *206*

12.6 Exploring the Mitotic Division of an Animal Cell *222*

13.8 Exploring the Meiotic Division of an Animal Cell *244*

21.2 Exploring Model Organisms for Genetic Studies of Development *412*

24.4 Exploring Reproductive Barriers *474*

27.13 Exploring Major Groups of Bacteria *542*

28.12 Exploring Structure and Function in the Ciliate *Paramecium caudatum* *557*

29.5 Exploring Derived Traits of Land Plants *576*

29.9 Exploring Bryophyte Diversity *582*

29.14 Exploring Seedless Vascular Plant Diversity *587*

30.4 Exploring Gymnosperm Diversity *594*

30.12 Exploring Angiosperm Diversity *602*

33.3 Exploring Invertebrate Diversity *639*

33.37 Exploring Insect Diversity *662*

34.36 Exploring Mammalian Diversity *698*

35.9 Exploring Examples of Differentiated Plant Cells *718*

37.13 Exploring Unusual Nutritional Adaptations in Plants *768*

38.3 Exploring Floral Variations *773*

40.5 Exploring Structure and Function in Animal Tissues *824*

41.2 Exploring Four Main Feeding Mechanisms of Animals *845*

42.4 Exploring Vertebrate Circulatory Systems *870*

44.18 Exploring Environmental Adaptations of the Vertebrate Kidney *939*

46.11 Exploring Human Oogenesis *974*

46.12 Exploring Human Spermatogenesis *975*

49.8 Exploring the Structure of the Human Ear *1051*

50.10 Exploring Global Climate Patterns *1088*

50.17 Exploring Aquatic Biomes *1094*

50.20 Exploring Terrestrial Biomes *1100*

54.17 Exploring Nutrient Cycles *1196*

55.22 Exploring Restoration Ecology Worldwide *1226*

Inquiry Figures

1.29 Does the presence of poisonous coral snakes affect predation rates on their mimics, king snakes? *23*

4.2 Could organic compounds have been synthesized abiotically on the early Earth? *59*

7.6 Do membrane proteins move? *127*

10.9 Which wavelengths of light are most effective in driving photosynthesis? *187*

12.8 During anaphase, do kinetochore microtubules shorten at their spindle pole ends or their kinetochore ends? *225*

12.13 Are there molecular signals in the cytoplasm that regulate the cell cycle? *228*

12.17 Does platelet-derived growth factor (PDGF) stimulate the division of human fibroblast cells in culture? *231*

14.3 When F_1 pea plants with purple flowers are allowed to self-pollinate, what flower color appears in the F_2 generation? *253*

14.8 Do the alleles for seed color and seed shape sort into gametes dependently (together) or independently? *257*

15.4 In a cross between a wild-type female fruit fly and a mutant white-eyed male, what color eyes will the F_1 and F_2 offspring have? *277*

15.5 Are the genes for body color and wing size in fruit flies located on the same chromosome or different chromosomes? *279*

16.2 Can the genetic trait of pathogenicity be transferred between bacteria? *294*

16.4 Is DNA or protein the genetic material of phage T2? *295*

16.11 Does DNA replication follow the conservative, semiconservative, or dispersive model? *300*

17.2 Do individual genes specify different enzymes in arginine biosynthesis? *311*

18.15 Can a bacterial cell acquire genes from another individual? *347*

21.5 Can a differentiated plant cell develop into a whole plant? *415*

21.6 Can the nucleus from a differentiated animal cell direct development of an organism? *416*

21.21 Which cell layers in the floral meristem determine the number of floral organs? *430*

22.12 Can predation pressure select for size and age at maturity in guppies? *447*

23.11 Does geographic variation in yarrow plants have a genetic component?   *464*

24.7 Can divergence of allopatric fruit fly populations lead to reproductive isolation?   *477*

24.10 Does sexual selection in cichlids result in reproductive isolation?   *480*

26.2 Can organic molecules form in a reducing atmosphere?   *513*

31.21 Does having mycorrhizae benefit a plant?   *620*

36.19 What causes phloem sap to flow from source to sink?   *753*

39.5 What part of a coleoptile senses light, and how is the signal transmitted?   *792*

39.6 Does asymmetric distribution of a growth-promoting chemical cause a coleoptile to grow toward the light?   *793*

39.7 What causes polar movement of auxin from shoot tip to base?   *795*

39.13 How does ethylene concentration affect the triple response in seedlings?   *799*

39.17 What wavelengths stimulate phototropic bending toward light?   *803*

39.18 How does the order of red and far-red illumination affect seed germination?   *803*

39.22 How does interrupting the dark period with a brief exposure to light affect flowering?   *807*

39.23 Is phytochrome the pigment that measures the interruption of dark periods in photoperiodic response?   *807*

39.24 Is there a flowering hormone?   *808*

44.6 What role does fur play in water conservation by camels?   *926*

47.4 What is the effect of sperm binding on on Ca^{2+} distribution in the egg?   *990*

47.21 Does fibronectin promote cell migration?   *1002*

47.22 Is cadherin required for development of the blastula?   *1003*

47.24 How does distribution of the gray crescent at the first cleavage affect the potency of the two daughter cells?   *1005*

47.25 Can the dorsal lip of the blastopore induce cells in another part of the amphibian embryo to change their developmental fate?   *1006*

47.27 What role does the zone of polarizing activity (ZPA) play in limb pattern formation in vertebrates?   *1008*

48.25 Are mammalian biological clocks influenced by external cues?   *1031*

49.13 How do insects detect different tastes?   *1055*

49.37 What are the energy costs of locomotion?   *1074*

50.8 Does feeding by sea urchins and limpets affect seaweed distribution?   *1086*

51.10 Are the different songs of closely related green lacewing species under genetic control?   *1112*

51.12 How does dietary environment affect mate choice by female *Drosophila mojavensis*?   *1113*

51.14 Does a digger wasp use landmarks to find her nest?   *1115*

52.7 How does caring for offspring affect parental survival in kestrals?   *1142*

52.18 How stable is the Isle Royale moose population?   *1150*

53.2 Can a species' niche be influenced by interspecific competition?   *1160*

53.28 How does species richness relate to area?   *1178*

54.6 Which nutrient limits phytoplankton production along the coast of Long Island?   *1189*

54.9 Is phosphorus or nitrogen the limiting nutrient in a Hudson Bay salt marsh?   *1191*

55.10 What caused the drastic decline of the Illinois greater prairie chicken population?   *1216*

Research Method Figures

2.5 Radioactive Tracers   *35*

5.24 X-Ray Crystallography   *86*

6.3 Light Microscopy   *96*

6.4 Electron Microscopy   *96*

6.5 Cell Fractionation   *97*

7.4 Freeze Fracture   *126*

10.8 Determining an Absorption Spectrum   *187*

13.3 Preparing a Karyotype   *240*

14.2 Crossing Pea Plants   *252*

14.7 The Testcross   *256*

15.7 Constructing a Linkage Map   *281*

20.4 Cloning a human gene in a Bacterial Plasmid   *387*

20.5 Nucleic Acid Probe Hybridization   *389*

20.7 The Polymerase Chain Reaction (PCR)   *391*

20.8 Gel Electrophoresis   *393*

20.10 Southern Blotting of DNA Fragments   *395*

20.12 Dideoxy Chain-Termination Method for Sequencing DNA   *397*

20.14 DNA Microarray Assay of Gene Expression Levels   *401*

20.19 Using the Ti Plasmid to Produce Transgenic Plants   *407*

21.7 Reproductive Cloning of a Mammal by Nuclear Transplantation   *417*

23.14 Using a Virtual Population to Study the Effects of Selection   *467*

25.15 Applying Parsimony to a Problem in Molecular Systematics   *502*

37.3 Hydroponic Culture   *757*

48.9 Intracellular Recording   *1016*

New to the Seventh Edition

The following list provides just a few highlights of what's new in *BIOLOGY*, Seventh Edition.

CHAPTER 1 Exploring Life

▶ Chapter 1 now includes a discussion of systems biology as one of the book's themes.

▶ The section on scientific inquiry is more robust and features a new case study of research on mimicry in snake populations.

UNIT ONE The Chemistry of Life

▶ At the suggestion of many instructors, the chapter on the basic principles of energy and metabolism, formerly Chapter 6, has been moved to Unit Two. In this edition, we provide a basic introduction to ATP in Chapter 4 and to enzymes in Chapter 5.

UNIT TWO The Cell

▶ The chapter "An Introduction to Metabolism" is now Chapter 8 in Unit Two, where it directly precedes the chapters on cellular respiration and photosynthesis. In addition to an improved presentation of the thermodynamic laws, Chapter 8 expands upon the introduction to ATP and enzymes given in Unit One.

UNIT THREE Genetics

▶ Chapter 19 has been updated throughout, including expanded coverage of histone modifications, DNA methylation, and epigenetic inheritance; a new discussion of regulation of gene expression by miRNAs and siRNAs; an updated discussion of the types of DNA sequences in the human genome; and a new section on genome evolution.

▶ In Chapter 20, new material ranges from a discussion of the current estimate of the number of human genes, to a more global view of gene interactions within a given genome, to comparisons of genomes of different species, all part of the current thrust to understand the biology of whole systems.

▶ Chapter 21 provides an expanded section on the evolution of development ("evo-devo"), including a new comparison of the genes involved in animal and plant development.

UNIT FOUR Mechanisms of Evolution

▶ Changes to this unit aim to combat misconceptions about evolutionary processes, as well as to eliminate hints of circular reasoning that are a target of anti-evolution arguments.

▶ New examples highlight vibrant research in evolutionary biology, including the continued impact of molecular systematics on phylogenetic studies and the use of virtual populations to model evolutionary processes.

▶ Chapter 25 has been revised to focus on the inquiry process involved in exploring phylogeny. Expanded coverage of genome evolution includes a new discussion of neutral theory.

UNIT FIVE The Evolutionary History of Biological Diversity

▶ Chapter 26, now titled "The Tree of Life: An Introduction to Biodiversity," is newly focused on placing life's diversity in the context of Earth's history, with emphasis on the major branchings in the tree of life.

▶ Updates in Chapter 27 (now titled "Prokaryotes") reflect new data regarding prokaryote classification and the growing evidence for cooperative relationships among prokaryotes.

▶ Chapters 28 (now titled "Protists"), 29, 30, and 31 include more information on the natural history, ecological roles, and human impact of various groups of protists, plants, and fungi. Updates include the implications of recent phylogenetic findings on classification, such as the recognition of a new fungal phylum (Glomeromycota).

▶ Chapters 32, 33, and 34 present a cohesive view of animal diversity, including an overview of hypotheses regarding animal phylogeny, an expanded survey of invertebrate phyla, added detail on natural history, updating of vertebrate classification, and recent findings relating to human origins.

UNIT SIX Plant Form and Function

▶ New examples highlight the role of biotechnology in agriculture, such as the development of genetically engineered "smart plants" that signal phosphorus deficiencies and the potential application of "terminator technology" to the problem of transgene escape from GM crops.

▶ New content in Chapter 39 focuses on the potential application of systems biology to the study of plant hormone interactions.

UNIT SEVEN Animal Form and Function

▶ New research examples highlight the physiology of diverse animals and relate physiological adaptations to the animals' ecological context.

▶ Content on thermoregulation has been moved from Chapter 44 (now titled "Osmoregulation and Excretion") to Chapter 40 ("Basic Principles of Animal Form and Function"), where it serves as an extended example of various animals' ability to maintain homeostasis.

▶ New sections on the vertebrate brain and on neurological disorders highlight recent discoveries as well as the tantalizing opportunities in these dynamic areas of research.

UNIT EIGHT Ecology

▶ A new Chapter 51 ("Behavioral Ecology") brings the subject into the 21st century, with expanded coverage of game theory, mate choice, and animal cognition.

▶ New examples throughout the unit highlight current research and applications, including facilitation and community structure, the FACTS-1 study of CO_2 impact on forests, and novel approaches in restoration ecology.

Brief Contents

1   **Exploring Life**   2

UNIT ONE   The Chemistry of Life
2   **The Chemical Context of Life**   32
3   **Water and the Fitness of the Environment**   47
4   **Carbon and the Molecular Diversity of Life**   58
5   **The Structure and Function of Macromolecules**   68

UNIT TWO   The Cell
6   **A Tour of the Cell**   94
7   **Membrane Structure and Function**   124
8   **An Introduction to Metabolism**   141
9   **Cellular Respiration: Harvesting Chemical Energy**   160
10   **Photosynthesis**   181
11   **Cell Communication**   201
12   **The Cell Cycle**   218

UNIT THREE   Genetics
13   **Meiosis and Sexual Life Cycles**   238
14   **Mendel and the Gene Idea**   251
15   **The Chromosomal Basis of Inheritance**   274
16   **The Molecular Basis of Inheritance**   293
17   **From Gene to Protein**   309
18   **The Genetics of Viruses and Bacteria**   334
19   **Eukaryotic Genomes: Organization, Regulation, and Evolution**   359
20   **DNA Technology and Genomics**   384
21   **The Genetic Basis of Development**   411

UNIT FOUR   Mechanisms of Evolution
22   **Descent with Modification: A Darwinian View of Life**   438
23   **The Evolution of Populations**   454
24   **The Origin of Species**   472
25   **Phylogeny and Systematics**   491

Detailed Contents

1   Exploring Life   2
OVERVIEW: Biology's Most Exciting Era   2
CONCEPT 1.1 Biologists explore life from the microscopic to the global scale   2
A Hierarchy of Biological Organization   3
A Closer Look at Ecosystems   6
A Closer Look at Cells   6
CONCEPT 1.2 Biological systems are much more than the sum of their parts   9
The Emergent Properties of Systems   9
The Power and Limitations of Reductionism   9
Systems Biology   10
Feedback Regulation in Biological Systems   11
CONCEPT 1.3 Biologists explore life across its great diversity of species   12
Grouping Species: The Basic Idea   12
The Three Domains of Life   13
Unity in the Diversity of Life   14
CONCEPT 1.4 Evolution accounts for life's unity and diversity   15
Natural Selection   16
The Tree of Life   17
CONCEPT 1.5 Biologists use various forms of inquiry to explore life   19
Discovery Science   19
Hypothesis-Based Science   20
A Case Study in Scientific Inquiry: Investigating Mimicry in Snake Populations   21
Limitations of Science   24
Theories in Science   24
Model-Building in Science   24
The Culture of Science   25
Science, Technology, and Society   25
CONCEPT 1.6 A set of themes connects the concepts of biology   26

UNIT ONE

The Chemistry of Life

2   The Chemical Context of Life   32
OVERVIEW: Chemical Foundations of Biology   32
CONCEPT 2.1 Matter consists of chemical elements in pure form and in combinations called compounds   32
Elements and Compounds   32
Essential Elements of Life   33
CONCEPT 2.2 An element's properties depend on the structure of its atoms   34
Subatomic Particles   34
Atomic Number and Atomic Mass   34
Isotopes   35
The Energy Levels of Electrons   36
Electron Configuration and Chemical Properties   37
Electron Orbitals   38
CONCEPT 2.3 The formation and function of molecules depend on chemical bonding between atoms   39
Covalent Bonds   39
Ionic Bonds   41
Weak Chemical Bonds   42
Molecular Shape and Function   42
CONCEPT 2.4 Chemical reactions make and break chemical bonds   44

3   Water and the Fitness of the Environment   47
OVERVIEW: The Molecule That Supports All of Life   47
CONCEPT 3.1 The polarity of water molecules results in hydrogen bonding   47
CONCEPT 3.2 Four emergent properties of water contribute to Earth's fitness for life   48
Cohesion   48
Moderation of Temperatures   49
Insulation of Bodies of Water by Floating Ice   50
The Solvent of Life   51
CONCEPT 3.3 Dissociation of water molecules leads to acidic and basic conditions that affect living organisms   53
Effects of Changes in pH   53
The Threat of Acid Precipitation   55

4   Carbon and the Molecular Diversity of Life   58
OVERVIEW: Carbon—The Backbone of Biological Molecules   58
CONCEPT 4.1 Organic chemistry is the study of carbon compounds   58

CONCEPT 4.2 Carbon atoms can form diverse molecules by bonding to four other atoms 59

The Formation of Bonds with Carbon 59
Molecular Diversity Arising from Carbon Skeleton Variation 61

CONCEPT 4.3 Functional groups are the parts of molecules involved in chemical reactions 63

The Functional Groups Most Important in the Chemistry of Life 63
ATP: An Important Source of Energy for Cellular Processes 66
The Chemical Elements of Life: *A Review* 66

5 The Structure and Function of Macromolecules 68

OVERVIEW: **The Molecules of Life** 68

CONCEPT 5.1 Most macromolecules are polymers, built from monomers 68

The Synthesis and Breakdown of Polymers 68
Diversity of Polymers 69

CONCEPT 5.2 Carbohydrates serve as fuel and building material 69

Sugars 70
Polysaccharides 71

CONCEPT 5.3 Lipids are a diverse group of hydrophobic molecules 74

Fats 75
Phospholipids 76
Steroids 77

CONCEPT 5.4 Proteins have many structures, resulting in a wide range of functions 77

Polypeptides 78
Protein Conformation and Function 81

CONCEPT 5.5 Nucleic acids store and transmit hereditary information 85

The Roles of Nucleic Acids 86
The Structure of Nucleic Acids 87
The DNA Double Helix 88
DNA and Proteins as Tape Measures of Evolution 89

The Theme of Emergent Properties in the Chemistry of Life: *A Review* 89

UNIT TWO

The Cell 92

6 A Tour of the Cell 94

OVERVIEW: **The Importance of Cells** 94

CONCEPT 6.1 To study cells, biologists use microscopes and the tools of biochemistry 94

Microscopy 95
Isolating Organelles by Cell Fractionation 97

CONCEPT 6.2 Eukaryotic cells have internal membranes that compartmentalize their functions 98

Comparing Prokaryotic and Eukaryotic Cells 98
A Panoramic View of the Eukaryotic Cell 99

CONCEPT 6.3 The eukaryotic cell's genetic instructions are housed in the nucleus and carried out by the ribosomes 102

The Nucleus: Genetic Library of the Cell 102
Ribosomes: Protein Factories in the Cell 102

CONCEPT 6.4 The endomembrane system regulates protein traffic and performs metabolic functions in the cell 104

The Endoplasmic Reticulum: Biosynthetic Factory 104
The Golgi Apparatus: Shipping and Receiving Center 105
Lysosomes: Digestive Compartments 107
Vacuoles: Diverse Maintenance Compartments 108
The Endomembrane System: *A Review* 108

CONCEPT 6.5 Mitochondria and chloroplasts change energy from one form to another 109

Mitochondria: Chemical Energy Conversion 109
Chloroplasts: Capture of Light Energy 110
Peroxisomes: Oxidation 110

CONCEPT 6.6 The cytoskeleton is a network of fibers that organizes structures and activities in the cell 112

Roles of the Cytoskeleton: Support, Motility, and Regulation 112
Components of the Cytoskeleton 113

CONCEPT 6.7 Extracellular components and connections between cells help coordinate cellular activities 118

Cell Walls of Plants 118
The Extracellular Matrix (ECM) of Animal Cells 119
Intercellular Junctions 120

THE CELL: **A Living Unit Greater Than the Sum of Its Parts** 120

7 Membrane Structure and Function 124

OVERVIEW: **Life at the Edge** 124

CONCEPT 7.1 Cellular membranes are fluid mosaics of lipids and proteins 124

Membrane Models: *Scientific Inquiry* 125
The Fluidity of Membranes 126
Membrane Proteins and Their Functions 127

The Role of Membrane Carbohydrates in Cell-Cell
Recognition   129
Synthesis and Sidedness of Membranes   129
CONCEPT 7.2 Membrane structure results in selective
permeability   130
The Permeability of the Lipid Bilayer   130
Transport Proteins   130
CONCEPT 7.3 Passive transport is diffusion of a substance
across a membrane with no energy investment   130
Effects of Osmosis on Water Balance   131
Facilitated Diffusion: Passive Transport Aided by
Proteins   133
CONCEPT 7.4 Active transport uses energy to move solutes
against their gradients   134
The Need for Energy in Active Transport   134
Maintenance of Membrane Potential by Ion Pumps   134
Cotransport: Coupled Transport by a Membrane
Protein   136
CONCEPT 7.5 Bulk transport across the plasma membrane
occurs by exocytosis and endocytosis   137
Exocytosis   137
Endocytosis   137

8   An Introduction to Metabolism   141
OVERVIEW: The Energy of Life   141
CONCEPT 8.1 An organism's metabolism transforms matter
and energy, subject to the laws of thermodynamics   141
Organization of the Chemistry of Life into Metabolic
Pathways   141
Forms of Energy   142
The Laws of Energy Transformation   143
CONCEPT 8.2 The free-energy change of a reaction tells us
whether the reaction occurs spontaneously   145
Free-Energy Change, ΔG 145
Free Energy, Stability, and Equilibrium   145
Free Energy and Metabolism   146
CONCEPT 8.3 ATP powers cellular work by coupling
exergonic reactions to endergonic reactions   148
The Structure and Hydrolysis of ATP   148
How ATP Performs Work   149
The Regeneration of ATP   150
CONCEPT 8.4 Enzymes speed up metabolic reactions by
lowering energy barriers   150
The Activation Energy Barrier   150
How Enzymes Lower the E_A Barrier   152
Substrate Specificity of Enzymes   152
Catalysis in the Enzyme's Active Site   152
Effects of Local Conditions on Enzyme Activity   154
CONCEPT 8.5 Regulation of enzyme activity helps control
metabolism   156
Allosteric Regulation of Enzymes   156
Specific Localization of Enzymes Within the Cell   157

9   Cellular Respiration: Harvesting
Chemical Energy   160
OVERVIEW: Life Is Work   160
CONCEPT 9.1 Catabolic pathways yield energy by oxidizing
organic fuels   161

Catabolic Pathways and Production of ATP   161
Redox Reactions: Oxidation and Reduction   161
The Stages of Cellular Respiration: A Preview   164
CONCEPT 9.2 Glycolysis harvests chemical energy by
oxidizing glucose to pyruvate   165
CONCEPT 9.3 The citric acid cycle completes
the energy-yielding oxidation of organic molecules   168
CONCEPT 9.4 During oxidative phosphorylation,
chemiosmosis couples electron transport to ATP
synthesis   170
The Pathway of Electron Transport   170
Chemiosmosis: The Energy-Coupling
Mechanism   171
An Accounting of ATP Production by Cellular
Respiration   173
CONCEPT 9.5 Fermentation enables some cells to
produce ATP without the use of oxygen   174
Types of Fermentation   175
Fermentation and Cellular Respiration
Compared   175
The Evolutionary Significance of Glycolysis   176
CONCEPT 9.6 Glycolysis and the citric acid cycle connect to
many other metabolic pathways   176
The Versatility of Catabolism   176
Biosynthesis (Anabolic Pathways)   177
Regulation of Cellular Respiration via Feedback
Mechanisms   177

10   Photosynthesis   181
OVERVIEW: The Process That Feeds the Biosphere   181
CONCEPT 10.1 Photosynthesis converts light energy to the
chemical energy of food   182
Chloroplasts: The Sites of Photosynthesis in Plants   182
Tracking Atoms Through Photosynthesis: Scientific
Inquiry   183
The Two Stages of Photosynthesis: A Preview   184
CONCEPT 10.2 The light reactions convert solar energy to
the chemical energy of ATP and NADPH   186
The Nature of Sunlight   186
Photosynthetic Pigments: The Light Receptors   186
Excitation of Chlorophyll by Light   188
A Photosystem: A Reaction Center Associated with Light-
Harvesting Complexes   189
Noncyclic Electron Flow   190
Cyclic Electron Flow   191
A Comparison of Chemiosmosis in Chloroplasts
and Mitochondria   192
CONCEPT 10.3 The Calvin cycle uses ATP and NADPH to
convert CO_2 to sugar   193
CONCEPT 10.4 Alternative mechanisms of carbon fixation
have evolved in hot, arid climates   195
Photorespiration: An Evolutionary Relic?   195
C_4 Plants   196
CAM Plants   196
The Importance of Photosynthesis: A Review   197

11 Cell Communication   201

OVERVIEW: The Cellular Internet   201

CONCEPT 11.1 External signals are converted into responses within the cell   201
- Evolution of Cell Signaling   201
- Local and Long-Distance Signaling   202
- The Three Stages of Cell Signaling: *A Preview*   203

CONCEPT 11.2 Reception: A signal molecule binds to a receptor protein, causing it to change shape   204
- Intracellular Receptors   205
- Receptors in the Plasma Membrane   205

CONCEPT 11.3 Transduction: Cascades of molecular interactions relay signals from receptors to target molecules in the cell   208
- Signal Transduction Pathways   208
- Protein Phosphorylation and Dephosphorylation   209
- Small Molecules and Ions as Second Messengers   210

CONCEPT 11.4 Response: Cell signaling leads to regulation of cytoplasmic activities or transcription   212
- Cytoplasmic and Nuclear Responses   212
- Fine-Tuning of the Response   213

12 The Cell Cycle   218

OVERVIEW: The Key Roles of Cell Division   218

CONCEPT 12.1 Cell division results in genetically identical daughter cells   219
- Cellular Organization of the Genetic Material   219
- Distribution of Chromosomes During Cell Division   219

CONCEPT 12.2 The mitotic phase alternates with interphase in the cell cycle   221
- Phases of the Cell Cycle   221
- The Mitotic Spindle: *A Closer Look*   221
- Cytokinesis: *A Closer Look*   224
- Binary Fission   226
- The Evolution of Mitosis   227

CONCEPT 12.3 The cell cycle is regulated by a molecular control system   228
- Evidence for Cytoplasmic Signals   228
- The Cell Cycle Control System   229
- Loss of Cell Cycle Controls in Cancer Cells   232

UNIT THREE

Genetics   236

13 Meiosis and Sexual Life Cycles   238

OVERVIEW: Hereditary Similarity and Variation   238

CONCEPT 13.1 Offspring acquire genes from parents by inheriting chromosomes   238
- Inheritance of Genes   239
- Comparison of Asexual and Sexual Reproduction   239

CONCEPT 13.2 Fertilization and meiosis alternate in sexual life cycles   240
- Sets of Chromosomes in Human Cells   240
- Behavior of Chromosome Sets in the Human Life Cycle   241
- The Variety of Sexual Life Cycles   242

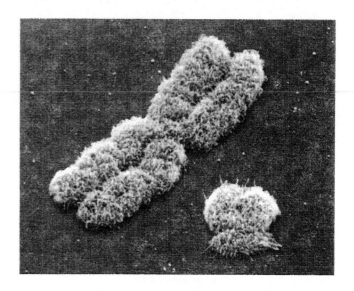

CONCEPT 13.3 Meiosis reduces the number of chromosome sets from diploid to haploid   243
- The Stages of Meiosis   243
- A Comparison of Mitosis and Meiosis   247

CONCEPT 13.4 Genetic variation produced in sexual life cycles contributes to evolution   247
- Origins of Genetic Variation Among Offspring   247
- Evolutionary Significance of Genetic Variation Within Populations   248

14 Mendel and the Gene Idea   251

OVERVIEW: Drawing from the Deck of Genes   251

CONCEPT 14.1 Mendel used the scientific approach to identify two laws of inheritance   251
- Mendel's Experimental, Quantitative Approach   252
- The Law of Segregation   253
- The Law of Independent Assortment   256

CONCEPT 14.2 The laws of probability govern Mendelian inheritance   258
- The Multiplication and Addition Rules Applied to Monohybrid Crosses   258
- Solving Complex Genetics Problems with the Rules of Probability   259

CONCEPT 14.3 Inheritance patterns are often more complex than predicted by simple Mendelian genetics   260
- Extending Mendelian Genetics for a Single Gene   260
- Extending Mendelian Genetics for Two or More Genes   262
- Nature and Nurture: The Environmental Impact on Phenotype   264
- Integrating a Mendelian View of Heredity and Variation   264

CONCEPT 14.4 Many human traits follow Mendelian patterns of inheritance   265
- Pedigree Analysis   265
- Recessively Inherited Disorders   266
- Dominantly Inherited Disorders   267
- Multifactorial Disorders   268
- Genetic Testing and Counseling   268

15 The Chromosomal Basis of Inheritance 274

OVERVIEW: Locating Genes on Chromosomes 274

CONCEPT 15.1 Mendelian inheritance has its physical basis in the behavior of chromosomes 274

Morgan's Experimental Evidence: *Scientific Inquiry* 276

CONCEPT 15.2 Linked genes tend to be inherited together because they are located near each other on the same chromosome 277

How Linkage Affects Inheritance: *Scientific Inquiry* 277
Genetic Recombination and Linkage 278
Linkage Mapping Using Recombination Data: *Scientific Inquiry* 279

CONCEPT 15.3 Sex-linked genes exhibit unique patterns of inheritance 282

The Chromosomal Basis of Sex 282
Inheritance of Sex-Linked Genes 283
X Inactivation in Female Mammals 284

CONCEPT 15.4 Alterations of chromosome number or structure cause some genetic disorders 285

Abnormal Chromosome Number 285
Alterations of Chromosome Structure 286
Human Disorders Due to Chromosomal Alterations 287

CONCEPT 15.5 Some inheritance patterns are exceptions to the standard chromosome theory 288

Genomic Imprinting 288
Inheritance of Organelle Genes 289

16 The Molecular Basis of Inheritance 293

OVERVIEW: Life's Operating Instructions 293

CONCEPT 16.1 DNA is the genetic material 293

The Search for the Genetic Material: *Scientific Inquiry* 293
Building a Structural Model of DNA: *Scientific Inquiry* 296

CONCEPT 16.2 Many proteins work together in DNA replication and repair 299

The Basic Principle: Base Pairing to a Template Strand 299
DNA Replication: *A Closer Look* 300
Proofreading and Repairing DNA 305
Replicating the Ends of DNA Molecules 306

17 From Gene to Protein 309

OVERVIEW: The Flow of Genetic Information 309

CONCEPT 17.1 Genes specify proteins via transcription and translation 309

Evidence from the Study of Metabolic Defects 309
Basic Principles of Transcription and Translation 311
The Genetic Code 312

CONCEPT 17.2 Transcription is the DNA-directed synthesis of RNA: *a closer look* 315

Molecular Components of Transcription 315
Synthesis of an RNA Transcript 316

CONCEPT 17.3 Eukaryotic cells modify RNA after transcription 317

Alteration of mRNA Ends 317
Split Genes and RNA Splicing 318

CONCEPT 17.4 Translation is the RNA-directed synthesis of a polypeptide: *a closer look* 320

Molecular Components of Translation 320
Building a Polypeptide 323
Completing and Targeting the Functional Protein 324

CONCEPT 17.5 RNA plays multiple roles in the cell: *a review* 327

CONCEPT 17.6 Comparing gene expression in prokaryotes and eukaryotes reveals key differences 327

CONCEPT 17.7 Point mutations can affect protein structure and function 328

Types of Point Mutations 328
Mutagens 329
What is a Gene? *Revisiting the Question* 330

18 The Genetics of Viruses and Bacteria 334

OVERVIEW: Microbial Model Systems 334

CONCEPT 18.1 A virus has a genome but can reproduce only within a host cell 334

The Discovery of Viruses: *Scientific Inquiry* 334
Structure of Viruses 335
General Features of Viral Reproductive Cycles 336
Reproductive Cycles of Phages 337
Reproductive Cycles of Animal Viruses 339
Evolution of Viruses 342

CONCEPT 18.2 Viruses, viroids, and prions are formidable pathogens in animals and plants 343

Viral Diseases in Animals 343
Emerging Viruses 344
Viral Diseases in Plants 345
Viroids and Prions: The Simplest Infectious Agents 345

CONCEPT 18.3 Rapid reproduction, mutation, and genetic recombination contribute to the genetic diversity of bacteria 346

The Bacterial Genome and Its Replication 346
Mutation and Genetic Recombination as Sources of Genetic Variation 346
Mechanisms of Gene Transfer and Genetic Recombination in Bacteria 348
Transposition of Genetic Elements 351

CONCEPT 18.4 Individual bacteria respond to environmental change by regulating their gene expression 352

Operons: The Basic Concept 353
Repressible and Inducible Operons: Two Types of Negative Gene Regulation 354
Positive Gene Regulation 356

19 Eukaryotic Genomes: Organization, Regulation, and Evolution 359

OVERVIEW: How Eukaryotic Genomes Work and Evolve 359

CONCEPT 19.1 Chromatin structure is based on successive levels of DNA packing 359

Nucleosomes, or "Beads on a String" 360
Higher Levels of DNA Packing 360

CONCEPT 19.2 Gene expression can be regulated at any stage, but the key step is transcription 362
Differential Gene Expression 362
Regulation of Chromatin Structure 363
Regulation of Transcription Initiation 364
Mechanisms of Post-Transcriptional Regulation 368

CONCEPT 19.3 Cancer results from genetic changes that affect cell cycle control 370
Types of Genes Associated with Cancer 370
Interference with Normal Cell-Signaling Pathways 371
The Multistep Model of Cancer Development 373
Inherited Predisposition to Cancer 374

CONCEPT 19.4 Eukaryotic genomes can have many noncoding DNA sequences in addition to genes 374
The Relationship Between Genomic Composition and Organismal Complexity 374
Transposable Elements and Related Sequences 375
Other Repetitive DNA, Including Simple Sequence DNA 376
Genes and Multigene Families 377

CONCEPT 19.5 Duplications, rearrangements, and mutations of DNA contribute to genome evolution 378
Duplication of Chromosome Sets 378
Duplication and Divergence of DNA Segments 378
Rearrangements of Parts of Genes: Exon Duplication and Exon Shuffling 380
How Transposable Elements Contribute to Genome Evolution 380

20 DNA Technology and Genomics 384
OVERVIEW: Understanding and Manipulating Genomes 384

CONCEPT 20.1 DNA cloning permits production of multiple copies of a specific gene or other DNA segment 385
DNA Cloning and Its Applications: A Preview 385
Using Restriction Enzymes to Make Recombinant DNA 386
Cloning a Eukaryotic Gene in a Bacterial Plasmid 386
Storing Cloned Genes in DNA Libraries 388
Cloning and Expressing Eukaryotic Genes 390
Amplifying DNA in Vitro: The Polymerase Chain Reaction (PCR) 391

CONCEPT 20.2 Restriction fragment analysis detects DNA differences that affect restriction sites 392
Gel Electrophoresis and Southern Blotting 392
Restriction Fragment Length Differences as Genetic Markers 394

CONCEPT 20.3 Entire genomes can be mapped at the DNA level 394
Genetic (Linkage) Mapping: Relative Ordering of Markers 396
Physical Mapping: Ordering DNA Fragments 396
DNA Sequencing 396

CONCEPT 20.4 Genome sequences provide clues to important biological questions 398
Identifying Protein-Coding Genes in DNA Sequences 399
Determining Gene Function 400
Studying Expression of Interacting Groups of Genes 400
Comparing Genomes of Different Species 400
Future Directions in Genomics 402

CONCEPT 20.5 The practical applications of DNA technology affect our lives in many ways 402
Medical Applications 402
Pharmaceutical Products 404
Forensic Evidence 404
Environmental Cleanup 405
Agricultural Applications 406
Safety and Ethical Questions Raised by DNA Technology 407

21 The Genetic Basis of Development 411
OVERVIEW: From Single Cell to Multicellular Organism 411

CONCEPT 21.1 Embryonic development involves cell division, cell differentiation, and morphogenesis 412

CONCEPT 21.2 Different cell types result from differential gene expression in cells with the same DNA 415
Evidence for Genomic Equivalence 415
Transcriptional Regulation of Gene Expression During Development 418
Cytoplasmic Determinants and Cell-Cell Signals in Cell Differentiation 420

CONCEPT 21.3 Pattern formation in animals and plants results from similar genetic and cellular mechanisms 421
Drosophila Development: A Cascade of Gene Activations 421
C. elegans: The Role of Cell Signaling 425
Plant Development: Cell Signaling and Transcriptional Regulation 429

CONCEPT 21.4 Comparative studies help explain how the evolution of development leads to morphological diversity 431
Widespread Conservation of Developmental Genes Among Animals 431
Comparison of Animal and Plant Development 433

UNIT FOUR

Mechanisms of Evolution 436

22 Descent with Modification: A Darwinian View of Life 438
OVERVIEW: Darwin Introduces a Revolutionary Theory 438

CONCEPT 22.1 The Darwinian revolution challenged traditional views of a young Earth inhabited by unchanging species 438
Resistance to the Idea of Evolution 439
Theories of Gradualism 440
Lamarck's Theory of Evolution 440

CONCEPT 22.2: In The Origin of Species, Darwin proposed that species change through natural selection 441
Darwin's Research 441
The Origin of Species 443

CONCEPT 22.3 Darwin's theory explains a wide range of observations 446
Natural Selection in Action 446
Homology, Biogeography, and the Fossil Record 448

What Is Theoretical about the Darwinian View of
  Life? 451

23 The Evolution of Populations 454

OVERVIEW: The Smallest Unit of Evolution 454

CONCEPT 23.1 Population genetics provides a foundation for studying evolution 454

The Modern Synthesis 455
Gene Pools and Allele Frequencies 455
The Hardy-Weinberg Theorem 456

CONCEPT 23.2 Mutation and sexual recombination produce the variation that makes evolution possible 459

Mutation 459
Sexual Recombination 460

CONCEPT 23.3 Natural selection, genetic drift, and gene flow can alter a population's genetic composition 460

Natural Selection 460
Genetic Drift 460
Gene Flow 462

CONCEPT 23.4 Natural selection is the primary mechanism of adaptive evolution 462

Genetic Variation 462
A Closer Look at Natural Selection 464
The Preservation of Genetic Variation 466
Sexual Selection 468
The Evolutionary Enigma of Sexual
  Reproduction 469
Why Natural Selection Cannot Fashion Perfect
  Organisms 469

24 The Origin of Species 472

OVERVIEW: That "Mystery of Mysteries" 472

CONCEPT 24.1 The biological species concept emphasizes reproductive isolation 473

The Biological Species Concept 473
Other Definitions of Species 476

CONCEPT 24.2 Speciation can take place with or without geographic separation 476

Allopatric ("Other Country") Speciation 477
Sympatric ("Same Country") Speciation 478
Allopatric and Sympatric Speciation: A
  Summary 480
Adaptive Radiation 480
Studying the Genetics of Speciation 481
The Tempo of Speciation 481

CONCEPT 24.3 Macroevolutionary changes can accumulate through many speciation events 482

Evolutionary Novelties 482
Evolution of the Genes That Control
  Development 484
Evolution Is Not Goal Oriented 486

25 Phylogeny and Systematics 491

OVERVIEW: Investigating the Tree of Life 491

CONCEPT 25.1 Phylogenies are based on common ancestries inferred from fossil, morphological, and molecular evidence 492

The Fossil Record 492
Morphological and Molecular Homologies 492

CONCEPT 25.2 Phylogenetic systematics connects classification with evolutionary history 495

Binomial Nomenclature 496
Hierarchical Classification 496
Linking Classification and Phylogeny 496

CONCEPT 25.3 Phylogenetic systematics informs the construction of phylogenetic trees based on shared characters 497

Cladistics 498
Phylogenetic Trees and Timing 499
Maximum Parsimony and Maximum
  Likelihood 501
Phylogenetic Trees as Hypotheses 501

CONCEPT 25.4 Much of an organism's evolutionary history is documented in its genome 504

Gene Duplications and Gene Families 505
Genome Evolution 505

CONCEPT 25.5 Molecular clocks help track evolutionary time 506

Molecular Clocks 506
The Universal Tree of Life 507

APPENDIX A Answers

APPENDIX B The Metric System

APPENDIX C A Comparison of the Light Microscope and the Electron Microscope

APPENDIX D Classification of Life

CREDITS

GLOSSARY

INDEX

Biology

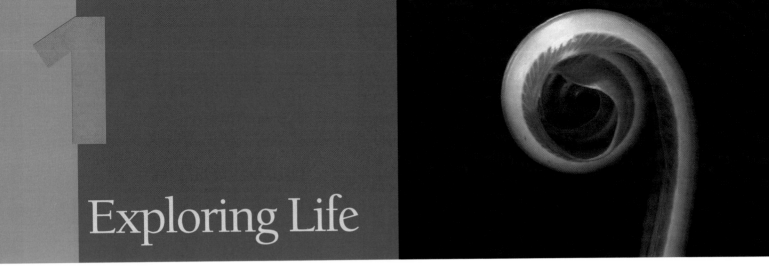

1

Exploring Life

▲ Figure 1.1 **Biology is the science that focuses on life.**

Key Concepts

1.1 Biologists explore life from the microscopic to the global scale

1.2 Biological systems are much more than the sum of their parts

1.3 Biologists explore life across its great diversity of species

1.4 Evolution accounts for life's unity and diversity

1.5 Biologists use various forms of inquiry to explore life

1.6 A set of themes connects the concepts of biology

Overview

Biology's Most Exciting Era

Welcome to **biology**, the scientific study of life. You are becoming involved with biology during its most exciting era. The largest and best-equipped community of scientists in history is beginning to solve biological puzzles that once seemed unsolvable. We are moving ever closer to understanding how a single microscopic cell develops into a complex plant or animal; how plants convert solar energy to the chemical energy of food; how the human mind works; how various forms of life network in biological communities such as forests and coral reefs; and how the great diversity of life on Earth evolved from the first microbes. The more we learn about life, the more fascinating it becomes, as progress on one question leads to even more questions that will captivate curious minds for decades to come. More than anything else, biology is a quest, an ongoing inquiry about the nature of life.

Modern biology is as important as it is inspiring. Research breakthroughs in genetics and cell biology are transforming medicine and agriculture. Molecular biology is providing new tools for fields as diverse as anthropology and criminal science. Neuroscience and evolutionary biology are reshaping psychology and sociology. New models in ecology are helping societies evaluate environmental issues, such as the causes and biological consequences of global warming. These are just a few examples of how biology weaves into the fabric of our culture more than ever before. There has never been a better time to explore life.

The phenomenon we call life defies a simple, one-sentence definition. Yet almost any child perceives that a dog or a bug or a plant, such as the fern "fiddlehead" that graces the cover of this book **(Figure 1.1)**, is alive, while a rock is not. We recognize life by what living things do. **Figure 1.2** highlights some of the properties and processes we associate with life.

As we set off to explore life, it helps to have a panoramic view of the vast field of study before us. This opening chapter introduces the wide scope of biology, highlights the diversity of life, describes themes, such as evolution, that unify all of biology, and examines methods of inquiry that biologists use to explore life.

Concept 1.1

Biologists explore life from the microscopic to the global scale

The study of life extends from the microscopic scale of the molecules and cells that make up organisms to the global scale of the entire living planet. We can divide this enormous range into different levels of biological organization.

(a) Order. This close-up of a sunflower illustrates the highly ordered structure that characterizes life.

(b) Evolutionary adaptation. The appearance of this pygmy seahorse camouflages the animal in its environment. Such adaptations evolve over many generations by the reproductive success of those individuals with heritable traits that are best suited to their environments.

(c) Response to the environment. This Venus' flytrap closed its trap rapidly in response to the environmental stimulus of a dragonfly landing on the open trap.

(d) Regulation. The regulation of blood flow through the blood vessels of this jackrabbit's ears helps maintain a constant body temperature by adjusting heat exchange with the surrounding air.

(e) Energy processing. This hummingbird obtains fuel in the form of nectar from flowers. The hummingbird will use the chemical energy stored in its food to power flight and other work.

(f) Growth and development. Inherited information carried by genes controls the pattern of growth and development of organisms, such as this Nile crocodile.

(g) Reproduction. Organisms (living things) reproduce their own kind. Here an emperor penguin protects its baby.

▲ **Figure 1.2 Some properties of life.**

A Hierarchy of Biological Organization

Imagine zooming in from space to take a closer and closer look at life on Earth. Our destination is a forest in Ontario, Canada, where we will eventually use microscopes and other instruments to explore a maple leaf right down to the molecular level. **Figure 1.3** (on the next two pages) narrates this journey into life, with the circled numbers leading you through the levels of biological organization illustrated by the photographs.

Figure 1.3
Exploring **Levels of Biological Organization**

❶ **The biosphere.** As soon as we are near enough to Earth to make out its continents and oceans, we begin to see signs of life — in the green mosaic of the planet's forests, for example. This is our first view of the biosphere, which consists of all the environments on Earth that are inhabited by life. The biosphere includes most regions of land; most bodies of water, such as oceans, lakes, and rivers; and the atmosphere to an altitude of several kilometers.

❷ **Ecosystems.** As we approach Earth's surface for an imaginary landing in Ontario, we can begin to make out a forest with an abundance of deciduous trees (trees that lose their leaves in the autumn and grow new ones in the spring). Such a deciduous forest is an example of an ecosystem. Grasslands, deserts, and the ocean's coral reefs are other types of ecosystems. An ecosystem consists of all the living things in a particular area, along with all the nonliving components of the environment with which life interacts, such as soil, water, atmospheric gases, and light. All of Earth's ecosystems combined make up the biosphere.

❸ **Communities.** The entire array of organisms inhabiting a particular ecosystem is called a biological community. The community in our forest ecosystem includes many kinds of trees and other plants, a diversity of animals, various mushrooms and other fungi, and enormous numbers of diverse microorganisms, which are living forms such as bacteria that are too small to see without a microscope. Each of these forms of life is called a *species*.

❹ **Populations.** A population consists of all the individuals of a species living within the bounds of a specified area. For example, our Ontario forest includes a population of sugar maple trees and a population of American black bears. We can now refine our definition of a community as the set of populations that inhabit a particular area.

❺ **Organisms.** Individual living things are called organisms. Each of the maple trees and other plants in the forest is an organism, and so is each forest animal such as a frog, squirrel, bear, and insect. The soil teems with microorganisms such as bacteria.

8 Cells. The cell is life's fundamental unit of structure and function. Some organisms, such as amoebas and most bacteria, are single cells. Other organisms, including plants and animals, are multicellular. Instead of a single cell performing all the functions of life, a multicellular organism has a division of labor among specialized cells. A human body consists of trillions of microscopic cells of many different kinds, including muscle cells and nerve cells, which are organized into the various specialized tissues. For example, muscle tissue consists of bundles of muscle cells. And note again the cells of the tissue within a leaf's interior. Each of the cells you see is only about 25 μm (micrometers) across. It would take more than 700 of these cells to reach across a penny. As small as these cells are, you can see that each contains numerous green structures called chloroplasts, which are responsible for photosynthesis.

Cell

1 μm

9 Organelles. Chloroplasts are examples of organelles, the various functional components that make up cells. In this figure, a very powerful tool called an electron microscope brings a single chloroplast into sharp focus.

Atoms

10 μm

7 Tissues. Our next scale change to see a leaf's tissues requires a microscope. The leaf on the left has been cut on an angle. The honey-combed tissue in the interior of the leaf (upper half of photo) is the main location of photosynthesis, the process that converts light energy to the chemical energy of sugar and other food. We are viewing the sliced leaf from a perspective that also enables us to see the jigsaw puzzle-like tissue called epidermis, the "skin" on the surface of the leaf (lower half of photo). The pores through the epidermis allow the gas carbon dioxide, a raw material for sugar production, to reach the photosynthetic tissue in the interior of the leaf. At this scale, we can also see that each tissue has a cellular structure. In fact, each kind of tissue is a group of similar cells.

10 Molecules. Our last scale change vaults us into a chloroplast for a view of life at the molecular level. A molecule is a chemical structure consisting of two or more small chemical units called *atoms,* which are represented as balls in this computer graphic of a chlorophyll molecule. Chlorophyll is the pigment molecule that makes a maple leaf green. One of the most important molecules on Earth, chlorophyll absorbs sunlight during the first step of photosynthesis. Within each chloroplast, millions of chlorophylls and other molecules are organized into the equipment that converts light energy to the chemical energy of food.

50 μm

6 Organs and organ systems. The structural hierarchy of life continues to unfold as we explore the architecture of the more complex organisms. A maple leaf is an example of an organ, a body part consisting of two or more tissues (which we'll see upon our next scale change). Stems and roots are the other major organs of plants. Examples of human organs are the brain, heart, and kidney. The organs of humans and other complex animals are organized into organ systems, each a team of organs that cooperate in a specific function. For example, the human digestive system includes such organs as the tongue, stomach, and intestines.

In Figure 1.3, we traced the greenness that we first saw in our extraterrestrial view of the biosphere all the way down to the molecular level of chlorophyll. As a follow-up to this overview of life's structural hierarchy, we'll take a closer look at just two biological levels near opposite ends of the size scale: ecosystems and cells.

A Closer Look at Ecosystems

Life does not exist in a vacuum. Each organism interacts continuously with its environment, which includes other organisms as well as nonliving factors. The roots of a tree, for example, absorb water and minerals from the soil. The leaves take in carbon dioxide from the air. Solar energy absorbed by chlorophyll drives photosynthesis, which converts water and carbon dioxide to sugar and oxygen. The tree releases oxygen to the air, and its roots help form soil by breaking up rocks. Both organism and environment are affected by the interactions between them. The tree also interacts with other life, including soil microorganisms associated with its roots and animals that eat its leaves and fruit.

Ecosystem Dynamics

The dynamics of any ecosystem include two major processes. One process is the cycling of nutrients. For example, minerals acquired by plants will eventually be returned to the soil by microorganisms that decompose leaf litter, dead roots, and other organic debris. The second major process in an ecosystem is the flow of energy from sunlight to producers to consumers. **Producers** are plants and other photosynthetic organisms that convert light energy to chemical energy. **Consumers** are organisms, such as animals, that feed on producers and other consumers.

Energy Conversion

Moving, growing, reproducing, and other activities of life require organisms to perform work. And work depends on a source of energy. The exchange of energy between an organism and its surroundings often involves the transformation of one form of energy to another. For example, when a leaf produces sugar, it converts solar energy to chemical energy in sugar molecules. When an animal's muscle cells use sugar as fuel to power movements, they convert chemical energy to kinetic energy, the energy of motion. And in all these energy conversions, some of the available energy is converted to thermal energy, which working organisms dissipate to their surroundings as heat. In contrast to chemical nutrients, which recycle within an ecosystem, energy flows *through* an ecosystem, usually entering as light and exiting as heat **(Figure 1.4)**.

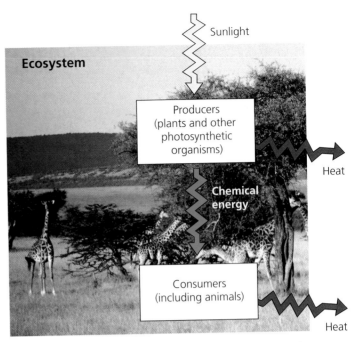

▲ Figure 1.4 **Basic scheme for energy flow through an ecosystem.**

A Closer Look at Cells

In life's structural hierarchy, the cell has a special place as the lowest level of organization that can perform *all* activities required for life. For example, the ability of cells to divide to form new cells is the basis for all reproduction and for the growth and repair of multicellular organisms **(Figure 1.5)**. Your every movement and thought are based on the activities of muscle cells and nerve cells. Even a global process such as the recycling of carbon, a chemical element essential to life, is the cumulative product of cellular activities, including the photosynthesis that occurs in the chloroplasts of leaf cells. Understanding how cells work is a major research focus of modern biology.

25 μm

▲ Figure 1.5 **A lung cell from a newt divides into two smaller cells that will grow and divide again.**

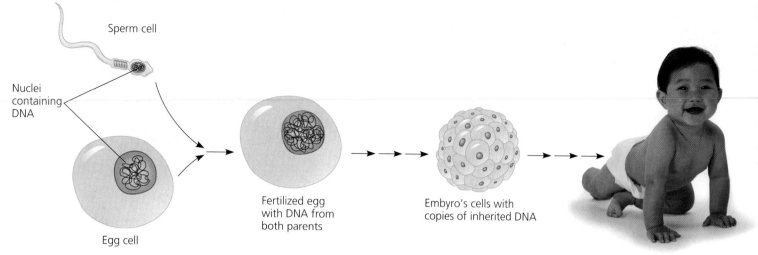

▲ Figure 1.6 **Inherited DNA directs development of an organism.**

The Cell's Heritable Information

Take another look at the dividing cell in Figure 1.5. Within the cells you can see structures called chromosomes, which are stained with a blue-glowing dye. The chromosomes are partly made of a substance called **deoxyribonucleic acid,** or **DNA** for short. DNA is the substance of **genes,** the units of inheritance that transmit information from parents to offspring. Your blood group (A, B, AB, or O), for example, is the result of certain genes that you inherited from your parents.

Each chromosome has one very long DNA molecule, with hundreds or thousands of genes arranged along its length. The DNA of chromosomes replicates as a cell prepares to divide; thus, each of the two cellular offspring inherits a complete set of genes.

Each of us began life as a single cell stocked with DNA inherited from our parents. Replication of that DNA transmitted those genes to our trillions of cells. In each cell, the genes along the length of DNA molecules encode the information for building the cell's other molecules. In this way, DNA directs the development and maintenance of the entire organism **(Figure 1.6).**

The molecular structure of DNA accounts for its information-rich nature. Each DNA molecule is made up of two long chains arranged into what is called a double helix. Each link of a chain is one of four kinds of chemical building blocks called nucleotides **(Figure 1.7).** The way DNA encodes a cell's information is analogous to the way we arrange the letters of the alphabet into precise sequences with specific meanings. The word *rat,* for example, conjures up an image of a rodent; the words *tar* and *art,* which contain the same letters, mean very different things. Libraries are filled with books containing information encoded in varying sequences of only 26 letters. We can think of nucleotides as the alphabet of

(a) DNA double helix. This model shows each atom in a segment of DNA. Made up of two long chains of building blocks called nucleotides, a DNA molecule takes the three-dimensional form of a double helix.

(b) Single strand of DNA. These geometric shapes and letters are simple symbols for the nucleotides in a small section of one chain of a DNA molecule. Genetic information is encoded in specific sequences of the four types of nucleotides (their names are abbreviated here as A, T, C, and G).

▲ Figure 1.7 **DNA: The genetic material.**

inheritance. Specific sequential arrangements of these four chemical letters encode the precise information in genes, which are typically hundreds or thousands of nucleotides long. One gene in a bacterial cell may be translated as "Build a purple pigment." A particular human gene may mean "Make the hormone insulin."

More generally, most genes program the cell's production of large molecules called proteins. The sequence of nucleotides along each gene codes for a specific protein with a unique shape and function in the cell. One protein might be part of the contractile apparatus of muscle cells. Another protein might be an antibody, part of the body's defense system against viruses and other disease agents. Still another protein might be an enzyme, a protein that catalyzes (speeds up) a specific chemical reaction in a cell. Almost all cellular activities involve the action of one or more proteins. DNA provides the heritable blueprints, but proteins are the tools that actually build and maintain the cell.

All forms of life employ essentially the same genetic code. A particular sequence of nucleotides says the same thing to one organism as it does to another. Differences between organisms reflect differences between their nucleotide sequences. But because the genetic code is universal, it is possible to engineer cells to produce proteins normally found only in some other organism. One of the first pharmaceutical products obtained using this technology was human insulin, produced by bacteria into which a gene for this human protein was inserted.

The entire "library" of genetic instructions that an organism inherits is called its **genome.** The chromosomes of each human cell pack a genome that is about 3 billion nucleotides long. If the one-letter symbols for this sequence of nucleotides were written in letters the size of those you are now reading, the genetic text would fill about 600 books the size of this one. Within this genomic library of nucleotide sequences are genes coding for the production of more than 75,000 different kinds of proteins, each with a specific function.

Two Main Forms of Cells

All cells share certain characteristics. For example, every cell is enclosed by a membrane that regulates the passage of materials between the cell and its surroundings. And every cell uses DNA as its genetic information.

We can distinguish two main forms of cells: prokaryotic cells and eukaryotic cells. The cells of two groups of microorganisms called bacteria and archaea are prokaryotic. All other forms of life, including plants and animals, are composed of eukaryotic cells.

A **eukaryotic cell** is subdivided by internal membranes into various membrane-enclosed organelles, including the chloroplasts of Figure 1.3. In most eukaryotic cells, the largest

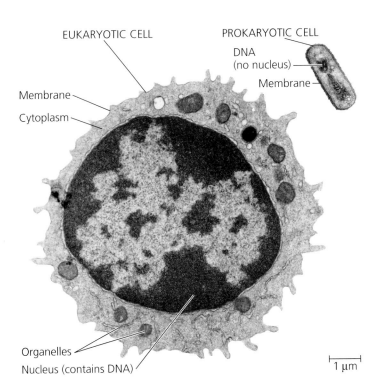

▲ **Figure 1.8 Contrasting eukaryotic and prokaryotic cells in size and complexity.**

organelle is the nucleus, which contains the cell's DNA (as chromosomal molecules). The other organelles are located in the cytoplasm, the entire region between the nucleus and outer membrane of the cell.

Prokaryotic cells are much simpler and generally smaller than eukaryotic cells **(Figure 1.8)**. In a **prokaryotic cell,** the DNA is not separated from the rest of the cell by enclosure in a membrane-bounded nucleus. Prokaryotic cells also lack the other kinds of membrane-enclosed organelles that characterize eukaryotic cells.

The prokaryote-eukaryote difference is an example of the biological diversity we will explore in Concept 1.3. But first, let's take one more look at the hierarchy of biological order, this time in the context of a research movement called systems biology.

Concept Check 1.1

1. For each biological level in Figure 1.3, write a sentence that includes the next "lower" level. Example: "A community consists of *populations* of the various species inhabiting a specific area."
2. What are the relationships between these three genetic terms: DNA, genes, and chromosomes?
3. Explain why, at the cellular level, plants have more in common with animals than they do with bacteria.

For suggested answers, see Appendix A.

Concept 1.2

Biological systems are much more than the sum of their parts

"The whole is greater than the sum of its parts." That familiar adage captures the important concept that a combination of components can form a more complex organization called a **system**. Examples of biological systems are cells, organisms, and ecosystems. To understand how such systems work, it is not enough to have a "parts list," even a complete one. The future of biology is in understanding the behavior of whole, integrated systems.

The Emergent Properties of Systems

Take another look at the levels of life in Figure 1.3. With each step upward in this hierarchy of biological order, novel properties emerge that are not present at the level just below. These **emergent properties** are due to the arrangement and interactions of parts as complexity increases. For example, a test-tube mixture of chlorophyll and all the other molecules found in a chloroplast cannot perform photosynthesis. The process of photosynthesis emerges from the very specific way in which the chlorophyll and other molecules are arranged in an intact chloroplast. To take another example, if a serious head injury disrupts the intricate architecture of a human brain, the mind may cease to function properly even though all of the brain parts are still present. Our thoughts and memories are emergent properties of a complex network of nerve cells. At an even higher level of biological organization—at the ecosystem level—the recycling of nutrients such as carbon depends on a network of diverse organisms interacting with each other and with the soil and air.

Emergent properties are neither supernatural nor unique to life. We can see the importance of arrangement in the distinction between a box of bicycle parts and a working bicycle. And while graphite and diamonds are both pure carbon, they have very different properties based on how their carbon atoms are arranged. But compared to such nonliving examples, the emergent properties of life are particularly challenging to study because of the unrivaled complexity of biological systems.

The Power and Limitations of Reductionism

Because the properties of life emerge from complex organization, scientists seeking to understand biological systems confront a dilemma. On the one hand, we cannot fully explain a higher level of order by breaking it down into its parts. A dissected animal no longer functions; a cell reduced to its chemical ingredients is no longer a cell. Disrupting a living system interferes with the meaningful understanding of its processes. On the other hand, something as complex as an organism or a cell cannot be analyzed without taking it apart.

Reductionism—reducing complex systems to simpler components that are more manageable to study—is a powerful strategy in biology. For example, by studying the molecular structure of DNA that had been extracted from cells, James Watson and Francis Crick inferred, in 1953, how this molecule could serve as the chemical basis of inheritance.

In 2001, almost half a century after the famous work of Watson and Crick, an international team of scientists published a "rough draft" of the sequence of 3 billion chemical letters in a human genome **(Figure 1.9)**. (Researchers have also sequenced the genomes of many other species.) The press and world leaders acclaimed the Human Genome Project as one of the greatest scientific achievements ever. But unlike past cultural zeniths, such as the moonwalk of Apollo astronauts, the sequencing of the human genome is more a

▶ **Figure 1.9 Modern biology as an information science.** Automatic DNA-sequencing machines and abundant computing power accelerated the Human Genome Project. This facility in Cambridge, United Kingdom, was one of many labs that collaborated in the international project.

commencement than a climax. As the quest continues, scientists are learning the functions of thousands of genes and their protein products. And research is now moving on to how the activities of these myriad molecules are coordinated in the development and maintenance of cells and whole organisms. At the cutting edge of this research is the approach called systems biology.

Systems Biology

Biology is turning in an exciting new direction as many researchers begin to complement reductionism with new strategies for understanding the emergent properties of life—how all the parts of biological systems such as cells are functionally integrated. This changing perspective is analogous to moving from ground level on a certain street corner to an aerial view above a city, where you can now see how variables such as time of day, construction projects, accidents, and traffic signal malfunctions affect traffic dynamics throughout the city.

The ultimate goal of **systems biology** is to model the dynamic behavior of whole biological systems. Accurate models will enable biologists to predict how a change in one or more variables will impact other components and the whole system. How, for example, will a slight increase in a muscle cell's calcium concentration affect the activities of the dozens of proteins that regulate muscle contraction? How will a drug that lowers blood pressure affect the function of organs throughout the human body and possibly cause harmful side effects? How will increasing the water supply to a crop impact key processes in the plants, such as the use of certain soil minerals and the storage of proteins essential for human nutrition? How will a gradual increase in atmospheric carbon dioxide alter ecosystems and the entire biosphere? The aim of systems biology is to make progress answering such big questions.

Systems biology is relevant to the study of life at all levels. Scientists investigating ecosystems pioneered the systems approach in the 1960s with elaborate models diagramming the network of interactions between species and nonliving components in salt marshes and other ecosystems. Even earlier, biologists studying the physiology (functioning) of humans and other organisms were integrating data on how multiple organs coordinate processes such as the regulation of sugar concentration in the blood. Such models of ecosystems and organisms have already been useful for predicting the responses of these systems to changing variables.

Systems biology is now taking hold in the study of life at the cellular and molecular levels, driven partly by the deluge of data from the sequencing of genomes and the growing catalog of known protein functions. In 2003, for example, a large research team published a network of protein interactions within the cell of a fruit fly, a popular research organism. The model is based on an extensive database of thousands of known proteins and their known interactions with other proteins. For example, protein A may bind to and alter the activities of proteins B, C, and D, which then go on to interact with still other proteins. **Figure 1.10** maps these protein partnerships to their cellular locales.

The basics of the systems strategy are straightforward enough. First, it is necessary to inventory as many parts as possible, such as all the known genes and proteins in a cell

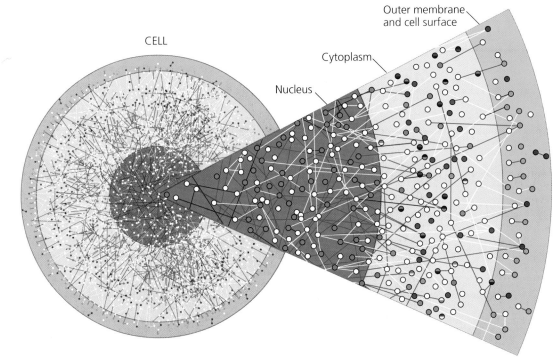

▶ **Figure 1.10 A systems map of interactions between proteins in a cell.** This diagram maps about 3,500 proteins (dots) and their network of interactions (lines connecting the proteins) in a fruit fly cell. Systems biologists develop such models from huge databases of information about molecules and their interactions in the cell. A major goal of this systems approach is to use such models to predict how one change, such as an increase in the activity of a particular protein, can ripple through the cell's molecular circuitry to cause other changes. One of the applications will be a more accurate prediction of the side effects of various drugs.

(reductionism). Then it is necessary to investigate how each part behaves in relation to others in the working system—all the protein-protein interactions, in the case of our fly cell example. Finally, with the help of computers and innovative software, it is possible to pool all the data from many research teams into the kind of system network modeled in Figure 1.10.

Though the basic idea of systems biology is simple, the practice is not, as you would expect from the complexity of biological systems. It has taken three key research developments to bring systems biology within reach:

▶ **High-throughput technology.** Systems biology depends on methods that can analyze biological materials very rapidly and produce enormous volumes of data. Such mega-data-collection methods are said to be "high-throughput." The automatic DNA-sequencing machines that made the Human Genome Project possible are examples of high-throughput devices (see Figure 1.9).

▶ **Bioinformatics.** The huge databases that result from high-throughput methods would be chaotic without the computing power, software, and mathematical models to process and integrate all this biological information. The new field of **bioinformatics** is extracting useful biological information from the enormous, ever-expanding data sets, such as DNA sequences and lists of protein interactions. The Internet is nurturing systems biology through dissemination of the digital data that feed bioinformatics.

▶ **Interdisciplinary research teams.** In 2003, Harvard Medical School formed a department of systems biology, its first new department in two decades. Nearby MIT is busy organizing over 80 faculty members from many departments into a new program for computational and systems biology. These and other systems biology start-ups are melting pots of diverse specialists, including engineers, medical scientists, chemists, physicists, mathematicians, computer scientists, and, of course, biologists from a variety of fields.

A number of prominent scientists are promoting systems biology with missionary zeal, but so far, the excitement exceeds the achievements. However, as systems biology gathers momentum, it is certain to have a growing impact on the questions biologists ask and the research they design. After all, scientists aspired to reach beyond reductionism to grasp how whole biological systems work long before new technology made modern systems biology possible. In fact, decades ago, biologists had already identified some of the key mechanisms that regulate the behavior of complex systems such as cells, organisms, and ecosystems.

Feedback Regulation in Biological Systems

A kind of supply-and-demand economy applies to some of the dynamics of biological systems. For example, when your muscle cells require more energy during exercise, they increase their consumption of the sugar molecules that provide fuel. In contrast, when you rest, a different set of chemical reactions converts surplus sugar to substances that store the fuel.

Like most of the cell's chemical processes, those that decompose or store sugar are accelerated, or catalyzed, by the specialized proteins called enzymes. Each type of enzyme catalyzes a specific chemical reaction. In many cases, these reactions are linked into chemical pathways, each step with its own enzyme. How does the cell coordinate its various chemical pathways? In our specific example of sugar management, how does the cell match fuel supply to demand by regulating its opposing pathways of sugar consumption and storage? The key is the ability of many biological processes to self-regulate by a mechanism called feedback.

In feedback regulation, the output, or product, of a process regulates that very process. In life, the most common form of regulation is **negative feedback,** in which accumulation of an end product of a process slows that process **(Figure 1.11)**. For example, the cell's breakdown of sugar generates chemical energy in the form of a substance called ATP. An excess accumulation of ATP "feeds back" and inhibits an enzyme near the beginning of the pathway.

Though less common than negative feedback, there are also many biological processes regulated by **positive feedback,** in which an end product *speeds up* its production. The clotting of your blood in response to injury is an example. When a blood vessel is damaged, structures in the blood called platelets begin to aggregate at the site. Positive feedback occurs as chemicals released by the platelets attract *more* platelets. The platelet pile then initiates a complex process that seals the

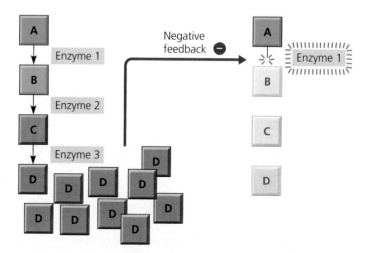

▲ **Figure 1.11 Negative feedback.** This three-step chemical pathway converts substance A to substance D. A specific enzyme catalyzes each chemical reaction. Accumulation of the final product (D) inhibits the first enzyme in the sequence, thus slowing down production of more D.

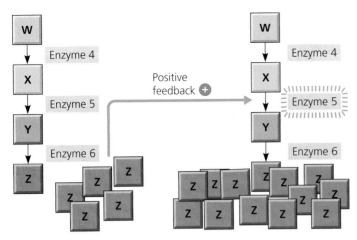

▲ Figure 1.12 **Positive feedback.** In positive feedback, a product stimulates an enzyme in the reaction sequence, increasing the rate of production of the product. Positive feedback is less common than negative feedback in living systems.

▲ Figure 1.13 **Drawers of diversity.** This is just a small sample of the tens of thousands of species in the moth and butterfly collection at the National Museum of Natural History in Washington, D.C.

wound with a clot. **Figure 1.12** shows a simple model of positive feedback.

Feedback is a regulatory motif common to life at all levels, from the molecular level to the biosphere. Such regulation is an example of the integration that makes living systems much greater than the sum of their parts.

Concept Check 1.2

1. Apply the principle of emergent properties to explain the relationship of a sentence to the alphabet of letters from which that sentence is constructed.
2. How does high-throughput technology complement bioinformatics?
3. When you flush a toilet, water begins to fill the tank and lift a float attached to a lever. When the water level reaches a certain height, the lever shuts the water valve and prevents the tank from overflowing. What type of regulatory mechanism is at work in this nonliving system?

For suggested answers, see Appendix A.

Concept 1.3

Biologists explore life across its great diversity of species

We can think of biology's enormous scope as having two dimensions. The "vertical" dimension, which we examined in this chapter's first two concepts, is the size scale that reaches all the way from molecules to the biosphere. But biology's scope also has a "horizontal" dimension stretching across the great diversity of species, now and over life's long history.

Diversity is a hallmark of life. Biologists have so far identified and named about 1.8 million species. This enormous diversity of life includes approximately 5,200 known species of prokaryotes, 100,000 fungi, 290,000 plants, 52,000 vertebrates (animals with backbones), and 1,000,000 insects (more than half of all known forms of life). Researchers identify thousands of additional species each year. Estimates of the total species count range from about 10 million to over 200 million. Whatever the actual number, the vast variety of life makes biology's scope very wide **(Figure 1.13)**.

Grouping Species: The Basic Idea

There seems to be a human tendency to group diverse items according to similarities. For instance, perhaps you organize your music collection according to artist. And then maybe you group the various artists into broader categories, such as dance music, party music, exercise music, and study-time music. In the same way, grouping species that are similar is natural for us. We may speak of squirrels and butterflies, though we recognize that many different species belong to each group. We may even sort groups into broader categories, such as rodents (which include squirrels) and insects (which include butterflies). Taxonomy, the branch of biology that names and classifies species, formalizes this ordering of species into a series of groups of increasing breadth **(Figure 1.14)**. You will learn more about this taxonomic scheme in Chapter 25. For now, we will focus on kingdoms and domains, the broadest units of classification.

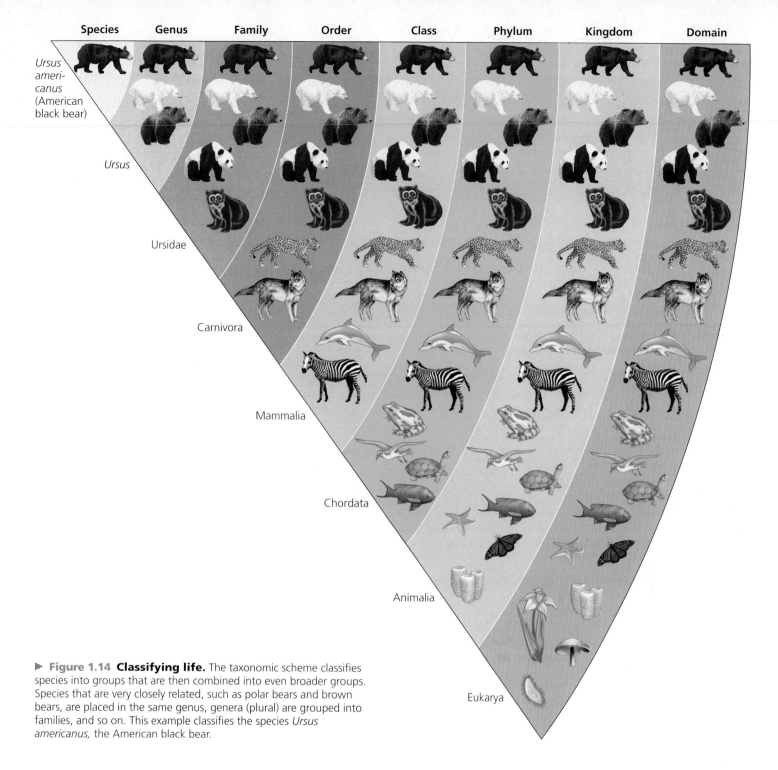

Species	Genus	Family	Order	Class	Phylum	Kingdom	Domain

Ursus americanus (American black bear)

Ursus

Ursidae

Carnivora

Mammalia

Chordata

Animalia

Eukarya

▶ **Figure 1.14 Classifying life.** The taxonomic scheme classifies species into groups that are then combined into even broader groups. Species that are very closely related, such as polar bears and brown bears, are placed in the same genus, genera (plural) are grouped into families, and so on. This example classifies the species *Ursus americanus,* the American black bear.

The Three Domains of Life

Until the last decade, most biologists adopted a taxonomic scheme that divided the diversity of life into five kingdoms, including the plant and animal kingdoms. But new methods, such as comparing the DNA sequences of diverse species, have led to an ongoing reevaluation of the number and boundaries of kingdoms. Different researchers have proposed anywhere from six kingdoms to dozens of kingdoms. But as debate continues at the kingdom level, there is more of a consensus that

the kingdoms of life can now be grouped into three even higher levels of classification called domains. The three domains are named Bacteria, Archaea, and Eukarya.

The first two domains, **domain Bacteria** and **domain Archaea,** both consist of prokaryotes (organisms with prokaryotic cells). Most prokaryotes are unicellular and microscopic. In the five-kingdom system, bacteria and archaea were combined in a single kingdom, called kingdom Monera, because they shared the prokaryotic form of cell structure. But evidence now supports the view that bacteria and archaea represent two very

Figure 1.15

Exploring **Life's Three Domains**

DOMAIN BACTERIA

Bacteria are the most diverse and widespread prokaryotes and are now divided among multiple kingdoms. Each of the rod-shaped structures in this photo is a bacterial cell.
4 μm

DOMAIN ARCHAEA

Many of the prokaryotes known as **archaea** live in Earth's extreme environments, such as salty lakes and boiling hot springs. Domain Archaea includes multiple kingdoms. The photo shows a colony composed of many cells.
0.5 μm

DOMAIN EUKARYA

Protists (multiple kingdoms) are unicellular eukaryotes and their relatively simple multicellular relatives. Pictured here is an assortment of protists inhabiting pond water. Scientists are currently debating how to split the protists into several kingdoms that better represent evolution and diversity.
100 μm

Kingdom Plantae consists of multicellular eukaryotes that carry out photosynthesis, the conversion of light energy to food.

Kindom Fungi is defined in part by the nutritional mode of its members, such as this mushroom, which absorb nutrients after decomposing organic material.

Kindom Animalia consists of multicellular eukaryotes that ingest other organisms.

distinct branches of prokaryotic life, different in key ways that you'll learn about in Chapter 27. There is also molecular evidence that archaea are at least as closely related to eukaryotic organisms as they are to bacteria.

All the eukaryotes (organisms with eukaryotic cells) are now grouped into the various kingdoms of **domain Eukarya (Figure 1.15)**. In the era of the five-kingdom scheme, most of the single-celled eukaryotes, including the microorganisms known as protozoans, were placed in a single kingdom, the kingdom Protista. Many biologists extended the boundaries of the kingdom Protista to include some multicellular forms, such as seaweeds, that are closely related to certain unicellular protists. The recent taxonomic trend has been to split the protists into several kingdoms. In addition to these protistan kingdoms, the domain Eukarya includes three kingdoms of multicellular eukaryotes: the kingdoms Plantae, Fungi, and Animalia. These three kingdoms are distinguished partly by their modes of nutrition. Plants produce their own sugars and other foods by

photosynthesis. Fungi are mostly decomposers that absorb nutrients by breaking down dead organisms and organic wastes, such as leaf litter and animal feces. Animals obtain food by ingestion, which is the eating and digesting of other organisms. It is, of course, the kingdom to which we belong.

Unity in the Diversity of Life

As diverse as life is, there is also evidence of remarkable unity, especially at the molecular and cellular levels. An example is the universal genetic language of DNA, which is common to organisms as different as bacteria and animals. And among eukaryotes, unity is evident in many features of cell structure **(Figure 1.16)**.

How can we account for life's dual nature of unity and diversity? The process of evolution, introduced in the next concept, illuminates both the similarities and differences among Earth's life.

15 μm

Cilia of *Paramecium*. The cilia of *Paramecium* propel the cell through pond water.

5 μm

Cilia of windpipe cells. The cells that line the human windpipe are equipped with cilia that help keep the lungs clean by moving a film of debris-trapping mucus upward.

0.1 μm

Cross section of cilium, as viewed with an electron microscope

▲ **Figure 1.16 An example of unity underlying the diversity of life: the architecture of cilia in eukaryotes.** Cilia (singular, cilium) are extensions of cells that function in locomotion. They occur in eukaryotes as diverse as the single-celled *Paramecium* and humans. But even organisms so different share a common architecture for their cilia, which have an elaborate system of tubules that is revealed in cross-sectional views.

Concept Check 1.3

1. How is a mailing address analogous to biology's hierarchical taxonomic system?
2. What is the key difference that distinguishes organisms of domain Eukarya from the other two domains?

For suggested answers, see Appendix A.

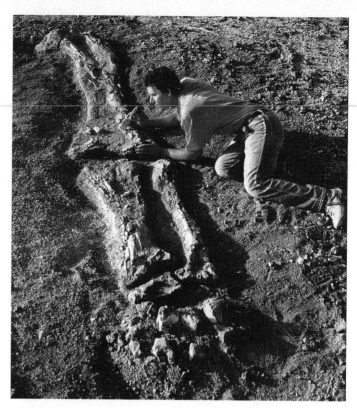

▲ **Figure 1.17 Digging into the past.** Paleontologist Paul Sereno gingerly excavates the leg bones of a dinosaur fossil in Niger, Africa.

Concept 1.4

Evolution accounts for life's unity and diversity

The history of life, as documented by fossils and other evidence, is a saga of a changing Earth billions of years old, inhabited by an evolving cast of living forms **(Figure 1.17)**. This evolutionary view of life came into sharp focus in November 1859, when Charles Robert Darwin published one of the most important and controversial books ever written. Entitled *On the Origin of Species by Natural Selection*, Darwin's book was an immediate best-seller and soon made "Darwinism" almost synonymous with the concept of evolution **(Figure 1.18)**.

The Origin of Species articulated two main points. First, Darwin presented evidence to support his view that contemporary species arose from

▲ **Figure 1.18 Charles Darwin in 1859, the year he published *The Origin of Species*.**

▲ **Figure 1.19 Unity and diversity in the orchid family.**
These three rain forest orchids are variations on a common floral theme. For example, each of these flowers has a liplike petal that helps attract pollinating insects and provides a landing platform for the pollinators.

OBSERVATION: **Individual variation.** Individuals in a population of any species vary in many heritable traits.

OBSERVATION: **Overproduction and competition.** A population of any species has the potential to produce far more offspring than will survive to produce offspring of their own. With more individuals than the environment can support, competition is inevitable.

INFERENCE: **Unequal reproductive success.** From the observable facts of heritable variation and overproduction of offspring, Darwin inferred that individuals are unequal in their likelihood of surviving and reproducing. Those individuals with heritable traits best suited to the local environment will generally produce a disproportionately large number of healthy, fertile offspring.

INFERENCE: **Evolutionary adaptation.** This unequal reproductive success can adapt a population to its environment. Over the generations, heritable traits that enhance survival and reproductive success tend to increase in frequency among a population's individuals. The population evolves.

Darwin called this mechanism of evolutionary adaptation "natural selection" because the natural environment "selects" for the propagation of certain traits. **Figure 1.20** summarizes Darwin's theory of natural selection. The example in **Figure 1.21** illustrates the ability of natural selection to "edit" a population's heritable variations. We see the products of natural selection in the exquisite adaptations of organisms to the special circumstances of their way of life and their environment **(Figure 1.22)**.

a succession of ancestors. (We will discuss the evidence for evolution in detail in Chapter 22.) Darwin called this evolutionary history of species "descent with modification." It was an insightful phrase, as it captured the duality of life's unity and diversity—unity in the kinship among species that descended from common ancestors; diversity in the modifications that evolved as species branched from their common ancestors **(Figure 1.19)**. Darwin's second main point was to propose a mechanism for descent with modification. He called this evolutionary mechanism natural selection.

Natural Selection

Darwin synthesized his theory of natural selection from observations that by themselves were neither new nor profound. Others had the pieces of the puzzle, but Darwin saw how they fit together. He inferred natural selection by connecting two readily observable features of life:

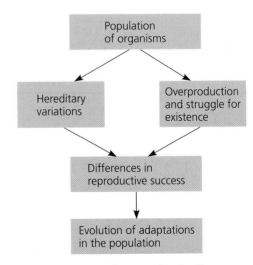

▲ **Figure 1.20 Summary of natural selection.**

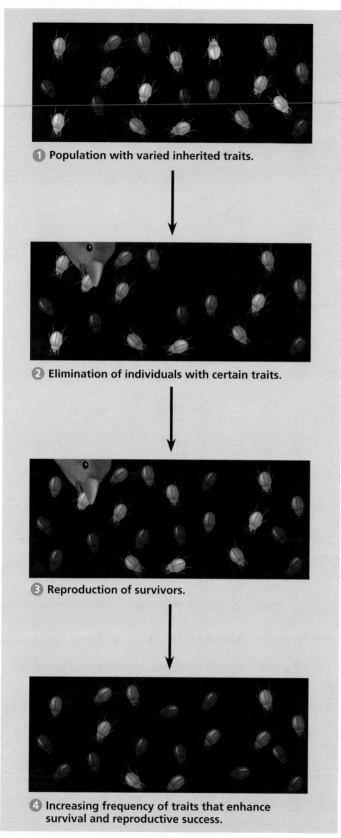

❶ Population with varied inherited traits.

❷ Elimination of individuals with certain traits.

❸ Reproduction of survivors.

❹ Increasing frequency of traits that enhance survival and reproductive success.

▲ **Figure 1.21 Natural selection.** This imaginary beetle population has colonized a locale where the soil has been blackened by a recent brush fire. Initially, the population varies extensively in the inherited coloration of the individuals, from very light gray to charcoal. For hungry birds that prey on the beetles, it is easiest to spot the beetles that are lightest in color.

▲ **Figure 1.22 Form fits function.** Bats, the only mammals capable of active flight, have wings with webbing between extended "fingers." In the Darwinian view of life, such adaptations are refined by natural selection.

The Tree of Life

Take another look at the skeletal architecture of the bat's wings in Figure 1.22. These forelimbs, though adapted for flight, actually have all the same bones, joints, nerves, and blood vessels found in other limbs as diverse as the human arm, the horse's foreleg, and the whale's flipper. Indeed, all mammalian forelimbs are anatomical variations of a common architecture, much as the flowers in Figure 1.19 are variations on an underlying "orchid" theme. Such examples of kinship connect life's "unity in diversity" to the Darwinian concept of "descent with modification." In this view, the unity of mammalian limb anatomy reflects inheritance of that structure from a common ancestor—the "prototype" mammal from which all other mammals descended, their diverse forelimbs modified by natural selection operating over millions of generations in different environmental contexts. Fossils and other evidence corroborate anatomical unity in supporting this view of mammalian descent from a common ancestor.

Thus, Darwin proposed that natural selection, by its cumulative effects over vast spans of time, could enable an ancestral species to "split" into two or more descendant species. This would occur, for example, if one population fragmented into several subpopulations isolated in different environments. In these various arenas of natural selection, one species could gradually radiate into many species as the geographically isolated populations adapted over many generations to different sets of environmental factors.

The "family tree" of 14 finches in **Figure 1.23**, on the next page, illustrates a famous example of adaptive radiation of new species from a common ancestor. Darwin collected specimens of these birds during his 1835 visit to the remote Galápagos Islands, 900 kilometers (km) off the Pacific coast of South America. These relatively young, volcanic islands are home to many species of plants and animals found nowhere else in the world, though Galápagos organisms are clearly related to species on the South American mainland. After volcanism built the Galápagos several million years ago, finches probably diversified on the various islands from an ancestral finch

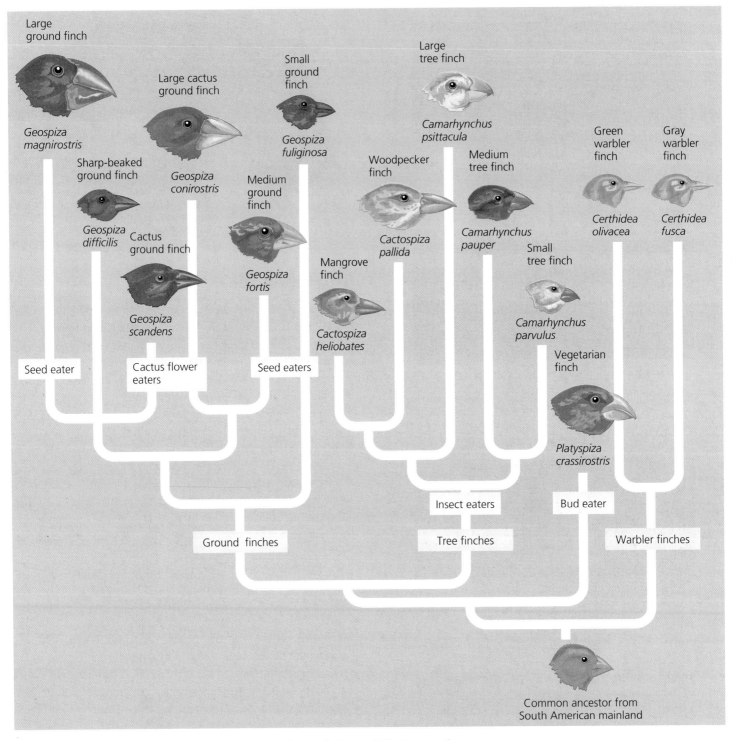

▲ **Figure 1.23 Descent with modification: adaptive radiation of finches on the Galápagos Islands.** Note the specialization of beaks, which are adapted to various food sources on the different islands.

species that by chance reached the archipelago from the mainland. Years after Darwin's collection of Galápagos finches, researchers began to sort out the relationships among the finch species, first from anatomical and geographic data and more recently with the help of DNA sequence comparisons.

Biologists' diagrams of evolutionary relationships generally take treelike forms, and for good reason. Just as an individual has a genealogy that can be diagrammed as a family tree, each

species is one twig of a branching tree of life extending back in time through ancestral species more and more remote. Species that are very similar, such as the Galápagos finches, share a common ancestor at a relatively recent branch point on the tree of life. But through an ancestor that lived much farther back in time, finches are related to sparrows, hawks, penguins, and all other birds. And birds, mammals, and all other vertebrates (animals with backbones) share a common ancestor even more ancient. We find evidence of still broader relationships in such similarities as the matching machinery of all eukaryotic cilia (see Figure 1.16). Trace life back far enough, and there are only fossils of the primeval prokaryotes that inhabited Earth over 3.5 billion years ago. We can recognize their vestiges in our own cells—in the universal genetic code, for example. All of life is connected through its long evolutionary history.

Concept Check 1.4

1. Explain why "editing" is better than "creating" as a metaphor for how natural selection acts on a population's heritable variation.
2. The three domains you learned about in Concept 1.3 can be represented in the tree of life as the three main branches. On the eukaryotic branch, three of the subbranches are the kingdoms Plantae, Fungi, and Animalia. Evidence supports the view that fungi and animals are more closely related to each other than either of these kingdoms is to plants. Draw a simple branching pattern that symbolizes the relationship between these three eukaryotic kingdoms.

For suggested answers, see Appendix A.

Concept 1.5

Biologists use various forms of inquiry to explore life

The word *science* is derived from a Latin verb meaning "to know." Science is a way of knowing. It developed out of our curiosity about ourselves, other life-forms, the world, and the universe. Striving to understand seems to be one of our basic urges.

At the heart of science is **inquiry,** a search for information and explanation, often focusing on specific questions. Inquiry drove Darwin to seek answers in nature for how species adapt to their environments. And inquiry is driving the analyses of genomes that are helping us understand biological unity and diversity at the molecular level. In fact, the inquisitive mind is the engine that drives all progress in biology.

There is no formula for successful scientific inquiry, no single scientific method with a rule book that researchers must rigidly follow. As in all quests, science includes elements of challenge, adventure, and surprise, along with careful planning, reasoning, creativity, cooperation, competition, patience, and the persistence to overcome setbacks. Such diverse elements of inquiry make science far less structured than most people realize. That said, it is possible to distill certain characteristics that help to distinguish science from other ways of describing and explaining nature.

Biology blends two main processes of scientific inquiry: discovery science and hypothesis-based science. Discovery science is mostly about *describing* nature. Hypothesis-based science is mostly about *explaining* nature. Most scientific inquiries combine these two research approaches.

Discovery Science

Sometimes called descriptive science, **discovery science** describes natural structures and processes as accurately as possible through careful observation and analysis of data. For example, discovery science gradually built our understanding of cell structure, and it is discovery science that is expanding our databases of genomes of diverse species.

Types of Data

Observation is the use of the senses to gather information, either directly or indirectly with the help of tools such as microscopes that extend our senses. Recorded observations are called **data.** Put another way, data are items of information on which scientific inquiry is based.

The term *data* implies numbers to many people. But some data are *qualitative,* often in the form of recorded descriptions rather than numerical measurements. For example, Jane Goodall spent decades recording her observations of chimpanzee behavior during field research in a Gambian jungle **(Figure 1.24)**. She also documented her observations with

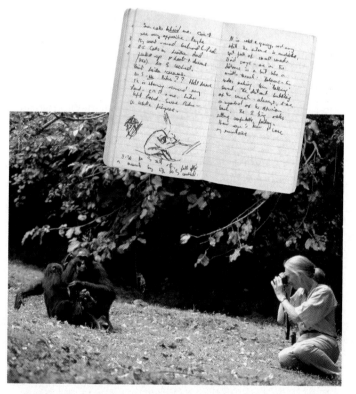

▲ **Figure 1.24 Jane Goodall collecting qualitative data on chimpanzee behavior.** Goodall recorded her observations in field notebooks, often with sketches of the animals' behavior.

photographs and movies. Along with these qualitative data, Goodall also enriched the field of animal behavior with volumes of *quantitative* data, which are generally recorded as measurements. Skim through any of the scientific journals in your college library, and you'll see many examples of quantitative data organized into tables and graphs.

Induction in Discovery Science

Discovery science can lead to important conclusions based on a type of logic called induction, or **inductive reasoning**. Through induction, we derive generalizations based on a large number of specific observations. "The sun always rises in the east" is an example. And so is "All organisms are made of cells." That generalization, part of the so-called cell theory, was based on two centuries of biologists discovering cells in the diverse biological specimens they observed with microscopes. The careful observations and data analyses of discovery science, along with the inductive generalizations they sometimes produce, are fundamental to our understanding of nature.

Hypothesis-Based Science

The observations and inductions of discovery science engage inquisitive minds to seek natural causes and explanations for those observations. What *caused* the diversification of finches on the Galápagos Islands? What *causes* the roots of a plant seedling to grow downward and the leaf-bearing shoot to grow upward? What *explains* the generalization that the sun always rises in the east? In science, such inquiry usually involves the proposing and testing of hypothetical explanations, or hypotheses.

The Role of Hypotheses in Inquiry

In science, a **hypothesis** is a tentative answer to a well-framed question—an explanation on trial. It is usually an educated postulate, based on past experience and the available data of discovery science. A scientific hypothesis makes predictions that can be tested by recording additional observations or by designing experiments.

We all use hypotheses in solving everyday problems. Let's say, for example, that your flashlight fails during a camp-out. That's an observation. The question is obvious: Why doesn't the flashlight work? Two reasonable hypotheses based on past experience are that (1) the batteries in the flashlight are dead or (2) the bulb is burnt out. Each of these alternative hypotheses makes predictions you can test with experiments. For example, the dead-battery hypothesis predicts that replacing the batteries will fix the problem. **Figure 1.25** diagrams this campground inquiry. Of course, we rarely dissect our thought processes this way when we are solving a problem using hypotheses, predictions, and experiments. But hypothesis-based science clearly has its origins in the human tendency to figure things out by tinkering.

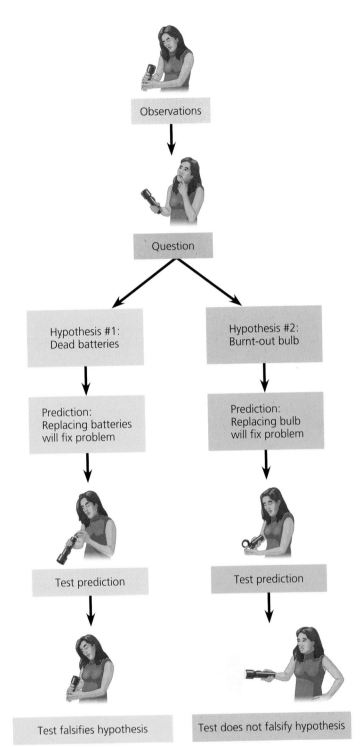

▲ **Figure 1.25 A campground example of hypothesis-based inquiry.**

Deduction: The "If . . . then" Logic of Hypothesis-Based Science

A type of logic called deduction is built into hypothesis-based science. Deduction contrasts with induction, which, remember, is reasoning from a set of specific observations to reach a general conclusion. In **deductive reasoning**, the logic flows in the opposite direction, from the general to the specific. From general premises, we extrapolate to the specific results we should expect if the premises are true. If all organisms are made of cells (premise 1), and humans are organisms (premise 2), then humans are composed of cells (deductive prediction about a specific case).

In hypothesis-based science, deduction usually takes the form of predictions about what outcomes of experiments or observations we should expect if a particular hypothesis (premise) is correct. We then test the hypothesis by performing the experiment to see whether or not the results are as predicted. This deductive testing takes the form of "If . . . then" logic. In the case of the flashlight example: *If* the dead-battery hypothesis is correct, and you replace the batteries with new ones, *then* the flashlight should work.

A Closer Look at Hypotheses in Scientific Inquiry

The flashlight example illustrates two important qualities of scientific hypotheses. First, a hypothesis must be *testable;* there must be some way to check the validity of the idea. Second, a hypothesis must be *falsifiable;* there must be some observation or experiment that *could* reveal if such an idea is actually *not* true. The hypothesis that dead batteries are the sole cause of the broken flashlight could be falsified by replacing the old batteries with new ones. But try to devise a test to falsify the hypothesis that invisible campground ghosts are fooling with your flashlight. Does restoring flashlight function by replacing the bulb falsify the ghost hypothesis? Not if the playful ghosts are continuing their mischief.

The flashlight inquiry illustrates another key point about hypothesis-based science. The ideal is to frame two or more alternative hypotheses and design experiments to falsify those candidate explanations. In addition to the two explanations tested in Figure 1.25, one of the many additional hypotheses is that *both* the batteries *and* the bulb are bad. What does this hypothesis predict about the outcome of the experiments in Figure 1.25? What additional experiment would you design to test this hypothesis of multiple malfunction?

We can mine the flashlight scenario for still one more important lesson about hypothesis-based science. Although the burnt-out bulb hypothesis stands up as the most likely explanation, notice that the testing supports that hypothesis *not* by proving that it is correct, but by not eliminating it through falsification. Perhaps the bulb was simply loose and the new bulb was inserted correctly. We could attempt to falsify the burnt-out bulb hypothesis by trying another experiment—removing the bulb and carefully reinstalling it. But no amount of experimental testing can *prove* a hypothesis beyond a shadow of doubt, because it is impossible to exhaust the testing of all alternative hypotheses. A hypothesis gains credibility by surviving various attempts to falsify it while testing eliminates (falsifies) alternative hypotheses.

The Myth of <u>the</u> Scientific Method

The steps in the flashlight example of Figure 1.25 trace an idealized process of inquiry called *the scientific method.* We can recognize the elements of this process in most of the research articles published by scientists, but rarely in such structured form. Very few scientific inquiries adhere rigidly to the sequence of steps prescribed by the "textbook" scientific method. For example, a scientist may start to design an experiment, but then backtrack upon realizing that more observations are necessary. In other cases, puzzling observations simply don't prompt well-defined questions until other research projects place those observations in a new context. For example, Darwin collected specimens of the Galápagos finches, but it wasn't until years later, as the idea of natural selection began to gel, that biologists began asking key questions about the history of those birds.

Moreover, scientists sometimes redirect their research when they realize they have been "barking up the wrong tree" by asking the wrong question. For example, in the early 20th century, much research on schizophrenia and manic-depressive disorder (now called bipolar disorder) got sidetracked by focusing too much on the question of how life experiences cause these serious maladies. Research on the causes and potential treatments became more productive when it was refocused on questions of how certain chemical imbalances in the brain contribute to mental illness. To be fair, we acknowledge that such twists and turns in scientific inquiry become more evident with the advantage of historical perspective.

There is still another reason that good science need not conform exactly to any one method of inquiry: Discovery science has contributed much to our understanding of nature without most of the steps of the so-called scientific method.

It is important for you to get some experience with the power of the scientific method—by using it for some of the laboratory inquiries in your biology course, for example. But it is also important to avoid stereotyping science as lock-step adherence to this method.

A Case Study in Scientific Inquiry: Investigating Mimicry in Snake Populations

Now that we have highlighted the key features of discovery science and hypothesis-based science, you should be able to recognize these forms of inquiry in a case study of actual scientific research.

The story begins with a set of observations and generalizations from discovery science. Many poisonous animals are brightly colored, often with distinctive patterns that stand out against the background. This is called warning coloration because it apparently signals "dangerous species" to potential predators. But there are also mimics. These imposters look like poisonous species, but are actually relatively harmless. An example is the flower fly, a nonstinging insect that mimics the appearance of a stinging honeybee (**Figure 1.26** on the next page).

Flower fly (nonstinging)

Honeybee (stinging)

▲ **Figure 1.26 A stinging honeybee and its nonstinging mimic, a flower fly.**

What is the function of such mimicry? What advantage does it confer on the mimics? In 1862, British scientist Henry Bates proposed the reasonable hypothesis that mimics such as flower flies benefit when predators confuse them with the harmful species. In other words, the deception may be an evolutionary adaptation that evolved by reducing the mimic's risk of being eaten. As intuitive as this hypothesis may be, it has been relatively difficult to test, especially with field experiments. But then, in 2001, biologists David and Karin Pfennig, along with William Harcombe, an undergraduate at the University of North Carolina, designed a simple but elegant set of field experiments to test Bates's mimicry hypothesis.

The team investigated a case of mimicry among snakes that live in North and South Carolina. A poisonous snake called the eastern coral snake has warning coloration: bold, alternating rings of red, yellow, and black. Predators rarely attack these snakes. It is unlikely that predators *learn* this avoidance behavior, as a first strike by a coral snake is usually deadly. Natural selection may have increased the frequency of predators that have inherited an instinctive recognition and avoidance of the warning coloration of the coral snake.

A nonpoisonous snake named the scarlet king snake mimics the ringed coloration of the coral snake. Both king snakes and coral snakes live in the Carolinas, but the king snakes' geographic range extends farther north and west into regions where no coral snakes are found **(Figure 1.27)**.

The geographic distribution of the Carolina snakes made it possible to test the key prediction of the mimicry hypothesis. Mimicry should help protect king snakes from predators, but *only* in regions where coral snakes also live. The mimicry hypothesis predicts that predators in non-coral snake areas will attack king snakes more frequently than will predators that live where coral snakes are present.

Field Experiments with Artificial Snakes

To test the mimicry hypothesis, Harcombe made hundreds of artificial snakes out of wire covered with a claylike substance called plasticine. He fashioned two versions of fake snakes: an *experimental group* with the red, black, and yellow ring pattern of king snakes; and a *control group* of plain brown artificial snakes as a basis of comparison.

Scarlet king snake

Key	
☐	Range of scarlet king snake
▨	Range of eastern coral snake

North Carolina

South Carolina

Eastern coral snake

Scarlet king snake

▲ **Figure 1.27 Geographic ranges of Carolina coral snakes and king snakes.** The scarlet king snake (*Lampropeltis triangulum*) mimics the warning coloration of the poisonous eastern coral snake (*Micrurus fulvius*). Though these two snake species cohabit many regions throughout North and South Carolina, the geographic range of the king snake extends north and west of the range of the coral snake.

The researchers placed equal numbers of the two types of artificial snakes in field sites throughout North and South Carolina, including the region where coral snakes are absent (see Figure 1.27). After four weeks, the scientists retrieved the fake snakes and recorded how many had been attacked by looking for bite or claw marks. The most common predators were foxes, coyotes, and raccoons, but black bears also attacked some of the artificial snakes (Figure 1.28).

The data fit the key prediction of the mimicry hypothesis. Compared to the brown artificial snakes, the ringed snakes were attacked by predators less frequently *only* in field sites within the geographic range of the poisonous coral snakes. Figure 1.29 summarizes the field experiments. This figure also introduces an illustration format we will use throughout the book to feature other examples of biological inquiry.

Designing Controlled Experiments

The snake mimicry experiment provides an example of how scientists design experiments to test the effect of one variable by canceling out the effects of any unwanted variables, such as the number of predators in this case. The design is called a **controlled experiment**, where an experimental group (the artificial king snakes, in this case) is compared with a control

(a) Artificial king snake

(b) Brown artificial snake that has been attacked

▲ **Figure 1.28 Artificial snakes used in field experiments to test the mimicry hypothesis.** You can see where a bear chomped on the brown artificial snake in (b).

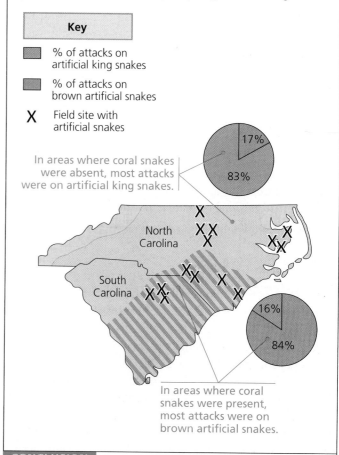

Figure 1.29

Inquiry **Does the presence of poisonous coral snakes affect predation rates on their mimics, king snakes?**

EXPERIMENT   David Pfennig and his colleagues made artificial snakes to test a prediction of the mimicry hypothesis: that king snakes benefit from mimicking the warning coloration of coral snakes *only* in regions where poisonous coral snakes are present. The Xs on the map below are field sites where the researchers placed equal numbers of artificial king snakes (experimental group) and brown artificial snakes (control group). The researchers recovered the artificial snakes after four weeks and tabulated predation data based on teeth and claw marks on the snakes (see Figure 1.28).

RESULTS   In field sites where coral snakes were present, predators attacked far fewer artificial king snakes than brown artificial snakes. The warning coloration of the "king snakes" afforded no such protection where coral snakes were absent. In fact, at those field sites, the artificial king snakes were *more* likely to be attacked than the brown artificial snakes, perhaps because the bright pattern is particularly easy to spot against the background.

Key

◼ % of attacks on artificial king snakes

▨ % of attacks on brown artificial snakes

X Field site with artificial snakes

In areas where coral snakes were absent, most attacks were on artificial king snakes.

17%
83%

North Carolina

South Carolina

16%
84%

In areas where coral snakes were present, most attacks were on brown artificial snakes.

CONCLUSION   The field experiments support the mimicry hypothesis by not falsifying the key prediction that imitation of coral snakes is only effective where coral snakes are present. The experiments also tested an alternative hypothesis that predators generally avoid all snakes with brightly colored rings, whether or not poisonous snakes with that coloration live in the environment. That alternative hypothesis was falsified by the data showing that the ringed coloration failed to repel predators where coral snakes were absent.

group (the brown artificial snakes). Ideally, the experimental and control groups differ only in the one factor the experiment is designed to test—in our example, the effect of the snakes' coloration on the behavior of predators.

What if the researchers had failed to control their experiment? Without the brown mock snakes as a control group, the number of attacks on the fake king snakes in different geographic regions would tell us nothing about the effect of snake coloration on predator behavior at the different field sites. Perhaps, for example, fewer predators attacked the artificial king snakes in the eastern and southern field sites simply because fewer predators live there. Or maybe warmer temperatures in those regions make predators less hungry. The brown artificial snakes enabled the scientists to rule out such variables as predator density and temperature because those factors would have had equal effects on the control group and experimental group. Yet predators in the eastern and southern field sites attacked more brown artificial snakes than "king snakes." The clever experimental design left coloration as the only factor that could account for the low predation rate on the artificial king snakes placed within the range of coral snakes. It was not the absolute number of attacks on the artificial king snakes that counted, but the difference between that number and the number of attacks on the brown snakes.

A common misconception is that the term *controlled experiment* means that scientists control the experimental environment to keep everything constant except the one variable being tested. But that's impossible in field research and not realistic even in highly regulated laboratory environments. Researchers usually "control" unwanted variables not by *eliminating* them through environmental regulation, but by *canceling* their effects by using control groups.

Limitations of Science

Scientific inquiry is a powerful way to know nature, but there are limitations to the kinds of questions it can answer. These limits are set by science's requirements that hypotheses be testable and falsifiable and that observations and experimental results be repeatable.

Observations that can't be verified may be interesting or even entertaining, but they cannot count as evidence in scientific inquiry. The headlines of supermarket tabloids would have you believe that humans are occasionally born with the head of a dog and that some of your classmates are extraterrestrials. The unconfirmed eyewitness accounts and the computer-rigged photos are amusing but unconvincing. In science, evidence from observations and experiments is only convincing if it stands up to the criterion of repeatability. The scientists who investigated snake mimicry in the Carolinas obtained similar data when they repeated their experiments with different species of coral snakes and king snakes in Arizona. And *you* should be able to obtain similar results if you were to repeat the snake experiments.

Ultimately, the limitations of science are imposed by its naturalism—its seeking of natural causes for natural phenomena. Science can neither support nor falsify hypotheses that angels, ghosts, or spirits, both benevolent and evil, cause storms, rainbows, illnesses, and cures. Such supernatural explanations are simply outside the bounds of science.

Theories in Science

"It's just a theory!" Our everyday use of the term *theory* often implies an untested speculation. But the term *theory* has a very different meaning in science. What is a scientific theory, and how is it different from a hypothesis or from mere speculation?

First, a scientific **theory** is much broader in scope than a hypothesis. *This* is a hypothesis: "Mimicking poisonous snakes is an adaptation that protects nonpoisonous snakes from predators." But *this* is a theory: "Evolutionary adaptations evolve by natural selection." Darwin's theory of natural selection accounts for an enormous diversity of adaptations, including mimicry.

Second, a theory is general enough to spin off many new, specific hypotheses that can be tested. For example, Peter and Rosemary Grant, of Princeton University, were motivated by the theory of natural selection to test the specific hypothesis that the beaks of the Galápagos finches evolve in response to changes in the types of available food.

And third, compared to any one hypothesis, a theory is generally supported by a much more massive body of evidence. Those theories that become widely adopted in science (such as the theory of natural selection) explain a great diversity of observations and are supported by an accumulation of evidence. In fact, scrutiny of general theories continues through testing of the specific, falsifiable hypotheses they spawn.

In spite of the body of evidence supporting a widely accepted theory, scientists must sometimes modify or even reject theories when new research methods produce results that don't fit. For example, the five-kingdom theory of biological diversity began to erode when new methods for comparing cells and molecules made it possible to test some of the hypothetical relationships between organisms that were based on the theory. If there is "truth" in science, it is conditional, based on the preponderance of available evidence.

Model Building in Science

You may work with many models in your biology course this year. Perhaps you'll model cell division by using pipe cleaners or other objects as chromosomes. Or maybe you'll practice using mathematical models to predict the growth of a bacterial population. Scientists often construct models as less abstract representations of ideas such as theories or

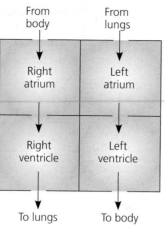

► Figure 1.30 **Modeling the pattern of blood flow through the four chambers of a human heart.**

From body → Right atrium → Right ventricle → To lungs

From lungs → Left atrium → Left ventricle → To body

► Figure 1.31 **Science as a social process.** In her New York University laboratory, plant biologist Gloria Coruzzi mentors one of her students in the methods of molecular biology.

natural phenomena such as biological processes. Scientific **models** can take many forms, such as diagrams, graphs, three-dimensional objects, computer programs, or mathematical equations.

The choice of a model type depends on how it will be used to help explain and communicate the object, idea, or process it represents. Some models are meant to be as lifelike as possible. Other models are more useful if they are symbolic schematics. For example, the simple diagram in **Figure 1.30** does a good job of modeling blood flow through the chambers of a human heart without looking anything like a real heart. A heart model designed to help train a physician to perform heart surgery would look very different. Whatever its design, the test of a model is how well it fits the available data, how comfortably it accommodates new observations, how accurately it predicts the outcomes of new experiments, and how effectively it clarifies and communicates the idea or process it represents.

The Culture of Science

Movies and cartoons sometimes portray scientists as loners working in isolated labs. In reality, science is an intensely social activity. Most scientists work in teams, which often include both graduate and undergraduate students **(Figure 1.31)**. And to succeed in science, it helps to be a good communicator. Research results have no impact until shared with a community of peers through seminars, publications, and websites.

Both cooperation and competition characterize the scientific culture. Scientists working in the same research field often check one another's claims by attempting to confirm observations or repeat experiments. And when several scientists converge on the same research question, there is all the excitement of a race. Scientists enjoy the challenge of "getting there first" with an important discovery or key experiment.

The biology community is part of society at large, embedded in the cultural milieu of the times. For example, changing attitudes about career choices have increased the proportion of women in biology, which has in turn affected the emphasis in certain research fields. A few decades ago, for instance, biologists who studied the mating behavior of animals focused mostly on competition among males for access to females. More recent research, however, emphasizes the important role that females play in choosing mates. For example, in many bird species, females prefer the bright coloration that "advertises" a male's vigorous health, a behavior that enhances the female's probability of having healthy offspring.

Some philosophers of science argue that scientists are so influenced by cultural and political values that science is no more objective than other ways of "knowing nature." At the other extreme are people who speak of scientific theories as though they were natural laws instead of human interpretations of nature. The reality of science is probably somewhere in between—rarely perfectly objective, but continuously vetted through the expectation that observations and experiments be repeatable and hypotheses be testable and falsifiable.

Science, Technology, and Society

The relationship of science to society becomes clearer when we add technology to the picture. Though science and technology sometimes employ similar inquiry patterns, their basic goals differ. The goal of science is to understand natural phenomena. In contrast, **technology** generally *applies* scientific knowledge for some specific purpose. Biologists and other scientists often speak of "discoveries," while engineers and other technologists more often speak of "inventions." And the beneficiaries of those inventions include scientists, who put new technology to work in their research; the impact of information technology on systems biology is just one example. Thus, science and technology are interdependent.

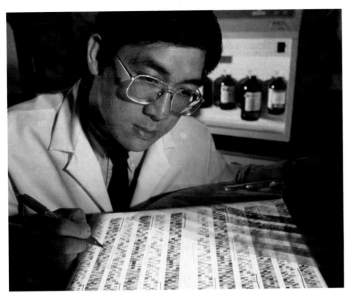

▲ **Figure 1.32 DNA technology and crime scene investigation.** Forensic technicians can use traces of DNA extracted from a blood sample or other body tissue collected at a crime scene to produce molecular fingerprints. The stained bands you see in this photograph represent fragments of DNA, and the pattern of bands varies from person to person.

The potent combination of science and technology has dramatic effects on society. For example, discovery of the structure of DNA by Watson and Crick 50 years ago and subsequent achievements in DNA science led to the many technologies of DNA engineering that are transforming a diversity of fields, including medicine, agriculture, and forensics **(Figure 1.32)**. Perhaps Watson and Crick envisioned that their discovery would someday produce important applications, but it is unlikely that they could have predicted exactly what those applications would be.

The directions that technology takes depend less on the curiosity that drives basic science than it does on the current needs and wants of people and on the social environment of the times. Debates about technology center more on "*should we do it*" than "*can we do it*." With advances in technology come difficult choices. For example, under what circumstances is it acceptable to use DNA technology to check if people have genes for hereditary diseases? Should such tests always be voluntary, or are there any circumstances when genetic testing should be mandatory? Should insurance companies or employers have access to the information, as they do for many other types of personal health data?

Such ethical issues have as much to do with politics, economics, and cultural values as with science and technology. But scientists and engineers have a responsibility to help educate politicians, bureaucrats, corporate leaders, and voters about how science works and about the potential benefits and risks of specific technologies. The crucial science-technology-society relationship is a theme that increases the significance of any biology course.

Concept Check 1.5

1. Contrast induction with deduction.
2. Critique this statement: "Scientists design controlled experiments to study a single variable by preventing all other factors from changing."
3. In the snake mimicry experiments, why did the researchers place some of their artificial snakes beyond the geographic range of coral snakes?
4. Contrast "theory" with "hypothesis."

For suggested answers, see Appendix A.

Concept 1.6

A set of themes connects the concepts of biology

In some ways, biology is the most demanding of all sciences, partly because living systems are so complex and partly because biology is an interdisciplinary science that requires knowledge of chemistry, physics, and mathematics. Modern biology is the decathlon of natural science. And of all the sciences, biology is the most connected to the humanities and social sciences. As biology students, you are definitely in the right place at the right time!

No matter what brings you to biology, you will find the study of life to be endlessly challenging and uplifting. But this ever-expanding subject can also be a bit intimidating, even to professional biologists. How, then, can beginning students develop a coherent view of life instead of hopelessly trying to memorize the details of a subject that is now far too big to memorize? One approach is to fit the many things you learn into a set of themes that pervade all of biology—ways of thinking about life that will still apply decades from now, when much of the specific information fossilized in any textbook will be obsolete. **Table 1.1** outlines a number of broad themes you will recognize from this first chapter of *Biology*. These unifying themes will reemerge throughout the book to provide touchstones as you explore life and begin asking important questions of your own.

Concept Check 1.6

1. Write a sentence relating the theme of "scientific inquiry" to the theme of "science, technology, and society."

For suggested answers, see Appendix A.

Table 1.1 Eleven Themes that Unify Biology

Theme	Description	Theme	Description
The cell 	Cells are every organism's basic units of structure and function. The two main types of cells are prokaryotic cells (in bacteria and archaea) and eukaryotic cells (in protists, plants, fungi, and animals).	**Unity and diversity** 	Biologists group the diversity of life into three domains: Bacteria, Archaea, and Eukarya. As diverse as life is, we can also find unity, such as a universal genetic code. The more closely related two species are, the more characteristics they share.
Heritable information 	The continuity of life depends on the inheritance of biological information in the form of DNA molecules. This genetic information is encoded in the nucleotide sequences of the DNA.	**Evolution** 	Evolution, biology's core theme, explains both the unity and diversity of life. The Darwinian theory of natural selection accounts for adaptation of populations to their environment through the differential reproductive success of varying individuals.
Emergent properties of biological systems 	The living world has a hierarchical organization, extending from molecules to the biosphere. With each step upward in level, system properties emerge as a result of interactions among components at the lower levels.	**Structure and function** 	Form and function are correlated at all levels of biological organization.
Regulation 	Feedback mechanisms regulate biological systems. In some cases, the regulation maintains a relatively steady state for internal factors such as body temperature.	**Scientific inquiry** 	The process of science includes observation-based discovery and the testing of explanations through hypothesis-based inquiry. Scientific credibility depends on the repeatability of observations and experiments.
Interaction with the environment 	Organisms are open systems that exchange materials and energy with their surroundings. An organism's environment includes other organisms as well as nonliving factors.	**Science, technology, and society** 	Many technologies are goal-oriented applications of science. The relationships of science and technology to society are now more crucial to understand than ever before.
Energy and life 	All organisms must perform work, which requires energy. Energy flows from sunlight to producers to consumers.		

Chapter 1 Review

Go to the Campbell Biology website (**www.campbellbiology.com**) or CD-ROM to explore Activities, Investigations, and other interactive study aids.

SUMMARY OF KEY CONCEPTS

Concept 1.1

Biologists explore life from the microscopic to the global scale

▶ **A Hierarchy of Biological Organization (pp. 3–6)** The hierarchy of life unfolds as follows: biosphere > ecosystem > community > population > organism > organ system > organ > tissue > cell > organelle > molecule > atom.
Activity *The Levels of Life Card Game*

▶ **A Closer Look at Ecosystems (p. 6)** Whereas chemical nutrients recycle within an ecosystem, energy flows through an ecosystem.
Activity *Energy Flow and Chemical Cycling*

▶ **A Closer Look at Cells (pp. 6–8)** The cell is the lowest level of organization that can perform all activities required for life. Cells contain DNA, the substance of genes, which program the cell's production of proteins and transmit information from parents to offspring. Eukaryotic cells contain membrane-enclosed organelles, including a DNA-containing nucleus. Prokaryotic cells lack such organelles.
Activity *Heritable Information: DNA*
Activity *Comparing Prokaryotic and Eukaryotic Cells*

Concept 1.2

Biological systems are much more than the sum of their parts

▶ **The Emergent Properties of Systems (p. 9)** Due to increasing complexity, new properties emerge with each step upward in the hierarchy of biological order.

▶ **The Power and Limitations of Reductionism (pp. 9–10)** Reductionism involves reducing complex systems to simpler components that are more manageable to study.

▶ **Systems Biology (pp. 10–11)** Systems biology seeks to create models of the dynamic behavior of whole biological systems. With such models, scientists will be able to predict how a change in one part of the system will affect the rest of the system.

▶ **Feedback Regulation in Biological Systems (pp. 11–12)** In negative feedback, accumulation of an end product slows the process that produces that product. In positive feedback, the end product speeds up its production.
Activity *Regulation: Negative and Positive Feedback*

Concept 1.3

Biologists explore life across its great diversity of species

▶ **Grouping Species: The Basic Idea (pp. 12–13)** Taxonomy is the branch of biology that names and classifies species according to a system of broader and broader groups.

▶ **The Three Domains of Life (pp. 13–14)** Domain Bacteria and Domain Archaea consist of prokaryotes. Domain Eukarya, the eukaryotes, includes the various protist kingdoms and the kingdoms Plantae, Fungi, and Animalia.
Activity *Classification Schemes*

▶ **Unity in the Diversity of Life (pp. 14–15)** As diverse as life is, there is also evidence of remarkable unity.

Concept 1.4

Evolution accounts for life's unity and diversity

▶ **Natural Selection (pp. 16–17)** Darwin called the evolutionary history of species "descent with modification." He proposed natural selection as the mechanism for evolutionary adaptation of populations to their environments. Natural selection is the evolutionary process that occurs when a population's heritable variations are exposed to environmental factors that favor the reproductive success of some individuals over others.
Investigation *How Do Environmental Changes Affect a Population?*
Activity *Form Fits Function: Cells*

▶ **The Tree of Life (pp. 17–19)** Each species is one twig of a branching tree of life extending back in time through ancestral species more and more remote. All of life is connected through its long evolutionary history.

Concept 1.5

Biologists use various forms of inquiry to explore life

▶ **Discovery Science (pp. 19–20)** In discovery science, scientists describe some aspect of the world and use inductive reasoning to draw general conclusions.
Graph It *An Introduction to Graphing*

▶ **Hypothesis-Based Science (pp. 20–21)** Based on observations, scientists propose hypotheses that lead to predictions and then test the hypotheses by seeing if the predictions come true. Deductive reasoning is used in testing hypotheses: *If* a hypothesis is correct, and we test it, *then* we can expect a particular outcome. Hypotheses must be testable and falsifiable.
Investigation *How Does Acid Precipitation Affect Trees?*

▶ **A Case Study in Scientific Inquiry: Investigating Mimicry in Snake Populations (pp. 21–24)** Experiments must be designed to test the effect of one variable by testing control groups and experimental groups that vary in only that one variable.

▶ **Limitations of Science (p. 24)** Science cannot address supernatural phenomena because hypotheses must be testable and falsifiable and observations and experimental results must be repeatable.

▶ **Theories in Science (p. 24)** A scientific theory is broad in scope, generates new hypotheses, and is supported by a large body of evidence.

▶ **Model Building in Science (pp. 24–25)** Models of ideas, structures, and processes help us understand scientific phenomena and make predictions.

▶ **The Culture of Science (p. 25)** Science is a social activity characterized by both cooperation and competition.

▶ **Science, Technology, and Society (pp. 25–26)** Technology applies scientific knowledge for some specific purpose.
Activity *Science, Technology, and Society: DDT*

Concept 1.6

A set of themes connects the concepts of biology

▶ Underlying themes provide a framework for understanding biology (pp. 26–27).

Self-Quiz

1. All the organisms on your campus make up
   a. an ecosystem.
   b. a community.
   c. a population.
   d. an experimental group.
   e. a taxonomic domain.

2. Which of the following is a correct sequence of levels in life's hierarchy, proceeding downward from an individual animal?
   a. brain, organ system, nerve cell, nervous tissue
   b. organ system, population of cells, nervous tissue, brain
   c. organism, organ system, tissue, cell, organ
   d. nervous system, brain, nervous tissue, nerve cell
   e. organ system, tissue, molecule, cell

3. Which of the following is *not* an observation or inference on which Darwin's theory of natural selection is based?
   a. Poorly adapted individuals never produce offspring.
   b. There is heritable variation among individuals.
   c. Because of overproduction of offspring, there is competition for limited resources.
   d. Individuals whose inherited characteristics best fit them to the environment will generally produce more offspring.
   e. A population can become adapted to its environment.

4. Systems biology is mainly an attempt to
   a. understand the integration of all levels of biological organization from molecules to the biosphere.
   b. simplify complex problems by reducing the system into smaller, less complex units.
   c. model one level of biological organization based on an understanding of the lower levels of organization.
   d. provide a systematic method for interpretation of large amounts of biological data.
   e. speed up the technological application of scientific knowledge.

5. Protists and bacteria are grouped into different domains because
   a. protists eat bacteria.
   b. bacteria are not made of cells.
   c. bacterial cells lack a nucleus.
   d. bacteria decompose protists.
   e. protists are photosynthetic.

6. Which of the following best demonstrates the unity among all organisms?
   a. matching DNA nucleotide sequences
   b. descent with modification
   c. the structure and function of DNA
   d. natural selection
   e. emergent properties

7. Which of the following is an example of qualitative data?
   a. The temperature decreased from 20°C to 15°C.
   b. The plant's height is 25 centimeters (cm).
   c. The fish swam in a zig-zag motion.
   d. The six pairs of robins hatched an average of three chicks.
   e. The contents of the stomach are mixed every 20 seconds.

8. Which of the following best describes the logic of hypothesis-based science?
   a. If I generate a testable hypothesis, tests and observations will support it.
   b. If my prediction is correct, it will lead to a testable hypothesis.
   c. If my observations are accurate, they will support my hypothesis.
   d. If my hypothesis is correct, I can expect certain test results.
   e. If my experiments are set up right, they will lead to a testable hypothesis.

9. A controlled experiment is one that
   a. proceeds slowly enough that a scientist can make careful records of the results.
   b. may include experimental groups and control groups tested in parallel.
   c. is repeated many times to make sure the results are accurate.
   d. keeps all environmental variables constant.
   e. is supervised by an experienced scientist.

10. Which of the following statements best distinguishes hypotheses from theories in science?
    a. Theories are hypotheses that have been proved.
    b. Hypotheses are guesses; theories are correct answers.
    c. Hypotheses usually are relatively narrow in scope; theories have broad explanatory power.
    d. Hypotheses and theories are essentially the same thing.
    e. Theories are proved true in all cases; hypotheses are usually falsified by tests.

For Self-Quiz answers, see Appendix A.

Go to the website or CD-ROM for more quiz questions.

Evolution Connection

A typical prokaryotic cell has about 3,000 genes in its DNA, while a human cell has about 25,000 genes. About 1,000 of these genes are present in both types of cells. Based on your understanding of evolution, explain how such different organisms could have the same subset of genes.

Scientific Inquiry

Based on the results of the snake mimicry case study, suggest another hypothesis researchers might investigate further.

Investigation *How Do Environmental Changes Affect a Population?*
Investigation *How Does Acid Precipitation Affect Trees?*

Science, Technology, and Society

The fruits of wild species of tomato are tiny compared to the giant beefsteak tomatoes available today. This difference in fruit size is almost entirely due to the larger number of cells in the domesticated fruits. Plant molecular biologists have recently discovered genes that are responsible for controlling cell division in tomatoes. Why would such a discovery be important to producers of other kinds of fruits and vegetables? To the study of human development and disease? To our basic understanding of biology?

The Chemistry of Life

AN INTERVIEW WITH
Lydia Makhubu

Until her recent retirement, Lydia Makhubu was the Vice Chancellor (in American terms, President) of the University of Swaziland, where she was also Professor of Chemistry. She received her higher education in Lesotho and at the Universities of Alberta and Toronto, where she earned a Ph.D. in Medicinal Chemistry. Building on her study of chemistry, Dr. Makhubu has had a distinguished career as a scientist in the area of health and traditional medicine, as a leader in higher education, and as a commentator on science, technology, and development in Africa and other developing regions. Among the many instances of her international service, she has been a consultant to several United Nations agencies and to the American Association for the Advancement of Science and has chaired the Association of Commonwealth Universities. Jane Reece met with her in Paris, where Dr. Makhubu was attending a meeting of the Executive Board of UNESCO, the United Nations Educational, Scientific and Cultural Organization.

Please tell us a little about Swaziland and its people.

Swaziland is a small landlocked country, only 17,400 square kilometers in area (smaller than New Jersey). It borders Mozambique on the east and South Africa on the west and south. The country ranges in altitude from high to low, and it has a great diversity of organisms, especially plants. The capital, Mbabane, is in the ecological zone called the highveld, where the altitude is close to 1,800 meters above sea level. The altitude drops to the middleveld, which has rich soils especially good for agriculture. As you go toward Mozambique and the sea, the land gets low and flat—the lowveld. The climate and the plant and animal species change as the altitude changes.

Swaziland is unusual these days because it is a kingdom, with a king who has executive authority. In the population of about 1 million, there is only one ethnic group, the Swazis, so we haven't had the conflicts that have afflicted some other African nations. Swaziland was a British colony, gaining independence in 1968. These days, the economy isn't as good as it used to be, in part because we've had a lot of drought and we're heavily dependent on agriculture.

What influenced you to become a medicinal chemist?

In the early days, my parents were teachers, but then my father took up a career in the Ministry of Health, becoming an orderly in a medical clinic. We lived at the clinic, and I could see him check people—since doctors were scarce, an orderly had a lot of responsibility. I wanted to be a medical doctor at that time. I ended up studying chemistry at college in Lesotho. From there, I went to Canada, where I did a master's degree and doctorate. I liked chemistry because it seemed to make sense: You mix this and that, and a product appears. I became interested in organic chemistry, and then, probably influenced by the importance of medicine in my society, I chose medicinal chemistry. I wanted to study the effects of drugs on the body.

What do you mean by "medicine in my society"?

The traditional medicine of my people. At college in Lesotho, we students used to argue about traditional medicine: Some believed it was absolute nonsense; others thought it worked. I was interested in this question. So when I came back from Canada, I immediately sought out traditional healers, including some of my relatives, and I was shown a few of the medicinal preparations they used. I started working in the laboratory to try to identify what was in those medicines.

In other countries of Southern Africa, traditional healers have organized themselves into associations and have even established some clinics. But in Swaziland, the British banned traditional medicine by the Witchcraft Act of 1901—and this law has not been repealed yet. Even people who had access to modern clinics, though, often continued to go to traditional healers, as well, and this continues today.

Tell us about the research on the plant *Phytolacca dodecandra* and its potential for preventing disease.

This plant, also called edod or soapberry, is a common bush in Africa. One day in 1964, an Ethiopian scientist, the late Aklilu Lemma of Addis Ababa University, was walking near a small stream, where he saw women washing clothes. He noticed a large pile of dead snails, of the type that transmits the disease schistosomiasis. He asked the women, "What are you using for soap?" and learned that they were using the berries of *Phytolacca*. He then took berries to the lab, along with some living snails, and found that extracts of the berries killed the snails.

What is schistosomiasis?

Also called bilharzia or snail fever, this is a debilitating disease that afflicts more than 200 million people worldwide. It is one of the greatest scourges in the developing world. The disease is caused by a parasitic flatworm (a fluke) that uses an aquatic snail as a host during part of its life cycle (see Figure 33.11). Fluke larvae released by the snails pierce the skin of people standing or swimming in the water, infecting them. You can control schistosomiasis by killing the parasite with a drug or by killing the snail with a synthetic molluscicide—but both are too expensive in Africa.

Is this where *Phytolacca* comes in?

Yes, *Phytolacca* berries are a better control method for schistosomiasis in Africa than synthetic chemicals of any sort because people can easily grow the plant and harvest the berries. Chemists have isolated the *Phytolacca* chemical that is lethal to snails, although it is not yet known exactly how it acts. Researchers have discovered that the chemical also kills some other parasites that live in African rivers, as well as the larvae of mosquitoes (which transmit malaria). And there are no bad environmental effects because the chemical readily decomposes.

At the University of Swaziland, we obtained seeds of *Phytolacca* from Ethiopia, grew the plants, and harvested the berries. The Ethiopians came to show us how to do everything; it was a true collaboration between Swazi and Ethiopian scientists, with help from some Zimbabwans and an American. Working in the lab, we discovered the concentration at which the berry extract killed the snails, and then we went into the field for further tests. Now we have selected an area in Swaziland where schistosomiasis is very prevalent, and we're working with the people there, teaching them how to grow and use *Phytolacca*. We hope that, in another year, the communities will be able to control the disease themselves.

What goes on at your university's institute of traditional medicine?

At this institute, officially the "Swaziland Institute of Research in Traditional Medicine, Medicinal and Indigenous Food Plants," multidisciplinary teams study all aspects of traditional medicine. Traditional healers are essential team members because they know the healing plants and how to use them. We have had several workshops

with traditional healers, trying to convince them of the importance of sharing their knowledge with us —because they are going to die, like all of us, and the knowledge may soon be lost. However, the healers—even my relatives!—are reluctant to help. They think, "You with your white coats are going to make loads of money from my knowledge." Their belief system is another obstacle. The healers believe that they are given the power of healing by their ancestors, and they are supposed to pass on this knowledge only to their children. But mostly it is suspicion. You know, for a long time they were called witches, and quite a few of the older ones are still sore about that; they ask me, "When is that Witchcraft Act of *yours* going to be repealed?"—as if I had written it! But slowly we are managing to convince them. We want to involve them for the long term, not only to show us the plants and help us grow them but to come into the lab to teach us how they prepare the medicine, so that we can quantify everything. But it's not easy.

It is also important, I think, to study the spiritual beliefs of the healers because the whole system is based on those beliefs. They say they are shown the plants in a dream by their ancestors' spirits, and they make diagnoses by throwing bones and going into a trance, during which the spirits speak to them.

What is the state of the environment and biological diversity in Swaziland?

Not very good. I think the underlying problem is overreliance on the natural environment, es-

pecially plant resources. In many rural areas, people have chopped down trees for wood until the land is completely bare; they do not know how to replant. Their grazing animals, such as cattle, often eat whatever plants remain. And the healers may overharvest medicinal plants from the wild. Many plants are disappearing.

Preservation of diversity goes along with preservation of the environment. So, you find that, in parts of Swaziland, certain animals have disappeared because the plants they lived on are no longer there. Even the climate is affected. For instance, in the forested highveld of Swaziland, there used to be lots of rain. But as the plants are removed, the rainfall lessens.

Another issue is damage that can result from projects associated with economic development, such as mining and dam construction. It is only recently that companies carrying out these big projects are being required to take care of the environment.

What are the challenges that science education faces in Africa?

We don't have enough resources to build proper science facilities, and we don't have enough science teachers. Another serious problem is the underrepresentation of women in science; this is particularly bad in Africa. Women are left behind. Science, especially physical science, is not considered a field for women. Many people think that if women go too far, they won't get a husband. But the situation is starting to change.

You are the President of the Third World Organization for Women in Science (TWOWS). What does this organization do?

We provide fellowships for postgraduate study, enlisting support from organizational benefactors. The fellowship recipients are usually sent to good universities in developing countries, such as South Africa or Pakistan, where the available money can go a long way. TWOWS also promotes collaboration among women from developing countries who are already established scientists.

But it's crucial to start at the earliest level, primary school. Researchers have learned that once girls get started in science, they do well. But they need to be encouraged by their teachers. If there is equipment available, it is used by the boys; the girls' role may be simply recording the results! So we are working hard to encourage the involvement of women scientists at all levels of education, to show the teachers that girls can be scientists.

"You can control schistosomiasis by killing the parasite with a drug or by killing the snail with a synthetic molluscicide—but both are too expensive in Africa. . . . *Phytolacca* berries are a better control method . . . because people can easily grow the plant."

2

The Chemical Context of Life

▲ Figure 2.1 **The bombardier beetle uses chemistry to defend itself.**

Key Concepts

2.1 Matter consists of chemical elements in pure form and in combinations called compounds

2.2 An element's properties depend on the structure of its atoms

2.3 The formation and function of molecules depend on chemical bonding between atoms

2.4 Chemical reactions make and break chemical bonds

Overview

Chemical Foundations of Biology

Like other animals, beetles have evolved structures and mechanisms that defend them from attack. The soil-dwelling bombardier beetle has a particularly effective mechanism for dealing with the ants that plague it. Upon detecting an ant on its body, this beetle ejects a spray of boiling hot liquid from glands in its abdomen, aiming the spray directly at the ant. (In **Figure 2.1**, the beetle aims its spray at a scientist's forceps.) The spray contains irritating chemicals that are generated at the moment of ejection by the explosive reaction of two sets of chemicals stored separately in the glands. The reaction produces heat and an audible pop.

Research on the bombardier beetle has involved chemistry, physics, and engineering, as well as biology. This is not surprising, for unlike a college catalog of courses, nature is not neatly packaged into the individual natural sciences. Biologists specialize in the study of life, but organisms and the world they live in are natural systems to which basic concepts of chemistry and physics apply. Biology is a multidisciplinary science.

This unit of chapters introduces key concepts of chemistry that will apply throughout our study of life. We will make many connections to the themes introduced in Chapter 1. One of those themes is the organization of life into a hierarchy of structural levels, with additional properties emerging at each successive level. In this unit, we will see how the theme of emergent properties applies to the lowest levels of biological organization—to the ordering of atoms into molecules and to the interactions of those molecules within cells. Somewhere in the transition from molecules to cells, we will cross the blurry boundary between nonlife and life. We begin by considering the chemical components that make up all matter. As Lydia Makhubu mentioned in the interview on pages 30 and 31, chemistry is an integral aspect of biology.

Concept 2.1

Matter consists of chemical elements in pure form and in combinations called compounds

Elements and Compounds

Organisms are composed of **matter,** which is anything that takes up space and has mass.* Matter exists in many diverse forms, each with its own characteristics. Rocks, metals, oils, gases, and humans are just a few examples of what seems an endless assortment of matter.

---

* Sometimes we substitute the term weight for mass, although the two are not identical. Mass is the amount of matter in an object, whereas the weight of an object is how strongly that mass is pulled by gravity. The weight of an astronaut walking on the moon is approximately 1/6 that on Earth, but his or her mass is the same. However, as long as we are earthbound, the weight of an object is a measure of its mass; in everyday language, therefore, we tend to use the terms interchangeably.

Sodium   Chlorine   Sodium chloride

▲ Figure 2.2 **The emergent properties of a compound.**
The metal sodium combines with the poisonous gas chlorine to form
the edible compound sodium chloride, or table salt.

Matter is made up of elements. An **element** is a substance that cannot be broken down to other substances by chemical reactions. Today, chemists recognize 92 elements occurring in nature; gold, copper, carbon, and oxygen are examples. Each element has a symbol, usually the first letter or two of its name. Some of the symbols are derived from Latin or German names; for instance, the symbol for sodium is Na, from the Latin word *natrium.*

A **compound** is a substance consisting of two or more different elements combined in a fixed ratio. Table salt, for example, is sodium chloride (NaCl), a compound composed of the elements sodium (Na) and chlorine (Cl) in a 1:1 ratio. Pure sodium is a metal and pure chlorine is a poisonous gas. When chemically combined, however, sodium and chlorine form an edible compound. This is a simple example of organized matter having emergent properties: A compound has characteristics different from those of its elements (**Figure 2.2**).

Essential Elements of Life

About 25 of the 92 natural elements are known to be essential to life. Just four of these—carbon (C), oxygen (O), hydrogen (H), and nitrogen (N)—make up 96% of living matter. Phos-

Table 2.1 Naturally Occurring Elements in the Human Body

Symbol	Element	Atomic Number (See p. 34)	Percentage of Human Body Weight
O	Oxygen	8	65.0
C	Carbon	6	18.5
H	Hydrogen	1	9.5
N	Nitrogen	7	3.3
Ca	Calcium	20	1.5
P	Phosphorus	15	1.0
K	Potassium	19	0.4
S	Sulfur	16	0.3
Na	Sodium	11	0.2
Cl	Chlorine	17	0.2
Mg	Magnesium	12	0.1

Trace elements (less than 0.01%): boron (B), chromium (Cr), cobalt (Co), copper (Cu), fluorine (F), iodine (I), iron (Fe), manganese (Mn), molybdenum (Mo), selenium (Se), silicon (Si), tin (Sn), vanadium (V), and zinc (Zn).

phorus (P), sulfur (S), calcium (Ca), potassium (K), and a few other elements account for most of the remaining 4% of an organism's weight. **Table 2.1** lists by percentage the elements that make up the human body; the percentages for other organisms are similar. **Figure 2.3a** illustrates the effect of a deficiency of nitrogen, an essential element, in a plant.

Trace elements are those required by an organism in only minute quantities. Some trace elements, such as iron (Fe), are needed by all forms of life; others are required only by certain species. For example, in vertebrates (animals with backbones), the element iodine (I) is an essential ingredient of a hormone produced by the thyroid gland. A daily intake of only 0.15 milligram (mg) of iodine is adequate for normal

▶ Figure 2.3 **The effects of essential-element deficiencies. (a)** This photo shows the effect of nitrogen deficiency in corn. In this controlled experiment, the plants on the left are growing in soil that was fertilized with compounds containing nitrogen, while the soil on the right is deficient in nitrogen. **(b)** Goiter, an enlarged thyroid gland, is the result of a deficiency of the trace element iodine. The goiter of this Malaysian woman can probably be reversed by iodine supplements.

(a) Nitrogen deficiency

(b) Iodine deficiency

activity of the human thyroid. An iodine deficiency in the diet causes the thyroid gland to grow to abnormal size, a condition called goiter **(Figure 2.3b)**. Where it is available, iodized salt has reduced the incidence of goiter.

Concept 2.2

An element's properties depend on the structure of its atoms

Each element consists of a certain kind of atom that is different from the atoms of any other element. An **atom** is the smallest unit of matter that still retains the properties of an element. Atoms are so small that it would take about a million of them to stretch across the period printed at the end of this sentence. We symbolize atoms with the same abbreviation used for the element made up of those atoms; thus, C stands for both the element carbon and a single carbon atom.

Subatomic Particles

Although the atom is the smallest unit having the properties of its element, these tiny bits of matter are composed of even smaller parts, called *subatomic particles*. Physicists have split the atom into more than a hundred types of particles, but only three kinds of particles are stable enough to be of relevance here: **neutrons, protons,** and **electrons.** Neutrons and protons are packed together tightly to form a dense core, or **atomic nucleus,** at the center of the atom. The electrons, moving at nearly the speed of light, form a cloud around the nucleus. **Figure 2.4** shows two models of the structure of the helium atom as an example.

Electrons and protons are electrically charged. Each electron has one unit of negative charge, and each proton has one unit of positive charge. A neutron, as its name implies, is electrically neutral. Protons give the nucleus a positive charge, and it is the attraction between opposite charges that keeps the rapidly moving electrons in the vicinity of the nucleus.

The neutron and proton are almost identical in mass, each about 1.7×10^{-24} gram (g). Grams and other conventional units are not very useful for describing the mass of objects so

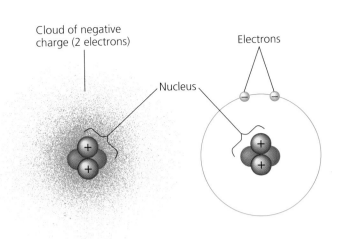

(a) This model represents the electrons as a cloud of negative charge, as if we had taken many snapshots of the 2 electrons over time, with each dot representing an electron's position at one point in time.

(b) In this even more simplified model, the electrons are shown as two small blue spheres on a circle around the nucleus.

▲ **Figure 2.4 Simplified models of a helium (He) atom.** The helium nucleus consists of 2 neutrons (brown) and 2 protons (pink). Two electrons (blue) move rapidly around the nucleus. These models are not to scale; they greatly overestimate the size of the nucleus in relation to the electron cloud.

minuscule. Thus, for atoms and subatomic particles (and for molecules as well), we use a unit of measurement called the **dalton,** in honor of John Dalton, the British scientist who helped develop atomic theory around 1800. (The dalton is the same as the *atomic mass unit,* or *amu,* a unit you may have encountered elsewhere.) Neutrons and protons have masses close to 1 dalton. Because the mass of an electron is only about $^1/_{2,000}$ that of a neutron or proton, we can ignore electrons when computing the total mass of an atom.

Atomic Number and Atomic Mass

Atoms of the various elements differ in their number of subatomic particles. All atoms of a particular element have the same number of protons in their nuclei. This number of protons, which is unique to that element, is called the **atomic number** and is written as a subscript to the left of the symbol for the element. The abbreviation $_2$He, for example, tells us that an atom of the element helium has 2 protons in its nucleus. Unless otherwise indicated, an atom is neutral in electrical charge, which means that its protons must be balanced by an equal number of electrons. Therefore, the atomic number tells us the number of protons and also the number of electrons in an electrically neutral atom.

We can deduce the number of neutrons from a second quantity, the **mass number,** which is the sum of protons plus neutrons in the nucleus of an atom. The mass number is written as a superscript to the left of an element's symbol. For example, we can use this shorthand to write an atom of helium as ^4_2He. Because the atomic number indicates how many protons there are, we can determine the number of neutrons by subtracting the atomic number from the mass number: A ^4_2He atom has 2 neutrons. An atom of sodium, $^{23}_{11}\text{Na}$, has 11 protons, 11 electrons, and 12 neutrons. The simplest atom is hydrogen ^1_1H, which has no neutrons; it consists of a lone proton with a single electron moving around it.

Almost all of an atom's mass is concentrated in its nucleus, because, as mentioned earlier, the contribution of electrons to mass is negligible. Because neutrons and protons each have a mass very close to 1 dalton, the mass number is an approximation of the total mass of an atom, called its **atomic mass.** So we might say that the atomic mass of sodium ($^{23}_{11}\text{Na}$) is 23 daltons, although more precisely it is 22.9898 daltons.

Isotopes

All atoms of a given element have the same number of protons, but some atoms have more neutrons than other atoms of the same element and therefore have greater mass. These different atomic forms are called **isotopes** of the element. In nature, an element occurs as a mixture of its isotopes. For example, consider the three isotopes of the element carbon, which has the atomic number 6. The most common isotope is carbon-12, $^{12}_6\text{C}$, which accounts for about 99% of the carbon in nature. It has 6 neutrons. Most of the remaining 1% of carbon consists of atoms of the isotope $^{13}_6\text{C}$, with 7 neutrons. A third, even rarer isotope, $^{14}_6\text{C}$, has 8 neutrons. Notice that all three isotopes of carbon have 6 protons—otherwise, they would not be carbon. Although isotopes of an element have slightly different masses, they behave identically in chemical reactions. (The number usually given as the atomic mass of an element, such as 22.9898 daltons for sodium, is actually an average of the atomic masses of all the element's naturally occurring isotopes.)

Both ^{12}C and ^{13}C are stable isotopes, meaning that their nuclei do not have a tendency to lose particles. The isotope ^{14}C, however, is unstable, or radioactive. A **radioactive isotope** is one in which the nucleus decays spontaneously, giving off particles and energy. When the decay leads to a change in the number of protons, it transforms the atom to an atom of a different element. For example, radioactive carbon decays to form nitrogen.

Radioactive isotopes have many useful applications in biology. In Chapter 26, you will learn how researchers use measurements of radioactivity in fossils to date those relics of past life. Radioactive isotopes are also useful as tracers to follow atoms through metabolism, the chemical processes of an organism. Cells use the radioactive atoms as they would nonradioactive isotopes of the same element, but the radioactive tracers can be readily detected. **Figure 2.5** presents an example of how biologists use radioactive tracers to monitor biological processes, in this case cells making copies of their DNA.

Figure 2.5

Research Method   **Radioactive Tracers**

APPLICATION   Scientists use radioactive isotopes to label certain chemical substances, creating tracers that can be used to follow a metabolic process or locate the substance within an organism. In this example, radioactive tracers are being used to determine the effect of temperature on the rate at which cells make copies of their DNA.

TECHNIQUE

Ingredients including radioactive tracer (bright blue)

Incubators

Human cells

❶ Ingredients for making DNA are added to human cells. One ingredient is labeled with ^3H, a radioactive isotope of hydrogen. Nine dishes of cells are incubated at different temperatures. The cells make new DNA, incorporating the radioactive tracer with ^3H.

❷ The cells are placed in test tubes, their DNA is isolated, and unused ingredients are removed.

DNA (old and new)

❸ A solution called scintillation fluid is added to the test tubes and they are placed in a scintillation counter. As the ^3H in the newly made DNA decays, it emits radiation that excites chemicals in the scintillation fluid, causing them to give off light. Flashes of light are recorded by the scintillation counter.

RESULTS   The frequency of flashes, which is recorded as counts per minute, is proportional to the amount of the radioactive tracer present, indicating the amount of new DNA. In this experiment, when the counts per minute are plotted against temperature, it is clear that temperature affects the rate of DNA synthesis—the most DNA was made at 35 °C.

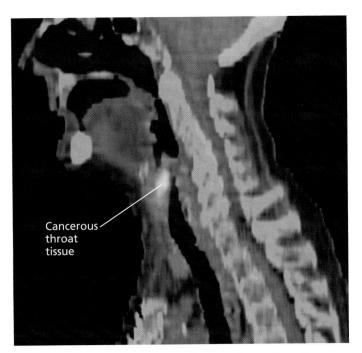

▲ **Figure 2.6** **A PET scan, a medical use for radioactive isotopes.** PET, an acronym for positron-emission tomography, detects locations of intense chemical activity in the body. The patient is first injected with a nutrient such as glucose labeled with a radioactive isotope that emits subatomic particles. These particles collide with electrons made available by chemical reactions in the body. A PET scanner detects the energy released in these collisions and maps "hot spots," the regions of an organ that are most chemically active at the time. The color of the image varies with the amount of the isotope present, with the bright yellow color here identifying a hot spot of cancerous throat tissue.

Radioactive tracers are important diagnostic tools in medicine. For example, certain kidney disorders can be diagnosed by injecting small doses of substances containing radioactive isotopes into the blood and then measuring the amount of tracer excreted in the urine. Radioactive tracers are also used in combination with sophisticated imaging instruments, such as PET scanners, which can monitor chemical processes, such as those involved in cancerous growth, as they actually occur in the body **(Figure 2.6)**.

Although radioactive isotopes are very useful in biological research and medicine, radiation from decaying isotopes also poses a hazard to life by damaging cellular molecules. The severity of this damage depends on the type and amount of radiation an organism absorbs. One of the most serious environmental threats is radioactive fallout from nuclear accidents. The doses of most isotopes used in medical diagnosis, however, are relatively safe.

The Energy Levels of Electrons

The simplified models of the atom in Figure 2.4 greatly exaggerate the size of the nucleus relative to the volume of the whole atom. If an atom of helium were the size of Yankee Stadium, the nucleus would be only the size of a pencil eraser in

the center of the field. Moreover, the electrons would be like two tiny gnats buzzing around the stadium, in a space approximately a million times as large as the nucleus. Atoms are mostly empty space.

When two atoms approach each other during a chemical reaction, their nuclei do not come close enough to interact. Of the three kinds of subatomic particles we have discussed, only electrons are directly involved in the chemical reactions between atoms.

An atom's electrons vary in the amount of energy they possess. **Energy** is defined as the capacity to cause change, for instance by doing work. **Potential energy** is the energy that matter possesses because of its location or structure. For example, because of its altitude, water in a reservoir on a hill has potential energy. When the gates of the reservoir's dam are opened and the water runs downhill, the energy can be used to do work, such as turning generators. Because energy has been expended, the water has less energy at the bottom of the hill than it did in the reservoir. Matter has a natural tendency to move to the lowest possible state of potential energy; in this example, water runs downhill. To restore the potential energy of a reservoir, work must be done to elevate the water against gravity.

The electrons of an atom also have potential energy because of how they are arranged in relation to the nucleus. The negatively charged electrons are attracted to the positively charged nucleus. It takes work to move an electron farther away from the nucleus, so the more distant the electrons are from the nucleus, the greater their potential energy. Unlike the continuous flow of water downhill, changes in the potential energy of electrons can occur only in steps of fixed amounts. An electron having a certain discrete amount of energy is something like a ball on a staircase **(Figure 2.7a)**. The ball can have different amounts of potential energy, depending on which step it is on, but it cannot spend much time between the steps. An electron cannot exist in between its fixed states of potential energy.

The different states of potential energy that electrons have in an atom are called **energy levels.** An electron's energy level is correlated with its average distance from the nucleus; these average distances are represented symbolically by **electron shells (Figure 2.7b).** The first shell is closest to the nucleus, and electrons in this shell have the lowest potential energy. Electrons in the second shell have more energy, electrons in the third shell more energy still, and so on. An electron can change the shell it occupies, but only by absorbing or losing an amount of energy equal to the difference in potential energy between its position in the old shell and that in the new shell. When an electron absorbs energy, it moves to a shell farther out from the nucleus. For example, light energy can excite an electron to a higher energy level. (Indeed, this is the first step taken when plants harness the energy of sunlight for photosynthesis, the process that produces food from carbon dioxide and water.) When an electron loses energy, it "falls back" to a

(a) A ball bouncing down a flight of stairs provides an analogy for energy levels of electrons, because the ball can only rest on each step, not between steps.

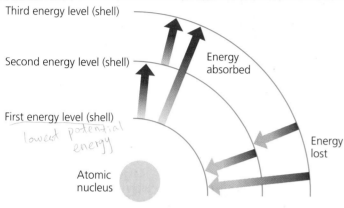

Third energy level (shell)

Second energy level (shell)

First energy level (shell)
lowest potential energy

Energy absorbed

Energy lost

Atomic nucleus

(b) An electron can move from one level to another only if the energy it gains or loses is exactly equal to the difference in energy between the two levels. Arrows indicate some of the step-wise changes in potential energy that are possible.

▲ **Figure 2.7 Energy levels of an atom's electrons.** Electrons exist only at fixed levels of potential energy, which are also called electron shells.

shell closer to the nucleus, and the lost energy is usually released to the environment in the form of heat. For example, sunlight excites electrons in the paint of a dark car to higher energy levels. When the electrons fall back to their original levels, the surface of the car heats up. This thermal energy can be transferred to the air or to your hand if you touch the car.

Electron Configuration and Chemical Properties

The chemical behavior of an atom is determined by its electron configuration—that is, the distribution of electrons in the atom's electron shells. Beginning with hydrogen, the simplest atom, we can imagine building the atoms of the other elements by adding 1 proton and 1 electron at a time (along with an appropriate number of neutrons). **Figure 2.8**, an abbreviated version of what is called the *periodic table of the elements*, shows this distribution of electrons for the first 18 elements, from hydrogen ($_1$H) to argon ($_{18}$Ar). The elements are arranged in three rows, or periods, corresponding to the number of electron shells in their atoms. The left-to-right sequence of elements in each row corresponds to the sequential addition of electrons (and protons).

Hydrogen's 1 electron and helium's 2 electrons are located in the first shell. Electrons, like all matter, tend to exist in the

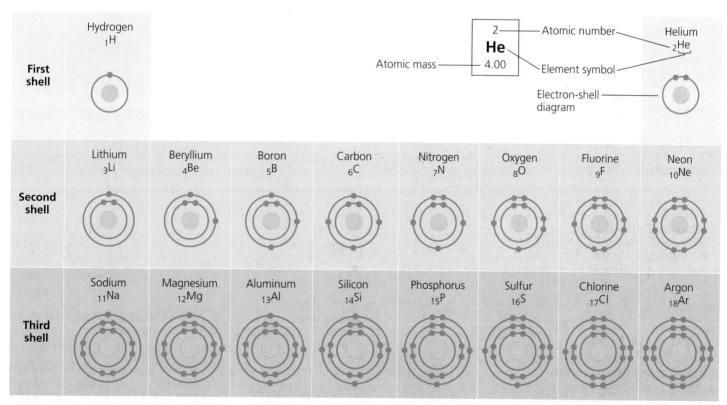

▲ **Figure 2.8 Electron-shell diagrams of the first 18 elements in the periodic table.** In a standard periodic table, information for each element is presented as shown for helium in the inset. In the diagrams in this modified table, electrons are shown as blue dots and electron shells (representing energy levels) as concentric rings. We are using these electron-shell diagrams as a convenient way to picture the distribution of an atom's electrons among its electron shells, but keep in mind that these are simplified models. The elements are arranged in rows, each representing the filling of an electron shell. As electrons are added, they occupy the lowest available shell.

lowest available state of potential energy, which they have in the first shell. However, the first shell can hold no more than 2 electrons; thus, there are only two elements (hydrogen and helium) in the first row of the table. An atom with more than 2 electrons must use higher shells because the first shell is full. The next element, lithium, has 3 electrons. Two of these electrons fill the first shell while the third electron occupies the second shell. The second shell holds a maximum of 8 electrons. Neon, at the end of the second row, has 8 electrons in the second shell, giving it a total of 10 electrons.

The chemical behavior of an atom depends mostly on the number of electrons in its *outermost* shell. We call those outer electrons **valence electrons** and the outermost electron shell the **valence shell**. In the case of lithium, there is only 1 valence electron, and the second shell is the valence shell. Atoms with the same number of electrons in their valence shells exhibit similar chemical behavior. For example, fluorine (F) and chlorine (Cl) both have 7 valence electrons, and both combine with the element sodium to form compounds (see Figure 2.2). An atom with a completed valence shell is unreactive; that is, it will not interact readily with other atoms it encounters. At the far right of the periodic table are helium, neon, and argon,

the only three elements shown in Figure 2.8 that have full valence shells. These elements are said to be *inert*, meaning chemically unreactive. All the other atoms in Figure 2.8 are chemically reactive because they have incomplete valence shells.

Electron Orbitals

Early in the 20th century, the electron shells of an atom were visualized as concentric paths of electrons orbiting the nucleus, somewhat like planets orbiting the sun. It is still convenient to use two-dimensional concentric-circle diagrams to symbolize electron shells, as in Figure 2.8, if we bear in mind that an electron shell represents the *average* distance of an electron from the nucleus. This is only a model, however, and it does not give a real picture of an atom. In reality, we can never know the exact path of an electron. What we can do instead is describe the space in which an electron spends most of its time. The three-dimensional space where an electron is found 90% of the time is called an **orbital.**

Each electron shell consists of a specific number of orbitals of distinctive shapes and orientations **(Figure 2.9)**. You can

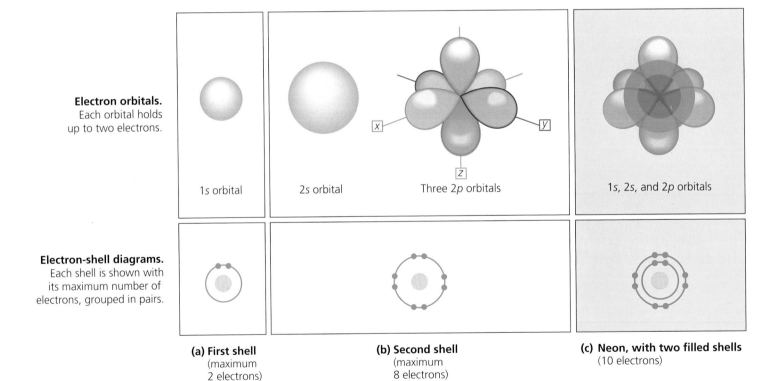

Electron orbitals.
Each orbital holds up to two electrons.

1s orbital   2s orbital   Three 2p orbitals   1s, 2s, and 2p orbitals

Electron-shell diagrams.
Each shell is shown with its maximum number of electrons, grouped in pairs.

(a) First shell
(maximum 2 electrons)

(b) Second shell
(maximum 8 electrons)

(c) Neon, with two filled shells
(10 electrons)

▲ **Figure 2.9 Electron orbitals.** The three-dimensional shapes in the top half of this figure represent electron orbitals—the volumes of space where the electrons of an atom are most likely to be found. Each orbital holds a maximum of 2 electrons. The bottom half of the figure shows the corresponding electron-shell diagrams. **(a)** The first electron shell has one spherical (s) orbital, designated 1s. **(b)** The second and all higher shells each have one larger s orbital (designated 2s for the second shell) plus three dumbbell-shaped orbitals called p orbitals (2p for the second shell). The three 2p orbitals lie at right angles to one another along imaginary x-, y-, and z-axes of the atom. Each 2p orbital is outlined here in a different color. **(c)** To symbolize the electron orbitals of the element neon, which has a total of 10 electrons, we superimpose the 1s orbital of the first shell and the 2s and three 2p orbitals of the second shell.

think of an orbital as a component of an electron shell. (Recall that an electron shell corresponds to a particular energy level.) The first electron shell has only one spherical s orbital (called 1s), but the second shell has four orbitals: one large spherical s orbital (called 2s) and three dumbbell-shaped p orbitals (called 2p orbitals). Each 2p orbital is oriented at right angles to the other two 2p orbitals (see Figure 2.9). (The third and higher electron shells also have s and p orbitals, as well as orbitals of more complex shapes.)

No more than 2 electrons can occupy a single orbital. The first electron shell can therefore accommodate a maximum of 2 electrons in its s orbital. The lone electron of a hydrogen atom occupies the 1s orbital, as do the 2 electrons of a helium atom. The four orbitals of the second electron shell can hold a maximum of 8 electrons. Electrons in each of the four orbitals have nearly the same energy, but they move in different volumes of space.

The reactivity of atoms arises from the presence of unpaired electrons in one or more orbitals of their valence shells. Notice that the electron configurations in Figure 2.8 build up with the addition of 1 electron at a time. For simplicity, we place 1 electron on each side of the outer shell until the shell is half full, and then pair up electrons until the shell is full. When atoms interact to complete their valence shells, it is the *unpaired* electrons that are involved.

Concept Check 2.2

1. A lithium atom has 3 protons and 4 neutrons. What is its atomic mass in daltons?
2. A nitrogen atom has 7 protons, and the most common isotope of nitrogen has 7 neutrons. A radioactive isotope of nitrogen has 8 neutrons. What is the atomic number and mass number of this radioactive nitrogen? Write as a chemical symbol with a subscript and superscript.
3. Look at Figure 2.8, and determine the atomic number of magnesium. How many protons and electrons does it have? How many electron shells? How many valence electrons are in the valence shell?
4. In an electron-shell diagram of phosphorus, in which shell do electrons have the most potential energy? In which shell do electrons have the least potential energy?
5. How many electrons does fluorine have? How many electron shells? Name the orbitals that are occupied. How many unpaired electrons does fluorine have?

For suggested answers, see Appendix A.

Concept 2.3

The formation and function of molecules depend on chemical bonding between atoms

Now that we have looked at the structure of atoms, we can move up the hierarchy of organization and see how atoms combine to form molecules and ionic compounds. Atoms with incomplete valence shells can interact with certain other atoms in such a way that each partner completes its valence shell: The atoms either share or transfer valence electrons. These interactions usually result in atoms staying close together, held by attractions called **chemical bonds**. The strongest kinds of chemical bonds are covalent bonds and ionic bonds.

Covalent Bonds

A **covalent bond** is the sharing of a pair of valence electrons by two atoms. For example, let's consider what happens when two hydrogen atoms approach each other. Recall that hydrogen has 1 valence electron in the first shell, but the shell's capacity is 2 electrons. When the two hydrogen atoms come close enough for their 1s orbitals to overlap, they share their electrons **(Figure 2.10)**. Each hydrogen atom now has 2 electrons associated with it in what amounts to a completed valence shell, shown in an electron-shell diagram in

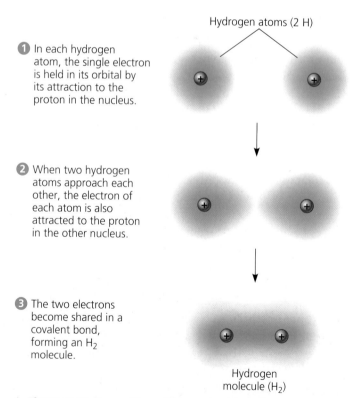

Hydrogen atoms (2 H)

1. In each hydrogen atom, the single electron is held in its orbital by its attraction to the proton in the nucleus.

2. When two hydrogen atoms approach each other, the electron of each atom is also attracted to the proton in the other nucleus.

3. The two electrons become shared in a covalent bond, forming an H_2 molecule.

Hydrogen molecule (H_2)

▲ **Figure 2.10 Formation of a covalent bond.**

Figure 2.11a. Two or more atoms held together by covalent bonds constitute a **molecule.** In this case, we have formed a hydrogen molecule. We can abbreviate the structure of this molecule as H—H, where the line represents a single covalent bond, or simply a **single bond**—that is, a pair of shared electrons. This notation, which represents both atoms and bonding, is called a **structural formula.** We can abbreviate even further by writing H_2, a **molecular formula** indicating simply that the molecule consists of two atoms of hydrogen.

With 6 electrons in its second electron shell, oxygen needs 2 more electrons to complete its valence shell. Two oxygen atoms form a molecule by sharing *two* pairs of valence electrons **(Figure 2.11b)**. The atoms are thus joined by what is called a double covalent bond, or simply a **double bond.**

Each atom that can share valence electrons has a bonding capacity corresponding to the number of covalent bonds the atom can form. When the bonds form, they give the atom a full complement of electrons in the valence shell. The bonding capacity of oxygen, for example, is 2. This bonding capacity is called the atom's **valence** and usually equals the number of unpaired electrons in the atom's outermost (valence) shell. See if you can determine the valences of hydrogen, oxygen, nitrogen, and carbon by studying the electron configurations in Figure 2.8. By counting the unpaired electrons, you can see that the valence of hydrogen is 1; oxygen, 2; nitrogen, 3; and carbon, 4. A more complicated case is phosphorus (P), another element important to life. Phosphorus can have a valence of 3, as we would predict from its 3 unpaired electrons. In biologically important molecules, however, we can consider it to have a valence of 5, forming three single bonds and one double bond.

The molecules H_2 and O_2 are pure elements, not compounds. (Recall that a compound is a combination of two or more *different* elements.) An example of a molecule that is a compound is water, with the molecular formula H_2O. It takes two atoms of hydrogen to satisfy the valence of one oxygen atom. **Figure 2.11c** shows the structure of a water molecule. Water is so important to life that Chapter 3 is devoted entirely to its structure and behavior.

Another molecule that is a compound is methane, the main component of natural gas, with the molecular formula CH_4 **(Figure 2.11d)**. It takes four hydrogen atoms, each with a valence of 1, to complement one atom of carbon, with its valence of 4. We will look at many other compounds of carbon in Chapter 4.

The attraction of a particular kind of atom for the electrons of a covalent bond is called its **electronegativity.** The more electronegative an atom, the more strongly it pulls shared electrons toward itself. In a covalent bond between two atoms of the same element, the outcome of the tug-of-war for common electrons is a standoff; the two atoms are equally electronegative. Such a bond, in which the electrons are shared equally, is a **nonpolar covalent bond.** For example, the covalent bond of H_2 is nonpolar, as is the double bond of O_2. In other compounds, however, where one atom is bonded to a more elec-

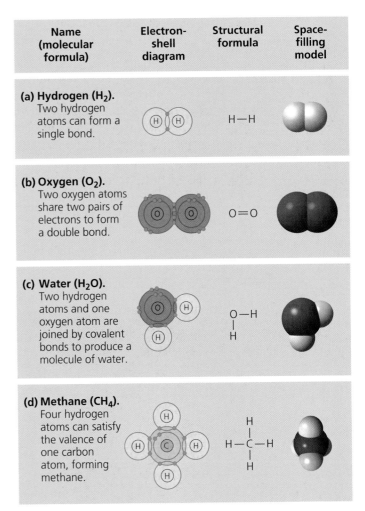

▲ **Figure 2.11 Covalent bonding in four molecules.** A single covalent bond consists of a pair of shared electrons. The number of electrons required to complete an atom's valence shell generally determines how many bonds that atom will form. Three ways of indicating bonds are shown; the space-filling model comes closest to representing the actual shape of the molecule (see also Figure 2.16).

tronegative atom, the electrons of the bond are not shared equally. This sort of bond is called a **polar covalent bond.** Such bonds vary in their polarity, depending on the relative electronegativity of the two atoms. For example, the individual bonds of methane (CH_4) are slightly polar because carbon and hydrogen differ slightly in electronegativity. In a more extreme example, the bonds between the oxygen and hydrogen atoms of a water molecule are quite polar **(Figure 2.12)**. Oxygen is one of the most electronegative of the 92 elements, attracting shared electrons much more strongly than hydrogen does. In a covalent bond between oxygen and hydrogen, the electrons spend more time near the oxygen nucleus than they do near the hydrogen nucleus. Because electrons have a negative charge, the unequal sharing of electrons in water causes the oxygen atom to have a partial negative charge (indicated by the Greek letter δ before a minus sign, $\delta-$, or "delta minus") and each hydrogen atom a partial positive charge ($\delta+$, or "delta plus").

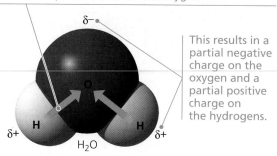

Because oxygen (O) is more electronegative than hydrogen (H), shared electrons are pulled more toward oxygen.

δ^-

This results in a partial negative charge on the oxygen and a partial positive charge on the hydrogens.

O

H   H
δ^+ δ^+
H_2O

▲ **Figure 2.12 Polar covalent bonds in a water molecule.**

Ionic Bonds

In some cases, two atoms are so unequal in their attraction for valence electrons that the more electronegative atom strips an electron completely away from its partner. This is what happens when an atom of sodium ($_{11}Na$) encounters an atom of chlorine ($_{17}Cl$) **(Figure 2.13)**. A sodium atom has a total of 11 electrons, with its single valence electron in the third electron shell. A chlorine atom has a total of 17 electrons, with 7 electrons in its valence shell. When these two atoms meet, the lone valence electron of sodium is transferred to the chlorine atom, and both atoms end up with their valence shells complete. (Because sodium no longer has an electron in the third shell, the second shell is now the valence shell.)

The electron transfer between the two atoms moves one unit of negative charge from sodium to chlorine. Sodium, now with 11 protons but only 10 electrons, has a net electrical charge of 1+. A charged atom (or molecule) is called an **ion.** When the charge is positive, the ion is specifically called a **cation;** the sodium atom has become a cation. Conversely, the chlorine atom, having gained an extra electron, now has 17 protons and 18 electrons, giving it a net electrical charge of 1−. It has become a chloride ion—an **anion,** or negatively

charged ion. Because of their opposite charges, cations and anions attract each other; this attraction is called an **ionic bond.** The transfer of an electron is not the formation of a bond; rather, it allows a bond to form because it results in two ions. Any two ions of opposite charge can form an ionic bond. The ions need not have acquired their charge by an electron transfer with each other.

Compounds formed by ionic bonds are called **ionic compounds,** or **salts.** We know the ionic compound sodium chloride (NaCl) as table salt **(Figure 2.14)**. Salts are often found in nature as crystals of various sizes and shapes, each an aggregate of vast numbers of cations and anions bonded by their electrical attraction and arranged in a three-dimensional lattice. A salt crystal does not consist of molecules in the sense that a covalent compound does, because a covalently bonded molecule has a definite size and number of atoms. The formula for an ionic compound, such as NaCl, indicates only the ratio of elements in a crystal of the salt. "NaCl" is not a molecule.

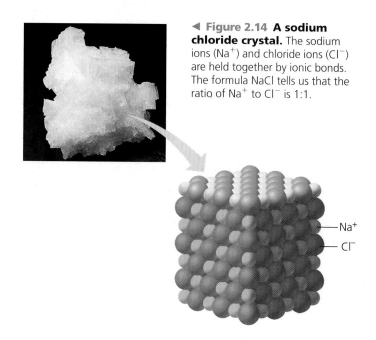

◀ **Figure 2.14 A sodium chloride crystal.** The sodium ions (Na^+) and chloride ions (Cl^-) are held together by ionic bonds. The formula NaCl tells us that the ratio of Na^+ to Cl^- is 1:1.

—Na^+
—Cl^-

1 The lone valence electron of a sodium atom is transferred to join the 7 valence electrons of a chlorine atom.

2 Each resulting ion has a completed valence shell. An ionic bond can form between the oppositely charged ions.

+   −

Na   Cl   Na   Cl

Na
Sodium atom

Cl
Chlorine atom

Na^+
Sodium ion
(a cation)

Cl^-
Chloride ion
(an anion)

Sodium chloride (NaCl)

▶ **Figure 2.13 Electron transfer and ionic bonding.** The attraction between oppositely charged atoms, or ions, is an ionic bond. An ionic bond can form between any two oppositely charged ions, even if they have not been formed by transfer of an electron from one to the other.

Not all salts have equal numbers of cations and anions. For example, the ionic compound magnesium chloride ($MgCl_2$) has two chloride ions for each magnesium ion. Magnesium ($_{12}Mg$) must lose 2 outer electrons if the atom is to have a complete valence shell, so it tends to become a cation with a net charge of $2+$ (Mg^{2+}). One magnesium cation can therefore form ionic bonds with two chloride anions.

The term *ion* also applies to entire molecules that are electrically charged. In the salt ammonium chloride (NH_4Cl), for instance, the anion is a single chloride ion (Cl^-), but the cation is ammonium (NH_4^+), a nitrogen atom with four covalently bonded hydrogen atoms. The whole ammonium ion has an electrical charge of $1+$ because it is 1 electron short.

Environment affects the strength of ionic bonds. In a dry salt crystal, the bonds are so strong that it takes a hammer and chisel to break enough of them to crack the crystal in two. Place the same salt crystal in water, however, and the salt dissolves as the attractions between its ions decrease. In the next chapter, you will learn how water dissolves salts.

Weak Chemical Bonds

In living organisms, most of the strongest chemical bonds are covalent ones, which link atoms to form a cell's molecules. But weaker bonding within and between molecules is also indispensable in the cell, where the properties of life emerge from such interactions. The most important large biological molecules are held in their functional form by weak bonds. In addition, when two molecules in the cell make contact, they may adhere temporarily by weak bonds. The reversibility of weak bonding can be an advantage: Two molecules can come together, respond to one another in some way, and then separate.

Several types of weak chemical bonds are important in living organisms. One is the ionic bond, which we just discussed. Another type of weak bond, crucial to life, is known as a hydrogen bond.

Hydrogen Bonds

Among the various kinds of weak chemical bonds, hydrogen bonds are so important in the chemistry of life that they deserve special attention. A **hydrogen bond** forms when a hydrogen atom covalently bonded to one electronegative atom is also attracted to another electronegative atom. In living cells, the electronegative partners involved are usually oxygen or nitrogen atoms. Refer to **Figure 2.15** to examine the simple case of hydrogen bonding between water (H_2O) and ammonia (NH_3). In the next chapter, we'll see how hydrogen bonds between water molecules allow some insects to walk on water.

Van der Waals Interactions

Even a molecule with nonpolar covalent bonds may have positively and negatively charged regions. Because electrons are in

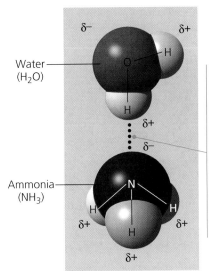

▲ Figure 2.15 **A hydrogen bond.**

A hydrogen bond results from the attraction between the partial positive charge on the hydrogen atom of water and the partial negative charge on the nitrogen atom of ammonia.

constant motion, they are not always symmetrically distributed in the molecule; at any instant, they may accumulate by chance in one part of the molecule or another. The results are ever-changing "hot spots" of positive and negative charge that enable all atoms and molecules to stick to one another. These **van der Waals interactions** are weak and occur only when atoms and molecules are very close together. In spite of their weakness, van der Waals interactions were recently shown to be responsible for the ability of a gecko lizard (right) to walk up a wall. Each gecko toe has hundreds of thousands of tiny hairs, with multiple projections at the hair's tip that increase surface area. Apparently, the van der Waals interactions between the hair tip molecules and the molecules of the wall's surface are so numerous that in spite of their individual weakness, together they can support the gecko's body weight.

Van der Waals interactions, hydrogen bonds, ionic bonds, and other weak bonds may form not only between molecules but also between different regions of a single large molecule, such as a protein. Although these bonds are individually weak, their cumulative effect is to reinforce the three-dimensional shape of a large molecule. You will learn more about the very important biological roles of weak bonds in Chapter 5.

Molecular Shape and Function

A molecule has a characteristic size and shape. The precise shape of a molecule is usually very important to its function in the living cell.

A molecule consisting of two atoms, such as H_2 or O_2, is always linear, but molecules with more than two atoms have

(a) Hybridization of orbitals. The single *s* and three *p* orbitals of a valence shell involved in covalent bonding combine to form four teardrop-shaped hybrid orbitals. These orbitals extend to the four corners of an imaginary tetrahedron (outlined in pink).

Space-filling model	Ball-and-stick model	Hybrid-orbital model (with ball-and-stick model superimposed)

Water (H_2O)

Unbonded electron pair

104.5°

Methane (CH_4)

(b) Molecular shape models. Three models representing molecular shape are shown for two examples: water and methane. The positions of the hybrid orbitals determine the shapes of the molecules.

▲ **Figure 2.16 Molecular shapes due to hybrid orbitals.**

more complicated shapes. These shapes are determined by the positions of the atoms' orbitals. When an atom forms covalent bonds, the orbitals in its valence shell rearrange. For atoms with valence electrons in both *s* and *p* orbitals (review Figure 2.9), the single *s* and three *p* orbitals hybridize to form four new hybrid orbitals shaped like identical teardrops extending from the region of the atomic nucleus **(Figure 2.16a)**. If we connect the larger ends of the teardrops with lines, we have the outline of a geometric shape called a tetrahedron, similar to a pyramid.

For the water molecule (H_2O), two of the hybrid orbitals in the oxygen atom's valence shell are shared with hydrogen atoms **(Figure 2.16b)**. The result is a molecule shaped roughly like a V, its two covalent bonds spread apart at an angle of 104.5°.

The methane molecule (CH_4) has the shape of a completed tetrahedron because all four hybrid orbitals of carbon are shared with hydrogen atoms (see Figure 2.16b). The nucleus

of the carbon is at the center, with its four covalent bonds radiating to hydrogen nuclei at the corners of the tetrahedron. Larger molecules containing multiple carbon atoms, including many of the molecules that make up living matter, have more complex overall shapes. However, the tetrahedral shape of a carbon atom bonded to four other atoms is often a repeating motif within such molecules.

Molecular shape is crucial in biology because it determines how biological molecules recognize and respond to one another with specificity. Only molecules with complementary shapes are able to bind to each other by weak bonds. An example of this specificity is provided by a mechanism of pain control. Natural signal molecules called endorphins bind to specific molecules, called receptors, on the surface of brain cells, producing euphoria and relieving pain. It turns out that molecules with shapes similar to endorphins have similar effects. Morphine, heroin, and other opiate drugs, for example, mimic endorphins by binding to endorphin receptors in the brain **(Figure 2.17)**. The role of molecular shape in brain chemistry illustrates the relationship between structure and function, one of biology's unifying themes.

■ Carbon ■ Nitrogen
□ Hydrogen ■ Sulfur
■ Oxygen

Natural endorphin

Morphine

(a) Structures of endorphin and morphine. The boxed portion of the endorphin molecule (left) binds to receptor molecules on target cells in the brain. The boxed portion of the morphine molecule (right) is a close match.

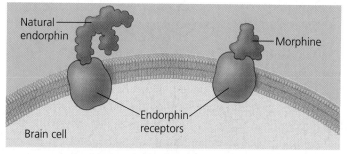

Natural endorphin

Morphine

Endorphin receptors

Brain cell

(b) Binding to endorphin receptors. Endorphin receptors on the surface of a brain cell can bind to both endorphin and morphine.

▲ **Figure 2.17 A molecular mimic.** Morphine affects pain perception and emotional state by mimicking the brain's natural endorphins.

Concept Check 2.3

1. Why does the following structure fail to make sense chemically?

$$H—C\equiv C—H$$

2. Explain what holds together the atoms in a crystal of magnesium chloride ($MgCl_2$).

For suggested answers, see Appendix A.

Concept 2.4

Chemical reactions make and break chemical bonds

The making and breaking of chemical bonds, leading to changes in the composition of matter, are called **chemical reactions.** An example is the reaction between hydrogen and oxygen to form water:

$$2\,H_2 \quad + \quad O_2 \quad \longrightarrow \quad 2\,H_2O$$

Reactants   **Reaction**   **Products**

This reaction breaks the covalent bonds of H_2 and O_2 and forms the new bonds of H_2O. When we write a chemical reaction, we use an arrow to indicate the conversion of the starting materials, called the **reactants,** to the **products.** The coefficients indicate the number of molecules involved; for example, the coefficient 2 in front of the H_2 means that the reaction starts with two molecules of hydrogen. Notice that all atoms of the reactants must be accounted for in the products. Matter is conserved in a chemical reaction: Reactions cannot create or destroy matter but can only rearrange it.

Photosynthesis, which takes place within the cells of green plant tissues, is a particularly important example of how chemical reactions rearrange matter. Humans and other animals ultimately depend on photosynthesis for food and oxygen, and this process is at the foundation of almost all ecosystems. The following chemical shorthand summarizes the process of photosynthesis:

$$6\,CO_2 + 6\,H_2O \longrightarrow C_6H_{12}O_6 + 6\,O_2$$

The raw materials of photosynthesis are carbon dioxide (CO_2), which is taken from the air, and water (H_2O), which is

absorbed from the soil. Within the plant cells, sunlight powers the conversion of these ingredients to a sugar called glucose ($C_6H_{12}O_6$) and oxygen molecules (O_2), a by-product that the plant releases into the surroundings **(Figure 2.18).** Although photosynthesis is actually a sequence of many chemical reactions, we still end up with the same number and kinds of atoms we had when we started. Matter has simply been rearranged, with an input of energy provided by sunlight.

Some chemical reactions go to completion; that is, all the reactants are converted to products. But most reactions are reversible, the products of the forward reaction becoming the reactants for the reverse reaction. For example, hydrogen and nitrogen molecules can combine to form ammonia, but ammonia can also decompose to regenerate hydrogen and nitrogen:

$$3\,H_2 + N_2 \rightleftharpoons 2\,NH_3$$

The opposite-headed arrows indicate that the reaction is reversible.

One of the factors affecting the rate of a reaction is the concentration of reactants. The greater the concentration of reactant molecules, the more frequently they collide with one another and have an opportunity to react to form products. The same holds true for the products. As products accumulate, collisions resulting in the reverse reaction become increasingly frequent. Eventually, the forward and reverse reactions occur at the same rate, and the relative concentrations of products and reactants stop changing. The point at which the reactions offset one another exactly is called **chemical equilibrium.** This is a dynamic equilibrium; reactions are still going on, but with no net effect on the concentrations of reactants and products. Equilibrium does *not* mean that the reactants and products are

▲ **Figure 2.18 Photosynthesis: a solar-powered rearrangement of matter.** *Elodea,* a freshwater plant, produces sugar by rearranging the atoms of carbon dioxide and water in the chemical process known as photosynthesis, which is powered by sunlight. Much of the sugar is then converted to other food molecules. Oxygen gas (O_2) is a by-product of photosynthesis; notice the bubbles of oxygen escaping from the leaves in the photo.

equal in concentration, but only that their concentrations have stabilized at a particular ratio. The reaction involving ammonia reaches equilibrium when ammonia decomposes as rapidly as it forms. In this case, there is far more ammonia than hydrogen and nitrogen at equilibrium.

We will return to the subject of chemical reactions after more detailed study of the various types of molecules that are important to life. In the next chapter, we focus on water, the substance in which all the chemical processes of living organisms occur.

Concept Check 2.4

1. Refer to the reaction between hydrogen and oxygen to form water, shown as a ball-and-stick model on page 44. Draw the electron-shell diagram representing this reaction.
2. Which occurs faster at equilibrium, the formation of products from reactants, or reactants from products?

For suggested answers, see Appendix A.

Chapter 2 Review

Go to the Campbell Biology website (**www.campbellbiology.com**) or CD-ROM to explore Activities, Investigations, and other interactive study aids.

SUMMARY OF KEY CONCEPTS

Concept 2.1

Matter consists of chemical elements in pure form and in combinations called compounds

▶ **Elements and Compounds (pp. 32–33)** Elements cannot be broken down chemically to other substances. A compound contains two or more elements in a fixed ratio.

▶ **Essential Elements of Life (pp. 33–34)** Carbon, oxygen, hydrogen, and nitrogen make up approximately 96% of living matter.
Investigation *How Are Space Rocks Analyzed for Signs of Life?*

Concept 2.2

An element's properties depend on the structure of its atoms

▶ **Subatomic Particles (p. 34)** An atom is the smallest unit of an element. An atom has a nucleus made up of positively charged protons and uncharged neutrons, as well as a surrounding cloud of negatively charged electrons.
Activity *Structure of the Atomic Nucleus*

▶ **Atomic Number and Atomic Mass (pp. 34–35)** The number of electrons in an electrically neutral atom equals the number of protons.

▶ **Isotopes (pp. 35–36)** Most elements have two or more isotopes, different in neutron number and therefore mass. Some isotopes are unstable and give off particles and energy as radioactivity. Radioactive tracers help biologists monitor biological processes.

▶ **The Energy Levels of Electrons (pp. 36–37)** In an atom, electrons occupy specific energy levels, each of which can be represented by an electron shell of that atom.

▶ **Electron Configuration and Chemical Properties (pp. 37–38)** Electron configuration determines the chemical behavior of an atom. Chemical behavior depends on the number of valence electrons—electrons in the outermost shell. An atom with an incomplete valence shell is reactive.
Activity *Electron Arrangement*

▶ **Electron Orbitals (pp. 38–39)** Electrons move within orbitals, three-dimensional spaces with specific shapes located within each successive shell.
Activity *Build an Atom*

Concept 2.3

The formation and function of molecules depend on chemical bonding between atoms

▶ **Covalent Bonds (pp. 39–41)** Chemical bonds form when atoms interact and complete their valence shells. A single covalent bond is the sharing of a pair of valence electrons by two atoms; double bonds are the sharing of two pairs of electrons. Molecules consist of two or more covalently bonded atoms. Electrons of a polar covalent bond are pulled closer to the more electronegative atom. A covalent bond is nonpolar if both atoms are the same and therefore equally electronegative.
Activity *Covalent Bonds*
Activity *Nonpolar and Polar Molecules*

▶ **Ionic Bonds (pp. 41–42)** Two atoms may differ so much in electronegativity that one or more electrons are actually transferred from one atom to the other. The result is a negatively charged ion (anion) and a positively charged ion (cation). The attraction between two ions of opposite charge is called an ionic bond.
Activity *Ionic Bonds*

▶ **Weak Chemical Bonds (p. 42)** A hydrogen bond is a weak attraction between one electronegative atom and a hydrogen atom that is covalently linked to another electronegative atom. Van der Waals interactions occur when transiently positive and negative regions of molecules attract each other. Weak bonds reinforce the shapes of large molecules and help molecules adhere to each other.
Activity *Hydrogen Bonds*

▶ **Molecular Shape and Function (pp. 42–44)** A molecule's shape is determined by the positions of its atoms' valence orbitals. When covalent bonds form, the s and p orbitals in the valence shell of an atom may combine to form four hybrid orbitals that extend to the corners of an imaginary tetrahedron; such orbitals are responsible for the shapes of H_2O, CH_4, and many more complex biological molecules. Shape is usually the basis for the recognition of one biological molecule by another.

Concept 2.4

Chemical reactions make and break chemical bonds

▶ Chemical reactions change reactants into products while conserving matter. Most chemical reactions are reversible. Chemical equilibrium is reached when the forward and reverse reaction rates are equal (pp. 44–45).

Self-Quiz

1. An element is to a (an) _____ as an organ is to a (an) _____.
   a. atom; organism 动物
   b. compound; organism
   c. molecule; cell
   d. atom; cell
   e. compound; organelle 细胞器

2. In the term *trace element,* the modifier *trace* means
   a. the element is required in very small amounts.
   b. the element can be used as a label to trace atoms through an organism's metabolism.
   c. the element is very rare on Earth.
   d. the element enhances health but is not essential for the organism's long-term survival.
   e. the element passes rapidly through the organism.

3. Compared to ^{31}P, the radioactive isotope ^{32}P has
   a. a different atomic number.
   b. one more neutron.
   c. one more proton. 质子
   d. one more electron.
   e. a different charge.

4. Atoms can be represented by simply listing the number of protons, neutrons, and electrons—for example, $2\,p^+$; $2\,n^0$; $2\,e^-$ for helium. Which atom represents the ^{18}O isotope of oxygen?
   a. $6\,p^+$; $8\,n^0$; $6\,e^-$
   b. $8\,p^+$; $10\,n^0$; $8\,e^-$
   c. $9\,p^+$; $9\,n^0$; $9\,e^-$
   d. $7\,p^+$; $2\,n^0$; $9\,e^-$
   e. $10\,p^+$; $8\,n^0$; $9\,e^-$

5. The atomic number of sulfur is 16. Sulfur combines with hydrogen by covalent bonding to form a compound, hydrogen sulfide. Based on the electron configuration of sulfur, we can predict that the molecular formula of the compound will be
   a. HS   b. HS_2 c. H_2S d. H_3S_2 e. H_4S

6. Review the valences of carbon, oxygen, hydrogen, and nitrogen, and then determine which of the following molecules is most likely to exist.

   a. $O\!=\!C\!-\!H$

   c. $H \qquad\quad H$
         $\;|\qquad\qquad|$
         $H\!-\!C\!-\!H\!-\!C\!=\!O$
         $\;|$
         H

   b. $H\quad H$
         $\;|\quad\;|$
         $H\!-\!O\!-\!C\!-\!C\!=\!O$
         $\qquad\quad|$
         $\qquad\quad H$

   d. O
         $|$
         $H\!-\!N\!=\!H$

7. The reactivity of an atom arises from
   a. the average distance of the outermost electron shell from the nucleus.
   b. the existence of unpaired electrons in the valence shell.
   c. the sum of the potential energies of all the electron shells.
   d. the potential energy of the valence shell.
   e. the energy difference between the s and p orbitals.

8. Which of these statements is true of all anionic atoms?
   a. The atom has more electrons than protons.
   b. The atom has more protons than electrons.
   c. The atom has fewer protons than does a neutral atom of the same element.
   d. The atom has more neutrons than protons.
   e. The net charge is $1-$.

9. What coefficients must be placed in the blanks so that all atoms are accounted for in the products?

   $$C_6H_{12}O_6 \longrightarrow \underline{2}\,C_2H_6O + \underline{2}\,CO_2$$

   a. 1; 2   b. 2; 2   c. 1; 3   d. 1; 1   e. 3; 1

10. Which of the following statements correctly describes any chemical reaction that has reached equilibrium?
    a. The concentration of products equals the concentration of reactants.
    b. The rate of the forward reaction equals the rate of the reverse reaction.
    c. Both forward and reverse reactions have halted.
    d. The reaction is now irreversible. 不可逆转
    e. No reactants remain.

For Self-Quiz Answers, see Appendix A.

Go to the website or CD-ROM for more quiz questions.

Evolution Connection

The text states that the percentages of naturally occurring elements making up the human body (see Table 2.1) are similar to the percentages of these elements found in other organisms. How could you account for this similarity among organisms?

Scientific Inquiry

Female silkworm moths (*Bombyx mori*) attract males by emitting chemical signals that spread through the air. A male hundreds of meters away can detect these molecules and fly toward their source. The sensory organs responsible for this behavior are the comblike antennae visible in the photograph here. Each filament of an antenna is equipped with thousands of receptor cells that detect the sex attractant. Based on what you learned in this chapter, propose a hypothesis to account for the ability of the male moth to detect a specific molecule in the presence of many other molecules in the air. What predictions does your hypothesis make? Design an experiment to test one of these predictions.

Investigation *How Are Space Rocks Analyzed for Signs of Life?*

Science, Technology, and Society

While waiting at an airport, Neil Campbell once overheard this claim: "It's paranoid and ignorant to worry about industry or agriculture contaminating the environment with their chemical wastes. After all, this stuff is just made of the same atoms that were already present in our environment." How would you counter this argument?

3 Water and the Fitness of the Environment

▲ **Figure 3.1 A view of Earth from space, showing our planet's abundance of water.**

Key Concepts

3.1 The polarity of water molecules results in hydrogen bonding

3.2 Four emergent properties of water contribute to Earth's fitness for life

3.3 Dissociation of water molecules leads to acidic and basic conditions that affect living organisms

Overview

The Molecule That Supports All of Life

As astronomers study newly discovered planets orbiting distant stars, they hope to find evidence of water on these far-off celestial bodies, for water is the substance that makes possible life as we know it here on Earth. All organisms familiar to us are made mostly of water and live in an environment dominated by water. Water is the biological medium here on Earth, and possibly on other planets as well.

Life on Earth began in water and evolved there for 3 billion years before spreading onto land. Modern life, even terrestrial (land-dwelling) life, remains tied to water. All living organisms require water more than any other substance. Human beings, for example, can survive for quite a few weeks without food, but only a week or so without water. Molecules of water participate in many chemical reactions necessary to sustain life. Most cells are surrounded by water, and cells themselves are about 70–95% water. Three-quarters of Earth's surface is submerged in water **(Figure 3.1)**. Although most of this water is in liquid form, water is also present on Earth as ice and vapor. Water is the only common substance to exist in the natural environment in all three physical states of matter: solid, liquid, and gas.

The abundance of water is a major reason Earth is habitable. In a classic book called *The Fitness of the Environment,* ecologist Lawrence Henderson highlights the importance of water to life. While acknowledging that life adapts to its environment through natural selection, Henderson emphasizes that for life to exist at all, the environment must first be a suitable abode. In this chapter, you will learn how the structure of a water molecule allows it to form weak chemical bonds with other molecules, including other water molecules. This ability leads to unique properties that support and maintain living systems on our planet. Your objective in this chapter is to develop a conceptual understanding of how water contributes to the fitness of Earth for life.

Concept 3.1

The polarity of water molecules results in hydrogen bonding

Water is so common that it is easy to overlook the fact that it is an exceptional substance with many extraordinary qualities. Following the theme of emergent properties, we can trace water's unique behavior to the structure and interactions of its molecules.

Studied in isolation, the water molecule is deceptively simple. Its two hydrogen atoms are joined to the oxygen atom by single covalent bonds. Because oxygen is more electronegative than hydrogen, the electrons of the polar bonds spend more time closer to the oxygen atom. In other words, the bonds that hold together the atoms in a water molecule are polar covalent bonds. The water molecule, shaped something like a wide V, is a **polar molecule,** meaning that opposite ends of the molecule have opposite charges: The oxygen region of the molecule has

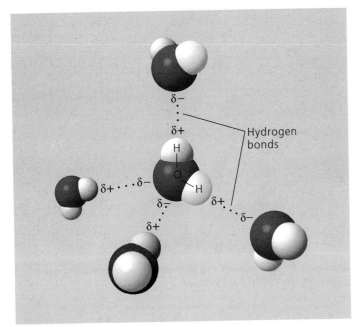

▲ **Figure 3.2 Hydrogen bonds between water molecules.** The charged regions of a polar water molecule are attracted to oppositely charged parts of neighboring molecules. Each molecule can hydrogen-bond to multiple partners, and these associations are constantly changing. At any instant in liquid water at 37°C (human body temperature), about 15% of the molecules are bonded to four partners in short-lived clusters.

a partial negative charge ($\delta-$), and the hydrogens have a partial positive charge ($\delta+$) (see Figure 2.12).

The anomalous properties of water arise from attractions between these polar molecules. The attraction is electrical; the slightly positive hydrogen of one molecule is attracted to the slightly negative oxygen of a nearby molecule. The two molecules are thus held together by a hydrogen bond **(Figure 3.2)**. Although the arrangement of molecules in a sample of liquid water is constantly changing, at any given moment, many of the molecules are linked by multiple hydrogen bonds. The extraordinary qualities of water are emergent properties resulting from the hydrogen bonding that orders molecules into a higher level of structural organization.

Concept Check 3.1

1. What is electronegativity and how does it affect interactions between water molecules?
2. Why is it unlikely that two neighboring water molecules would be arranged like this?

For suggested answers, see Appendix A.

Four emergent properties of water contribute to Earth's fitness for life

We will examine four of water's properties that contribute to the suitability of Earth as an environment for life. These are water's cohesive behavior, its ability to moderate temperature, its expansion upon freezing, and its versatility as a solvent.

Cohesion 内聚力

Water molecules stay close to each other as a result of hydrogen bonding. When water is in its liquid form, its hydrogen bonds are very fragile, about one-twentieth as strong as covalent bonds. They form, break, and re-form with great frequency. Each hydrogen bond lasts only a few trillionths of a second, but the molecules are constantly forming new bonds with a succession of partners. Thus, at any instant, a substantial percentage of all the water molecules are bonded to their neighbors, making water more structured than most other liquids. Collectively, the hydrogen bonds hold the substance together, a phenomenon called **cohesion.**

Cohesion due to hydrogen bonding contributes to the transport of water and dissolved nutrients against gravity in plants **(Figure 3.3)**. Water from the roots reaches the leaves through

Water-conducting cells

100 μm

▲ **Figure 3.3 Water transport in plants.** Evaporation from leaves pulls water upward from the roots through water-conducting cells, in this case located in the trunk of a tree. Cohesion due to hydrogen bonding helps hold together the column of water within the cells. Adhesion of the water to cell walls helps resist the downward pull of gravity. Because of these properties, the tallest trees can transport water more than 100 meters (m) upward—approximately one-quarter the height of the Empire State Building in New York City.

▲ **Figure 3.4 Walking on water.** The high surface tension of water, resulting from the collective strength of its hydrogen bonds, allows the water strider to walk on the surface of a pond.

a network of water-conducting cells. As water evaporates from a leaf, hydrogen bonds cause water molecules leaving the veins to tug on molecules farther down, and the upward pull is transmitted through the water-conducting cells all the way down to the roots. **Adhesion,** the clinging of one substance to another, also plays a role. Adhesion of water to the walls of the cells helps counter the downward pull of gravity.

Related to cohesion is **surface tension,** a measure of how difficult it is to stretch or break the surface of a liquid. Water has a greater surface tension than most other liquids. At the interface between water and air is an ordered arrangement of water molecules, hydrogen-bonded to one another and to the water below. This makes the water behave as though coated with an invisible film. You can observe the surface tension of water by slightly overfilling a drinking glass; the water will stand above the rim. In a more biological example, some animals can stand, walk, or run on water without breaking the surface **(Figure 3.4).**

Moderation of Temperature

Water moderates air temperature by absorbing heat from air that is warmer and releasing the stored heat to air that is cooler. Water is effective as a heat bank because it can absorb or release a relatively large amount of heat with only a slight change in its own temperature. To understand this capability of water, we must first look briefly at heat and temperature.

Heat and Temperature

Anything that moves has **kinetic energy,** the energy of motion. Atoms and molecules have kinetic energy because they are always moving, although not necessarily in any particular direction. The faster a molecule moves, the greater its kinetic

energy. **Heat** is a measure of the *total* amount of kinetic energy due to molecular motion in a body of matter. **Temperature** measures the intensity of heat due to the *average* kinetic energy of the molecules. When the average speed of the molecules increases, a thermometer records this as a rise in temperature. Heat and temperature are related, but they are not the same. A swimmer crossing the English Channel has a higher temperature than the water, but the ocean contains far more heat because of its volume.

Whenever two objects of different temperature are brought together, heat passes from the warmer to the cooler object until the two are the same temperature. Molecules in the cooler object speed up at the expense of the kinetic energy of the warmer object. An ice cube cools a drink not by adding coldness to the liquid, but by absorbing heat from the liquid as the ice itself melts.

Throughout this book, we will use the **Celsius scale** to indicate temperature (Celsius degrees are abbreviated as °C). At sea level, water freezes at 0°C and boils at 100°C. The temperature of the human body averages 37°C, and comfortable room temperature is about 20–25°C.

One convenient unit of heat used in this book is the **calorie (cal).** A calorie is the amount of heat it takes to raise the temperature of 1 g of water by 1°C. Conversely, a calorie is also the amount of heat that 1 g of water releases when it cools by 1°C. A **kilocalorie (kcal),** 1,000 cal, is the quantity of heat required to raise the temperature of 1 kilogram (kg) of water by 1°C. (The "calories" on food packages are actually kilocalories.) Another energy unit used in this book is the **joule (J).** One joule equals 0.239 cal; one calorie equals 4.184 J.

Water's High Specific Heat

The ability of water to stabilize temperature stems from its relatively high specific heat. The **specific heat** of a substance is defined as the amount of heat that must be absorbed or lost for 1 g of that substance to change its temperature by 1°C. We already know water's specific heat because we have defined a calorie as the amount of heat that causes 1 g of water to change its temperature by 1°C. Therefore, the specific heat of water is 1 calorie per gram per degree Celsius, abbreviated as 1 cal/g/°C. Compared with most other substances, water has an unusually high specific heat. For example, ethyl alcohol, the type of alcohol in alcoholic beverages, has a specific heat of 0.6 cal/g/°C—that is, only 0.6 cal is required to raise the temperature of 1g of ethyl alcohol 1°C.

Because of the high specific heat of water relative to other materials, water will change its temperature less when it absorbs or loses a given amount of heat. The reason you can burn your fingers by touching the metal handle of a pot on the stove when the water in the pot is still lukewarm is that the specific heat of water is ten times greater than that of iron. In other words, it will take only 0.1 cal to raise the temperature of 1 g of iron 1°C. Specific heat can be thought of as a measure of how well a substance resists changing its temperature when it absorbs or releases heat. Water resists changing its temperature; when it does change its temperature, it absorbs or loses a relatively large quantity of heat for each degree of change.

We can trace water's high specific heat, like many of its other properties, to hydrogen bonding. Heat must be absorbed in order to break hydrogen bonds, and heat is released when hydrogen bonds form. A calorie of heat causes a relatively small change in the temperature of water because much of the heat is used to disrupt hydrogen bonds before the water molecules can begin moving faster. And when the temperature of water drops slightly, many additional hydrogen bonds form, releasing a considerable amount of energy in the form of heat.

What is the relevance of water's high specific heat to life on Earth? A large body of water can absorb and store a huge amount of heat from the sun in the daytime and during summer while warming up only a few degrees. And at night and during winter, the gradually cooling water can warm the air. This is the reason coastal areas generally have milder climates than inland regions. The high specific heat of water also tends to stabilize ocean temperatures, creating a favorable environment for marine life. Thus, because of its high specific heat, the water that covers most of Earth keeps temperature fluctuations on land and in water within limits that permit life. Also, because organisms are made primarily of water, they are more able to resist changes in their own temperature than if they were made of a liquid with a lower specific heat.

Evaporative Cooling

Molecules of any liquid stay close together because they are attracted to one another. Molecules moving fast enough to overcome these attractions can depart the liquid and enter the air as gas. This transformation from a liquid to a gas is called vaporization, or *evaporation*. Recall that the speed of molecular movement varies and that temperature is the *average* kinetic energy of molecules. Even at low temperatures, the speediest molecules can escape into the air. Some evaporation occurs at any temperature; a glass of water at room temperature, for example, will eventually evaporate. If a liquid is heated, the average kinetic energy of molecules increases and the liquid evaporates more rapidly.

Heat of vaporization is the quantity of heat a liquid must absorb for 1 g of it to be converted from the liquid to the gaseous state. For the same reason that water has a high specific heat, it also has a high heat of vaporization relative to most other liquids. To evaporate 1 g of water at 25°C, about 580 cal of heat is needed—nearly double the amount needed to vaporize a gram of alcohol or ammonia. Water's high heat of vaporization is another emergent property caused by hydrogen bonds, which must be broken before the molecules can make their exodus from the liquid.

Water's high heat of vaporization helps moderate Earth's climate. A considerable amount of solar heat absorbed by tropical seas is consumed during the evaporation of surface water. Then, as moist tropical air circulates poleward, it releases heat as it condenses to form rain.

As a liquid evaporates, the surface of the liquid that remains behind cools down. This **evaporative cooling** occurs because the "hottest" molecules, those with the greatest kinetic energy, are the most likely to leave as gas. It is as if the hundred fastest runners at a college transferred to another school; the average speed of the remaining students would decline.

Evaporative cooling of water contributes to the stability of temperature in lakes and ponds and also provides a mechanism that prevents terrestrial organisms from overheating. For example, evaporation of water from the leaves of a plant helps keep the tissues in the leaves from becoming too warm in the sunlight. Evaporation of sweat from human skin dissipates body heat and helps prevent overheating on a hot day or when excess heat is generated by strenuous activity. High humidity on a hot day increases discomfort because the high concentration of water vapor in the air inhibits the evaporation of sweat from the body.

Insulation of Bodies of Water by Floating Ice

Water is one of the few substances that are less dense as a solid than as a liquid. In other words, ice floats in liquid water. While other materials contract when they solidify, water expands. The cause of this exotic behavior is, once again, hydrogen bonding. At temperatures above 4°C, water behaves like other liquids, expanding as it warms and contracting as it cools. Water begins to freeze when its molecules are no longer moving vigorously enough to break their hydrogen bonds. As the temperature falls to 0°C, the water becomes locked into a crystalline lattice, each water molecule bonded to four partners **(Figure 3.5)**. The hydrogen bonds keep the molecules at "arm's length," far enough apart to make ice about 10% less dense (10% fewer molecules for the same volume) than liquid water at 4°C. When ice absorbs enough heat for its temperature to rise above 0°C, hydrogen bonds between molecules are disrupted. As the crystal collapses, the ice melts, and molecules are free to slip closer together. Water reaches its greatest density at 4°C and then begins to expand as the molecules move faster. Keep in mind, however, that even in liquid water, many of the molecules are connected by hydrogen bonds, though only transiently: The hydrogen bonds are constantly breaking and re-forming.

The ability of ice to float because of the expansion of water as it solidifies is an important factor in the fitness of the environment. If ice sank, then eventually all ponds, lakes, and even oceans would freeze solid, making life as we know it impossible on Earth. During summer, only the upper few inches of the ocean would thaw. Instead, when a deep body of

Hydrogen
bond

Ice
Hydrogen bonds are stable

▲ Figure 3.5 **Ice: crystalline structure and floating barrier.** In ice, each molecule is hydrogen-bonded to four neighbors in a three-dimensional crystal. Because the crystal is

spacious, ice has fewer molecules than an equal volume of liquid water. In other words, ice is less dense than liquid water. Floating ice becomes a barrier that protects the liquid

Liquid water
Hydrogen bonds
constantly break and re-form

water below from the colder air. The marine organism shown here is called a euphausid shrimp; it was photographed beneath the antarctic ice.

water cools, the floating ice insulates the liquid water below, preventing it from freezing and allowing life to exist under the frozen surface, as shown in the photo in Figure 3.5.

The Solvent of Life

A sugar cube placed in a glass of water will dissolve. The glass will then contain a uniform mixture of sugar and water; the concentration of dissolved sugar will be the same everywhere in the mixture. A liquid that is a completely homogeneous mixture of two or more substances is called a **solution**. The dissolving agent of a solution is the **solvent**, and the substance that is dissolved is the **solute**. In this case, water is the solvent and sugar is the solute. An **aqueous solution** is one in which water is the solvent.

The medieval alchemists tried to find a universal solvent, one that would dissolve anything. They learned that nothing works better than water. However, water is not a universal solvent; if it were, it would dissolve any container in which it was stored, including our cells. But water is a very versatile solvent, a quality we can trace to the polarity of the water molecule.

Suppose, for example, that a crystal of the ionic compound sodium chloride (NaCl) is placed in water **(Figure 3.6)**. At the surface of the crystal, the sodium and chloride ions are exposed to the solvent. These ions and the water molecules have a mutual affinity through electrical attraction. The oxygen regions of the water molecules are negatively charged and cling to sodium cations. The hydrogen regions of the water molecules are positively charged and are attracted to chloride anions. As a result, water molecules surround the individual sodium and chloride ions, separating and shielding them from one another. The sphere of water molecules around each dissolved ion

is called a **hydration shell**. Working inward from the surface of the salt crystal, water eventually dissolves all the ions. The result is a solution of two solutes, sodium cations and chloride anions, homogeneously mixed with water, the solvent. Other ionic compounds also dissolve in water. Seawater, for instance, contains a great variety of dissolved ions, as do living cells.

A compound does not need to be ionic to dissolve in water; compounds made up of nonionic polar molecules, such as

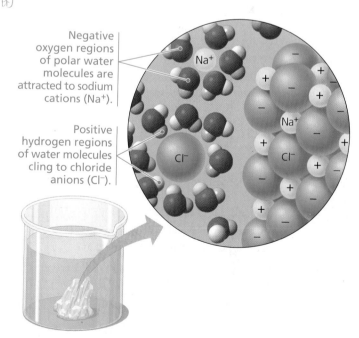

Negative oxygen regions of polar water molecules are attracted to sodium cations (Na⁺).

Positive hydrogen regions of water molecules cling to chloride anions (Cl⁻).

▲ Figure 3.6 **A crystal of table salt dissolving in water.** A sphere of water molecules, called a hydration shell, surrounds each solute ion.

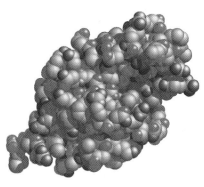

(a) Lysozyme molecule in a nonaqueous environment

(b) Lysozyme molecule (purple) in an aqueous environment such as tears or saliva

This oxygen is attracted to a slight positive charge on the lysozyme molecule.

This hydrogen is attracted to a slight negative charge on the lysozyme molecule.

(c) Ionic and polar regions on the protein's surface attract water molecules.

▲ **Figure 3.7 A water-soluble protein.** This figure shows human lysozyme, a protein found in tears and saliva that has antibacterial action.

sugars, are also water-soluble. Such compounds dissolve when water molecules surround each of the solute molecules. Even molecules as large as proteins can dissolve in water if they have ionic and polar regions on their surface **(Figure 3.7)**. Many different kinds of polar compounds are dissolved (along with ions) in the water of such biological fluids as blood, the sap of plants, and the liquid within all cells. Water is the solvent of life.

Hydrophilic and Hydrophobic Substances

Whether ionic or polar, any substance that has an affinity for water is said to be **hydrophilic** (from the Greek *hydro,* water, and *philios,* loving). In some cases, substances can be hydrophilic without actually dissolving. For example, some components in cells are such large molecules (or complexes of multiple molecules) that they do not dissolve. Instead, they remain suspended in the aqueous liquid of the cell. Such a mixture is an example of a **colloid,** a stable suspension of fine particles in a liquid. Another example of a hydrophilic substance that does not dissolve is cotton, a plant product. Cotton consists of giant molecules of cellulose, a compound with numerous regions of partial positive and partial negative charges associated with polar bonds. Water adheres to the cellulose fibers. Thus, a cotton towel does a great job of drying the body, yet does not dissolve in the washing machine. Cellulose is also present in the walls of water-conducting cells in a plant; you read earlier how the adhesion of water to these hydrophilic walls allows water transport to occur.

There are, of course, substances that do not have an affinity for water. Substances that are nonionic and nonpolar actually seem to repel water; these substances are said to be **hydrophobic** (from the Greek *phobos,* fearing). An example from the kitchen is vegetable oil, which, as you know, does not mix stably with water-based substances such as vinegar. The hydrophobic behavior of the oil molecules results from a preva-

lence of relatively nonpolar bonds, in this case bonds between carbon and hydrogen, which share electrons almost equally. Hydrophobic molecules related to oils are major ingredients of cell membranes. (Imagine what would happen to a cell if its membrane dissolved.)

Solute Concentration in Aqueous Solutions

Biological chemistry is "wet" chemistry. Most of the chemical reactions in organisms involve solutes dissolved in water. To understand chemical reactions, we need to know how many atoms and molecules are involved. Thus, it is important to learn how to calculate the concentration of solutes in an aqueous solution (the number of solute molecules in a volume of solution).

When carrying out experiments, we use mass to calculate the number of molecules. We know the mass of each atom in a given molecule, so we can calculate its **molecular mass,** which is simply the sum of the masses of all the atoms in a molecule. As an example, let's calculate the molecular mass of table sugar (sucrose), which has the molecular formula $C_{12}H_{22}O_{11}$. In round numbers of daltons, the mass of a carbon atom is 12, the mass of a hydrogen atom is 1, and the mass of an oxygen atom is 16. Thus, sucrose has a molecular mass of 342 daltons. Of course, weighing out small numbers of molecules is not practical. For this reason, we usually measure substances in units called moles. Just as a dozen always means 12 objects, a **mole (mol)** represents an exact number of objects—6.02×10^{23}, which is called Avogadro's number. Because of the way in which Avogadro's number and the unit *dalton* were originally defined, there are 6.02×10^{23} daltons in 1 gram. This is significant because once we determine the molecular mass of a molecule such as sucrose, we can use the same number (342), but with the unit *gram,* to represent the mass of 6.02×10^{23} molecules of sucrose, or one mole of sucrose (this is sometimes called the *molar mass*).

To obtain one mole of sucrose in the lab, therefore, we weigh out 342 g.

The practical advantage of measuring a quantity of chemicals in moles is that a mole of one substance has exactly the same number of molecules as a mole of any other substance. If the molecular mass of substance A is 342 daltons and that of substance B is 10 daltons, then 342 g of A will have the same number of molecules as 10 g of B. A mole of ethyl alcohol (C_2H_6O) also contains 6.02×10^{23} molecules, but its mass is only 46 g because the mass of a molecule of ethyl alcohol is less than that of a molecule of sucrose. Measuring in moles makes it convenient for scientists working in the laboratory to combine substances in fixed ratios of molecules.

How would we make a liter (L) of solution consisting of 1 mol of sucrose dissolved in water? We would measure out 342 g of sucrose and then gradually add water, while stirring, until the sugar was completely dissolved. We would then add enough water to bring the total volume of the solution up to 1 L. At that point, we would have a 1-molar (1 *M*) solution of sucrose. **Molarity**—the number of moles of solute per liter of solution—is the unit of concentration most often used by biologists for aqueous solutions.

Concept 3.3

Dissociation of water molecules leads to acidic and basic conditions that affect living organisms

Occasionally, a hydrogen atom participating in a hydrogen bond between two water molecules shifts from one molecule to the other. When this happens, the hydrogen atom leaves its electron behind, and what is actually transferred is a **hydrogen ion,** a single proton with a charge of 1+. The water molecule that lost a proton is now a **hydroxide ion** (OH^-), which has a charge of 1−. The proton binds to the other water molecule, making that molecule a hydronium ion (H_3O^+). We can picture the chemical reaction this way:

Hydronium ion (H_3O^+) Hydroxide ion (OH^-)

Although this is what actually happens, we can think of the process in a simplified way, as the dissociation (separation) of a water molecule into a hydrogen ion and a hydroxide ion:

$$H_2O \rightleftharpoons H^+ + OH^-$$

Hydrogen ion   Hydroxide ion

As the double arrows indicate, this is a reversible reaction that will reach a state of dynamic equilibrium when water dissociates at the same rate that it is being re-formed from H^+ and OH^-. At this equilibrium point, the concentration of water molecules greatly exceeds the concentrations of H^+ and OH^-. In fact, in pure water, only one water molecule in every 554 million is dissociated. The concentration of each ion in pure water is 10^{-7} M (at 25°C). This means that there is only one ten-millionth of a mole of hydrogen ions per liter of pure water and an equal number of hydroxide ions.

Although the dissociation of water is reversible and statistically rare, it is exceedingly important in the chemistry of life. Hydrogen and hydroxide ions are very reactive. Changes in their concentrations can drastically affect a cell's proteins and other complex molecules. As we have seen, the concentrations of H^+ and OH^- are equal in pure water, but adding certain kinds of solutes, called acids and bases, disrupts this balance. Biologists use something called the pH scale to describe how acidic or basic (the opposite of acidic) a solution is. In the remainder of this chapter, you will learn about acids, bases, and pH and why changes in pH can adversely affect organisms.

Effects of Changes in pH

Before discussing the pH scale, let's see what acids and bases are and how they interact with water.

Acids and Bases

What would cause an aqueous solution to have an imbalance in its H^+ and OH^- concentrations? When the substances called acids dissolve in water, they donate additional H^+ to the solution. An **acid,** according to the definition often used by biologists, is a substance that increases the hydrogen ion concentration of a solution. For example, when hydrochloric acid (HCl) is added to water, hydrogen ions dissociate from chloride ions:

$$HCl \longrightarrow H^+ + Cl^-$$

This additional source of H^+ (dissociation of water is the other source) results in the solution having more H^+ than OH^-. Such a solution is known as an acidic solution.

A substance that reduces the hydrogen ion concentration of a solution is called a **base**. Some bases reduce the H^+ concentration directly by accepting hydrogen ions. Ammonia (NH_3), for instance, acts as a base when the unshared electron pair in nitrogen's valence shell attracts a hydrogen ion from the solution, resulting in an ammonium ion (NH_4^+):

$$NH_3 + H^+ \rightleftharpoons NH_4^+$$

Other bases reduce the H^+ concentration indirectly by dissociating to form hydroxide ions, which then combine with hydrogen ions in the solution to form water. One base that acts this way is sodium hydroxide (NaOH), which in water dissociates into its ions:

$$NaOH \longrightarrow Na^+ + OH^-$$

In either case, the base reduces the H^+ concentration. Solutions with a higher concentration of OH^- than H^+ are known as basic solutions. A solution in which the H^+ and OH^- concentrations are equal is said to be neutral.

Notice that single arrows were used in the reactions for HCl and NaOH. These compounds dissociate completely when mixed with water, and so hydrochloric acid is called a strong acid and sodium hydroxide a strong base. In contrast, ammonia is a relatively weak base. The double arrows in the reaction for ammonia indicate that the binding and release of hydrogen ions are reversible reactions, although at equilibrium there will be a fixed ratio of NH_4^+ to NH_3.

There are also weak acids, which reversibly release and accept back hydrogen ions. An example is carbonic acid, which has essential functions in many organisms:

$$\underset{\substack{\text{Carbonic} \\ \text{acid}}}{H_2CO_3} \quad \rightleftharpoons \quad \underset{\substack{\text{Bicarbonate} \\ \text{ion}}}{HCO_3^-} \quad + \quad \underset{\substack{\text{Hydrogen} \\ \text{ion}}}{H^+}$$

Here the equilibrium so favors the reaction in the left direction that when carbonic acid is added to water, only 1% of the molecules are dissociated at any particular time. Still, that is enough to shift the balance of H^+ and OH^- from neutrality.

The pH Scale

In any aqueous solution at 25°C, the *product* of the H^+ and OH^- concentrations is constant at 10^{-14}. This can be written

$$[H^+][OH^-] = 10^{-14}$$

In such an equation, brackets indicate molar concentration for the substance enclosed within them. In a neutral solution at room temperature (25°C), $[H^+] = 10^{-7}$ and $[OH^-] = 10^{-7}$, so in this case, 10^{-14} is the product of $10^{-7} \times 10^{-7}$. If enough acid is added to a solution to increase $[H^+]$ to 10^{-5} M, then $[OH^-]$ will decline by an equivalent amount to 10^{-9} M (note that $10^{-5} \times 10^{-9} = 10^{-14}$). This constant relationship expresses the behavior of acids and bases in an aqueous solution. An acid not only adds hydrogen ions to a solution, but also removes hydroxide ions because of the tendency for H^+ to combine with OH^- to form water. A base has the opposite effect, increasing OH^- concentration but also reducing H^+ concentration by the formation of water. If enough of a base is added to raise the OH^- concentration to 10^{-4} M, it will cause the H^+ concentration to drop to 10^{-10} M. Whenever we know the concentration of either H^+ or OH^- in an aqueous solution, we can deduce the concentration of the other ion.

Because the H^+ and OH^- concentrations of solutions can vary by a factor of 100 trillion or more, scientists have developed a way to express this variation more conveniently than in moles per liter. The pH scale (Figure 3.8) compresses the range of H^+ and OH^- concentrations by employing logarithms. The **pH** of a solution is defined as the negative logarithm (base 10) of the hydrogen ion concentration:

$$pH = -\log [H^+]$$

For a neutral aqueous solution, $[H^+]$ is 10^{-7} M, giving us

$$-\log 10^{-7} = -(-7) = 7$$

▲ **Figure 3.8 The pH scale and pH values of some aqueous solutions.**

Notice that pH *declines* as H^+ concentration *increases*. Notice, too, that although the pH scale is based on H^+ concentration, it also implies OH^- concentration. A solution of pH 10 has a hydrogen ion concentration of 10^{-10} M and a hydroxide ion concentration of 10^{-4} M.

The pH of a neutral aqueous solution is 7, the midpoint of the scale. A pH value less than 7 denotes an acidic solution; the lower the number, the more acidic the solution. The pH for basic solutions is above 7. Most biological fluids are within the range pH 6–8. There are a few exceptions, however, including the strongly acidic digestive juice of the human stomach, which has a pH of about 2.

Remember that each pH unit represents a tenfold difference in H^+ and OH^- concentrations. It is this mathematical feature that makes the pH scale so compact. A solution of pH 3 is not twice as acidic as a solution of pH 6, but a thousand times more acidic. When the pH of a solution changes slightly, the actual concentrations of H^+ and OH^- in the solution change substantially.

Buffers

The internal pH of most living cells is close to 7. Even a slight change in pH can be harmful, because the chemical processes of the cell are very sensitive to the concentrations of hydrogen and hydroxide ions.

The presence of buffers in biological fluids allows for a relatively constant pH despite the addition of acids or bases. **Buffers** are substances that minimize changes in the concentrations of H^+ and OH^- in a solution. For example, buffers normally maintain the pH of human blood very close to 7.4, which is slightly basic. A person cannot survive for more than a few minutes if the blood pH drops to 7 (neutral) or rises to 7.8. Under normal circumstances, the buffering capacity of the blood prevents such swings in pH.

A buffer works by accepting hydrogen ions from the solution when they are in excess and donating hydrogen ions to the solution when they have been depleted. Most buffer solutions contain a weak acid and its corresponding base, which combine reversibly with hydrogen ions. There are several buffers that contribute to pH stability in human blood and many other biological solutions. One of these is carbonic acid (H_2CO_3), which, as already mentioned, dissociates to yield a bicarbonate ion (HCO_3^-) and a hydrogen ion (H^+):

$$H_2CO_3 \underset{\text{Response to a drop in pH}}{\overset{\text{Response to a rise in pH}}{\rightleftharpoons}} HCO_3^- + H^+$$

| H^+ donor (acid) | | H^+ acceptor (base) | Hydrogen ion |

The chemical equilibrium between carbonic acid and bicarbonate acts as a pH regulator, the reaction shifting left or right as other processes in the solution add or remove hydrogen ions. If the H^+ concentration in blood begins to fall (that is, if pH rises), the reaction proceeds to the right and more carbonic acid disso-

ciates, replenishing hydrogen ions. But when H^+ concentration in blood begins to rise (when pH drops), the reaction proceeds to the left, with HCO_3^- (the base) removing the hydrogen ions from the solution to form H_2CO_3. Thus, the carbonic acid–bicarbonate buffering system consists of an acid and a base in equilibrium with each other. Most other buffers are also acid-base pairs.

The Threat of Acid Precipitation

Considering the dependence of all life on water, contamination of rivers, lakes, and seas is a dire environmental problem. One of the most serious assaults on water quality is acid precipitation. Uncontaminated rain has a pH of about 5.6, slightly acidic, owing to the formation of carbonic acid from carbon dioxide and water. **Acid precipitation** refers to rain, snow, or fog with a pH lower or more acidic than pH 5.6.

Acid precipitation is caused primarily by the presence in the atmosphere of sulfur oxides and nitrogen oxides, gaseous compounds that react with water in the air to form strong acids, which fall to earth with rain or snow. A major source of these oxides is the burning of fossil fuels (coal, oil, and gas) in factories and automobiles. Electrical power plants that burn coal produce more of these pollutants than any other single source. Winds carry the pollutants away, and acid rain may fall hundreds of kilometers away from industrial centers. In certain sites in Pennsylvania and New York, the pH of rainfall in December 2001 averaged 4.3, about 20 times more acidic than normal rain. Acid precipitation falls on many other regions, including eastern Canada, the Cascade Mountains of the Pacific Northwest, and certain parts of Europe and Asia **(Figure 3.9)**.

Acid precipitation can damage life in lakes and streams. In addition, acid precipitation falling on land washes away certain mineral ions, such as calcium and magnesium ions, that

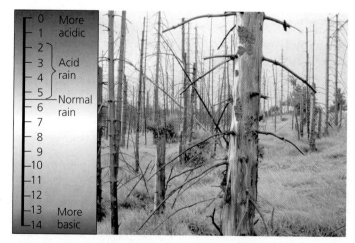

▲ **Figure 3.9 Acid precipitation and its effects on a forest.** Acid rain is thought to be responsible for killing trees in many forests, including the fir forest shown here in the Czech Republic.

ordinarily help buffer the soil solution and are essential nutrients for plant growth. At the same time, other minerals, such as aluminum, reach toxic concentrations when acidification increases their solubility. The effects of acid precipitation on soil chemistry have taken a toll on some North American forests and are contributing to the decline of European forests (see Figure 3.9). Nevertheless, studies indicate that the majority of North American forests are not currently suffering substantially from acid precipitation.

If there is reason for optimism about the future quality of water resources, it is that we have made progress in reducing acid precipitation (see Chapter 54). Continued progress can come only from the actions of people who are concerned about environmental quality. This requires understanding the crucial role that water plays in the environment's fitness for continued life on Earth.

Concept Check 3.3

1. Compared to a basic solution at pH 9, the same volume of an acidic solution at pH 4 has _____ times more hydrogen ions (H^+).
2. HCl is a strong acid that dissociates completely in water: $HCl \rightarrow H^+ + Cl^-$. What is the pH of 0.01 M HCl?

For suggested answers, see Appendix A.

Chapter 3 Review

Go to the Campbell Biology website (**www.campbellbiology.com**) or CD-ROM to explore Activities, Investigations, and other interactive study aids.

SUMMARY OF KEY CONCEPTS

Concept 3.1

The polarity of water molecules results in hydrogen bonding

▶ A hydrogen bond forms when the oxygen of one water molecule is electrically attracted to the hydrogen of a nearby molecule. Hydrogen bonding between water molecules is the basis for water's unusual properties (pp. 47–48).
Activity *The Polarity of Water*

Concept 3.2

Four emergent properties of water contribute to Earth's fitness for life

▶ **Cohesion (pp. 48–49)** Hydrogen bonding keeps water molecules close to each other, and this cohesion helps pull water upward in the microscopic vessels of plants. Hydrogen bonding is also responsible for water's surface tension.
Activity *Cohesion of Water*

▶ **Moderation of Temperature (pp. 49–50)** Hydrogen bonding gives water a high specific heat. Heat is absorbed when hydrogen bonds break and is released when hydrogen bonds form, helping minimize temperature fluctuations to within limits that permit life. Evaporative cooling is based on water's high heat of vaporization. Water molecules must have a relatively high kinetic energy to break hydrogen bonds. The evaporative loss of these energetic water molecules cools a surface.

▶ **Insulation of Bodies of Water by Floating Ice (pp. 50–51)** Ice is less dense than liquid water because its more organized hydrogen bonding causes expansion into a crystal formation. The lower density causes ice to float, which allows life to exist under the frozen surfaces of lakes and polar seas.

▶ **The Solvent of Life (pp. 51–53)** Water is an unusually versatile solvent because its polar molecules are attracted to charged and polar substances. Ions or polar substances surrounded by water molecules dissolve and are called solutes. Hydrophilic substances have an affinity for water; hydrophobic substances do not. Molarity, the number of moles of solute per liter of solution, is used as a measure of solute concentration in solutions. A mole is a certain number of molecules of a substance. The mass of a mole of the substance in grams is the same as the molecular mass in daltons.

Concept 3.3

Dissociation of water molecules leads to acidic and basic conditions that affect living organisms

▶ **Effects of Changes in pH (pp. 53–55)** Water can dissociate into H^+ and OH^-. The concentration of H^+ is expressed as pH, where pH $= -\log [H^+]$. Acids donate additional H^+ in aqueous solutions; bases donate OH^- or accept H^+. In a neutral solution at 25°C, $[H^+] = [OH^-] = 10^{-7}$, and pH = 7. In an acidic solution, $[H^+]$ is greater than $[OH^-]$, and the pH is less than 7. In a basic solution, $[H^+]$ is less than $[OH^-]$, and the pH is greater than 7. Buffers in biological fluids resist changes in pH. A buffer consists of an acid-base pair that combines reversibly with hydrogen ions.
Activity *Dissociation of Water Molecules*
Activity *Acids, Bases, and pH*

▶ **The Threat of Acid Precipitation (pp. 55–56)** Acid precipitation is rain, snow, or fog with a pH below 5.6. It often results from a reaction in the air between water vapor and sulfur oxides and nitrogen oxides produced by the combustion of fossil fuels.
Investigation *How Does Acid Precipitation Affect Trees?*

TESTING YOUR KNOWLEDGE

Self-Quiz

1. What is the best explanation of the phrase "fitness of the environment," as used in this chapter?
   a. Earth's environment is constant.
   b. It is the physical environment, not life, that has changed.
   c. The environment of Earth has adapted to life.
   d. Life as we know it depends on certain environmental qualities on Earth.
   e. Water and other aspects of Earth's environment exist because they make the planet more suitable for life.

2. Many mammals control their body temperature by sweating. Which property of water is most directly responsible for the ability of sweat to lower body temperature?
   a. water's change in density when it condenses
   b. water's ability to dissolve molecules in the air
   c. the release of heat by the formation of hydrogen bonds
   d. the absorption of heat by the breaking of hydrogen bonds
   e. water's high surface tension

3. For two bodies of matter in contact, heat always flows from
   a. the body with greater heat to the one with less heat.
   b. the body of higher temperature to the one of lower temperature.
   c. the denser body to the less dense body.
   d. the body with more water to the one with less water.
   e. the larger body to the smaller body.

4. A slice of pizza has 500 kcal. If we could burn the pizza and use all the heat to warm a 50-L container of cold water, what would be the approximate increase in the temperature of the water? (*Note:* A liter of cold water weighs about 1 kg.)
   a. 50°C   d. 100°C
   b. 5°C   e. 1°C
   c. 10°C

5. The bonds that are broken when water vaporizes are
   a. ionic bonds.
   b. bonds between water molecules.
   c. bonds between atoms within individual water molecules.
   d. polar covalent bonds.
   e. nonpolar covalent bonds.

6. Which of the following is an example of a hydrophobic material?
   a. paper   d. sugar
   b. table salt   e. pasta
   c. wax

7. We can be sure that a mole of table sugar and a mole of vitamin C are equal in their
   a. mass in daltons.   d. number of atoms.
   b. mass in grams.   e. volume.
   c. number of molecules.

8. How many grams of acetic acid ($C_2H_4O_2$) would you use to make 10 L of a 0.1 M aqueous solution of acetic acid? (*Note:* The atomic masses, in daltons, are approximately 12 for carbon, 1 for hydrogen, and 16 for oxygen.)
   a. 10.0 g   d. 60.0 g
   b. 0.1 g   e. 0.6 g
   c. 6.0 g

9. Acid precipitation has lowered the pH of a particular lake to 4.0. What is the hydrogen ion concentration of the lake?
   a. 4.0 M   d. 10^4 M
   b. 10^{-10} M   e. 4%
   c. 10^{-4} M

10. What is the *hydroxide* ion concentration of the lake described in question 9?
    a. 10^{-7} M   d. 10^{-14} M
    b. 10^{-4} M   e. 10 M
    c. 10^{-10} M

For Self-Quiz answers, see Appendix A.

Go to the website or CD-ROM for more quiz questions.

Evolution Connection

The surface of the planet Mars has many landscape features reminiscent of those formed by flowing water on Earth, including what appear to be meandering channels and outwash areas. Recent probes sent to Mars have revealed strong evidence that liquid water was once present on its surface. Ice exists at the Martian poles today, and some scientists suspect a great deal more water may be present beneath the Martian surface. Why has there been so much interest in the presence of water on Mars? Does the presence of water make it more likely that life had evolved there? What other physical factors might also be important?

Scientific Inquiry

1. Design a controlled experiment to test the hypothesis that acid precipitation inhibits the growth of *Elodea*, a common freshwater plant.

2. In agricultural areas, farmers pay close attention to the weather forecast. Right before a predicted overnight freeze, farmers spray water on crops to protect the plants. Use the properties of water to explain how this works. Be sure to mention why hydrogen bonds are responsible for this phenomenon.

Investigation *How Does Acid Precipitation Affect Trees?*

Science, Technology, and Society

Agriculture, industry, and the growing populations of cities all compete, through political influence, for water. If you were in charge of water resources in an arid region, what would your priorities be for allocating the limited water supply for various uses? How would you try to build consensus among the different special-interest groups?

4 Carbon and the Molecular Diversity of Life

▲ Figure 4.1 **Life is based on carbon.**

Key Concepts

4.1 Organic chemistry is the study of carbon compounds

4.2 Carbon atoms can form diverse molecules by bonding to four other atoms

4.3 Functional groups are the parts of molecules involved in chemical reactions

Overview

Carbon—The Backbone of Biological Molecules

Although water is the universal medium for life on Earth, living organisms, including all the plants and the snail you see in **Figure 4.1**, are made up of chemicals based mostly on the element carbon. Carbon enters the biosphere through the action of plants, which use the sun's energy to transform CO_2 in the atmosphere into the molecules of life. These molecules are then passed along to animals that feed on plants, such as the snail in the photo. Of all chemical elements, carbon is unparalleled in its ability to form molecules that are large, complex, and diverse, and this molecular diversity has made possible the diversity of organisms that have evolved on Earth. Proteins, DNA, carbohydrates, and other molecules that distinguish living matter from inanimate material are all composed of carbon atoms bonded to one another and to atoms of other elements. Hydrogen (H), oxygen (O), nitrogen (N), sulfur (S), and phosphorus (P) are other common ingredients of these compounds, but it is carbon (C) that accounts for the large diversity of biological molecules.

Proteins and other very large molecules are the main focus of Chapter 5. In this chapter, we investigate the properties of smaller molecules, using them to illustrate a few concepts of molecular architecture that highlight carbon's importance to life and the theme that emergent properties arise from the organization of the matter of living organisms.

Concept 4.1

Organic chemistry is the study of carbon compounds

Compounds containing carbon are said to be organic, and the branch of chemistry that specializes in the study of carbon compounds is called **organic chemistry.** Organic compounds range from simple molecules, such as methane (CH_4), to colossal ones, such as proteins, with thousands of atoms and molecular masses in excess of 100,000 daltons. Most organic compounds contain hydrogen atoms in addition to carbon atoms.

The overall percentages of the major elements of life—C, H, O, N, S, and P—are quite uniform from one organism to another. Because of carbon's versatility, however, this limited assortment of atomic building blocks, taken in roughly the same proportions, can be used to build an inexhaustible variety of organic molecules. Different species of organisms, and different individuals within a species, are distinguished by variations in their organic molecules.

Since the dawn of human history, people have used other organisms as sources of valued substances—from foods to medicines and fabrics. The science of organic chemistry originated in attempts to purify and improve the yield of such products. By the early 19th century, chemists had learned to make many simple compounds in the laboratory by combining elements under the right conditions. Artificial synthesis of the complex molecules extracted from living matter seemed impossible, however. At that time, the Swedish chemist Jöns

Jakob Berzelius made the distinction between organic compounds, those that seemingly could arise only within living organisms, and inorganic compounds, those that were found in the nonliving world. The new discipline of organic chemistry was first built on a foundation of *vitalism*, the belief in a life force outside the jurisdiction of physical and chemical laws.

Chemists began to chip away at the foundation of vitalism when they learned to synthesize organic compounds in their laboratories. In 1828, Friedrich Wöhler, a German chemist who had studied with Berzelius, attempted to make an "inorganic" salt, ammonium cyanate, by mixing solutions of ammonium ions (NH_4^+) and cyanate ions (CNO^-). Wöhler was astonished to find that instead of the expected product, he had made urea, an organic compound present in the urine of animals. Wöhler challenged the vitalists when he wrote, "I must tell you that I can prepare urea without requiring a kidney or an animal, either man or dog." However, one of the ingredients used in the synthesis, the cyanate, had been extracted from animal blood, and the vitalists were not swayed by Wöhler's discovery. A few years later, however, Hermann Kolbe, a student of Wöhler's, made the organic compound acetic acid from inorganic substances that could themselves be prepared directly from pure elements.

The foundation of vitalism finally crumbled after several more decades of laboratory synthesis of increasingly complex organic compounds. In 1953, Stanley Miller, then a graduate student at the University of Chicago, helped bring this abiotic (nonliving) synthesis of organic compounds into the context of evolution. Miller used a laboratory simulation of chemical conditions on the primitive Earth to demonstrate that the spontaneous synthesis of organic compounds could have been an early stage in the origin of life **(Figure 4.2)**.

The pioneers of organic chemistry helped shift the mainstream of biological thought from vitalism to *mechanism*, the view that all natural phenomena, including the processes of life, are governed by physical and chemical laws. Organic chemistry was redefined as the study of carbon compounds, regardless of their origin. Most naturally occurring organic compounds are produced by organisms, and these molecules represent a diversity and range of complexity unrivaled by inorganic compounds. However, the same rules of chemistry apply to inorganic and organic molecules alike. The foundation of organic chemistry is not some intangible life force, but the unique chemical versatility of the element carbon.

Figure 4.2

Inquiry Could organic compounds have been synthesized abiotically on the early Earth?

EXPERIMENT   In 1953, Stanley Miller simulated what were thought to be environmental conditions on the lifeless, primordial Earth. As shown in this recreation, Miller used electrical discharges (simulated lightning) to trigger reactions in a primitive "atmosphere" of H_2O, H_2, NH_3 (ammonia), and CH_4 (methane)—some of the gases released by volcanoes.

RESULTS   A variety of organic compounds that play key roles in living cells were synthesized in Miller's apparatus.

CONCLUSION   Organic compounds may have been synthesized abiotically on the early Earth, setting the stage for the origin of life. (We will explore this hypothesis in more detail in Chapter 26.)

Concept 4.2

Carbon atoms can form diverse molecules by bonding to four other atoms

The key to the chemical characteristics of an atom, as you learned in Chapter 2, is in its configuration of electrons. Electron configuration determines the kinds and number of bonds an atom will form with other atoms.

The Formation of Bonds with Carbon

Carbon has a total of 6 electrons, with 2 in the first electron shell and 4 in the second shell. Having 4 valence electrons in a shell that holds 8, carbon would have to donate or accept 4 electrons to complete its valence shell and become an ion. Instead, a carbon atom usually completes its valence shell by sharing its 4 electrons with other atoms in covalent bonds so that 8 electrons are present. Each carbon atom thus acts as an intersection point from which a molecule can branch off in up to

Concept Check 4.1

1. In Stanley Miller's experiment, what conclusion could be drawn from the presence of urea in the products?

For suggested answers, see Appendix A.

meth- "甲基"

Name and Comment	Molecular Formula	Structural Formula	Ball-and-Stick Model	Space-Filling Model
(a) Methane. When a carbon atom has four single bonds to other atoms, the molecule is tetrahedral.	CH_4	H | H — C — H | H		
(b) Ethane. A molecule may have more than one tetrahedral group of single-bonded atoms. (Ethane consists of two such groups.)	C_2H_6	H H | | H — C — C — H | | H H		
(c) Ethene (ethylene). When two carbon atoms are joined by a double bond, all atoms attached to those carbons are in the same plane; the molecule is flat.	C_2H_4	H H \ / C = C / \ H H		

▲ **Figure 4.3 The shapes of three simple organic molecules.**

four directions. This *tetravalence* is one facet of carbon's versatility that makes large, complex molecules possible.

In Chapter 2, you also learned that when a carbon atom forms single covalent bonds, the arrangement of its four hybrid orbitals causes the bonds to angle toward the corners of an imaginary tetrahedron (see Figure 2.16b). The bond angles in methane (CH_4) are 109.5° **(Figure 4.3a)**, and they are approximately the same in any group of atoms where carbon has four single bonds. For example, ethane (C_2H_6) is shaped like two tetrahedrons overlapping at their apexes **(Figure 4.3b)**. In molecules with still more carbons, every grouping of a carbon bonded to four other atoms has a tetrahedral shape. But when two carbon atoms are joined by a double bond, all bonds around those carbons are in the same plane. For example, ethene (C_2H_4) is a flat molecule; its atoms all lie in the same plane **(Figure 4.3c)**. We find it convenient to write all structural formulas as though the molecules represented were flat, but keep in mind that molecules are three-dimensional and that the shape of a molecule often determines its function.

The electron configuration of carbon gives it covalent compatibility with many different elements. **Figure 4.4** shows electron-shell diagrams of the four major atomic components of organic molecules. As you may recall from Chapter 2, these models allow us to see the valences of carbon and its most frequent partners—oxygen, hydrogen, and nitrogen. We can think of these valences as the basis for the rules of covalent bonding in organic chemistry—the building code that governs the architecture of organic molecules.

Hydrogen (valence = 1)	Oxygen (valence = 2)	Nitrogen (valence = 3)	Carbon (valence = 4)

▲ **Figure 4.4 Electron-shell diagrams showing valences for the major elements of organic molecules.** Valence is the number of covalent bonds an atom can form. It is generally equal to the number of electrons required to complete the atom's outermost (valence) electron shell (see Figure 2.8).

A couple of additional examples will show how the rules of covalent bonding apply to carbon atoms with partners other than hydrogen. In the carbon dioxide molecule (CO_2), a single carbon atom is joined to two atoms of oxygen by double covalent bonds. The structural formula for CO_2 is shown here:

$$O = C = O$$

Each line in a structural formula represents a pair of shared electrons. Notice that the carbon atom in CO_2 is involved in two double bonds, the equivalent of four single covalent bonds. The arrangement completes the valence shells of all atoms in the molecule. Because carbon dioxide is a very simple molecule and lacks hydrogen, it is often considered inorganic, even though it contains carbon. Whether we call CO_2 organic or inorganic, there is no question about its importance to the living world. As previously mentioned, CO_2 is the source of carbon for all the organic molecules found in organisms.

Another relatively simple molecule is urea, $CO(NH_2)_2$. This is the organic compound found in urine that Wöhler

Ethane   Propane

(a) Length. Carbon skeletons vary in length.

1-Butene   2-Butene

(c) Double bonds. The skeleton may have double bonds, which can vary in location.

Butane   2-methylpropane (commonly called isobutane)

(b) Branching. Skeletons may be unbranched or branched.

Cyclohexane   Benzene

(d) Rings. Some carbon skeletons are arranged in rings. In the abbreviated structural formula for each compound (at the right), each corner represents a carbon and its attached hydrogens.

▲ **Figure 4.5 Variations in carbon skeletons.** Hydrocarbons, organic molecules consisting only of carbon and hydrogen, illustrate the diversity of the carbon skeletons of organic molecules.

learned to synthesize in the early 19th century. The structural formula for urea is shown at the right.

Urea

Again, each atom has the required number of covalent bonds. In this case, one carbon atom is involved in both single and double bonds.

Both urea and carbon dioxide are molecules with only one carbon atom. But as Figure 4.3 shows, a carbon atom can also use one or more of its valence electrons to form covalent bonds to other carbon atoms, making it possible to link the atoms into chains of seemingly infinite variety.

Molecular Diversity Arising from Carbon Skeleton Variation

Carbon chains form the skeletons of most organic molecules **(Figure 4.5).** The skeletons vary in length and may be straight, branched, or arranged in closed rings. Some carbon skeletons have double bonds, which vary in number and location. Such variation in carbon skeletons is one important source of the molecular complexity and diversity that characterize living matter. In addition, atoms of other elements can be bonded to the skeletons at available sites.

Hydrocarbons

All the molecules shown in Figures 4.3 and 4.5 are **hydrocarbons,** organic molecules consisting only of carbon and hydrogen. Atoms of hydrogen are attached to the carbon skeleton wherever electrons are available for covalent bonding. Hydrocarbons are the major components of petroleum, which

is called a fossil fuel because it consists of the partially decomposed remains of organisms that lived millions of years ago.

Although hydrocarbons are not prevalent in living organisms, many of a cell's organic molecules have regions consisting of only carbon and hydrogen. For example, the molecules known as fats have long hydrocarbon tails attached to a non-hydrocarbon component **(Figure 4.6).** Neither petroleum nor fat dissolves in water; both are hydrophobic compounds

Fat droplets (stained red)

100 μm

(a) A fat molecule   **(b) Mammalian adipose cells**

▲ **Figure 4.6 The role of hydrocarbons in fats. (a)** A fat molecule consists of a small, non-hydrocarbon component joined to three hydrocarbon tails. The tails can be broken down to provide energy. They also account for the hydrophobic behavior of fats. (Black = carbon; gray = hydrogen; red = oxygen.) **(b)** Mammalian adipose cells stockpile fat molecules as a fuel reserve. Each adipose cell in this micrograph is almost filled by a large fat droplet, which contains a huge number of fat molecules.

because the great majority of their bonds are nonpolar carbon-to-hydrogen linkages. Another characteristic of hydrocarbons is that they can undergo reactions that release a relatively large amount of energy. The gasoline that fuels a car consists of hydrocarbons, and the hydrocarbon tails of fat molecules serve as stored fuel for animal bodies.

Isomers

Variation in the architecture of organic molecules can be seen in **isomers**, compounds that have the same numbers of atoms of the same elements but different structures and hence different properties. Compare, for example, the two pentanes in **Figure 4.7a**. Both have the molecular formula C_5H_{12}, but they differ in the covalent arrangement of their carbon skeletons. The skeleton is straight in one form of pentane but branched in the other. We will examine three types of isomers: structural isomers, geometric isomers, and enantiomers.

Structural isomers differ in the covalent arrangements of their atoms. The number of possible isomers increases tremendously as carbon skeletons increase in size. There are only three pentanes (two are shown in Figure 4.7a), but there are 18 variations of C_8H_{18} and 366,319 possible structural isomers of $C_{20}H_{42}$. Structural isomers may also differ in the location of double bonds.

Geometric isomers have the same covalent partnerships, but they differ in their spatial arrangements. Geometric isomers arise from the inflexibility of double bonds, which, unlike single bonds, will not allow the atoms they join to rotate freely about the bond axis. If a double bond joins two carbon atoms, and each C also has two different atoms (or groups of atoms) attached to it, then two distinct geometric isomers are possible. Consider the simple example in **Figure 4.7b**. Each of the carbons has an H and an X attached to it, but one isomer has a "cis" arrangement, with two Xs on the same side relative to the double bond, and the other isomer has a "trans" arrangement, with the Xs on opposite sides. The subtle difference in shape between geometric isomers can dramatically affect the biological activities of organic molecules. For example, the biochemistry of vision involves a light-induced change of rhodopsin, a chemical compound in the eye, from the cis isomer to the trans isomer (see Chapter 49).

Enantiomers are molecules that are mirror images of each other. In the ball-and-stick models shown in **Figure 4.7c**, the middle carbon is called an *asymmetric carbon* because it is attached to four different atoms or groups of atoms. The four groups can be arranged in space about the asymmetric carbon in two different ways that are mirror images. They are, in a way, left-handed and right-handed versions of the molecule. A cell can distinguish these isomers based on their different shapes. Usually, one isomer is biologically active and the other is inactive.

The concept of enantiomers is important in the pharmaceutical industry because the two enantiomers of a drug

(a) **Structural isomers** differ in covalent partners, as shown in this example of two isomers of pentane.

cis isomer: The two Xs are on the same side.

trans isomer: The two Xs are on opposite sides.

(b) **Geometric isomers** differ in arrangement about a double bond. In these diagrams, X represents an atom or group of atoms attached to a double-bonded carbon.

L isomer

D isomer

(c) **Enantiomers** differ in spatial arrangement around an asymmetric carbon, resulting in molecules that are mirror images, like left and right hands. The two isomers are designated the L and D isomers from the Latin for left and right (*levo* and *dextro*). Enantiomers cannot be superimposed on each other.

▲ Figure 4.7 **Three types of isomers.** Compounds with the same molecular formula but different structures, isomers are a source of diversity in organic molecules.

may not be equally effective. For example, L-dopa is effective against Parkinson's disease, while its enantiomer, D-dopa, is not (**Figure 4.8**). In some cases, one of the isomers may even produce harmful effects. This was the case with thalidomide, a drug prescribed for thousands of pregnant women in the late 1950s and early 1960s. The drug was a mixture of two enantiomers. One enantiomer reduced morning sickness, the desired effect, but the other caused severe birth defects. (Unfortunately, even if the "good" thalidomide enantiomer is used in purified form, some of it soon converts to the "bad" enantiomer in the patient's body.) The differing effects of enantiomers in the body demonstrate that organisms are sensitive to even

L-Dopa
(effective against
Parkinson's disease)

D-Dopa
(biologically
inactive)

▲ **Figure 4.8 The pharmacological importance of enantiomers.** L-Dopa is a drug used to treat Parkinson's disease, a disorder of the central nervous system. The drug's enantiomer, the mirror-image molecule designated D-dopa, has no effect on patients.

the most subtle variations in molecular architecture. Once again, we see that molecules have emergent properties that depend on the specific arrangement of their atoms.

Concept Check 4.2

1. Draw a structural formula for C_2H_4.
2. Look at Figure 4.5, and determine which pair(s) of molecules is (are) isomers of each other, identifying the type(s) of isomer.
3. What is the chemical similarity between gasoline and fat?

For suggested answers, see Appendix A.

Concept 4.3

Functional groups are the parts of molecules involved in chemical reactions

The distinctive properties of an organic molecule depend not only on the arrangement of its carbon skeleton, but also on the molecular components attached to that skeleton. We will now examine certain groups of atoms that are frequently attached to the skeletons of organic molecules.

The Functional Groups Most Important in the Chemistry of Life

The components of organic molecules that are most commonly involved in chemical reactions are known as **functional groups.** If we think of hydrocarbons as the simplest organic molecules, we can view functional groups as attachments that

Female lion

Male lion

▲ **Figure 4.9 A comparison of functional groups of female (estradiol) and male (testosterone) sex hormones.** The two molecules differ only in the functional groups attached to a common carbon skeleton of four fused rings, which is shown here in abbreviated form. These subtle variations in molecular architecture influence the development of the anatomical and physiological differences between female and male vertebrates.

replace one or more of the hydrogens bonded to the carbon skeleton of the hydrocarbon. (However, some functional groups include atoms of the carbon skeleton, as we will see.)

Each functional group behaves consistently from one organic molecule to another, and the number and arrangement of the groups help give each molecule its unique properties. Consider the differences between testosterone and estradiol (a type of estrogen). These compounds are male and female sex hormones, respectively, in humans and other vertebrates **(Figure 4.9).** Both are steroids, organic molecules with a common carbon skeleton in the form of four fused rings. These sex hormones differ only in the functional groups attached to the rings. The different actions of these two molecules on many targets throughout the body help produce the contrasting features of females and males. Thus, even our sexuality has its biological basis in variations of molecular architecture.

The six functional groups most important in the chemistry of life are the hydroxyl, carbonyl, carboxyl, amino, sulfhydryl, and phosphate groups. These groups are hydrophilic and thus increase the solubility of organic compounds in water. Before reading further, take time to familiarize yourself with the functional groups in **Figure 4.10** on the next two pages.

Figure 4.10

Exploring Some Important Functional Groups of Organic Compounds

FUNCTIONAL GROUP	HYDROXYL	CARBONYL	CARBOXYL
	[handwritten: lhai'drɒksɪl / 羟基] —OH (may be written HO—)	*[handwritten: 羰基]* 	*[handwritten: 羧基]*
STRUCTURE	In a **hydroxyl group** (—OH), a hydrogen atom is bonded to an oxygen atom, which in turn is bonded to the carbon skeleton of the organic molecule. (Do not confuse this functional group with the hydroxide ion, OH⁻.)	The **carbonyl group** (>CO) consists of a carbon atom joined to an oxygen atom by a double bond.	When an oxygen atom is double-bonded to a carbon atom that is also bonded to a hydroxyl group, the entire assembly of atoms is called a **carboxyl group** (—COOH).
NAME OF COMPOUNDS	*[handwritten: 酒精 乙醇]* **Alcohols** (their specific names usually end in *-ol*)	*[handwritten: 'kiːtəʊn / 酮] [handwritten: >C=O]* **Ketones** if the carbonyl group is within a carbon skeleton *[handwritten: 醛]* **Aldehydes** if the carbonyl group is at the end of the carbon skeleton *[handwritten: —C⁄⁄O H]*	**Carboxylic acids**, or organic acids
EXAMPLE	*[handwritten: C₂H₅OH]* *[handwritten: 乙醇] [handwritten: 'eθənɒl]* **Ethanol**, the alcohol present in alcoholic beverages *[handwritten: 饮料]*	*[handwritten: "aceto-" 乙酰 "醋酸"]* **Acetone**, the simplest ketone *[handwritten: 丙酮]* **Propanal**, an aldehyde *[handwritten: 丙醛]*	*[handwritten: 乙酸] [handwritten: ə'siːtɪk]* **Acetic acid**, which gives vinegar its sour taste
FUNCTIONAL PROPERTIES	▶ Is polar as a result of the electronegative oxygen atom drawing electrons toward itself. ▶ Attracts water molecules, helping dissolve organic compounds such as sugars (see Figure 5.3).	▶ A ketone and an aldehyde may be structural isomers with different properties, as is the case for acetone and propanal.	▶ Has acidic properties because it is a source of hydrogen ions. ▶ The covalent bond between oxygen and hydrogen is so polar that hydrogen ions (H⁺) tend to dissociate reversibly; for example, *[handwritten: 分离] [handwritten: 可逆的]* Acetic acid ⇌ Acetate ion + H⁺ ▶ In cells, found in the ionic form, which is called a carboxylate group.

AMINO	SULFHYDRYL	PHOSPHATE	FUNCTIONAL GROUP
	(may be written HS —)		STRUCTURE
The **amino group** (—NH$_2$) consists of a nitrogen atom bonded to two hydrogen atoms and to the carbon skeleton.	The **sulfhydryl group** consists of a sulfur atom bonded to an atom of hydrogen; resembles a hydroxyl group in shape.	In a **phosphate group**, a phosphorus atom is bonded to four oxygen atoms; one oxygen is bonded to the carbon skeleton; two oxygens carry negative charges; abbreviated ⑫. The phosphate group (—OPO$_3$$^{2-}$) is an ionized form of a phosphoric acid group (—OPO$_3$H$_2$; note the two hydrogens).	
Amines	Thiols	Organic phosphates	NAME OF COMPOUNDS
Glycine	Ethanethiol	Glycerol phosphate	EXAMPLE
Because it also has a carboxyl group, glycine is both an amine and a carboxylic acid; compounds with both groups are called amino acids.			
▶ Acts as a base; can pick up a proton from the surrounding solution: (nonionized) (ionized) ▶ Ionized, with a charge of 1+, under cellular conditions.	▶ Two sulfhydryl groups can interact to help stabilize protein structure (see Figure 5.20).	▶ Makes the molecule of which it is a part an anion (negatively charged ion). ▶ Can transfer energy between organic molecules.	FUNCTIONAL PROPERTIES

ATP: An Important Source of Energy for Cellular Processes

[handwritten: lə'denəsin # 腺苷]

The "Phosphate" column in Figure 4.10 shows a simple example of an organic phosphate molecule. A more complicated organic phosphate, **adenosine triphosphate**, or **ATP**, is worth mentioning because it is the primary energy-transferring molecule in the cell. ATP consists of an organic molecule called adenosine attached to a string of three phosphate groups:

Where three phosphates are present in series, as in ATP, one phosphate may split off as an inorganic phosphate ion. This ion, $HOPO_3^{2-}$, is often abbreviated $\textcircled{P}_i$ in this book. Losing one phosphate, ATP becomes adenosine *di*phosphate, or ADP. The reaction releases energy that can be used by the cell, as you will learn in more detail in Chapter 8.

$$\textcircled{P}—\textcircled{P}—\textcircled{P}—\boxed{\text{Adenosine}} \longrightarrow \textcircled{P}_i + \textcircled{P}—\textcircled{P}—\boxed{\text{Adenosine}} + \text{Energy}$$

| ATP | Inorganic phosphate | ADP |

The Chemical Elements of Life: *A Review*

Living matter, as you have learned, consists mainly of carbon, oxygen, hydrogen, and nitrogen, with smaller amounts of sulfur and phosphorus. These elements share the characteristic of forming strong covalent bonds, a quality that is essential in the architecture of complex organic molecules. Of all these elements, carbon is the virtuoso of the covalent bond. The versatility of carbon makes possible the great diversity of organic molecules, each with particular properties that emerge from the unique arrangement of its carbon skeleton and the functional groups appended to that skeleton. At the foundation of all biological diversity lies this variation at the molecular level.

Chapter 4 Review

Go to the Campbell Biology website (**www.campbellbiology.com**) or CD-ROM to explore Activities, Investigations, and other interactive study aids.

SUMMARY OF KEY CONCEPTS

Concept 4.1

Organic chemistry is the study of carbon compounds

▶ Organic compounds were once thought to arise only within living organisms, but this idea (vitalism) was disproved when chemists were able to synthesize organic compounds in the laboratory (pp. 58–59).

Concept 4.2

Carbon atoms can form diverse molecules by bonding to four other atoms

▶ **The Formation of Bonds with Carbon (pp. 59–61)** A covalent-bonding capacity of four contributes to carbon's ability to form diverse molecules. Carbon can bond to a variety of atoms, including O, H, and N. Carbon atoms can also bond to other carbons, forming the carbon skeletons of organic compounds.

▶ **Molecular Diversity Arising from Carbon Skeleton Variation (pp. 61–63)** The carbon skeletons of organic molecules vary in length and shape and have bonding sites for atoms of other elements. Hydrocarbons consist only of carbon and hydrogen. Isomers are molecules with the same molecular formula but different structures and properties. Three types of isomers are structural isomers, geometric isomers, and enantiomers.
Activity Diversity of Carbon-Based Molecules

Activity Isomers
Investigation What Factors Determine the Effectiveness of Drugs?

Concept 4.3

Functional groups are the parts of molecules involved in chemical reactions

▶ **The Functional Groups Most Important in the Chemistry of Life (pp. 63–65)** Functional groups are chemically reactive groups of atoms within an organic molecule that give the molecule distinctive chemical properties. The hydroxyl group (—OH) is polar, thus helping compounds dissolve in water. The carbonyl group ($>$CO) can be either at the end of a carbon skeleton (aldehyde) or within the skeleton (ketone). The carboxyl group (—COOH) is found in carboxylic acids. The hydrogen of this group can dissociate, making such molecules weak acids. The amino group (—NH_2) can accept a proton (H^+), thereby acting as a base. The sulfhydryl group (—SH) helps stabilize the structure of some proteins. The phosphate group (—OPO_3^{2-}) has an important role in the transfer of energy.
Activity Functional Groups

▶ **ATP: An Important Source of Energy for Cellular Processes (p. 66)** When a phosphate group splits off from ATP, energy is released that can be used by the cell.

▶ **The Chemical Elements of Life: A Review (p. 66)** Living matter is made mostly of carbon, oxygen, hydrogen, and nitrogen, with some sulfur and phosphorus. Biological diversity has its molecular basis in carbon's ability to form a huge number of molecules with particular shapes and chemical properties.

Self-Quiz

1. Organic chemistry is currently defined as
   a. the study of compounds that can be made only by living cells.
   b. the study of carbon compounds.
   c. the study of vital forces.
   d. the study of natural (as opposed to synthetic) compounds.
   e. the study of hydrocarbons.

2. Choose the pair of terms that correctly completes this sentence:
   Hydroxyl is to _____ as _____ is to aldehyde.
   a. carbonyl; ketone
   b. oxygen; carbon
   c. alcohol; carbonyl
   d. amine; carboxyl
   e. alcohol; ketone

3. Which of the following hydrocarbons has a double bond in its carbon skeleton?
   a. C_3H_8
   b. C_2H_6
   c. CH_4
   d. C_2H_4
   e. C_2H_2

4. The gasoline consumed by an automobile is a fossil fuel consisting mostly of
   a. aldehydes.
   b. amino acids.
   c. alcohols.
   d. hydrocarbons.
   e. thiols.

5. Choose the term that correctly describes the relationship between these two sugar molecules:

   a. structural isomers
   b. geometric isomers
   c. enantiomers
   d. isotopes

6. Identify the asymmetric carbon in this molecule:

7. Which functional group is *not* present in this molecule?

   a. carboxyl
   b. sulfhydryl
   c. hydroxyl
   d. amino

8. Which action could produce a carbonyl group?
   a. the replacement of the hydroxyl of a carboxyl group with hydrogen
   b. the addition of a thiol to a hydroxyl
   c. the addition of a hydroxyl to a phosphate
   d. the replacement of the nitrogen of an amine with oxygen
   e. the addition of a sulfhydryl to a carboxyl

9. Which functional group is most likely to be responsible for an organic molecule behaving as a base?
   a. hydroxyl
   b. carbonyl
   c. carboxyl
   d. amino
   e. phosphate

10. Given what you know about the electronegativity of oxygen, predict which of the following molecules would be the strongest acid. (*Hint:* Study Figure 4.10.) Explain your answer.

For Self-Quiz answers, see Appendix A.

Go to the website or CD-ROM for more quiz questions.

Evolution Connection

Some scientists believe that life elsewhere in the universe might be based on the element silicon, rather than on carbon, as on Earth. What properties does silicon share with carbon that would make silicon-based life more likely than, say, neon-based life or aluminum-based life? (See Figure 2.8.)

Scientific Inquiry

In 1918, an epidemic of sleeping sickness caused an unusual rigid paralysis in some survivors, similiar to symptoms of advanced Parkinson's disease. Years later, L-dopa, a chemical used to treat Parkinson's disease (see Figure 4.8), was given to some of these patients, as dramatized in the movie *Awakenings*. L-Dopa was remarkably effective at eliminating the paralysis, at least temporarily. However, its enantiomer, D-dopa, was subsequently shown to have no effect at all, as is the case for Parkinson's disease. Suggest a hypothesis to explain why, for *both* diseases, one enantiomer is effective and the other is not.

Investigation *What Factors Determine the Effectiveness of Drugs?*

Science, Technology, and Society

Thalidomide achieved notoriety 50 years ago because of a wave of birth defects among children born to women who took thalidomide during pregnancy as a treatment for morning sickness. However, in 1998 the U.S. Food and Drug Administration (FDA) approved this drug for the treatment of certain conditions associated with Hansen's disease (leprosy). In clinical trials, thalidomide also shows promise for use in treating patients suffering from AIDS, tuberculosis, and some types of cancer. Do you think approval of this drug is appropriate? If so, under what conditions? What criteria do you think the FDA should use in weighing a drug's benefits against its dangers?

5 The Structure and Function of Macromolecules

▲ Figure 5.1 **Scientists working with computer models of proteins.**

Key Concepts

5.1 Most macromolecules are polymers, built from monomers

5.2 Carbohydrates serve as fuel and building material

5.3 Lipids are a diverse group of hydrophobic molecules

5.4 Proteins have many structures, resulting in a wide range of functions

5.5 Nucleic acids store and transmit hereditary information

Overview

The Molecules of Life

We have seen how the concept of emergent properties applies to water and relatively simple organic molecules. Each type of small molecule has unique properties arising from the orderly arrangement of its atoms. Another level in the hierarchy of biological organization is reached when small organic molecules are joined inside cells, forming larger molecules. The four main classes of large biological molecules are carbohydrates, lipids, proteins, and nucleic acids. Many of these cellular molecules are, on the molecular scale, huge. For example, a protein may consist of thousands of covalently connected atoms that form a molecular colossus with a mass of over 100,000 daltons. Biologists use the term **macromolecule** for such giant molecules.

Considering the size and complexity of macromolecules, it is remarkable that biochemists have determined the detailed structures of so many of them **(Figure 5.1)**. The architecture of a macromolecule helps explain how that molecule works. Life's large molecules are the main subject of this chapter. For these molecules, as at all levels in the biological hierarchy, form and function are inseparable.

Concept 5.1

Most macromolecules are polymers, built from monomers

The large molecules in three of the four classes of life's organic compounds—carbohydrates, proteins, and nucleic acids—are chain-like molecules called polymers (from the Greek *polys*, many, and *meris*, part). A **polymer** is a long molecule consisting of many similar or identical building blocks linked by covalent bonds, much as a train consists of a chain of cars. The repeating units that serve as the building blocks of a polymer are small molecules called **monomers.** Some of the molecules that serve as monomers also have other functions of their own.

The Synthesis and Breakdown of Polymers

The classes of polymeric macromolecules differ in the nature of their monomers, but the chemical mechanisms by which cells make and break polymers are basically the same in all cases **(Figure 5.2)**. Monomers are connected by a reaction in which two molecules are covalently bonded to each other through loss of a water molecule; this is called a **condensation reaction,** specifically a **dehydration reaction,** because the molecule lost is water **(Figure 5.2a)**. When a bond forms between two monomers, each monomer contributes part of the water molecule that is lost: One molecule provides a hydroxyl group (—OH), while the other provides a hydrogen (—H). In making a polymer, this reaction is repeated as monomers are added to the chain one by one. The cell must expend energy to carry out these dehydration reactions, and the process oc-

(a) Dehydration reaction in the synthesis of a polymer

Short polymer

Unlinked monomer

Dehydration removes a water molecule, forming a new bond

H_2O

Longer polymer

Hydrolysis adds a water molecule, breaking a bond

H_2O

(b) Hydrolysis of a polymer

▲ Figure 5.2 **The synthesis and breakdown of polymers.**

curs only with the help of enzymes, specialized proteins that speed up chemical reactions in cells.

Polymers are disassembled to monomers by **hydrolysis**, a process that is essentially the reverse of the dehydration reaction **(Figure 5.2b)**. Hydrolysis means to break with water (from the Greek *hydro*, water, and *lysis*, break). Bonds between monomers are broken by the addition of water molecules, a hydrogen from the water attaching to one monomer and a hydroxyl group attaching to the adjacent monomer. An example of hydrolysis working in our bodies is the process of digestion. The bulk of the organic material in our food is in the form of polymers that are much too large to enter our cells. Within the digestive tract, various enzymes attack the polymers, speeding up hydrolysis. The released monomers are then absorbed into the bloodstream for distribution to all body cells. Those cells can then use dehydration reactions to assemble the monomers into new polymers that differ from the ones that were digested. The new polymers perform specific functions required by the cell.

The Diversity of Polymers

Each cell has thousands of different kinds of macromolecules; the collection varies from one type of cell to another even in the same organism. The inherent differences between human

siblings reflect variations in polymers, particularly DNA and proteins. Molecular differences between unrelated individuals are more extensive and between species greater still. The diversity of macromolecules in the living world is vast, and the possible variety is effectively limitless.

What is the basis for such diversity in life's polymers? These molecules are constructed from only 40 to 50 common monomers and some others that occur rarely. Building an enormous variety of polymers from such a limited list of monomers is analogous to constructing hundreds of thousands of words from only 26 letters of the alphabet. The key is arrangement—variation in the linear sequence that the units follow. However, this analogy falls far short of describing the great diversity of macromolecules, because most biological polymers are much longer than the longest word. Proteins, for example, are built from 20 kinds of amino acids arranged in chains that are typically hundreds of amino acids long. The molecular logic of life is simple but elegant: Small molecules common to all organisms are ordered into unique macromolecules.

We are now ready to investigate the specific structures and functions of the four major classes of organic compounds found in cells. For each class, we will see that the large molecules have emergent properties not found in their individual building blocks.

Concept Check 5.1

1. What are the four main classes of large biological molecules?
2. How many molecules of water are needed to completely hydrolyze a polymer that is 10 monomers long?
3. After you eat a slice of apple, which reactions must occur for the amino acid monomers in the protein of the apple to be converted into proteins in your body?

For suggested answers, see Appendix A.

Concept 5.2

Carbohydrates serve as fuel and building material

Carbohydrates include both sugars and the polymers of sugars. The simplest carbohydrates are the monosaccharides, or single sugars, also known as simple sugars. Disaccharides are double sugars, consisting of two monosaccharides joined by a condensation reaction. The carbohydrates that are macromolecules are polysaccharides, polymers composed of many sugar building blocks.

Sugars

Monosaccharides (from the Greek *monos,* single, and *sacchar,* sugar) generally have molecular formulas that are some multiple of the unit CH_2O **(Figure 5.3)**. Glucose ($C_6H_{12}O_6$), the most common monosaccharide, is of central importance in the chemistry of life. In the structure of glucose, we can see the trademarks of a sugar: The molecule has a carbonyl group ($>C=O$) and multiple hydroxyl groups (—OH). Depending on the location of the carbonyl group, a sugar is either an aldose (aldehyde sugar) or a ketose (ketone sugar). Glucose, for example, is an aldose; fructose, a structural isomer of glucose, is a ketose. (Most names for sugars end in *-ose.*) Another criterion for classifying sugars is the size of the carbon skeleton, which ranges from three to seven carbons long. Glucose, fructose, and other sugars that have six carbons are called hexoses. Trioses (three-carbon sugars) and pentoses (five-carbon sugars) are also common.

Still another source of diversity for simple sugars is in the spatial arrangement of their parts around asymmetric carbons. (Recall from Chapter 4 that an asymmetric carbon is a carbon attached to four different kinds of partners.) Glucose and galactose, for example, differ only in the placement of parts around one asymmetric carbon (see the purple boxes in Figure 5.3). What seems like a small difference is significant enough to give the two sugars distinctive shapes and behaviors.

Although it is convenient to draw glucose with a linear carbon skeleton, this representation is not completely accurate. In aqueous solutions, glucose molecules, as well as most other sugars, form rings **(Figure 5.4)**.

Monosaccharides, particularly glucose, are major nutrients for cells. In the process known as cellular respiration, cells extract the energy stored in glucose molecules. Not only are simple sugar molecules a major fuel for cellular work, but their carbon skeletons serve as raw material for the synthesis of other types of small organic molecules, such as amino acids and fatty acids. Sugar molecules that are not immediately used in these ways are generally incorporated as monomers into disaccharides or polysaccharides.

A **disaccharide** consists of two monosaccharides joined by a **glycosidic linkage,** a covalent bond formed between two monosaccharides by a dehydration reaction. For example, maltose is a disaccharide formed by the linking of two molecules of glucose **(Figure 5.5a)**. Also known as malt sugar, maltose is an ingredient used in brewing beer. The most prevalent disaccharide is sucrose, which is table sugar. Its two monomers are glucose and fructose **(Figure 5.5b)**. Plants generally transport carbohydrates from leaves to roots and other nonphotosynthetic organs in the form of sucrose. Lactose, the sugar present in milk, is another disaccharide, in this case a glucose molecule joined to a galactose molecule.

	Triose sugars ($C_3H_6O_3$)	Pentose sugars ($C_5H_{10}O_5$)	Hexose sugars ($C_6H_{12}O_6$)

▶ **Figure 5.3 The structure and classification of some monosaccharides.** Sugars may be aldoses (aldehyde sugars, top row) or ketoses (ketone sugars, bottom row), depending on the location of the carbonyl group (dark orange). Sugars are also classified according to the length of their carbon skeletons. A third point of variation is the spatial arrangement around asymmetric carbons (compare, for example, the purple portions of glucose and galactose).

(a) **Linear and ring forms.** Chemical equilibrium between the linear and ring structures greatly favors the formation of rings. To form the glucose ring, carbon 1 bonds to the oxygen attached to carbon 5.

(b) **Abbreviated ring structure.** Each corner represents a carbon. The ring's thicker edge indicates that you are looking at the ring edge-on; the components attached to the ring lie above or below the plane of the ring.

▲ Figure 5.4 **Linear and ring forms of glucose.**

(a) **Dehydration reaction in the synthesis of maltose.** The bonding of two glucose units forms maltose. The glycosidic link joins the number 1 carbon of one glucose to the number 4 carbon of the second glucose. Joining the glucose monomers in a different way would result in a different disaccharide.

Glucose   Glucose   1–4 glycosidic linkage   Maltose

(b) **Dehydration reaction in the synthesis of sucrose.** Sucrose is a disaccharide formed from glucose and fructose. Notice that fructose, though a hexose like glucose, forms a five-sided ring.

Glucose   Fructose   1–2 glycosidic linkage   Sucrose

▲ Figure 5.5 **Examples of disaccharide synthesis.**

Polysaccharides

Polysaccharides are macromolecules, polymers with a few hundred to a few thousand monosaccharides joined by glycosidic linkages. Some polysaccharides serve as storage material, hydrolyzed as needed to provide sugar for cells. Other polysaccharides serve as building material for structures that protect the cell or the whole organism. The architecture and function of a polysaccharide are determined by its sugar monomers and by the positions of its glycosidic linkages.

Storage Polysaccharides

Starch, a storage polysaccharide of plants, is a polymer consisting entirely of glucose monomers. Most of these monomers are joined by 1–4 linkages (number 1 carbon to number 4 carbon), like the glucose units in maltose (see Figure 5.5a). The angle of these bonds makes the polymer helical. The simplest form of starch, amylose, is unbranched. Amylopectin, a more complex form of starch, is a branched polymer with 1–6 linkages at the branch points.

Plants store starch as granules within cellular structures called plastids, which include chloroplasts (**Figure 5.6a**). Synthesizing starch enables the plant to stockpile surplus glucose. Because glucose is a major cellular fuel, starch represents stored energy. The sugar can later be withdrawn from this carbohydrate "bank" by hydrolysis, which breaks the bonds between the glucose monomers. Most animals, including humans, also have enzymes that can hydrolyze plant starch, making glucose

Amylose

Amylopectin

(a) Starch: a plant polysaccharide. Two forms of starch are amylose (unbranched) and amylopectin (branched). The light ovals in the micrograph are granules of starch within a chloroplast of a plant cell.

Glycogen

(b) Glycogen: an animal polysaccharide. Glycogen is more branched than amylopectin. Animal cells stockpile glycogen as dense clusters of granules within liver and muscle cells. (The micrograph shows part of a liver cell; mitochondria are organelles that help break down sugars.)

▲ **Figure 5.6 Storage polysaccharides of plants and animals.** These examples, starch and glycogen, are composed entirely of glucose monomers, represented here by hexagons. Due to their molecular structure, the polymer chains tend to form helices.

available as a nutrient for cells. Potato tubers and grains—the fruits of wheat, corn, rice, and other grasses—are the major sources of starch in the human diet.

Animals store a polysaccharide called **glycogen,** a polymer of glucose that is like amylopectin but more extensively branched **(Figure 5.6b).** Humans and other vertebrates store glycogen mainly in liver and muscle cells. Hydrolysis of glycogen in these cells releases glucose when the demand for sugar increases. This stored fuel cannot sustain an animal for long, however. In humans, for example, glycogen stores are depleted in about a day unless they are replenished by consumption of food.

Structural Polysaccharides

Organisms build strong materials from structural polysaccharides. For example, the polysaccharide called **cellulose** is a major component of the tough walls that enclose plant cells. On a global scale, plants produce almost 10^{11} (100 billion) tons of cellulose per year; it is the most abundant organic compound on Earth. Like starch, cellulose is a polymer of

glucose, but the glycosidic linkages in these two polymers differ. The difference is based on the fact that there are actually two slightly different ring structures for glucose **(Figure 5.7a).** When glucose forms a ring, the hydroxyl group attached to the number 1 carbon is positioned either below or above the plane of the ring. These two ring forms for glucose are called alpha (α) and beta (β), respectively. In starch, all the glucose monomers are in the α configuration **(Figure 5.7b),** the arrangement we saw in Figures 5.4 and 5.5. In contrast, the glucose monomers of cellulose are all in the β configuration, making every other glucose monomer upside down with respect to its neighbors **(Figure 5.7c).**

The differing glycosidic links in starch and cellulose give the two molecules distinct three-dimensional shapes. Whereas a starch molecule is mostly helical, a cellulose molecule is straight (and never branched), and its hydroxyl groups are free to hydrogen-bond with the hydroxyls of other cellulose molecules lying parallel to it. In plant cell walls, parallel cellulose molecules held together in this way are grouped into units called microfibrils **(Figure 5.8).** These cable-like microfibrils

(a) α and β glucose ring structures. These two interconvertible forms of glucose differ in the placement of the hydroxyl group attached to the number 1 carbon.

▲ Figure 5.7 **Starch and cellulose structures.**

(b) Starch: 1–4 linkage of α glucose monomers.

(c) Cellulose: 1–4 linkage of β glucose monomers. The angles of the bonds that link the rings make every other glucose monomer upside down with respect to its neighbors. Compare the positions of the highlighted –OH groups in (b) starch and (c) cellulose.

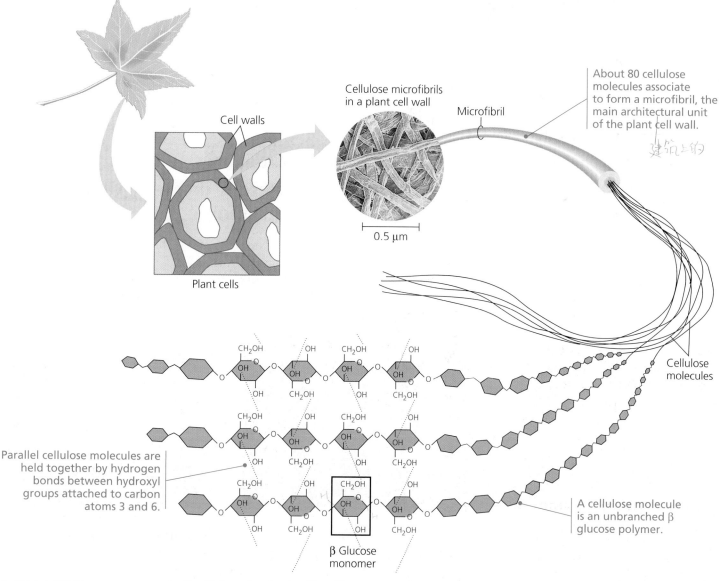

Cell walls

Plant cells

Cellulose microfibrils in a plant cell wall

0.5 μm

Microfibril

About 80 cellulose molecules associate to form a microfibril, the main architectural unit of the plant cell wall.

Cellulose molecules

Parallel cellulose molecules are held together by hydrogen bonds between hydroxyl groups attached to carbon atoms 3 and 6.

A cellulose molecule is an unbranched β glucose polymer.

β Glucose monomer

▲ Figure 5.8 **The arrangement of cellulose in plant cell walls.**

▲ Figure 5.9 **Cellulose-digesting bacteria are found in grazing animals such as this cow.**

are a strong building material for plants as well as for humans, who use wood, which is rich in cellulose, for lumber.

Enzymes that digest starch by hydrolyzing its α linkages are unable to hydrolyze the β linkages of cellulose because of the distinctly different shapes of these two molecules. In fact, few organisms possess enzymes that can digest cellulose. Humans do not; the cellulose in our food passes through the digestive tract and is eliminated with the feces. Along the way, the cellulose abrades the wall of the digestive tract and stimulates the lining to secrete mucus, which aids in the smooth passage of food through the tract. Thus, although cellulose is not a nutrient for humans, it is an important part of a healthful diet. Most fresh fruits, vegetables, and whole grains are rich in cellulose. On food packages, "insoluble fiber" refers mainly to cellulose.

Some microbes can digest cellulose, breaking it down to glucose monomers. A cow harbors cellulose-digesting bacteria in the rumen, the first compartment in its stomach (Figure 5.9). The bacteria hydrolyze the cellulose of hay and grass and convert the glucose to other nutrients that nourish the cow. Simi-

larly, a termite, which is unable to digest cellulose by itself, has microbes living in its gut that can make a meal of wood. Some fungi can also digest cellulose, thereby helping recycle chemical elements within Earth's ecosystems.

Another important structural polysaccharide is **chitin**, the carbohydrate used by arthropods (insects, spiders, crustaceans, and related animals) to build their exoskeletons (**Figure 5.10**). An exoskeleton is a hard case that surrounds the soft parts of an animal. Pure chitin is leathery, but it becomes hardened when encrusted with calcium carbonate, a salt. Chitin is also found in many fungi, which use this polysaccharide rather than cellulose as the building material for their cell walls. Chitin is similar to cellulose, except that the glucose monomer of chitin has a nitrogen-containing appendage (see Figure 5.10a).

Concept Check 5.2

1. Write the formula for a monosaccharide that has three carbons.
2. A dehydration reaction joins two glucose molecules to form maltose. The formula for glucose is $C_6H_{12}O_6$. What is the formula for maltose?
3. Compare and contrast starch and cellulose.

For suggested answers, see Appendix A.

Concept 5.3

Lipids are a diverse group of hydrophobic molecules

Lipids are the one class of large biological molecules that does not consist of polymers. The compounds called **lipids** are grouped together because they share one important trait:

(a) The structure of the chitin monomer.

(b) Chitin forms the exoskeleton of arthropods. This cicada is molting, shedding its old exoskeleton and emerging in adult form.

(c) Chitin is used to make a strong and flexible surgical thread that decomposes after the wound or incision heals.

▲ Figure 5.10 **Chitin, a structural polysaccharide.**

They have little or no affinity for water. The hydrophobic behavior of lipids is based on their molecular structure. Although they may have some polar bonds associated with oxygen, lipids consist mostly of hydrocarbons. Smaller than true (polymeric) macromolecules, lipids are a highly varied group in both form and function. Lipids include waxes and certain pigments, but we will focus on the most biologically important types of lipids: fats, phospholipids, and steroids.

Fats

Although fats are not polymers, they are large molecules, and they are assembled from smaller molecules by dehydration reactions. A **fat** is constructed from two kinds of smaller molecules: glycerol and fatty acids (**Figure 5.11a**). Glycerol is an alcohol with three carbons, each bearing a hydroxyl group. A **fatty acid** has a long carbon skeleton, usually 16 or 18 carbon atoms in length. At one end of the fatty acid is a carboxyl group, the functional group that gives these molecules the name fatty *acid*. Attached to the carboxyl group is a long hydrocarbon chain. The nonpolar C—H bonds in the hydrocarbon chains of fatty acids are the reason fats are hydrophobic. Fats separate from water because the water molecules hydrogen-bond to one

another and exclude the fats. A common example of this phenomenon is the separation of vegetable oil (a liquid fat) from the aqueous vinegar solution in a bottle of salad dressing.

In making a fat, three fatty acid molecules each join to glycerol by an ester linkage, a bond between a hydroxyl group and a carboxyl group. The resulting fat, also called a **triacylglycerol**, thus consists of three fatty acids linked to one glycerol molecule. (Still another name for a fat is *triglyceride,* a word often found in the list of ingredients on packaged foods.) The fatty acids in a fat can be the same, as in **Figure 5.11b**, or they can be of two or three different kinds.

Fatty acids vary in length and in the number and locations of double bonds. The terms *saturated fats* and *unsaturated fats* are commonly used in the context of nutrition (**Figure 5.12**). These terms refer to the structure of the hydrocarbon chains of the fatty acids. If there are no double bonds between carbon atoms composing the chain, then as many hydrogen atoms as possible are bonded to the carbon skeleton. Such a structure is described as being *saturated* with hydrogen, so the resulting fatty acid is called a **saturated fatty acid** (**Figure 5.12a**). An **unsaturated**

Fatty acid
(palmitic acid)

Glycerol

(a) Dehydration reaction in the synthesis of a fat

Ester linkage

(b) Fat molecule (triacylglycerol)

▲ **Figure 5.11 The synthesis and structure of a fat, or triacylglycerol.** The molecular building blocks of a fat are one molecule of glycerol and three molecules of fatty acids. **(a)** One water molecule is removed for each fatty acid joined to the glycerol. **(b)** A fat molecule with three identical fatty acid units. The carbons of the fatty acids are arranged zig-zag to suggest the actual orientations of the four single bonds extending from each carbon (see Figure 4.3a).

Stearic acid

(a) Saturated fat and fatty acid. At room temperature, the molecules of a saturated fat such as this butter are packed closely together, forming a solid.

Oleic acid

cis double bond causes bending

(b) Unsaturated fat and fatty acid. At room temperature, the molecules of an unsaturated fat such as this olive oil cannot pack together closely enough to solidify because of the kinks in their fatty acid tails.

▲ **Figure 5.12 Examples of saturated and unsaturated fats and fatty acids.**

fatty acid has one or more double bonds, formed by the removal of hydrogen atoms from the carbon skeleton. The fatty acid will have a kink in its hydrocarbon chain wherever a *cis* double bond occurs **(Figure 5.12b)**.

A fat made from saturated fatty acids is called a saturated fat. Most animal fats are saturated: The hydrocarbon chains of their fatty acids—the "tails" of the fat molecules—lack double bonds, and the molecules can pack tightly, side by side. Saturated animal fats—such as lard and butter—are solid at room temperature. In contrast, the fats of plants and fishes are generally unsaturated, meaning that they are built of one or more types of unsaturated fatty acids. Usually liquid at room temperature, plant and fish fats are referred to as oils—olive oil and cod liver oil are examples. The kinks where the *cis* double bonds are located prevent the molecules from packing together closely enough to solidify at room temperature. The phrase "hydrogenated vegetable oils" on food labels means that unsaturated fats have been synthetically converted to saturated fats by adding hydrogen. Peanut butter, margarine, and many other products are hydrogenated to prevent lipids from separating out in liquid (oil) form.

A diet rich in saturated fats is one of several factors that may contribute to the cardiovascular disease known as atherosclerosis. In this condition, deposits called plaques develop within the walls of blood vessels, causing inward bulges that impede blood flow and reduce the resilience of the vessels. Recent studies have shown that the process of hydrogenating vegetable oils produces not only saturated fats but also unsat-

urated fats with *trans* double bonds. These *trans* fat molecules may contribute more than saturated fats to atherosclerosis (see Chapter 42) and other problems.

Fat has come to have such a negative connotation in our culture that you might wonder whether fats serve any useful purpose. The major function of fats is energy storage. The hydrocarbon chains of fats are similar to gasoline molecules and just as rich in energy. A gram of fat stores more than twice as much energy as a gram of a polysaccharide, such as starch. Because plants are relatively immobile, they can function with bulky energy storage in the form of starch. (Vegetable oils are generally obtained from seeds, where more compact storage is an asset to the plant.) Animals, however, must carry their energy stores with them, so there is an advantage to having a more compact reservoir of fuel—fat. Humans and other mammals stock their long-term food reserves in adipose cells (see Figure 4.6b), which swell and shrink as fat is deposited and withdrawn from storage. In addition to storing energy, adipose tissue also cushions such vital organs as the kidneys, and a layer of fat beneath the skin insulates the body. This subcutaneous layer is especially thick in whales, seals, and most other marine mammals, protecting them from cold ocean water.

Phospholipids

A **phospholipid**, as shown in **Figure 5.13**, is similar to a fat, but has only two fatty acids attached to glycerol rather than three. The third hydroxyl group of glycerol is joined to a phosphate

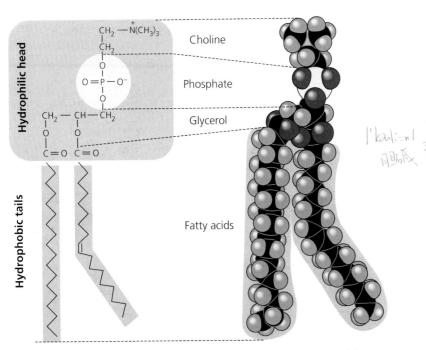

(a) Structural formula   **(b) Space-filling model**   **(c) Phospholipid symbol**

Choline

Phosphate

Glycerol

Fatty acids

Hydrophilic head

Hydrophobic tails

◀ **Figure 5.13 The structure of a phospholipid.** A phospholipid has a hydrophilic (polar) head and two hydrophobic (nonpolar) tails. Phospholipid diversity is based on differences in the two fatty acids and in the groups attached to the phosphate group of the head. This particular phospholipid, called a phosphatidylcholine, has an attached choline group. The kink in one of its tails is due to a *cis* double bond. **(a)** The structural formula follows a common chemical convention of omitting the carbons and attached hydrogens of the hydrocarbon tails. **(b)** In the space-filling model, black = carbon, gray = hydrogen, red = oxygen, yellow = phosphorus, and blue = nitrogen. **(c)** This symbol for a phospholipid will appear throughout the book.

Hydrophilic head

Hydrophobic tails

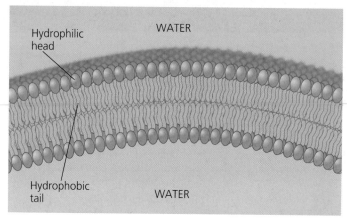

▲ **Figure 5.14 Bilayer structure formed by self-assembly of phospholipids in an aqueous environment.** The phospholipid bilayer shown here is the main fabric of biological membranes. Note that the hydrophilic heads of the phospholipids are in contact with water in this structure, whereas the hydrophobic tails are in contact with each other and remote from water.

▲ **Figure 5.15 Cholesterol, a steroid.** Cholesterol is the molecule from which other steroids, including the sex hormones, are synthesized. Steroids vary in the functional groups attached to their four interconnected rings (shown in gold).

group, which has a negative electrical charge. Additional small molecules, usually charged or polar, can be linked to the phosphate group to form a variety of phospholipids.

Phospholipids show ambivalent behavior toward water. Their hydrocarbon tails are hydrophobic and are excluded from water. However, the phosphate group and its attachments form a hydrophilic head that has an affinity for water. When phospholipids are added to water, they self-assemble into double-layered aggregates—bilayers—that shield their hydrophobic portions from water (**Figure 5.14**).

At the surface of a cell, phospholipids are arranged in a similar bilayer. The hydrophilic heads of the molecules are on the outside of the bilayer, in contact with the aqueous solutions inside and outside the cell. The hydrophobic tails point toward the interior of the bilayer, away from the water. The phospholipid bilayer forms a boundary between the cell and its external environment; in fact, phospholipids are major components of all cell membranes. This behavior provides another example of how form fits function at the molecular level.

Steroids

Steroids are lipids characterized by a carbon skeleton consisting of four fused rings (**Figure 5.15**). Different steroids vary in the functional groups attached to this ensemble of rings. One steroid, **cholesterol,** is a common component of animal cell membranes and is also the precursor from which other steroids are synthesized. Many hormones, including vertebrate sex hormones, are steroids produced from cholesterol (see Figure 4.9). Thus, cholesterol is a crucial molecule in animals, although a high level of it in the blood may contribute to atherosclerosis. Both saturated fats

and *trans* fats exert their negative impact on health by affecting cholesterol levels.

Concept 5.4

Proteins have many structures, resulting in a wide range of functions

The importance of proteins is implied by their name, which comes from the Greek word *proteios,* meaning "first place." Proteins account for more than 50% of the dry mass of most cells, and they are instrumental in almost everything organisms do. Some proteins speed up chemical reactions, while others play a role in structural support, storage, transport, cellular communications, movement, and defense against foreign substances (**Table 5.1**, on the next page).

The most important type of protein may be **enzymes.** Enzymatic proteins regulate metabolism by acting as **catalysts,** chemical agents that selectively speed up chemical reactions in

Table 5.1 An Overview of Protein Functions

Type of Protein	Function	Examples
Enzymatic proteins	Selective acceleration of chemical reactions	Digestive enzymes catalyze the hydrolysis of the polymers in food.
Structural proteins	Support	Insects and spiders use silk fibers to make their cocoons and webs, respectively. Collagen and elastin provide a fibrous framework in animal connective tissues. Keratin is the protein of hair, horns, feathers, and other skin appendages.
Storage proteins	Storage of amino acids	Ovalbumin is the protein of egg white, used as an amino acid source for the developing embryo. Casein, the protein of milk, is the major source of amino acids for baby mammals. Plants have storage proteins in their seeds.
Transport proteins	Transport of other substances	Hemoglobin, the iron-containing protein of vertebrate blood, transports oxygen from the lungs to other parts of the body. Other proteins transport molecules across cell membranes.
Hormonal proteins	Coordination of an organism's activities	Insulin, a homone secreted by the pancreas, helps regulate the concentration of sugar in the blood of vertebrates.
Receptor proteins	Response of cell to chemical stimuli	Receptors built into the membrane of a nerve cell detect chemical signals released by other nerve cells.
Contractile and motor proteins	Movement	Actin and myosin are responsible for the movement of muscles. Other proteins are responsible for the undulations of the organelles called cilia and flagella.
Defensive proteins	Protection against disease	Antibodies combat bacteria and viruses.

the cell without being consumed by the reaction **(Figure 5.16)**. Because an enzyme can perform its function over and over again, these molecules can be thought of as workhorses that keep cells running by carrying out the processes of life.

A human has tens of thousands of different proteins, each with a specific structure and function; proteins, in fact, are the most structurally sophisticated molecules known. Consistent with their diverse functions, they vary extensively in structure, each type of protein having a unique three-dimensional shape, or conformation.

Polypeptides

Diverse as proteins are, they are all polymers constructed from the same set of 20 amino acids. Polymers of amino acids are called **polypeptides**. A **protein** consists of one or more polypeptides folded and coiled into specific conformations.

Amino Acid Monomers

Amino acids are organic molecules possessing both carboxyl and amino groups (see Chapter 4). The illustration at the right shows the general formula for an amino acid. At the center of the amino acid is an asymmetric carbon atom called the *alpha (α) carbon*. Its four different partners are an amino group, a carboxyl group, a hydrogen atom, and a variable group symbolized by R. The R group, also called the side chain, differs with each amino acid. **Figure 5.17** shows the 20 amino acids that cells use to

① Active site is available for a molecule of substrate, the reactant on which the enzyme acts.

② Substrate binds to enzyme.

Substrate (sucrose)

Glucose

OH

Enzyme (sucrase)

H_2O

Fructose

HO

④ Products are released.

③ Substrate is converted to products.

▲ **Figure 5.16 The catalytic cycle of an enzyme.** The enzyme sucrase accelerates hydrolysis of sucrose into glucose and fructose. Acting as a catalyst, the sucrase protein is not consumed during the cycle, but is available for further catalysis.

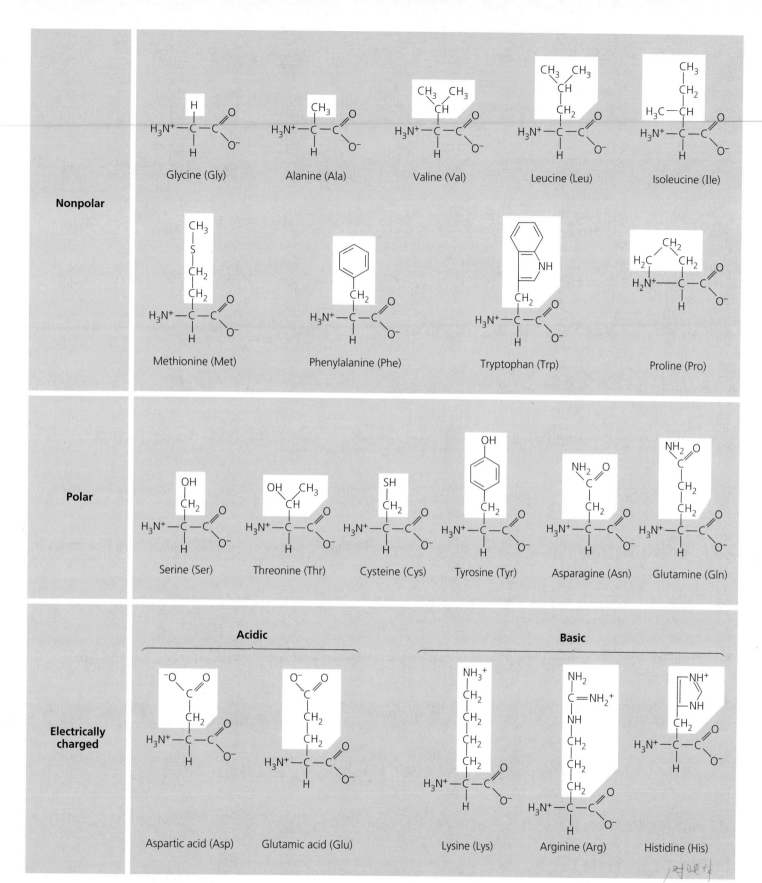

Nonpolar

Glycine (Gly)   Alanine (Ala)   Valine (Val)   Leucine (Leu)   Isoleucine (Ile)

Methionine (Met)   Phenylalanine (Phe)   Tryptophan (Trp)   Proline (Pro)

Polar

Serine (Ser)   Threonine (Thr)   Cysteine (Cys)   Tyrosine (Tyr)   Asparagine (Asn)   Glutamine (Gln)

Electrically charged

Acidic

Basic

Aspartic acid (Asp)   Glutamic acid (Glu)   Lysine (Lys)   Arginine (Arg)   Histidine (His)

▲ **Figure 5.17 The 20 amino acids of proteins.** The amino acids are grouped here according to the properties of their side chains (R groups), highlighted in white. The amino acids are shown in their prevailing ionic forms at pH 7.2, the pH within a cell. The three-letter abbreviations for the amino acids are in parentheses. All the amino acids used in proteins are the same enantiomer, called the L form, as shown here (see Figure 4.7).

build their thousands of proteins. Here the amino and carboxyl groups are all depicted in ionized form, the way they usually exist at the pH in a cell. The R group may be as simple as a hydrogen atom, as in the amino acid glycine (the one amino acid lacking an asymmetric carbon, since two of its α carbon's partners are hydrogen atoms), or it may be a carbon skeleton with various functional groups attached, as in glutamine. (Organisms do have other amino acids, some of which are occasionally found in proteins. Because these are relatively rare, they are not shown in Figure 5.17.)

The physical and chemical properties of the side chain determine the unique characteristics of a particular amino acid. In Figure 5.17, the amino acids are grouped according to the properties of their side chains. One group consists of amino acids with nonpolar side chains, which are hydrophobic. Another group consists of amino acids with polar side chains, which are hydrophilic. Acidic amino acids are those with side chains that are generally negative in charge owing to the presence of a carboxyl group, which is usually dissociated (ionized) at cellular pH. Basic amino acids have amino groups in their side chains that are generally positive in charge. (Notice that *all* amino acids have carboxyl groups and amino groups; the terms *acidic* and *basic* in this context refer only to groups on the side chains.) Because they are charged, acidic and basic side chains are also hydrophilic.

Amino Acid Polymers

Now that we have examined amino acids, let's see how they are linked to form polymers **(Figure 5.18)**. When two amino acids are positioned so that the carboxyl group of one is adjacent to the amino group of the other, an enzyme can cause them to join by catalyzing a dehydration reaction, with the removal of a water molecule. The resulting covalent bond is called a **peptide bond.** Repeated over and over, this process yields a polypeptide, a polymer of many amino acids linked by peptide bonds. At one end of the polypeptide chain is a free amino group; at the opposite end is a free carboxyl group. Thus, the chain has an amino end (N-terminus) and a carboxyl end (C-terminus). The repeating sequence of atoms highlighted in purple in Figure 5.18b is called the polypeptide backbone. Attached to this backbone are different kinds of appendages, the side chains of the amino acids. Polypeptides range in length from a few monomers to a thousand or more. Each specific polypeptide has a unique linear sequence of amino acids. The immense variety of polypeptides in nature illustrates an important concept introduced earlier—that cells can make many different polymers by linking a limited set of monomers into diverse sequences.

Determining the Amino Acid Sequence of a Polypeptide

The pioneer in determining the amino acid sequence of proteins was Frederick Sanger, who, with his colleagues at

(a)

(b)

▲ **Figure 5.18 Making a polypeptide chain. (a)** Peptide bonds formed by dehydration reactions link the carboxyl group of one amino acid to the amino group of the next. **(b)** The peptide bonds are formed one at a time, starting with the amino acid at the amino end (N-terminus). The polypeptide has a repetitive backbone (purple) to which the amino acid side chains are attached.

Cambridge University in England, worked on the hormone insulin in the late 1940s and early 1950s. His approach was to use protein-digesting enzymes and other catalysts that break polypeptides at specific places rather than completely hydrolyzing the chains to amino acids. Treatment with one of these agents cleaves a polypeptide into fragments (each consisting of multiple amino acid subunits) that can be separated by a technique called chromatography. Hydrolysis with a different agent breaks the polypeptide at different sites, yielding a second group of fragments. Sanger used chemical methods to determine the sequence of amino acids in these small fragments. Then he searched for overlapping regions among the pieces obtained by hydrolyzing with the different agents. Consider, for instance, two fragments with the following sequences:

Cys-Ser-Leu-Tyr-Gln-Leu
Tyr-Gln-Leu-Glu-Asn

We can deduce from the overlapping regions that the intact polypeptide contains in its primary structure the following segment:

Cys-Ser-Leu-Tyr-Gln-Leu-Glu-Asn

Just as we could reconstruct this sentence from a collection of fragments with overlapping sequences of letters, Sanger and his co-workers were able, after years of effort, to reconstruct the complete primary structure of insulin. Since then, most of the steps involved in sequencing a polypeptide have been automated.

Protein Conformation and Function

Once we have learned the amino acid sequence of a polypeptide, what can it tell us about protein conformation and function? The term *polypeptide* is not quite synonymous with the term *protein*. Even for a protein consisting of a single polypeptide, the relationship is somewhat analogous to that between a long strand of yarn and a sweater of particular size and shape that one can knit from the yarn. A functional protein is not *just* a polypeptide chain, but one or more polypeptides precisely twisted, folded, and coiled into a molecule of unique shape (**Figure 5.19**). It is the amino acid sequence of a polypeptide that determines what three-dimensional conformation the protein will take.

When a cell synthesizes a polypeptide, the chain generally folds spontaneously, assuming the functional conformation for that protein. This folding is driven and reinforced by the formation of a variety of bonds between parts of the chain, which in turn depends on the sequence of amino acids. Many proteins are globular (roughly spherical), while others are fibrous in shape. Even within these broad categories, countless variations are possible.

A protein's specific conformation determines how it works. In almost every case, the function of a protein depends on its ability to recognize and bind to some other molecule. For instance, an antibody (a protein) binds to a particular foreign substance that has invaded the body, and an enzyme (another type of protein) recognizes and binds to its substrate, the substance the enzyme works on. In Chapter 2, you learned that natural signal molecules called endorphins bind to specific receptor proteins on the surface of brain cells in humans, producing euphoria and relieving pain. Morphine, heroin, and other opiate drugs are able to mimic endorphins because they all share a similar shape with endorphins and can thus fit into and bind to endorphin receptors in the brain. This fit is very specific, something like a lock and key (see Figure 2.17). Thus, the function of a protein—for instance, the ability of a receptor protein to identify and associate with a particular pain-relieving signal molecule—is an emergent property resulting from exquisite molecular order.

Four Levels of Protein Structure

In the complex architecture of a protein, we can recognize three superimposed levels of structure, known as primary, secondary, and tertiary structure. A fourth level, quaternary structure, arises when a protein consists of two or more polypeptide chains. **Figure 5.20**, on the following two pages, describes these four levels of protein structure. Be sure to study this figure thoroughly before going on to the next section.

(a) A **ribbon model** shows how the single polypeptide chain folds and coils to form the functional protein. (The yellow lines represent one type of chemical bond that stabilizes the protein's shape.)

(b) A **space-filling model** shows more clearly the globular shape seen in many proteins, as well as the specific conformation unique to lysozyme.

▲ **Figure 5.19 Conformation of a protein, the enzyme lysozyme.** Present in our sweat, tears, and saliva, lysozyme is an enzyme that helps prevent infection by binding to and destroying specific molecules on the surface of many kinds of bacteria. The groove is the part of the protein that recognizes and binds to the target molecules on bacterial walls.

Figure 5.20

Exploring Levels of Protein Structure

β pleated sheet

α helix

Amino end

Amino acid subunits

PRIMARY STRUCTURE

SECONDARY STRUCTURE

The **primary structure** of a protein is its unique sequence of amino acids. As an example, let's consider transthyretin, a globular protein found in the blood that transports vitamin A and a particular thyroid hormone throughout the body. Each of the four identical polypeptide chains that, together, make up transthyretin is composed of 127 amino acids. Shown here is one of these chains unraveled for a closer look at its primary structure. A specific one of the 20 amino acids, indicated here by its three-letter abbreviation, occupies each of the 127 positions along the chain. The primary structure is like the order of letters in a very long word. If left to chance, there would be 20^{127} different ways of making a polypeptide chain 127 amino acids long. However, the precise primary structure of a protein is determined not by the random linking of amino acids, but by inherited genetic information.

Carboxyl end

Most proteins have segments of their polypeptide chains repeatedly coiled or folded in patterns that contribute to the protein's overall conformation. These coils and folds, collectively referred to as **secondary structure**, are the result of hydrogen bonds between the repeating constituents of the polypeptide backbone (not the amino acid side chains). Both the oxygen and the nitrogen atoms of the backbone are electronegative, with partial negative charges (see Figure 2.15). The weakly positive hydrogen atom attached to the nitrogen atom has an affinity for the oxygen atom of a nearby peptide bond. Individually, these hydrogen bonds are weak, but because they are repeated many times over a relatively long region of the polypeptide chain, they can support a particular shape for that part of the protein.

One such secondary structure is the **α helix,** a delicate coil held together by hydrogen bonding between every fourth amino acid, shown above for transthyretin. Although transthyretin has only one α helix region (see tertiary structure), other globular proteins have multiple stretches of α helix separated by nonhelical regions. Some fibrous proteins, such as α-keratin, the structural protein of hair, have the α helix formation over most of their length.

The other main type of secondary structure is the **β pleated sheet.** As shown above, in this structure two or more regions of the polypeptide chain lying side by side are connected by hydrogen bonds between parts of the two parallel polypeptide backbones. Pleated sheets make up the core of many globular proteins, as is the case for transthyretin, and dominate some fibrous proteins, including the silk protein of a spider's web. The teamwork of so many hydrogen bonds makes each spider silk fiber stronger than a steel strand of the same weight.

Abdominal glands of the spider secrete silk fibers that form the web.

The radiating strands, made of dry silk fibers, maintain the shape of the web.

The spiral strands (capture strands) are elastic, stretching in response to wind, rain, and the touch of insects.

Spider silk: a structural protein containing β pleated sheets

TERTIARY STRUCTURE

QUATERNARY STRUCTURE

Superimposed on the patterns of secondary structure is a protein's **tertiary structure,** shown above for the transthyretin polypeptide. Rather than involving interactions between backbone constituents, tertiary structure is the overall shape of a polypeptide resulting from interactions between the side chains (R groups) of the various amino acids. One type of interaction that contributes to tertiary structure is—somewhat misleadingly—called a **hydrophobic interaction.** As a polypeptide folds into its functional conformation, amino acids with hydrophobic (nonpolar) side chains usually end up in clusters at the core of the protein, out of contact with water. Thus, what we call a hydrophobic interaction is actually caused by the action of water molecules, which exclude nonpolar substances as they form hydrogen bonds with each other and with hydrophilic parts of the protein. Once nonpolar amino acid side chains are close together, van der Waals interactions help hold them together. Meanwhile, hydrogen bonds between polar side chains and ionic bonds between positively and negatively charged side chains also help stabilize tertiary structure. These are all weak interactions, but their cumulative effect helps give the protein a unique shape.

The conformation of a protein may be reinforced further by covalent bonds called **disulfide bridges.** Disulfide bridges form where two cysteine monomers, amino acids with sulfhydryl groups (—SH) on their side chains, are brought close together by the folding of the protein. The sulfur of one cysteine bonds to the sulfur of the second, and the disulfide bridge (—S—S—) rivets parts of the protein together (see yellow lines in Figure 5.19a). All of these different kinds of bonds can occur in one protein, as shown above in a small part of a hypothetical protein.

Hydrophobic interactions and van der Waals interactions

— Polypeptide backbone

Hydrogen bond

Disulfide bridge

Ionic bond

Some proteins consist of two or more polypeptide chains aggregated into one functional macromolecule. **Quaternary structure** is the overall protein structure that results from the aggregation of these polypeptide subunits. For example, shown above is the complete, globular transthyretin protein, made up of its four polypeptides. Another example is collagen, shown on the right, which is a fibrous protein that has helical subunits intertwined into a larger triple helix, giving the long fibers great strength. This suits collagen fibers to their function as the girders of connective tissue in skin, bone, tendons, ligaments, and other body parts (collagen accounts for 40% of the protein in a human body). Hemoglobin, the oxygen-binding protein of red blood cells shown below, is another example of a globular protein with quaternary structure. It consists of four polypeptide subunits, two of one kind (α chains) and two of another kind (β chains). Both α and β subunits consist primarily of α-helical secondary structure. Each subunit has a nonpolypeptide component, called heme, with an iron atom that binds oxygen.

Polypeptide chain

Collagen

β Chains

Iron

Heme

α Chains

Hemoglobin

Sickle-Cell Disease: A Simple Change in Primary Structure

Even a slight change in primary structure can affect a protein's conformation and ability to function. For instance, the substitution of one amino acid (valine) for the normal one (glutamic acid) at a particular position in the primary structure of hemoglobin, the protein that carries oxygen in red blood cells, can cause *sickle-cell disease*, an inherited blood disorder. Normal red blood cells are disk-shaped, but in sickle-cell disease, the abnormal hemoglobin molecules tend to crystallize, deforming some of the cells into a sickle shape (Figure 5.21). The life of someone with the disease is punctuated by 'sickle-cell crises,' which occur when the angular cells clog tiny blood vessels, impeding blood flow. The toll taken on such patients is a dramatic example of how a simple change in protein structure can have devastating effects on protein function.

What Determines Protein Conformation?

You've learned that a unique shape endows each protein with a specific function. But what are the key factors determining protein conformation? You already know most of the answer: A polypeptide chain of a given amino acid sequence can spontaneously arrange itself into a three-dimensional shape determined and maintained by the interactions responsible for secondary and tertiary structure. This folding normally occurs as the protein is being synthesized within the cell. However, protein conformation also depends on the physical and chemical conditions of the protein's environment. If the pH, salt concentration, temperature, or other aspects of its environment are altered, the protein may unravel and lose its native conformation, a change called **denaturation** (Figure 5.22). Because it is misshapen, the denatured protein is biologically inactive.

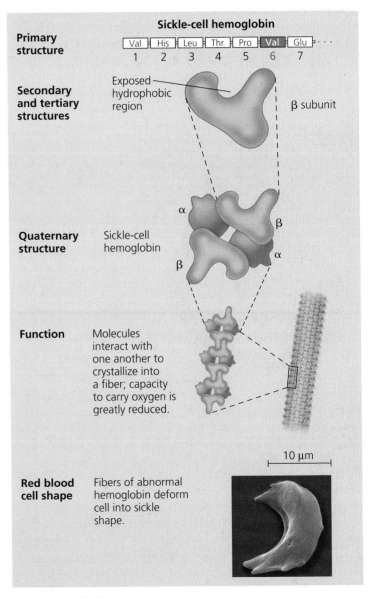

▲ Figure 5.21 **A single amino acid substitution in a protein causes sickle-cell disease.**
To show fiber formation clearly, the orientation of the hemoglobin molecule here is different from that in Figure 5.20.

Denaturation

Normal protein

Denatured protein

Renaturation

變性 /diː.neɪt(ə'reɪʃən/

▲ **Figure 5.22 Denaturation and renaturation of a protein.**
High temperatures or various chemical treatments will denature a protein, causing it to lose its conformation and hence its ability to function. If the denatured protein remains dissolved, it can often renature when the chemical and physical aspects of its environment are restored to normal.

Most proteins become denatured if they are transferred from an aqueous environment to an organic solvent, such as ether or chloroform; the polypeptide chain refolds so that its hydrophobic regions face outward toward the solvent. Other denaturation agents include chemicals that disrupt the hydrogen bonds, ionic bonds, and disulfide bridges that maintain a protein's shape. Denaturation can also result from excessive heat, which agitates the polypeptide chain enough to overpower the weak interactions that stabilize conformation. The white of an egg becomes opaque during cooking because the denatured proteins are insoluble and solidify. This also explains why extremely high fevers can be fatal: Proteins in the blood become denatured by such high body temperatures.

When a protein in a test-tube solution has been denatured by heat or chemicals, it will often return to its functional shape when the denaturing agent is removed. We can conclude that the information for building specific shape is intrinsic to the protein's primary structure. The sequence of amino acids determines conformation—where an α helix can form, where β pleated sheets can occur, where disulfide bridges are located, where ionic bonds can form, and so on. However, in the crowded environment inside a cell, correct folding may be more of a problem than it is in a test tube.

The Protein-Folding Problem

Biochemists now know the amino acid sequences of more than 875,000 proteins and the three-dimensional shapes of about 7,000. One would think that by correlating the primary structures of many proteins with their conformations, it would be relatively easy to discover the rules of protein folding. Unfortunately, the protein-folding problem is not that simple. Most proteins probably go through several intermediate states on their way to a stable conformation, and looking at the mature conformation does not reveal the stages of folding required to achieve that form. However, biochemists have developed methods for tracking a protein through its intermediate stages of folding. Researchers have also discovered **chaperonins** (also called chaperone proteins), protein molecules that assist the proper folding of other proteins **(Figure 5.23)**. Chaperonins do not actually specify the correct final structure of a polypeptide. Instead, they work by keeping the new polypeptide segregated from "bad influences" in the cytoplasmic environment while it folds spontaneously. The well-studied chaperonin shown in Figure 5.23, from the bacterium *E. coli,* is a giant multiprotein complex shaped like a hollow cylinder. The cavity provides a shelter for folding polypeptides of various types.

Even when scientists have an actual protein in hand, determining its exact three-dimensional structure is not simple, for a single protein molecule is built of thousands of atoms. **X-ray crystallography** is an important method used to determine a protein's three-dimensional structure **(Figure 5.24)**. Another method that has recently been applied to this problem is nuclear magnetic resonance (NMR) spectroscopy, which does not require protein crystallization. These approaches have contributed greatly to our understanding of protein structure and have also given us valuable hints about protein function.

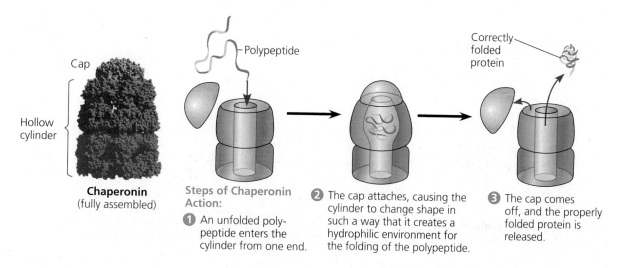

▶ **Figure 5.23**
A chaperonin in action. The computer graphic (left) shows a large chaperonin protein complex with an interior space that provides a shelter for the proper folding of newly made polypeptides. The complex consists of two proteins: One protein is a hollow cylinder; the other is a cap that can fit on either end.

Cap

Hollow cylinder

Chaperonin (fully assembled)

Polypeptide

Correctly folded protein

Steps of Chaperonin Action:
1. An unfolded polypeptide enters the cylinder from one end.
2. The cap attaches, causing the cylinder to change shape in such a way that it creates a hydrophilic environment for the folding of the polypeptide.
3. The cap comes off, and the properly folded protein is released.

Figure 5.24
X-Ray Crystallography

APPLICATION Scientists use X-ray crystallography to determine the three-dimensional structure of macromolecules such as nucleic acids and proteins. In this figure we will examine how researchers at the University of California, Riverside, determined the structure of the protein ribonuclease, an enzyme whose function involves binding to a nucleic acid molecule.

TECHNIQUE Researchers aim an X-ray beam through the crystallized protein. The atoms of the crystal diffract (deflect) the X-rays into an orderly array. The diffracted X-rays expose photographic film, producing a pattern of spots known as an X-ray diffraction pattern.

RESULTS Using data from X-ray diffraction patterns, as well as the amino acid sequence determined by chemical methods, scientists build a 3D computer model of the protein, such as this model of the protein ribonuclease (purple) bound to a short strand of nucleic acid (green).

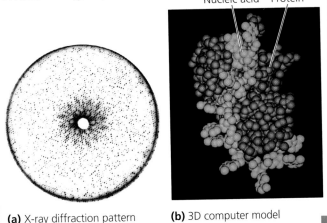

(a) X-ray diffraction pattern   **(b)** 3D computer model

Concept Check 5.4

1. Why does a denatured protein no longer function normally?
2. Differentiate between secondary and tertiary structure by describing the parts of the polypeptide chain that participate in the bonds that hold together each level of structure.
3. A genetic mutation can change a protein's primary structure. How can this destroy the protein's function?

For suggested answers, see Appendix A.

Concept 5.5

Nucleic acids store and transmit hereditary information

If the primary structure of polypeptides determines the conformation of a protein, what determines primary structure? The amino acid sequence of a polypeptide is programmed by a unit of inheritance known as a **gene**. Genes consist of DNA, which is a polymer belonging to the class of compounds known as **nucleic acids**.

The Roles of Nucleic Acids

There are two types of nucleic acids: **deoxyribonucleic acid (DNA)** and **ribonucleic acid (RNA)**. These are the molecules that enable living organisms to reproduce their complex components from one generation to the next. Unique among molecules, DNA provides directions for its own replication. DNA also directs RNA synthesis and, through RNA, controls protein synthesis **(Figure 5.25)**.

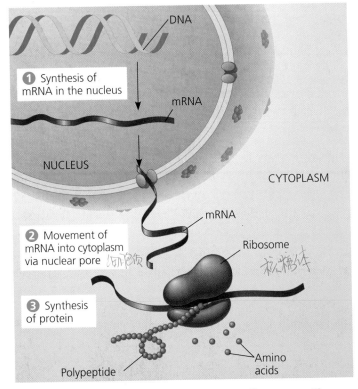

▲ **Figure 5.25 DNA → RNA → protein: a diagrammatic overview of information flow in a cell.** In a eukaryotic cell, DNA in the nucleus programs protein production in the cytoplasm by dictating the synthesis of messenger RNA (mRNA), which travels to the cytoplasm and binds to ribosomes. As a ribosome (greatly enlarged in this drawing) moves along the mRNA, the genetic message is translated into a polypeptide of specific amino acid sequence.

DNA is the genetic material that organisms inherit from their parents. Each chromosome contains one long DNA molecule, usually consisting of from several hundred to more than a thousand genes. When a cell reproduces itself by dividing, its DNA molecules are copied and passed along from one generation of cells to the next. Encoded in the structure of DNA is the information that programs all the cell's activities. The DNA, however, is not directly involved in running the operations of the cell, any more than computer software by itself can print a bank statement or read the bar code on a box of cereal. Just as a printer is needed to print out a statement and a scanner is needed to read a bar code, proteins are required to implement genetic programs. The molecular hardware of the cell—the tools for most biological functions—consists of proteins. For example, the oxygen carrier in the blood is the protein hemoglobin, not the DNA that specifies its structure.

How does RNA, the other type of nucleic acid, fit into the flow of genetic information from DNA to proteins? Each gene along the length of a DNA molecule directs the synthesis of a type of RNA called *messenger RNA* (mRNA). The mRNA molecule then interacts with the cell's protein-synthesizing machinery to direct the production of a polypeptide. We can summarize the flow of genetic information as DNA → RNA → protein (see Figure 5.25). The actual sites of protein synthesis are cellular structures called ribosomes. In a eukaryotic cell, ribosomes are located in the cytoplasm, but DNA resides in the nucleus. Messenger RNA conveys the genetic instructions for building proteins from the nucleus to the cytoplasm. Prokaryotic cells lack nuclei, but they still use RNA to send a message from the DNA to the ribosomes and other equipment of the cell that translate the coded information into amino acid sequences.

The Structure of Nucleic Acids

Nucleic acids are macromolecules that exist as polymers called **polynucleotides** (**Figure 5.26a**). As indicated by the name, each polynucleotide consists of monomers called **nucleotides**. A nucleotide is itself composed of three parts: a nitrogenous base, a pentose (five-carbon sugar), and a phosphate group (**Figure 5.26b**). The portion of this unit without the phosphate group is called a *nucleoside*.

▲ Figure 5.26 **The components of nucleic acids. (a)** A polynucleotide has a regular sugar-phosphate backbone with variable appendages, the four kinds of nitrogenous bases. RNA usually exists in the form of a single polynucleotide, like the one shown here. **(b)** A nucleotide monomer is made up of three components: a nitrogenous base, a sugar, and a phosphate group, linked together as shown here. Without the phosphate group, the resulting structure is called a nucleoside. **(c)** The components of the nucleoside include a nitrogenous base (either a purine or a pyrimidine) and a pentose sugar (either deoxyribose or ribose).

Nucleotide Monomers

To build a nucleotide, let's first consider the two components of the nucleoside: the nitrogenous base and the sugar **(Figure 5.26c)**. There are two families of nitrogenous bases: pyrimidines and purines. A **pyrimidine** has a six-membered ring of carbon and nitrogen atoms. (The nitrogen atoms tend to take up H⁺ from solution, which explains the term *nitrogenous base*.) The members of the pyrimidine family are cytosine (C), thymine (T), and uracil (U). **Purines** are larger, with a six-membered ring fused to a five-membered ring. The purines are adenine (A) and guanine (G). The specific pyrimidines and purines differ in the functional groups attached to the rings. Adenine, guanine, and cytosine are found in both types of nucleic acid; thymine is found only in DNA and uracil only in RNA.

The pentose connected to the nitrogenous base is **ribose** in the nucleotides of RNA and **deoxyribose** in DNA (see Figure 5.26c). The only difference between these two sugars is that deoxyribose lacks an oxygen atom on the second carbon in the ring; hence its name. Because the atoms in both the nitrogenous base and the sugar are numbered, the sugar atoms have a prime (′) after the number to distinguish them. Thus, the second carbon in the sugar ring is the 2′ ("2 prime") carbon, and the carbon that sticks up from the ring is called the 5′ carbon.

So far, we have built a nucleoside. To complete the construction of a nucleotide, we attach a phosphate group to the 5′ carbon of the sugar (see Figure 5.26b). The molecule is now a nucleoside monophosphate, better known as a nucleotide.

Nucleotide Polymers

Now we can see how these nucleotides are linked together to build a polynucleotide. Adjacent nucleotides are joined by covalent bonds called phosphodiester linkages between the —OH group on the 3′ carbon of one nucleotide and the phosphate on the 5′ carbon of the next. This bonding results in a backbone with a repeating pattern of sugar-phosphate units (see Figure 5.26a). The two free ends of the polymer are distinctly different from each other. One end has a phosphate attached to a 5′ carbon, and the other end has a hydroxyl group on a 3′ carbon; we refer to these as the 5′ end and the 3′ end, respectively. So we can say that the DNA strand has a built-in directionality along its sugar-phosphate backbone, from 5′ to 3′, somewhat like a one-way street. All along this sugar-phosphate backbone are appendages consisting of the nitrogenous bases.

The sequence of bases along a DNA (or mRNA) polymer is unique for each gene. Because genes are hundreds to thousands of nucleotides long, the number of possible base sequences is effectively limitless. A gene's meaning to the cell is encoded in its specific sequence of the four DNA bases. For example, the sequence AGGTAACTT means one thing, whereas the sequence CGCTTTAAC has a different meaning. (Real genes, of course, are much longer.) The linear order of bases in a gene specifies the amino acid sequence—the primary structure—of a protein, which in turn specifies that protein's three-dimensional conformation and function in the cell.

The DNA Double Helix

The RNA molecules of cells consist of a single polynucleotide chain like the one shown in Figure 5.26. In contrast, cellular DNA molecules have two polynucleotides that spiral around an imaginary axis, forming a **double helix (Figure 5.27)**. James Watson and Francis Crick, working at Cambridge University,

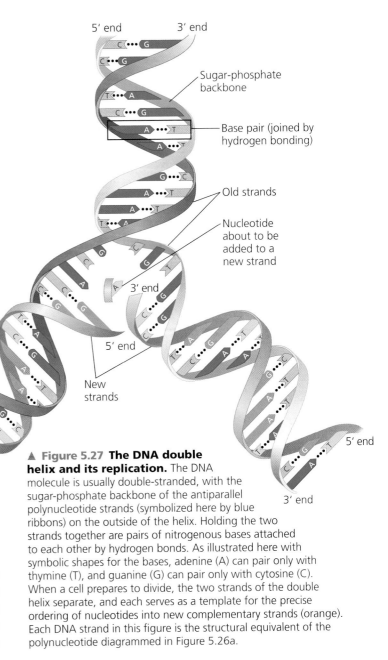

▲ **Figure 5.27 The DNA double helix and its replication.** The DNA molecule is usually double-stranded, with the sugar-phosphate backbone of the antiparallel polynucleotide strands (symbolized here by blue ribbons) on the outside of the helix. Holding the two strands together are pairs of nitrogenous bases attached to each other by hydrogen bonds. As illustrated here with symbolic shapes for the bases, adenine (A) can pair only with thymine (T), and guanine (G) can pair only with cytosine (C). When a cell prepares to divide, the two strands of the double helix separate, and each serves as a template for the precise ordering of nucleotides into new complementary strands (orange). Each DNA strand in this figure is the structural equivalent of the polynucleotide diagrammed in Figure 5.26a.

first proposed the double helix as the three-dimensional structure of DNA in 1953. The two sugar-phosphate backbones run in opposite $5' \rightarrow 3'$ directions from each other, an arrangement referred to as **antiparallel**, somewhat like a divided highway. The sugar-phosphate backbones are on the outside of the helix, and the nitrogenous bases are paired in the interior of the helix. The two polynucleotides, or strands, as they are called, are held together by hydrogen bonds between the paired bases and by van der Waals interactions between the stacked bases. Most DNA molecules are very long, with thousands or even millions of base pairs connecting the two chains. One long DNA double helix includes many genes, each one a particular segment of the molecule.

Only certain bases in the double helix are compatible with each other. Adenine (A) always pairs with thymine (T), and guanine (G) always pairs with cytosine (C). If we were to read the sequence of bases along one strand as we traveled the length of the double helix, we would know the sequence of bases along the other strand. If a stretch of one strand has the base sequence 5'-AGGTCCG-3', then the base-pairing rules tell us that the same stretch of the other strand must have the sequence 3'-TCCAGGC-5'. The two strands of the double helix are *complementary*, each the predictable counterpart of the other. It is this feature of DNA that makes possible the precise copying of genes that is responsible for inheritance (see Figure 5.27). In preparation for cell division, each of the two strands of a DNA molecule serves as a template to order nucleotides into a new complementary strand. The result is two identical copies of the original double-stranded DNA molecule, which are then distributed to the two daughter cells. Thus, the structure of DNA accounts for its function in transmitting genetic information whenever a cell reproduces.

DNA and Proteins as Tape Measures of Evolution

We are accustomed to thinking of shared traits, such as hair and milk production in mammals, as evidence of shared ancestors. Because we now understand that DNA carries heritable information in the form of genes, we can see that genes and their products (proteins) document the hereditary background of an organism. The linear sequences of nucleotides in DNA molecules are passed from parents to offspring; these sequences determine the amino acid sequences of proteins. Siblings have greater similarity in their DNA and proteins than do unrelated individuals of the same species. If the evolutionary view of life is valid, we should be able to extend this concept of "molecular genealogy" to relationships *between* species: We should expect two species that appear to be closely related based on fossil and anatomical evidence to also share a greater proportion of their DNA and protein sequences than do more distantly related species. In fact, that is the case. For example, if we compare a polypeptide chain of human hemoglobin with the corresponding hemoglobin polypeptide in five other vertebrates, we find

the following. In this chain of 146 amino acids, humans and gorillas differ in just 1 amino acid, humans and gibbons differ in 2 amino acids, and humans and rhesus monkeys differ in 8 amino acids. More distantly related species have chains that are less similar. Humans and mice differ in 27 amino acids, and humans and frogs differ in 67 amino acids. Molecular biology has added a new tape measure to the toolkit biologists use to assess evolutionary kinship.

Concept Check 5.5

1. Go to Figure 5.26a and number all the carbons in the sugars for the top three nucleotides; circle the nitrogenous bases and star the phosphates.
2. In a DNA double helix, a region along one DNA strand has this sequence of nitrogenous bases: 5'-TAGGCCT-3'. List the base sequence along the other strand of the molecule, clearly indicating the 5' and 3' ends of this strand.

For suggested answers, see Appendix A.

The Theme of Emergent Properties in the Chemistry of Life: *A Review*

Recall that life is organized along a hierarchy of structural levels (see Figure 1.3). With each increasing level of order, new properties emerge in addition to those of the component parts. In Chapters 2–5, we have dissected the chemistry of life using the strategy of the reductionist. But we have also begun to develop a more integrated view of life as we have seen how properties emerge with increasing order.

We have seen that the unusual behavior of water, so essential to life on Earth, results from interactions of the water molecules, themselves an ordered arrangement of hydrogen and oxygen atoms. We reduced the great complexity and diversity of organic compounds to the chemical characteristics of carbon, but we also saw that the unique properties of organic compounds are related to the specific structural arrangements of carbon skeletons and their appended functional groups. We learned that small organic molecules are often assembled into giant molecules, but we also discovered that a macromolecule does not behave like a composite of its monomers but rather takes on additional properties owing to the interactions between those monomers.

By completing our overview of the molecular basis of life with an introduction to the important classes of macromolecules that build living cells, we have built a bridge to Unit Two, where we will study the cell's structure and function. We will maintain our balance between the need to reduce life to a conglomerate of simpler processes and the ultimate satisfaction of viewing those processes in their integrated context.

Go to the Campbell Biology website (**www.campbellbiology.com**) or CD-ROM to explore Activities, Investigations, and other interactive study aids.

SUMMARY OF KEY CONCEPTS

Concept 5.1

Most macromolecules are polymers, built from monomers

▶ **The Synthesis and Breakdown of Polymers (pp. 68–69)** Carbohydrates, lipids, proteins, and nucleic acids are the four major classes of organic compounds in cells. Many of these compounds are very large molecules. Most macromolecules are polymers, chains of identical or similar monomers. Monomers form larger molecules by condensation reactions, in which water molecules are released (dehydration). Polymers can disassemble by the reverse process, hydrolysis.
Activity Making and Breaking Polymers

▶ **The Diversity of Polymers (p. 69)** Each class of polymer is formed from a specific set of monomers. Although organisms share the same limited number of monomer types, each organism is unique because of the specific arrangement of monomers into polymers. An immense variety of polymers can be built from a small set of monomers.

Concept 5.2

Carbohydrates serve as fuel and building material

▶ **Sugars (pp. 70–71)** Sugars, the smallest carbohydrates, serve as fuel and carbon sources. Monosaccharides are the simplest sugars. They are used for fuel, converted to other organic molecules, or combined into polymers. Disaccharides consist of two monosaccharides connected by a glycosidic linkage.
Activity Models of Glucose

▶ **Polysaccharides (pp. 71–74)** Polysaccharides, polymers of sugars, have storage and structural roles. The monomers of polysaccharides are connected by glycosidic linkages. Starch in plants and glycogen in animals are both storage polymers of glucose. Cellulose is an important structural polymer of glucose in plant cell walls. Starch, glycogen, and cellulose differ in the positions and orientations of their glycosidic linkages.
Activity Carbohydrates

Concept 5.3

Lipids are a diverse group of hydrophobic molecules

▶ **Fats (pp. 75–76)** Fats store large amounts of energy. Also known as triacylglycerols, fats are constructed by the joining of a glycerol molecule to three fatty acids by dehydration reactions. Saturated fatty acids have the maximum number of hydrogen atoms. Unsaturated fatty acids (present in oils) have one or more double bonds in their hydrocarbon chains.

▶ **Phospholipids (pp. 76–77)** Phospholipids, which are major components of cell membranes, consist of two fatty acids and a phosphate group linked to glycerol. Thus, the "head" of a phospholipid is hydrophilic and the "tail" hydrophobic.

▶ **Steroids (p. 77)** Steroids include cholesterol and certain hormones. Steroids have a basic structure of four fused rings of carbon atoms.
Activity Lipids

Concept 5.4

Proteins have many structures, resulting in a wide range of functions

▶ **Polypeptides (pp. 78–81)** A polypeptide is a polymer of amino acids connected in a specific sequence. A protein consists of one or more polypeptide chains folded into a specific three-dimensional conformation. Polypeptides are constructed from 20 different amino acids, each with a characteristic side chain (R group). The carboxyl and amino groups of adjacent amino acids link together in peptide bonds.

▶ **Protein Conformation and Function (pp. 81–86)** The primary structure of a protein is its unique sequence of amino acids. Secondary structure is the folding or coiling of the polypeptide into repeating configurations, mainly the α helix and the β pleated sheet, which result from hydrogen bonding between parts of the polypeptide backbone. Tertiary structure is the overall three-dimensional shape of a polypeptide and results from interactions between amino acid R groups. Proteins made of more than one polypeptide chain have a quaternary level of structure. Protein shape is ultimately determined by its primary structure, but the structure and function of a protein are sensitive to physical and chemical conditions.
Activity Protein Functions
Activity Protein Structure
Biology Labs On-Line HemoglobinLab

Concept 5.5

Nucleic acids store and transmit hereditary information

▶ **The Roles of Nucleic Acids (pp. 86–87)** DNA stores information for the synthesis of specific proteins. RNA (specifically, mRNA) carries this genetic information to the protein-synthesizing machinery.

▶ **The Structure of Nucleic Acids (pp. 87–88)** Each nucleotide monomer consists of a pentose covalently bonded to a phosphate group and to one of four different nitrogenous bases (A, G, C, and T or U). RNA has ribose as its pentose; DNA has deoxyribose. RNA has U; DNA, T. In a polynucleotide, nucleotides are joined to form a sugar-phosphate backbone from which the nitrogenous bases project. Each polynucleotide strand has polarity, with a 5′ end and a 3′ end. The sequence of bases along a gene specifies the amino acid sequence of a particular protein.

▶ **The DNA Double Helix (pp. 88–89)** DNA is a helical, double-stranded macromolecule with bases projecting into the interior of the molecule from the two antiparallel polynucleotide strands. Because A always hydrogen-bonds to T, and C to G, the nucleotide sequences of the two strands are complementary. One strand can serve as a template for the formation of the other. This unique feature of DNA provides a mechanism for the continuity of life.

▶ **DNA and Proteins as Tape Measures of Evolution (p. 89)** Molecular comparisons help biologists sort out the evolutionary connections among species.
Activity Nucleic Acid Functions
Activity Nucleic Acid Structure

• • •

▶ **The Theme of Emergent Properties in the Chemistry of Life: A Review (p. 89)** Higher levels of organization result in the emergence of new properties. Organization is the key to the chemistry of life.

Self-Quiz

1. Which term includes all others in the list?
   a. monosaccharide
   b. disaccharide
   c. starch
   d. carbohydrate
   e. polysaccharide

2. The molecular formula for glucose is $C_6H_{12}O_6$. What would be the molecular formula for a polymer made by linking ten glucose molecules together by dehydration reactions?
   a. $C_{60}H_{120}O_{60}$
   b. $C_6H_{12}O_6$
   c. $C_{60}H_{102}O_{51}$
   d. $C_{60}H_{100}O_{50}$
   e. $C_{60}H_{111}O_{51}$

3. The enzyme amylase can break glycosidic linkages between glucose monomers only if the monomers are the α form. Which of the following could amylase break down? (Choose all that apply.)
   a. cellulose
   b. chitin
   c. glycogen
   d. starch
   e. amylopectin

4. Choose the pair of terms that correctly completes this sentence: Nucleotides are to _____ as _____ are to proteins.
   a. nucleic acids; amino acids
   b. amino acids; polypeptides
   c. glycosidic linkages; polypeptide linkages
   d. genes; enzymes
   e. polymers; polypeptides

5. Which of the following statements concerning *unsaturated* fats is true?
   a. They are more common in animals than in plants.
   b. They have double bonds in the carbon chains of their fatty acids.
   c. They generally solidify at room temperature.
   d. They contain more hydrogen than saturated fats having the same number of carbon atoms.
   e. They have fewer fatty acid molecules per fat molecule.

6. The structural level of a protein least affected by a disruption in hydrogen bonding is the
   a. primary level.
   b. secondary level.
   c. tertiary level.
   d. quaternary level.
   e. All structural levels are equally affected.

7. Which of the following pairs of base sequences could form a short stretch of a normal double helix of DNA?
   a. 5′-purine-pyrimidine-purine-pyrimidine-3′ with 3′-purine-pyrimidine-purine-pyrimidine-5′
   b. 5′-A-G-C-T-3′ with 5′-T-C-G-A-3′
   c. 5′-G-C-G-C-3′ with 5′-T-A-T-A-3′
   d. 5′-A-T-G-C-3′ with 5′-G-C-A-T-3′
   e. a, b, and d are all correct

8. Enzymes that break down DNA catalyze the hydrolysis of the covalent bonds that join nucleotides together. What would happen to DNA molecules treated with these enzymes?
   a. The two strands of the double helix would separate.
   b. The phosphodiester bonds between deoxyribose sugars would be broken.
   c. The purines would be separated from the deoxyribose sugars.
   d. The pyrimidines would be separated from the deoxyribose sugars.
   e. All bases would be separated from the deoxyribose sugars.

9. Which of the following is *not* a protein?
   a. hemoglobin
   b. cholesterol
   c. an antibody
   d. an enzyme
   e. insulin

10. Which of the following statements about the 5′ end of a polynucleotide strand is correct?
    a. The 5′ end has a hydroxyl group.
    b. The 5′ end has a phosphate group.
    c. The 5′ end is identical to the 3′ end.
    d. The 5′ end is antiparallel to the 3′ end.
    e. The 5′ end is the fifth position on one of the nitrogenous bases.

For Self-Quiz answers, see Appendix A.

Go to the website or CD-ROM for more quiz questions.

Evolution Connection

Comparisons of the amino acid sequences of proteins or the nucleotide sequences of genes can shed light on the evolutionary divergence of related organisms. Would you expect all the proteins or genes of a given set of organisms living on Earth today to show the same degree of divergence? Why or why not?

Scientific Inquiry

During the Napoleonic Wars in the early 1800s, there was a sugar shortage in Europe because supply ships were blockaded from harbors. To create artificial sweeteners, German scientists hydrolyzed wheat starch. They did this by adding hydrochloric acid to heated starch solutions, which caused some of the glycosidic linkages between the glucose monomers to break. The process broke only about 50% of the glycosidic linkages, however, so the sweetener was less sweet than sugar. In addition, consumers complained of a slight bitterness resulting from by-products of the reaction. Sketch a glycosidic linkage in starch using Figures 5.5a and 5.7b for reference. Show how the acid was able to break this bond. Why do you think the acid broke only 50% of the linkages in the wheat starch?

Biological Inquiry: A Workbook of Investigative Cases *Explore macromolecules further with the case "Picture Perfect."*
Biology Labs On-Line *HemoglobinLab*

Science, Technology, and Society

Some amateur and professional athletes take anabolic steroids to help them "bulk up" or build strength. The health risks of this practice are extensively documented. Apart from health considerations, how do you feel about the use of chemicals to enhance athletic performance? Do you think an athlete who takes anabolic steroids is cheating, or is the use of such chemicals just part of the preparation required to succeed in a competitive sport? Defend your answer.

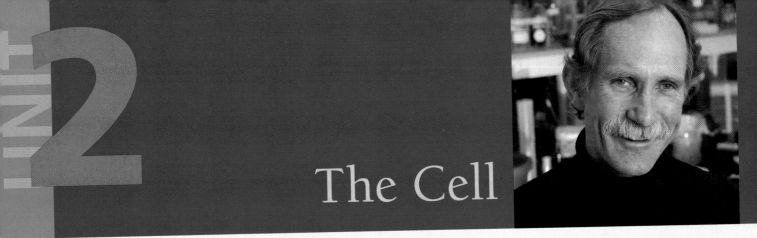

The Cell

AN INTERVIEW WITH
Peter Agre

In 2003 Peter Agre received the Nobel Prize in Chemistry for the discovery of aquaporins, "water pore" proteins that allow water molecules to rapidly cross the cell membrane. (He shared the prize with Roderick MacKinnon of Rockefeller University, who works on the other main aspect of cellular "plumbing"—the transport of ions.) A medical doctor as well as a researcher in basic science, Dr. Agre is a professor in the Departments of Biological Chemistry and Medicine at the Johns Hopkins University School of Medicine.

How did you start in science?

As a little kid, really. I grew up in Northfield, Minnesota, where my dad was teaching chemistry at St. Olaf College. The kids in our family had an idyllic life, playing in apple orchards and roaming the campus. We lived right across the street from my dad's laboratory, a really nice lab with cheerful students who did summer research. I'd do little experiments with my father's help. We'd change the pH of some solution, and the indicator dye would turn pink or blue—it was amazing! As an adolescent I didn't want anything to do with any of that. But the first merit badge I ever earned as a Boy Scout was in chemistry. Then I became more interested in medicine.

What was the appeal of medicine?

In part, the people. The local doctors were really interesting and nice people, and it seemed like they did a lot of good things.

High school was a bit of a detour—I was kind of a hellraiser then. My friends and I started an underground newspaper (this was 1967, and I thought a revolution was about to occur). I didn't do a lot of school work. So I was invited to leave high school. I went to night school and then got into Augsberg College.

What turned you on to research?

At medical school, I spent time in a research lab, and that really fired me up. I got to work with a group of vibrant scientists from all over the world. I learned you could approach complex problems at a molecular level—reductionist biology. We purified a variant of cholera toxin produced by certain strains of the bacterium *E. coli*. Like the toxin of the true cholera bacterium (*Vibrio cholerae*), this can cause a terrible and sometimes fatal diarrhea.

If young people saw scientists the way I did in that lab, they would all want to be scientists. Too many people still stereotype scientists in a negative way—something like Doc from *Back to the Future*. I'm afraid we've lost good role models in science. And too often we scientists are so stressed out trying to get grants funded that our work doesn't look appealing to students.

People need to realize how much science is a social endeavor. Scientists have personalities and interests and fears and limitations. We're not cybertronic machines. And we collaborate. Unless you're at the level of Leonardo da Vinci, you get a lot of ideas from other people.

Tell us about combining medical practice with basic research.

Until 1993, I was an attending physician in Hematology here. I stopped in part because I was busy with starting a new graduate program in cellular and molecular medicine. (It provides Ph.D. training in basic science but with direct medical relevance.) Combining medical practice with basic research is a challenge because there are only so many hours in the day. I'm married with four children, and, as much as I liked my patients, my heart was more in the research. In practicing medicine, you can help individual patients, but with research, you might make a discovery that would help thousands of patients. As a student, I doubted I had what it took to succeed in basic science, but I wanted to try it.

I still have my medical license, which I use for Boy Scout camp physicals, ringside positions as medical doctor to amateur wrestlers, and inner city kids—I'm their doc. Anyway, my wife's not convinced that research is going to carry me to retirement. She may be right. I think it's better in life not to be overconfident.

Let's talk about the research that led to the discovery of aquaporins.

I'm a blood specialist (hematologist), and my particular interest has been proteins found in the plasma membrane of red blood cells. The plasma membrane is a phospholipid bilayer with inserted cholesterol molecules, "integral" proteins that span the bilayer, and membrane-associated proteins that bind to the membrane's inner surface. With red cells, it's easy to study plasma membrane in pure form, and there are interesting disorders associated with defects in the proteins.

When I joined the faculty at Hopkins, I began to study the Rh blood antigens. Blood group antigens are membrane glycoproteins of red cells that exist in the population in two or more forms. The differences can be in the attached carbohydrate, as with the antigens of the ABO blood groups (see Chapter 43), or they can be within the core protein. Rh is of medical importance because of Rh incompatibility, which occurs when Rh negative mothers have Rh positive babies and become sensitized to the Rh antigen. Unless the mother is treated, there's a significant risk that in subsequent pregnancies, her immune system will attack the baby's red blood cells. Surprisingly, as of the late 1980s, no one had yet been able to isolate the Rh antigen.

Membrane-spanning proteins like the Rh protein are really messy to work with. But we worked out a method to isolate and partially purify the Rh protein. Our sample seemed to consist of two proteins, but we were sure that the smaller one was just a breakdown product of the larger one. We were completely wrong, though: It was a water channel protein, which we later named aquaporin-1.

How did you figure that out?

It took a lot of convincing to make myself believe that this protein was even a new discovery. Using antibodies we made to the protein, we showed it to be one of the most abundant proteins in red cell membranes (200,000 copies per cell!) and even more abundant in certain renal (kidney) cells. I talked to 15 or so membrane biochemists: What could it be? Although many people study red cells, no one had ever seen this protein before because it doesn't stain with the usual protein stains. It was John Parker, a hematologist and superb red-cell physiologist, who finally said, "Maybe this protein is involved in water transport."

To test this hypothesis, we performed a simple experiment using frog egg cells: We injected the cells with mRNA that the cells translated into aquaporin and found that we could turn the cells from being almost watertight (without aquaporin) into highly water-permeable (with aquaporin). The cells with aquaporin would swell and explode in distilled water as a result of osmosis: With aquaporins, the cell membrane became permeable to water but not to things dissolved in it (solutes), so water molecules crossed the membrane from the side with less solute (distilled water) to the side with more (the cell interior).

You know, as a scientist, you can benefit from being a bit like Huckleberry Finn. You should explore your fancy to some degree. If something interesting shows up, it's good to go for it.

Why do cells have water channel proteins?

Not all cells do. Before our discovery, however, many physiologists thought that diffusion through the phospholipid bilayer was enough for getting water into and out of *all* cells. Others said this couldn't be enough, especially for cells whose water permeability needs to be very high or regulated—for example, cells forming the tubules of the kidneys, which control the concentration of the urine. A number of researchers had made observations indicating that diffusion through the phospholipid bilayer wasn't everything. But there was a lot of skepticism until our experiment with frog eggs ended the controversy.

Water transport is very important in our bodies. For example, our kidneys must filter and reabsorb many liters of water every day. If we don't reabsorb that water, we die of dehydration. Aquaporins allow us to reabsorb enough water, without reabsorbing ions.

How do aquaporins work?

The structure of an aquaporin molecule helps explain how it functions. The protein looks like an hourglass spanning the membrane. The two halves are symmetrical with opposite orientations. An hourglass works equally well if it's

right side up or upside down, and aquaporins work equally well for the uptake or release of water. The driving force is not some kind of a pump action, but simply osmosis. An aquaporin allows osmosis to occur extremely rapidly. Nothing larger than water molecules can fit through the channel. In addition, the passage of ions is prevented—even small ones like the hydronium ions (H_3O^+) formed by the combining of H^+ with H_2O (see p. 51). They are repelled by positively charged amino acids at the narrowest part of the channel.

What happens when mutations disrupt aquaporin function?

Mutations in aquaporin genes can cause health problems. People whose kidney cells have defective aquaporin-2 molecules need to drink 20 liters of water a day to prevent dehydration. They can't concentrate their urine enough. Individuals who can't make aquaporin-1 generally do OK in modern life, but they get dehydrated much more easily than other people. In addition, some patients make too much aquaporin, causing them to retain too much fluid. Fluid retention in pregnant women is caused by the synthesis of too much aquaporin-2.

Knowledge of aquaporins may in the future contribute to the *solution* of medical problems. Specific aquaporins, such as those of the malaria parasite, might be useful targets for new drugs.

What has the study of aquaporins revealed about evolution?

Several hundred aquaporins are known so far. Plants have the most; rice has around 50, whereas mammals have only about 10. Apparently, aquaporins are even more important for plants than animals. The presence of aquaporins in almost all organisms and similarities among the molecules suggest that aquaporin arose very early in evolution.

What are your major goals now?

Of great importance to me right now is the success of the next generation of scientists. As a scientist, there are three things that count: original discoveries, the respect of your peers, and training future scientists—and the third is perhaps the most important in the long run. Almost everything we scientists do eventually gets revised. We usually pick up a story and carry it for a while until someone else takes it over. So the educating of young scientists is a big issue, as is scientific literacy for everyone.

"Science is a social endeavor. Scientists have personalities and interests and fears and limitations. We're not cybertronic machines. And we collaborate. Unless you're at the level of Leonardo da Vinci, you get a lot of ideas from other people."

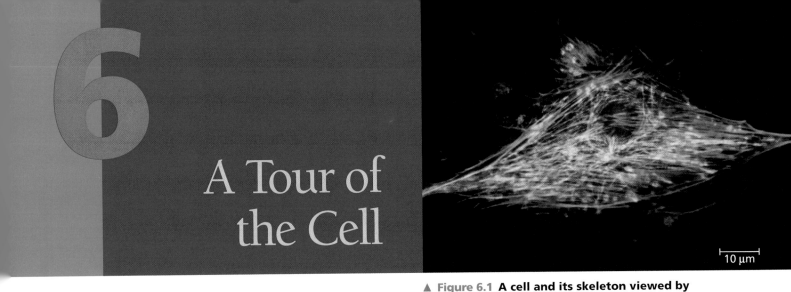

6

A Tour of the Cell

10 μm

▲ Figure 6.1 **A cell and its skeleton viewed by fluorescence microscopy.**

Key Concepts

6.1 To study cells, biologists use microscopes and the tools of biochemistry

6.2 Eukaryotic cells have internal membranes that compartmentalize their functions

6.3 The eukaryotic cell's genetic instructions are housed in the nucleus and carried out by the ribosomes

6.4 The endomembrane system regulates protein traffic and performs metabolic functions in the cell

6.5 Mitochondria and chloroplasts change energy from one form to another

6.6 The cytoskeleton is a network of fibers that organizes structures and activities in the cell

6.7 Extracellular components and connections between cells help coordinate cellular activities

Overview

The Importance of Cells

The cell is as fundamental to biology as the atom is to chemistry: All organisms are made of cells. In the hierarchy of biological organization, the cell is the simplest collection of matter that can live. Indeed, there are diverse forms of life existing as single-celled organisms. More complex organisms, including plants and animals, are multicellular; their bodies are cooperatives of many kinds of specialized cells that could not survive for long on their own. However, even when they are arranged into higher levels of organization, such as tissues and organs, cells can be singled out as the organism's basic units of structure and function. The contraction of muscle cells moves your eyes as you read this sentence; when you decide to turn the next page, nerve cells will transmit that decision from your brain to the muscle cells of your hand. Everything an organism does occurs fundamentally at the cellular level.

The cell is a microcosm that demonstrates most of the themes introduced in Chapter 1. Life at the cellular level arises from structural order, reinforcing the themes of emergent properties and the correlation between structure and function. For example, the movement of an animal cell depends on an intricate interplay of the structures that make up a cellular skeleton (green and red in the micrograph in **Figure 6.1**). Another recurring theme in biology is the interaction of organisms with their environment. Cells sense and respond to environmental fluctuations. And keep in mind the one biological theme that unifies all others: evolution. All cells are related by their descent from earlier cells. However, they have been modified in many different ways during the long evolutionary history of life on Earth.

Although cells can differ substantially from each other, they share certain common characteristics. In this chapter, we'll first learn about the tools and experimental approaches that have allowed us to understand subcellular details; then we'll tour the cell and become acquainted with its components.

Concept 6.1

To study cells, biologists use microscopes and the tools of biochemistry

It can be difficult to understand how a cell, usually too small to be seen by the unaided eye, can be so complex. How can cell biologists possibly investigate the inner workings of such tiny entities? Before we actually tour the cell, it will be helpful to learn how cells are studied.

Microscopy

The advance of a scientific field often parallels the invention of instruments that extend human senses to new limits. The discovery and early study of cells progressed with the invention of microscopes in 1590 and their improvement in the 17th century. Microscopes of various types are still indispensable tools for the study of cells.

The microscopes first used by Renaissance scientists, as well as the microscopes you are likely to use in the laboratory, are all **light microscopes (LMs).** Visible light is passed through the specimen and then through glass lenses. The lenses refract (bend) the light in such a way that the image of the specimen is magnified as it is projected into the eye, onto photograph film, or onto a video screen. (See the diagram of microscope structure in Appendix C.)

Two important parameters in microscopy are magnification and resolving power, or resolution. *Magnification* in microscopy is the ratio of an object's image to its real size. *Resolution* is a measure of the clarity of the image; it is the minimum distance two points can be separated and still be distinguished as two separate points. For example, what appears to the unaided eye as one star in the sky may be resolved as twin stars with a telescope.

Just as the resolving power of the human eye is limited, the resolution of telescopes and microscopes is limited. Microscopes can be designed to magnify objects as much as desired, but the light microscope cannot resolve detail finer than about 0.2 micrometer (μm), or 200 nanometers (nm), the size of a small bacterium **(Figure 6.2)**. This resolution is limited by the shortest wavelength of light used to illuminate the specimen. Light microscopes can magnify effectively to about 1,000 times the size of the actual specimen; at greater magnifications, the image becomes increasingly blurry. Most of the improvements in light microscopy since the beginning of the 20th century have involved new methods for enhancing contrast, which clarifies the details that can be resolved **(Figure 6.3**, next page). In addition, scientists have developed methods for staining or labeling particular cell components so that they stand out visually.

Although cells were discovered by Robert Hooke in 1665, the geography of the cell was largely uncharted until the 1950s. Most subcellular structures, or **organelles,** are too small to be resolved by the light microscope. Cell biology advanced rapidly in the 1950s with the introduction of the electron microscope. Instead of using light, the **electron microscope (EM)** focuses a beam of electrons through the specimen or onto its surface (see Appendix C). Resolution is inversely related to the wavelength of the radiation a microscope uses for imaging, and electron beams have wavelengths much shorter than the wavelengths of visible light. Modern electron microscopes can theoretically achieve a resolution of about 0.002 nm, but the practical limit for biological structures is generally only about 2 nm—still a hundredfold improvement over the light microscope. Biologists use the term *cell ultrastructure* to refer to a cell's anatomy as revealed by an electron microscope.

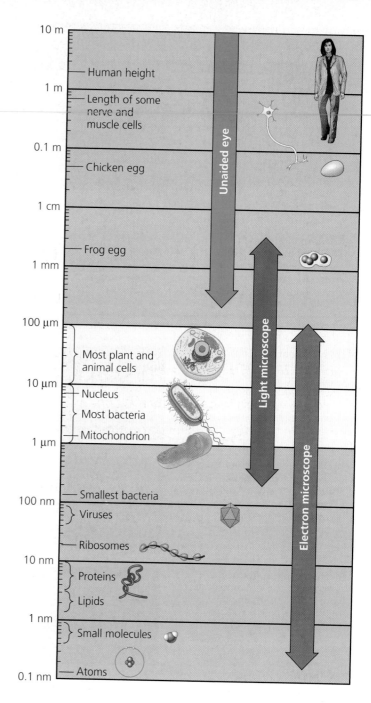

Measurements
1 centimeter (cm) = 10^{-2} meter (m) = 0.4 inch
1 millimeter (mm) = 10^{-3} m
1 micrometer (μm) = 10^{-3} mm = 10^{-6} m
1 nanometer (nm) = 10^{-3} μm = 10^{-9} m

▲ **Figure 6.2 The size range of cells.** Most cells are between 1 and 100 μm in diameter (yellow region of chart) and are therefore visible only under a microscope. Notice that the scale along the left side is logarithmic to accommodate the range of sizes shown. Starting at the top of the scale with 10 m and going down, each reference measurement marks a tenfold decrease in diameter or length. For a complete table of the metric system, see Appendix B.

Figure 6.3
Research Method Light Microscopy

TECHNIQUE	RESULTS

(a) Brightfield (unstained specimen). Passes light directly through specimen. Unless cell is naturally pigmented or artificially stained, image has little contrast. [Parts (a)–(d) show a human cheek epithelial cell.]

50 μm

(b) Brightfield (stained specimen). Staining with various dyes enhances contrast, but most staining procedures require that cells be fixed (preserved).

(c) Phase-contrast. Enhances contrast in unstained cells by amplifying variations in density within specimen; especially useful for examining living, unpigmented cells.

(d) Differential-interference-contrast (Nomarski). Like phase-contrast microscopy, it uses optical modifications to exaggerate differences in density, making the image appear almost 3D.

(e) Fluorescence. Shows the locations of specific molecules in the cell by tagging the molecules with fluorescent dyes or antibodies. These fluorescent substances absorb ultraviolet radiation and emit visible light, as shown here in a cell from an artery.

50 μm

(f) Confocal. Uses lasers and special optics for "optical sectioning" of fluorescently-stained specimens. Only a single plane of focus is illuminated; out-of-focus fluorescence above and below the plane is subtracted by a computer. A sharp image results, as seen in stained nervous tissue (top), where nerve cells are green, support cells are red, and regions of overlap are yellow. A standard fluorescence micrograph (bottom) of this relatively thick tissue is blurry.

50 μm

Figure 6.4
Research Method Electron Microscopy

TECHNIQUE	RESULTS

(a) Scanning electron microscopy (SEM). Micrographs taken with a scanning electron microscope show a 3D image of the surface of a specimen. This SEM shows the surface of a cell from a rabbit trachea (windpipe) covered with motile organelles called cilia. Beating of the cilia helps move inhaled debris upward toward the throat.

Cilia   1 μm

(b) Transmission electron microscopy (TEM). A transmission electron microscope profiles a thin section of a specimen. Here we see a section through a tracheal cell, revealing its ultrastructure. In preparing the TEM, some cilia were cut along their lengths, creating longitudinal sections, while other cilia were cut straight across, creating cross sections.

Longitudinal section of cilium   Cross section of cilium   1 μm

There are two basic types of electron microscopes: the **scanning electron microscope (SEM)** and the **transmission electron microscope (TEM)**. The SEM is especially useful for detailed study of the surface of a specimen **(Figure 6.4a)**. The electron beam scans the surface of the sample, which is usually coated with a thin film of gold. The beam excites electrons on the sample's surface, and these secondary electrons are detected by a device that translates the pattern of electrons into an electronic signal to a video screen. The result is an image of the topography of the specimen. The SEM has great depth of field, which results in an image that appears three-dimensional.

Cell biologists use the TEM mainly to study the internal ultrastructure of cells **(Figure 6.4b)**. The TEM aims an electron beam through a very thin section of the specimen, similar to the way a light microscope transmits light through a slide. The specimen has been stained with atoms of heavy metals, which attach to certain cellular structures, thus enhancing the electron density of some parts of the cell more than others. The electrons passing through the specimen are scattered more in the denser regions, so fewer electrons are transmitted. The image is created by the pattern of transmitted electrons. Instead of using glass lenses, the TEM uses electromagnets as lenses to bend the paths of the electrons, ultimately focusing the image onto a screen for viewing or onto photographic film. Some microscopes are equipped with a digital camera to photograph the image on the screen; others are equipped with a digital detector in place of both screen and camera.

Electron microscopes reveal many organelles that are impossible to resolve with the light microscope. But the light microscope offers advantages, especially for the study of living cells. A disadvantage of electron microscopy is that the methods used to prepare the specimen kill the cells. Also, specimen preparation can introduce artifacts, structural features seen in micrographs that do not exist in the living cell (as is true for all microscopy techniques). From this point on in the book, micrographs are identified by the type of microscopy: LM for a light micrograph, SEM for a scanning electron micrograph, and TEM for a transmission electron micrograph.

Microscopes are the most important tools of *cytology*, the study of cell structure. But simply describing the diverse organelles within the cell reveals little about their function. Modern cell biology developed from an integration of cytology with *biochemistry*, the study of the molecules and chemical processes (metabolism) of cells. A biochemical approach called cell fractionation has been particularly important in cell biology.

Isolating Organelles by Cell Fractionation

The goal of **cell fractionation** is to take cells apart and separate the major organelles from one another **(Figure 6.5)**. The instrument used to fractionate cells is the centrifuge, which can spin test tubes holding mixtures of disrupted cells at various speeds. The centrifugal force separates the cell components by size and density. The most powerful machines, called **ultracentrifuges**, can spin as fast as 130,000 revolutions per minute (rpm) and apply forces on particles of more than 1 million times the force of gravity (1,000,000 *g*).

Cell fractionation enables the researcher to prepare specific components of cells in bulk quantity to study their composition and functions. By following this approach, biologists have been able to assign various functions of the cell to the different organelles, a task that would be far more difficult with intact cells. For example, one cellular fraction collected by centrifugation has enzymes that function in the metabolic process known as cellular respiration. The electron microscope reveals this fraction to be very rich in the organelles called mitochondria. This evidence helped cell biologists determine that mitochondria are the sites of cellular respiration. Cytology and biochemistry complement each other in correlating cellular structure and function.

Concept Check 6.1

1. Which type of microscope would you use to study
   (a) the changes in shape of a living white blood cell,
   (b) the details of surface texture of a hair, and (c) the detailed structure of an organelle?

For suggested answers, see Appendix A.

Figure 6.5

Research Method   Cell Fractionation

APPLICATION   Cell fractionation is used to isolate (fractionate) cell components, based on size and density.

TECHNIQUE   First, cells are homogenized in a blender to break them up. The resulting mixture (cell homogenate) is then centrifuged at various speeds and durations to fractionate the cell components, forming a series of pellets.

Homogenization

Tissue cells

Homogenate

1000 *g*
(1000 times the force of gravity)
10 min

Differential centrifugation

Supernatant poured into next tube

20,000 *g*
20 min

80,000 *g*
60 min

150,000 *g*
3 hr

Pellet rich in nuclei and cellular debris

Pellet rich in mitochondria (and chloroplasts if cells are from a plant)

Pellet rich in "microsomes" (pieces of plasma membranes and cells' internal membranes)

Pellet rich in ribosomes

RESULTS   In the original experiments, the researchers used microscopy to identify the organelles in each pellet, establishing a baseline for further experiments. In the next series of experiments, researchers used biochemical methods to determine the metabolic functions associated with each type of organelle. Researchers currently use cell fractionation to isolate particular organelles in order to study further details of their function.

Concept 6.2

Eukaryotic cells have internal membranes that compartmentalize their functions

The basic structural and functional unit of every organism is one of two types of cells—prokaryotic or eukaryotic. Only organisms of the domains Bacteria and Archaea consist of prokaryotic cells. Protists, fungi, animals, and plants all consist of eukaryotic cells. This chapter focuses on generalized animal and plant cells, after first comparing them with prokaryotic cells.

Comparing Prokaryotic and Eukaryotic Cells

All cells have several basic features in common: They are all bounded by a membrane, called a *plasma membrane*. Within the membrane is a semifluid substance, *cytosol*, in which organelles are found. All cells contain *chromosomes*, carrying genes in the form of DNA. And all cells have *ribosomes*, tiny organelles that make proteins according to instructions from the genes.

A major difference between prokaryotic and eukaryotic cells, indicated by their names, is that the chromosomes of a eukaryotic cell are located in a membrane-enclosed organelle called the *nucleus*. The word *prokaryotic* is from the Greek *pro*, meaning "before," and *karyon*, meaning "kernel," referring here to the nucleus. In a **prokaryotic cell (Figure 6.6)**, the DNA is concentrated in a region called the **nucleoid**, but no membrane

separates this region from the rest of the cell. In contrast, the **eukaryotic cell** (Greek *eu*, true, and *karyon*) has a true nucleus, bounded by a membranous nuclear envelope (see Figure 6.9, pp. 100–101). The entire region between the nucleus and the plasma membrane is called the **cytoplasm**, a term also used for the interior of a prokaryotic cell. Within the cytoplasm of a eukaryotic cell, suspended in cytosol, are a variety of membrane-bounded organelles of specialized form and function. These are absent in prokaryotic cells. Thus, the presence or absence of a true nucleus is just one example of the disparity in structural complexity between the two types of cells.

Eukaryotic cells are generally quite a bit bigger than prokaryotic cells (see Figure 6.2). Size is a general aspect of cell structure that relates to function. The logistics of carrying out cellular metabolism sets limits on cell size. At the lower limit, the smallest cells known are bacteria called mycoplasmas, which have diameters between 0.1 and 1.0 μm. These are perhaps the smallest packages with enough DNA to program metabolism and enough enzymes and other cellular equipment to carry out the activities necessary for a cell to sustain itself and reproduce. Most bacteria are 1–10 μm in diameter, a dimension about ten times greater than that of mycoplasmas. Eukaryotic cells are typically 10–100 μm in diameter.

Metabolic requirements also impose theoretical upper limits on the size that is practical for a single cell. As an object of a particular shape increases in size, its volume grows proportionately more than its surface area. (Area is proportional to a linear dimension squared, whereas volume is proportional to the linear dimension cubed.) Thus, the smaller the object, the greater its ratio of surface area to volume **(Figure 6.7)**.

Pili: attachment structures on the surface of some prokaryotes

Nucleoid: region where the cell's DNA is located (not enclosed by a membrane)

Ribosomes: organelles that synthesize proteins

Plasma membrane: membrane enclosing the cytoplasm

Cell wall: rigid structure outside the plasma membrane

Capsule: jelly-like outer coating of many prokaryotes

Bacterial chromosome

Flagella: locomotion organelles of some bacteria

(a) A typical rod-shaped bacterium

0.5 μm

(b) A thin section through the bacterium *Bacillus coagulans* (TEM)

▲ **Figure 6.6 A prokaryotic cell.** Lacking a true nucleus and the other membrane-enclosed organelles of the eukaryotic cell, the prokaryotic cell is much simpler in structure. Only bacteria and archaea are prokaryotes.

Surface area increases while
total volume remains constant

Total surface area (height × width × number of sides × number of boxes)	6	150	750
Total volume (height × width × length × number of boxes)	1	125	125
Surface-to-volume ratio (surface area ÷ volume)	6	1.2	6

▲ **Figure 6.7 Geometric relationships between surface area and volume.** In this diagram, cells are represented as boxes. Using arbitrary units of length, we can calculate the cell's surface area (in square units), volume (in cubic units), and ratio of surface area to volume. The smaller the cell, the higher the surface-to-volume ratio. A high surface-to-volume ratio facilitates the exchange of materials between a cell and its environment.

At the boundary of every cell, the **plasma membrane** functions as a selective barrier that allows sufficient passage of oxygen, nutrients, and wastes to service the entire volume of the cell **(Figure 6.8)**. For each square micrometer of membrane, only so much of a particular substance can cross per second. Rates of chemical exchange with the extracellular environment might be inadequate to maintain a cell with a very large cytoplasm. The need for a surface area sufficiently large to accommodate the volume helps explain the microscopic size of most cells. Larger organisms do not generally have *larger* cells than smaller organisms—simply *more* cells. A sufficiently high ratio of surface area to volume is especially important in cells that exchange a lot of material with their surroundings, such as

intestinal cells. Such cells may have many long, thin projections from their surface called microvilli, which increase surface area without an appreciable increase in volume.

Prokaryotic cells will be described in detail in Chapters 18 and 27 (see Table 27.2 for a comparison of prokaryotes and eukaryotes), and the possible evolutionary relationships between prokaryotic and eukaryotic cells will be discussed in Chapter 28. Most of the discussion of cell structure that follows in this chapter applies to eukaryotic cells.

A Panoramic View of the Eukaryotic Cell

In addition to the plasma membrane at its outer surface, a eukaryotic cell has extensive and elaborately arranged internal membranes, which partition the cell into compartments—the membranous organelles mentioned earlier. These membranes also participate directly in the cell's metabolism, because many enzymes are built right into the membranes. Furthermore, the cell's compartments provide different local environments that facilitate specific metabolic functions, so incompatible processes can go on simultaneously inside the same cell.

Membranes of various kinds are fundamental to the organization of the cell. In general, biological membranes consist of a double layer of phospholipids and other lipids. Embedded in this lipid bilayer or attached to its surfaces are diverse proteins (see Figure 6.8). However, each type of membrane has a unique composition of lipids and proteins suited to that membrane's specific functions. For example, enzymes embedded in the membranes of the organelles called mitochondria function in cellular respiration.

Before continuing with this chapter, examine the overviews of eukaryotic cells in **Figure 6.9** on the next two pages. These generalized cell diagrams introduce the various organelles and provide a map of the cell for the detailed tour upon which we will now embark. Figure 6.9 also contrasts animal and plant cells. As eukaryotic cells, they have much more in common than either has with any prokaryotic cell. As you will see, however, there are important differences between animal and plant cells.

Outside of cell

Inside of cell | 0.1 μm |

(a) TEM of a plasma membrane. The plasma membrane, here in a red blood cell, appears as a pair of dark bands separated by a light band.

Carbohydrate side chain

Hydrophilic region

Hydrophobic region

Hydrophilic region

Phospholipid   Proteins

(b) Structure of the plasma membrane

◀ **Figure 6.8 The plasma membrane.** The plasma membrane and the membranes of organelles consist of a double layer (bilayer) of phospholipids with various proteins attached to or embedded in it. The phospholipid tails in the interior of a membrane are hydrophobic; the interior portions of membrane proteins are also hydrophobic. The phospholipid heads, exterior proteins, exterior parts of proteins, and carbohydrate side chains are hydrophilic and in contact with the aqueous solution on either side of the membrane. Carbohydrate side chains are found only on the outer surface of the plasma membrane. The specific functions of a membrane depend on the kinds of phospholipids and proteins present.

Figure 6.9
Exploring **Animal and Plant Cells**

ANIMAL CELL

This drawing of a generalized animal cell incorporates the most common structures of animal cells (no cell actually looks just like this). As shown by this cutaway view, the cell has a variety of organelles ("little organs"), many of which are bounded by membranes. The most prominent organelle in an animal cell is usually the nucleus.

Most of the cell's metabolic activities occur in the cytoplasm, the entire region between the nucleus and the plasma membrane. The cytoplasm contains many organelles suspended in a semifluid medium, the cytosol. Pervading much of the cytoplasm is a labyrinth of membranes called the endoplasmic reticulum (ER).

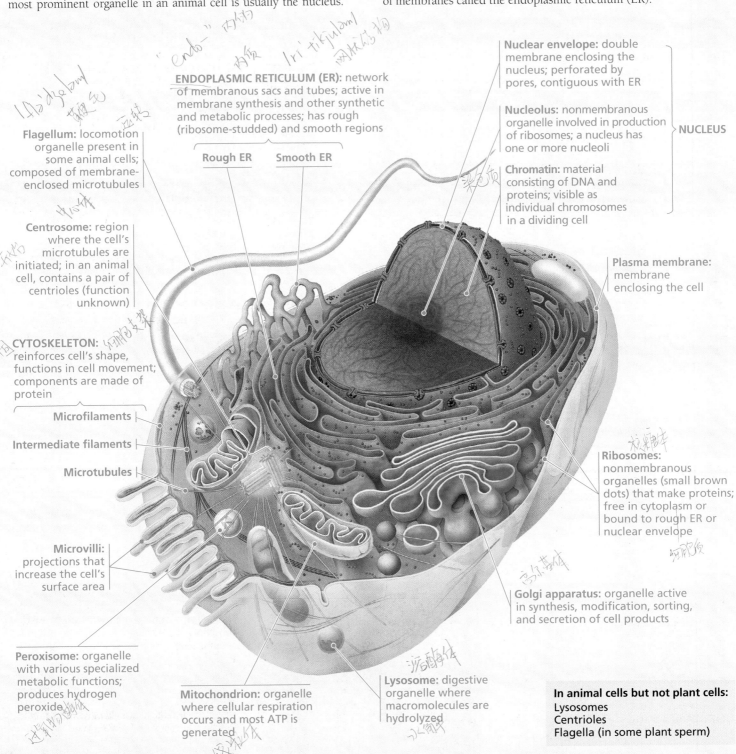

ENDOPLASMIC RETICULUM (ER): network of membranous sacs and tubes; active in membrane synthesis and other synthetic and metabolic processes; has rough (ribosome-studded) and smooth regions

Rough ER **Smooth ER**

Flagellum: locomotion organelle present in some animal cells; composed of membrane-enclosed microtubules

Centrosome: region where the cell's microtubules are initiated; in an animal cell, contains a pair of centrioles (function unknown)

CYTOSKELETON: reinforces cell's shape, functions in cell movement; components are made of protein

Microfilaments

Intermediate filaments

Microtubules

Microvilli: projections that increase the cell's surface area

Peroxisome: organelle with various specialized metabolic functions; produces hydrogen peroxide

Mitochondrion: organelle where cellular respiration occurs and most ATP is generated

Lysosome: digestive organelle where macromolecules are hydrolyzed

Nuclear envelope: double membrane enclosing the nucleus; perforated by pores, contiguous with ER

Nucleolus: nonmembranous organelle involved in production of ribosomes; a nucleus has one or more nucleoli

Chromatin: material consisting of DNA and proteins; visible as individual chromosomes in a dividing cell

NUCLEUS

Plasma membrane: membrane enclosing the cell

Ribosomes: nonmembranous organelles (small brown dots) that make proteins; free in cytoplasm or bound to rough ER or nuclear envelope

Golgi apparatus: organelle active in synthesis, modification, sorting, and secretion of cell products

In animal cells but not plant cells:
Lysosomes
Centrioles
Flagella (in some plant sperm)

This drawing of a generalized plant cell reveals the similarities and differences between an animal cell and a plant cell. In addition to most of the features seen in an animal cell, a plant cell has membrane-enclosed organelles called plastids. The most important type of plastid is the chloroplast, which carries out photosynthesis. Many plant cells have a large central vacuole; some may have one or more smaller vacuoles. Outside a plant cell's plasma membrane is a thick cell wall, perforated by channels called plasmodesmata.

NUCLEUS
- Nuclear envelope
- Nucleolus
- Chromatin

Centrosome: region where the cell's microtubules are initiated; lacks centrioles in plant cells

Rough endoplasmic reticulum

If you preview the rest of the chapter now, you'll see Figure 6.9 repeated in miniature as orientation diagrams. In each case, a particular organelle is highlighted, color-coded to its appearance in Figure 6.9. As we take a closer look at individual organelles, the orientation diagrams will help you place those structures in the context of the whole cell.

Smooth endoplasmic reticulum

Ribosomes (small brown dots)

Central vacuole: prominent organelle in older plant cells; functions include storage, breakdown of waste products, hydrolysis of macromolecules; enlargement of vacuole is a major mechanism of plant growth

Tonoplast: membrane enclosing the central vacuole

Golgi apparatus

Microfilaments

Intermediate filaments

Microtubules

CYTOSKELETON

Mitochondrion

Peroxisome

Plasma membrane

Cell wall: outer layer that maintains cell's shape and protects cell from mechanical damage; made of cellulose, other polysaccharides, and protein

Wall of adjacent cell

Chloroplast: photosynthetic organelle; converts energy of sunlight to chemical energy stored in sugar molecules

Plasmodesmata: channels through cell walls that connect the cytoplasms of adjacent cells

In plant cells but not animal cells:
Chloroplasts
Central vacuole and tonoplast
Cell wall
Plasmodesmata

Concept 6.3

The eukaryotic cell's genetic instructions are housed in the nucleus and carried out by the ribosomes

On the first stop of our detailed tour of the cell, let's look at two organelles involved in the genetic control of the cell: the nucleus, which houses most of the cell's DNA, and the ribosomes, which use information from the DNA to make proteins.

The Nucleus: Genetic Library of the Cell

The **nucleus** contains most of the genes in the eukaryotic cell (some genes are located in mitochondria and chloroplasts). It is generally the most conspicuous organelle in a eukaryotic cell, averaging about 5 μm in diameter. The **nuclear envelope** encloses the nucleus **(Figure 6.10)**, separating its contents from the cytoplasm.

The nuclear envelope is a *double* membrane. The two membranes, each a lipid bilayer with associated proteins, are separated by a space of 20–40 nm. The envelope is perforated by pores that are about 100 nm in diameter. At the lip of each pore, the inner and outer membranes of the nuclear envelope are continuous. An intricate protein structure called a *pore complex* lines each pore and regulates the entry and exit of certain large macromolecules and particles. Except at the pores, the nuclear side of the envelope is lined by the **nuclear lamina**, a netlike array of protein filaments that maintains the shape of the nucleus by mechanically supporting the nuclear envelope. There is also much evidence for a *nuclear matrix*, a framework of fibers extending throughout the nuclear interior. (In Chapter 19, we will examine possible functions of the nuclear lamina and matrix in organizing the genetic material.)

Within the nucleus, the DNA is organized into discrete units called **chromosomes**, structures that carry the genetic information. Each chromosome is made up of a material called **chromatin**, a complex of proteins and DNA. Stained chromatin usually appears through both light microscopes and electron microscopes as a diffuse mass. As a cell prepares to divide, however, the thin chromatin fibers coil up (condense), becoming thick enough to be distinguished as the familiar separate structures we know as chromosomes. Each eukaryotic species has a characteristic number of chromosomes. A typical human cell, for example, has 46 chromosomes in its nucleus; the exceptions are the sex cells (eggs and sperm), which have only 23 chromosomes in humans. A fruit fly cell has 8 chromosomes in most cells, with 4 in the sex cells.

A prominent structure within the nondividing nucleus is the **nucleolus** (plural, *nucleoli*), which appears through the electron microscope as a mass of densely stained granules and fibers adjoining part of the chromatin. Here a special type of RNA called *ribosomal RNA* (rRNA) is synthesized from instructions in the DNA. Also, proteins imported from the cytoplasm are assembled with rRNA into large and small ribosomal subunits in the nucleolus. These subunits then exit the nucleus through the nuclear pores to the cytoplasm, where a large and a small subunit can assemble into a ribosome. Sometimes there are two or more nucleoli; the number depends on the species and the stage in the cell's reproductive cycle. Recent studies have suggested that the nucleolus may perform additional functions as well.

As we saw in Figure 5.25, the nucleus directs protein synthesis by synthesizing messenger RNA (mRNA) according to instructions provided by the DNA. The mRNA is then transported to the cytoplasm via the nuclear pores. Once an mRNA molecule reaches the cytoplasm, ribosomes translate the mRNA's genetic message into the primary structure of a specific polypeptide. This process of transcribing and translating genetic information is described in detail in Chapter 17.

Ribosomes: Protein Factories in the Cell

Ribosomes, particles made of ribosomal RNA and protein, are the organelles that carry out protein synthesis **(Figure 6.11)**. Cells that have high rates of protein synthesis have a particularly large number of ribosomes. For example, a human pancreas cell has a few million ribosomes. Not surprisingly, cells active in protein synthesis also have prominent nucleoli. (Keep in mind that both nucleoli and ribosomes, unlike most other organelles, are not enclosed in membrane.)

Ribosomes build proteins in two cytoplasmic locales (see Figure 6.11). *Free ribosomes* are suspended in the cytosol, while *bound ribosomes* are attached to the outside of the endoplasmic reticulum or nuclear envelope. Most of the proteins made on free ribosomes function within the cytosol; examples are enzymes that catalyze the first steps of sugar breakdown. Bound ribosomes generally make proteins that are destined either for insertion into membranes, for packaging within certain organelles such as lysosomes (see Figure 6.9), or for export from the cell (secretion). Cells that specialize in protein secretion—for instance, the cells of the pancreas that secrete digestive enzymes—frequently have a high proportion of bound ribosomes. Bound and free ribosomes are structurally

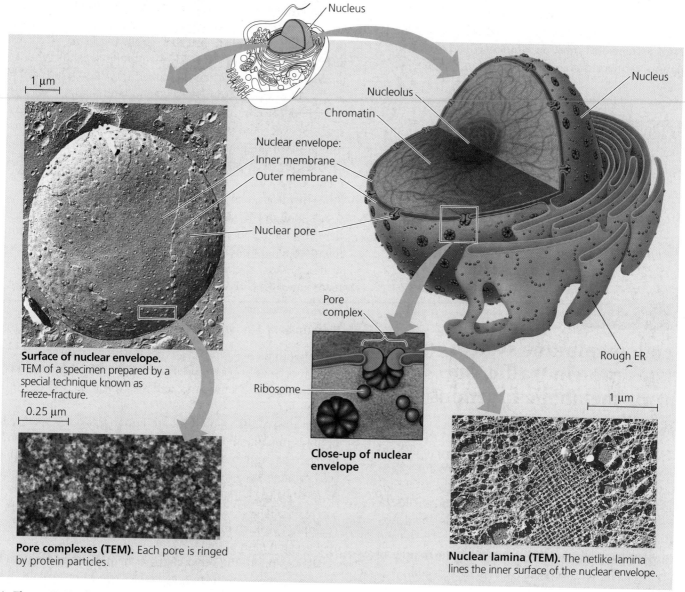

1 μm

Nucleus

Nucleolus

Chromatin

Nuclear envelope:
Inner membrane
Outer membrane

Nuclear pore

Nucleus

Rough ER

1 μm

Surface of nuclear envelope.
TEM of a specimen prepared by a
special technique known as
freeze-fracture.

0.25 μm

Pore
complex

Ribosome

**Close-up of nuclear
envelope**

Pore complexes (TEM). Each pore is ringed
by protein particles.

Nuclear lamina (TEM). The netlike lamina
lines the inner surface of the nuclear envelope.

▲ **Figure 6.10 The nucleus and its envelope.** Within the nucleus are the chromosomes, which
appear as a mass of chromatin (DNA and associated proteins), and one or more nucleoli (singular,
nucleolus), which function in ribosome synthesis. The nuclear envelope, which consists of two
membranes separated by a narrow space, is perforated with pores and lined by the nuclear lamina.

Ribosomes

ER

Cytosol

Endoplasmic reticulum (ER)

Free ribosomes

Bound ribosomes

Large
subunit

Small
subunit

0.5 μm

TEM showing ER and ribosomes

Diagram of a ribosome

◄ **Figure 6.11 Ribosomes.** This electron
micrograph of part of a pancreas cell shows
many ribosomes, both free (in the cytosol) and
bound (to the endoplasmic reticulum). The
simplified diagram of a ribosome shows its two
subunits.

identical and can alternate between the two roles; the cell adjusts the relative numbers of each as metabolic changes alter the types of proteins that must be synthesized. You will learn more about ribosome structure and function in Chapter 17.

Concept Check 6.3

1. What role do the ribosomes play in carrying out the genetic instructions?
2. Describe the composition of chromatin and of nucleoli and the function(s) of each.

For suggested answers, see Appendix A.

Concept 6.4

The endomembrane system regulates protein traffic and performs metabolic functions in the cell

Many of the different membranes of the eukaryotic cell are part of an **endomembrane system,** which carries out a variety of tasks in the cell. These tasks include synthesis of proteins and their transport into membranes and organelles or out of the cell, metabolism and movement of lipids, and detoxification of poisons. The membranes of this system are related either through direct physical continuity or by the transfer of membrane segments as tiny **vesicles** (sacs made of membrane). Despite these relationships, the various membranes are not identical in structure and function. Moreover, the thickness, molecular composition, and types of chemical reactions carried out by proteins in a given membrane are not fixed, but may be modified several times during the membrane's life. The endomembrane system includes the nuclear envelope, endoplasmic reticulum, Golgi apparatus, lysosomes, various kinds of vacuoles, and the plasma membrane (not actually an *endo*membrane in physical location, but nevertheless related to the endoplasmic reticulum and other internal membranes). We have already discussed the nuclear envelope and will now focus on the endoplasmic reticulum and the other endomembranes to which the endoplasmic reticulum gives rise.

The Endoplasmic Reticulum: Biosynthetic Factory

The **endoplasmic reticulum (ER)** is such an extensive network of membranes that it accounts for more than half the total membrane in many eukaryotic cells. (The word *endo-*

plasmic means "within the cytoplasm," and *reticulum* is Latin for "little net.") The ER consists of a network of membranous tubules and sacs called cisternae (from the Latin *cisterna,* a reservoir for a liquid). The ER membrane separates the internal compartment of the ER, called the ER lumen (cavity) or cisternal space, from the cytosol. And because the ER membrane is continuous with the nuclear envelope, the space between the two membranes of the envelope is continuous with the lumen of the ER **(Figure 6.12)**.

There are two distinct, though connected, regions of ER that differ in structure and function: smooth ER and rough ER. **Smooth ER** is so named because its outer surface lacks ribosomes. **Rough ER** has ribosomes that stud the outer surface of the membrane and thus appears rough through the electron microscope. As already mentioned, ribosomes are also attached to the cytoplasmic side of the nuclear envelope's outer membrane, which is continuous with rough ER.

Functions of Smooth ER

The smooth ER of various cell types functions in diverse metabolic processes. These processes include synthesis of lipids, metabolism of carbohydrates, and detoxification of drugs and poisons.

Enzymes of the smooth ER are important to the synthesis of lipids, including oils, phospholipids, and steroids. Among the steroids produced by the smooth ER in animal cells are the sex hormones of vertebrates and the various steroid hormones secreted by the adrenal glands. The cells that actually synthesize and secrete these hormones—in the testes and ovaries, for example—are rich in smooth ER, a structural feature that fits the function of these cells.

In the smooth ER, other enzymes help detoxify drugs and poisons, especially in liver cells. Detoxification usually involves adding hydroxyl groups to drugs, making them more soluble and easier to flush from the body. The sedative phenobarbital and other barbiturates are examples of drugs metabolized in this manner by smooth ER in liver cells. In fact, barbiturates, alcohol, and many other drugs induce the proliferation of smooth ER and its associated detoxification enzymes, thus increasing the rate of detoxification. This, in turn, increases tolerance to the drugs, meaning that higher doses are required to achieve a particular effect, such as sedation. Also, because some of the detoxification enzymes have relatively broad action, the proliferation of smooth ER in response to one drug can increase tolerance to other drugs as well. Barbiturate abuse, for example, may decrease the effectiveness of certain antibiotics and other useful drugs.

The smooth ER also stores calcium ions. In muscle cells, for example, a specialized smooth ER membrane pumps calcium ions from the cytosol into the ER lumen. When a muscle cell is stimulated by a nerve impulse, calcium ions rush back across the ER membrane into the cytosol and trigger contraction of the muscle cell. In other cell types, calcium ion release from the smooth ER can trigger different responses.

Functions of Rough ER

Many types of specialized cells secrete proteins produced by ribosomes attached to rough ER. For example, certain cells in the pancreas secrete the protein insulin, a hormone, into the

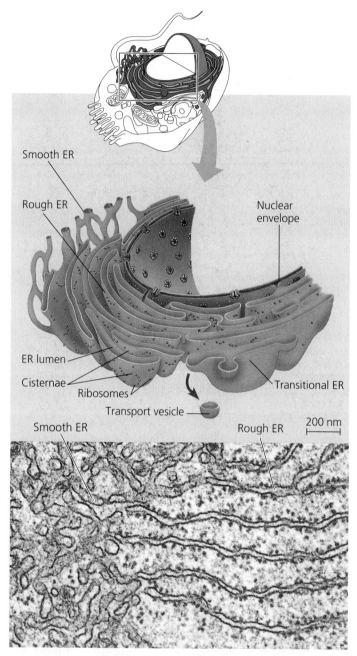

Smooth ER

Rough ER

Nuclear envelope

ER lumen

Cisternae

Ribosomes

Transport vesicle

Smooth ER

Transitional ER

Rough ER

200 nm

▲ **Figure 6.12 Endoplasmic reticulum (ER).** A membranous system of interconnected tubules and flattened sacs called cisternae, the ER is also continuous with the nuclear envelope. (The drawing is a cutaway view.) The membrane of the ER encloses a continuous compartment called the ER lumen (or cisternal space). Rough ER, which is studded on its outer surface with ribosomes, can be distinguished from smooth ER in the electron micrograph (TEM). Transport vesicles bud off from a region of the rough ER called transitional ER and travel to the Golgi apparatus and other destinations.

bloodstream (see Figure 6.11). As a polypeptide chain grows from a bound ribosome, it is threaded into the ER lumen through a pore formed by a protein complex in the ER membrane. As the new protein enters the ER lumen, it folds into its native conformation. Most secretory proteins are **glycoproteins,** proteins that have carbohydrates covalently bonded to them. The carbohydrate is attached to the protein in the ER by specialized molecules built into the ER membrane.

Once secretory proteins are formed, the ER membrane keeps them separate from the proteins, produced by free ribosomes, that will remain in the cytosol. Secretory proteins depart from the ER wrapped in the membranes of vesicles that bud like bubbles from a specialized region called transitional ER (see Figure 6.12). Vesicles in transit from one part of the cell to another are called **transport vesicles;** we will learn their fate in the next section.

In addition to making secretory proteins, rough ER is a membrane factory for the cell; it grows in place by adding membrane proteins and phospholipids to its own membrane. As polypeptides destined to be membrane proteins grow from the ribosomes, they are inserted into the ER membrane itself and are anchored there by their hydrophobic portions. The rough ER also makes its own membrane phospholipids; enzymes built into the ER membrane assemble phospholipids from precursors in the cytosol. The ER membrane expands and is transferred in the form of transport vesicles to other components of the endomembrane system.

The Golgi Apparatus: Shipping and Receiving Center

After leaving the ER, many transport vesicles travel to the **Golgi apparatus.** We can think of the Golgi as a center of manufacturing, warehousing, sorting, and shipping. Here, products of the ER are modified and stored and then sent to other destinations. Not surprisingly, the Golgi apparatus is especially extensive in cells specialized for secretion.

The Golgi apparatus consists of flattened membranous sacs—cisternae—looking like a stack of pita bread (**Figure 6.13,** on the next page). A cell may have many or even hundreds of these stacks. The membrane of each cisterna in a stack separates its internal space from the cytosol. Vesicles concentrated in the vicinity of the Golgi apparatus are engaged in the transfer of material between the parts of the Golgi and other structures.

A Golgi stack has a distinct polarity, with the membranes of cisternae on opposite sides of the stack differing in thickness and molecular composition. The two poles of a Golgi stack are referred to as the *cis* face and the *trans* face; these act, respectively, as the receiving and shipping departments of the Golgi apparatus. The *cis* face is usually located near the ER. Transport vesicles move material from the ER to the Golgi apparatus. A vesicle that buds from the ER can add its membrane and the contents of its lumen to the *cis* face by fusing with a

cis face ("receiving" side of Golgi apparatus)

6 Vesicles also transport certain proteins back to ER

1 Vesicles move from ER to Golgi

2 Vesicles coalesce to form new *cis* Golgi cisternae

Cisternae

3 Cisternal maturation: Golgi cisternae move in a *cis*-to-*trans* direction

4 Vesicles form and leave Golgi, carrying specific proteins to other locations or to the plasma membrane for secretion

5 Vesicles transport specific proteins backward to newer Golgi cisternae

trans face ("shipping" side of Golgi apparatus)

0.1 µm

TEM of Golgi apparatus

▲ **Figure 6.13 The Golgi apparatus.** The Golgi apparatus consists of stacks of flattened sacs, or cisternae, which, unlike ER cisternae, are not physically connected. (The drawing is a cutaway view.) A Golgi stack receives and dispatches transport vesicles and the products they contain. A Golgi stack has a structural and functional polarity, with a *cis* face that receives vesicles containing ER products and a *trans* face that dispatches vesicles. The cisternal maturation model suggests that the Golgi cisternae themselves appear to "mature," moving from the *cis* to the *trans* face while carrying some proteins along. In addition, some vesicles recycle enzymes that had been carried forward, in moving cisternae, "backward" to a newer region where their functions are needed (TEM).

Golgi membrane. The *trans* face gives rise to vesicles, which pinch off and travel to other sites.

Products of the ER are usually modified during their transit from the *cis* region to the *trans* region of the Golgi. Proteins and phospholipids of membranes may be altered. For example, various Golgi enzymes modify the carbohydrate portions of glycoproteins. Carbohydrates are first added to proteins in the rough ER, often during the process of polypeptide synthesis. The carbohydrate on the resulting glycoprotein is then modified as it passes through the rest of the ER and the Golgi. The Golgi removes some sugar monomers and substitutes others, producing a large variety of carbohydrates.

In addition to its finishing work, the Golgi apparatus manufactures certain macromolecules by itself. Many polysaccharides secreted by cells are Golgi products, including pectins and certain other non-cellulose polysaccharides made by plant cells and incorporated along with cellulose into their cell walls. (Cellulose is made by enzymes located within the plasma membrane, which directly deposit this polysaccharide on the outside surface.) Golgi products that will be secreted depart from the *trans* face of the Golgi inside transport vesicles that eventually fuse with the plasma membrane.

The Golgi manufactures and refines its products in stages, with different cisternae between the *cis* and *trans* regions containing unique teams of enzymes. Until recently, we viewed the Golgi as a static structure, with products in various stages of processing transferred from one cisterna to the next by vesicles. While this may occur, recent research has given rise to a new model of the Golgi as a more dynamic structure. According to the model called the *cisternal maturation model*, the cisternae of the Golgi actually progress forward from the *cis* to the *trans* face of the Golgi, carrying and modifying their protein cargo as they move. Figure 6.13 shows the details of this model.

Before a Golgi stack dispatches its products by budding vesicles from the *trans* face, it sorts these products and targets them for various parts of the cell. Molecular identification tags, such as phosphate groups that have been added to the Golgi products, aid in sorting by acting like ZIP codes on mailing labels. Finally, transport vesicles budded from the Golgi may have external molecules on their membranes that recognize "docking sites" on the surface of specific organelles or on the plasma membrane, thus targeting them appropriately.

Lysosomes: Digestive Compartments

A **lysosome** is a membranous sac of hydrolytic enzymes that an animal cell uses to digest all kinds of macromolecules. Lysosomal enzymes work best in the acidic environment found in lysosomes. If a lysosome breaks open or leaks its contents, the released enzymes are not very active, because the cytosol has a neutral pH. However, excessive leakage from a large number of lysosomes can destroy a cell by autodigestion.

Hydrolytic enzymes and lysosomal membrane are made by rough ER and then transferred to the Golgi apparatus for further processing. At least some lysosomes probably arise by budding from the *trans* face of the Golgi apparatus (see Figure 6.13).

Proteins of the inner surface of the lysosomal membrane and the digestive enzymes themselves are thought to be spared from destruction by having three-dimensional conformations that protect vulnerable bonds from enzymatic attack.

Lysosomes carry out intracellular digestion in a variety of circumstances. Amoebas and many other protists eat by engulfing smaller organisms or other food particles, a process called **phagocytosis** (from the Greek *phagein*, to eat, and *kytos*, vessel, referring here to the cell). The *food vacuole* formed in this way then fuses with a lysosome, whose enzymes digest the food **(Figure 6.14a)**. Digestion products, including simple sugars, amino acids, and other monomers, pass into the cytosol and become nutrients for the cell. Some human cells also carry out phagocytosis. Among them are macrophages, a type of white blood cell that helps defend the body by engulfing and destroying bacteria and other invaders (see Figure 6.32).

Lysosomes also use their hydrolytic enzymes to recycle the cell's own organic material, a process called *autophagy*. During autophagy, a damaged organelle or small amount of cytosol

(a) Phagocytosis: lysosome digesting food

(b) Autophagy: lysosome breaking down damaged organelle

▲ **Figure 6.14 Lysosomes.** Lysosomes digest (hydrolyze) materials taken into the cell and recycle intracellular materials. **(a)** *Top* In this macrophage (a type of white blood cell) from a rat, the lysosomes are very dark because of a specific stain that reacts with one of the products of digestion within the lysosome (TEM). Macrophages ingest bacteria and viruses and destroy them using lysosomes. *Bottom* This diagram shows one lysosome fusing with a food vacuole during the process of phagocytosis. **(b)** *Top* In the cytoplasm of this rat liver cell, a lysosome has engulfed two disabled organelles, a mitochondrion and a peroxisome, in the process of autophagy (TEM). *Bottom* This diagram shows a lysosome fusing with a vesicle containing a damaged mitochondrion.

becomes surrounded by a membrane, and a lysosome fuses with this vesicle **(Figure 6.14b)**. The lysosomal enzymes dismantle the enclosed material, and the organic monomers are returned to the cytosol for reuse. With the help of lysosomes, the cell continually renews itself. A human liver cell, for example, recycles half of its macromolecules each week.

The cells of people with inherited lysosomal storage diseases lack a functioning hydrolytic enzyme normally present in lysosomes. The lysosomes become engorged with indigestible substrates, which begin to interfere with other cellular activities. In Tay-Sachs disease, for example, a lipid-digesting enzyme is missing or inactive, and the brain becomes impaired by an accumulation of lipids in the cells. Fortunately, lysosomal storage diseases are rare in the general population.

Vacuoles: Diverse Maintenance Compartments

A plant or fungal cell may have one or several vacuoles. While vacuoles carry out hydrolysis and are thus similar to lysosomes, they carry out other functions as well. **Food vacuoles,** formed by phagocytosis, have already been mentioned (see Figure 6.14a). Many freshwater protists have **contractile vacuoles** that pump excess water out of the cell, thereby maintaining the appropriate concentration of salts and other molecules (see Figure 7.14). Mature plant cells generally contain a large **central vacuole (Figure 6.15)** enclosed by a membrane called the **tonoplast.** The central vacuole develops by the coalescence of smaller vacuoles, themselves derived from the endoplasmic reticulum and Golgi apparatus. The vacuole is in this way an integral part of a plant cell's endomembrane system. Like all cellular membranes, the tonoplast is selective in transporting solutes; as a result, the solution inside the vacuole, called cell sap, differs in composition from the cytosol.

The plant cell's central vacuole is a versatile compartment. It can hold reserves of important organic compounds, such as the proteins stockpiled in the vacuoles of storage cells in seeds. It is also the plant cell's main repository of inorganic ions, such as potassium and chloride. Many plant cells use their vacuoles as disposal sites for metabolic by-products that would endanger the cell if they accumulated in the cytosol. Some vacuoles contain pigments that color the cells, such as the red and blue pigments of petals that help attract pollinating insects to flowers. Vacuoles may also help protect the plant against predators by containing compounds that are poisonous or unpalatable to animals. The vacuole has a major role in the growth of plant cells, which enlarge as their vacuoles absorb water, enabling the cell to become larger with a minimal investment in new cytoplasm. And because of the large vacuole, the cytosol often occupies only a thin layer between the plasma membrane and the tonoplast, so the ratio of membrane surface to cytosolic volume is great, even for a large plant cell.

The Endomembrane System: *A Review*

Figure 6.16 reviews the endomembrane system, showing the flow of membrane lipids and proteins through the various organelles. As the membrane moves from the ER to the Golgi and then elsewhere, its molecular composition and metabolic functions are modified, along with those of its contents. The endomembrane system is a complex and dynamic player in the cell's compartmental organization.

We'll continue our tour of the cell with some membranous organelles that are *not* closely related to the endomembrane system, but play crucial roles in the energy transformations carried out by cells.

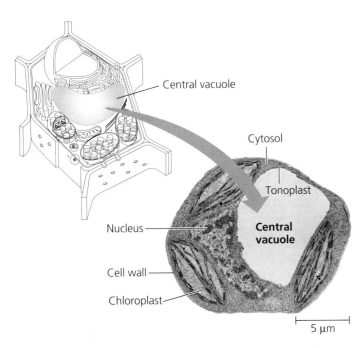

▲ **Figure 6.15 The plant cell vacuole.** The central vacuole is usually the largest compartment in a plant cell; the rest of the cytoplasm is generally confined to a narrow zone between the vacuolar membrane (tonoplast) and the plasma membrane (TEM).

Central vacuole
Cytosol
Tonoplast
Central vacuole
Nucleus
Cell wall
Chloroplast
5 μm

Concept Check 6.4

1. Describe the structural and functional distinctions between rough and smooth ER.
2. Imagine a protein that functions in the ER, but requires modification in the Golgi apparatus before it can achieve that function. Describe the protein's path through the cell, starting with the mRNA molecule that specifies the protein.
3. How do transport vesicles serve to integrate the endomembrane system?

For suggested answers, see Appendix A.

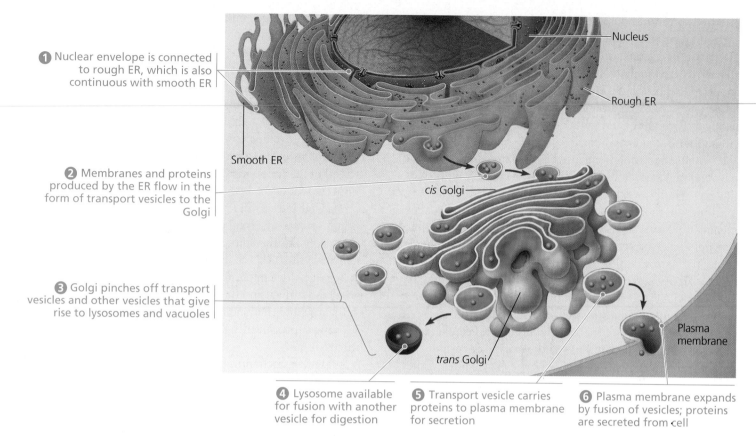

① Nuclear envelope is connected to rough ER, which is also continuous with smooth ER

Nucleus

Rough ER

Smooth ER

② Membranes and proteins produced by the ER flow in the form of transport vesicles to the Golgi

cis Golgi

③ Golgi pinches off transport vesicles and other vesicles that give rise to lysosomes and vacuoles

Plasma membrane

trans Golgi

④ Lysosome available for fusion with another vesicle for digestion

⑤ Transport vesicle carries proteins to plasma membrane for secretion

⑥ Plasma membrane expands by fusion of vesicles; proteins are secreted from cell

▲ **Figure 6.16 Review: relationships among organelles of the endomembrane system.** The red arrows show some of the migration pathways for membranes and the materials they enclose.

Concept **6.5**

Mitochondria and chloroplasts change energy from one form to another

Organisms transform energy they acquire from their surroundings. In eukaryotic cells, mitochondria and chloroplasts are the organelles that convert energy to forms that cells can use for work. **Mitochondria** (singular, *mitochondrion*) are the sites of cellular respiration, the metabolic process that generates ATP by extracting energy from sugars, fats, and other fuels with the help of oxygen. **Chloroplasts,** found only in plants and algae, are the sites of photosynthesis. They convert solar energy to chemical energy by absorbing sunlight and using it to drive the synthesis of organic compounds such as sugars from carbon dioxide and water.

Although mitochondria and chloroplasts are enclosed by membranes, they are not part of the endomembrane system. In contrast to organelles of the endomembrane system, each of these organelles has at least two membranes separating the innermost space from the cytosol. Their membrane proteins are made not by the ER, but by free ribosomes in the cytosol and by ribosomes contained within these organelles themselves. Not only do these organelles have ribosomes, but they also contain a small amount of DNA. It is this DNA that programs the synthesis of the proteins made on the organelle's own ribosomes. (Proteins imported from the cytosol—constituting most of the organelle's proteins—are programmed by nuclear DNA.) Mitochondria and chloroplasts are semiautonomous organelles that grow and reproduce within the cell. In Chapters 9 and 10, we will focus on how mitochondria and chloroplasts function. We will consider the evolution of these organelles in Chapter 28. Here we are concerned mainly with the structure of these energy transformers.

In this section, we will also consider the **peroxisome,** an oxidative organelle that is not part of the endomembrane system. Like mitochondria and chloroplasts, the peroxisome imports its proteins primarily from the cytosol.

Mitochondria: Chemical Energy Conversion

Mitochondria are found in nearly all eukaryotic cells, including those of plants, animals, fungi, and protists. Some cells have a single large mitochondrion, but more often a cell has hundreds or even thousands of mitochondria; the number is correlated with the cell's level of metabolic activity. For example, motile or contractile cells have proportionally more mitochondria per volume than less active cells. Mitochondria are about 1–10 μm long. Time-lapse films of living cells reveal mitochondria moving around, changing their shapes, and dividing in two, unlike the static cylinders seen in electron micrographs of dead cells.

The mitochondrion is enclosed by two membranes, each a phospholipid bilayer with a unique collection of embedded proteins **(Figure 6.17)**. The outer membrane is smooth, but the inner membrane is convoluted, with infoldings called **cristae**. The inner membrane divides the mitochondrion into two internal compartments. The first is the intermembrane space, the narrow region between the inner and outer membranes. The second compartment, the **mitochondrial matrix,** is enclosed by the inner membrane. The matrix contains many different enzymes as well as the mitochondrial DNA and ribosomes. Some of the metabolic steps of cellular respiration are catalyzed by enzymes in the matrix. Other proteins that function in respiration, including the enzyme that makes ATP, are built into the inner membrane. As highly folded surfaces, the cristae give the inner mitochondrial membrane a large surface area for these proteins, thus enhancing the productivity of cellular respiration. This is another example of structure fitting function.

Chloroplasts: Capture of Light Energy

The chloroplast is a specialized member of a family of closely related plant organelles called **plastids.** *Amyloplasts* are colorless plastids that store starch (amylose), particularly in roots and tubers. *Chromoplasts* have pigments that give fruits and flowers their orange and yellow hues. *Chloroplasts* contain the green pigment chlorophyll, along with enzymes and other molecules that function in the photosynthetic production of sugar. These lens-shaped organelles, measuring about 2 μm by 5 μm, are found in leaves and other green organs of plants and in algae **(Figure 6.18)**.

The contents of a chloroplast are partitioned from the cytosol by an envelope consisting of two membranes separated by a very narrow intermembrane space. Inside the chloroplast is another membranous system in the form of flattened, interconnected sacs called **thylakoids.** In some regions, thylakoids are stacked like poker chips; each stack is called a **granum** (plural, *grana*). The fluid outside the thylakoids is the **stroma,** which contains the chloroplast DNA and ribosomes as well as many enzymes. The membranes of the chloroplast divide the chloroplast space into three compartments: the intermembrane space, the stroma, and the thylakoid space. In Chapter 10, you will learn how this compartmental organization enables the chloroplast to convert light energy to chemical energy during photosynthesis.

As with mitochondria, the static and rigid appearance of chloroplasts in micrographs or schematic diagrams is not true to their dynamic behavior in the living cell. Their shapes are changeable, and they grow and occasionally pinch in two, reproducing themselves. They are mobile and move around the cell with mitochondria and other organelles along tracks of the cytoskeleton, a structural network we will consider later in this chapter.

Peroxisomes: Oxidation

The peroxisome is a specialized metabolic compartment bounded by a single membrane **(Figure 6.19)**. Peroxisomes

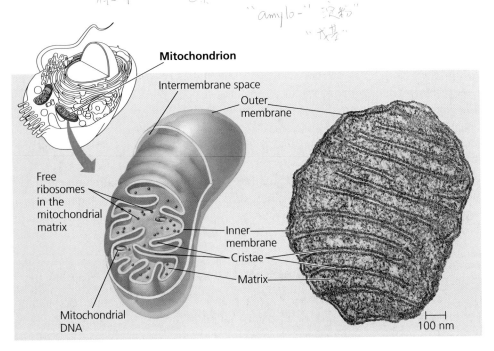

Mitochondrion

Intermembrane space

Outer membrane

Free ribosomes in the mitochondrial matrix

Inner membrane

Cristae

Matrix

Mitochondrial DNA

100 nm

◀ **Figure 6.17 The mitochondrion, site of cellular respiration.** The inner and outer membranes of the mitochondrion are evident in the drawing and micrograph (TEM). The cristae are infoldings of the inner membrane. The cutaway drawing shows the two compartments bounded by the membranes: the intermembrane space and the mitochondrial matrix. Free ribosomes are seen in the matrix, along with one to several copies of the mitochondrial genome (DNA). The DNA molecules are usually circular and are attached to the inner mitochondrial membrane.

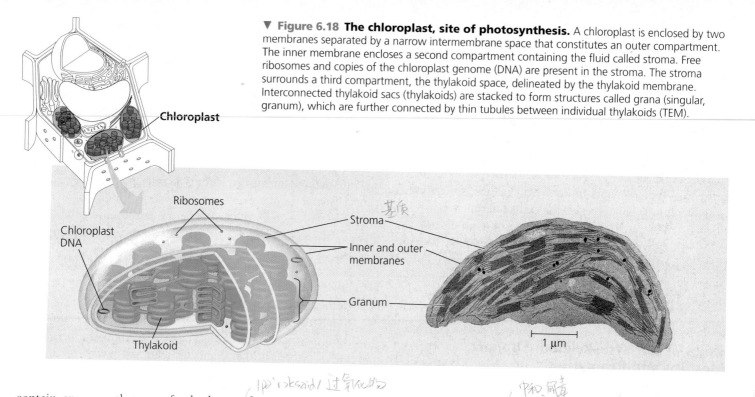

▼ **Figure 6.18 The chloroplast, site of photosynthesis.** A chloroplast is enclosed by two membranes separated by a narrow intermembrane space that constitutes an outer compartment. The inner membrane encloses a second compartment containing the fluid called stroma. Free ribosomes and copies of the chloroplast genome (DNA) are present in the stroma. The stroma surrounds a third compartment, the thylakoid space, delineated by the thylakoid membrane. Interconnected thylakoid sacs (thylakoids) are stacked to form structures called grana (singular, granum), which are further connected by thin tubules between individual thylakoids (TEM).

contain enzymes that transfer hydrogen from various substrates to oxygen, producing hydrogen peroxide (H_2O_2) as a by-product, from which the organelle derives its name. These reactions may have many different functions. Some peroxisomes use oxygen to break fatty acids down into smaller molecules that can then be transported to mitochondria, where they are used as fuel for cellular respiration. Peroxisomes in the liver detoxify alcohol and other harmful compounds by transferring hydrogen from the poisons to oxygen. The H_2O_2 formed by peroxisome metabolism is itself toxic, but the organelle contains an enzyme that converts the H_2O_2 to water. Enclosing in the same space both the enzymes that produce hydrogen peroxide and those that dispose of this toxic compound is another example of how the cell's compartmental structure is crucial to its functions.

Specialized peroxisomes called *glyoxysomes* are found in the fat-storing tissues of plant seeds. These organelles contain enzymes that initiate the conversion of fatty acids to sugar, which the emerging seedling can use as a source of energy and carbon until it is able to produce its own sugar by photosynthesis.

Unlike lysosomes, peroxisomes do not bud from the endomembrane system. They grow larger by incorporating proteins made primarily in the cytosol, lipids made in the ER, and lipids synthesized within the peroxisome itself. Peroxisomes may increase in number by splitting in two when they reach a certain size.

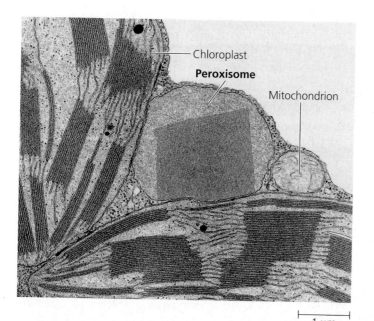

▲ **Figure 6.19 Peroxisomes.** Peroxisomes are roughly spherical and often have a granular or crystalline core that is thought to be a dense collection of enzyme molecules. This peroxisome is in a leaf cell. Notice its proximity to two chloroplasts and a mitochondrion. These organelles cooperate with peroxisomes in certain metabolic functions (TEM).

Concept Check 6.5

1. Describe at least two common characteristics of chloroplasts and mitochondria.
2. Explain the characteristics of mitochondria and chloroplasts that place them in a separate category from organelles in the endomembrane system.

For suggested answers, see Appendix A.

The cytoskeleton is a network of fibers that organizes structures and activities in the cell

In the early days of electron microscopy, biologists thought that the organelles of a eukaryotic cell floated freely in the cytosol. But improvements in both light microscopy and electron microscopy have revealed the **cytoskeleton,** a network of fibers extending throughout the cytoplasm **(Figure 6.20)**. The cytoskeleton, which plays a major role in organizing the structures and activities of the cell, is composed of three types of molecular structures: microtubules, microfilaments, and intermediate filaments **(Table 6.1)**.

Roles of the Cytoskeleton: Support, Motility, and Regulation

The most obvious function of the cytoskeleton is to give mechanical support to the cell and maintain its shape. This is especially important for animal cells, which lack walls. The remarkable strength and resilience of the cytoskeleton as a whole is based on its architecture. Like a geodesic dome, the cytoskeleton is stabilized by a balance between opposing forces exerted by its elements. And just as the skeleton of an animal helps fix the positions of other body parts, the cytoskeleton provides anchorage for many organelles and even cytosolic enzyme molecules. The cytoskeleton is more dynamic than an animal skeleton, however. It can be quickly dismantled in one part of the cell and reassembled in a new location, changing the shape of the cell.

The cytoskeleton is also involved in several types of cell motility (movement). The term *cell motility* encompasses both changes in cell location and more limited movements of parts of the cell. Cell motility generally requires the interaction of the cytoskeleton with proteins called **motor proteins.** Examples of such cell motility abound. Cytoskeletal elements and motor proteins work together with plasma membrane molecules to allow whole cells to move along fibers outside the cell. Motor proteins bring about the movements of cilia and flagella by gripping microtubules within those organelles and propelling them past each other. A similar mechanism involving microfilaments causes muscle cells to contract. Inside the cell, vesicles often travel to their destinations along "monorails" provided by the cytoskeleton. For example, this is how vesicles containing neurotransmitter molecules migrate to the tips of axons, the long extensions of nerve cells that release these molecules as chemical signals to adjacent nerve cells **(Figure 6.21)**. The vesicles that bud off from the ER travel to the Golgi along tracks built of cytoskeletal elements. It is the cytoskeleton that manipulates the plasma membrane to form food vacuoles during phagocytosis. Finally, the streaming of cytoplasm that circulates materials within many large plant cells is yet another kind of cellular movement brought about by components of the cytoskeleton.

(a) Motor proteins that attach to receptors on organelles can "walk" the organelles along microtubules or, in some cases, microfilaments.

(b) Vesicles containing neurotransmitters migrate to the tips of nerve cell axons via the mechanism in (a). In this SEM of a squid giant axon, two vesicles can be seen moving along a microtubule. (A separate part of the experiment provided the evidence that they were in fact moving.)

▲ Figure 6.21 **Motor proteins and the cytoskeleton.**

▲ Figure 6.20 **The cytoskeleton.** In this TEM, prepared by a method known as deep-etching, the thicker, hollow microtubules and the thinner, solid microfilaments are visible. A third component of the cytoskeleton, intermediate filaments, is not evident here.

Table 6.1 The Structure and Function of the Cytoskeleton

Property	Microtubules (Tubulin Polymers)	Microfilaments (Actin Filaments)	Intermediate Filaments
Structure	Hollow tubes; wall consists of 13 columns of tubulin molecules	Two intertwined strands of actin, each a polymer of actin subunits	Fibrous proteins supercoiled into thicker cables
Diameter	25 nm with 15-nm lumen	7 nm	8–12 nm
Protein subunits	Tubulin, consisting of α-tubulin and β-tubulin	Actin	One of several different proteins of the keratin family, depending on cell type
Main functions	Maintenance of cell shape (compression-resisting "girders") Cell motility (as in cilia or flagella) Chromosome movements in cell division Organelle movements	Maintenance of cell shape (tension-bearing elements) Changes in cell shape Muscle contraction Cytoplasmic streaming Cell motility (as in pseudopodia) Cell division (cleavage furrow formation)	Maintenance of cell shape (tension-bearing elements) Anchorage of nucleus and certain other organelles Formation of nuclear lamina

Micrographs of fibroblasts, a favorite cell type for cell biology studies. Each has been experimentally treated to fluorescently tag the structure of interest.

10 μm

10 μm

5 μm

Column of tubulin dimers
25 nm
α   β   Tubulin dimer

Actin subunit
7 nm

Protein subunits (keratins)
Fibrous subunits
8–12 nm

The most recent addition to the list of possible cytoskeletal functions is the regulation of biochemical activities in the cell. Mounting evidence suggests that the cytoskeleton can transmit mechanical forces exerted by extracellular molecules via surface proteins of the cell to its interior—and even into the nucleus. In one experiment, investigators used a micromanipulation device to pull on certain plasma membrane proteins attached to the cytoskeleton. A video microscope captured almost instantaneous rearrangements of nucleoli and other structures in the nucleus. In this way, the transmission of naturally occurring mechanical signals by the cytoskeleton may help regulate cell function.

Components of the Cytoskeleton

Now let's look more closely at the three main types of fibers that make up the cytoskeleton (see Table 6.1). **Microtubules** are the thickest of the three types; **microfilaments** (also called actin filaments) are the thinnest; and **intermediate filaments** are fibers with diameters in a middle range.

Microtubules

Microtubules are found in the cytoplasm of all eukaryotic cells. They are hollow rods measuring about 25 nm in diameter and from 200 nm to 25 µm in length. The wall of the hollow tube is constructed from a globular protein called tubulin. Each tubulin molecule is a dimer consisting of two slightly different polypeptide subunits, α-tubulin and β-tubulin. A microtubule grows in length by adding tubulin dimers to its ends. Microtubules can be disassembled and their tubulin used to build microtubules elsewhere in the cell.

Microtubules shape and support the cell and also serve as tracks along which organelles equipped with motor proteins can move (see Figure 6.21). For example, microtubules guide secretory vesicles from the Golgi apparatus to the plasma membrane. Microtubules are also responsible for the separation of chromosomes during cell division (see Chapter 12).

Centrosomes and Centrioles. In many cells, microtubules grow out from a **centrosome**, a region often located near the nucleus that is considered to be a "microtubule-organizing center." These microtubules function as compression-resisting girders of the cytoskeleton. Within the centrosome of an animal cell are a pair of **centrioles**, each composed of nine sets of triplet microtubules arranged in a ring **(Figure 6.22)**. Before a cell divides, the centrioles replicate. Although centrioles may help organize microtubule assembly, they are not essential for this function in all eukaryotes; centrosomes of most plants lack centrioles, but have well-organized microtubules.

Cilia and Flagella. In eukaryotes, a specialized arrangement of microtubules is responsible for the beating of **flagella** (singular, *flagellum*) and **cilia** (singular, *cilium*), locomotor appendages that protrude from some cells. Many unicellular eukaryotic organisms are propelled through water by cilia or flagella, and the sperm of animals, algae, and some plants have flagella. When cilia or flagella extend from cells that are held in place as part of a tissue layer, they can move fluid over the surface of the tissue. For example, the ciliated lining of the windpipe sweeps mucus containing trapped debris out of the lungs (see Figure 6.4). In a woman's reproductive tract, the cilia lining the oviducts (fallopian tubes) help move an egg toward the uterus.

Cilia usually occur in large numbers on the cell surface. They are about 0.25 µm in diameter and about 2–20 µm in length. Flagella are the same diameter but longer than cilia, measuring 10–200 µm in length. Also, flagella are usually limited to just one or a few per cell.

Flagella and cilia differ in their beating patterns **(Figure 6.23)**. A flagellum has an undulating motion that generates force in the same direction as the flagellum's axis. In contrast, cilia work more like oars, with alternating power and recovery strokes generating force in a direction perpendicular to the cilium's axis.

Though different in length, number per cell, and beating pattern, cilia and flagella share a common ultrastructure. A

▲ **Figure 6.22 Centrosome containing a pair of centrioles.** An animal cell has a pair of centrioles within its centrosome, the region near the nucleus where the cell's microtubules are initiated. The centrioles, each about 250 nm (0.25 µm) in diameter, are found at right angles to each other, and each is made up of nine sets of three microtubules. The blue portions of the drawing represent nontubulin proteins that connect the microtubule triplets (TEM).

cilium or flagellum has a core of microtubules sheathed in an extension of the plasma membrane **(Figure 6.24)**. Nine doublets of microtubules, the members of each pair sharing part of their walls, are arranged in a ring. In the center of the ring are two single microtubules. This arrangement, referred to as the "9 + 2" pattern, is found in nearly all eukaryotic flagella and cilia. (The flagella of motile prokaryotes, discussed in Chapter 27, do not contain microtubules.) Flexible "wagon wheels" of cross-linking proteins, evenly spaced along the length of the cilium or flagellum, connect the outer doublets to each other (the wheel rim) and to the two central microtubules (the wheel spokes). Each outer doublet also has pairs of side-arms spaced along its length and reaching toward the neighboring doublet; these are motor proteins. The microtubule assembly of a cilium or flagellum is anchored in the cell by a **basal body**, which is structurally identical to a centriole. In fact, in many animals (including humans), the basal body of the fertilizing sperm's flagellum enters the egg and becomes a centriole.

Each motor protein extending from one microtubule doublet to the next is a large protein called **dynein**, which is composed

(a) Motion of flagella. A flagellum usually undulates, its snakelike motion driving a cell in the same direction as the axis of the flagellum. Propulsion of a human sperm cell is an example of flagellate locomotion (LM).

Direction of swimming

5 µm

(b) Motion of cilia. Cilia have a back-and-forth motion that moves the cell in a direction perpendicular to the axis of the cilium. A dense nap of cilia, beating at a rate of about 40 to 60 strokes a second, covers this *Colpidium*, a freshwater protozoan (SEM).

Direction of organism's movement

Direction of active stroke   Direction of recovery stroke

15 µm

Microtubules

Plasma membrane

Basal body

0.5 µm

(a) A longitudinal section of a cilium shows microtubules running the length of the structure (TEM).

0.1 µm

Outer microtubule doublet

Plasma membrane

Dynein arms

Central microtubule

Cross-linking proteins inside outer doublets

Radial spoke

(b) A cross section through the cilium shows the "9 + 2" arrangement of microtubules (TEM). The outer microtubule doublets and the two central microtubules are held together by cross-linking proteins (purple in art), including the radial spokes. The doublets also have attached motor proteins, the dynein arms (red in art).

0.1 µm

Triplet

(c) Basal body: The nine outer doublets of a cilium or flagellum extend into the basal body, where each doublet joins another microtubule to form a ring of nine triplets. Each triplet is connected to the next by nontubulin proteins (blue). The two central microtubules terminate above the basal body (TEM).

Cross section of basal body

▲ **Figure 6.24 Ultrastructure of a eukaryotic flagellum or cilium.**

of several polypeptides. These dynein arms are responsible for the bending movements of cilia and flagella. A dynein arm performs a complex cycle of movements caused by changes in the conformation of the protein, with ATP providing the energy for these changes (Figure 6.25).

The mechanics of dynein "walking" are reminiscent of a cat climbing a tree by attaching its claws, moving its legs, releasing its front claws, and grabbing again farther up the tree. Similarly, the dynein arms of one doublet attach to an adjacent doublet and pull so that the doublets slide past each other in opposite directions. The arms then release from the other doublet and reattach a little farther along its length. Without any restraints on the movement of the microtubule doublets, one doublet would continue to "walk" along and slide past the surface of the other, elongating the cilium or flagellum rather than bending it (see Figure 6.25a). For lateral movement of a cilium or flagellum, the dynein "walking" must have something to pull against, as when the muscles in your leg pull against your bones to move your knee. In cilia and flagella, the microtubule doublets seem to be held in place by the cross-linking proteins just inside the outer doublets and by the radial spokes and other structural elements. Thus, neighboring doublets cannot slide past each other very far. Instead, the forces exerted by the dynein arms cause the doublets to curve, bending the cilium or flagellum (see Figure 6.25b and c).

Microfilaments (Actin Filaments)

Microfilaments are solid rods about 7 nm in diameter. They are also called actin filaments, because they are built from molecules of **actin**, a globular protein. A microfilament is a twisted double chain of actin subunits (see Table 6.1). Besides occurring as linear filaments, microfilaments can form structural networks, due to the presence of proteins that bind along the side of an actin filament and allow a new filament to extend as a branch. Microfilaments seem to be present in all eukaryotic cells.

In contrast to the compression-resisting role of microtubules, the structural role of microfilaments in the cytoskeleton is to bear tension (pulling forces). The ability of microfilaments to form a three-dimensional network just inside the plasma membrane helps support the cell's shape. This network gives the cortex (outer cytoplasmic layer) of a cell the semisolid consistency of a gel, in contrast with the more fluid (sol) state of the interior cytoplasm. In animal cells specialized for transporting materials across the plasma membrane, such as intestinal cells, bundles of microfilaments make up the core of microvilli, the previously mentioned delicate projections that increase the cell surface area (Figure 6.26).

Microfilaments are well known for their role in cell motility, particularly as part of the contractile apparatus of muscle

(a) Dynein "walking." Powered by ATP, the dynein arms of one microtubule doublet grip the adjacent doublet, push it up, release, and then grip again. If the two microtubule doublets were not attached, they would slide relative to each other.

(b) Effect of cross-linking proteins. In a cilium or flagellum, two adjacent doublets cannot slide far because they are physically restrained by proteins, so they bend. (Only two of the nine outer doublets in Figure 6.24b are shown here.)

(c) Wavelike motion. Localized, synchronized activation of many dynein arms probably causes a bend to begin at the base of the cilium or flagellum and move outward toward the tip. Many successive bends, such as the ones shown here to the left and right, result in a wavelike motion. In this diagram, the two central microtubules and the cross-linking proteins are not shown.

▲ Figure 6.25 **How dynein "walking" moves flagella and cilia.**

Microvillus

Plasma membrane

Microfilaments (actin filaments)

Intermediate filaments

0.25 µm

▲ **Figure 6.26 A structural role of microfilaments.** The surface area of this nutrient-absorbing intestinal cell is increased by its many microvilli (singular, microvillus), cellular extensions reinforced by bundles of microfilaments. These actin filaments are anchored to a network of intermediate filaments (TEM).

Muscle cell

Actin filament

Myosin filament
Myosin arm

(a) Myosin motors in muscle cell contraction. The "walking" of myosin arms drives the parallel myosin and actin filaments past each other so that the actin filaments approach each other in the middle (red arrows). This shortens the muscle and the cell. Muscle contraction involves contraction of many muscle cells at the same time.

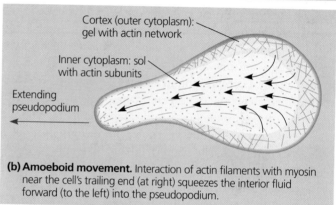

Cortex (outer cytoplasm): gel with actin network

Inner cytoplasm: sol with actin subunits

Extending pseudopodium

(b) Amoeboid movement. Interaction of actin filaments with myosin near the cell's trailing end (at right) squeezes the interior fluid forward (to the left) into the pseudopodium.

Nonmoving cytoplasm (gel)

Chloroplast

Streaming cytoplasm (sol)

Vacuole

Parallel actin filaments

Cell wall

(c) Cytoplasmic streaming in plant cells. A layer of cytoplasm cycles around the cell, moving over a carpet of parallel actin filaments. Myosin motors attached to organelles in the fluid cytosol may drive the streaming by interacting with the actin.

▲ **Figure 6.27 Microfilaments and motility.** In the three examples shown in this figure, cell nuclei and most other organelles have been omitted for clarity.

cells. Thousands of actin filaments are arranged parallel to one another along the length of a muscle cell, interdigitated with thicker filaments made of a protein called **myosin (Figure 6.27a)**. Myosin acts as a motor protein by means of projections (arms) that "walk" along the actin filaments. Contraction of the muscle cell results from the actin and myosin filaments sliding past one another in this way, shortening the cell. In other kinds of cells, actin filaments are associated with myosin in miniature and less elaborate versions of the arrangement in muscle cells. These actin-myosin aggregates are responsible for localized contractions of cells. For example, a contracting belt of microfilaments forms a cleavage furrow that pinches a dividing animal cell into two daughter cells.

Localized contraction brought about by actin and myosin also plays a role in amoeboid movement **(Figure 6.27b)**, in which a cell, such as an amoeba, for example, crawls along a surface by extending and flowing into cellular extensions called **pseudopodia** (from the Greek *pseudes*, false, and *pod,* foot). Pseudopodia extend and contract through the reversible assembly of actin subunits into microfilaments and of microfilaments into networks that convert cytoplasm from sol to

gel. According to a widely accepted model, filaments near the cell's trailing end interact with myosin, causing contraction. Like squeezing on a toothpaste tube, this contraction forces the interior fluid into the pseudopodium, where the actin network has been weakened. The pseudopodium extends until the actin reassembles into a network. Amoebas are not the only cells that move by crawling; so do many cells in the animal body, including some white blood cells.

In plant cells, both actin-myosin interactions and sol-gel transformations brought about by actin may be involved in **cytoplasmic streaming,** a circular flow of cytoplasm within cells **(Figure 6.27c)**. This movement, which is especially common in large plant cells, speeds the distribution of materials within the cell.

Intermediate Filaments

Intermediate filaments are named for their diameter, which, at 8–12 nm, is larger than the diameter of microfilaments but smaller than that of microtubules (see Table 6.1, p. 113). Specialized for bearing tension (like microfilaments), intermediate filaments are a diverse class of cytoskeletal elements. Each type is constructed from a different molecular subunit belonging to a family of proteins whose members include the keratins. Microtubules and microfilaments, in contrast, are consistent in diameter and composition in all eukaryotic cells.

Intermediate filaments are more permanent fixtures of cells than are microfilaments and microtubules, which are often disassembled and reassembled in various parts of a cell. Even after cells die, intermediate filament networks often persist; for example, the outer layer of our skin consists of dead skin cells full of keratin proteins. Chemical treatments that remove microfilaments and microtubules from the cytoplasm of living cells leave a web of intermediate filaments that retains its original shape. Such experiments suggest that intermediate filaments are especially important in reinforcing the shape of a cell and fixing the position of certain organelles. For example, the nucleus commonly sits within a cage made of intermediate filaments, fixed in location by branches of the filaments that extend into the cytoplasm. Other intermediate filaments make up the nuclear lamina that lines the interior of the nuclear envelope (see Figure 6.10). In cases where the shape of the entire cell is correlated with function, intermediate filaments support that shape. For instance, the long extensions (axons) of nerve cells that transmit impulses are strengthened by one class of intermediate filament. Thus, the various kinds of intermediate filaments may function as the framework of the entire cytoskeleton.

Extracellular components and connections between cells help coordinate cellular activities

Having crisscrossed the interior of the cell to explore various organelles, we complete our tour of the cell by returning to the surface of this microscopic world, where there are additional structures with important functions. The plasma membrane is usually regarded as the boundary of the living cell, but most cells synthesize and secrete materials of one kind or another that are external to the plasma membrane. Although they are outside the cell, the study of these extracellular structures is central to cell biology because they are involved in so many cellular functions.

Cell Walls of Plants

The **cell wall** is an extracellular structure of plant cells that distinguishes them from animal cells. The wall protects the plant cell, maintains its shape, and prevents excessive uptake of water. On the level of the whole plant, the strong walls of specialized cells hold the plant up against the force of gravity. Prokaryotes, fungi, and some protists also have cell walls, but we will postpone discussion of them until Unit Five.

Plant cell walls are much thicker than the plasma membrane, ranging from 0.1 μm to several micrometers. The exact chemical composition of the wall varies from species to species and even from one cell type to another in the same plant, but the basic design of the wall is consistent. Microfibrils made of the polysaccharide cellulose (see Figure 5.8) are embedded in a matrix of other polysaccharides and protein. This combination of materials, strong fibers in a "ground substance" (matrix), is the same basic architectural design found in steel-reinforced concrete and in fiberglass.

A young plant cell first secretes a relatively thin and flexible wall called the **primary cell wall (Figure 6.28)**. Between primary walls of adjacent cells is the **middle lamella,** a thin layer rich in sticky polysaccharides called pectins. The middle lamella glues adjacent cells together (pectin is used as a thickening agent in jams and jellies). When the cell matures and stops growing, it strengthens its wall. Some plant cells do this simply by secreting hardening substances into the primary wall. Other cells add a **secondary cell wall** between the plasma membrane and the primary wall. The secondary wall, often deposited in several laminated layers, has a strong and durable matrix that affords the cell protection and support. Wood, for example, consists mainly of secondary walls. Plant cell walls are commonly perforated by channels between adjacent cells called plasmodesmata (see Figure 6.28), which will be discussed shortly.

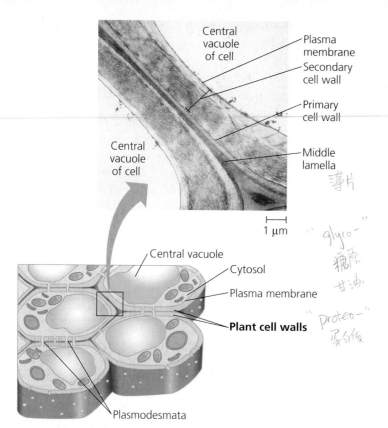

Figure 6.28 labels (clockwise):
- Central vacuole of cell
- Plasma membrane
- Secondary cell wall
- Primary cell wall
- Middle lamella
- Central vacuole of cell

1 μm

- Central vacuole
- Cytosol
- Plasma membrane
- **Plant cell walls**
- Plasmodesmata

▲ **Figure 6.28 Plant cell walls.** The orientation drawing shows several cells, each with a large vacuole, a nucleus, and several chloroplasts and mitochondria. The transmission electron micrograph (TEM) shows the cell walls where two cells come together. The multilayered partition between plant cells consists of adjoining walls individually secreted by the cells.

The Extracellular Matrix (ECM) of Animal Cells

Although animal cells lack walls akin to those of plant cells, they do have an elaborate **extracellular matrix (ECM)** (Figure 6.29). The main ingredients of the ECM are glycoproteins secreted by the cells. (Recall that glycoproteins are proteins with covalently bonded carbohydrate, usually short chains of sugars.) The most abundant glycoprotein in the ECM of most animal cells is **collagen**, which forms strong fibers outside the cells. In fact, collagen accounts for about half of the total protein in the human body. The collagen fibers are embedded in a network woven from **proteoglycans**, which are glycoproteins of another class. A proteoglycan molecule consists of a small core protein with many carbohydrate chains covalently attached, so that it may be up to 95% carbohydrate. Large proteoglycan complexes can form when hundreds of proteoglycans become noncovalently attached to a single long polysaccharide molecule, as shown in Figure 6.29. Some cells are attached to the ECM by still other ECM glycoproteins, including **fibronectin**. Fibronectin and other ECM proteins bind to cell surface receptor proteins called **integrins** that are built into the plasma membrane. Integrins span the membrane and bind on their cytoplasmic side to associated proteins attached to microfilaments of the cytoskeleton. The name integrin is based on the word *integrate*: Integrins are in a position to transmit changes between the ECM and the cytoskeleton and thus to integrate changes occurring outside and inside the cell.

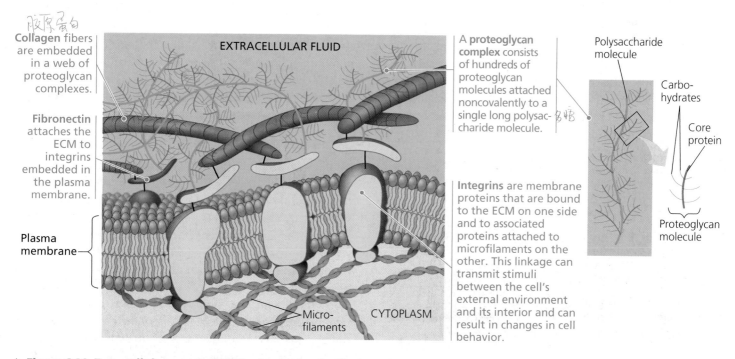

Collagen fibers are embedded in a web of proteoglycan complexes.

Fibronectin attaches the ECM to integrins embedded in the plasma membrane.

Plasma membrane

EXTRACELLULAR FLUID

A **proteoglycan complex** consists of hundreds of proteoglycan molecules attached noncovalently to a single long polysaccharide molecule.

Integrins are membrane proteins that are bound to the ECM on one side and to associated proteins attached to microfilaments on the other. This linkage can transmit stimuli between the cell's external environment and its interior and can result in changes in cell behavior.

Micro-filaments

CYTOPLASM

Polysaccharide molecule

Carbohydrates

Core protein

Proteoglycan molecule

▲ **Figure 6.29 Extracellular matrix (ECM) of an animal cell.** The molecular composition and structure of the ECM varies from one cell type to another. In this example, three different types of glycoproteins are present: proteoglycans, collagen, and fibronectin.

Current research on fibronectin, other ECM molecules, and integrins is revealing the influential role of the extracellular matrix in the lives of cells. By communicating with a cell through integrins, the ECM can regulate a cell's behavior. For example, some cells in a developing embryo migrate along specific pathways by matching the orientation of their microfilaments to the "grain" of fibers in the extracellular matrix. Researchers are also learning that the extracellular matrix around a cell can influence the activity of genes in the nucleus. Information about the ECM probably reaches the nucleus by a combination of mechanical and chemical signaling pathways. Mechanical signaling involves fibronectin, integrins, and microfilaments of the cytoskeleton. Changes in the cytoskeleton may in turn trigger chemical signaling pathways inside the cell, leading to changes in the set of proteins being made by the cell and therefore changes in the cell's function. In this way, the extracellular matrix of a particular tissue may help coordinate the behavior of all the cells within that tissue. Direct connections between cells also function in this coordination, as we discuss next.

Intercellular Junctions

The many cells of an animal or plant are organized into tissues, organs, and organ systems. Neighboring cells often adhere, interact, and communicate through special patches of direct physical contact.

Plants: Plasmodesmata

It might seem that the nonliving cell walls of plants would isolate cells from one another. But in fact, as shown in **Figure 6.30**, plant cell walls are perforated with channels called **plasmodesmata** (singular, *plasmodesma;* from the Greek *desmos,* to bind). Cytosol passes through the plasmodesmata and connects the chemical environments of adjacent cells. These connections unify most of the plant into one living continuum. The plasma membranes of adjacent cells line the channel of each plasmodesma and thus are continuous. Water and small solutes can pass freely from cell to cell, and recent experiments have shown that in certain circumstances, specific proteins and RNA molecules can also do this. The macromolecules to be transported to neighboring cells seem to reach the plasmodesmata by moving along fibers of the cytoskeleton.

Animals: Tight Junctions, Desmosomes, and Gap Junctions

In animals, there are three main types of intercellular junctions: *tight junctions, desmosomes,* and *gap junctions* (which are most like the plasmodesmata of plants). All three types are especially common in epithelial tissue, which lines the internal surfaces of the body. **Figure 6.31** uses epithelial cells of the intestinal lining to illustrate these junctions: please study this figure before moving on.

The Cell: A Living Unit Greater Than the Sum of Its Parts

From our panoramic view of the cell's overall compartmental organization to our close-up inspection of each organelle's architecture, this tour of the cell has provided many opportunities to correlate structure with function. (This would be a good time to review cell structure by returning to Figure 6.9, pp. 100 and 101.) But even as we dissect the cell, remember that none of its organelles works alone. As an example of cellular integration, consider the microscopic scene in **Figure 6.32**. The large cell is a macrophage (see Figure 6.14a). It helps defend the body against infections by ingesting bacteria (the smaller cells) into phagocytic vesicles. The macrophage crawls along a surface and reaches out to the bacteria with thin pseudopodia (called filopodia). Actin filaments interact with other elements of the cytoskeleton in these movements. After the macrophage engulfs the bacteria, they are destroyed by lysosomes. The elaborate endomembrane system produces the lysosomes. The digestive enzymes of the lysosomes and the proteins of the cytoskeleton are all made on ribosomes. And the synthesis of these proteins is programmed by genetic messages dispatched from the DNA in the nucleus. All these processes require energy, which mitochondria supply in the form of ATP. Cellular functions arise from cellular order: The cell is a living unit greater than the sum of its parts.

Cell walls

Interior of cell

Interior of cell

0.5 μm

Plasmodesmata   Plasma membranes

▲ **Figure 6.30 Plasmodesmata between plant cells.** The cytoplasm of one plant cell is continuous with the cytoplasm of its neighbors via plasmodesmata, channels through the cell walls (TEM).

Figure 6.31

Exploring **Intercellular Junctions in Animal Tissues**

Tight junctions prevent fluid from moving across a layer of cells

Tight junction

Tight junctions

Intermediate filaments

Desmosome

Gap junctions

Space between cells

Plasma membranes of adjacent cells

Extracellular matrix

TIGHT JUNCTIONS

At **tight junctions**, the membranes of neighboring cells are very tightly pressed against each other, bound together by specific proteins (purple). Forming continuous seals around the cells, tight junctions prevent leakage of extracellular fluid across a layer of epithelial cells.

0.5 μm

DESMOSOMES

Desmosomes (also called *anchoring junctions*) function like rivets, fastening cells together into strong sheets. Intermediate filaments made of sturdy keratin proteins anchor desmosomes in the cytoplasm.

1 μm

GAP JUNCTIONS

Gap junction

Gap junctions (also called *communicating junctions*) provide cytoplasmic channels from one cell to an adjacent cell. Gap junctions consist of special membrane proteins that surround a pore through which ions, sugars, amino acids, and other small molecules may pass. Gap junctions are necessary for communication between cells in many types of tissues, including heart muscle and animal embryos.

0.1 μm

▶ **Figure 6.32 The emergence of cellular functions from the cooperation of many organelles.** The ability of this macrophage (brown) to recognize, apprehend, and destroy bacteria (yellow) is a coordinated activity of the whole cell. Its cytoskeleton, lysosomes, and plasma membrane are among the components that function in phagocytosis (colorized SEM).

5 μm

Chapter 6 Review

Go to the Campbell Biology website (**www.campbellbiology.com**) or CD-ROM to explore Activities, Investigations, and other interactive study aids.

SUMMARY OF KEY CONCEPTS

Concept 6.1

To study cells, biologists use microscopes and the tools of biochemistry

▶ **Microscopy** (pp. 95–97) Improvements in microscopy have catalyzed progress in the study of cell structure.
Activity *Metric System Review*
Investigation *What Is the Size and Scale of Our World?*

▶ **Isolating Organelles by Cell Fractionation** (p. 97) Cell biologists can obtain pellets enriched in specific organelles by centrifuging disrupted cells.

Concept 6.2

Eukaryotic cells have internal membranes that compartmentalize their functions

▶ **Comparing Prokaryotic and Eukaryotic Cells** (pp. 98–99) All cells are bounded by a plasma membrane. Unlike eukaryotic cells, prokaryotic cells lack nuclei and other membrane-enclosed organelles.
Activity *Prokaryotic Cell Structure and Function*
Activity *Comparing Prokaryotic and Eukaryotic Cells*

▶ **A Panoramic View of the Eukaryotic Cell** (pp. 99–101) Plant and animal cells have most of the same organelles.
Activity *Build an Animal Cell and a Plant Cell*

Concept 6.3

The eukaryotic cell's genetic instructions are housed in the nucleus and carried out by the ribosomes

▶ **The Nucleus: Genetic Library of the Cell** (pp. 102–103) The nucleus houses DNA and nucleoli, where ribosomal subunits are made. Materials pass through pores in the nuclear envelope.

▶ **Ribosomes: Protein Factories in the Cell** (pp. 102–104) Free ribosomes in the cytosol and bound ribosomes on the outside of the ER and the nuclear envelope synthesize proteins.
Activity *Role of the Nucleus and Ribosomes in Protein Synthesis*

Concept 6.4

The endomembrane system regulates protein traffic and performs metabolic functions in the cell

▶ The membranes of the endomembrane system are connected by physical continuity or through transport vesicles (p. 104).

▶ **The Endoplasmic Reticulum: Biosynthetic Factory** (pp. 104–105) Smooth ER synthesizes lipids, metabolizes carbohydrates, stores calcium, and detoxifies poisons. Rough ER has bound ribosomes and produces proteins and membranes, which are distributed by transport vesicles from the ER.

▶ **The Golgi Apparatus: Shipping and Receiving Center** (pp. 105–107) Proteins are transported from the ER to the Golgi, where they are modified, sorted, and released in transport vesicles.

▶ **Lysosomes: Digestive Compartments** (pp. 107–108) Lysosomes are sacs of hydrolytic enzymes. They break down ingested substances and cell macromolecules for recycling.

▶ **Vacuoles: Diverse Maintenance Compartments** (p. 108) A plant cell's central vacuole functions in digestion, storage, waste disposal, cell growth, and protection.

▶ **The Endomembrane System: *A Review*** (pp. 108–109)
Activity *The Endomembrane System*

Concept 6.5

Mitochondria and chloroplasts change energy from one form to another

▶ **Mitochondria: Chemical Energy Conversion** (pp. 109–110) Mitochondria, the sites of cellular respiration, have an outer membrane and an inner membrane that is folded into cristae.

▶ **Chloroplasts: Capture of Light Energy** (pp. 110–111) Chloroplasts contain pigments that function in photosynthesis. Two membranes surround the fluid stroma, which contains thylakoids stacked into grana.
Activity *Build a Chloroplast and a Mitochondrion*

▶ **Peroxisomes: Oxidation** (pp. 110–111) Peroxisomes produce hydrogen peroxide (H_2O_2) and convert it to water.

Concept 6.6

The cytoskeleton is a network of fibers that organizes structures and activities in the cell

▶ **Roles of the Cytoskeleton: Support, Motility, and Regulation** (pp. 112–113) The cytoskeleton functions in structural support for the cell, motility, and signal transmission.

▶ **Components of the Cytoskeleton** (pp. 113–118) Microtubules shape the cell, guide movement of organelles, and help separate the chromosome copies in dividing cells. Cilia and flagella are motile appendages containing microtubules. Microfilaments are thin rods built from actin; they function in muscle contraction, amoeboid movement, cytoplasmic streaming, and support for microvilli. Intermediate filaments support cell shape and fix organelles in place.
Activity *Cilia and Flagella*

Concept 6.7

Extracellular components and connections between cells help coordinate cellular activities

▶ **Cell Walls of Plants** (pp. 118–119) Plant cell walls are made of cellulose fibers embedded in other polysaccharides and protein.

▶ **The Extracellular Matrix (ECM) of Animal Cells** (pp. 119–120) Animal cells secrete glycoproteins that form the ECM, which functions in support, adhesion, movement, and regulation.

▶ **Intercellular Junctions** (pp. 120–121) Plants have plasmodesmata that pass through adjoining cell walls. Animal cells have tight junctions, desmosomes, and gap junctions.
Activity *Cell Junctions*

▶ **The Cell: A Living Unit Greater Than the Sum of Its Parts** (pp. 120–121)
Activity *Review: Animal Cell Structure and Function*
Activity *Review: Plant Cell Structure and Function*

Self-Quiz

1. The symptoms of a certain inherited disorder in humans include breathing problems and, in males, sterility. Which of the following is a reasonable hypothesis for the molecular basis of this disorder? (Explain your answer.)
   a. a defective enzyme in the mitochondria
   b. defective actin molecules in cellular microfilaments
   c. defective dynein molecules in cilia and flagella
   d. abnormal hydrolytic enzymes in the lysosomes
   e. defective ribosome assembly in the nucleolus

2. Choose the statement that correctly characterizes bound ribosomes.
   a. Bound ribosomes are enclosed in their own membrane.
   b. Bound and free ribosomes are structurally different.
   c. Bound ribosomes generally synthesize membrane proteins and secretory proteins.
   d. The most common location for bound ribosomes is the cytoplasmic surface of the plasma membrane.
   e. All of the above.

3. Which of the following is not considered part of the endomembrane system?
   a. nuclear envelope   d. plasma membrane
   b. chloroplast   e. ER
   c. Golgi apparatus

4. Cells of the pancreas will incorporate radioactively labeled amino acids into proteins. This "tagging" of newly synthesized proteins enables a researcher to track the location of these proteins in a cell. In this case, we are tracking an enzyme that is eventually secreted by pancreatic cells. Which of the following is the most likely pathway for movement of this protein in the cell?
   a. ER→Golgi→nucleus
   b. Golgi→ER→lysosome
   c. nucleus→ER→Golgi
   d. ER→Golgi→vesicles that fuse with plasma membrane
   e. ER→lysosomes→vesicles that fuse with plasma membrane

5. Which of the following structures is common to plant *and* animal cells?
   a. chloroplast   d. mitochondrion
   b. wall made of cellulose   e. centriole
   c. tonoplast

6. Which of the following is present in a prokaryotic cell?
   a. mitochondrion   d. chloroplast
   b. ribosome   e. ER
   c. nuclear envelope

7. Which type of cell would probably provide the best opportunity to study lysosomes?
   a. muscle cell   d. leaf cell of a plant
   b. nerve cell   e. bacterial cell
   c. phagocytic white blood cell

8. Which of the following statements is a correct distinction between prokaryotic and eukaryotic cells attributable to the absence of a prokaryotic cytoskeleton?
   a. Organelles are found only in eukaryotic cells.
   b. Cytoplasmic streaming is not observed in prokaryotes.
   c. Only eukaryotic cells are capable of movement.
   d. Prokaryotic cells have cell walls.
   e. Only the eukaryotic cell concentrates its genetic material in a region separate from the rest of the cell.

9. Which of the following structure-function pairs is *mismatched*?
   a. nucleolus; ribosome production
   b. lysosome; intracellular digestion
   c. ribosome; protein synthesis
   d. Golgi; protein trafficking
   e. microtubule; muscle contraction

10. Cyanide binds with at least one of the molecules involved in the production of ATP. Following exposure of a cell to cyanide, most of the cyanide could be expected to be found within the
    a. mitochondria.   d. lysosomes.
    b. ribosomes.   e. endoplasmic reticulum.
    c. peroxisomes.

For Self-Quiz Answers, see Appendix A.

Go to the website or CD-ROM for more quiz questions.

Evolution Connection

Although the similarities among cells reveal the evolutionary unity of life, cells can differ dramatically in structure. Which aspects of cell structure best reveal their evolutionary unity? What are some examples of specialized cellular modifications?

Scientific Inquiry

Imagine protein X, destined to go to the plasma membrane of a cell. Assume that the mRNA carrying the genetic message for protein X has already been translated by ribosomes in a cell culture. You collect the cells, break them open, and then fractionate their contents by differential centrifugation as shown in Figure 6.5. In the pellet of which fraction would you expect to find protein X? Explain your answer by describing the transit of protein X through the cell.

Investigation *What Is the Size and Scale of Our World?*

Science, Technology, and Society

Doctors at a California university removed a man's spleen, standard treatment for a type of leukemia. The disease did not recur. Researchers kept some of the spleen cells alive in a nutrient medium. They found that some of the cells produced a blood protein that showed promise for treating cancer and AIDS. The researchers patented the cells. The patient sued, claiming a share in profits from any products derived from his cells. The California Supreme Court ruled against the patient, stating that his suit "threatens to destroy the economic incentive to conduct important medical research." The U.S. Supreme Court agreed. Do you think the patient was treated fairly? What else would you like to know about this case that might help you make up your mind?

7

Membrane Structure and Function

▲ Figure 7.1 **The plasma membrane.**

Key Concepts

7.1 Cellular membranes are fluid mosaics of lipids and proteins

7.2 Membrane structure results in selective permeability

7.3 Passive transport is diffusion of a substance across a membrane with no energy investment

7.4 Active transport uses energy to move solutes against their gradients

7.5 Bulk transport across the plasma membrane occurs by exocytosis and endocytosis

Overview

Life at the Edge

The plasma membrane is the edge of life, the boundary that separates the living cell from its nonliving surroundings. A remarkable film only about 8 nm thick—it would take over 8,000 to equal the thickness of this page—the plasma membrane controls traffic into and out of the cell it surrounds. Like all biological membranes, the plasma membrane exhibits **selective permeability;** that is, it allows some substances to cross it more easily than others. One of the earliest episodes in the evolution of life may have been the formation of a membrane that enclosed a solution different from the surrounding solution while still permitting the uptake of nutrients and elimination of waste products. This ability of the cell to discriminate in its chemical exchanges with its environment is fundamental to life, and it is the plasma membrane and its component molecules that make this selectivity possible.

In this chapter, you will learn how cellular membranes control the passage of substances. The importance of selective

permeability was highlighted when the 2003 Nobel Prize in Chemistry was awarded to Peter Agre (see the interview on pp. 92–93) and Roderick MacKinnon, two scientists who worked out how water and specific ions are transported into and out of the cell. We will concentrate on the plasma membrane, the outermost membrane of the cell, represented in **Figure 7.1**. However, the same general principles of membrane traffic also apply to the many varieties of internal membranes that partition the eukaryotic cell. To understand how membranes work, we begin by examining their architecture.

Concept **7.1**

Cellular membranes are fluid mosaics of lipids and proteins

Lipids and proteins are the staple ingredients of membranes, although carbohydrates are also important. The most abundant lipids in most membranes are phospholipids. The ability of phospholipids to form membranes is inherent in their molecular structure. A phospholipid is an **amphipathic molecule,** meaning it has both a hydrophilic region and a hydrophobic region (see Figure 5.13). Other types of membrane lipids are also amphipathic. Furthermore, most of the proteins of membranes have both hydrophobic and hydrophilic regions.

How are phospholipids and proteins arranged in the membranes of cells? You encountered the currently accepted model for the arrangement of these molecules in Chapter 6 (see Figure 6.8). In this **fluid mosaic model**, the membrane is a fluid structure with a "mosaic" of various proteins embedded in or attached to a double layer (bilayer) of phospholipids. We'll discuss this model in detail, starting with the story of how it was developed.

Membrane Models: *Scientific Inquiry*

Scientists began building molecular models of the membrane decades before membranes were first seen with the electron microscope in the 1950s. In 1915, membranes isolated from red blood cells were chemically analyzed and found to be composed of lipids and proteins. Ten years later, two Dutch scientists, E. Gorter and F. Grendel, reasoned that cell membranes must actually be phospholipid bilayers. Such a double layer of molecules could exist as a stable boundary between two aqueous compartments because the molecular arrangement shelters the hydrophobic tails of the phospholipids from water while exposing the hydrophilic heads to water **(Figure 7.2)**.

With the conclusion that a phospholipid bilayer was the main fabric of a membrane, the next question was where to place the proteins. Although the heads of phospholipids are hydrophilic, the surface of a membrane consisting of a pure phospholipid bilayer adheres less strongly to water than does the surface of a biological membrane. Given these data, in 1935, Hugh Davson and James Danielli suggested that this difference could be accounted for if the membrane were coated on both sides with hydrophilic proteins. They proposed a sandwich model: a phospholipid bilayer between two layers of proteins.

When researchers first used electron microscopes to study cells in the 1950s, the pictures seemed to support the Davson-Danielli model. By the 1960s, the Davson-Danielli sandwich had become widely accepted as the structure not only of the plasma membrane, but of all the internal membranes of the cell. By the end of that decade, however, many cell biologists recognized two problems with the model. First, the generalization that all membranes of the cell are identical was challenged. Whereas the plasma membrane is 7–8 nm thick and has a three-layered structure in electron micrographs, the inner membrane of the mitochondrion is only 6 nm thick and looks like a row of beads. Mitochondrial membranes also have a substantially greater percentage of proteins than do plasma membranes, and there are differences in the specific kinds of phospholipids and other lipids. In short, membranes with different functions differ in chemical composition and structure.

A second, more serious problem with the sandwich model was the placement of the proteins. Unlike proteins dissolved in the cytosol, membrane proteins are not very soluble in water. Membrane proteins have hydrophobic regions as well as hydrophilic regions (that is, they are amphipathic). If such proteins were layered on the surface of the membrane, their hydrophobic parts would be in an aqueous environment.

In 1972, S. J. Singer and G. Nicolson proposed that membrane proteins are dispersed and individually inserted into the phospholipid bilayer, with only their hydrophilic regions protruding far enough from the bilayer to be exposed to water **(Figure 7.3)**. This molecular arrangement would maximize contact of hydrophilic regions of proteins and phospholipids with water while providing their hydrophobic parts with a nonaqueous environment. According to this model, the membrane is a mosaic of protein molecules bobbing in a fluid bilayer of phospholipids.

A method of preparing cells for electron microscopy called freeze-fracture has demonstrated visually that proteins are indeed embedded in the phospholipid bilayer of the membrane. Freeze-fracture splits a membrane along the middle of the phospholipid bilayer. When the halves of the fractured membrane are viewed in the electron microscope, the interior of the bilayer appears cobblestoned, with protein particles interspersed in a smooth matrix, as in the fluid mosaic model (**Figure 7.4**, next page). Other kinds of evidence further support this arrangement.

Models are proposed by scientists as hypotheses, ways of organizing and explaining existing information. Replacing one model of membrane structure with another does not imply that the original model was worthless. The acceptance or rejection of a model depends on how well it fits observations and explains experimental results. A good model also makes predictions that shape future research. Models inspire experiments, and few models survive these tests without modification. New findings may make a model obsolete; even then, it may not be totally scrapped, but revised to incorporate the new observations. The fluid mosaic model is continually being refined and may one day undergo further revision.

Now let's take a closer look at membrane structure, beginning with the ability of lipids and proteins to drift laterally within the membrane.

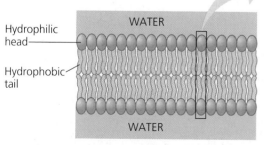

▲ Figure 7.2 **Phospholipid bilayer (cross section).**

▲ Figure 7.3 **The fluid mosaic model for membranes.**

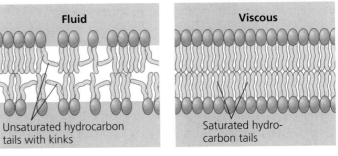

(a) Movement of phospholipids. Lipids move laterally in a membrane, but flip-flopping across the membrane is quite rare.

Figure 7.4
Research Method **Freeze-Fracture**

APPLICATION   A cell membrane can be split into its two layers, revealing the ultrastructure of the membrane's interior.

TECHNIQUE   A cell is frozen and fractured with a knife. The fracture plane often follows the hydrophobic interior of a membrane, splitting the phospholipid bilayer into two separated layers. The membrane proteins go wholly with one of the layers.

Extracellular layer

Knife

Proteins

Plasma membrane

Cytoplasmic layer

RESULTS   These SEMs show membrane proteins (the "bumps") in the two layers, demonstrating that proteins are embedded in the phospholipid bilayer.

Extracellular layer

Cytoplasmic layer

(b) Membrane fluidity. Unsaturated hydrocarbon tails of phospholipids have kinks that keep the molecules from packing together, enhancing membrane fluidity.

Fluid

Viscous

Unsaturated hydrocarbon tails with kinks

Saturated hydro-carbon tails

Cholesterol

(c) Cholesterol within the animal cell membrane. Cholesterol reduces membrane fluidity at moderate temperatures by reducing phospholipid movement, but at low temperatures it hinders solidification by disrupting the regular packing of phospholipids.

▲ **Figure 7.5 The fluidity of membranes.**

The Fluidity of Membranes

Membranes are not static sheets of molecules locked rigidly in place. A membrane is held together primarily by hydrophobic interactions, which are much weaker than covalent bonds (see Figure 5.20). Most of the lipids and some of the proteins can drift about laterally—that is, in the plane of the membrane **(Figure 7.5a)**. It is quite rare, however, for a molecule to flip-flop transversely across the membrane, switching from one phospholipid layer to the other; to do so, the hydrophilic part of the molecule must cross the hydrophobic core of the membrane.

The lateral movement of phospholipids within the membrane is rapid. Adjacent phospholipids switch positions about 10^7 times per second, which means that a phospholipid can travel about 2 μm—the length of a typical bacterial cell—in 1 second. Proteins are much larger than lipids and move more slowly, but some membrane proteins do, in fact, drift **(Figure 7.6)**. And some membrane proteins seem to move in a highly directed manner, perhaps driven along cytoskeletal fibers by motor proteins connected to the membrane proteins' cytoplasmic regions. However, many other membrane proteins seem to be held virtually immobile by their attachment to the cytoskeleton.

A membrane remains fluid as temperature decreases, until finally the phospholipids settle into a closely packed arrangement and the membrane solidifies, much as bacon grease

forms lard when it cools. The temperature at which a membrane solidifies depends on the types of lipids it is made of. The membrane remains fluid to a lower temperature if it is rich in phospholipids with unsaturated hydrocarbon tails (see Figures 5.12 and 5.13). Because of kinks in the tails where double bonds are located, unsaturated hydrocarbons cannot pack together as closely as saturated hydrocarbons, and this makes the membrane more fluid **(Figure 7.5b)**.

The steroid cholesterol, which is wedged between phospholipid molecules in the plasma membranes of animal cells, has different effects on membrane fluidity at different temperatures **(Figure 7.5c)**. At relatively warm temperatures—at 37°C, the body temperature of humans, for example—cholesterol makes the membrane less fluid by restraining the movement of phospholipids. However, because cholesterol

Figure 7.6
Inquiry Do membrane proteins move?

EXPERIMENT   Researchers labeled the plasma membrane proteins of a mouse cell and a human cell with two different markers and fused the cells. Using a microscope, they observed the markers on the hybrid cell.

RESULTS

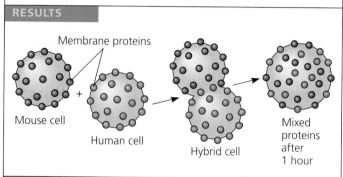

Membrane proteins

Mouse cell

Human cell

Hybrid cell

Mixed proteins after 1 hour

CONCLUSION   The mixing of the mouse and human membrane proteins indicates that at least some membrane proteins move sideways within the plane of the plasma membrane.

also hinders the close packing of phospholipids, it lowers the temperature required for the membrane to solidify. Thus, cholesterol can be thought of as a "temperature buffer" for the membrane, resisting changes in membrane fluidity that can be caused by changes in temperature.

Membranes must be fluid to work properly; they are usually about as fluid as salad oil. When a membrane solidifies, its permeability changes, and enzymatic proteins in the membrane may become inactive—for example, if their activity requires them to be able to move laterally in the membrane. The lipid composition of cell membranes can change as an adjustment to changing temperature. For instance, in many plants that tolerate extreme cold, such as winter wheat, the percentage of unsaturated phospholipids increases in autumn, an adaptation that keeps the membranes from solidifying during winter.

Membrane Proteins and Their Functions

Now we come to the *mosaic* aspect of the fluid mosaic model. A membrane is a collage of different proteins embedded in the fluid matrix of the lipid bilayer **(Figure 7.7)**. More than 50 kinds

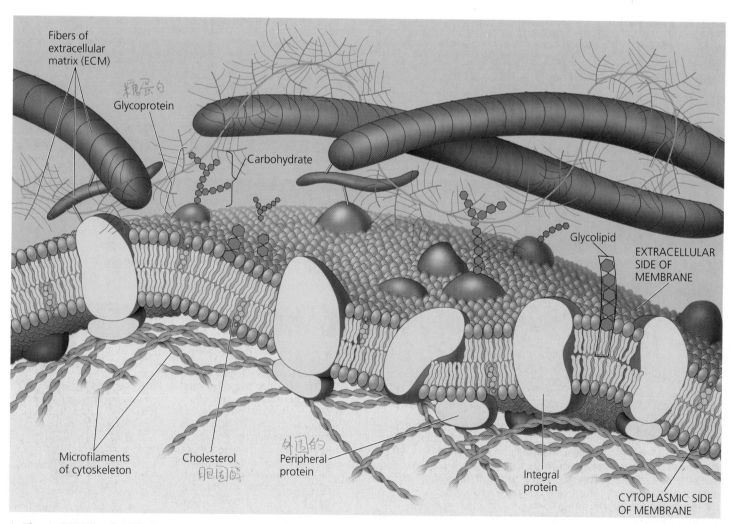

Fibers of extracellular matrix (ECM)

Glycoprotein

Carbohydrate

Glycolipid

EXTRACELLULAR SIDE OF MEMBRANE

Microfilaments of cytoskeleton

Cholesterol

Peripheral protein

Integral protein

CYTOPLASMIC SIDE OF MEMBRANE

▲ **Figure 7.7 The detailed structure of an animal cell's plasma membrane, in cross section.**

of proteins have been found so far in the plasma membrane of red blood cells, for example. Phospholipids form the main fabric of the membrane, but proteins determine most of the membrane's specific functions. Different types of cells contain different sets of membrane proteins, and the various membranes within a cell each have a unique collection of proteins.

Notice in Figure 7.7 that there are two major populations of membrane proteins. **Integral proteins** penetrate the hydrophobic core of the lipid bilayer. Many are *transmembrane* proteins, which completely span the membrane. The hydrophobic regions of an integral protein consist of one or more stretches of nonpolar amino acids (see Figure 5.17), usually coiled into α helices **(Figure 7.8)**. The hydrophilic parts of the molecule are exposed to the aqueous solutions on either side of the membrane. **Peripheral proteins** are not embedded in the lipid bilayer at all; they are appendages loosely bound to the surface of the membrane, often to the exposed parts of integral proteins (see Figure 7.7).

On the cytoplasmic side of the plasma membrane, some membrane proteins are held in place by attachment to the cytoskeleton. And on the exterior side, certain membrane proteins are attached to fibers of the extracellular matrix (see Figure 6.29; *integrins* are one type of integral protein). These attachments combine to give animal cells a stronger framework than the plasma membrane itself could provide.

Figure 7.9 gives an overview of six major functions performed by proteins of the plasma membrane. A single cell may

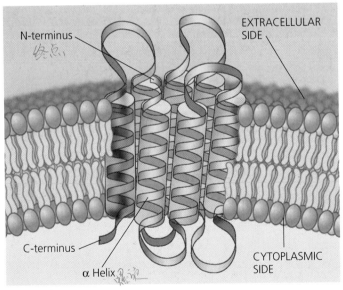

▲ Figure 7.8 The structure of a transmembrane protein. The protein shown here, bacteriorhodopsin (a bacterial transport protein), has a distinct orientation in the membrane, with the N-terminus outside the cell and the C-terminus inside. This ribbon model highlights the α-helical secondary structure of the hydrophobic parts of the protein, which lie mostly within the hydrophobic core of the membrane. The protein includes seven transmembrane helices (outlined with cylinders for emphasis). The nonhelical hydrophilic segments of the protein are in contact with the aqueous solutions on the extracellular and cytoplasmic sides of the membrane.

(a) Transport. (left) A protein that spans the membrane may provide a hydrophilic channel across the membrane that is selective for a particular solute. **(right)** Other transport proteins shuttle a substance from one side to the other by changing shape. Some of these proteins hydrolyze ATP as an energy source to actively pump substances across the membrane.

(b) Enzymatic activity. A protein built into the membrane may be an enzyme with its active site exposed to substances in the adjacent solution. In some cases, several enzymes in a membrane are organized as a team that carries out sequential steps of a metabolic pathway.

(c) Signal transduction. A membrane protein may have a binding site with a specific shape that fits the shape of a chemical messenger, such as a hormone. The external messenger (signal) may cause a conformational change in the protein (receptor) that relays the message to the inside of the cell.

(d) Cell-cell recognition. Some glycoproteins serve as identification tags that are specifically recognized by other cells.

(e) Intercellular joining. Membrane proteins of adjacent cells may hook together in various kinds of junctions, such as gap junctions or tight junctions (see Figure 6.31).

(f) Attachment to the cytoskeleton and extracellular matrix (ECM). Microfilaments or other elements of the cytoskeleton may be bonded to membrane proteins, a function that helps maintain cell shape and stabilizes the location of certain membrane proteins. Proteins that adhere to the ECM can coordinate extracellular and intracellular changes (see Figure 6.29).

▲ Figure 7.9 Some functions of membrane proteins. In many cases, a single protein performs some combination of these tasks.

have membrane proteins carrying out several of these functions, and a single protein may have multiple functions. Thus, the membrane is a functional mosaic as well as a structural one.

The Role of Membrane Carbohydrates in Cell-Cell Recognition

Cell-cell recognition, a cell's ability to distinguish one type of neighboring cell from another, is crucial to the functioning of an organism. It is important, for example, in the sorting of cells into tissues and organs in an animal embryo. It is also the basis for the rejection of foreign cells (including those of transplanted organs) by the immune system, an important line of defense in vertebrate animals (see Chapter 43). The way cells recognize other cells is by binding to surface molecules, often carbohydrates, on the plasma membrane (see Figure 7.9d).

Membrane carbohydrates are usually short, branched chains of fewer than 15 sugar units. Some of these carbohydrates are covalently bonded to lipids, forming molecules called **glycolipids.** (Recall that *glyco* refers to the presence of carbohydrate.) Most, however, are covalently bonded to proteins, which are thereby **glycoproteins** (see Figure 7.7).

The carbohydrates on the external side of the plasma membrane vary from species to species, among individuals of the same species, and even from one cell type to another in a single individual. The diversity of the molecules and their location on the cell's surface enable membrane carbohydrates to function as markers that distinguish one cell from another. For example, the four human blood types designated A, B, AB, and O reflect variation in the carbohydrates on the surface of red blood cells.

Synthesis and Sidedness of Membranes

Membranes have distinct inside and outside faces. The two lipid layers may differ in specific lipid composition, and each protein has directional orientation in the membrane (see Figure 7.8). When a vesicle fuses with the plasma membrane, the outside layer of the vesicle becomes continuous with the cytoplasmic layer of the plasma membrane. Therefore, molecules that start out on the *inside* face of the ER end up on the *outside* face of the plasma membrane.

The process, shown in **Figure 7.10**, starts with ❶ the synthesis of membrane proteins and lipids in the endoplasmic reticulum. Carbohydrates (green) are added to the proteins (purple), making them glycoproteins. The carbohydrate portions may then be modified. ❷ Inside the Golgi apparatus, the glycoproteins undergo further carbohydrate modification, and lipids acquire carbohydrates, becoming glycolipids. ❸ Transmembrane proteins (purple dumbbells), membrane glycolipids, and secretory proteins (purple spheres) are transported in vesicles to the plasma membrane. ❹ There the vesicles fuse with the membrane, releasing secretory proteins from the cell. Vesicle fusion positions the carbohydrates of membrane

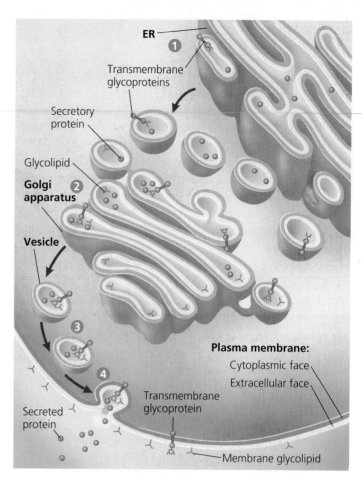

▲ Figure 7.10 **Synthesis of membrane components and their orientation on the resulting membrane.** The plasma membrane has distinct cytoplasmic and extracellular sides, or faces, with the extracellular face arising from the inside face of ER, Golgi, and vesicle membranes.

glycoproteins and glycolipids on the outside of the plasma membrane. Thus, the asymmetrical distribution of proteins, lipids, and their associated carbohydrates in the plasma membrane is determined as the membrane is being built by the ER and Golgi apparatus.

Concept Check 7.1

1. How would you expect the saturation levels of membrane fatty acids to differ in plants adapted to cold environments and plants adapted to hot environments?

2. The carbohydrates attached to some of the proteins and lipids of the plasma membrane are added as the membrane is made and refined in the ER and Golgi apparatus; the new membrane then forms transport vesicles that travel to the cell surface. On which side of the vesicle membrane are the carbohydrates?

For suggested answers, see Appendix A.

Membrane structure results in selective permeability

The biological membrane is an exquisite example of a supramolecular structure—many molecules ordered into a higher level of organization—with emergent properties beyond those of the individual molecules. The remainder of this chapter focuses on one of the most important of those properties: the ability to regulate transport across cellular boundaries, a function essential to the cell's existence. We will see once again that form fits function: The fluid mosaic model helps explain how membranes regulate the cell's molecular traffic.

A steady traffic of small molecules and ions moves across the plasma membrane in both directions. Consider the chemical exchanges between a muscle cell and the extracellular fluid that bathes it. Sugars, amino acids, and other nutrients enter the cell, and metabolic waste products leave it. The cell takes in oxygen for cellular respiration and expels carbon dioxide. It also regulates its concentrations of inorganic ions, such as Na^+, K^+, Ca^{2+}, and Cl^-, by shuttling them one way or the other across the plasma membrane. Although traffic through the membrane is extensive, cell membranes are selectively permeable, and substances do not cross the barrier indiscriminately. The cell is able to take up many varieties of small molecules and ions and exclude others. Moreover, substances that move through the membrane do so at different rates.

The Permeability of the Lipid Bilayer

Hydrophobic (nonpolar) molecules, such as hydrocarbons, carbon dioxide, and oxygen, can dissolve in the lipid bilayer of the membrane and cross it with ease, without the aid of membrane proteins. However, the hydrophobic core of the membrane impedes the direct passage of ions and polar molecules, which are hydrophilic, through the membrane. Polar molecules such as glucose and other sugars pass only slowly through a lipid bilayer, and even water, an extremely small polar molecule, does not cross very rapidly. A charged atom or molecule and its surrounding shell of water (see Figure 3.6) find the hydrophobic layer of the membrane even more difficult to penetrate. Fortunately, the lipid bilayer is only part of the story of a membrane's selective permeability. Proteins built into the membrane play key roles in regulating transport.

Transport Proteins

Cell membranes *are* permeable to specific ions and a variety of polar molecules. These hydrophilic substances can avoid contact with the lipid bilayer by passing through **transport proteins** that span the membrane. Some transport proteins, called *channel proteins*, function by having a hydrophilic channel that certain molecules or atomic ions use as a tunnel through the membrane (see Figure 7.9a, left). For example, the passage of water molecules through the membrane in certain cells is greatly facilitated by channel proteins known as **aquaporins**. (These were discovered in the laboratory of Peter Agre; see pp. 92–93.) Other transport proteins, called *carrier proteins*, hold onto their passengers and change shape in a way that shuttles them across the membrane (see Figure 7.9a, right). In both cases, the transport protein is specific for the substance it translocates (moves), allowing only a certain substance (or substances) to cross the membrane. For example, glucose carried in blood and needed by red blood cells for cellular activities enters these cells rapidly through specific transport proteins in the plasma membrane. This "glucose transporter" is so selective as a carrier protein that it even rejects fructose, a structural isomer of glucose.

Thus, the selective permeability of a membrane depends on both the discriminating barrier of the lipid bilayer and the specific transport proteins built into the membrane. But what determines the *direction* of traffic across a membrane? At a given time, will a particular substance enter or leave the cell? And what mechanisms actually drive molecules across membranes? We will address these questions next as we explore two modes of membrane traffic: passive transport and active transport.

Concept Check 7.2

1. Two molecules that can cross a lipid bilayer without help from membrane proteins are O_2 and CO_2. What properties allow this to occur?
2. Why would water molecules need a transport protein (aquaporin) to move rapidly and in large quantities across a membrane?

For suggested answers, see Appendix A.

Passive transport is diffusion of a substance across a membrane with no energy investment

Molecules have a type of energy called thermal motion (heat). One result of thermal motion is **diffusion**, the tendency for molecules of any substance to spread out evenly into the available space. Each molecule moves randomly, yet diffusion of a *population* of molecules may be directional. A good way to visualize this is to imagine a synthetic membrane separating pure water from a solution of a dye in water. Assume that this membrane has microscopic pores and is permeable to the dye molecules **(Figure 7.11a)**. Each dye molecule wanders randomly, but there will be a *net* movement of the dye molecules across the membrane to the side that began as pure water. The dye molecules will continue to spread across the membrane until both solutions have equal concentrations of the dye. Once that point is reached, there will be a dynamic equilibrium, with as many dye molecules crossing the membrane each second in one direction as in the other.

We can now state a simple rule of diffusion: In the absence of other forces, a substance will diffuse from where it is more concentrated to where it is less concentrated. Put another way, any substance will diffuse down its **concentration gradient.** No work must be done to make this happen; diffusion is a spontaneous process. Note that each substance diffuses down its *own* concentration gradient, unaffected by the concentration differences of other substances **(Figure 7.11b)**.

Much of the traffic across cell membranes occurs by diffusion. When a substance is more concentrated on one side of a membrane than on the other, there is a tendency for the substance to diffuse across the membrane down its concentration gradient (assuming that the membrane is permeable to that substance). One important example is the uptake of oxygen by a cell performing cellular respiration. Dissolved oxygen diffuses into the cell across the plasma membrane. As long as cellular respiration consumes the O_2 as it enters, diffusion into the cell will continue, because the concentration gradient favors movement in that direction.

The diffusion of a substance across a biological membrane is called **passive transport** because the cell does not have to expend energy to make it happen. The concentration gradient itself represents potential energy (see Chapter 2, p. 36) and drives diffusion. Remember, however, that membranes are selectively permeable and therefore have different effects on the rates of diffusion of various molecules. In the case of water, aquaporins allow water to diffuse very rapidly across the membranes of certain cells. The movement of water across the plasma membrane has important consequences for cells.

Effects of Osmosis on Water Balance

To see how two solutions with different solute concentrations interact, picture a U-shaped glass tube with a selectively permeable membrane separating two sugar solutions **(Figure 7.12)**. Pores in this synthetic membrane are too small for sugar molecules to pass through but large enough for water molecules. How does this affect the *water* concentration? It seems logical that the solution with the higher concentration of solute would have the lower concentration of water and that water would diffuse into it from the other side for that reason. However, for a dilute solution like most biological fluids,

(a) Diffusion of one solute. The membrane has pores large enough for molecules of dye to pass through. Random movement of dye molecules will cause some to pass through the pores; this will happen more often on the side with more molecules. The dye diffuses from where it is more concentrated to where it is less concentrated (called diffusing down a concentration gradient). This leads to a dynamic equilibrium: The solute molecules continue to cross the membrane, but at equal rates in both directions.

Molecules of dye — Membrane (cross section)

WATER

Net diffusion — Net diffusion — Equilibrium

(b) Diffusion of two solutes. Solutions of two different dyes are separated by a membrane that is permeable to both. Each dye diffuses down its own concentration gradient. There will be a net diffusion of the purple dye toward the left, even though the *total* solute concentration was initially greater on the left side.

▲ **Figure 7.11 The diffusion of solutes across a membrane.** Each of the large arrows under the diagrams shows the net diffusion of the dye molecules of that color.

Net diffusion — Net diffusion — Equilibrium
Net diffusion — Net diffusion — Equilibrium

Lower concentration of solute (sugar)

Higher concentration of sugar

Same concentration of sugar

H₂O

Selectively permeable membrane: sugar molecules cannot pass through pores, but water molecules can

Water molecules cluster around sugar molecules

More free water molecules (higher concentration)

Fewer free water molecules (lower concentration)

Osmosis

Water moves from an area of higher free water concentration to an area of lower free water concentration

▲ **Figure 7.12 Osmosis.** Two sugar solutions of different concentrations are separated by a selectively permeable membrane, which the solvent (water) can pass through but the solute (sugar) cannot. Water molecules move randomly and may cross through the pores in either direction, but overall, water diffuses from the solution with less concentrated solute to that with more concentrated solute. This transport of water, or osmosis, eventually equalizes the sugar concentrations on both sides of the membrane.

solutes do not affect the water concentration significantly. Instead, tight clustering of water molecules around the hydrophilic solute molecules makes some of the water unavailable to cross the membrane. It is the difference in *free* water concentration that is important. But the effect is the same: Water diffuses across the membrane from the region of lower solute concentration to that of higher solute concentration until the solute concentrations on both sides of the membrane are equal. The diffusion of water across a selectively permeable membrane is called **osmosis.** The movement of water across cell membranes and the balance of water between the cell and its environment are crucial to organisms. Let's now apply to living cells what we have learned about osmosis in artificial systems.

Water Balance of Cells Without Walls

When considering the behavior of a cell in a solution, both solute concentration and membrane permeability must be considered. Both factors are taken into account in the concept of **tonicity,** the ability of a solution to cause a cell to gain or lose water. The tonicity of a solution depends in part on its

concentration of solutes that cannot cross the membrane (nonpenetrating solutes), relative to that in the cell itself. If there are more nonpenetrating solutes in the surrounding solution, water will tend to leave the cell, and vice versa.

If a cell without a wall, such as an animal cell, is immersed in an environment that is **isotonic** to the cell (*iso* means "same"), there will be no *net* movement of water across the plasma membrane. Water flows across the membrane, but at the same rate in both directions. In an isotonic environment, the volume of an animal cell is stable **(Figure 7.13a)**.

Now let's transfer the cell to a solution that is **hypertonic** to the cell (*hyper* means "more," in this case more nonpenetrating solutes). The cell will lose water to its environment, shrivel, and probably die. This is one reason why an increase in the salinity (saltiness) of a lake can kill the animals there—if the lake water becomes hypertonic to the animals' cells, the cells might shrivel and die. However, taking up too much water can be just as hazardous to an animal cell as losing water. If we place the cell in a solution that is **hypotonic** to the cell (*hypo* means "less"), water will enter the cell faster than it leaves, and the cell will swell and lyse (burst) like an overfilled water balloon.

A cell without rigid walls can tolerate neither excessive uptake nor excessive loss of water. This problem of water balance is automatically solved if such a cell lives in isotonic surroundings. Seawater is isotonic to many marine invertebrates. The cells of most terrestrial (land-dwelling) animals are bathed in an extracellular fluid that is isotonic to the cells. Animals and other organisms without rigid cell walls living in hypertonic or hypotonic environments must have special adaptations for **osmoregulation,** the control of water balance. For example, the protist *Paramecium* lives in pond water, which is hypotonic to the cell. *Paramecium* has a plasma membrane that is much less permeable to water than the membranes of most other cells, but this only slows the uptake of water, which continually enters the cell. *Paramecium* doesn't burst because it is also equipped with a contractile vacuole, an organelle that functions as a bilge pump to force water out of the cell as fast as it enters by osmosis **(Figure 7.14)**. We will examine other evolutionary adaptations for osmoregulation in Chapter 44.

Water Balance of Cells with Walls

The cells of plants, prokaryotes, fungi, and some protists have walls. When such a cell is immersed in a hypotonic solution—bathed in rainwater, for example—the wall helps maintain the cell's water balance. Consider a plant cell. Like an animal cell, the plant cell swells as water enters by osmosis **(Figure 7.13b)**. However, the elastic wall will expand only so much before it exerts a back pressure on the cell that opposes further water uptake. At this point, the cell is **turgid** (very firm), which is the healthy state for most plant cells. Plants that are not

► **Figure 7.13 The water balance of living cells.** How living cells react to changes in the solute concentration of their environment depends on whether or not they have cell walls. **(a)** Animal cells such as this red blood cell do not have cell walls. **(b)** Plant cells do. (Arrows indicate net water movement since the cells were first placed in these solutions.)

(a) Animal cell. An animal cell fares best in an isotonic environment unless it has special adaptations to offset the osmotic uptake or loss of water.

(b) Plant cell. Plant cells are turgid (firm) and generally healthiest in a hypotonic environment, where the uptake of water is eventually balanced by the elastic wall pushing back on the cell.

Hypotonic solution	Isotonic solution	Hypertonic solution
H_2O	H_2O → H_2O	→ H_2O
Lysed	Normal	Shriveled
H_2O	H_2O → H_2O	→ H_2O
Turgid (normal)	Flaccid	Plasmolyzed

woody, such as most houseplants, depend for mechanical support on cells kept turgid by a surrounding hypotonic solution. If a plant's cells and their surroundings are isotonic, there is no net tendency for water to enter, and the cells become **flaccid** (limp).

However, a wall is of no advantage if the cell is immersed in a hypertonic environment. In this case, a plant cell, like an an-imal cell, will lose water to its surroundings and shrink. As the plant cell shrivels, its plasma membrane pulls away from the wall. This phenomenon, called **plasmolysis,** causes the plant to wilt and can be lethal. The walled cells of bacteria and fungi also plasmolyze in hypertonic environments.

Facilitated Diffusion: Passive Transport Aided by Proteins

Let's look more closely at how water and certain hydrophilic solutes cross a membrane. As mentioned earlier, many polar molecules and ions impeded by the lipid bilayer of the membrane diffuse passively with the help of transport proteins that span the membrane. This phenomenon is called **facilitated diffusion.** Cell biologists are still trying to learn exactly how various transport proteins facilitate diffusion. Most transport proteins are very specific: They transport only particular substances but not others.

As described earlier, the two types of transport proteins are channel proteins and carrier proteins. Channel proteins simply provide corridors that allow a specific molecule or ion to cross the membrane **(Figure 7.15a)**. The hydrophilic passageways provided by these proteins allow water molecules or small ions to flow very quickly from one side of the membrane to the other. While water molecules are small enough to cross through the phospholipid bilayer, the rate of water movement by this route is relatively slow because of their polarity. Aquaporins, the water channel proteins, facilitate the massive amounts of diffusion that occur in plant cells and in animal cells such as red blood cells (see Figure 7.13). Another group of channels are **ion channels,** many of which function as **gated channels;** a stimulus causes them to open or close. The stimulus may be electrical or chemical; if chemical, the stimulus is a substance other than the one to be transported. For example, stimulation of a nerve cell by

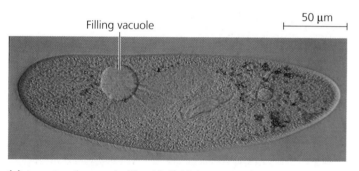

Filling vacuole   50 μm

(a) A contractile vacuole fills with fluid that enters from a system of canals radiating throughout the cytoplasm.

Contracting vacuole   50 μm

(b) When full, the vacuole and canals contract, expelling fluid from the cell.

▲ **Figure 7.14 The contractile vacuole of *Paramecium*: an evolutionary adaptation for osmoregulation.** The contractile vacuole of this freshwater protist offsets osmosis by bailing water out of the cell.

(a) A channel protein (purple) has a channel through which water molecules or a specific solute can pass.

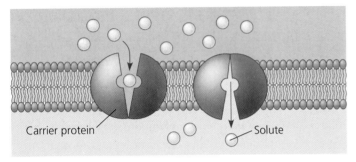

(b) A carrier protein alternates between two conformations, moving a solute across the membrane as the shape of the protein changes. The protein can transport the solute in either direction, with the net movement being down the concentration gradient of the solute.

▲ **Figure 7.15 Two types of transport proteins that carry out facilitated diffusion.** In both cases, the protein transports the solute down its concentration gradient.

certain neurotransmitter molecules opens gated channels that allow sodium ions into the cell.

Carrier proteins seem to undergo a subtle change in shape that somehow translocates the solute-binding site across the membrane (**Figure 7.15b**). These changes in shape may be triggered by the binding and release of the transported molecule.

In certain inherited diseases, specific transport systems are either defective or missing altogether. An example is cystinuria, a human disease characterized by the absence of a protein that transports cysteine and some other amino acids across the membranes of kidney cells. Kidney cells normally reabsorb these amino acids from the urine and return them to the blood, but an individual afflicted with cystinuria develops painful stones from amino acids that accumulate and crystallize in the kidneys.

Concept Check 7.3

1. If a *Paramecium* were to swim from a hypotonic environment to an isotonic one, would the activity of its contractile vacuole increase or decrease? Why?

For suggested answers, see Appendix A.

Active transport uses energy to move solutes against their gradients

Despite the help of transport proteins, facilitated diffusion is still considered passive transport because the solute being transported is moving down its concentration gradient. Facilitated diffusion speeds the transport of a solute by providing an efficient passage through the membrane, but it does not alter the direction of transport. Some transport proteins, however, can move solutes against their concentration gradients, across the plasma membrane from the side where they are less concentrated to the side where they are more concentrated.

The Need for Energy in Active Transport

To pump a molecule across a membrane against its gradient requires work; the cell must expend energy. Therefore, this type of membrane traffic is called **active transport.** The transport proteins that move solutes against a concentration gradient are all carrier proteins, rather than channel proteins. This makes sense, because when channel proteins are open, they merely allow molecules to flow down their concentration gradient, rather than picking them up and transporting them against their gradient.

Active transport enables a cell to maintain internal concentrations of small molecules that differ from concentrations in its environment. For example, compared to its surroundings, an animal cell has a much higher concentration of potassium ions and a much lower concentration of sodium ions. The plasma membrane helps maintain these steep gradients by pumping sodium out of the cell and potassium into the cell.

As in other types of cellular work, ATP supplies the energy for most active transport. One way ATP can power active transport is by transferring its terminal phosphate group directly to the transport protein. This may induce the protein to change its conformation in a manner that translocates a solute bound to the protein across the membrane. One transport system that works this way is the **sodium-potassium pump,** which exchanges sodium (Na^+) for potassium (K^+) across the plasma membrane of animal cells (**Figure 7.16**). **Figure 7.17** reviews the distinction between passive transport and active transport.

Maintenance of Membrane Potential by Ion Pumps

All cells have voltages across their plasma membranes. Voltage is electrical potential energy—a separation of opposite charges.

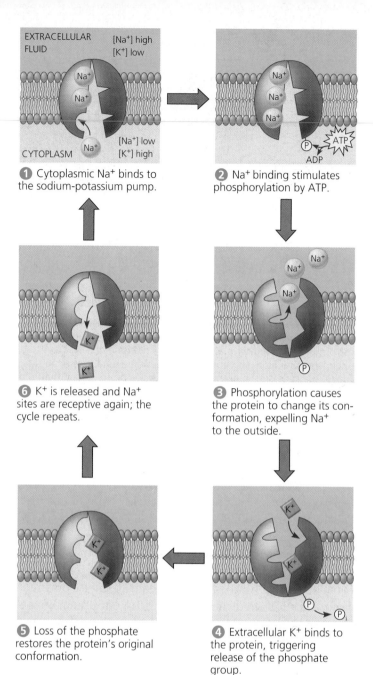

1 Cytoplasmic Na⁺ binds to the sodium-potassium pump.

2 Na⁺ binding stimulates phosphorylation by ATP.

3 Phosphorylation causes the protein to change its conformation, expelling Na⁺ to the outside.

4 Extracellular K⁺ binds to the protein, triggering release of the phosphate group.

5 Loss of the phosphate restores the protein's original conformation.

6 K⁺ is released and Na⁺ sites are receptive again; the cycle repeats.

▲ **Figure 7.16** **The sodium-potassium pump: a specific case of active transport.** This transport system pumps ions against steep concentration gradients: Sodium ion concentration (represented as [Na⁺]) is high outside the cell and low inside, while potassium ion concentration ([K⁺]) is low outside the cell and high inside. The pump oscillates between two conformational states in a pumping cycle that translocates three sodium ions out of the cell for every two potassium ions pumped into the cell. ATP powers the changes in conformation by phosphorylating the transport protein (that is, by transferring a phosphate group to the protein).

The cytoplasm of a cell is negative in charge compared to the extracellular fluid because of an unequal distribution of anions and cations on opposite sides of the membrane. The voltage across a membrane, called a **membrane potential**, ranges from

Passive transport. Substances diffuse spontaneously down their concentration gradients, crossing a membrane with no expenditure of energy by the cell. The rate of diffusion can be greatly increased by transport proteins in the membrane.

Active transport. Some transport proteins act as pumps, moving substances across a membrane against their concentration gradients. Energy for this work is usually supplied by ATP.

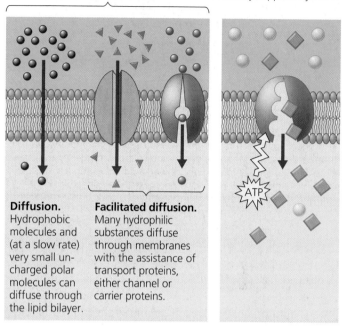

Diffusion. Hydrophobic molecules and (at a slow rate) very small uncharged polar molecules can diffuse through the lipid bilayer.

Facilitated diffusion. Many hydrophilic substances diffuse through membranes with the assistance of transport proteins, either channel or carrier proteins.

▲ **Figure 7.17** **Review: passive and active transport compared.**

about −50 to −200 millivolts (mV). (The minus sign indicates that the inside of the cell is negative compared to the outside.)

The membrane potential acts like a battery, an energy source that affects the traffic of all charged substances across the membrane. Because the inside of the cell is negative compared to the outside, the membrane potential favors the passive transport of cations into the cell and anions out of the cell. Thus, *two* forces drive the diffusion of ions across a membrane: a chemical force (the ion's concentration gradient) and an electrical force (the effect of the membrane potential on the ion's movement). This combination of forces acting on an ion is called the **electrochemical gradient**. In the case of ions, we must refine our concept of passive transport: An ion does not simply diffuse down its *concentration* gradient, but diffuses down its *electrochemical* gradient. For example, the concentration of sodium ions (Na⁺) inside a resting nerve cell is much lower than outside it. When the cell is stimulated, gated channels that facilitate Na⁺ diffusion open. Sodium ions then "fall" down their electrochemical gradient, driven by the concentration gradient of Na⁺ and by the attraction of cations to the negative side of the membrane.

Some membrane proteins that actively transport ions contribute to the membrane potential. An example is the sodium-potassium pump. Notice in Figure 7.16 that the pump does not

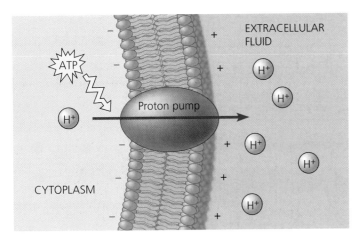

▲ **Figure 7.18 An electrogenic pump.** Proton pumps, the main electrogenic pumps of plants, fungi, and bacteria, are membrane proteins that store energy by generating voltage (charge separation) across membranes. Using ATP for power, a proton pump translocates positive charge in the form of hydrogen ions. The voltage and H⁺ concentration gradient represent a dual energy source that can drive other processes, such as the uptake of nutrients.

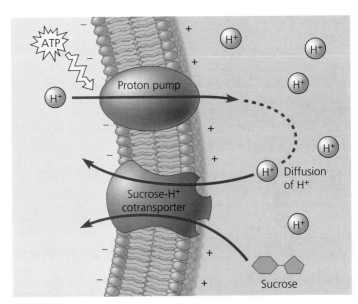

▲ **Figure 7.19 Cotransport: active transport driven by a concentration gradient.** A special carrier protein such as this sucrose-H⁺ cotransporter is able to use the diffusion of H⁺ down its electrochemical gradient into the cell to drive the uptake of sucrose. The H⁺ gradient is maintained by an ATP-driven proton pump that concentrates H⁺ outside the cell, thus storing potential energy that can be used for active transport, in this case of sucrose. Thus, ATP is indirectly providing the energy necessary for cotransport.

translocate Na^+ and K^+ one for one, but actually pumps three sodium ions out of the cell for every two potassium ions it pumps into the cell. With each "crank" of the pump, there is a net transfer of one positive charge from the cytoplasm to the extracellular fluid, a process that stores energy in the form of voltage. A transport protein that generates voltage across a membrane is called an **electrogenic pump.** The sodium-potassium pump seems to be the major electrogenic pump of animal cells. The main electrogenic pump of plants, fungi, and bacteria is a **proton pump,** which actively transports hydrogen ions (protons) out of the cell. The pumping of H⁺ transfers positive charge from the cytoplasm to the extracellular solution **(Figure 7.18).** By generating voltage across membranes, electrogenic pumps store energy that can be tapped for cellular work, including a type of membrane traffic called cotransport.

Cotransport: Coupled Transport by a Membrane Protein

A single ATP-powered pump that transports a specific solute can indirectly drive the active transport of several other solutes in a mechanism called **cotransport.** A substance that has been pumped across a membrane can do work as it moves back across the membrane by diffusion, analogous to water that has been pumped uphill and performs work as it flows back down. Another specialized transport protein, a cotransporter separate from the pump, can couple the "downhill" diffusion of this substance to the "uphill" transport of a second substance against its own concentration gradient. For example, a plant cell uses the gradient of hydrogen ions generated by its proton pumps to drive the active transport

of amino acids, sugars, and several other nutrients into the cell. One specific transport protein couples the return of hydrogen ions to the transport of sucrose into the cell **(Figure 7.19).** The protein can translocate sucrose into the cell against a concentration gradient, but only if the sucrose molecule travels in the company of a hydrogen ion. The hydrogen ion uses the common transport protein as an avenue to diffuse down the electrochemical gradient maintained by the proton pump. Plants use the mechanism of sucrose-H⁺ cotransport to load sucrose produced by photosynthesis into specialized cells in the veins of leaves. The sugar can then be distributed by the vascular tissue of the plant to nonphotosynthetic organs, such as roots.

What we know about cotransport proteins, osmosis, and water balance in animal cells has helped us find more effective treatments for the dehydration resulting from diarrhea, a serious problem in developing countries where intestinal parasites are prevalent. Patients are given a solution to drink containing a high concentration of glucose and salt. The solutes are taken up by transport proteins on the intestinal cell surface and passed through the cells into the blood. The resulting osmotic pressure causes a flow of water from the intestine through the intestinal cells into the blood, rehydrating the patient. Because of the specific proteins involved, both glucose and the sodium ion from salt must be present. The same principle underlies athletes' consumption of solute-rich solutions after a demanding athletic event.

Concept 7.5

Bulk transport across the plasma membrane occurs by exocytosis and endocytosis

Water and small solutes enter and leave the cell by passing through the lipid bilayer of the plasma membrane or by being pumped or carried across the membrane by transport proteins. However, large molecules, such as proteins and polysaccharides, as well as larger particles, generally cross the membrane by a different mechanism—one involving vesicles.

Exocytosis

As we described in Chapter 6, the cell secretes macromolecules by the fusion of vesicles with the plasma membrane; this is called **exocytosis.** A transport vesicle that has budded from the Golgi apparatus moves along microtubules of the cytoskeleton to the plasma membrane. When the vesicle membrane and plasma membrane come into contact, the lipid molecules of the two bilayers rearrange themselves so that the two membranes fuse. The contents of the vesicle then spill to the outside of the cell, and the vesicle membrane becomes part of the plasma membrane (see Figure 7.10).

Many secretory cells use exocytosis to export their products. For example, certain cells in the pancreas manufacture the hormone insulin and secrete it into the blood by exocytosis. Another example is the neuron, or nerve cell, which uses exocytosis to release neurotransmitters that signal other neurons or muscle cells. When plant cells are making walls, exocytosis delivers proteins and certain carbohydrates from Golgi vesicles to the outside of the cell.

Endocytosis

In **endocytosis,** the cell takes in macromolecules and particulate matter by forming new vesicles from the plasma membrane. Although the proteins involved in the processes are different, the events of endocytosis look like the reverse of exocytosis. A small area of the plasma membrane sinks inward to form a pocket. As the pocket deepens, it pinches in, forming a vesicle containing material that had been outside the cell. There are three types of endocytosis: phagocytosis ("cellular eating"), pinocytosis ("cellular drinking"), and receptor-mediated endocytosis. Please study **Figure 7.20** on page 138, which describes these processes, before going on.

Human cells use receptor-mediated endocytosis to take in cholesterol for use in the synthesis of membranes and as a precursor for the synthesis of other steroids. Cholesterol travels in the blood in particles called low-density lipoproteins (LDLs), complexes of lipids and proteins. These particles act as **ligands** (a general term for any molecule that binds specifically to a receptor site of another molecule) by binding to LDL receptors on membranes and then entering the cells by endocytosis. In humans with familial hypercholesterolemia, an inherited disease characterized by a very high level of cholesterol in the blood, the LDL receptor proteins are defective or missing, and the LDL particles cannot enter cells. Instead, cholesterol accumulates in the blood, where it contributes to early atherosclerosis, the buildup of lipid deposits within the walls of blood vessels, causing them to bulge inward and impede blood flow.

Vesicles not only transport substances between the cell and its surroundings but also provide a mechanism for rejuvenating or remodeling the plasma membrane. Endocytosis and exocytosis occur continually to some extent in most eukaryotic cells, and yet the amount of plasma membrane in a nongrowing cell remains fairly constant over the long run. Apparently, the addition of membrane by one process offsets the loss of membrane by the other.

Energy and cellular work have figured prominently in our study of membranes. We have seen, for example, that active transport is powered by ATP. In the next three chapters, you will learn more about how cells acquire chemical energy to do the work of life.

Figure 7.20
Exploring Endocytosis in Animal Cells

PHAGOCYTOSIS

In **phagocytosis**, a cell engulfs a particle by wrapping pseudopodia around it and packaging it within a membrane-enclosed sac large enough to be classified as a vacuole. The particle is digested after the vacuole fuses with a lysosome containing hydrolytic enzymes.

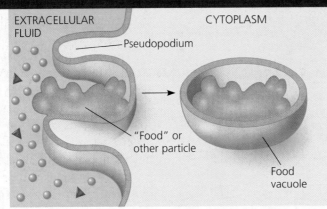

EXTRACELLULAR FLUID

CYTOPLASM

Pseudopodium

"Food" or other particle

Food vacuole

1 µm

Pseudopodium of amoeba

Bacterium

Food vacuole

An amoeba engulfing a bacterium via phagocytosis (TEM).

PINOCYTOSIS

In **pinocytosis**, the cell "gulps" droplets of extracellular fluid into tiny vesicles. It is not the fluid itself that is needed by the cell, but the molecules dissolved in the droplet. Because any and all included solutes are taken into the cell, pinocytosis is nonspecific in the substances it transports.

Plasma membrane

Vesicle

0.5 µm

Pinocytosis vesicles forming (arrows) in a cell lining a small blood vessel (TEM).

RECEPTOR-MEDIATED ENDOCYTOSIS

Receptor-mediated endocytosis enables the cell to acquire bulk quantities of specific substances, even though those substances may not be very concentrated in the extracellular fluid. Embedded in the membrane are proteins with specific receptor sites exposed to the extracellular fluid. The receptor proteins are usually already clustered in regions of the membrane called coated pits, which are lined on their cytoplasmic side by a fuzzy layer of coat proteins. Extracellular substances (ligands) bind to these receptors. When binding occurs, the coated pit forms a vesicle containing the ligand molecules. Notice that there are relatively more bound molecules (purple) inside the vesicle, but other molecules (green) are also present. After this ingested material is liberated from the vesicle, the receptors are recycled to the plasma membrane by the same vesicle.

Coat protein

Receptor

Coated vesicle

Coated pit

Ligand

Coat protein

Plasma membrane

A coated pit and a coated vesicle formed during receptor-mediated endocytosis (TEMs).

0.25 µm

Go to the Campbell Biology website (**www.campbellbiology.com**) or CD-ROM to explore Activities, Investigations, and other interactive study aids.

SUMMARY OF KEY CONCEPTS

Concept 7.1

Cellular membranes are fluid mosaics of lipids and proteins

▶ **Membrane Models: *Scientific Inquiry* (pp. 125–126)** The Davson-Danielli sandwich model of the membrane has been replaced by the fluid mosaic model, in which amphipathic proteins are embedded in the phospholipid bilayer.

▶ **The Fluidity of Membranes (pp. 126–127)** Phospholipids and, to a lesser extent, proteins move laterally within the membrane. Cholesterol and unsaturated hydrocarbon tails in the phospholipids affect membrane fluidity.

▶ **Membrane Proteins and Their Functions (pp. 127–129)** Integral proteins are embedded in the lipid bilayer; peripheral proteins are attached to the surfaces. The functions of membrane proteins include transport, enzymatic activity, signal transduction, cell-cell recognition, intercellular joining, and attachment to the cytoskeleton and extracellular matrix.

▶ **The Role of Membrane Carbohydrates in Cell-Cell Recognition (p. 129)** Short chains of sugars are linked to proteins and lipids on the exterior side of the plasma membrane, where they can interact with the surface molecules of other cells.

▶ **Synthesis and Sidedness of Membranes (p. 129)** Membrane proteins and lipids are synthesized in the ER and modified in the ER and Golgi apparatus. The inside and outside faces of the membrane differ in composition.
Activity *Membrane Structure*

Concept 7.2

Membrane structure results in selective permeability

▶ A cell must exchange small molecules and ions with its surroundings, a process controlled by the plasma membrane (p. 130).

▶ **The Permeability of the Lipid Bilayer (p. 130)** Hydrophobic substances are soluble in lipid and pass through membranes rapidly.

▶ **Transport Proteins (p. 130)** Polar molecules and ions generally require specific transport proteins to help them cross.
Activity *Selective Permeability of Membranes*

Concept 7.3

Passive transport is diffusion of a substance across a membrane with no energy investment

▶ Diffusion is the spontaneous movement of a substance down its concentration gradient (pp. 130–131).
Activity *Diffusion*

▶ **Effects of Osmosis on Water Balance (pp. 131–133)** Water flows across a membrane from the side where solute is less concentrated (hypotonic) to the side where solute is more concentrated (hypertonic). If the concentrations are equal (isotonic), no net osmosis occurs. Cell survival depends on

balancing water uptake and loss. Cells lacking walls (as in animals and some protists) are isotonic with their environments or have adaptations for osmoregulation. Plants, prokaryotes, fungi, and some protists have elastic cell walls, so the cells don't burst in a hypotonic environment.
Activity *Osmosis and Water Balance in Cells*
Investigation *How Do Salt Concentrations Affect Cells?*

▶ **Facilitated Diffusion: Passive Transport Aided by Proteins (pp. 133–134)** In facilitated diffusion, a transport protein speeds the movement of water or a solute across a membrane down its concentration gradient.
Activity *Facilitated Diffusion*

Concept 7.4

Active transport uses energy to move solutes against their gradients

▶ **The Need for Energy in Active Transport (pp. 134–135)** Specific membrane proteins use energy, usually in the form of ATP, to do the work of active transport.
Activity *Active Transport*

▶ **Maintenance of Membrane Potential by Ion Pumps (pp. 134–136)** Ions can have both a concentration (chemical) gradient and an electrical gradient (voltage). These forces combine in the electrochemical gradient, which determines the net direction of ionic diffusion. Electrogenic pumps, such as sodium-potassium pumps and proton pumps, are transport proteins that contribute to electrochemical gradients.

▶ **Cotransport: Coupled Transport by a Membrane Protein (p. 136)** One solute's "downhill" diffusion drives the other's "uphill" transport.

Concept 7.5

Bulk transport across the plasma membrane occurs by exocytosis and endocytosis

▶ **Exocytosis (p. 137)** In exocytosis, transport vesicles migrate to the plasma membrane, fuse with it, and release their contents.

▶ **Endocytosis (pp. 137–138)** In endocytosis, molecules enter cells within vesicles pinched inward from the plasma membrane. The three types of endocytosis are phagocytosis, pinocytosis, and receptor-mediated endocytosis.
Activity *Exocytosis and Endocytosis*

TESTING YOUR KNOWLEDGE

Self-Quiz

1. In what way do the various membranes of a eukaryotic cell differ?
   a. Phospholipids are found only in certain membranes.
   b. Certain proteins are unique to each membrane.
   c. Only certain membranes of the cell are selectively permeable.
   d. Only certain membranes are constructed from amphipathic molecules.
   e. Some membranes have hydrophobic surfaces exposed to the cytoplasm, while others have hydrophilic surfaces facing the cytoplasm.

2. According to the fluid mosaic model of membrane structure, proteins of the membrane are mostly
   a. spread in a continuous layer over the inner and outer surfaces of the membrane.
   b. confined to the hydrophobic core of the membrane.
   c. embedded in a lipid bilayer.
   d. randomly oriented in the membrane, with no fixed inside-outside polarity.
   e. free to depart from the fluid membrane and dissolve in the surrounding solution.

3. Which of the following factors would tend to increase membrane fluidity?
   a. a greater proportion of unsaturated phospholipids
   b. a greater proportion of saturated phospholipids
   c. a lower temperature
   d. a relatively high protein content in the membrane
   e. a greater proportion of relatively large glycolipids compared to lipids having smaller molecular masses

4. Which of the following processes includes all others?
   a. osmosis
   b. diffusion of a solute across a membrane
   c. facilitated diffusion
   d. passive transport
   e. transport of an ion down its electrochemical gradient

5. Based on the model of sucrose uptake in Figure 7.19, which of the following experimental treatments would increase the rate of sucrose transport into the cell?
   a. decreasing extracellular sucrose concentration
   b. decreasing extracellular pH
   c. decreasing cytoplasmic pH
   d. adding an inhibitor that blocks the regeneration of ATP
   e. adding a substance that makes the membrane more permeable to hydrogen ions

Questions 6–10
An artificial cell consisting of an aqueous solution enclosed in a selectively permeable membrane has just been immersed in a beaker containing a different solution. The membrane is permeable to water and to the simple sugars glucose and fructose but completely impermeable to the disaccharide sucrose.

"Cell"
0.03 *M* sucrose
0.02 *M* glucose

Environment
0.01 *M* sucrose
0.01 *M* glucose
0.01 *M* fructose

6. Which solute(s) will exhibit a net diffusion into the cell?

7. Which solute(s) will exhibit a net diffusion out of the cell?

8. Which solution—the cell contents or the environment—is hypertonic to the other?

9. In which direction will there be a net osmotic movement of water?

10. After the cell is placed in the beaker, which of the following changes will occur? (Choose all that apply.)
    a. The artificial cell will become more flaccid.
    b. The artificial cell will become more turgid.
    c. Some water molecules will flow out of the cell, but the majority will flow into it.
    d. The membrane potential will decrease.
    e. In spite of the inability of sucrose to cross the membrane, eventually the two solutions will become isotonic.

For Self-Quiz answers, see Appendix A.

Go to the website or CD-ROM for more quiz questions.

Evolution Connection

Paramecium and other protists that live in hypotonic environments have cell membrane adaptations that slow osmotic water uptake, while those living in isotonic environments have more permeable cell membranes. What water regulation adaptations would you expect to have evolved in protists living in hypertonic habitats such as Great Salt Lake? How about those living in habitats where salt concentration fluctuates?

Scientific Inquiry

An experiment is designed to study the mechanism of sucrose uptake by plant cells. Cells are immersed in a sucrose solution, and the pH of the solution is monitored with a pH meter. Samples of the cells are taken at intervals, and the sucrose in the sampled cells is measured. The measurements show that sucrose uptake by the cells correlates with a rise in the pH of the surrounding solution. The magnitude of the pH change is proportional to the starting concentration of sucrose in the extracellular solution. A metabolic poison known to block the ability of cells to regenerate ATP is found to inhibit the pH changes in the extracellular solution. Propose a hypothesis accounting for these results. Suggest an additional experiment to test your hypothesis.

Investigation *How Do Salt Concentrations Affect Cells?*

Science, Technology, and Society

Extensive irrigation in arid regions causes salts to accumulate in the soil. (The water contains low concentrations of salts, but when the water evaporates from the fields, the salts are left behind to concentrate in the soil.) Based on what you have learned about water balance in plant cells, explain why increasing soil salinity (saltiness) has an adverse effect on agriculture. Suggest some ways to minimize this damage. What costs are attached to your solutions?

8

An Introduction to Metabolism

▲ Figure 8.1 **Bioluminescence by a fungus.**

Key Concepts

8.1 An organism's metabolism transforms matter and energy, subject to the laws of thermodynamics

8.2 The free-energy change of a reaction tells us whether the reaction occurs spontaneously

8.3 ATP powers cellular work by coupling exergonic reactions to endergonic reactions

8.4 Enzymes speed up metabolic reactions by lowering energy barriers

8.5 Regulation of enzyme activity helps control metabolism

Overview

The Energy of Life

The living cell is a chemical factory in miniature, where thousands of reactions occur within a microscopic space. Sugars can be converted to amino acids that are linked together into proteins when needed, and proteins are dismantled into amino acids that can be converted to sugars when food is digested. Small molecules are assembled into polymers, which may be hydrolyzed later as the needs of the cell change. In multicellular organisms, many cells export chemical products that are used in other parts of the organism. The process known as cellular respiration drives the cellular economy by extracting the energy stored in sugars and other fuels. Cells apply this energy to perform various types of work, such as the transport of solutes across the plasma membrane, which we discussed in Chapter 7. In a more exotic example, cells of the fungus in **Figure 8.1** convert the energy stored in certain organic molecules to light, a process called bioluminescence. (The glow may attract insects that benefit the fungus by dispersing its spores.) Bioluminescence and all other metabolic activities carried out by a cell are precisely coordinated and controlled. In its complexity, its efficiency, its integration, and its responsiveness to subtle changes, the cell is peerless as a chemical factory. The concepts of metabolism that you learn in this chapter will help you understand how matter and energy flow during life's processes and how that flow is regulated.

Concept 8.1

An organism's metabolism transforms matter and energy, subject to the laws of thermodynamics

The totality of an organism's chemical reactions is called **metabolism** (from the Greek *metabole*, change). Metabolism is an emergent property of life that arises from interactions between molecules within the orderly environment of the cell.

Organization of the Chemistry of Life into Metabolic Pathways

We can picture a cell's metabolism as an elaborate road map of the thousands of chemical reactions that occur in a cell, arranged as intersecting metabolic pathways. A **metabolic pathway** begins with a specific molecule, which is then altered in a series of defined steps, resulting in a certain product. Each step of the pathway is catalyzed by a specific enzyme:

Analogous to the red, yellow, and green stoplights that control the flow of traffic, mechanisms that regulate enzymes balance metabolic supply and demand, averting deficits or surpluses of important cellular molecules.

Metabolism as a whole manages the material and energy resources of the cell. Some metabolic pathways release energy by breaking down complex molecules to simpler compounds. These degradative processes are called **catabolic pathways**, or breakdown pathways. A major pathway of catabolism is cellular respiration, in which the sugar glucose and other organic fuels are broken down in the presence of oxygen to carbon dioxide and water. (Pathways can have more than one starting molecule and/or product.) Energy that was stored in the organic molecules becomes available to do the work of the cell, such as ciliary beating or membrane transport. **Anabolic pathways**, in contrast, consume energy to build complicated molecules from simpler ones; they are sometimes called biosynthetic pathways. An example of anabolism is the synthesis of a protein from amino acids. Catabolic and anabolic pathways are the "downhill" and "uphill" avenues of the metabolic map. Energy released from the downhill reactions of catabolism can be stored and then used to drive the uphill reactions of the anabolic pathways.

In this chapter, we will focus on the mechanisms common to metabolic pathways. Because energy is fundamental to all metabolic processes, a basic knowledge of energy is necessary to understand how the living cell works. Although we will use some nonliving examples to study energy, keep in mind that the concepts demonstrated by these examples also apply to **bioenergetics**, the study of how organisms manage their energy resources.

Forms of Energy

Energy is the capacity to cause change. In everyday life, energy is important because some forms of energy can be used to do work—that is, to move matter against opposing forces, such as gravity and friction. Put another way, energy is the ability to rearrange a collection of matter. For example, you expend energy to turn the pages of this book, and your cells expend energy in transporting certain substances across membranes. Energy exists in various forms, and the work of life depends on the ability of cells to transform energy from one type into another.

Energy can be associated with the relative motion of objects; this energy is called **kinetic energy**. Moving objects can perform work by imparting motion to other matter: A pool player uses the motion of the cue stick to push the cue ball, which in turn moves the other balls; water gushing over a dam turns turbines; and the contraction of leg muscles pushes bicycle pedals. Light is also a type of energy that can be harnessed to perform work, such as powering photosynthesis in green plants. **Heat**, or **thermal energy**, is kinetic energy associated with the random movement of atoms or molecules.

An object not presently moving may still possess energy. Energy that is not kinetic is called **potential energy**; it is energy that matter possesses because of its location or structure. Water behind a dam, for instance, stores energy because of its altitude above sea level. Molecules store energy because of the arrangement of their atoms. **Chemical energy** is a term used by biologists to refer to the potential energy available for release in a chemical reaction. Recall that catabolic pathways release energy by breaking down complex molecules. Biologists say that these complex molecules, such as glucose, are high in chemical energy. During a catabolic reaction, atoms are rearranged and energy is released, resulting in lower-energy breakdown products. This transformation also occurs, for example, in the engine of a car when the hydrocarbons of gasoline react explosively with oxygen, releasing the energy that pushes the pistons and producing exhaust. Although less explosive, a similar reaction of food molecules with oxygen provides chemical energy in biological systems, producing carbon dioxide and water as waste products. It is the structures and biochemical pathways of cells that enable them to release chemical energy from food molecules, powering life processes.

How is energy converted from one form to another? Consider the divers in **Figure 8.2**. The young man climbing the

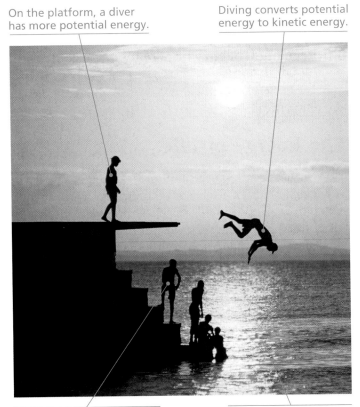

On the platform, a diver has more potential energy.

Diving converts potential energy to kinetic energy.

Climbing up converts kinetic energy of muscle movement to potential energy.

In the water, a diver has less potential energy.

▲ **Figure 8.2 Transformations between kinetic and potential energy.**

steps to the diving platform is releasing chemical energy from the food he ate for lunch and using some of that energy to perform the work of climbing. The kinetic energy of muscle movement is thus being transformed into potential energy owing to his increasing height above the water. The young man diving is converting his potential energy to kinetic energy, which is then transferred to the water as he enters it. A small amount of energy is lost as heat due to friction.

Now let's go back one step and consider the original source of the organic food molecules that provided the necessary chemical energy for the divers to climb the steps. This chemical energy was itself derived from light energy by plants during photosynthesis. Organisms are energy transformers.

The Laws of Energy Transformation

The study of the energy transformations that occur in a collection of matter is called **thermodynamics.** Scientists use the word *system* to denote the matter under study; they refer to the rest of the universe—everything outside the system—as the *surroundings.* A *closed system,* such as that approximated by liquid in a thermos bottle, is isolated from its surroundings. In an *open system,* energy (and often matter) can be transferred between the system and its surroundings. Organisms are open systems. They absorb energy—for instance, light energy or chemical energy in the form of organic molecules—and release heat and metabolic waste products, such as carbon dioxide, to the surroundings. Two laws of thermodynamics govern energy transformations in organisms and all other collections of matter.

The First Law of Thermodynamics

According to the **first law of thermodynamics,** the energy of the universe is constant. *Energy can be transferred and transformed, but it cannot be created or destroyed.* The first law is also known as the *principle of conservation of energy.* The electric company does not make energy, but merely converts it to a form that is convenient to use. By converting sunlight to chemical energy, a green plant acts as an energy transformer, not an energy producer.

The cheetah in **Figure 8.3a** will convert the chemical energy of the organic molecules in its food to kinetic and other forms of energy as it carries out biological processes. What happens to this energy after it has performed work? The second law helps to answer this question.

The Second Law of Thermodynamics

If energy cannot be destroyed, why can't organisms simply recycle their energy over and over again? It turns out that during every energy transfer or transformation, some energy becomes unusable energy, unavailable to do work. In most energy transformations, more usable forms of energy are at least partly converted to heat, which is the energy associated with the random motion of atoms or molecules. Only a small fraction of the chemical energy from the food in Figure 8.3a is transformed into the motion of the cheetah shown in **Figure 8.3b**; most is lost as heat, which dissipates rapidly through the surroundings.

In the process of carrying out chemical reactions that perform various kinds of work, living cells unavoidably convert organized forms of energy to heat. A system can put heat to work only when there is a temperature difference that results in the heat flowing from a warmer location to a cooler one. If temperature is uniform, as it is in a living cell, then the only use for heat energy generated during a chemical reaction is to warm a body of matter, such as the organism. (This can make a room crowded with people uncomfortably

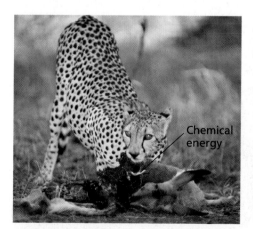

(a) First law of thermodynamics: Energy can be transferred or transformed but neither created nor destroyed. For example, the chemical (potential) energy in food will be converted to the kinetic energy of the cheetah's movement in (b).

(b) Second law of thermodynamics: Every energy transfer or transformation increases the disorder (entropy) of the universe. For example, disorder is added to the cheetah's surroundings in the form of heat and the small molecules that are the by-products of metabolism.

▲ **Figure 8.3 The two laws of thermodynamics.**

warm, as each person is carrying out a multitude of chemical reactions!)

A logical consequence of the loss of usable energy during energy transfer or transformation is that each such event makes the universe more disordered. Scientists use a quantity called **entropy** as a measure of disorder, or randomness. The more randomly arranged a collection of matter is, the greater its entropy. We can now state the **second law of thermodynamics** as follows: *Every energy transfer or transformation increases the entropy of the universe.* Although order can increase locally, there is an unstoppable trend toward randomization of the universe as a whole.

In many cases, increased entropy is evident in the physical disintegration of a system's organized structure. For example, you can observe increasing entropy in the gradual decay of an unmaintained building. Much of the increasing entropy of the universe is less apparent, however, because it appears as increasing amounts of heat and less ordered forms of matter. As the cheetah in Figure 8.3b converts chemical energy to kinetic energy, it is also increasing the disorder of its surroundings by producing heat and the small molecules that are the breakdown products of food.

The concept of entropy helps us understand why certain processes occur. It turns out that for a process to occur on its own, without outside help (an input of energy), it must increase the entropy of the universe. Let's first agree to use the word *spontaneous* for a process that can occur without an input of energy. Note that as we're using it here, the word *spontaneous* does not imply that such a process would occur quickly. Some spontaneous processes may be virtually instantaneous, such as an explosion, while others may be much slower, such as the rusting of an old car over time. A process that cannot occur on its own is said to be nonspontaneous; it will happen only if energy is added to the system. We know from experience that certain events occur spontaneously and others do not. For instance, we know that water flows downhill spontaneously, but moves uphill only with an input of energy, for instance when a machine pumps the water against gravity. In fact, another way to state the second law is: *For a process to occur spontaneously, it must increase the entropy of the universe.*

Biological Order and Disorder

Living systems increase the entropy of their surroundings, as predicted by thermodynamic law. It is true that cells create ordered structures from less organized starting materials. For example, amino acids are ordered into the specific sequences of polypeptide chains. At the organismal level, **Figure 8.4** shows the extremely symmetrical anatomy of a plant's root, formed by biological processes from simpler starting materials. However, an organism also takes in organized forms of matter and energy from the surroundings and replaces them with less ordered forms. For example, an animal obtains starch,

50 μm

▲ **Figure 8.4 Order as a characteristic of life.** Order is evident in the detailed anatomy of this root tissue from a buttercup plant (LM, cross section). As open systems, organisms can increase their order as long as the order of their surroundings decreases.

proteins, and other complex molecules from the food it eats. As catabolic pathways break these molecules down, the animal releases carbon dioxide and water—small molecules that store less chemical energy than the food did. The depletion of chemical energy is accounted for by heat generated during metabolism. On a larger scale, energy flows into an ecosystem in the form of light and leaves in the form of heat.

During the early history of life, complex organisms evolved from simpler ancestors. For example, we can trace the ancestry of the plant kingdom to much simpler organisms called green algae. However, this increase in organization over time in no way violates the second law. The entropy of a particular system, such as an organism, may actually decrease, so long as the total entropy of the *universe*—the system plus its surroundings—increases. Thus, organisms are islands of low entropy in an increasingly random universe. The evolution of biological order is perfectly consistent with the laws of thermodynamics.

Concept Check 8.1

1. How does the second law of thermodynamics help explain the diffusion of a substance across a membrane?
2. What is the relationship between energy and work?
3. Describe the forms of energy found in an apple as it grows on a tree, then falls and is digested by someone who eats it.

For suggested answers, see Appendix A.

The free-energy change of a reaction tells us whether the reaction occurs spontaneously

The laws of thermodynamics that we've just discussed apply to the universe as a whole. As biologists, we want to understand the chemical reactions of life—for example, to know which reactions occur spontaneously and which ones require some input of energy from outside. But how can we know this without assessing the energy and entropy changes in the entire universe for each separate reaction?

Free-Energy Change, ΔG

Recall that the universe is really equivalent to "the system" plus "the surroundings." In 1878, J. Willard Gibbs, a professor at Yale, defined a very useful function called the Gibbs free energy of a system (without considering its surroundings), symbolized by the letter G. We'll refer to the Gibbs free energy simply as free energy. **Free energy** measures the portion of a system's energy that can perform work when temperature and pressure are uniform throughout the system, as in a living cell. Let's consider how we determine the free energy change that occurs when a system changes—for example, during a chemical reaction.

The change in free energy, ΔG, can be calculated for any specific chemical reaction with the following formula:

$$\Delta G = \Delta H - T\Delta S$$

This formula uses only properties of the system (the reaction) itself: ΔH symbolizes the change in the system's *enthalpy* (in biological systems, equivalent to total energy); ΔS is the change in the system's entropy; and T is the absolute temperature in Kelvin (K) units (K = °C + 273; see Appendix B).

Once we know the value of ΔG for a process, we can use it to predict whether the process will be spontaneous (that is, whether it will run without an outside input of energy). A century of experiments has shown that only processes with a negative ΔG are spontaneous. For a process to occur spontaneously, therefore, the system must either give up enthalpy (H must decrease), give up order (TS must increase), or both: When the changes in H and TS are tallied, ΔG must have a negative value (ΔG < 0). This means that every spontaneous process decreases the system's free energy. Processes that have a positive or zero ΔG are never spontaneous.

This information is immensely interesting to biologists, for it gives us the power to predict which kinds of change can happen without help. Such spontaneous changes can be harnessed to perform work. This principle is very important in the study of metabolism, where a major goal is to determine which reactions can supply energy to do work in the living cell.

Free Energy, Stability, and Equilibrium

As we saw in the previous section, when a process occurs spontaneously in a system, we can be sure that ΔG is negative. Another way to think of ΔG is to realize that it represents the difference between the free energy of the final state and the free energy of the initial state:

$$\Delta G = G_{\text{final state}} - G_{\text{initial state}}$$

Thus, ΔG can only be negative when the process involves a loss of free energy during the change from initial state to final state. Because it has less free energy, the system in its final state is less likely to change and is therefore more stable than it was previously.

We can think of free energy as a measure of a system's instability—its tendency to change to a more stable state. Unstable systems (higher G) tend to change in such a way that they become more stable (lower G). For example, a diver on top of a platform is less stable than when floating in the water, a drop of concentrated dye is less stable than when the dye is spread randomly through the liquid, and a sugar molecule is less stable than the simpler molecules into which it can be broken (**Figure 8.5**, on the next page). Unless something prevents it, each of these systems will move toward greater stability: The diver falls, the solution becomes uniformly colored, and the sugar molecule is broken down.

Another term for a state of maximum stability is *equilibrium*, which you learned about in Chapter 2 in connection with chemical reactions. There is an important relationship between free energy and equilibrium, including chemical equilibrium. Recall that most chemical reactions are reversible and proceed to a point at which the forward and backward reactions occur at the same rate. The reaction is then said to be at chemical equilibrium, and there is no further net change in the relative concentration of products and reactants.

As a reaction proceeds toward equilibrium, the free energy of the mixture of reactants and products decreases. Free energy increases when a reaction is somehow pushed away from equilibrium, perhaps by removing some of the products (and thus changing their concentration relative to that of the reactants). For a system at equilibrium, G is at its lowest possible value in that system. We can think of the equilibrium state as an energy valley. Any small change from the equilibrium position will have a positive ΔG and will not be spontaneous. For this reason, systems never spontaneously move away from equilibrium. Because a system at equilibrium cannot spontaneously change, it can do no work. A process is spontaneous and can perform work only when it is moving toward equilibrium.

- More free energy (higher G)
- Less stable
- Greater work capacity

In a **spontaneous change**
- The free energy of the system decreases ($\Delta G < 0$)
- The system becomes more stable
- The released free energy can be harnessed to do work

- Less free energy (lower G)
- More stable
- Less work capacity

(a) Gravitational motion. Objects move spontaneously from a higher altitude to a lower one.

(b) Diffusion. Molecules in a drop of dye diffuse until they are randomly dispersed.

(c) Chemical reaction. In a cell, a sugar molecule is broken down into simpler molecules.

▲ Figure 8.5 **The relationship of free energy to stability, work capacity, and spontaneous change.** Unstable systems (top diagrams) are rich in free energy, or G. They have a tendency to change spontaneously to a more stable state (bottom), and it is possible to harness this "downhill" change to perform work.

Free Energy and Metabolism

We can now apply the free-energy concept more specifically to the chemistry of life's processes.

Exergonic and Endergonic Reactions in Metabolism

Based on their free-energy changes, chemical reactions can be classified as either exergonic ("energy outward") or endergonic ("energy inward"). An **exergonic reaction** proceeds with a net release of free energy **(Figure 8.6a)**. Because the chemical mixture loses free energy (G decreases), ΔG is negative for an exergonic reaction. Using ΔG as a standard for spontaneity, exergonic reactions are those that occur spontaneously. (Remember, the word *spontaneous* does not imply that a reaction will occur instantaneously, or even rapidly.) The magnitude of ΔG for an exergonic reaction represents the maximum amount of work the reaction can perform.* The greater the decrease in free energy, the greater the amount of work that can be done.

We can use the overall reaction for cellular respiration as an example:

$$C_6H_{12}O_6 + O_2 \rightarrow 6\ CO_2 + 6\ H_2O$$

$$\Delta G = -686\ \text{kcal/mol}\ (-2{,}870\ \text{kJ/mol})$$

---

* The word *maximum* qualifies this statement, because some of the free energy is released as heat and cannot do work. Therefore, ΔG represents a theoretical upper limit of available energy.

For each mole (180 g) of glucose broken down by respiration under what are called "standard conditions" (1 M of each reactant and product, 25°C, pH 7), 686 kcal (2,870 kJ) of energy are made available for work. Because energy must be conserved, the chemical products of respiration store 686 kcal less free energy per mole than the reactants. The products are, in a sense, the spent exhaust of a process that tapped the free energy stored in the sugar molecules.

An **endergonic reaction** is one that absorbs free energy from its surroundings **(Figure 8.6b)**. Because this kind of reaction essentially *stores* free energy in molecules (G increases), ΔG is positive. Such reactions are nonspontaneous, and the magnitude of ΔG is the quantity of energy required to drive the reaction. If a chemical process is exergonic (downhill) in one direction, then the reverse process must be endergonic (uphill). A reversible process cannot be downhill in both directions. If $\Delta G = -686$ kcal/mol for respiration, which converts sugar to carbon dioxide and water, then the reverse process—the conversion of carbon dioxide and water to sugar—must be strongly endergonic, with $\Delta G = +686$ kcal/mol. Such a reaction would never happen by itself.

How, then, do plants make the sugar that all the living world consumes for energy? They get the required energy—686 kcal to make a mole of sugar—from the environment by capturing light and converting its energy to chemical energy. Next, in a long series of exergonic steps, they gradually spend that chemical energy to assemble sugar molecules.

(a) **Exergonic reaction: energy released**

(b) **Endergonic reaction: energy required**

▲ Figure 8.6 **Free energy changes (ΔG) in exergonic and endergonic reactions.**

Equilibrium and Metabolism

Reactions in a closed system eventually reach equilibrium and can then do no work, as illustrated by the closed hydroelectric system in **Figure 8.7a**. The chemical reactions of metabolism are reversible, and they, too, would reach equilibrium if they occurred in the isolation of a test tube. Because systems at equilibrium are at a minimum of G and can do no work, a cell that has reached metabolic equilibrium is dead! The fact that metabolism as a whole is never at equilibrium is one of the defining features of life.

Like most systems, a cell in our body is not in equilibrium. The constant flow of materials in and out of the cell keeps the metabolic pathways from ever reaching equilibrium, and the cell continues to do work throughout its life. This principle is illustrated by the open (and more realistic) hydroelectric system in **Figure 8.7b**. However, unlike this simple single-step system, a catabolic pathway in a cell releases free energy in a series of reactions. An example is cellular respiration, illustrated by analogy in **Figure 8.7c**. Some of the reversible reactions of respiration are constantly "pulled" in one direction—that is, they are kept out of equilibrium. The key to maintaining this lack of equilibrium is that the product of one reaction does not accumulate, but instead becomes a reactant in the next step; finally, waste products are expelled from the cell. The overall sequence of reactions is kept going by the huge free-energy difference between glucose at the top of the energy "hill" and carbon dioxide and water at the "downhill" end. As long as our cells have a steady supply of glucose or other fuels and oxygen and are able to expel waste products to the surroundings, their metabolic pathways never reach equilibrium and can continue to do the work of life.

We see once again how important it is to think of organisms as open systems. Sunlight provides a daily source of free energy for an ecosystem's plants and other photosynthetic organisms. Animals and other nonphotosynthetic organisms in an ecosystem must have a source of free energy in the form of the organic products of photosynthesis. Now that we have

(a) **A closed hydroelectric system.** Water flowing downhill turns a turbine that drives a generator providing electricity to a light bulb, but only until the system reaches equilibrium.

(b) **An open hydroelectric system.** Flowing water keeps driving the generator because intake and outflow of water keep the system from reaching equilibrium.

(c) **A multistep open hydroelectric system.** Cellular respiration is analogous to this system: Glucose is broken down in a series of exergonic reactions that power the work of the cell. The product of each reaction becomes the reactant for the next, so no reaction reaches equilibrium.

▲ Figure 8.7 **Equilibrium and work in closed and open systems.**

applied the free-energy concept to metabolism, we are ready to see how a cell actually performs the work of life.

Concept 8.3

ATP powers cellular work by coupling exergonic reactions to endergonic reactions

A cell does three main kinds of work:

▶ *Mechanical work,* such as the beating of cilia (see Chapter 6), the contraction of muscle cells, and the movement of chromosomes during cellular reproduction
▶ *Transport work,* the pumping of substances across membranes against the direction of spontaneous movement (see Chapter 7)
▶ *Chemical work,* the pushing of endergonic reactions, which would not occur spontaneously, such as the synthesis of polymers from monomers (the focus of this chapter, and Chapters 9 and 10)

A key feature in the way cells manage their energy resources to do this work is **energy coupling,** the use of an exergonic process to drive an endergonic one. ATP is responsible for mediating most energy coupling in cells, and in most cases it acts as the immediate source of energy that powers cellular work.

The Structure and Hydrolysis of ATP

ATP (adenosine triphosphate) was introduced in Chapter 4 when we discussed the phosphate group as a functional group. Here we will look more closely at the structure of this molecule. ATP contains the sugar ribose, with the nitrogenous base adenine and a chain of three phosphate groups bonded to it **(Figure 8.8)**.

▲ **Figure 8.8 The structure of adenosine triphosphate (ATP).** In the cell, most hydroxyl groups of phosphates are ionized (—O⁻).

The bonds between the phosphate groups of ATP's tail can be broken by hydrolysis. When the terminal phosphate bond is broken, a molecule of inorganic phosphate (abbreviated Ⓟᵢ throughout this book) leaves the ATP, which becomes adenosine diphosphate, or ADP **(Figure 8.9)**. The reaction is exergonic and under standard conditions releases 7.3 kcal of energy per mole of ATP hydrolyzed:

$$ATP + H_2O \rightarrow ADP + Ⓟ_i$$

$$\Delta G = -7.3 \text{ kcal/mol} (-30.5 \text{ kJ/mol}) \text{ (standard conditions)}*$$

The free-energy change for many different reactions has been measured in the laboratory under standard conditions. If the ΔG of an endergonic reaction is less than the amount of energy released by ATP hydrolysis, then the two reactions can be coupled so that, overall, the coupled reactions are exergonic **(Figure 8.10)**.

Because their hydrolysis releases energy, the phosphate bonds of ATP are sometimes referred to as high-energy phosphate

▲ **Figure 8.9 The hydrolysis of ATP.** The hydrolysis of ATP yields inorganic phosphate (Ⓟᵢ) and ADP.

---

* In the cell, the conditions do not conform to standard conditions, owing in large part to reactant and product concentrations that differ from 1 M. For example, when ATP hydrolysis occurs under cellular conditions, the actual ΔG is about −13 kcal/mol, 78% greater than the energy released by ATP hydrolysis under standard conditions.

bonds, but the term is misleading. The phosphate bonds of ATP are not unusually strong bonds, as "high-energy" may imply; rather, the molecule itself has high energy in relation to that of the products (ADP and P_i). The release of energy during the hydrolysis of ATP comes from the chemical change to a state of lower free energy, not from the phosphate bonds themselves.

ATP is useful to the cell because the energy it releases on hydrolyzing a phosphate group is somewhat greater than the energy most other molecules could deliver. But why does this hydrolysis release so much energy? If we reexamine the ATP molecule in Figure 8.8, we can see that all three phosphate groups are negatively charged. These like charges are crowded together, and their mutual repulsion contributes to the instability of this region of the ATP molecule. The triphosphate tail of ATP is the chemical equivalent of a compressed spring.

How ATP Performs Work

When ATP is hydrolyzed in a test tube, the release of free energy merely heats the surrounding water. In an organism, this same generation of heat can sometimes be beneficial. For instance, the process of shivering uses ATP hydrolysis during muscle contraction to generate heat and warm the body. In most cases in the cell, however, the generation of heat alone would be an inefficient (and potentially dangerous) use of a valuable energy resource.

Instead, with the help of specific enzymes, the cell is able to couple the energy of ATP hydrolysis directly to endergonic processes by transferring a phosphate group from ATP to some other molecule, such as the reactant. The recipient of the phosphate group is then said to be **phosphorylated.** The key to coupling exergonic and endergonic reactions is the formation of this phosphorylated intermediate, which is more reactive (less stable) than the original unphosphorylated molecule.

The three types of cellular work—mechanical, transport, and chemical—are nearly always powered by the hydrolysis of ATP **(Figure 8.11)**. In each case, a phosphate group is transferred from ATP to some other molecule, and this phosphorylated molecule undergoes a change that performs work. An example is the synthesis of the amino acid glutamine from glutamic acid (another amino acid)

Endergonic reaction: ΔG is positive, reaction is not spontaneous

Glutamic acid + Ammonia → Glutamine $\Delta G = +3.4$ kcal/mol

Exergonic reaction: ΔG is negative, reaction is spontaneous

ATP + H_2O → ADP + P_i $\Delta G = -7.3$ kcal/mol

Coupled reactions: Overall ΔG is negative; together, reactions are spontaneous $\Delta G = -3.9$ kcal/mol

▲ **Figure 8.10 Energy coupling using ATP hydrolysis.** In this example, the exergonic process of ATP hydrolysis is used to drive an endergonic process—the synthesis of the amino acid glutamine from glutamic acid and ammonia.

(a) **Mechanical work: ATP phosphorylates motor proteins**

(b) **Transport work: ATP phosphorylates transport proteins**

(c) **Chemical work: ATP phosphorylates key reactants**

▲ **Figure 8.11 How ATP drives cellular work.** Phosphate group transfer is the mechanism responsible for most types of cellular work. For example, **(a)** ATP drives mechanical work by phosphorylating motor proteins, such as the ones that move organelles along cytoskeletal "tracks" in the cell. ATP also **(b)** drives active transport by phosphorylating certain membrane proteins. And ATP **(c)** drives chemical work by phosphorylating key reactants, in this case glutamic acid that is then converted to glutamine. The phosphorylated molecules lose the phosphate groups as work is performed, leaving ADP and inorganic phosphate (P_i) as products. Cellular respiration replenishes the ATP supply by powering the phosphorylation of ADP, as we will see in the next chapter.

and ammonia (see Figure 8.11c). First, ATP phosphorylates glutamic acid (Glu), making it a less stable phosphorylated intermediate. Second, ammonia displaces the phosphate group, forming glutamine (Glu—NH$_2$). Because the overall process is exergonic, it occurs spontaneously (see Figure 8.10).

The Regeneration of ATP

An organism at work uses ATP continuously, but ATP is a renewable resource that can be regenerated by the addition of phosphate to ADP (Figure 8.12). The free energy required to phosphorylate ADP comes from exergonic breakdown reactions (catabolism) in the cell. This shuttling of inorganic phosphate and energy is called the ATP cycle, and it couples the cell's energy-yielding (exergonic) processes to the energy-consuming (endergonic) ones. The ATP cycle moves at an astonishing pace. For example, a working muscle cell recycles its entire pool of ATP in less than a minute. That turnover represents 10 million molecules of ATP consumed and regenerated per second per cell. If ATP could not be regenerated by the phosphorylation of ADP, humans would use up nearly their body weight in ATP each day.

Because both directions of a reversible process cannot go downhill, the regeneration of ATP from ADP and $\circled{P}_i$ is necessarily endergonic:

$$ADP + \circled{P}_i \rightarrow ATP + H_2O$$

$$\Delta G = +7.3 \text{ kcal/mol } (+30.5 \text{ kJ/mol}) \text{ (standard conditions)}$$

Because ATP formation from ADP and $\circled{P}_i$ is not spontaneous, free energy must be spent to make it occur. Catabolic (exergonic) pathways, especially cellular respiration, provide the energy for the endergonic process of making ATP. Plants also use light energy to produce ATP.

Thus, the ATP cycle is a turnstile through which energy passes during its transfer from catabolic to anabolic pathways. In fact, the chemical potential energy temporarily stored in ATP drives most cellular work.

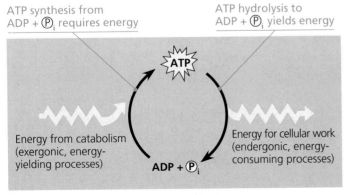

▲ **Figure 8.12 The ATP cycle.** Energy released by breakdown reactions (catabolism) in the cell is used to phosphorylate ADP, regenerating ATP. Energy stored in ATP drives most cellular work.

Concept Check 8.3

1. In most cases, how does ATP transfer energy from exergonic to endergonic processes in the cell?
2. Which of the following groups has more free energy: glutamic acid + ammonia + ATP, or glutamine + ADP + $\circled{P}_i$? Explain your answer.

For suggested answers, see Appendix A.

Concept 8.4

Enzymes speed up metabolic reactions by lowering energy barriers

The laws of thermodynamics tell us what will and will not happen under given conditions but say nothing about the rate of these processes. A spontaneous chemical reaction occurs without any requirement for outside energy, but it may occur so slowly that it is imperceptible. For example, even though the hydrolysis of sucrose (table sugar) to glucose and fructose is exergonic, occurring spontaneously with a release of free energy ($\Delta G = -7$ kcal/mol), a solution of sucrose dissolved in sterile water will sit for years at room temperature with no appreciable hydrolysis. However, if we add a small amount of a catalyst, such as the enzyme sucrase, to the solution, then all the sucrose may be hydrolyzed within seconds (Figure 8.13). How does an enzyme do this?

A **catalyst** is a chemical agent that speeds up a reaction without being consumed by the reaction; an **enzyme** is a catalytic protein. (Another class of biological catalysts, made of RNA and called ribozymes, is discussed in Chapters 17 and 26.) In the absence of regulation by enzymes, chemical traffic through the pathways of metabolism would become hopelessly congested because many chemical reactions would take such a long time. In the next two sections, we will see what impedes a spontaneous reaction from occurring faster and how an enzyme changes the situation.

The Activation Energy Barrier

Every chemical reaction between molecules involves both bond breaking and bond forming. For example, the hydrolysis of sucrose involves breaking the bond between glucose and fructose and one of the bonds of a water molecule, and then forming two new bonds, as shown in Figure 8.13. Changing one molecule into another generally involves contorting the starting molecule into a highly unstable state before the reaction can proceed. This contortion can be compared to a metal

▲ **Figure 8.13 Example of an enzyme-catalyzed reaction: hydrolysis of sucrose by sucrase.**

Sucrose
$C_{12}H_{22}O_{11}$

Glucose
$C_6H_{12}O_6$

Fructose
$C_6H_{12}O_6$

key ring when you bend it and pry it open to add a new key. The key ring is highly unstable in its opened form but returns to a stable state once the key is threaded all the way onto the ring. To reach the contorted state where bonds can change, reactant molecules must absorb energy from their surroundings. When the new bonds of the product molecules form, energy is released as heat, and the molecules return to stable shapes with lower energy.

The initial investment of energy for starting a reaction—the energy required to contort the reactant molecules so the bonds can change—is known as the **free energy of activation,** or **activation energy,** abbreviated E_A in this book. We can think of activation energy as the amount of energy needed to push the reactants over an energy barrier, or hill, so that the "downhill" part of the reaction can begin. **Figure 8.14** graphs the energy changes for a hypothetical exergonic reaction that swaps portions of two reactant molecules:

$$AB + CD \rightarrow AC + BD$$

The energizing, or activation, of the reactants is represented by the uphill portion of the graph, with the free-energy content of the reactant molecules increasing. At the summit, the reactants are in an unstable condition known as the *transition state:* They are activated, and the breaking and making of bonds can occur. The bond-forming phase of the reaction corresponds to the downhill part of the curve, which shows the loss of free energy by the molecules.

Activation energy is often supplied in the form of heat that the reactant molecules absorb from the surroundings. The bonds of the reactants break only when the molecules have absorbed enough energy to become unstable and are therefore more reactive (in the transition state at the peak of the curve in Figure 8.14). The absorption of thermal energy increases the speed of the reactant molecules, so they collide more often and more forcefully. Also, thermal agitation of the atoms in the molecules makes the bonds more likely to break. As the molecules settle into their new, more stable bonding arrangements, energy is released to the surroundings. If the reaction is exergonic, E_A will be repaid with dividends, as the formation of new bonds releases more energy than was invested in the breaking of old bonds.

The reactants AB and CD must absorb enough energy from the surroundings to reach the unstable transition state, where bonds can break.

Bonds break and new bonds form, releasing energy to the surroundings.

Transition state

E_A

Reactants

Free energy

$\Delta G < 0$

Products

Progress of the reaction ⟶

▲ **Figure 8.14 Energy profile of an exergonic reaction.** The "molecules" are hypothetical, with A, B, C, and D representing portions of the molecules. Thermodynamically, this is an exergonic reaction, with a negative ΔG, and the reaction occurs spontaneously. However, the activation energy (E_A) provides a barrier that determines the rate of the reaction.

The reaction shown in Figure 8.14 is exergonic and occurs spontaneously. However, the activation energy provides a barrier that determines the rate of the reaction. The reactants must absorb enough energy to reach the top of the activation energy barrier before the reaction can occur. For some reactions, E_A is modest enough that even at room temperature there is sufficient thermal energy for many of the reactants to reach the transition state in a short time. In most cases, however, E_A is so high and the transition state is reached so rarely that the reaction will hardly proceed at all. In these cases, the reaction will occur at a noticeable rate only if the reactants are heated. The spark plugs in an automobile engine energize the gasoline-oxygen mixture so that the molecules reach the transition state and react; only then can there be the explosive release of energy that pushes the pistons. Without a spark, a mixture of gasoline hydrocarbons and oxygen will not react because the E_A barrier is too high.

How Enzymes Lower the E_A Barrier

Proteins, DNA, and other complex molecules of the cell are rich in free energy and have the potential to decompose spontaneously; that is, the laws of thermodynamics favor their breakdown. These molecules persist only because at temperatures typical for cells, few molecules can make it over the hump of activation energy. However, the barriers for selected reactions must occasionally be surmounted for cells to carry out the processes necessary for life. Heat speeds a reaction by allowing reactants to attain the transition state more often, but this solution would be inappropriate for biological systems. First, high temperature denatures proteins and kills cells. Second, heat would speed up *all* reactions, not just those that are necessary. Organisms therefore use an alternative: catalysis.

An enzyme catalyzes a reaction by lowering the E_A barrier (Figure 8.15), enabling the reactant molecules to absorb enough energy to reach the transition state even at moderate temperatures. An enzyme cannot change the ΔG for a reaction; it cannot make an endergonic reaction exergonic. Enzymes can only hasten reactions that would occur eventually anyway, but this function makes it possible for the cell to have a dynamic metabolism, routing chemical traffic smoothly through the cell. And because enzymes are very selective in the reactions they catalyze, they determine which chemical processes will be going on in the cell at any particular time.

Substrate Specificity of Enzymes

The reactant an enzyme acts on is referred to as the enzyme's **substrate.** The enzyme binds to its substrate (or substrates, when there are two or more reactants), forming an **enzyme-substrate complex.** While enzyme and substrate are joined, the catalytic action of the enzyme converts the substrate to the product (or products) of the reaction. The overall process can be summarized as follows:

$$\text{Enzyme} + \text{Substrate(s)} \rightleftharpoons \begin{array}{c}\text{Enzyme-}\\\text{substrate}\\\text{complex}\end{array} \rightleftharpoons \text{Enzyme} + \text{Product(s)}$$

For example, the enzyme sucrase (most enzyme names end in *-ase*) catalyzes the hydrolysis of the disaccharide sucrose into its two monosaccharides, glucose and fructose (see Figure 8.13):

$$\begin{array}{c}\text{Sucrase} +\\\text{Sucrose} +\\H_2O\end{array} \rightleftharpoons \begin{array}{c}\text{Sucrase-}\\\text{sucrose-}H_2O\\\text{complex}\end{array} \rightleftharpoons \begin{array}{c}\text{Sucrase} +\\\text{Glucose} +\\\text{Fructose}\end{array}$$

The reaction catalyzed by each enzyme is very specific; an enzyme can recognize its specific substrate even among closely related compounds, such as isomers. For instance, sucrase will act only on sucrose and will not bind to other disaccharides, such as maltose. What accounts for this molecular recognition? Recall that enzymes are proteins, and proteins are macromolecules with unique three-dimensional conformations. The specificity of an enzyme results from its shape, which is a consequence of its amino acid sequence.

Only a restricted region of the enzyme molecule actually binds to the substrate. This region, called the **active site,** is typically a pocket or groove on the surface of the protein (Figure 8.16a). Usually, the active site is formed by only a few of the enzyme's amino acids, with the rest of the protein molecule providing a framework that determines the configuration of the active site. The specificity of an enzyme is attributed to a compatible fit between the shape of its active site and the shape of the substrate. The active site, however, is not a rigid receptacle for the substrate. As the substrate enters the active site, interactions between its chemical groups and those on the amino acids of the protein cause the enzyme to change its shape slightly so that the active site fits even more snugly around the substrate (Figure 8.16b). This **induced fit** is like a clasping handshake. Induced fit brings chemical groups of the active site into positions that enhance their ability to catalyze the chemical reaction.

Catalysis in the Enzyme's Active Site

In an enzymatic reaction, the substrate binds to the active site (Figure 8.17). In most cases, the substrate is held in the active site by weak interactions, such as hydrogen bonds and ionic bonds. Side chains (R groups) of a few of the amino acids that make up the active site catalyze the conversion of substrate to product, and the product departs from the active site. The enzyme is then free to take another substrate molecule into its active site. The entire cycle happens so fast that a single enzyme molecule typically acts on about a thousand substrate molecules per second. Some enzymes are much faster. Enzymes, like other catalysts, emerge from the reaction in their original form. There-

▲ **Figure 8.15 The effect of enzymes on reaction rate.** Without affecting the free-energy change (ΔG) for a reaction, an enzyme speeds the reaction by reducing its activation energy (E_A).

▶ **Figure 8.16 Induced fit between an enzyme and its substrate. (a)** In this computer graphic model, the active site of this enzyme (hexokinase, shown in blue) forms a groove on its surface. Its substrate is glucose (red). **(b)** When the substrate enters the active site, it induces a change in the shape of the protein. This change allows more weak bonds to form, causing the active site to embrace the substrate and hold it in place.

Substrate

Active site

Enzyme

Enzyme-substrate complex

(a)   **(b)**

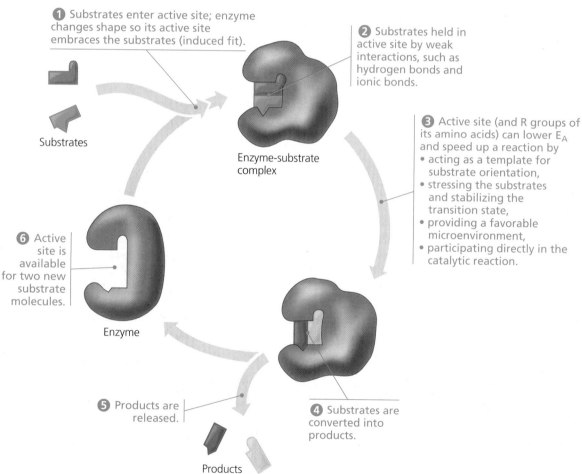

▶ **Figure 8.17 The active site and catalytic cycle of an enzyme.** An enzyme can convert one or more reactant molecules to one or more product molecules. The enzyme shown here converts two substrate molecules to two product molecules.

❶ Substrates enter active site; enzyme changes shape so its active site embraces the substrates (induced fit).

❷ Substrates held in active site by weak interactions, such as hydrogen bonds and ionic bonds.

❸ Active site (and R groups of its amino acids) can lower E_A and speed up a reaction by
• acting as a template for substrate orientation,
• stressing the substrates and stabilizing the transition state,
• providing a favorable microenvironment,
• participating directly in the catalytic reaction.

Substrates

Enzyme-substrate complex

❻ Active site is available for two new substrate molecules.

Enzyme

❺ Products are released.

❹ Substrates are converted into products.

Products

fore, very small amounts of enzyme can have a huge metabolic impact by functioning over and over again in catalytic cycles.

Most metabolic reactions are reversible, and an enzyme can catalyze both the forward and the reverse reactions. Which reaction prevails depends mainly on the relative concentrations of reactants and products. The enzyme always catalyzes the reaction in the direction of equilibrium.

Enzymes use a variety of mechanisms that lower activation energy and speed up a reaction (see Figure 8.17, step ❸). First, in reactions involving two or more reactants, the active site provides a template for the substrates to come together in the proper orientation for a reaction to occur between them. Second, as the active site of an enzyme clutches the bound substrates, the enzyme may stretch the substrate molecules toward their transition-state conformation, stressing and bending critical chemical bonds that must be broken during the reaction. Because E_A is proportional to the difficulty of breaking the bonds, distorting the substrate makes it approach the transition state and thus reduces the amount of free energy that must be absorbed to achieve a transition state.

Third, the active site may also provide a microenvironment that is more conducive to a particular type of reaction than the solution itself would be without the enzyme. For example, if the active site has amino acids with acidic side chains (R groups), the active site may be a pocket of low pH in an otherwise neutral cell. In such cases, an acidic amino acid may facilitate H^+ transfer to the substrate as a key step in catalyzing the reaction.

A fourth mechanism of catalysis is the direct participation of the active site in the chemical reaction. Sometimes this process even involves brief covalent bonding between the substrate and a side chain of an amino acid of the enzyme. Subsequent steps of the reaction restore the side chains to their original states, so the active site is the same after the reaction as it was before.

The rate at which a particular amount of enzyme converts substrate to product is partly a function of the initial concentration of the substrate: The more substrate molecules are available, the more frequently they access the active sites of the enzyme molecules. However, there is a limit to how fast the reaction can be pushed by adding more substrate to a fixed concentration of enzyme. At some point, the concentration of substrate will be high enough that all enzyme molecules have their active sites engaged. As soon as the product exits an active site, another substrate molecule enters. At this substrate concentration, the enzyme is said to be *saturated*, and the rate of the reaction is determined by the speed at which the active site can convert substrate to product. When an enzyme population is saturated, the only way to increase the rate of product formation is to add more enzyme. Cells sometimes do this by making more enzyme molecules.

Effects of Local Conditions on Enzyme Activity

The activity of an enzyme—how efficiently the enzyme functions—is affected by general environmental factors, such as temperature and pH. It can also be affected by chemicals that specifically influence that enzyme.

Effects of Temperature and pH

Recall from Chapter 5 that the three-dimensional structures of proteins are sensitive to their environment. As a consequence, each enzyme works better under some conditions than under others, because these *optimal conditions* favor the most active conformation for the enzyme molecule.

Temperature and pH are environmental factors important in the activity of an enzyme. Up to a point, the rate of an enzymatic reaction increases with increasing temperature, partly because substrates collide with active sites more frequently when the molecules move rapidly. Above that temperature, however, the speed of the enzymatic reaction drops sharply. The thermal agitation of the enzyme molecule disrupts the hydrogen bonds, ionic bonds, and other weak interactions that stabilize the active conformation, and the protein molecule eventually denatures. Each enzyme has an optimal temperature at which its reaction rate is greatest. Without denaturing the enzyme, this temperature allows the greatest number of molecular collisions and the fastest conversion of the reactants to product molecules. Most human enzymes have optimal temperatures of about 35–40°C (close to human body temperature). Bacteria that live in hot springs contain enzymes with optimal temperatures of 70°C or higher **(Figure 8.18a)**.

Just as each enzyme has an optimal temperature, it also has a pH at which it is most active. The optimal pH values for most enzymes fall in the range of pH 6–8, but there are exceptions. For example, pepsin, a digestive enzyme in the stomach, works best at pH 2. Such an acidic environment denatures most enzymes, but the active conformation of pepsin is adapted to maintain its functional three-dimensional structure in the acidic environment of the stomach. In contrast, trypsin, a digestive enzyme residing in the alkaline environment of the intestine, has an optimal pH of 8 and would be denatured in the stomach **(Figure 8.18b)**.

(a) Optimal temperature for two enzymes

(b) Optimal pH for two enzymes

▲ **Figure 8.18 Environmental factors affecting enzyme activity.** Each enzyme has an optimal **(a)** temperature and **(b)** pH that favor the most active conformation of the protein molecule.

Cofactors

Many enzymes require nonprotein helpers for catalytic activity. These adjuncts, called **cofactors**, may be bound tightly to the enzyme as permanent residents, or they may bind loosely and reversibly along with the substrate. The cofactors of some enzymes are inorganic, such as the metal atoms zinc, iron, and copper in ionic form. If the cofactor is an organic molecule, it is more specifically called a **coenzyme.** Most vitamins are coenzymes or raw materials from which coenzymes are made. Cofactors function in various ways, but in all cases where they are used, they perform a crucial function in catalysis. You'll encounter examples of cofactors later in the book.

Enzyme Inhibitors

Certain chemicals selectively inhibit the action of specific enzymes, and we have learned a lot about enzyme function by studying the effects of these molecules. If the inhibitor attaches to the enzyme by covalent bonds, inhibition is usually irreversible.

Many enzyme inhibitors, however, bind to the enzyme by weak bonds, in which case inhibition is reversible. Some reversible inhibitors resemble the normal substrate molecule and compete for admission into the active site (**Figure 8.19a** and **b**). These mimics, called **competitive inhibitors**, reduce the productivity of enzymes by blocking substrates from entering active sites. This kind of inhibition can be overcome by increasing the concentration of substrate so that as active sites become available, more substrate molecules than inhibitor molecules are around to gain entry to the sites.

In contrast, **noncompetitive inhibitors** do not directly compete with the substrate to bind to the enzyme at the active site (**Figure 8.19c**). Instead, they impede enzymatic reactions by binding to another part of the enzyme. This interaction causes the enzyme molecule to change its shape, rendering the active site less effective at catalyzing the conversion of substrate to product.

Toxins and poisons are often irreversible enzyme inhibitors. An example is sarin, a nerve gas that caused the death of several people and injury to many others when it was released by terrorists in the Tokyo subway in 1995. This small molecule binds covalently to the R group on the amino acid serine, which is found in the active site of acetylcholinesterase, an enzyme important in the nervous system. Other examples include the pesticides DDT and parathion, inhibitors of key enzymes in the nervous system. Finally, many antibiotics are inhibitors of specific enzymes in bacteria. For instance, penicillin blocks the active site of an enzyme that many bacteria use to make their cell walls.

Citing enzyme inhibitors that are metabolic poisons may give the impression that enzyme inhibition is generally abnormal and harmful. In fact, molecules naturally present in the cell often regulate enzyme activity by acting as inhibitors.

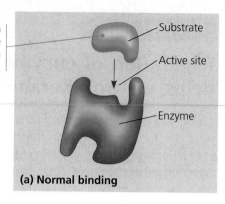

A substrate can bind normally to the active site of an enzyme.

Substrate

Active site

Enzyme

(a) Normal binding

A competitive inhibitor mimics the substrate, competing for the active site.

Competitive inhibitor

(b) Competitive inhibition

A noncompetitive inhibitor binds to the enzyme away from the active site, altering the conformation of the enzyme so that its active site no longer functions.

Noncompetitive inhibitor

(c) Noncompetitive inhibition

▲ **Figure 8.19 Inhibition of enzyme activity.**

Such regulation—selective inhibition—is essential to the control of cellular metabolism, as we discuss next.

Concept Check 8.4

1. Many spontaneous reactions occur very slowly. Why don't all spontaneous reactions occur instantly?
2. Describe why enzymes act only on very specific substrates.
3. Malonate is a competitive inhibitor of the enzyme succinate dehydrogenase. Describe how malonate would prevent the enzyme from acting on its normal substrate succinate.

For suggested answers, see Appendix A.

Regulation of enzyme activity helps control metabolism

Chemical chaos would result if all of a cell's metabolic pathways were operating simultaneously. Intrinsic to the process of life is a cell's ability to tightly regulate its metabolic pathways by controlling when and where its various enzymes are active. It does this either by switching on and off the genes that encode specific enzymes (as we will discuss in Unit Three) or, as we discuss here, by regulating the activity of enzymes once they are made.

Allosteric Regulation of Enzymes

In many cases, the molecules that naturally regulate enzyme activity in a cell behave something like reversible noncompetitive inhibitors (see Figure 8.19c): These regulatory molecules change an enzyme's shape and the functioning of its active site by binding to a site elsewhere on the molecule, via noncovalent bonds. **Allosteric regulation** is the term used to describe any case in which a protein's function at one site is affected by the binding of a regulatory molecule to a separate site. It may result in either inhibition or stimulation of an enzyme's activity.

Allosteric Activation and Inhibition

Most allosterically regulated enzymes are constructed from two or more polypeptide chains, or subunits **(Figure 8.20)**. Each subunit has its own active site. The entire complex oscillates between two conformational states, one catalytically active and the other inactive **(Figure 8.20a)**. In the simplest case of allosteric regulation, an activating or inhibiting regulatory molecule binds to a regulatory site (sometimes called an allosteric site), often located where subunits join. The binding of an *activator* to a regulatory site stabilizes the conformation that has functional active sites, whereas the binding of an *inhibitor* stabilizes the inactive form of the enzyme. The subunits of an allosteric enzyme fit together in such a way that a conformational change in one subunit is transmitted to all others. Through this interaction of subunits, a single activator or inhibitor molecule that binds to one regulatory site will affect the active sites of all subunits.

Fluctuating concentrations of regulators can cause a sophisticated pattern of response in the activity of cellular enzymes. The products of ATP hydrolysis (ADP and Ⓟᵢ), for example, play a major role in balancing the flow of traffic between anabolic and catabolic pathways by their effects on key enzymes. For example, ATP binds to several catabolic enzymes allosterically, lowering their affinity for substrate and thus inhibiting their activity. ADP, however, functions as an activator of the same enzymes. This is logical because a major function of catabolism is to regenerate ATP. If ATP production lags behind its

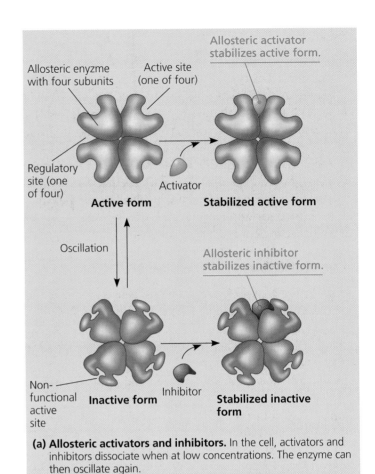

(a) Allosteric activators and inhibitors. In the cell, activators and inhibitors dissociate when at low concentrations. The enzyme can then oscillate again.

(b) Cooperativity: another type of allosteric activation. Note that the inactive form shown on the left oscillates back and forth with the active form when the active form is not stabilized by substrate.

▲ **Figure 8.20 Allosteric regulation of enzyme activity.**

use, ADP accumulates and activates these key enzymes that speed up catabolism, producing more ATP. If the supply of ATP exceeds demand, then catabolism slows down as ATP molecules accumulate and bind these same enzymes, inhibiting them. ATP, ADP, and other related molecules also affect key enzymes in anabolic pathways. In this way, allosteric enzymes control the rates of key reactions in metabolic pathways.

In another kind of allosteric activation, a substrate molecule binding to one active site may stimulate the catalytic powers of a multi-subunit enzyme by affecting the other active sites (Figure 8.20b). If an enzyme has two or more subunits, a substrate molecule causing induced fit in one subunit can trigger the same favorable conformational change in all the other subunits of the enzyme. Called **cooperativity**, this mechanism amplifies the response of enzymes to substrates: One substrate molecule primes an enzyme to accept additional substrate molecules more readily.

Feedback Inhibition

When ATP allosterically inhibits an enzyme in an ATP-generating pathway, the result is feedback inhibition, a common method of metabolic control. In **feedback inhibition**, a metabolic pathway is switched off by the inhibitory binding of its end product to an enzyme that acts early in the pathway. **Figure 8.21** shows an example of this control mechanism operating on an anabolic pathway. Some cells use this pathway of five steps to synthesize the amino acid isoleucine from threonine, another amino acid. As isoleucine accumulates, it slows down its own synthesis by allosterically inhibiting the enzyme for the very first step of the pathway. Feedback inhi-

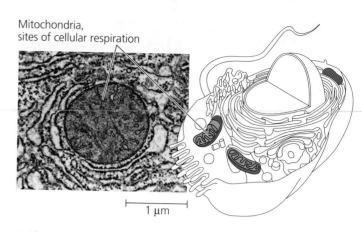

▲ **Figure 8.22 Organelles and structural order in metabolism.** Organelles such as these mitochondria (TEM) contain enzymes that carry out specific functions, in this case cellular respiration.

bition thereby prevents the cell from wasting chemical resources by synthesizing more isoleucine than is necessary.

Specific Localization of Enzymes Within the Cell

The cell is not just a bag of chemicals with thousands of different kinds of enzymes and substrates in a random mix. Structures within the cell help bring order to metabolic pathways. In some cases, a team of enzymes for several steps of a metabolic pathway is assembled into a multienzyme complex. The arrangement controls and speeds up the sequence of reactions, as the product from the first enzyme becomes the substrate for an adjacent enzyme in the complex, and so on, until the end product is released. Some enzymes and enzyme complexes have fixed locations within the cell, and act as structural components of particular membranes. Others are in solution within specific membrane-enclosed eukaryotic organelles, each with its own internal chemical environment. For example, in eukaryotic cells, the enzymes for cellular respiration reside in specific locations within mitochondria. **(Figure 8.22)**.

In this chapter we have learned that metabolism, the intersecting set of chemical pathways characteristic of life, is a choreographed interplay of thousands of different kinds of cellular molecules. In the next chapter we explore cellular respiration, the major catabolic pathway that breaks down organic molecules, releasing energy for the crucial processes of life.

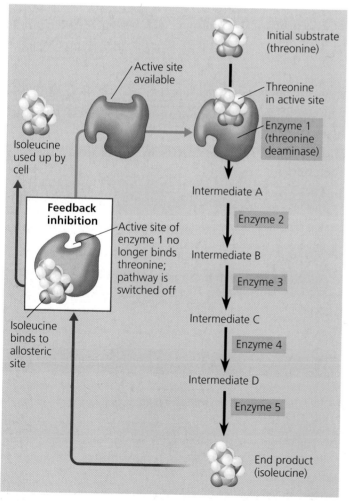

▲ **Figure 8.21 Feedback inhibition in isoleucine synthesis.**

Concept Check **8.5**

1. How can an activator and an inhibitor have different effects on an allosterically regulated enzyme?

For suggested answers, see Appendix A.

Chapter 8 Review

Go to the Campbell Biology website (**www.campbellbiology.com**) or CD-ROM to explore Activities, Investigations, and other interactive study aids.

SUMMARY OF KEY CONCEPTS

Concept 8.1

An organism's metabolism transforms matter and energy, subject to the laws of thermodynamics

▶ **Organization of the Chemistry of Life into Metabolic Pathways (pp. 141–142)** Metabolism is the collection of chemical reactions that occur in an organism. Aided by enzymes, it follows intersecting pathways, which may be catabolic (breaking down molecules, releasing energy) or anabolic (building molecules, consuming energy).

▶ **Forms of Energy (pp. 142–143)** Energy is the capacity to cause change; some forms of energy do work by moving matter. Kinetic energy is associated with motion. Potential energy is stored in the location or structure of matter and includes chemical energy stored in molecular structure.

▶ **The Laws of Energy Transformation (pp. 143–144)** The first law, conservation of energy, states that energy cannot be created or destroyed, only transferred or transformed. The second law states that spontaneous changes, those requiring no outside input of energy, increase the entropy (disorder) of the universe. *Activity Energy Transformations*

Concept 8.2

The free-energy change of a reaction tells us whether the reaction occurs spontaneously

▶ **Free-Energy Change, ΔG (p. 145)** A living system's free energy is energy that can do work under cellular conditions. The change in free energy (ΔG) during a biological process is related directly to enthalpy change (ΔH) and to the change in entropy (ΔS): $\Delta G = \Delta H - T\Delta S$.

▶ **Free Energy, Stability, and Equilibrium (pp. 145–146)** Organisms live at the expense of free energy. During a spontaneous change, free energy decreases and the stability of a system increases. At maximum stability, the system is at equilibrium.

▶ **Free Energy and Metabolism (pp. 146–148)** In an exergonic (spontaneous) chemical reaction, the products have less free energy than the reactants ($-\Delta G$). Endergonic (nonspontaneous) reactions require an input of energy ($+\Delta G$). The addition of starting materials and the removal of end products prevent metabolism from reaching equilibrium.

Concept 8.3

ATP powers cellular work by coupling exergonic reactions to endergonic reactions

▶ **The Structure and Hydrolysis of ATP (pp. 148–149)** ATP is the cell's energy shuttle. Release of its terminal phosphate group produces ADP, inorganic phosphate, and free energy. *Activity The Structure of ATP*

▶ **How ATP Performs Work (pp. 149–150)** ATP drives endergonic reactions by phosphorylation, the transfer of a phosphate group to specific reactants, making them more reactive. In this way, cells can carry out work, such as movement and anabolism. *Activity Chemical Reactions and ATP*

▶ **The Regeneration of ATP (p. 150)** Catabolic pathways drive the regeneration of ATP from ADP and phosphate.

Concept 8.4

Enzymes speed up metabolic reactions by lowering energy barriers

▶ **The Activation Energy Barrier (pp. 150–152)** In a chemical reaction, the energy necessary to break the bonds of the reactants is the activation energy, E_A.

▶ **How Enzymes Lower the E_A Barrier (p. 152)** Enzymes, which are proteins, are biological catalysts. They speed up reactions by lowering the activation energy barrier.

▶ **Substrate Specificity of Enzymes (p. 152)** Each type of enzyme has a unique active site that combines specifically with its substrate, the reactant molecule on which it acts. The enzyme changes shape slightly when it binds the substrate (induced fit). *Activity How Enzymes Work*

▶ **Catalysis in the Enzyme's Active Site (pp. 152–154)** The active site can lower an E_A barrier by orienting substrates correctly, straining their bonds, providing a favorable microenvironment, and even covalently bonding with the substrate.

▶ **Effects of Local Conditions on Enzyme Activity (pp. 154–155)** Each enzyme has an optimal temperature and pH. Inhibitors reduce enzyme function. A competitive inhibitor binds to the active site, while a noncompetitive inhibitor binds to a different site on the enzyme. *Investigation How Is the Rate of Enzyme Catalysis Measured?* *Biology Labs On-Line EnzymeLab*

Concept 8.5

Regulation of enzyme activity helps control metabolism

▶ **Allosteric Regulation of Enzymes (pp. 156–157)** Many enzymes are allosterically regulated: They change shape when regulatory molecules, either activators or inhibitors, bind to specific regulatory sites, affecting enzymatic function. In feedback inhibition, the end product of a metabolic pathway allosterically inhibits the enzyme for an earlier step in the pathway.

▶ **Specific Localization of Enzymes Within the Cell (p. 157)** Some enzymes are grouped into complexes, some are incorporated into membranes, and others are contained inside organelles.

TESTING YOUR KNOWLEDGE

Self-Quiz

1. Choose the pair of terms that correctly completes this sentence: Catabolism is to anabolism as _____ is to _____.
   a. exergonic; spontaneous
   b. exergonic; endergonic
   c. free energy; entropy
   d. work; energy
   e. entropy; enthalpy

2. Most cells cannot harness heat to perform work because
   a. heat is not a form of energy.
   b. cells do not have much heat; they are relatively cool.
   c. temperature is usually uniform throughout a cell.
   d. heat can never be used to do work.
   e. heat denatures enzymes.

3. According to the first law of thermodynamics,
   a. matter can be neither created nor destroyed.
   b. energy is conserved in all processes.
   c. all processes increase the order of the universe.
   d. systems rich in energy are intrinsically stable.
   e. the universe constantly loses energy because of friction.

4. Which of the following metabolic processes can occur without
   a net influx of energy from some other process?
   a. $ADP + \textcircled{P}_i \rightarrow ATP + H_2O$
   b. $C_6H_{12}O_6 + 6 O_2 \rightarrow 6 CO_2 + 6 H_2O$
   c. $6 CO_2 + 6 H_2O \rightarrow C_6H_{12}O_6 + 6 O_2$
   d. amino acids $\rightarrow$ protein
   e. glucose + fructose $\rightarrow$ sucrose

5. If an enzyme has been inhibited noncompetitively,
   a. the ΔG for the reaction it catalyzes will always be negative.
   b. the active site will be occupied by the inhibitor molecule.
   c. raising substrate concentration will increase inhibition.
   d. more energy will be necessary to initiate the reaction.
   e. the inhibitor molecule may be chemically unrelated to the substrate.

6. If an enzyme solution is saturated with substrate, the most
   effective way to obtain an even faster yield of products is to
   a. add more of the enzyme.
   b. heat the solution to 90°C.
   c. add more substrate.
   d. add an allosteric inhibitor.
   e. add a noncompetitive inhibitor.

7. If an enzyme is added to a solution where its substrate and
   products are in equilibrium, what would occur?
   a. Additional product would be formed.
   b. Additional substrate would be formed.
   c. The reaction would change from endergonic to exergonic.
   d. The free energy of the system would change.
   e. Nothing; the reaction would stay at equilibrium.

8. Some bacteria are metabolically active in hot springs because
   a. they are able to maintain a cooler internal temperature.
   b. high temperatures make catalysis unnecessary.
   c. their enzymes have high optimal temperatures.
   d. their enzymes are completely insensitive to temperature.
   e. they use molecules other than proteins as their main catalysts.

9. Which of the following characteristics is not associated with
   allosteric regulation of an enzyme's activity?
   a. A mimic of the substrate competes for the active site.
   b. A naturally occurring molecule stabilizes a catalytically
      active conformation.
   c. Regulatory molecules bind to a site remote from the active site.
   d. Inhibitors and activators may compete with one another.
   e. The enzyme usually has a quaternary structure.

10. In this branched metabolic pathway, a red arrow with a minus
    sign symbolizes inhibition of a metabolic step by an end product:

Which reaction would prevail if both Q and S were present in
the cell in high concentrations?
   a. $L \rightarrow M$ c. $L \rightarrow N$ e. $R \rightarrow S$
   b. $M \rightarrow O$ d. $O \rightarrow P$

For Self-Quiz answers, see Appendix A.

Go to the website or CD-ROM for more quiz questions.

Evolution Connection

A recent revival of the anti-evolutionary "argument from design"
holds that biochemical pathways are too complex to have evolved,
because all intermediate steps in a given pathway must be present
to produce the final product. Critique this argument. How could
you use the existing diversity of metabolic pathways that produce
the same or similar products to support your case?

Scientific Inquiry

A researcher has developed an assay to measure the activity of an
important enzyme present in liver cells being grown in culture.
She adds the enzyme's substrate to a dish of cells, then measures
the appearance of reaction products. The results are graphed as the
amount of product on the *y*-axis versus time on the *x*-axis. The researcher notes four sections of the graph. For a short period of
time, no products appeared (section A). Then (section B) the reaction rate was quite high (the slope of the line was steep). After
some time, the reaction slowed down considerably (section C), although products continued to appear (the line was not flat). Still
later, the reaction resumed its original rapid rate (section D). Draw
the graph, and propose a model to explain the molecular events
underlying this interesting reaction profile.

Investigation *How Is the Rate of Enzyme Catalysis Measured?*
Biology Labs On-Line *EnzymeLab*

Science, Technology, and Society

The EPA is evaluating the safety of the most commonly used
organophosphate insecticides (organic compounds containing
phosphate groups). Organophosphates typically interfere with
nerve transmission by inhibiting the enzymes that degrade the
transmitter molecules diffusing from one neuron to another.
Noxious insects are not uniquely susceptible; humans and other
vertebrates can be affected as well. Thus, the use of organophosphate pesticides creates some health risks. As a consumer, what
level of risk are you willing to accept in exchange for an abundant
and affordable food supply? What other facts would you like to
know before you defend your opinion?

9

Cellular Respiration
Harvesting Chemical Energy

▲ Figure 9.1 **This giant panda is consuming fuel to power the work of life.**

Key Concepts

9.1 Catabolic pathways yield energy by oxidizing organic fuels

9.2 Glycolysis harvests chemical energy by oxidizing glucose to pyruvate

9.3 The citric acid cycle completes the energy-yielding oxidation of organic molecules

9.4 During oxidative phosphorylation, chemiosmosis couples electron transport to ATP synthesis

9.5 Fermentation enables some cells to produce ATP without the use of oxygen

9.6 Glycolysis and the citric acid cycle connect to many other metabolic pathways

Overview

Life Is Work

Living cells require transfusions of energy from outside sources to perform their many tasks—for example, assembling polymers, pumping substances across membranes, moving, and reproducing. The giant panda in **Figure 9.1** obtains energy for its cells by eating plants; some animals feed on other organisms that eat plants. The energy stored in the organic molecules of food ultimately comes from the sun. Energy flows into an ecosystem as sunlight and leaves as heat **(Figure 9.2)**. In contrast, the chemical elements essential to life are recycled. Photosynthesis generates oxygen and organic molecules used by the mitochondria of eukaryotes (including plants and algae) as fuel for cellular respiration. Respiration breaks this fuel down, generating ATP. The waste products of respiration, carbon dioxide and water, are the raw materials for photosynthesis. In this chapter, we consider how cells harvest the chemical energy stored in organic molecules and use it to generate ATP, the molecule that drives most cellular work. After presenting some basics about respiration, we will focus on the three key pathways of respiration: glycolysis, the citric acid cycle, and oxidative phosphorylation.

▲ Figure 9.2 **Energy flow and chemical recycling in ecosystems.** Energy flows into an ecosystem as sunlight and ultimately leaves as heat, while the chemical elements essential to life are recycled.

Catabolic pathways yield energy by oxidizing organic fuels

In this section, we consider several processes that are central to cellular respiration and related pathways.

Catabolic Pathways and Production of ATP

Organic compounds store energy in their arrangement of atoms. With the help of enzymes, a cell systematically degrades complex organic molecules that are rich in potential energy to simpler waste products that have less energy. Some of the energy taken out of chemical storage can be used to do work; the rest is dissipated as heat. As you learned in Chapter 8, metabolic pathways that release stored energy by breaking down complex molecules are called catabolic pathways. One catabolic process, **fermentation,** is a partial degradation of sugars that occurs without the use of oxygen. However, the most prevalent and efficient catabolic pathway is **cellular respiration,** in which oxygen is consumed as a reactant along with the organic fuel. In eukaryotic cells, mitochondria house most of the metabolic equipment for cellular respiration.

Although very different in mechanism, respiration is in principle similar to the combustion of gasoline in an automobile engine after oxygen is mixed with the fuel (hydrocarbons). Food provides the fuel for respiration, and the exhaust is carbon dioxide and water. The overall process can be summarized as follows:

$$\text{Organic compounds} + \text{Oxygen} \rightarrow \text{Carbon dioxide} + \text{Water} + \text{Energy}$$

Although carbohydrates, fats, and proteins can all be processed and consumed as fuel, it is helpful to learn the steps of cellular respiration by tracking the degradation of the sugar glucose ($C_6H_{12}O_6$), the fuel that cells most often use:

$$C_6H_{12}O_6 + 6\ O_2 \rightarrow 6\ CO_2 + 6\ H_2O + \text{Energy (ATP + heat)}$$

This breakdown of glucose is exergonic, having a free-energy change of -686 kcal ($-2{,}870$ kJ) per mole of glucose decomposed ($\Delta G = -686$ kcal/mol). Recall that a negative ΔG indicates that the products of the chemical process store less energy than the reactants and that the reaction can happen spontaneously—in other words, without an input of energy.

Catabolic pathways do not directly move flagella, pump solutes across membranes, polymerize monomers, or perform other cellular work. Catabolism is linked to work by a chemical drive shaft—ATP, which you learned about in Chapter 8. To keep working, the cell must regenerate its supply of ATP from ADP and $\textcircled{P}_i$ (see Figure 8.11). To understand how cellular respiration accomplishes this, let's examine the fundamental chemical processes known as oxidation and reduction.

Redox Reactions: Oxidation and Reduction

Why do the catabolic pathways that decompose glucose and other organic fuels yield energy? The answer is based on the transfer of electrons during the chemical reactions. The relocation of electrons releases energy stored in organic molecules, and this energy ultimately is used to synthesize ATP.

The Principle of Redox

In many chemical reactions, there is a transfer of one or more electrons (e^-) from one reactant to another. These electron transfers are called oxidation-reduction reactions, or **redox reactions** for short. In a redox reaction, the loss of electrons from one substance is called **oxidation,** and the addition of electrons to another substance is known as **reduction.** (Note that *adding* electrons is called *reduction;* negatively charged electrons added to an atom *reduce* the amount of positive charge of that atom.) To take a simple, nonbiological example, consider the reaction between the elements sodium (Na) and chlorine (Cl) that forms table salt:

We could generalize a redox reaction this way:

In the generalized reaction, substance X, the electron donor, is called the **reducing agent;** it reduces Y, which accepts the donated electron. Substance Y, the electron acceptor, is the **oxidizing agent;** it oxidizes X by removing its electron. Because an electron transfer requires both a donor and an acceptor, oxidation and reduction always go together.

Not all redox reactions involve the complete transfer of electrons from one substance to another; some change the degree of electron sharing in covalent bonds. The reaction between methane and oxygen, shown in **Figure 9.3** on the next page, is an example. As explained in Chapter 2, the covalent electrons in methane are shared nearly equally between the bonded atoms because carbon and hydrogen have about the same affinity for valence electrons; they are about equally electronegative. But when methane reacts with oxygen, forming carbon dioxide, electrons end up farther away from the carbon atom and closer to their new covalent partners, the oxygen atoms, which are very electronegative. In effect, the carbon atom has partially "lost" its shared electrons; thus, methane has been oxidized.

Now let's examine the fate of the reactant O_2. The two atoms of the oxygen molecule (O_2) share their electrons equally. But when oxygen reacts with the hydrogen from methane, forming water, the electrons of the covalent bonds are drawn closer to

Reactants		Products

becomes oxidized

$$CH_4 \;+\; 2\,O_2 \;\longrightarrow\; CO_2 \;+\; \text{Energy} \;+\; 2\,H_2O$$

becomes reduced

Methane (reducing agent)   Oxygen (oxidizing agent)   Carbon dioxide   Water

▲ **Figure 9.3 Methane combustion as an energy-yielding redox reaction.** The reaction releases energy to the surroundings because the electrons lose potential energy when they end up closer to electronegative atoms such as oxygen.

the oxygen (see Figure 9.3). In effect, each oxygen atom has partially "gained" electrons, and so the oxygen molecule has been reduced. Because oxygen is so electronegative, it is one of the most potent of all oxidizing agents.

Energy must be added to pull an electron away from an atom, just as energy is required to push a ball uphill. The more electronegative the atom (the stronger its pull on electrons), the more energy is required to take an electron away from it. An electron loses potential energy when it shifts from a less electronegative atom toward a more electronegative one, just as a ball loses potential energy when it rolls downhill. A redox reaction that relocates electrons closer to oxygen, such as the burning of methane, therefore releases chemical energy that can be put to work.

Oxidation of Organic Fuel Molecules During Cellular Respiration

The oxidation of methane by oxygen is the main combustion reaction that occurs at the burner of a gas stove. The combustion of gasoline in an automobile engine is also a redox reaction; the energy released pushes the pistons. But the energy-yielding redox process of greatest interest here is respiration: the oxidation of glucose and other molecules in food. Examine again the summary equation for cellular respiration, but this time think of it as a redox process:

becomes oxidized

$$C_6H_{12}O_6 \;+\; 6\,O_2 \;\longrightarrow\; 6\,CO_2 \;+\; 6\,H_2O \;+\; \text{Energy}$$

becomes reduced

As in the combustion of methane or gasoline, the fuel (glucose) is oxidized and oxygen is reduced. The electrons lose potential energy along the way, and energy is released.

In general, organic molecules that have an abundance of hydrogen are excellent fuels because their bonds are a source of "hilltop" electrons, whose energy may be released as these electrons "fall" down an energy gradient when they are transferred to oxygen. The summary equation for respiration indicates that hydrogen is transferred from glucose to oxygen. But the important point, not visible in the summary equation, is that the status of electrons changes as hydrogen is transferred to oxygen, liberating energy (ΔG is negative). By oxidizing glucose, respiration liberates stored energy from glucose and makes it available for ATP synthesis.

The main energy foods, carbohydrates and fats, are reservoirs of electrons associated with hydrogen. Only the barrier of activation energy holds back the flood of electrons to a lower energy state (see Figure 8.14). Without this barrier, a food substance like glucose would combine almost instantaneously with O_2. When we supply the activation energy by igniting glucose, it burns in air, releasing 686 kcal (2,870 kJ) of heat per mole of glucose (about 180 g). Body temperature is not high enough to initiate burning, of course. Instead, if you swallow some glucose, enzymes in your cells will lower the barrier of activation energy, allowing the sugar to be oxidized in a series of steps.

Stepwise Energy Harvest via NAD$^+$ and the Electron Transport Chain

If energy is released from a fuel all at once, it cannot be harnessed efficiently for constructive work. For example, if a gasoline tank explodes, it cannot drive a car very far. Cellular respiration does not oxidize glucose in a single explosive step either. Rather, glucose and other organic fuels are broken down in a series of steps, each one catalyzed by an enzyme. At key steps, electrons are stripped from the glucose. As is often the case in oxidation reactions, each electron travels with a proton—thus, as a hydrogen atom. The hydrogen atoms are not transferred directly to oxygen, but instead are usually passed first to a coenzyme called **NAD$^+$** (nicotinamide adenine dinucleotide, a derivative of the vitamin niacin). As an electron acceptor, NAD$^+$ functions as an oxidizing agent during respiration.

How does NAD$^+$ trap electrons from glucose and other organic molecules? Enzymes called dehydrogenases remove a pair of hydrogen atoms (two electrons and two protons) from the substrate (a sugar, for example), thereby oxidizing it. The enzyme delivers the two electrons along with *one* proton to its coenzyme, NAD$^+$ **(Figure 9.4)**. The other proton is released as a hydrogen ion (H$^+$) into the surrounding solution:

$$H-\overset{\textstyle |}{\underset{\textstyle |}{C}}-OH \;+\; NAD^+ \xrightarrow{\text{Dehydrogenase}} \overset{\textstyle |}{\underset{\textstyle |}{C}}=O \;+\; NADH \;+\; H^+$$

By receiving two negatively charged electrons but only one positively charged proton, NAD$^+$ has its charge neutralized when it is reduced to NADH. The name NADH shows the hydrogen that has been received in the reaction. NAD$^+$ is the most versa-

NAD⁺

$$H \quad O$$
$$C - NH_2$$

Nicotinamide
(oxidized form)

+ 2[H]
(from food)

Dehydrogenase

Reduction of NAD⁺ ⇌ Oxidation of NADH

NADH

$$H \quad H \quad O$$
$$C - NH_2$$

Nicotinamide
(reduced form)

+ H⁺

◀ **Figure 9.4 NAD⁺ as an electron shuttle.** The full name for NAD⁺, nicotinamide adenine dinucleotide, describes its structure; the molecule consists of two nucleotides joined together at their phosphate groups (shown in yellow). (Nicotinamide is a nitrogenous base, although not one that is present in DNA or RNA.) The enzymatic transfer of two electrons and one proton (H⁺) from an organic molecule in food to NAD⁺ reduces the NAD⁺ to NADH; the second proton (H⁺) is released. Most of the electrons removed from food are transferred initially to NAD⁺.

tile electron acceptor in cellular respiration and functions in several of the redox steps during the breakdown of sugar.

Electrons lose very little of their potential energy when they are transferred from food to NAD⁺. Each NADH molecule formed during respiration represents stored energy that can be tapped to make ATP when the electrons complete their "fall" down an energy gradient from NADH to oxygen.

How do electrons that are extracted from food and stored by NADH finally reach oxygen? It will help to compare the redox chemistry of cellular respiration to a much simpler reaction: the reaction between hydrogen and oxygen to form water **(Figure 9.5a)**. Mix H₂ and O₂, provide a spark for activation

energy, and the gases combine explosively. The explosion represents a release of energy as the electrons of hydrogen fall closer to the electronegative oxygen atoms. Cellular respiration also brings hydrogen and oxygen together to form water, but there are two important differences. First, in cellular respiration, the hydrogen that reacts with oxygen is derived from organic molecules rather than H₂. Second, respiration uses an **electron transport chain** to break the fall of electrons to oxygen into several energy-releasing steps instead of one explosive reaction **(Figure 9.5b)**. The transport chain consists of a number of molecules, mostly proteins, built into the inner membrane of a mitochondrion. Electrons removed from food are shuttled

▶ **Figure 9.5 An introduction to electron transport chains. (a)** The uncontrolled exergonic reaction of hydrogen with oxygen to form water releases a large amount of energy in the form of heat and light: an explosion. **(b)** In cellular respiration, the same reaction occurs in stages: An electron transport chain breaks the "fall" of electrons in this reaction into a series of smaller steps and stores some of the released energy in a form that can be used to make ATP. (The rest of the energy is released as heat.)

(a) Uncontrolled reaction

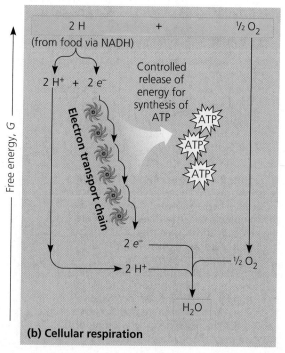

(b) Cellular respiration

by NADH to the "top," higher-energy end of the chain. At the "bottom," lower-energy end, oxygen captures these electrons along with hydrogen nuclei (H⁺), forming water.

Electron transfer from NADH to oxygen is an exergonic reaction with a free-energy change of −53 kcal/mol (−222 kJ/mol). Instead of this energy being released and wasted in a single explosive step, electrons cascade down the chain from one carrier molecule to the next, losing a small amount of energy with each step until they finally reach oxygen, the terminal electron acceptor, which has a very great affinity for electrons. Each "downhill" carrier is more electronegative than its "uphill" neighbor, with oxygen at the bottom of the chain. Thus, the electrons removed from food by NAD⁺ fall down an energy gradient in the electron transport chain to a far more stable location in the electronegative oxygen atom. Put another way, oxygen pulls electrons down the chain in an energy-yielding tumble analogous to gravity pulling objects downhill.

In summary, during cellular respiration, most electrons travel the following "downhill" route: food → NADH → electron transport chain → oxygen. Later in this chapter, you will learn more about how the cell uses the energy released from this exergonic electron fall to regenerate its supply of ATP.

Now that we have covered the basic redox mechanisms of cellular respiration, let's look at the entire process.

The Stages of Cellular Respiration: *A Preview*

Respiration is a cumulative function of three metabolic stages:

1. Glycolysis (color-coded teal throughout the chapter)
2. The citric acid cycle (color-coded salmon)
3. Oxidative phosphorylation: electron transport and chemiosmosis (color-coded violet)

Technically, cellular respiration is defined as including only the processes that require O_2: the citric acid cycle and oxidative phosphorylation. We include glycolysis, even though it doesn't require O_2, because most respiring cells deriving energy from glucose use this process to produce starting material for the citric acid cycle.

As diagrammed in **Figure 9.6**, the first two stages of cellular respiration, glycolysis and the citric acid cycle, are the catabolic pathways that decompose glucose and other organic fuels. **Glycolysis**, which occurs in the cytosol, begins the degradation process by breaking glucose into two molecules of a compound called pyruvate. The **citric acid cycle**, which takes place within the mitochondrial matrix, completes the breakdown of glucose by oxidizing a derivative of pyruvate to carbon dioxide. Thus, the carbon dioxide produced by respiration represents fragments of oxidized organic molecules.

Some of the steps of glycolysis and the citric acid cycle are redox reactions in which dehydrogenase enzymes transfer electrons from substrates to NAD⁺, forming NADH. In the third stage of respiration, the electron transport chain accepts electrons from the breakdown products of the first two stages (most often via NADH) and passes these electrons from one molecule to another. At the end of the chain, the electrons are combined with molecular oxygen and hydrogen ions (H⁺), forming water (see Figure 9.5b). The energy released at each step of the chain is stored in a form the mitochondrion can use to make ATP. This mode of ATP synthesis is called **oxidative phosphorylation** because it is powered by the redox reactions of the electron transport chain.

The inner membrane of the mitochondrion is the site of electron transport and chemiosmosis, the processes that together constitute oxidative phosphorylation. Oxidative phosphorylation accounts for almost 90% of the ATP generated by

▶ **Figure 9.6 An overview of cellular respiration.** During glycolysis, each glucose molecule is broken down into two molecules of the compound pyruvate. The pyruvate enters the mitochondrion, where the citric acid cycle oxidizes it to carbon dioxide. NADH and a similar coenzyme called FADH₂ transfer electrons derived from glucose to electron transport chains, which are built into the inner mitochondrial membrane. During oxidative phosphorylation, electron transport chains convert the chemical energy to a form used for ATP synthesis in the process called chemiosmosis.

▲ Figure 9.7 **Substrate-level phosphorylation.** Some ATP is made by direct enzymatic transfer of a phosphate group from an organic substrate to ADP.

Energy investment phase

Glucose

$2 ADP + 2 P$ ⟸ $2 ATP$ used

Energy payoff phase

$4 ADP + 4 P$ ⟹ $4 ATP$ formed

$2 NAD^+ + 4 e^- + 4 H^+$ ⟹ $2 NADH + 2 H^+$

→ 2 Pyruvate + 2 H_2O

Net

Glucose ⟶ 2 Pyruvate + 2 H_2O

4 ATP formed – 2 ATP used ⟶ 2 ATP

$2 NAD^+ + 4 e^- + 4 H^+$ ⟶ $2 NADH + 2 H^+$

▲ Figure 9.8 **The energy input and output of glycolysis.**

respiration. A smaller amount of ATP is formed directly in a few reactions of glycolysis and the citric acid cycle by a mechanism called **substrate-level phosphorylation (Figure 9.7).** This mode of ATP synthesis occurs when an enzyme transfers a phosphate group from a substrate molecule to ADP, rather than adding an inorganic phosphate to ADP as in oxidative phosphorylation. "Substrate molecule" here refers to an organic molecule generated during the catabolism of glucose.

For each molecule of glucose degraded to carbon dioxide and water by respiration, the cell makes up to about 38 molecules of ATP, each with 7.3 kcal/mol of free energy. Respiration cashes in the large denomination of energy banked in a single molecule of glucose (686 kcal/mol) for the small change of many molecules of ATP, which is more practical for the cell to spend on its work.

This preview has introduced how glycolysis, the citric acid cycle, and oxidative phosphorylation fit into the overall process of cellular respiration. We are now ready to take a closer look at each of these three stages of respiration.

Concept Check 9.1

1. In the following redox reaction, which compound is oxidized and which is reduced?

$$C_4H_6O_5 + NAD^+ \rightarrow C_4H_4O_5 + NADH + H^+$$

reduced
oxidized   **For suggested answers, see Appendix A.**

Concept 9.2

Glycolysis harvests chemical energy by oxidizing glucose to pyruvate

The word *glycolysis* means "splitting of sugar," and that is exactly what happens during this pathway. Glucose, a six-carbon sugar, is split into two three-carbon sugars. These smaller sugars are then oxidized and their remaining atoms rearranged to form two molecules of pyruvate. (Pyruvate is the ionized form of pyruvic acid.)

As summarized in **Figure 9.8** and described in detail in **Figure 9.9**, on the next two pages, the pathway of glycolysis consists of ten steps, which can be divided into two phases. During the energy investment phase, the cell actually spends ATP. This investment is repaid with dividends during the energy payoff phase, when ATP is produced by substrate-level phosphorylation and NAD^+ is reduced to NADH by electrons released from the oxidation of the food (glucose in this example). The net energy yield from glycolysis, per glucose molecule, is 2 ATP plus 2 NADH.

Notice in Figure 9.9 that all of the carbon originally present in glucose is accounted for in the two molecules of pyruvate; no CO_2 is released during glycolysis. Glycolysis occurs whether or not O_2 is present. However, if O_2 *is* present, the chemical energy stored in pyruvate and NADH can be extracted by the citric acid cycle and oxidative phosphorylation, respectively.

Concept Check 9.2

1. During the redox reaction in glycolysis, which molecule acts as the oxidizing agent? The reducing agent?

For suggested answers, see Appendix A.

▼ **Figure 9.9 A closer look at glycolysis.** The orientation diagram at the right relates glycolysis to the whole process of respiration. Do not let the chemical detail in the main diagram block your view of glycolysis as a source of ATP and NADH.

ENERGY INVESTMENT PHASE

1 Glucose enters the cell and is phosphorylated by the enzyme hexokinase, which transfers a phosphate group from ATP to the sugar. The charge of the phosphate group traps the sugar in the cell because the plasma membrane is impermeable to ions. Phosphorylation also makes glucose more chemically reactive. In this diagram, the transfer of a phosphate group or pair of electrons from one reactant to another is indicated by coupled arrows:

2 Glucose-6-phosphate is rearranged to convert it to its isomer, fructose-6-phosphate.

3 This enzyme transfers a phosphate group from ATP to the sugar, investing another molecule of ATP in glycolysis. So far, 2 ATP have been used. With phosphate groups on its opposite ends, the sugar is now ready to be split in half. This is a key step for regulation of glycolysis; phosphofructokinase is allosterically regulated by ATP and its products.

4 This is the reaction from which glycolysis gets its name. The enzyme cleaves the sugar molecule into two different three-carbon sugars: dihydroxyacetone phosphate and glyceraldehyde-3-phosphate. These two sugars are isomers of each other.

5 Isomerase catalyzes the reversible conversion between the two three-carbon sugars. This reaction never reaches equilibrium in the cell because the next enzyme in glycolysis uses only glyceraldehyde-3-phosphate as its substrate (and not dihydroxyacetone phosphate). This pulls the equilibrium in the direction of glyceraldehyde-3-phosphate, which is removed as fast as it forms. Thus, the net result of steps 4 and 5 is cleavage of a six-carbon sugar into two molecules of glyceraldehyde-3-phosphate; each will progress through the remaining steps of glycolysis.

ENERGY PAYOFF PHASE

连续的,相继的

6 This enzyme catalyzes two sequential reactions while it holds glyceraldehyde-3-phosphate in its active site. First, the sugar is oxidized by the transfer of electrons and H⁺ to NAD⁺, forming NADH (a redox reaction). This reaction is very exergonic, and the enzyme uses the released energy to attach a phosphate group to the oxidized substrate, making a product of very high potential energy. The source of the phosphates is the pool of inorganic phosphate ions that are always present in the cytosol. Notice that the coefficient 2 precedes all molecules in the energy payoff phase; these steps occur after glucose is split into two three-carbon sugars (step 4).

7 Glycolysis produces some ATP by substrate-level phosphorylation. The phosphate group added in the previous step is transferred to ADP in an exergonic reaction. For each glucose molecule that began glycolysis, step 7 produces 2 ATP, since every product after the sugar-splitting step (step 4) is doubled. Recall that 2 ATP were invested to get sugar ready for splitting; this ATP debt has now been repaid. Glucose has been converted to two molecules of 3-phosphoglycerate, which is not a sugar. The carbonyl group that characterizes a sugar has been oxidized to a carboxyl group (— COO⁻), the hallmark of an organic acid. The sugar was oxidized in step 6, and now the energy made available by that oxidation has been used to make ATP.

8 Next, this enzyme relocates the remaining phosphate group. This step prepares the substrate for the next reaction.

9 This enzyme causes a double bond to form in the substrate by extracting a water molecule, yielding phosphoenolpyruvate (PEP). The electrons of the substrate are rearranged in such a way that the remaining phosphate bond becomes very unstable, preparing the substrate for the next reaction.

10 The last reaction of glycolysis produces more ATP by transferring the phosphate group from PEP to ADP, a second example of substrate-level phosphorylation. Since this step occurs twice for each glucose molecule, 2 ATP are produced. Overall, glycolysis has used 2 ATP in the energy investment phase (steps 1 and 3) and produced 4 ATP in the energy payoff phase (steps 7 and 10), for a net gain of 2 ATP. Glycolysis has repaid the ATP investment with 100% interest. Additional energy was stored by step 6 in NADH, which can be used to make ATP by oxidative phosphorylation if oxygen is present. Glucose has been broken down and oxidized to two molecules of pyruvate, the end product of the glycolytic pathway. If oxygen is present, the chemical energy in pyruvate can be extracted by the citric acid cycle.

The citric acid cycle completes the energy-yielding oxidation of organic molecules

Glycolysis releases less than a quarter of the chemical energy stored in glucose; most of the energy remains stockpiled in the two molecules of pyruvate. If molecular oxygen is present, the pyruvate enters the mitochondrion, where the enzymes of the citric acid cycle complete the oxidation of the organic fuel.

Upon entering the mitochondrion via active transport, pyruvate is first converted to a compound called acetyl coenzyme A, or **acetyl CoA (Figure 9.10)**. This step, the junction between glycolysis and the citric acid cycle, is accomplished by a multi-enzyme complex that catalyzes three reactions: ❶ Pyruvate's carboxyl group (—COO⁻), which is already fully oxidized and thus has little chemical energy, is removed and given off as a molecule of CO_2. (This is the first step in which CO_2 is released during respiration.) ❷ The remaining two-carbon fragment is oxidized, forming a compound named acetate (the ionized form of acetic acid). An enzyme transfers the extracted electrons to NAD^+, storing energy in the form of NADH. ❸ Finally, coenzyme A, a sulfur-containing compound derived from a B vitamin, is attached to the acetate by an unstable bond that makes the acetyl group (the attached acetate) very reactive. The product of this chemical grooming, acetyl CoA, is now ready to feed its acetyl group into the citric acid cycle for further oxidation.

The citric acid cycle is also called the tricarboxylic acid cycle or the Krebs cycle, the latter honoring Hans Krebs, the German-British scientist who was largely responsible for elucidating the pathway in the 1930s. The cycle functions as a metabolic furnace that oxidizes organic fuel derived from pyruvate. **Figure 9.11** summarizes the inputs and outputs as pyruvate is broken down to 3 CO_2 molecules, including the molecule of CO_2 released during the conversion of pyruvate to acetyl CoA. The cycle generates 1 ATP per turn by substrate-level phosphorylation, but most of the chemical energy is transferred to NAD^+ and the related coenzyme FAD during the redox reactions. The reduced coenzymes, NADH and $FADH_2$, shuttle their cargo of high-energy electrons to the electron transport chain.

Now let's look at the citric acid cycle in more detail. The cycle has eight steps, each catalyzed by a specific enzyme. You can see in **Figure 9.12** that for each turn of the citric acid cycle, two carbons (red) enter in the relatively reduced form of an acetyl group (step 1), and two different carbons (blue) leave in the completely oxidized form of CO_2 (steps 3 and 4). The acetyl group of acetyl CoA joins the cycle by combining with the compound oxaloacetate, forming citrate (step 1).

▲ **Figure 9.10 Conversion of pyruvate to acetyl CoA, the junction between glycolysis and the citric acid cycle.** Because pyruvate is a charged molecule, it must enter the mitochondrion via active transport, with the help of a transport protein. Next, a complex of several enzymes (the pyruvate dehydrogenase complex) catalyzes the three numbered steps, which are described in the text. The acetyl group of acetyl CoA will enter the citric acid cycle. The CO_2 molecule will diffuse out of the cell.

▲ **Figure 9.11 An overview of the citric acid cycle.** To calculate the inputs and outputs on a per-glucose basis, multiply by 2, because each glucose molecule is split during glycolysis into two pyruvate molecules.

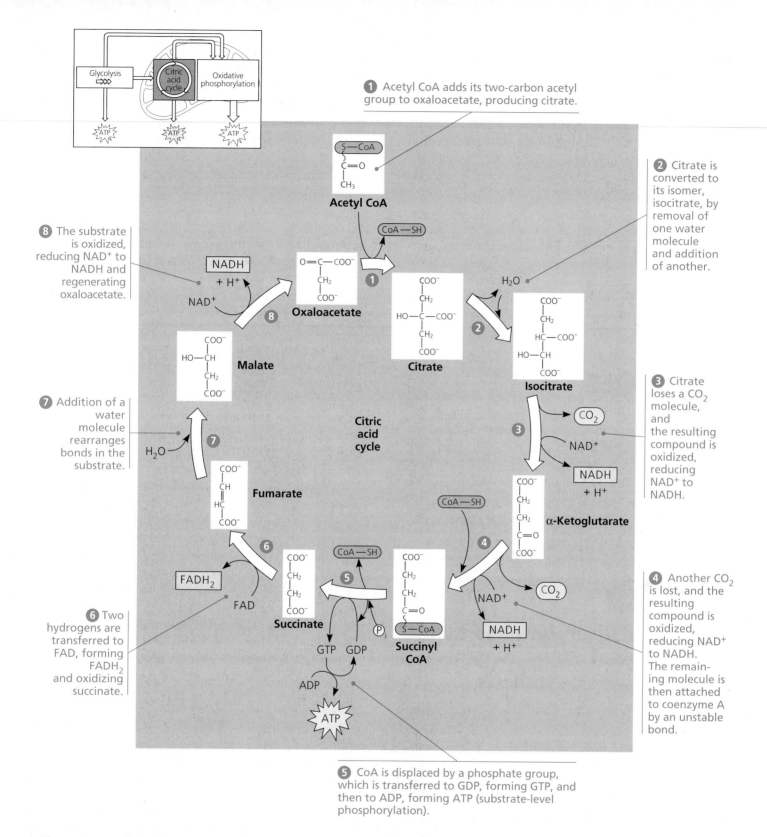

① Acetyl CoA adds its two-carbon acetyl group to oxaloacetate, producing citrate.

② Citrate is converted to its isomer, isocitrate, by removal of one water molecule and addition of another.

③ Citrate loses a CO₂ molecule, and the resulting compound is oxidized, reducing NAD⁺ to NADH.

④ Another CO₂ is lost, and the resulting compound is oxidized, reducing NAD⁺ to NADH. The remaining molecule is then attached to coenzyme A by an unstable bond.

⑤ CoA is displaced by a phosphate group, which is transferred to GDP, forming GTP, and then to ADP, forming ATP (substrate-level phosphorylation).

⑥ Two hydrogens are transferred to FAD, forming FADH₂ and oxidizing succinate.

⑦ Addition of a water molecule rearranges bonds in the substrate.

⑧ The substrate is oxidized, reducing NAD⁺ to NADH and regenerating oxaloacetate.

Acetyl CoA
Oxaloacetate
Citrate
Isocitrate
α-Ketoglutarate
Succinyl CoA
Succinate
Fumarate
Malate

Citric acid cycle

▲ Figure 9.12 **A closer look at the citric acid cycle.** In the chemical structures, red type traces the fate of the two carbon atoms that enter the cycle via acetyl CoA (step 1), and blue type indicates the two carbons that exit the cycle as CO₂ in steps 3 and 4. (The red labeling only goes through step 5, but you can continue to trace the fate of those carbons.) Notice that the carbon atoms that enter the cycle from acetyl CoA do not leave the cycle in the same turn. They remain in the cycle, occupying a different location in the molecules on their next turn after another acetyl group is added. As a consequence, the oxaloacetate that is regenerated at step 8 is composed of different carbon atoms each time around. All the citric acid cycle enzymes are located in the mitochondrial matrix except for the enzyme that catalyzes step 6, which resides in the inner mitochondrial membrane. Carboxylic acids are represented in their ionized forms, as —COO⁻, because the ionized forms prevail at the pH within the mitochondrion. For example, citrate is the ionized form of citric acid.

(Citrate is the ionized form of citric acid, for which the citric acid cycle is named.) The next seven steps decompose the citrate back to oxaloacetate. It is this regeneration of oxaloacetate that makes this process a *cycle*.

For each acetyl group that enters the cycle, 3 NAD^+ are reduced to NADH (steps 3, 4, and 8). In step 6, electrons are transferred not to NAD^+, but to a different electron acceptor, FAD (flavin adenine dinucleotide, derived from riboflavin, a B vitamin). Step 5 in the citric acid cycle forms a GTP molecule directly by substrate-level phosphorylation, similar to the ATP-generating steps of glycolysis. This GTP is then used to synthesize an ATP, the only ATP generated directly by the citric acid cycle. Most of the ATP output of respiration results from oxidative phosphorylation, when the NADH and $FADH_2$ produced by the citric acid cycle relay the electrons extracted from food to the electron transport chain. In the process, they supply the necessary energy for the phosphorylation of ADP to ATP. We will explore this process in the next section.

Concept Check 9.3

1. In which molecules is most of the energy from the citric acid cycle's redox reactions conserved? How will these molecules convert their energy to a form that can be used to make ATP?
2. What cellular processes produce the carbon dioxide that you exhale?

For suggested answers, see Appendix A.

Concept 9.4

During oxidative phosphorylation, chemiosmosis couples electron transport to ATP synthesis

Our main objective in this chapter is to learn how cells harvest the energy of food to make ATP. But the metabolic components of respiration we have dissected so far, glycolysis and the citric acid cycle, produce only 4 ATP molecules per glucose molecule, all by substrate-level phosphorylation: 2 net ATP from glycolysis and 2 ATP from the citric acid cycle. At this point, molecules of NADH (and $FADH_2$) account for most of the energy extracted from the food. These electron escorts link glycolysis and the citric acid cycle to the machinery of oxidative phosphorylation, which uses energy released by the electron transport chain to power ATP synthesis. In this section, you will learn first how the electron transport chain works, then how the inner membrane of the mitochondrion couples electron flow down the chain to ATP synthesis.

The Pathway of Electron Transport

The electron transport chain is a collection of molecules embedded in the inner membrane of the mitochondrion. The folding of the inner membrane to form cristae increases its surface area, providing space for thousands of copies of the chain in each mitochondrion. (Once again, we see that structure fits function.) Most components of the chain are proteins, which exist in multiprotein complexes numbered I through IV. Tightly bound to these proteins are *prosthetic groups*, nonprotein components essential for the catalytic functions of certain enzymes.

Figure 9.13 shows the sequence of electron carriers in the electron transport chain and the drop in free energy as electrons travel down the chain. During electron transport along the chain, electron carriers alternate between reduced and oxidized states as they accept and donate electrons. Each component of the chain becomes reduced when it accepts electrons from its "uphill" neighbor, which has a lower affinity for electrons (is less electronegative). It then returns to its oxidized form as it passes electrons to its "downhill," more electronegative neighbor.

Now let's take a closer look at the electron transport chain in Figure 9.13. Electrons removed from food by NAD^+, during glycolysis and the citric acid cycle, are transferred from NADH to the first molecule of the electron transport chain. This molecule is a flavoprotein, so named because it has a prosthetic group called flavin mononucleotide (FMN in complex I). In the next redox reaction, the flavoprotein returns to its oxidized form as it passes electrons to an iron-sulfur protein (Fe·S in complex I), one of a family of proteins with both iron and sulfur tightly bound. The iron-sulfur protein then passes the electrons to a compound called ubiquinone (Q in Figure 9.13). This electron carrier is a small hydrophobic molecule, the only member of the electron transport chain that is not a protein. Ubiquinone is mobile within the membrane rather than residing in a particular complex.

Most of the remaining electron carriers between ubiquinone and oxygen are proteins called **cytochromes.** Their prosthetic group, called a heme group, has an iron atom that accepts and donates electrons. (It is similar to the heme group in hemoglobin, the protein of red blood cells, except that the iron in hemoglobin carries oxygen, not electrons.) The electron transport chain has several types of cytochromes, each a different protein with a slightly different electron-carrying heme group. The last cytochrome of the chain, cyt a_3, passes its electrons to oxygen, which is *very* electronegative. Each oxygen atom also picks up a pair of hydrogen ions from the aqueous solution, forming water.

Another source of electrons for the transport chain is $FADH_2$, the other reduced product of the citric acid cycle. Notice in Figure 9.13 that $FADH_2$ adds its electrons to the electron transport chain at complex II, at a lower energy level than NADH does. Consequently, the electron transport chain provides about one-third less energy for ATP synthesis when the electron donor is $FADH_2$ rather than NADH.

The electron transport chain makes no ATP directly. Its function is to ease the fall of electrons from food to oxygen, breaking a large free-energy drop into a series of smaller steps that release energy in manageable amounts. How does the mitochondrion couple this electron transport and energy release to ATP synthesis? The answer is a mechanism called chemiosmosis.

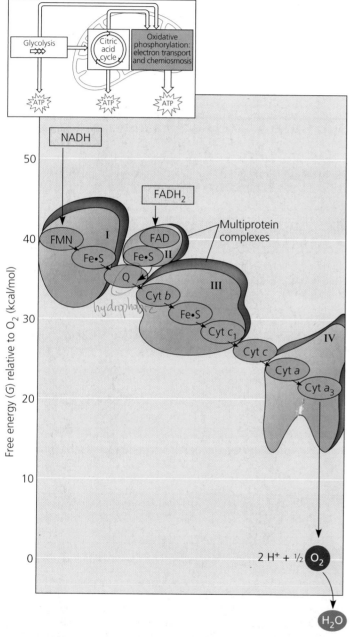

▲ **Figure 9.13 Free-energy change during electron transport.** The overall energy drop (ΔG) for electrons traveling from NADH to oxygen is 53 kcal/mol, but this "fall" is broken up into a series of smaller steps by the electron transport chain. (An oxygen atom is represented here as ½ O_2 to emphasize that the electron transport chain reduces molecular oxygen, O_2, not individual oxygen atoms. For every 2 NADH molecules, 1 O_2 molecule is reduced to 2 H_2O.)

Chemiosmosis: The Energy-Coupling Mechanism

Populating the inner membrane of the mitochondrion are many copies of a protein complex called **ATP synthase**, the enzyme that actually makes ATP from ADP and inorganic phosphate **(Figure 9.14)**. ATP synthase works like an ion pump running in reverse. Recall from Chapter 7 that ion pumps use ATP as an energy source to transport ions against their gradients. In the reverse of that process, ATP synthase uses the energy of an existing ion gradient to power ATP synthesis. The ion gradient that drives phosphorylation is a proton (hydrogen ion) gradient; that is, the power source for the ATP synthase is a difference in the concentration of H^+ on opposite sides of the inner mitochondrial membrane. (We can also think of this gradient as a difference in pH, since pH is a measure of H^+ concentration.) This process, in which energy stored in the form of a hydrogen ion gradient across a membrane is used to drive cellular work such as the synthesis of ATP, is called **chemiosmosis** (from the Greek *osmos*, push). We have previously used the word *osmosis* in discussing water transport, but here it refers to the flow of H^+ across a membrane.

From studying the structure of ATP synthase, scientists have learned how the flow of H^+ through this large enzyme powers ATP generation. ATP synthase is a multisubunit complex with

A **rotor** within the membrane spins clockwise when H^+ flows past it down the H^+ gradient.

A **stator** anchored in the membrane holds the knob stationary.

A **rod** (or "stalk") extending into the knob also spins, activating catalytic sites in the knob.

Three catalytic sites in the stationary **knob** join inorganic phosphate to ADP to make ATP.

▲ **Figure 9.14 ATP synthase, a molecular mill.** The ATP synthase protein complex functions as a mill, powered by the flow of hydrogen ions. This complex resides in mitochondrial and chloroplast membranes of eukaryotes and in the plasma membranes of prokaryotes. Each of the four parts of ATP synthase consists of a number of polypeptide subunits.

four main parts, each made up of multiple polypeptides (see Figure 9.14): a rotor in the inner mitochondrial membrane; a knob that protrudes into the mitochondrial matrix; an internal rod extending from the rotor into the knob; and a stator, anchored next to the rotor, that holds the knob stationary. Hydrogen ions flow down a narrow space between the stator and rotor, causing the rotor and its attached rod to rotate, much as a rushing stream turns a waterwheel. The spinning rod causes conformational changes in the stationary knob, activating three catalytic sites in the subunits that make up the knob, such that ADP and inorganic phosphate combine to make ATP.

So how does the inner mitochondrial membrane generate and maintain the H^+ gradient that drives ATP synthesis in the ATP synthase protein complex? Creating the H^+ gradient is the function of the electron transport chain, which is shown in its mitochondrial location in **Figure 9.15**. The chain is an energy converter that uses the exergonic flow of electrons to pump H^+ across the membrane, from the mitochondrial matrix into the intermembrane space. The H^+ has a tendency to move back across the membrane, diffusing down its gradient. And the ATP synthases are the only sites on the membrane that are freely permeable to H^+. The ions pass through a channel in ATP synthase, which uses the exergonic flow of H^+ to drive the phosphorylation of ADP (see Figure 9.14). Thus, the energy stored in an H^+ gradient across a membrane couples the redox reactions of the electron transport chain to ATP synthesis, an example of chemiosmosis.

At this point, you may be wondering how the electron transport chain pumps hydrogen ions. Researchers have found that certain members of the electron transport chain

▲ **Figure 9.15 Chemiosmosis couples the electron transport chain to ATP synthesis.** NADH and FADH$_2$ shuttle high-energy electrons extracted from food during glycolysis and the citric acid cycle to an electron transport chain built into the inner mitochondrial membrane. The yellow arrow traces the transport of electrons, which finally pass to oxygen at the "downhill" end of the chain, forming water. As Figure 9.13 showed, most of the electron carriers of the chain are grouped into four complexes. Two mobile carriers, ubiquinone (Q) and cytochrome c (Cyt c), move rapidly along the membrane, ferrying electrons between the large complexes. As complexes I, III, and IV accept and then donate electrons, they pump hydrogen ions (protons) from the mitochondrial matrix into the intermembrane space. (Note that FADH$_2$ deposits its electrons via complex II and so results in fewer protons being pumped into the intermembrane space than NADH.) Chemical energy originally harvested from food is transformed into a proton-motive force, a gradient of H^+ across the membrane. The hydrogen ions flow back down their gradient through a channel in an ATP synthase, another protein complex built into the membrane. The ATP synthase harnesses the proton-motive force to phosphorylate ADP, forming ATP. The use of an H^+ gradient (proton-motive force) to transfer energy from redox reactions to cellular work (ATP synthesis, in this case) is called chemiosmosis. Together, electron transport and chemiosmosis compose oxidative phosphorylation.

accept and release protons (H^+) along with electrons. At certain steps along the chain, electron transfers cause H^+ to be taken up and released into the surrounding solution. The electron carriers are spatially arranged in the membrane in such a way that H^+ is accepted from the mitochondrial matrix and deposited in the intermembrane space (see Figure 9.15). The H^+ gradient that results is referred to as a **proton-motive force,** emphasizing the capacity of the gradient to perform work. The force drives H^+ back across the membrane through the specific H^+ channels provided by ATP synthases.

In general terms, *chemiosmosis is an energy-coupling mechanism that uses energy stored in the form of an H^+ gradient across a membrane to drive cellular work.* In mitochondria, the energy for gradient formation comes from exergonic redox reactions, and ATP synthesis is the work performed. But chemiosmosis also occurs elsewhere and in other variations. Chloroplasts use chemiosmosis to generate ATP during photosynthesis; in these organelles, light (rather than chemical energy) drives both electron flow down an electron transport chain and the resulting H^+ gradient formation. Prokaryotes, which lack both mitochondria and chloroplasts, generate H^+ gradients across their plasma membranes. They then tap the proton-motive force not only to make ATP but also to pump nutrients and waste products across the membrane and to rotate their flagella. Because of its central importance to energy conversions in prokaryotes and eukaryotes, chemiosmosis has helped unify the study of bioenergetics. Peter Mitchell was awarded the Nobel Prize in 1978 for originally proposing the chemiosmotic model.

An Accounting of ATP Production by Cellular Respiration

Now that we have looked more closely at the key processes of cellular respiration, let's return to its overall function: harvesting the energy of food for ATP synthesis.

During respiration, most energy flows in this sequence: glucose → NADH → electron transport chain → proton-motive force → ATP. We can do some bookkeeping to calculate the ATP profit when cellular respiration oxidizes a molecule of glucose to six molecules of carbon dioxide. The three main departments of this metabolic enterprise are glycolysis, the citric acid cycle, and the electron transport chain, which drives oxidative phosphorylation. **Figure 9.16** gives a detailed accounting of the ATP yield per glucose molecule oxidized. The tally adds the 4 ATP produced directly by substrate-level phosphorylation during glycolysis and the citric acid cycle to the many more molecules of ATP generated by oxidative phosphorylation. Each NADH that transfers a pair of electrons from food to the electron transport chain contributes enough to the proton-motive force to generate a maximum of about 3 ATP.

Why are the numbers in Figure 9.16 inexact? There are three reasons we cannot state an exact number of ATP molecules generated by the breakdown of one molecule of glucose. First, phos-

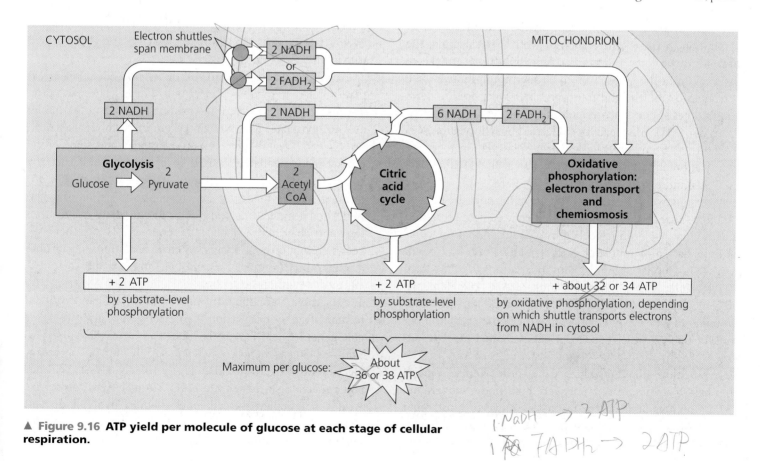

▲ **Figure 9.16 ATP yield per molecule of glucose at each stage of cellular respiration.**

phorylation and the redox reactions are not directly coupled to each other, so the ratio of number of NADH molecules to number of ATP molecules is not a whole number. We know that 1 NADH results in 10 H^+ being transported out across the inner mitochondrial membrane, and we also know that somewhere between 3 and 4 H^+ must reenter the mitochondrial matrix via ATP synthase to generate 1 ATP. Therefore, 1 NADH generates enough proton-motive force for synthesis of 2.5 to 3.3 ATP; generally, we round off and say that 1 NADH can generate about 3 ATP. The citric acid cycle also supplies electrons to the electron transport chain via $FADH_2$, but since it enters later in the chain, each molecule of this electron carrier is responsible for transport of only enough H^+ for the synthesis of 1.5 to 2 ATP.

Second, the ATP yield varies slightly depending on the type of shuttle used to transport electrons from the cytosol into the mitochondrion. The mitochondrial inner membrane is impermeable to NADH, so NADH in the cytosol is segregated from the machinery of oxidative phosphorylation. The two electrons of NADH captured in glycolysis must be conveyed into the mitochondrion by one of several electron shuttle systems. Depending on the type of shuttle in a particular cell type, the electrons are passed either to NAD^+ or to FAD. If the electrons are passed to FAD, as in brain cells, only about 2 ATP can result from each cytosolic NADH. If the electrons are passed to mitochondrial NAD^+, as in liver cells and heart cells, the yield is about 3 ATP.

A third variable that reduces the yield of ATP is the use of the proton-motive force generated by the redox reactions of respiration to drive other kinds of work. For example, the proton-motive force powers the mitochondrion's uptake of pyruvate from the cytosol. So, if *all* the proton-motive force generated by the electron transport chain were used to drive ATP synthesis, one glucose molecule could generate a maximum of 34 ATP produced by oxidative phosphorylation plus 4 ATP (net) from substrate-level phosphorylation to give a total yield of about 38 ATP (or only about 36 ATP if the less efficient shuttle were functioning).

We can now make a rough estimate of the efficiency of respiration—that is, the percentage of chemical energy stored in glucose that has been restocked in ATP. Recall that the complete oxidation of a mole of glucose releases 686 kcal of energy ($\Delta G = -686$ kcal/mol). Phosphorylation of ADP to form ATP stores at least 7.3 kcal per mole of ATP. Therefore, the efficiency of respiration is 7.3 kcal per mole of ATP times 38 moles of ATP per mole of glucose divided by 686 kcal per mole of glucose, which equals 0.4. Thus, about 40% of the energy stored in glucose has been transferred to storage in ATP. The rest of the stored energy is lost as heat. We use some of this heat to maintain our relatively high body temperature (37°C), and we dissipate the rest through sweating and other cooling mechanisms. Cellular respiration is remarkably efficient in its energy conversion. By comparison, the most efficient automobile converts only about 25% of the energy stored in gasoline to energy that moves the car.

Concept Check 9.4

1. What effect would an absence of O_2 have on the process shown in Figure 9.15?
2. In the absence of O_2, as above, what do you think would happen if you decreased the pH of the intermembrane space of the mitochondrion? Explain your answer.

For suggested answers, see Appendix A.

Concept 9.5

Fermentation enables some cells to produce ATP without the use of oxygen

Because most of the ATP generated by cellular respiration is the work of oxidative phosphorylation, our estimate of ATP yield from respiration is contingent upon an adequate supply of oxygen to the cell. Without the electronegative oxygen to pull electrons down the transport chain, oxidative phosphorylation ceases. However, fermentation provides a mechanism by which some cells can oxidize organic fuel and generate ATP *without* the use of oxygen.

How can food be oxidized without oxygen? Remember, oxidation refers to the loss of electrons to *any* electron acceptor, not just to oxygen. Glycolysis oxidizes glucose to two molecules of pyruvate. The oxidizing agent of glycolysis is NAD^+, not oxygen. Overall, glycolysis is exergonic, and some of the energy made available is used to produce 2 ATP (net) by substrate-level phosphorylation. If oxygen *is* present, then additional ATP is made by oxidative phosphorylation when NADH passes electrons removed from glucose to the electron transport chain. But glycolysis generates 2 ATP whether oxygen is present or not—that is, whether conditions are **aerobic** or **anaerobic** (from the Greek *aer*, air, and *bios*, life; the prefix *an-* means "without").

Anaerobic catabolism of organic nutrients can occur by fermentation. Fermentation is an extension of glycolysis that can generate ATP solely by substrate-level phosphorylation—as long as there is a sufficient supply of NAD^+ to accept electrons during the oxidation step of glycolysis. Without some mechanism to recycle NAD^+ from NADH, glycolysis would soon deplete the cell's pool of NAD^+ by reducing it all to NADH and shut itself down for lack of an oxidizing agent. Under aerobic conditions, NAD^+ is recycled productively from NADH by the transfer of electrons to the electron transport chain. The anaerobic alternative is to transfer electrons from NADH to pyruvate, the end product of glycolysis.

Types of Fermentation

Fermentation consists of glycolysis plus reactions that regenerate NAD^+ by transferring electrons from NADH to pyruvate or derivatives of pyruvate. The NAD^+ can then be reused to oxidize sugar by glycolysis, which nets two molecules of ATP by substrate-level phosphorylation. There are many types of fermentation, differing in the end products formed from pyruvate. Two common types are alcohol fermentation and lactic acid fermentation.

In **alcohol fermentation** **(Figure 9.17a)**, pyruvate is converted to ethanol (ethyl alcohol) in two steps. The first step releases carbon dioxide from the pyruvate, which is converted to the two-carbon compound acetaldehyde. In the second step, acetaldehyde is reduced by NADH to ethanol. This regenerates the supply of NAD^+ needed for the continuation of glycolysis. Many bacteria carry out alcohol fermentation under anaerobic conditions. Yeast (a fungus) also carries out alcohol fermentation. For thousands of years, humans have used yeast in brewing, winemaking, and baking. The CO_2 bubbles generated by baker's yeast allow bread to rise.

During **lactic acid fermentation** **(Figure 9.17b)**, pyruvate is reduced directly by NADH to form lactate as an end product, with no release of CO_2. (Lactate is the ionized form of lactic acid.) Lactic acid fermentation by certain fungi and bacteria is used in the dairy industry to make cheese and yogurt. Other types of microbial fermentation that are commercially important produce acetone and methanol (methyl alcohol).

Human muscle cells make ATP by lactic acid fermentation when oxygen is scarce. This occurs during the early stages of strenuous exercise, when sugar catabolism for ATP production outpaces the muscle's supply of oxygen from the blood. Under these conditions, the cells switch from aerobic respiration to fermentation. The lactate that accumulates may cause muscle fatigue and pain, but the lactate is gradually carried away by the blood to the liver. Lactate is converted back to pyruvate by liver cells.

Fermentation and Cellular Respiration Compared

Fermentation and cellular respiration are anaerobic and aerobic alternatives, respectively, for producing ATP by harvesting the chemical energy of food. Both pathways use glycolysis to oxidize glucose and other organic fuels to pyruvate, with a net production of 2 ATP by substrate-level phosphorylation. And in both fermentation and respiration, NAD^+ is the oxidizing agent that accepts electrons from food during glycolysis. A key difference is the contrasting mechanisms for oxidizing NADH back to NAD^+, which is required to sustain glycolysis. In fermentation, the final electron acceptor is an organic molecule such as pyruvate (lactic acid fermentation) or acetaldehyde (alcohol fermentation). In respiration, by contrast, the final acceptor for electrons from NADH is oxygen. This not only regenerates the NAD^+ required for glycolysis but pays an ATP bonus when the stepwise electron transport from NADH to oxygen drives oxidative phosphorylation. An even bigger ATP payoff comes from the oxidation of pyruvate in the citric acid cycle, which is unique to respiration. Without oxygen, the energy still stored in pyruvate is unavailable to the cell. Thus, cellular respiration harvests much more energy from each

(a) Alcohol fermentation

(b) Lactic acid fermentation

▲ **Figure 9.17 Fermentation.** In the absence of oxygen, many cells use fermentation to produce ATP by substrate-level phosphorylation. Pyruvate, the end product of glycolysis, serves as an electron acceptor for oxidizing NADH back to NAD^+, which can then be reused in glycolysis. Two of the common end products formed from fermentation are **(a)** ethanol and **(b)** lactate, the ionized form of lactic acid.

sugar molecule than fermentation can. In fact, respiration yields as much as 19 times more ATP per glucose molecule than does fermentation—up to 38 ATP for respiration, compared to 2 ATP produced by substrate-level phosphorylation in fermentation.

Some organisms, including yeasts and many bacteria, can make enough ATP to survive using either fermentation or respiration. Such species are called **facultative anaerobes.** On the cellular level, our muscle cells behave as facultative anaerobes. In a facultative anaerobe, pyruvate is a fork in the metabolic road that leads to two alternative catabolic routes **(Figure 9.18)**. Under aerobic conditions, pyruvate can be converted to acetyl CoA, and oxidation continues in the citric acid cycle. Under anaerobic conditions, pyruvate is diverted from the citric acid cycle, serving instead as an electron acceptor to recycle NAD^+. To make the same amount of ATP, a facultative anaerobe would have to consume sugar at a much faster rate when fermenting than when respiring.

The Evolutionary Significance of Glycolysis

The role of glycolysis in both fermentation and respiration has an evolutionary basis. Ancient prokaryotes probably used glycolysis to make ATP long before oxygen was present in Earth's atmosphere. The oldest known fossils of bacteria date back 3.5 billion years, but appreciable quantities of oxygen probably did not begin to accumulate in the atmosphere until about 2.7 billion years ago. Cyanobacteria produced this

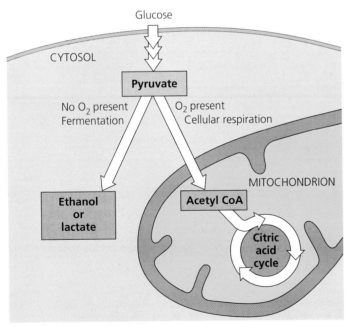

▲ **Figure 9.18 Pyruvate as a key juncture in catabolism.** Glycolysis is common to fermentation and cellular respiration. The end product of glycolysis, pyruvate, represents a fork in the catabolic pathways of glucose oxidation. In a cell capable of both cellular respiration and fermentation, pyruvate is committed to one of those two pathways, usually depending on whether or not oxygen is present.

O_2 as a by-product of photosynthesis. Therefore, early prokaryotes may have generated ATP exclusively from glycolysis, which does not require oxygen. In addition, glycolysis is the most widespread metabolic pathway, which suggests that it evolved very early in the history of life. The cytosolic location of glycolysis also implies great antiquity; the pathway does not require any of the membrane-bounded organelles of the eukaryotic cell, which evolved approximately 1 billion years after the prokaryotic cell. Glycolysis is a metabolic heirloom from early cells that continues to function in fermentation and as the first stage in the breakdown of organic molecules by respiration.

Concept Check 9.5

1. Consider the NADH formed during glycolysis. What is the final acceptor for its electrons during fermentation? What is the final acceptor for its electrons during respiration?
2. A glucose-fed yeast cell is moved from an aerobic environment to an anaerobic one. For the cell to continue generating ATP at the same rate, how would its rate of glucose consumption need to change?

For suggested answers, see Appendix A.

Concept 9.6

Glycolysis and the citric acid cycle connect to many other metabolic pathways

So far, we have treated the oxidative breakdown of glucose in isolation from the cell's overall metabolic economy. In this section, you will learn that glycolysis and the citric acid cycle are major intersections of various catabolic and anabolic (biosynthetic) pathways.

The Versatility of Catabolism

Throughout this chapter, we have used glucose as the fuel for cellular respiration. But free glucose molecules are not common in the diets of humans and other animals. We obtain most of our calories in the form of fats, proteins, sucrose and other disaccharides, and starch, a polysaccharide. All these organic molecules in food can be used by cellular respiration to make ATP **(Figure 9.19)**.

Glycolysis can accept a wide range of carbohydrates for catabolism. In the digestive tract, starch is hydrolyzed to glucose, which can then be broken down in the cells by glycolysis and the citric acid cycle. Similarly, glycogen, the polysaccharide that humans and many other animals store in their liver and muscle cells, can be hydrolyzed to glucose between meals as fuel for respiration. The digestion of disaccharides, including sucrose, provides glucose and other monosaccharides as fuel for respiration.

Proteins can also be used for fuel, but first they must be digested to their constituent amino acids. Many of the amino acids, of course, are used by the organism to build new proteins. Amino acids present in excess are converted by enzymes to intermediates of glycolysis and the citric acid cycle. Before amino acids can feed into glycolysis or the citric acid cycle, their amino groups must be removed, a process called deamination. The nitrogenous refuse is excreted from the animal in the form of ammonia, urea, or other waste products.

Catabolism can also harvest energy stored in fats obtained either from food or from storage cells in the body. After fats are digested to glycerol and fatty acids, the glycerol is converted to glyceraldehyde-3-phosphate, an intermediate of glycolysis. Most of the energy of a fat is stored in the fatty acids. A metabolic sequence called **beta oxidation** breaks the fatty acids down to two-carbon fragments, which enter the citric acid cycle as acetyl CoA. Fats make excellent fuel. A gram of fat oxidized by respiration produces more than twice as much ATP as a gram of carbohydrate. Unfortunately, this also means that a person who is trying to lose weight must work hard to use up fat stored in the body, because so many calories are stockpiled in each gram of fat.

Biosynthesis (Anabolic Pathways)

Cells need substance as well as energy. Not all the organic molecules of food are destined to be oxidized as fuel to make ATP. In addition to calories, food must also provide the carbon skeletons that cells require to make their own molecules. Some organic monomers obtained from digestion can be used directly. For example, as previously mentioned, amino acids from the hydrolysis of proteins in food can be incorporated into the organism's own proteins. Often, however, the body needs specific molecules that are not present as such in food. Compounds formed as intermediates of glycolysis and the citric acid cycle can be diverted into anabolic pathways as precursors from which the cell can synthesize the molecules it requires. For example, humans can make about half of the 20 amino acids in proteins by modifying compounds siphoned away from the citric acid cycle. Also, glucose can be made from pyruvate, and fatty acids can be synthesized from acetyl CoA. Of course, these anabolic, or biosynthetic, pathways do not generate ATP, but instead consume it.

In addition, glycolysis and the citric acid cycle function as metabolic interchanges that enable our cells to convert some kinds of molecules to others as we need them. For example, an intermediate compound generated during glycolysis, dihydroxyacetone phosphate (see Figure 9.9, step 5), can be converted into one of the major precursors of fats. If we eat more food than we need, we store fat even if our diet is fat-free. Metabolism is remarkably versatile and adaptable.

Regulation of Cellular Respiration via Feedback Mechanisms

Basic principles of supply and demand regulate the metabolic economy. The cell does not waste energy making more of a particular substance than it needs. If there is a glut of a certain amino acid, for example, the anabolic pathway that synthesizes that amino acid from an intermediate of the citric acid cycle is switched off. The most common mechanism for this control is feedback inhibition: The end product of the anabolic pathway inhibits the enzyme that catalyzes an early step of the pathway (see Figure 8.20). This prevents the needless

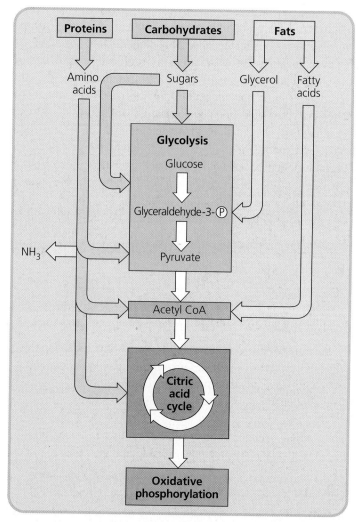

▲ **Figure 9.19 The catabolism of various molecules from food.** Carbohydrates, fats, and proteins can all be used as fuel for cellular respiration. Monomers of these molecules enter glycolysis or the citric acid cycle at various points. Glycolysis and the citric acid cycle are catabolic funnels through which electrons from all kinds of organic molecules flow on their exergonic fall to oxygen.

diversion of key metabolic intermediates from uses that are more urgent.

The cell also controls its catabolism. If the cell is working hard and its ATP concentration begins to drop, respiration speeds up. When there is plenty of ATP to meet demand, respiration slows down, sparing valuable organic molecules for other functions. Again, control is based mainly on regulating the activity of enzymes at strategic points in the catabolic pathway. One important switch is phosphofructokinase (Figure 9.20), the enzyme that catalyzes step 3 of glycolysis (see Figure 9.9). That is the earliest step that commits substrate irreversibly to the glycolytic pathway. By controlling the rate of this step, the cell can speed up or slow down the entire catabolic process; phosphofructokinase can thus be considered the pacemaker of respiration.

Phosphofructokinase is an allosteric enzyme with receptor sites for specific inhibitors and activators. It is inhibited by ATP and stimulated by AMP (adenosine monophosphate), which the cell derives from ADP. As ATP accumulates, inhibition of the enzyme slows down glycolysis. The enzyme becomes active again as cellular work converts ATP to ADP (and AMP) faster than ATP is being regenerated. Phosphofructokinase is also sensitive to citrate, the first product of the citric acid cycle. If citrate accumulates in mitochondria, some of it passes into the cytosol and inhibits phosphofructokinase. This mechanism helps synchronize the rates of glycolysis and the citric acid cycle. As citrate accumulates, glycolysis slows down, and the supply of acetyl groups to the citric acid cycle decreases. If citrate consumption increases, either because of a demand for more ATP or because anabolic pathways are draining off intermediates of the citric acid cycle, glycolysis accelerates and meets the demand. Metabolic balance is augmented by the control of other enzymes at other key locations in glycolysis and the citric acid cycle. Cells are thrifty, expedient, and responsive in their metabolism.

Examine Figure 9.2 again to put cellular respiration into the broader context of energy flow and chemical cycling in ecosystems. The energy that keeps us alive is *released*, but not *produced*, by cellular respiration. We are tapping energy that was stored in food by photosynthesis. In the next chapter, you will learn how photosynthesis captures light and converts it to chemical energy.

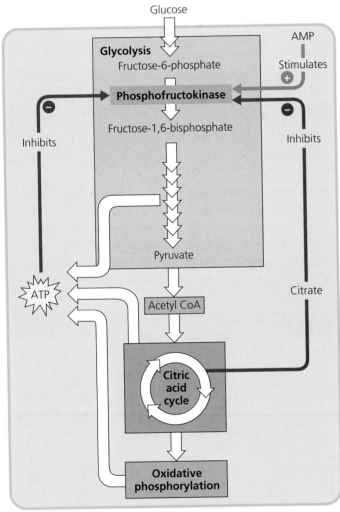

▲ **Figure 9.20 The control of cellular respiration.** Allosteric enzymes at certain points in the respiratory pathway respond to inhibitors and activators that help set the pace of glycolysis and the citric acid cycle. Phosphofructokinase, the enzyme that catalyzes step 3 of glycolysis (see Figure 9.9), is one such enzyme. It is stimulated by AMP (derived from ADP) but is inhibited by ATP and by citrate. This feedback regulation adjusts the rate of respiration as the cell's catabolic and anabolic demands change.

Concept Check 9.6

1. Compare the structure of a fat (see Figure 5.11) with that of a carbohydrate (see Figure 5.3). What features of their structures make fat a much better fuel?
2. Under what circumstances might your body synthesize fat molecules?
3. What will happen in a muscle cell that has used up its supply of oxygen and ATP? (See Figure 9.20.)

For suggested answers, see Appendix A.

Go to the Campbell Biology website (**www.campbellbiology.com**) or CD-ROM to explore Activities, Investigations, and other interactive study aids.

SUMMARY OF KEY CONCEPTS

▶ Life's processes require energy that enters the ecosystem in the form of sunlight. Energy is used for work or dissipated as heat, while the essential chemical elements are recycled by respiration and photosynthesis (p. 160).
Activity *Build a Chemical Cycling System*

Concept 9.1

Catabolic pathways yield energy by oxidizing organic fuels

▶ **Catabolic Pathways and Production of ATP (p. 161)** The breakdown of glucose and other organic fuels is exergonic. Starting with glucose or another organic molecule and using O_2, cellular respiration yields H_2O, CO_2, and energy in the form of ATP and heat. To keep working, a cell must regenerate ATP.

▶ **Redox Reactions: Oxidation and Reduction (pp. 161–164)** The cell taps the energy stored in food molecules through redox reactions, in which one substance partially or totally shifts electrons to another. The substance receiving electrons is reduced; the substance losing electrons is oxidized. During cellular respiration, glucose ($C_6H_{12}O_6$) is oxidized to CO_2, and O_2 is reduced to H_2O. Electrons lose potential energy during their transfer from organic compounds to oxygen. Electrons from organic compounds are usually passed first to NAD^+, reducing it to NADH. NADH passes the electrons to an electron transport chain, which conducts them to O_2 in energy-releasing steps. The energy released is used to make ATP.

▶ **The Stages of Cellular Respiration: A Preview (pp. 164–165)** Glycolysis and the citric acid cycle supply electrons (via NADH or $FADH_2$) to the electron transport chain, which drives oxidative phosphorylation. Oxidative phosphorylation generates ATP.
Activity *Overview of Cellular Respiration*

Concept 9.2

Glycolysis harvests chemical energy by oxidizing glucose to pyruvate

▶ Glycolysis breaks down glucose into two pyruvate molecules and nets 2 ATP and 2 NADH per glucose molecule (pp. 165–167).
Activity *Glycolysis*

Concept 9.3

The citric acid cycle completes the energy-yielding oxidation of organic molecules

▶ The import of pyruvate into the mitochondrion and its conversion to acetyl CoA links glycolysis to the citric acid cycle. The two-carbon acetyl group of acetyl CoA joins the four-carbon oxaloacetate, forming the six-carbon citrate, which is degraded back to oxaloacetate. The cycle releases 2 CO_2, forms 1 ATP, and passes electrons to NAD^+ and FAD, yielding 3 NADH and 1 $FADH_2$ per turn (pp. 168–170).
Activity *The Citric Acid Cycle*

Concept 9.4

During oxidative phosphorylation, chemiosmosis couples electron transport to ATP synthesis

▶ NADH and $FADH_2$ donate electrons to the electron transport chain, which powers ATP synthesis via oxidative phosphorylation (p. 170).

▶ **The Pathway of Electron Transport (pp. 170–171)** In the electron transport chain, electrons from NADH and $FADH_2$ lose energy in several energy-releasing steps. At the end of the chain, electrons are passed to O_2, reducing it to H_2O.

▶ **Chemiosmosis: The Energy-Coupling Mechanism (pp. 171–173)** At certain steps along the electron transport chain, electron transfer causes protein complexes to move H^+ from the mitochondrial matrix to the intermembrane space, storing energy as a proton-motive force (H^+ gradient). As H^+ diffuses back into the matrix through ATP synthase, its passage drives the phosphorylation of ADP.
Activity *Electron Transport*

▶ **An Accounting of ATP Production by Cellular Respiration (pp. 173–174)** About 40% of the energy stored in a glucose molecule is transferred to ATP during cellular respiration, producing a maximum of about 38 ATP.
Biology Labs On-Line *MitochondriaLab*
Investigation *How Is the Rate of Cellular Respiration Measured?*

Concept 9.5

Fermentation enables some cells to produce ATP without the use of oxygen

▶ **Types of Fermentation (p. 175)** Glycolysis nets two ATP by substrate-level phosphorylation whether oxygen is present or not. Under anaerobic conditions, the electrons from NADH are passed to pyruvate or a derivative of pyruvate, regenerating the NAD^+ required to oxidize more glucose. Two common types of fermentation are alcohol fermentation and lactic acid fermentation.
Activity *Fermentation*

▶ **Fermentation and Cellular Respiration Compared (pp. 175–176)** Both use glycolysis to oxidize glucose, but differ in their final electron acceptor. Respiration yields more ATP.

▶ **The Evolutionary Significance of Glycolysis (p. 176)** Glycolysis occurs in nearly all organisms and probably evolved in ancient prokaryotes before there was O_2 in the atmosphere.

Concept 9.6

Glycolysis and the citric acid cycle connect to many other metabolic pathways

▶ **The Versatility of Catabolism (pp. 176–177)** Catabolic pathways funnel electrons from many kinds of organic molecules into cellular respiration.

▶ **Biosynthesis (Anabolic Pathways) (p. 177)** The body can use small molecules from food directly or use them to build other substances through glycolysis or the citric acid cycle.

▶ **Regulation of Cellular Respiration via Feedback Mechanisms (pp. 177–178)** Cellular respiration is controlled by allosteric enzymes at key points in glycolysis and the citric acid cycle.

Self-Quiz

1. What is the reducing agent in the following reaction?

$$Pyruvate + NADH + H^+ \rightarrow Lactate + NAD^+$$

   a. oxygen   b. NADH   c. NAD^+
   d. lactate   e. pyruvate

2. The *immediate* energy source that drives ATP synthesis by ATP synthase during oxidative phosphorylation is
   a. the oxidation of glucose and other organic compounds.
   b. the flow of electrons down the electron transport chain.
   c. the affinity of oxygen for electrons.
   d. the H^+ concentration gradient across the inner mitochondrial membrane.
   e. the transfer of phosphate to ADP.

3. Which metabolic pathway is common to both fermentation and cellular respiration?
   a. the citric acid cycle
   b. the electron transport chain
   c. glycolysis
   d. synthesis of acetyl CoA from pyruvate
   e. reduction of pyruvate to lactate

4. In mitochondria, exergonic redox reactions
   a. are the source of energy driving prokaryotic ATP synthesis.
   b. are directly coupled to substrate-level phosphorylation.
   c. provide the energy to establish the proton gradient.
   d. reduce carbon atoms to carbon dioxide.
   e. are coupled via phosphorylated intermediates to endergonic processes.

5. The final electron acceptor of the electron transport chain that functions in oxidative phosphorylation is
   a. oxygen.   b. water.   c. NAD^+.
   d. pyruvate.   e. ADP.

6. When electrons flow along the electron transport chains of mitochondria, which of the following changes occurs?
   a. The pH of the matrix increases.
   b. ATP synthase pumps protons by active transport.
   c. The electrons gain free energy.
   d. The cytochromes phosphorylate ADP to form ATP.
   e. NAD^+ is oxidized.

7. In the presence of a metabolic poison that specifically and completely inhibits all function of mitochondrial ATP synthase, which would you expect?
   a. a decrease in the pH difference across the inner mitochondrial membrane
   b. an increase in the pH difference across the inner mitochondrial membrane
   c. increased synthesis of ATP
   d. increased oxygen consumption
   e. an accumulation of NAD^+

8. Cells do not catabolize carbon dioxide because
   a. its double bonds are too stable to be broken.
   b. CO_2 has fewer bonding electrons than other organic compounds.
   c. CO_2 is already completely reduced.
   d. CO_2 is already completely oxidized.
   e. the molecule has too few atoms.

9. Which of the following is a true distinction between fermentation and cellular respiration?
   a. Only respiration oxidizes glucose.
   b. NADH is oxidized by the electron transport chain in respiration only.
   c. Fermentation, but not respiration, is an example of a catabolic pathway.
   d. Substrate-level phosphorylation is unique to fermentation.
   e. NAD^+ functions as an oxidizing agent only in respiration.

10. Most CO_2 from catabolism is released during
   a. glycolysis.
   b. the citric acid cycle.
   c. lactate fermentation.
   d. electron transport.
   e. oxidative phosphorylation.

For Self-Quiz Answers, see Appendix A.

Go to the website or CD-ROM for more quiz questions.

Evolution Connection

ATP synthase enzymes are found in the prokaryotic plasma membrane and in mitochondria and chloroplasts. What does this suggest about the evolutionary relationship of these eukaryotic organelles to prokaryotes? How might the amino acid sequences of the ATP synthases from the different sources support or refute your hypothesis?

Scientific Inquiry

In the 1940s, some physicians prescribed low doses of a drug called dinitrophenol (DNP) to help patients lose weight. This unsafe method was abandoned after a few patients died. DNP uncouples the chemiosmotic machinery by making the lipid bilayer of the inner mitochondrial membrane leaky to H^+. Explain how this causes weight loss.

**Biology Labs On-Line *MitochondriaLab*
Investigation *How Is the Rate of Cellular Respiration Measured?***

Science, Technology, and Society

Nearly all human societies use fermentation to produce alcoholic drinks such as beer and wine. The practice dates back to the earliest days of agriculture. How do you suppose this use of fermentation was first discovered? Why did wine prove to be a more useful beverage, especially to a preindustrial culture, than the grape juice from which it was made?

Biological Inquiry: A Workbook of Investigative Cases *Explore fermentation further in the case "Bean Brew."*

10
Photosynthesis

Key Concepts

10.1 Photosynthesis converts light energy to the chemical energy of food

10.2 The light reactions convert solar energy to the chemical energy of ATP and NADPH

10.3 The Calvin cycle uses ATP and NADPH to convert CO_2 to sugar

10.4 Alternative mechanisms of carbon fixation have evolved in hot, arid climates

Overview

The Process That Feeds the Biosphere

Life on Earth is solar powered. The chloroplasts of plants capture light energy that has traveled 150 million kilometers from the sun and convert it to chemical energy stored in sugar and other organic molecules. This conversion process is called **photosynthesis.** Let's begin by placing photosynthesis in its ecological context.

Photosynthesis nourishes almost the entire living world directly or indirectly. An organism acquires the organic compounds it uses for energy and carbon skeletons by one of two major modes: autotrophic nutrition or heterotrophic nutrition. **Autotrophs** are "self-feeders" (*auto* means "self," and *trophos* means "feed"); they sustain themselves without eating anything derived from other organisms. Autotrophs produce their organic molecules from CO_2 and other inorganic raw materials obtained from the environment. They are the ultimate sources of organic compounds for all nonautotrophic

organisms, and for this reason, biologists refer to autotrophs as the *producers* of the biosphere.

Almost all plants are autotrophs; the only nutrients they require are water and minerals from the soil and carbon dioxide from the air. Specifically, plants are *photo*autotrophs, organisms that use light as a source of energy to synthesize organic substances **(Figure 10.1)**. Photosynthesis also occurs in algae, certain other protists, and some prokaryotes **(Figure 10.2,** on the next page). In this chapter, our emphasis will be on plants; variations in autotrophic nutrition that occur in prokaryotes and algae will be discussed in Chapters 27 and 28.

Heterotrophs obtain their organic material by the second major mode of nutrition. Unable to make their own food, they live on compounds produced by other organisms (*hetero* means "other"). Heterotrophs are the biosphere's *consumers.* The most obvious form of this "other-feeding" occurs when an animal eats plants or other animals. But heterotrophic nutrition may be more subtle. Some heterotrophs consume the remains of dead organisms by decomposing and feeding on organic litter such as carcasses, feces, and fallen leaves; they are known as decomposers. Most fungi and many types of prokaryotes get their nourishment this way. Almost all heterotrophs, including humans, are completely dependent on photoautotrophs for food—and also for oxygen, a by-product of photosynthesis.

In this chapter, you will learn how photosynthesis works. After a discussion of the general principles of photosynthesis, we will consider the two stages of photosynthesis: the light reactions, in which solar energy is captured and transformed into chemical energy; and the Calvin cycle, in which the chemical energy is used to make organic molecules of food. Finally, we will consider photosynthesis from an evolutionary perspective.

▶ **Figure 10.2 Photoautotrophs.** These organisms use light energy to drive the synthesis of organic molecules from carbon dioxide and (in most cases) water. They feed not only themselves, but the entire living world. **(a)** On land, plants are the predominant producers of food. In aquatic environments, photosynthetic organisms include **(b)** multicellular algae, such as this kelp; **(c)** some unicellular protists, such as *Euglena;* **(d)** the prokaryotes called cyanobacteria; and **(e)** other photosynthetic prokaryotes, such as these purple sulfur bacteria, which produce sulfur (spherical globules) (c, d, e: LMs).

(a) Plants

(b) Multicellular algae

(c) Unicellular protist   10 μm

(d) Cyanobacteria   40 μm

(e) Purple sulfur bacteria   1.5 μm

Concept 10.1

Photosynthesis converts light energy to the chemical energy of food

You were introduced to the chloroplast in Chapter 6. This remarkable organelle is responsible for feeding the vast majority of organisms on our planet. Chloroplasts are present in a variety of photosynthesizing organisms (see Figure 10.2), but here we will focus on plants.

Chloroplasts: The Sites of Photosynthesis in Plants

All green parts of a plant, including green stems and unripened fruit, have chloroplasts, but the leaves are the major sites of photosynthesis in most plants **(Figure 10.3)**. There are about half a million chloroplasts per square millimeter of leaf surface. The color of the leaf is from **chlorophyll,** the green pigment located within chloroplasts. It is the light energy absorbed by chlorophyll that drives the synthesis of organic molecules in the chloroplast. Chloroplasts are found mainly in the cells of the **mesophyll,** the tissue in the interior of the leaf. Carbon dioxide enters the leaf, and oxygen exits, by way of microscopic pores called **stomata** (singular, *stoma;* from the Greek, meaning "mouth"). Water absorbed by the roots is delivered to the leaves in veins. Leaves also use veins to export sugar to roots and other nonphotosynthetic parts of the plant.

A typical mesophyll cell has about 30 to 40 chloroplasts, each organelle measuring about 2–4 μm by 4–7 μm. An envelope of two membranes encloses the **stroma,** the dense fluid within the chloroplast. An elaborate system of interconnected membranous sacs called **thylakoids** segregates the stroma from another compartment, the interior of the thylakoids, or *thylakoid space.* In some places, thylakoid sacs are stacked in columns called *grana* (singular, *granum*). Chlorophyll resides

▶ **Figure 10.3 Focusing in on the location of photosynthesis in a plant.** Leaves are the major organs of photosynthesis in plants. These pictures take you into a leaf, then into a cell, and finally into a chloroplast, the organelle where photosynthesis occurs (middle, LM; bottom, TEM).

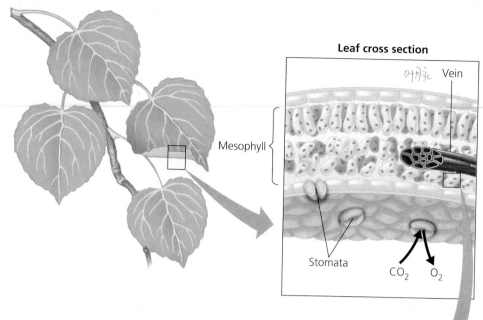

Leaf cross section

Vein

Mesophyll

Stomata CO_2 O_2

in the thylakoid membranes. (Photosynthetic prokaryotes lack chloroplasts, but they do have photosynthetic membranes arising from infolded regions of the plasma membrane that function in a manner similar to the thylakoid membranes of chloroplasts; see Figure 27.7b.) Now that we have looked at the sites of photosynthesis in plants, we are ready to look more closely at the process of photosynthesis.

Tracking Atoms Through Photosynthesis: *Scientific Inquiry*

Scientists have tried for centuries to piece together the process by which plants make food. Although some of the steps are still not completely understood, the overall photosynthetic equation has been known since the 1800s: In the presence of light, the green parts of plants produce organic compounds and oxygen from carbon dioxide and water. Using molecular formulas, we can summarize photosynthesis with this chemical equation:

$$6 \ CO_2 + 12 \ H_2O + \text{Light energy} \rightarrow C_6H_{12}O_6 + 6 \ O_2 + 6 \ H_2O$$

The carbohydrate $C_6H_{12}O_6$ is glucose.* Water appears on both sides of the equation because 12 molecules are consumed and 6 molecules are newly formed during photosynthesis. We can simplify the equation by indicating only the net consumption of water:

$$6 \ CO_2 + 6 \ H_2O + \text{Light energy} \rightarrow C_6H_{12}O_6 + 6 \ O_2$$

Writing the equation in this form, we can see that the overall chemical change during photosynthesis is the reverse of the one that occurs during cellular respiration. Both of these metabolic processes occur in plant cells. However, as you will soon learn, plants do not make food by simply reversing the steps of respiration.

Now let's divide the photosynthetic equation by 6 to put it in its simplest possible form:

$$CO_2 + H_2O \rightarrow [CH_2O] + O_2$$

Here, the brackets indicate that CH_2O is not an actual sugar but represents the general formula for a carbohydrate. In

Mesophyll cell

Chloroplast

5 μm

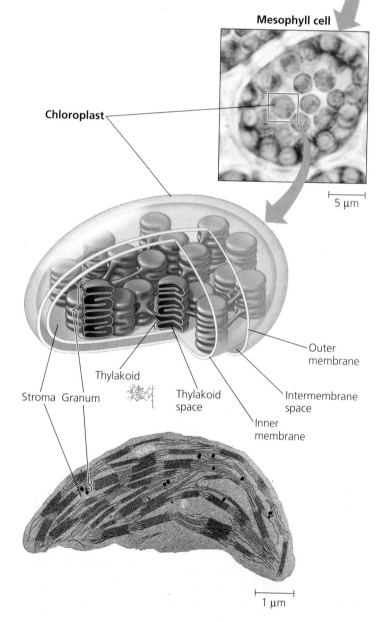

Thylakoid

Stroma Granum

Thylakoid space

Inner membrane

Outer membrane

Intermembrane space

1 μm

---

* The direct product of photosynthesis is actually a three-carbon sugar. Glucose is used here only to simplify the relationship between photosynthesis and respiration.

other words, we are imagining the synthesis of a sugar molecule one carbon at a time. Six repetitions would produce a glucose molecule. Let's now use this simplified formula to see how researchers tracked the chemical elements (C, H, and O) from the reactants of photosynthesis to the products.

The Splitting of Water

One of the first clues to the mechanism of photosynthesis came from the discovery that the oxygen given off by plants through their stomata is derived from water and not from carbon dioxide. The chloroplast splits water into hydrogen and oxygen. Before this discovery, the prevailing hypothesis was that photosynthesis split carbon dioxide ($CO_2 \rightarrow C + O_2$) and then added water to the carbon ($C + H_2O \rightarrow [CH_2O]$). This hypothesis predicted that the O_2 released during photosynthesis came from CO_2. This idea was challenged in the 1930s by C. B. van Niel of Stanford University. Van Niel was investigating photosynthesis in bacteria that make their carbohydrate from CO_2 but do not release O_2. Van Niel concluded that, at least in these bacteria, CO_2 is not split into carbon and oxygen. One group of bacteria used hydrogen sulfide (H_2S) rather than water for photosynthesis, forming yellow globules of sulfur as a waste product (these globules are visible in Figure 10.2e). Here is the chemical equation for photosynthesis in these sulfur bacteria:

$$CO_2 + 2\ H_2S \rightarrow [CH_2O] + H_2O + 2\ S$$

Van Niel reasoned that the bacteria split H_2S and used the hydrogen atoms to make sugar. He then generalized that idea, proposing that all photosynthetic organisms require a hydrogen source but that the source varies:

$$\begin{aligned}
\text{Sulfur bacteria:} \quad & CO_2 + 2\ H_2S \rightarrow [CH_2O] + H_2O + 2\ S \\
\text{Plants:} \quad & CO_2 + 2\ H_2O \rightarrow [CH_2O] + H_2O + O_2 \\
\text{General:} \quad & CO_2 + 2\ H_2X \rightarrow [CH_2O] + H_2O + 2\ X
\end{aligned}$$

Thus, van Niel hypothesized that plants split water as a source of electrons from hydrogen atoms, releasing oxygen as a by-product.

Nearly 20 years later, scientists confirmed van Niel's hypothesis by using oxygen-18 (^{18}O), a heavy isotope, as a radioactive tracer to follow the fate of oxygen atoms during photosynthesis. The experiments showed that the O_2 from plants was labeled with ^{18}O *only* if water was the source of the tracer (experiment 1). If the ^{18}O was introduced to the plant in the form of CO_2, the label did not turn up in the released O_2 (experiment 2). In the following summary, red denotes labeled atoms of oxygen (^{18}O):

$$\begin{aligned}
\text{Experiment 1:} \quad & CO_2 + 2\ H_2O \rightarrow [CH_2O] + H_2O + O_2 \\
\text{Experiment 2:} \quad & CO_2 + 2\ H_2O \rightarrow [CH_2O] + H_2O + O_2
\end{aligned}$$

A significant result of the shuffling of atoms during photosynthesis is the extraction of hydrogen from water and its incorporation into sugar. The waste product of photosynthesis,

▲ **Figure 10.4 Tracking atoms through photosynthesis.**

O_2, is released to the atmosphere. **Figure 10.4** shows the fates of all atoms in photosynthesis.

Photosynthesis as a Redox Process

Let's briefly compare photosynthesis with cellular respiration. Both processes involve redox reactions. During cellular respiration, energy is released from sugar when electrons associated with hydrogen are transported by carriers to oxygen, forming water as a by-product. The electrons lose potential energy as they "fall" down the electron transport chain toward electronegative oxygen, and the mitochondrion harnesses that energy to synthesize ATP (see Figure 9.15). Photosynthesis reverses the direction of electron flow. Water is split, and electrons are transferred along with hydrogen ions from the water to carbon dioxide, reducing it to sugar. Because the electrons increase in potential energy as they move from water to sugar, this process requires energy. This energy boost is provided by light.

The Two Stages of Photosynthesis: *A Preview*

The equation for photosynthesis is a deceptively simple summary of a very complex process. Actually, photosynthesis is not a single process, but two processes, each with multiple steps. These two stages of photosynthesis are known as the **light reactions** (the *photo* part of photosynthesis) and the **Calvin cycle** (the *synthesis* part) **(Figure 10.5)**.

The light reactions are the steps of photosynthesis that convert solar energy to chemical energy. Light absorbed by chlorophyll drives a transfer of electrons and hydrogen from water to an acceptor called **NADP+** (nicotinamide adenine dinucleotide phosphate), which temporarily stores the energized electrons. Water is split in the process, and thus it is the light reactions of photosynthesis that give off O_2 as a by-product. The electron acceptor of the light reactions, $NADP^+$, is first cousin to NAD^+, which functions as an electron carrier in cellular respiration; the two molecules differ only by the presence of an extra phosphate group in the $NADP^+$ molecule. The light reactions use solar power to reduce $NADP^+$ to NADPH by adding a pair of electrons along with a hydrogen nucleus, or H^+. The light reactions also generate ATP, using chemiosmosis to power the addition of a phosphate

▶ **Figure 10.5 An overview of photosynthesis: cooperation of the light reactions and the Calvin cycle.** In the chloroplast, the thylakoid membranes are the sites of the light reactions, whereas the Calvin cycle occurs in the stroma. The light reactions use solar energy to make ATP and NADPH, which function as chemical energy and reducing power, respectively, in the Calvin cycle. The Calvin cycle incorporates CO_2 into organic molecules, which are converted to sugar. (Recall from Chapter 5 that most simple sugars have formulas that are some multiple of $[CH_2O]$.)

A smaller version of this diagram will reappear in several subsequent figures as a reminder of whether the events being described occur in the light reactions or in the Calvin cycle.

group to ADP, a process called **photophosphorylation.** Thus, light energy is initially converted to chemical energy in the form of two compounds: NADPH, a source of energized electrons ("reducing power"), and ATP, the versatile energy currency of cells. Notice that the light reactions produce no sugar; that happens in the second stage of photosynthesis, the Calvin cycle.

The Calvin cycle is named for Melvin Calvin, who, along with his colleagues, began to elucidate its steps in the late 1940s. The cycle begins by incorporating CO_2 from the air into organic molecules already present in the chloroplast. This initial incorporation of carbon into organic compounds is known as **carbon fixation.** The Calvin cycle then reduces the fixed carbon to carbohydrate by the addition of electrons. The reducing power is provided by NADPH, which acquired energized electrons in the light reactions. To convert CO_2 to carbohydrate, the Calvin cycle also requires chemical energy in the form of ATP, which is also generated by the light reactions. Thus, it is the Calvin cycle that makes sugar, but it can do so only with the help of the NADPH and ATP produced by the light reactions. The metabolic steps of the Calvin cycle are sometimes referred to as the dark reactions, or light-independent reactions, because none of the steps requires light *directly.* Nevertheless, the Calvin cycle in most plants occurs during daylight, for only then can the light reactions provide the NADPH and

ATP that the Calvin cycle requires. In essence, the chloroplast uses light energy to make sugar by coordinating the two stages of photosynthesis.

As Figure 10.5 indicates, the thylakoids of the chloroplast are the sites of the light reactions, while the Calvin cycle occurs in the stroma. In the thylakoids, molecules of $NADP^+$ and ADP pick up electrons and phosphate, respectively, and then are released to the stroma, where they transfer their high-energy cargo to the Calvin cycle. The two stages of photosynthesis are treated in this figure as metabolic modules that take in ingredients and crank out products. Our next step toward understanding photosynthesis is to look more closely at how the two stages work, beginning with the light reactions.

Concept Check 10.1

1. How do the reactant molecules of photosynthesis reach the chloroplasts in leaves?
2. How did the use of an oxygen isotope help elucidate the chemistry of photosynthesis?
3. Describe how the two stages of photosynthesis are dependent on each other.

For suggested answers, see Appendix A.

The light reactions convert solar energy to the chemical energy of ATP and NADPH

Chloroplasts are chemical factories powered by the sun. Their thylakoids transform light energy into the chemical energy of ATP and NADPH. To understand this conversion better, we need to know about some important properties of light.

The Nature of Sunlight

Light is a form of energy known as electromagnetic energy, also called electromagnetic radiation. Electromagnetic energy travels in rhythmic waves analogous to those created by dropping a pebble into a pond. Electromagnetic waves, however, are disturbances of electrical and magnetic fields rather than disturbances of a material medium such as water.

The distance between the crests of electromagnetic waves is called the **wavelength.** Wavelengths range from less than a nanometer (for gamma rays) to more than a kilometer (for radio waves). This entire range of radiation is known as the **electromagnetic spectrum (Figure 10.6).** The segment most important to life is the narrow band from about 380 nm to 750 nm in wavelength. This radiation is known as **visible light** because it is detected as various colors by the human eye.

The model of light as waves explains many of light's properties, but in certain respects light behaves as though it consists of discrete particles, called **photons.** Photons are not tangible objects, but they act like objects in that each of them has a fixed quantity of energy. The amount of energy is inversely related to the wavelength of the light; the shorter the wavelength, the greater the energy of each photon of that light. Thus, a photon of violet light packs nearly twice as much energy as a photon of red light.

Although the sun radiates the full spectrum of electromagnetic energy, the atmosphere acts like a selective window, allowing visible light to pass through while screening out a substantial fraction of other radiation. The part of the spectrum we can see—visible light—is also the radiation that drives photosynthesis.

Photosynthetic Pigments: The Light Receptors

When light meets matter, it may be reflected, transmitted, or absorbed. Substances that absorb visible light are known as pigments. Different pigments absorb light of different wavelengths, and the wavelengths that are absorbed disappear. If a pigment is illuminated with white light, the color we see is the color most reflected or transmitted by the pigment. (If a pigment absorbs all wavelengths, it appears black.) We see green when we look at a leaf because chlorophyll absorbs violet-blue and red light while transmitting and reflecting green light **(Figure 10.7).** The ability of a pigment to absorb various wavelengths of light can be measured with an instrument called a **spectrophotometer.** This machine directs beams of light of different wavelengths through a solution of the pigment and measures the fraction of the light transmitted

▲ **Figure 10.6 The electromagnetic spectrum.** White light is a mixture of all wavelengths of visible light. A prism can sort white light into its component colors by bending light of different wavelengths at different angles. (Droplets of water in the atmosphere can act as prisms, forming a rainbow; see Figure 10.1.) Visible light drives photosynthesis.

▲ **Figure 10.7 Why leaves are green: interaction of light with chloroplasts.** The chlorophyll molecules of chloroplasts absorb violet-blue and red light (the colors most effective in driving photosynthesis) and reflect or transmit green light. This is why leaves appear green.

at each wavelength **(Figure 10.8)**. A graph plotting a pigment's light absorption versus wavelength is called an **absorption spectrum.**

The absorption spectra of chloroplast pigments provide clues to the relative effectiveness of different wavelengths for driving photosynthesis, since light can perform work in chloroplasts only if it is absorbed. **Figure 10.9a** shows the absorption spectra of three types of pigments in chloroplasts. If we look first at the absorption spectrum of **chlorophyll *a*,** it suggests that violet-blue and red light work best for photosynthesis, since they are

Figure 10.8
Research Method **Determining an Absorption Spectrum**

APPLICATION   An absorption spectrum is a visual representation of how well a particular pigment absorbs different wavelengths of visible light. Absorption spectra of various chloroplast pigments help scientists decipher each pigment's role in a plant.

TECHNIQUE   A spectrophotometer measures the relative amounts of light of different wavelengths absorbed and transmitted by a pigment solution.

1 White light is separated into colors (wavelengths) by a prism.

2 One by one, the different colors of light are passed through the sample (chlorophyll in this example). Green light and blue light are shown here.

3 The transmitted light strikes a photoelectric tube, which converts the light energy to electricity.

4 The electrical current is measured by a galvanometer. The meter indicates the fraction of light transmitted through the sample, from which we can determine the amount of light absorbed.

The high transmittance (low absorption) reading indicates that chlorophyll absorbs very little green light.

The low transmittance (high absorption) reading indicates that chlorophyll absorbs most blue light.

RESULTS   See Figure 10.9a for absorption spectra of three types of chloroplast pigments.

Figure 10.9
Inquiry **Which wavelengths of light are most effective in driving photosynthesis?**

EXPERIMENT   Three different experiments helped reveal which wavelengths of light are photosynthetically important. The results are shown below.

RESULTS

(a) Absorption spectra. The three curves show the wavelengths of light best absorbed by three types of chloroplast pigments.

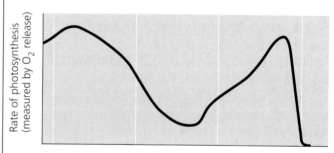

(b) Action spectrum. This graph plots the rate of photosynthesis versus wavelength. The resulting action spectrum resembles the absorption spectrum for chlorophyll *a* but does not match exactly (see part a). This is partly due to the absorption of light by accessory pigments such as chlorophyll *b* and carotenoids.

(c) Engelmann's experiment. In 1883, Theodor W. Engelmann illuminated a filamentous alga with light that had been passed through a prism, exposing different segments of the alga to different wavelengths. He used aerobic bacteria, which concentrate near an oxygen source, to determine which segments of the alga were releasing the most O_2 and thus photosynthesizing most. Bacteria congregated in greatest numbers around the parts of the alga illuminated with violet-blue or red light. Notice the close match of the bacterial distribution to the action spectrum in part b.

CONCLUSION   Light in the violet-blue and red portions of the spectrum are most effective in driving photosynthesis.

absorbed, while green is the least effective color. This is confirmed by an **action spectrum** for photosynthesis **(Figure 10.9b)**, which profiles the relative effectiveness of different wavelengths of radiation in driving the process. An action spectrum is prepared by illuminating chloroplasts with light of different colors and then plotting wavelength against some measure of photosynthetic rate, such as CO_2 consumption or O_2 release. The action spectrum for photosynthesis was first demonstrated in 1883 in an elegant experiment performed by German botanist Theodor W. Engelmann, who used bacteria to measure rates of photosynthesis in filamentous algae **(Figure 10.9c)**.

Notice by comparing Figures 10.9a and 10.9b that the action spectrum for photosynthesis does not exactly match the absorption spectrum of chlorophyll *a*. The absorption spectrum of chlorophyll *a* alone underestimates the effectiveness of certain wavelengths in driving photosynthesis. This is partly because accessory pigments with different absorption spectra are also photosynthetically important in chloroplasts and broaden the spectrum of colors that can be used for photosynthesis. One of these accessory pigments is another form of chlorophyll, **chlorophyll *b*.** Chlorophyll *b* is almost identical to chlorophyll *a*, but a slight structural difference between them **(Figure 10.10)** is enough to give the two pigments slightly different absorption spectra (see Figure 10.9a). As a result, they have different colors—chlorophyll *a* is blue-green, whereas chlorophyll *b* is yellow-green.

Other accessory pigments include **carotenoids**, hydrocarbons that are various shades of yellow and orange because they absorb violet and blue-green light (see Figure 10.9a). Carotenoids may broaden the spectrum of colors that can drive photosynthesis. However, a more important function of at least some carotenoids seems to be *photoprotection*: These compounds absorb and dissipate excessive light energy that would otherwise damage chlorophyll or interact with oxygen, forming reactive oxidative molecules that are dangerous to the cell. Interestingly, carotenoids similar to the photoprotective ones in chloroplasts have a photoprotective role in the human eye. These and other related molecules are highlighted in health food products as "phytochemicals" (from the Greek *phyton*, plant) that have antioxidant powers. Plants can synthesize all the antioxidants they require, whereas humans and other animals must obtain some of them from their diets.

Excitation of Chlorophyll by Light

What exactly happens when chlorophyll and other pigments absorb light? The colors corresponding to the absorbed wavelengths disappear from the spectrum of the transmitted and reflected light, but energy cannot disappear. When a molecule absorbs a photon of light, one of the molecule's electrons is elevated to an orbital where it has more potential energy. When the electron is in its normal orbital, the pigment molecule is said to be in its ground state. Absorption of a photon boosts

Porphyrin ring: light-absorbing "head" of molecule; note magnesium atom at center

Hydrocarbon tail: interacts with hydrophobic regions of proteins inside thylakoid membranes of chloroplasts; H atoms not shown

▲ **Figure 10.10 Structure of chlorophyll molecules in chloroplasts of plants.** Chlorophyll *a* and chlorophyll *b* differ only in one of the functional groups bonded to the porphyrin ring.

an electron to an orbital of higher energy, and the pigment molecule is then said to be in an excited state. The only photons absorbed are those whose energy is exactly equal to the energy difference between the ground state and an excited state, and this energy difference varies from one kind of atom or molecule to another. Thus, a particular compound absorbs only photons corresponding to specific wavelengths, which is why each pigment has a unique absorption spectrum.

Once absorption of a photon raises an electron from the ground state to an excited state, the electron cannot remain there long. The excited state, like all high-energy states, is unstable. Generally, when isolated pigment molecules absorb light, their excited electrons drop back down to the ground-state orbital in a billionth of a second, releasing their excess energy as heat. This conversion of light energy to heat is what makes the top of an automobile so hot on a sunny day. (White cars are coolest because their paint reflects all wavelengths of visible light, although it may absorb ultraviolet and other invisible radiation.) In isolation, some pigments, including chlorophyll, emit light as well as heat after absorbing photons. As excited electrons fall back to the ground state, photons are given off. This afterglow is called fluorescence. If a solution of chlorophyll isolated from chloroplasts is illuminated, it will fluoresce in the red-orange part of the spectrum and also give off heat **(Figure 10.11)**.

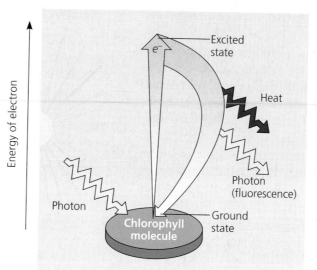

◀ **Figure 10.11 Excitation of isolated chlorophyll by light. (a)** Absorption of a photon causes a transition of the chlorophyll molecule from its ground state to its excited state. The photon boosts an electron to an orbital where it has more potential energy. If the illuminated molecule exists in isolation, its excited electron immediately drops back down to the ground-state orbital, and its excess energy is given off as heat and fluorescence (light). **(b)** A chlorophyll solution excited with ultraviolet light fluoresces with a red-orange glow.

(a) Excitation of isolated chlorophyll molecule

(b) Fluorescence

A Photosystem: A Reaction Center Associated with Light-Harvesting Complexes

Chlorophyll molecules excited by the absorption of light energy produce very different results in an intact chloroplast than they do in isolation (see Figure 10.11). In their native environment of the thylakoid membrane, chlorophyll molecules are organized along with other small organic molecules and proteins into photosystems.

A **photosystem** is composed of a reaction center surrounded by a number of light-harvesting complexes (**Figure 10.12**). Each **light-harvesting complex** consists of pigment molecules (which may include chlorophyll *a*, chlorophyll *b*, and carotenoids) bound to particular proteins. The number and variety of pigment molecules enable a photosystem to harvest light over a larger surface and a larger portion of the spectrum than any single pigment molecule alone could. Together, these light-harvesting complexes act as an antenna for the reaction center. When a pigment molecule absorbs a photon, the energy is transferred from pigment molecule to pigment molecule within a light-harvesting complex until it is funneled into the reaction center. The **reaction center** is a protein complex that includes two special chlorophyll *a* molecules and a molecule called the **primary electron acceptor.** These chlorophyll *a* molecules are special because their molecular environment—their location and the other molecules with which they are associated—enables them to use the energy from light to boost one of their electrons to a higher energy level.

The solar-powered transfer of an electron from a special chlorophyll *a* molecule to the primary electron acceptor is the first step of the light reactions. As soon as the chlorophyll electron is excited to a higher energy level, the primary electron acceptor captures it; this is a redox reaction. Isolated chlorophyll fluoresces because there is no electron acceptor, so electrons of photoexcited chlorophyll drop right back to the ground state.

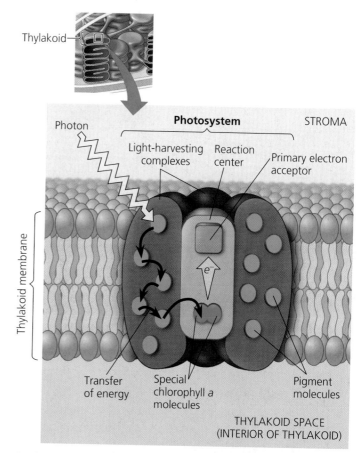

▲ **Figure 10.12 How a photosystem harvests light.** When a photon strikes a pigment molecule in a light-harvesting complex, the energy is passed from molecule to molecule until it reaches the reaction center. At the reaction center, an excited electron from one of the two special chlorophyll *a* molecules is captured by the primary electron acceptor.

In a chloroplast, this immediate plunge of high-energy electrons back to the ground state is prevented. Thus, each photosystem—a reaction center surrounded by light-harvesting complexes—functions in the chloroplast as a unit. It converts light energy to chemical energy, which will ultimately be used for the synthesis of sugar.

The thylakoid membrane is populated by two types of photosystems that cooperate in the light reactions of photosynthesis. They are called **photosystem II (PS II)** and **photosystem I (PS I).** (They were named in order of their discovery, but the two function sequentially, with photosystem II functioning first.) Each has a characteristic reaction center—a particular kind of primary electron acceptor next to a pair of special chlorophyll *a* molecules associated with specific proteins. The reaction-center chlorophyll *a* of photosystem II is known as P680 because this pigment is best at absorbing light having a wavelength of 680 nm (in the red part of the spectrum). The chlorophyll *a* at the reaction center of photosystem I is called P700 because it most effectively absorbs light of wavelength 700 nm (in the far red part of the spectrum). These two pigments, P680 and P700, are actually identical chlorophyll *a* molecules. However, their association with different proteins in the thylakoid membrane affects the electron distribution in the chlorophyll molecules and accounts for the slight differences in light-absorbing properties. Now let's see how the two photosystems work together in using light energy to generate ATP and NADPH, the two main products of the light reactions.

Noncyclic Electron Flow

Light drives the synthesis of NADPH and ATP by energizing the two photosystems embedded in the thylakoid membranes of chloroplasts. The key to this energy transformation is a flow of electrons through the photosystems and other molecular components built into the thylakoid membrane. During the light reactions of photosynthesis, there are two possible routes for electron flow: cyclic and noncyclic. **Noncyclic electron flow**, the predominant route, is shown in **Figure 10.13**. The numbers in the text description correspond to the numbered steps in the figure.

1 A photon of light strikes a pigment molecule in a light-harvesting complex and is relayed to other pigment molecules until it reaches one of the two P680 chlorophyll *a* molecules in the PS II reaction center. It excites one of the P680 electrons to a higher energy state.

2 This electron is captured by the primary electron acceptor.

3 An enzyme splits a water molecule into two electrons, two hydrogen ions, and an oxygen atom. The electrons are supplied one by one to the P680 molecules, each replacing an electron lost to the primary electron acceptor. (Missing an electron, P680 is the strongest biological oxidizing agent known; its electron hole must be filled.)

▼ **Figure 10.13 How noncyclic electron flow during the light reactions generates ATP and NADPH.** The gold arrows trace the current of light-driven electrons from water to NADPH.

The oxygen atom immediately combines with another oxygen atom, forming O_2.

④ Each photoexcited electron passes from the primary electron acceptor of PS II to PS I via an electron transport chain (similar to the electron transport chain that functions in cellular respiration). The electron transport chain between PS II and PS I is made up of the electron carrier plastoquinone (Pq), a cytochrome complex, and a protein called plastocyanin (Pc).

⑤ The exergonic "fall" of electrons to a lower energy level provides energy for the synthesis of ATP.

⑥ Meanwhile, light energy was transferred via a light-harvesting complex to the PS I reaction center, exciting an electron of one of the two P700 chlorophyll *a* molecules located there. The photoexcited electron was then captured by PS I's primary electron acceptor, creating an electron "hole" in the P700. The hole is filled by an electron that reaches the bottom of the electron transport chain from PS II.

⑦ Photoexcited electrons are passed from PS I's primary electron acceptor down a second electron transport chain through the protein ferredoxin (Fd).

⑧ The enzyme NADP$^+$ reductase transfers electrons from Fd to NADP$^+$. Two electrons are required for its reduction to NADPH.

As complicated as the scheme shown in Figure 10.13 is, do not lose track of its functions: The light reactions use solar power to generate ATP and NADPH, which provide chemical energy and reducing power, respectively, to the sugar-making reactions of the Calvin cycle. The energy changes of electrons as they flow through the light reactions are shown by analogy in **Figure 10.14**.

Cyclic Electron Flow

Under certain conditions, photoexcited electrons take an alternative path called **cyclic electron flow**, which uses photosystem I but not photosystem II. You can see in **Figure 10.15**

▲ **Figure 10.14 A mechanical analogy for the light reactions.**

that cyclic flow is a short circuit: The electrons cycle back from ferredoxin (Fd) to the cytochrome complex and from there continue on to a P700 chlorophyll in the PS I reaction center. There is no production of NADPH and no release of oxygen. Cyclic flow does, however, generate ATP.

What is the function of cyclic electron flow? Noncyclic electron flow produces ATP and NADPH in roughly equal quantities, but the Calvin cycle consumes more ATP than NADPH. Cyclic electron flow makes up the difference, since it produces ATP but no NADPH. The concentration of NADPH in the chloroplast may help regulate which pathway, cyclic versus noncyclic, electrons take through the light reactions. If the chloroplast runs low on ATP for the Calvin cycle, NADPH will begin to accumulate as the Calvin cycle slows down. The rise in NADPH may stimulate a temporary shift from noncyclic to cyclic electron flow until ATP supply catches up with demand.

Whether ATP synthesis is driven by noncyclic or cyclic electron flow, the actual mechanism is the same. This is a good

▶ **Figure 10.15 Cyclic electron flow.** Photoexcited electrons from PS I are occasionally shunted back from ferredoxin (Fd) to chlorophyll via the cytochrome complex and plastocyanin (Pc). This electron shunt supplements the supply of ATP (via chemiosmosis) but produces no NADPH. The "shadow" of noncyclic electron flow is included in the diagram for comparison with the cyclic route. The two ferredoxin molecules shown in this diagram are actually one and the same—the final electron carrier in the electron transport chain of PS I.

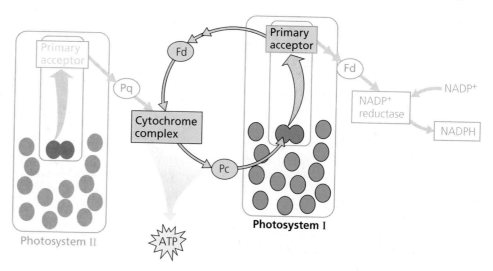

time to review chemiosmosis, the process that uses membranes to couple redox reactions to ATP production.

A Comparison of Chemiosmosis in Chloroplasts and Mitochondria

Chloroplasts and mitochondria generate ATP by the same basic mechanism: chemiosmosis. An electron transport chain assembled in a membrane pumps protons across the membrane as electrons are passed through a series of carriers that are progressively more electronegative. In this way, electron transport chains transform redox energy to a proton-motive force, potential energy stored in the form of an H^+ gradient across a membrane. Built into the same membrane is an ATP synthase complex that couples the diffusion of hydrogen ions down their gradient to the phosphorylation of ADP. Some of the electron carriers, including the iron-containing proteins called cytochromes, are very similar in chloroplasts and mitochondria. The ATP synthase complexes of the two organelles are also very much alike. But there are noteworthy differences between oxidative phosphorylation in mitochondria and photophosphorylation in chloroplasts. In mitochondria, the high-energy electrons dropped down the transport chain are extracted from organic molecules (which are thus oxidized). Chloroplasts do not need molecules from food to make ATP; their photosystems capture light energy and use it to drive electrons to the top of the transport chain. In other words, mitochondria transfer chemical energy from food molecules to ATP (and NADH), whereas chloroplasts transform light energy into chemical energy in ATP (and NADPH).

The spatial organization of chemiosmosis also differs in chloroplasts and mitochondria **(Figure 10.16)**. The inner membrane of the mitochondrion pumps protons from the mitochondrial matrix out to the intermembrane space, which then serves as a reservoir of hydrogen ions that powers the ATP synthase. The thylakoid membrane of the chloroplast pumps protons from the stroma into the thylakoid space (interior of the thylakoid), which functions as the H^+ reservoir. The thylakoid membrane makes ATP as the hydrogen ions diffuse down their concentration gradient from the thylakoid space back to the stroma through ATP synthase complexes, whose catalytic knobs are on the stroma side of the membrane. Thus, ATP forms in the stroma, where it is used to help drive sugar synthesis during the Calvin cycle.

The proton (H^+) gradient, or pH gradient, across the thylakoid membrane is substantial. When chloroplasts are illuminated, the pH in the thylakoid space drops to about 5 (the H^+ concentration increases), and the pH in the stroma increases to about 8 (the H^+ concentration decreases). This gradient of three pH units corresponds to a thousandfold difference in H^+ concentration. If in the laboratory the lights are

▲ **Figure 10.16 Comparison of chemiosmosis in mitochondria and chloroplasts.** In both kinds of organelles, electron transport chains pump protons (H^+) across a membrane from a region of low H^+ concentration (light gray in this diagram) to one of high H^+ concentration (dark gray). The protons then diffuse back across the membrane through ATP synthase, driving the synthesis of ATP.

turned off, the pH gradient is abolished, but it can quickly be restored by turning the lights back on. Such experiments provide strong evidence in support of the chemiosmotic model.

Based on studies in several laboratories, **Figure 10.17** shows a current model for the organization of the light-reaction "machinery" within the thylakoid membrane. Each of the molecules and molecular complexes in the figure is present in numerous copies in each thylakoid. Notice that NADPH, like ATP, is produced on the side of the membrane facing the stroma, where the Calvin cycle reactions take place.

Let's summarize the light reactions. Noncyclic electron flow pushes electrons from water, where they are at a low state of potential energy, to NADPH, where they are stored at a high state of potential energy. The light-driven electron current also generates ATP. Thus, the equipment of the thylakoid membrane converts light energy to chemical energy stored in NADPH and ATP. (Oxygen is a by-product.) Let's now see how the Calvin cycle uses the products of the light reactions to synthesize sugar from CO_2.

STROMA
(Low H⁺ concentration)

Photosystem II **Cytochrome complex** **Photosystem I** **NADP⁺ reductase**

THYLAKOID SPACE
(High H⁺ concentration)

Thylakoid membrane

STROMA
(Low H⁺ concentration)

ATP synthase

To Calvin cycle

▲ **Figure 10.17 The light reactions and chemiosmosis: the organization of the thylakoid membrane.** This diagram shows a current model for the organization of the thylakoid membrane. The gold arrows track the noncyclic electron flow outlined in Figure 10.13. As electrons pass from carrier to carrier in redox reactions, hydrogen ions removed from the stroma are deposited in the thylakoid space, storing energy as a proton-motive force (H⁺ gradient). At least three steps in the light reactions contribute to the proton gradient: ❶ Water is split by photosystem II on the side of the membrane facing the thylakoid space; ❷ as plastoquinone (Pq), a mobile carrier, transfers electrons to the cytochrome complex, protons are translocated across the membrane into the thylakoid space; and ❸ a hydrogen ion is removed from the stroma when it is taken up by NADP⁺. Notice how, as in Figure 10.16, hydrogen ions are being pumped from the stroma into the thylakoid space. The diffusion of H⁺ from the thylakoid space back to the stroma (along the H⁺ concentration gradient) powers the ATP synthase. These light-driven reactions store chemical energy in NADPH and ATP, which shuttle the energy to the sugar-producing Calvin cycle.

Concept Check 10.2

1. What color of light is *least* effective in driving photosynthesis? Explain.
2. Compared to a solution of isolated chlorophyll, why do intact chloroplasts release less heat and fluorescence when illuminated?
3. In the light reactions, what is the electron donor? Where do the electrons end up?

For suggested answers, see Appendix A.

Concept 10.3

The Calvin cycle uses ATP and NADPH to convert CO₂ to sugar

The Calvin cycle is similar to the citric acid cycle in that a starting material is regenerated after molecules enter and leave the cycle. However, while the citric acid cycle is catabolic, oxidizing glucose and releasing energy, the Calvin cycle is anabolic, building sugar from smaller molecules and consuming energy. Carbon enters the Calvin cycle in the form of CO_2 and leaves in the form of sugar. The cycle spends ATP as an energy source and consumes NADPH as reducing power for adding high-energy electrons to make the sugar.

The carbohydrate produced directly from the Calvin cycle is actually not glucose, but a three-carbon sugar named **glyceraldehyde-3-phosphate (G3P)**. For the net synthesis of one molecule of this sugar, the cycle must take place three times, fixing three molecules of CO_2. (Recall that carbon fixation refers to the initial incorporation of CO_2 into organic material.) As we trace the steps of the cycle, keep in mind that we are following three molecules of CO_2 through the reactions. **Figure 10.18** divides the Calvin cycle into three phases:

Phase 1: Carbon fixation. The Calvin cycle incorporates each CO_2 molecule, one at a time, by attaching it to a five-carbon sugar named ribulose bisphosphate (abbreviated RuBP). The enzyme that catalyzes this first step is RuBP carboxylase, or **rubisco.** (It is the most abundant protein in chloroplasts and probably the most abundant protein on Earth.) The product of the reaction is a six-carbon intermediate so unstable that it immediately splits in half, forming two molecules of 3-phosphoglycerate (for each CO_2).

Phase 2: Reduction. Each molecule of 3-phosphoglycerate receives an additional phosphate group from ATP, becoming 1,3-bisphosphoglycerate. Next, a pair of electrons donated from NADPH reduces 1,3-bisphosphoglycerate to G3P. Specifically, the electrons from NADPH reduce the

▶ **Figure 10.18 The Calvin cycle.** This diagram tracks carbon atoms (gray balls) through the cycle. The three phases of the cycle correspond to the phases discussed in the text. For every three molecules of CO_2 that enter the cycle, the net output is one molecule of glyceraldehyde-3-phosphate (G3P), a three-carbon sugar. The light reactions sustain the Calvin cycle by regenerating ATP and NADPH.

carboyxl group of 3-phosphoglycerate to the aldehyde group of G3P, which stores more potential energy. G3P is a sugar—the same three-carbon sugar formed in glycolysis by the splitting of glucose. Notice in Figure 10.18 that for every *three* molecules of CO_2, there are *six* molecules of G3P. But only one molecule of this three-carbon sugar can be counted as a net gain of carbohydrate. The cycle began with 15 carbons' worth of carbohydrate in the form of three molecules of the five-carbon sugar RuBP. Now there are 18 carbons' worth of carbohydrate in the form of six molecules of G3P. One molecule exits the cycle to be used by the plant cell, but the other five molecules must be recycled to regenerate the three molecules of RuBP.

Phase 3: Regeneration of the CO_2 acceptor (RuBP). In a complex series of reactions, the carbon skeletons of five molecules of G3P are rearranged by the last steps of the Calvin cycle into three molecules of RuBP. To accomplish this, the cycle spends three more molecules of ATP. The RuBP is now prepared to receive CO_2 again, and the cycle continues.

For the net synthesis of one G3P molecule, the Calvin cycle consumes a total of nine molecules of ATP and six molecules of NADPH. The light reactions regenerate the ATP and NADPH. The G3P spun off from the Calvin cycle becomes the starting material for metabolic pathways that synthesize other organic compounds, including glucose and other carbohydrates. Neither the light reactions nor the Calvin cycle alone can make sugar from CO_2. Photosynthesis is an emergent property of the intact chloroplast, which integrates the two stages of photosynthesis.

Concept Check 10.3

1. To synthesize one glucose molecule, the Calvin cycle uses _____ molecules of CO_2, _____ molecules of ATP, and _____ molecules of NADPH.
2. Explain why the high number of ATP and NADPH molecules used during the Calvin cycle is consistent with the high value of glucose as an energy source.
3. Explain why a poison that inhibits an enzyme of the Calvin cycle will also inhibit the light reactions.

For suggested answers, see Appendix A.

Concept 10.4

Alternative mechanisms of carbon fixation have evolved in hot, arid climates

Ever since plants first moved onto land about 475 million years ago, they have been adapting to the problems of terrestrial life, particularly the problem of dehydration. In Chapters 29 and 36, we will consider anatomical adaptations that help plants conserve water. Here we are concerned with metabolic adaptations. The solutions often involve trade-offs. An important example is the compromise between photosynthesis and the prevention of excessive water loss from the plant. The CO_2 required for photosynthesis enters a leaf via stomata, the pores through the leaf surface (see Figure 10.3). However, stomata are also the main avenues of transpiration, the evaporative loss of water from leaves. On a hot, dry day, most plants close their stomata, a response that conserves water. This response also reduces photosynthetic yield by limiting access to CO_2. With stomata even partially closed, CO_2 concentrations begin to decrease in the air spaces within the leaf, and the concentration of O_2 released from the light reactions begins to increase. These conditions within the leaf favor a seemingly wasteful process called photorespiration.

Photorespiration: An Evolutionary Relic?

In most plants, initial fixation of carbon occurs via rubisco, the Calvin cycle enzyme that adds CO_2 to ribulose bisphosphate. Such plants are called **C_3 plants** because the first organic product of carbon fixation is a three-carbon compound, 3-phosphoglycerate (see Figure 10.18). Rice, wheat, and soybeans are C_3 plants that are important in agriculture. When their stomata partially close on hot, dry days, C_3 plants produce less sugar because the declining level of CO_2 in the leaf starves the Calvin cycle. In addition, rubisco can bind O_2 in place of CO_2. As CO_2 becomes scarce within the air spaces of the leaf, rubisco adds O_2 to the Calvin cycle instead of CO_2. The product splits, and a two-carbon compound leaves the chloroplast. Peroxisomes and mitochondria rearrange and split this compound, releasing CO_2. The process is called **photorespiration** because it occurs in the light (*photo*) and consumes O_2 while producing CO_2 (*respiration*). However, unlike normal cellular respiration, photorespiration generates no ATP; in fact, photorespiration consumes ATP. And unlike photosynthesis, photorespiration produces no sugar. In fact, photorespiration *decreases* photosynthetic output by siphoning organic material from the Calvin cycle.

How can we explain the existence of a metabolic process that seems to be counterproductive for the plant? According to one hypothesis, photorespiration is evolutionary baggage—a metabolic relic from a much earlier time, when the atmosphere had less O_2 and more CO_2 than it does today. In the ancient atmosphere that prevailed when rubisco first evolved, the inability of the enzyme's active site to exclude O_2 would have made little difference. The hypothesis speculates that modern rubisco retains some of its chance affinity for O_2, which is now so concentrated in the atmosphere that a certain amount of photorespiration is inevitable.

It is not known whether photorespiration is beneficial to plants in any way. It *is* known that in many types of plants—

including crop plants—photorespiration drains away as much as 50% of the carbon fixed by the Calvin cycle. As heterotrophs that depend on carbon fixation in chloroplasts for our food, we naturally view photorespiration as wasteful. Indeed, if photorespiration could be reduced in certain plant species without otherwise affecting photosynthetic productivity, crop yields and food supplies might increase.

In certain plant species, alternate modes of carbon fixation have evolved that minimize photorespiration and optimize the Calvin cycle—even in hot, arid climates. The two most important of these photosynthetic adaptations are C_4 photosynthesis and CAM.

C_4 Plants

The **C_4 plants** are so named because they preface the Calvin cycle with an alternate mode of carbon fixation that forms a four-carbon compound as its first product. Several thousand species in at least 19 plant families use the C_4 pathway. Among the C_4 plants important to agriculture are sugarcane and corn, members of the grass family.

A unique leaf anatomy is correlated with the mechanism of C_4 photosynthesis (**Figure 10.19**; compare with Figure 10.3). In C_4 plants, there are two distinct types of photosynthetic cells: bundle-sheath cells and mesophyll cells. **Bundle-sheath cells** are arranged into tightly packed sheaths around the veins of the leaf. Between the bundle sheath and the leaf surface are the more loosely arranged **mesophyll cells.** The Calvin cycle is confined to the chloroplasts of the bundle sheath. However, the cycle is preceded by incorporation of CO_2 into organic compounds in the mesophyll. The first step,

carried out by the enzyme **PEP carboxylase**, is the addition of CO_2 to phosphoenolpyruvate (PEP), forming the four-carbon product oxaloacetate. PEP carboxylase has a much higher affinity for CO_2 than rubisco and no affinity for O_2. Therefore, PEP carboxylase can fix carbon efficiently when rubisco cannot—that is, when it is hot and dry and stomata are partially closed, causing CO_2 concentration in the leaf to fall and O_2 concentration to rise. After the C_4 plant fixes carbon from CO_2, the mesophyll cells export their four-carbon products (malate in the example shown in Figure 10.19) to bundle-sheath cells through plasmodesmata (see Figure 6.30). Within the bundle-sheath cells, the four-carbon compounds release CO_2, which is reassimilated into organic material by rubisco and the Calvin cycle. Pyruvate is also regenerated for conversion to PEP in mesophyll cells.

In effect, the mesophyll cells of a C_4 plant pump CO_2 into the bundle sheath, keeping the CO_2 concentration in the bundle-sheath cells high enough for rubisco to bind carbon dioxide rather than oxygen. The cyclic series of reactions involving PEP carboxylase and the regeneration of PEP can be thought of as a CO_2-concentrating pump that is powered by ATP. In this way, C_4 photosynthesis minimizes photorespiration and enhances sugar production. This adaptation is especially advantageous in hot regions with intense sunlight, where stomata partially close during the day, and it is in such environments that C_4 plants evolved and thrive today.

CAM Plants

A second photosynthetic adaptation to arid conditions has evolved in succulent (water-storing) plants (including jade

▶ **Figure 10.19 C_4 leaf anatomy and the C_4 pathway.** The structure and biochemical functions of the leaves of C_4 plants are an evolutionary adaptation to hot, dry climates. This adaptation maintains a CO_2 concentration in the bundle sheath that favors photosynthesis over photorespiration.

plants), many cacti, pineapples, and representatives of several other plant families. These plants open their stomata during the night and close them during the day, just the reverse of how other plants behave. Closing stomata during the day helps desert plants conserve water, but it also prevents CO_2 from entering the leaves. During the night, when their stomata are open, these plants take up CO_2 and incorporate it into a variety of organic acids. This mode of carbon fixation is called **crassulacean acid metabolism**, or **CAM**, after the plant family Crassulaceae, the succulents in which the process was first discovered. The mesophyll cells of **CAM plants** store the organic acids they make during the night in their vacuoles until morning, when the stomata close. During the day, when the light reactions can supply ATP and NADPH for the Calvin cycle, CO_2 is released from the organic acids made the night before to become incorporated into sugar in the chloroplasts.

Notice in **Figure 10.20** that the CAM pathway is similar to the C_4 pathway in that carbon dioxide is first incorporated into organic intermediates before it enters the Calvin cycle. The difference is that in C_4 plants, the initial steps of carbon fixation are separated structurally from the Calvin cycle, whereas in CAM plants, the two steps occur at separate times but within the same cell. (Keep in mind that CAM, C_4, and C_3 plants all eventually use the Calvin cycle to make sugar from carbon dioxide.)

Concept Check 10.4

1. Explain why photorespiration lowers photosynthetic output for plants.
2. How would you expect the relative abundance of C_3 versus C_4 and CAM species to change in a geographic region whose climate becomes much hotter and drier?

For suggested answers, see Appendix A.

The Importance of Photosynthesis: *A Review*

In this chapter, we have followed photosynthesis from photons to food. The light reactions capture solar energy and use

Sugarcane

Pineapple

▶ **Figure 10.20 C₄ and CAM photosynthesis compared.** Both adaptations are characterized by ❶ preliminary incorporation of CO_2 into organic acids, followed by ❷ transfer of CO_2 to the Calvin cycle. The C_4 and CAM pathways are two evolutionary solutions to the problem of maintaining photosynthesis with stomata partially or completely closed on hot, dry days.

C_4

Mesophyll cell — Organic acid — CO_2

Bundle-sheath cell — CO_2 — CALVIN CYCLE — Sugar

❶ CO_2 incorporated into four-carbon organic acids (carbon fixation)

❷ Organic acids release CO_2 to Calvin cycle

CAM

Night — CO_2 — Organic acid

Day — CO_2 — CALVIN CYCLE — Sugar

(a) Spatial separation of steps. In C_4 plants, carbon fixation and the Calvin cycle occur in different types of cells.

(b) Temporal separation of steps. In CAM plants, carbon fixation and the Calvin cycle occur in the same cells at different times.

► **Figure 10.21 A review of photosynthesis.** This diagram outlines the main reactants and products of the light reactions and the Calvin cycle as they occur in the chloroplasts of plant cells. The entire ordered operation depends on the structural integrity of the chloroplast and its membranes. Enzymes in the chloroplast and cytosol convert glyceraldehyde-3-phosphate (G3P), the direct product of the Calvin cycle, into many other organic compounds.

Light reactions:
- Are carried out by molecules in the thylakoid membranes
- Convert light energy to the chemical energy of ATP and NADPH
- Split H_2O and release O_2 to the atmosphere

Calvin cycle reactions:
- Take place in the stroma
- Use ATP and NADPH to convert CO_2 to the sugar G3P
- Return ADP, inorganic phosphate, and $NADP^+$ to the light reactions

it to make ATP and transfer electrons from water to $NADP^+$. The Calvin cycle uses the ATP and NADPH to produce sugar from carbon dioxide. The energy that enters the chloroplasts as sunlight becomes stored as chemical energy in organic compounds. See **Figure 10.21** for a review of the entire process.

What are the fates of photosynthetic products? The sugar made in the chloroplasts supplies the entire plant with chemical energy and carbon skeletons for the synthesis of all the major organic molecules of plant cells. About 50% of the organic material made by photosynthesis is consumed as fuel for cellular respiration in the mitochondria of the plant cells. Sometimes there is a loss of photosynthetic products to photorespiration.

Technically, green cells are the only autotrophic parts of the plant. The rest of the plant depends on organic molecules exported from leaves via veins. In most plants, carbohydrate is transported out of the leaves in the form of sucrose, a disaccharide. After arriving at nonphotosynthetic cells, the sucrose provides raw material for cellular respiration and a multitude of anabolic pathways that synthesize proteins, lipids, and other products. A considerable amount of sugar in the form of glucose is linked together to make the polysaccharide cellulose, especially in plant cells that are still growing and maturing.

Cellulose, the main ingredient of cell walls, is the most abundant organic molecule in the plant—and probably on the surface of the planet.

Most plants manage to make more organic material each day than they need to use as respiratory fuel and precursors for biosynthesis. They stockpile the extra sugar by synthesizing starch, storing some in the chloroplasts themselves and some in storage cells of roots, tubers, seeds, and fruits. In accounting for the consumption of the food molecules produced by photosynthesis, let's not forget that most plants lose leaves, roots, stems, fruits, and sometimes their entire bodies to heterotrophs, including humans.

On a global scale, photosynthesis is the process that is responsible for the presence of oxygen in our atmosphere. Furthermore, in terms of food production, the collective productivity of the minute chloroplasts is prodigious; it is estimated that photosynthesis makes about 160 billion metric tons of carbohydrate per year (a metric ton is 1,000 kg, about 1.1 tons). That's organic matter equivalent to a stack of about 60 trillion copies of this textbook—17 stacks of books reaching from Earth to the sun! No other chemical process on the planet can match the output of photosynthesis. And no process is more important than photosynthesis to the welfare of life on Earth.

Go to the Campbell Biology website (**www.campbellbiology.com**) or CD-ROM to explore Activities, Investigations, and other interactive study aids.

SUMMARY OF KEY CONCEPTS

▶ Plants and other autotrophs are the producers of the biosphere. Photoautotrophs use the energy of sunlight to make organic molecules from CO_2 and H_2O. Heterotrophs consume organic molecules from other organisms for energy and carbon (p. 181).

Concept 10.1
Photosynthesis converts light energy to the chemical energy of food

▶ **Chloroplasts: The Sites of Photosynthesis in Plants** (pp. 182–183) In autotrophic eukaryotes, photosynthesis occurs in chloroplasts, organelles containing thylakoids. Stacks of thylakoids form grana.
Activity *The Sites of Photosynthesis*

▶ **Tracking Atoms Through Photosynthesis:** *Scientific Inquiry* (pp. 183–184) Photosynthesis is summarized as

$$6\ CO_2 + 12\ H_2O + \text{Light energy} \rightarrow C_6H_{12}O_6 + 6\ O_2 + 6\ H_2O$$

Chloroplasts split water into hydrogen and oxygen, incorporating the electrons of hydrogen into sugar molecules. Photosynthesis is a redox process: H_2O is oxidized, CO_2 is reduced.

▶ **The Two Stages of Photosynthesis:** *A Preview* (pp. 184–185) The light reactions in the grana split water, releasing O_2, producing ATP, and forming NADPH. The Calvin cycle in the stroma forms sugar from CO_2, using ATP for energy and NADPH for reducing power.
Activity *Overview of Photosynthesis*

Concept 10.2
The light reactions convert solar energy to the chemical energy of ATP and NADPH

▶ **The Nature of Sunlight** (p. 186) Light is a form of electromagnetic energy. The colors we see as visible light include those wavelengths that drive photosynthesis.

▶ **Photosynthetic Pigments: The Light Receptors** (pp. 186–188) A pigment absorbs visible light of specific wavelengths. Chlorophyll *a* is the main photosynthetic pigment in plants. Other accessory pigments absorb different wavelengths of light and pass the energy on to chlorophyll *a*.
Activity *Light Energy and Pigments*
Investigation *How Does Paper Chromatography Separate Plant Pigments?*

▶ **Excitation of Chlorophyll by Light** (p. 188) A pigment goes from a ground state to an excited state when a photon boosts one of its electrons to a higher-energy orbital. This excited state is unstable. Electrons from isolated pigments tend to fall back to the ground state, giving off heat and/or light.

▶ **A Photosystem: A Reaction Center Associated with Light-Harvesting Complexes** (pp. 189–190) A photosystem is composed of a reaction center surrounded by light-harvesting complexes that funnel the energy of photons to the reaction center. When a reaction-center chlorophyll *a* molecule absorbs energy, one of its electrons gets bumped up to the primary electron acceptor. Photosystem I contains P700 chlorophyll *a* molecules at the reaction center; photosystem II contains P680 molecules.

▶ **Noncyclic Electron Flow** (pp. 190–191) Noncyclic electron flow produces NADPH, ATP, and oxygen.

▶ **Cyclic Electron Flow** (pp. 191–192) Cyclic electron flow employs only photosystem I, producing ATP but no NADPH or O_2.

▶ **A Comparison of Chemiosmosis in Chloroplasts and Mitochondria** (pp. 192–193) In both organelles, the redox reactions of electron transport chains generate an H^+ gradient across a membrane. ATP synthase uses this proton-motive force to make ATP.
Activity *The Light Reactions*

Concept 10.3
The Calvin cycle uses ATP and NADPH to convert CO_2 to sugar

▶ The Calvin cycle occurs in the stroma and consists of carbon fixation, reduction, and regeneration of the CO_2 acceptor. Using electrons from NADPH and energy from ATP, the cycle synthesizes a three-carbon sugar (G3P). Most of the G3P is reused in the cycle, but some exits the cycle and is converted to glucose and other organic molecules (pp. 193–195).
Activity *The Calvin Cycle*
Investigation *How Is the Rate of Photosynthesis Measured?*
Biology Labs On-Line *LeafLab*

Concept 10.4
Alternative mechanisms of carbon fixation have evolved in hot, arid climates

▶ **Photorespiration: An Evolutionary Relic?** (pp. 195–196) On dry, hot days, plants close their stomata, conserving water. Oxygen from the light reactions builds up. In photorespiration, O_2 substitutes for CO_2 in the active site of rubisco. This process consumes organic fuel and releases CO_2 without producing ATP or sugar.

▶ **C_4 Plants** (p. 196) C_4 plants minimize the cost of photorespiration by incorporating CO_2 into four-carbon compounds in mesophyll cells. These compounds are exported to bundle-sheath cells, where they release carbon dioxide for use in the Calvin cycle.

▶ **CAM Plants** (pp. 196–197) CAM plants open their stomata at night, incorporating CO_2 into organic acids, which are stored in mesophyll cells. During the day the stomata close, and the CO_2 is released from the organic acids for use in the Calvin cycle.
Activity *Photosynthesis in Dry Climates*

▶ **The Importance of Photosynthesis:** *A Review* (pp. 197–198) Organic compounds produced by photosynthesis provide the energy and building material for ecosystems.

TESTING YOUR KNOWLEDGE

Self-Quiz

1. The light reactions of photosynthesis supply the Calvin cycle with
   a. light energy.
   b. CO_2 and ATP.
   c. H_2O and NADPH.
   d. ATP and NADPH.
   e. sugar and O_2.

2. Which of the following sequences correctly represents the flow of electrons during photosynthesis?
   a. NADPH → O_2 → CO_2
   b. H_2O → NADPH → Calvin cycle
   c. NADPH → chlorophyll → Calvin cycle
   d. H_2O → photosystem I → photosystem II
   e. NADPH → electron transport chain → O_2

3. Which of the following conclusions does *not* follow from studying the absorption spectrum for chlorophyll *a* and the action spectrum for photosynthesis (see Figure 10.9a and b)?
   a. Not all wavelengths are equally effective for photosynthesis.
   b. There must be accessory pigments that broaden the spectrum of light that contributes to photosynthesis.
   c. The red and blue areas of the spectrum are most effective in driving photosynthesis.
   d. Chlorophyll owes its color to the absorption of green light.
   e. Chlorophyll *a* has two absorption peaks.

4. Cooperation of the *two* photosystems is required for
   a. ATP synthesis.
   b. reduction of $NADP^+$.
   c. cyclic photophosphorylation.
   d. oxidation of the reaction center of photosystem I.
   e. generation of a proton-motive force.

5. In *mechanism*, photophosphorylation is most similar to
   a. substrate-level phosphorylation in glycolysis.
   b. oxidative phosphorylation in cellular respiration.
   c. the Calvin cycle.
   d. carbon fixation.
   e. reduction of $NADP^+$.

6. In what respect are the photosynthetic adaptations of C_4 plants and CAM plants similar?
   a. In both cases, only photosystem I is used.
   b. Both types of plants make sugar without the Calvin cycle.
   c. In both cases, an enzyme other than rubisco carries out the first step in carbon fixation.
   d. Both types of plants make most of their sugar in the dark.
   e. Neither C_4 plants nor CAM plants have thylakoids.

7. Which of the following processes is most directly driven by light energy?
   a. creation of a pH gradient by pumping protons across the thylakoid membrane
   b. carbon fixation in the stroma
   c. reduction of $NADP^+$ molecules
   d. removal of electrons from chlorophyll molecules
   e. ATP synthesis

8. Which of the following statements is a correct distinction between cyclic and noncyclic electron flow?
   a. Only noncyclic electron flow produces ATP.
   b. In addition to ATP, cyclic electron flow also produces O_2 and NADPH.
   c. Only cyclic electron flow utilizes light at 700 nm.
   d. Chemiosmosis is unique to noncyclic electron flow.
   e. Only cyclic electron flow can operate in the absence of photosystem II.

9. Which of the following statements is a correct distinction between autotrophs and heterotrophs?
   a. Only heterotrophs require chemical compounds from the environment.
   b. Cellular respiration is unique to heterotrophs.
   c. Only heterotrophs have mitochondria.
   d. Autotrophs, but not heterotrophs, can nourish themselves beginning with CO_2 and other nutrients that are inorganic.
   e. Only heterotrophs require oxygen.

10. Which of the following does *not* occur during the Calvin cycle?
    a. carbon fixation
    b. oxidation of NADPH
    c. release of oxygen
    d. regeneration of the CO_2 acceptor
    e. consumption of ATP

For Self-Quiz answers, see Appendix A.

Go to the website or CD-ROM for more quiz questions.

Evolution Connection

Photorespiration can substantially decrease soybeans' photosynthetic output by about 50%. Would you expect this figure to be higher or lower in wild relatives of soybeans? Why?

Scientific Inquiry

The diagram below represents an experiment with isolated chloroplasts. The chloroplasts were first made acidic by soaking them in a solution at pH 4. After the thylakoid space reached pH 4, the chloroplasts were transferred to a basic solution at pH 8. The chloroplasts then made ATP in the dark. Explain this result.

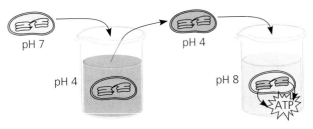

Investigation *How Does Paper Chromatography Separate Plant Pigments?*
Investigation *How Is the Rate of Photosynthesis Measured?*
Biology Labs On-Line *LeafLab*

Science, Technology, and Society

CO_2 in the atmosphere traps heat and warms the air, just as clear glass does in a greenhouse. Scientific evidence indicates that the CO_2 added to the air by the burning of wood and fossil fuels is contributing to a rise in global temperature. Tropical rain forests are estimated to be responsible for more than 20% of global photosynthesis. It seems reasonable to expect that the rain forests would reduce global warming by consuming large amounts of CO_2, but many experts now think that rain forests make little or no *net* contribution to reduction of global warming. Why might this be? (*Hint:* What happens to the food produced by a rain forest tree when it is eaten by animals or the tree dies?)

11

Cell Communication

▲ **Figure 11.1 Viagra (multicolored) bound to an enzyme (purple) involved in a signaling pathway.**

Key Concepts

11.1 External signals are converted into responses within the cell

11.2 Reception: A signal molecule binds to a receptor protein, causing it to change shape

11.3 Transduction: Cascades of molecular interactions relay signals from receptors to target molecules in the cell

11.4 Response: Cell signaling leads to regulation of cytoplasmic activities or transcription

Overview

The Cellular Internet

A hiker slips and falls down a steep ravine, injuring her leg in the fall. Tragedy is averted when she is able to pull out a cell phone and call for help. Cell phones, the Internet, e-mail, instant messaging—no one would deny the importance of communication in our lives. The role of communication in life at the cellular level is equally critical. Cell-to-cell communication is absolutely essential for multicellular organisms such as humans and oak trees. The trillions of cells in a multicellular organism must communicate with each other to coordinate their activities in a way that enables the organism to develop from a fertilized egg, then survive and reproduce in turn. Communication between cells is also important for many unicellular organisms. Networks of communication between cells can be even more complicated than the World Wide Web.

In studying how cells signal to each other and how they interpret the signals they receive, biologists have discovered some universal mechanisms of cellular regulation, additional evidence for the evolutionary relatedness of all life. The same small set of cell-signaling mechanisms shows up again and again in many lines of biological research—from embryonic development to hormone action to cancer. In one example, a common cell-to-cell signaling pathway leads to dilation of blood vessels. Once the signal subsides, the response is shut down by the enzyme shown in purple in **Figure 11.1**. Also shown is a multicolored molecule that blocks the action of this enzyme and keeps blood vessels dilated. Enzyme-inhibiting compounds like this one are often prescribed for treatment of medical conditions. The action of the multicolored compound, known as Viagra, will be discussed later in the chapter. The signals received by cells, whether originating from other cells or from changes in the physical environment, take various forms, including light and touch. However, cells most often communicate with each other by chemical signals. In this chapter, we focus on the main mechanisms by which cells receive, process, and respond to chemical signals sent from other cells.

Concept 11.1

External signals are converted into responses within the cell

What does a "talking" cell say to a "listening" cell, and how does the latter cell respond to the message? Let's approach these questions by first looking at communication among microorganisms, for modern microbes are a window on the role of cell signaling in the evolution of life on Earth.

Evolution of Cell Signaling

One topic of cell "conversation" is sex—at least for the yeast *Saccharomyces cerevisiae,* which people have used for millennia to make bread, wine, and beer. Researchers have learned that cells of this yeast identify their mates by chemical signaling. There are two sexes, or mating types, called **a** and α **(Figure 11.2)**. Cells of mating type **a** secrete a chemical signal called **a** factor, which can bind to specific receptor proteins on nearby α cells. At the same time, α cells secrete α factor, which binds to receptors on **a** cells. Without actually entering the cells, the two mating factors cause the cells to grow toward each other and bring about other cellular changes. The result is the fusion, or mating, of two cells of opposite type. The new **a**/α cell contains all the genes of both original cells, a combination of genetic resources that provides advantages to the cell's descendants, which arise by subsequent cell divisions.

How is the mating signal at the yeast cell surface changed, or *transduced,* into a form that brings about the cellular response of mating? The process by which a signal on a cell's surface is converted into a specific cellular response is a series of steps called a **signal transduction pathway.** Many such pathways have been extensively studied in both yeast and animal cells. Amazingly, the molecular details of signal transduction in yeast and mammals are strikingly similar, even though

the last common ancestor of these two groups of organisms lived over a billion years ago. These similarities—and others more recently uncovered between signaling systems in bacteria and plants—suggest that early versions of the cell-signaling mechanisms used today evolved well before the first multicellular creatures appeared on Earth. Scientists think that signaling mechanisms evolved first in ancient prokaryotes and single-celled eukaryotes and were then adopted for new uses by their multicellular descendants.

Local and Long-Distance Signaling

Like yeast cells, cells in a multicellular organism usually communicate via chemical messengers targeted for cells that may or may not be immediately adjacent. Cells may communicate by direct contact, as we saw in Chapters 6 and 7. Both animals and plants have cell junctions that, where present, directly connect the cytoplasms of adjacent cells **(Figure 11.3a)**. In these cases, signaling substances dissolved in the cytosol can pass freely between adjacent cells. Moreover, animal cells may communicate via direct contact between membrane-bound cell surface molecules **(Figure 11.3b)**. This sort of signaling, called cell-cell recognition, is important in such processes as embryonic development and the immune response.

In many other cases, messenger molecules are secreted by the signaling cell. Some of these travel only short distances; such **local regulators** influence cells in the vicinity. One class of local regulators in animals, *growth factors,* are compounds

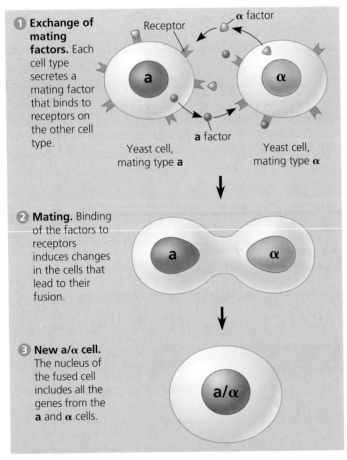

① Exchange of mating factors. Each cell type secretes a mating factor that binds to receptors on the other cell type.

Receptor
α factor
a
α
a factor

Yeast cell, mating type **a**

Yeast cell, mating type α

② Mating. Binding of the factors to receptors induces changes in the cells that lead to their fusion.

a
α

③ New a/α cell. The nucleus of the fused cell includes all the genes from the **a** and α cells.

a/α

▲ **Figure 11.2 Communication between mating yeast cells.** *Saccharomyces cerevisiae* cells use chemical signaling to identify cells of opposite mating type and initiate the mating process. The two mating types and their corresponding chemical signals, or mating factors, are called **a** and α.

Plasma membranes

Gap junctions between animal cells

Plasmodesmata between plant cells

(a) Cell junctions. Both animals and plants have cell junctions that allow molecules to pass readily between adjacent cells without crossing plasma membranes.

(b) Cell-cell recognition. Two cells in an animal may communicate by interaction between molecules protruding from their surfaces.

▲ **Figure 11.3 Communication by direct contact between cells.**

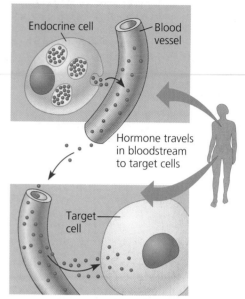

(a) Paracrine signaling. A secreting cell acts on nearby target cells by discharging molecules of a local regulator (a growth factor, for example) into the extracellular fluid.

(b) Synaptic signaling. A nerve cell releases neurotransmitter molecules into a synapse, stimulating the target cell.

(c) Hormonal signaling. Specialized endocrine cells secrete hormones into body fluids, often the blood. Hormones may reach virtually all body cells.

▲ **Figure 11.4 Local and long-distance cell communication in animals.** In both local and long-distance signaling, only specific target cells recognize and respond to a given chemical signal.

that stimulate nearby target cells to grow and multiply. Numerous cells can simultaneously receive and respond to the molecules of growth factor produced by a single cell in their vicinity. This type of local signaling in animals is called *paracrine signaling* (**Figure 11.4a**).

Another, more specialized type of local signaling called *synaptic signaling* occurs in the animal nervous system. An electrical signal along a nerve cell triggers the secretion of a chemical signal in the form of neurotransmitter molecules. These diffuse across the synapse, the narrow space between the nerve cell and its target cell (often another nerve cell). The neurotransmitter stimulates the target cell (**Figure 11.4b**).

Local signaling in plants is not as well understood. Because of their cell walls, plants must use mechanisms somewhat different from those operating locally in animals.

Both animals and plants use chemicals called **hormones** for long-distance signaling. In hormonal signaling in animals, also known as endocrine signaling, specialized cells release hormone molecules into vessels of the circulatory system, by which they travel to target cells in other parts of the body (**Figure 11.4c**). Plant hormones (often called *growth regulators*) sometimes travel in vessels but more often reach their targets by moving through cells (see Chapter 39) or by diffusion through the air as a gas. Hormones vary widely in molecular size and type, as do local regulators. For instance, the plant hormone ethylene, a gas that promotes fruit ripening and helps regulate growth, is a hydrocarbon of only six atoms (C_2H_4) that can pass through cell walls. In contrast, the mam-

malian hormone insulin, which regulates sugar levels in the blood, is a protein with thousands of atoms.

The transmission of a signal through the nervous system can also be considered an example of long-distance signaling. An electrical signal travels the length of a nerve cell and is then converted back to a chemical signal that crosses the synapse to another nerve cell. Here it is converted back into an electrical signal. In this way, a nerve signal can travel along a series of nerve cells. Since some nerve cells are quite long, the nerve signal can quickly travel great distances—from your brain to your big toe, for example. This type of long-distance signaling will be covered in detail in Chapter 48.

What happens when a cell encounters a signal? The signal must be recognized by a specific receptor molecule, and the information it carries must be changed into another form—transduced—inside the cell before the cell can respond. The remainder of the chapter discusses this process, primarily as it occurs in animal cells.

The Three Stages of Cell Signaling: *A Preview*

Our current understanding of how chemical messengers act via signal transduction pathways had its origins in the pioneering work of Earl W. Sutherland, whose research led to a Nobel Prize in 1971. Sutherland and his colleagues at Vanderbilt University were investigating how the animal hormone epinephrine stimulates the breakdown of the storage polysaccharide glycogen within liver cells and skeletal muscle cells. Glycogen

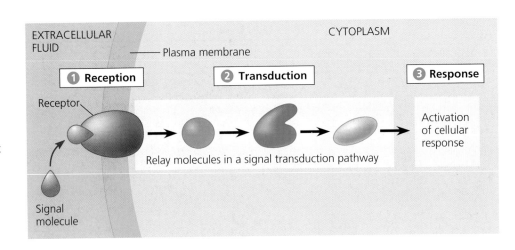

▶ **Figure 11.5 Overview of cell signaling.** From the perspective of the cell receiving the message, cell signaling can be divided into three stages: signal reception, signal transduction, and cellular response. When reception occurs at the plasma membrane, as shown here, the transduction stage is usually a pathway of several steps, with each molecule in the pathway bringing about a change in the next molecule. The last molecule in the pathway triggers the cell's response. The three stages are explained in the text.

EXTRACELLULAR FLUID

CYTOPLASM

— Plasma membrane

1 Reception

2 Transduction

3 Response

Receptor

Relay molecules in a signal transduction pathway

Activation of cellular response

Signal molecule

---

breakdown releases the sugar glucose-1-phosphate, which the cell converts to glucose-6-phosphate. The cell (a liver cell, for example) can then use this compound, an early intermediate in glycolysis, for energy production. Alternatively, the compound can be stripped of phosphate and released from the liver cell into the blood as glucose, which can fuel cells throughout the body. Thus, one effect of epinephrine, which is secreted from the adrenal gland during times of physical or mental stress, is the mobilization of fuel reserves.

Sutherland's research team discovered that epinephrine stimulates glycogen breakdown by somehow activating a cytosolic enzyme, glycogen phosphorylase. However, when epinephrine was added to a test-tube mixture containing the enzyme and its substrate, glycogen, no breakdown occurred. Epinephrine could activate glycogen phosphorylase only when the hormone was added to a solution containing *intact* cells. This result told Sutherland two things. First, epinephrine does not interact directly with the enzyme responsible for glycogen breakdown; an intermediate step or series of steps must be occurring inside the cell. Second, the plasma membrane is somehow involved in transmitting the epinephrine signal.

Sutherland's early work suggested that the process going on at the receiving end of a cellular conversation can be dissected into three stages: reception, transduction, and response **(Figure 11.5)**:

❶ **Reception.** Reception is the target cell's detection of a signal molecule coming from outside the cell. A chemical signal is "detected" when it binds to a receptor protein located at the cell's surface or inside the cell.

❷ **Transduction.** The binding of the signal molecule changes the receptor protein in some way, initiating the process of transduction. The transduction stage converts the signal to a form that can bring about a specific cellular response. In Sutherland's system, the binding of epinephrine to a receptor protein in a liver cell's plasma membrane leads to activation of glycogen phosphorylase. Transduction sometimes occurs in a single step but more often requires a sequence of changes in a series of

different molecules—a *signal transduction pathway*. The molecules in the pathway are often called relay molecules.

❸ **Response.** In the third stage of cell signaling, the transduced signal finally triggers a specific cellular response. The response may be almost any imaginable cellular activity—such as catalysis by an enzyme (for example, glycogen phosphorylase), rearrangement of the cytoskeleton, or activation of specific genes in the nucleus. The cell-signaling process helps ensure that crucial activities like these occur in the right cells, at the right time, and in proper coordination with the other cells of the organism. We'll now explore the mechanisms of cell signaling in more detail.

Concept Check 11.1

1. Explain how nerve cells provide examples of both local and long-distance signaling.
2. When epinephrine is mixed with glycogen phosphorylase and glycogen in a test tube, is glucose-1-phosphate generated? Why or why not?

For suggested answers, see Appendix A.

Concept 11.2

Reception: A signal molecule binds to a receptor protein, causing it to change shape

When we speak to someone, others nearby may hear our message, sometimes with unfortunate consequences. However, errors of this kind rarely occur among cells. The signals emitted by an **a** yeast cell are "heard" only by its prospective mates, α cells. Similarly, although epinephrine encounters many types of cells as it circulates in the blood, only certain target cells detect and react to the hormone. A receptor protein on or in the target cell allows the cell to "hear" the signal and respond to it. The signal molecule is complementary in shape to a specific site on the receptor and attaches there, like a key in a lock or a substrate in the catalytic site of an enzyme. The signal molecule behaves as a **ligand,** the term for a molecule that specifically binds to another molecule, often a larger one. Ligand binding generally causes a receptor protein to undergo a change in conformation—that is, to change shape. For many receptors, this shape change directly activates the receptor, enabling it to interact with other cellular molecules. For other kinds of receptors, the immediate effect of ligand binding is to cause the aggregation of two or more receptor molecules, which leads to further molecular events inside the cell.

Most signal receptors are plasma membrane proteins. Their ligands are water-soluble and generally too large to pass freely through the plasma membrane. Other signal receptors, however, are located inside the cell. We discuss these next, before returning to membrane receptors.

Intracellular Receptors

Intracellular receptor proteins are found in either the cytoplasm or nucleus of target cells. To reach such a receptor, a chemical messenger passes through the target cell's plasma membrane. A number of important signaling molecules can do this because they are either hydrophobic enough or small enough to cross the phospholipid interior of the membrane. Such hydrophobic chemical messengers include the steroid hormones and thyroid hormones of animals. Another chemical signal with an intracellular receptor is nitric oxide (NO), a gas; its very small molecules readily pass between the membrane phospholipids.

The behavior of testosterone is representative of steroid hormones. Secreted by cells of the testis, the hormone travels through the blood and enters cells all over the body. In the cytoplasm of target cells, the only cells that contain receptor molecules for testosterone, the hormone binds to the receptor protein, activating it **(Figure 11.6)**. With the hormone attached, the active form of the receptor protein then enters the nucleus and turns on specific genes that control male sex characteristics.

How does the activated hormone-receptor complex turn on genes? Recall that the genes in a cell's DNA function by being transcribed and processed into messenger RNA (mRNA), which leaves the nucleus and is translated into a specific protein by ribosomes in the cytoplasm (see Figure 5.25). Special proteins called *transcription factors* control which genes are turned on—that is, which genes are transcribed into mRNA—in a particular cell at a particular time. The testosterone receptor, when activated, acts as a transcription factor that turns on specific genes.

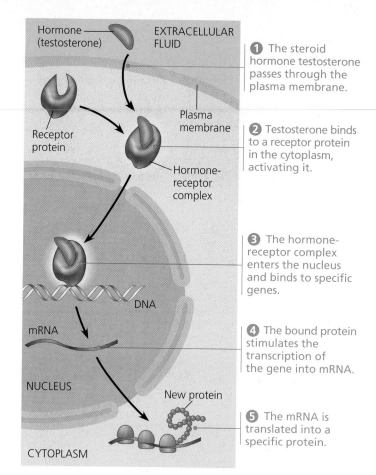

▲ Figure 11.6 **Steroid hormone interacting with an intracellular receptor.**

❶ The steroid hormone testosterone passes through the plasma membrane.

❷ Testosterone binds to a receptor protein in the cytoplasm, activating it.

❸ The hormone-receptor complex enters the nucleus and binds to specific genes.

❹ The bound protein stimulates the transcription of the gene into mRNA.

❺ The mRNA is translated into a specific protein.

By acting as a transcription factor, the testosterone receptor itself carries out the complete transduction of the signal. Most other intracellular receptors function in the same way, although many of them are already in the nucleus before the signal molecule reaches them (an example is the thyroid hormone receptor). Interestingly, many of these intracellular receptor proteins are structurally similar, suggesting an evolutionary kinship. We will look more closely at hormones with intracellular receptors in Chapter 45.

Receptors in the Plasma Membrane

Most water-soluble signal molecules bind to specific sites on receptor proteins embedded in the cell's plasma membrane. Such a receptor transmits information from the extracellular environment to the inside of the cell by changing shape or aggregating when a specific ligand binds to it. We can see how membrane receptors work by looking at three major types: G-protein-linked receptors, receptor tyrosine kinases, and ion channel receptors. These receptors are discussed and illustrated in **Figure 11.7** on the next three pages; please study this figure before going on.

Figure 11.7
Exploring **Membrane Receptors**

G-PROTEIN-LINKED RECEPTORS

G-protein-linked receptor

A **G-protein-linked receptor** is a plasma membrane receptor that works with the help of a protein called a **G protein**. Many different signal molecules use G-protein-linked receptors, including yeast mating factors, epinephrine and many other hormones, and neurotransmitters. These receptors vary in their binding sites for recognizing signal molecules and for recognizing different G proteins inside the cell. Nevertheless, G-protein-linked receptor proteins are all remarkably similar in structure. They each have seven α helices spanning the membrane, as shown above.

A large family of eukaryotic receptor proteins has this secondary structure, where the single polypeptide, represented here as a ribbon, has seven transmembrane α helices, represented as cylinders and depicted in a row for clarity. Specific loops between the helices form binding sites for signal and G-protein molecules.

G-protein-linked receptor systems are extremely widespread and diverse in their functions, including roles in embryonic development and sensory reception. In humans, for example, both vision and smell depend on such proteins. Similarities in structure among G proteins and G-protein-linked receptors of modern organisms suggest that G proteins and associated receptors evolved very early.

G-protein systems are involved in many human diseases, including bacterial infections. The bacteria that cause cholera, pertussis (whooping cough), and botulism, among others, make their victims ill by producing toxins that interfere with G-protein function. Pharmacologists now realize that up to 60% of all medicines used today exert their effects by influencing G-protein pathways.

❶ Loosely attached to the cytoplasmic side of the membrane, the G protein functions as a molecular switch that is either on or off, depending on which of two guanine nucleotides is attached, GDP or GTP—hence the term G protein. (GTP, or guanosine triphosphate, is similar to ATP.) When GDP is bound to the G protein, as shown above, the G protein is inactive. The receptor and G protein work together with another protein, usually an enzyme.

❷ When the appropriate signal molecule binds to the extracellular side of the receptor, the receptor is activated and changes shape. Its cytoplasmic side then binds an inactive G protein, causing a GTP to displace the GDP. This activates the G protein.

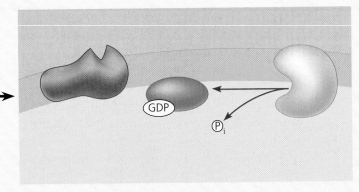

❸ The activated G protein dissociates from the receptor and diffuses along the membrane, then binds to an enzyme and alters *its* activity. When the enzyme is activated, it can trigger the next step in a pathway leading to a cellular response.

❹ The changes in the enzyme and G protein are only temporary, because the G protein also functions as a GTPase enzyme and soon hydrolyzes its bound GTP to GDP. Now inactive again, the G protein leaves the enzyme, which returns to its original state. The G protein is now available for reuse. The GTPase function of the G protein allows the pathway to shut down rapidly when the signal molecule is no longer present.

Continued on next page

A **receptor tyrosine kinase** can trigger more than one signal transduction pathway at once, helping the cell regulate and coordinate many aspects of cell growth and cell reproduction. This receptor is one of a major class of plasma membrane receptors characterized by having enzymatic activity. A *kinase* is an enzyme that catalyzes the transfer of phosphate groups. The part of the receptor protein extending into the cytoplasm functions as an enzyme, called tyrosine kinase, that catalyzes the transfer of a phosphate group from ATP to the amino acid tyrosine on a substrate protein. Thus, receptor tyrosine kinases are membrane receptors that attach phosphates to tyrosines.

One receptor tyrosine kinase complex may activate ten or more different transduction pathways and cellular responses. The ability of a single ligand-binding event to trigger so many pathways is a key difference between receptor tyrosine kinases and G-protein-linked receptors. Abnormal receptor tyrosine kinases that dimerize even in the absence of signal molecules may contribute to some kinds of cancer.

1 Many receptor tyrosine kinases have the structure depicted schematically here. Before the signal molecule binds, the receptors exist as individual polypeptides. Notice that each has an extracellular signal-binding site, an α helix spanning the membrane, and an intracellular tail containing multiple tyrosines.

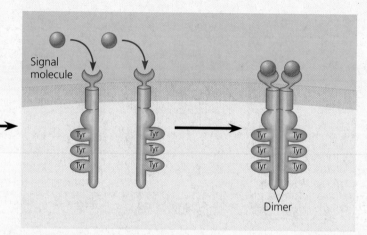

2 The binding of a signal molecule (such as a growth factor) causes two receptor polypeptides to associate closely with each other, forming a dimer (dimerization).

3 Dimerization activates the tyrosine-kinase region of each polypeptide; each tyrosine kinase adds a phosphate from an ATP molecule to a tyrosine on the tail of the other polypeptide.

4 Now that the receptor protein is fully activated, it is recognized by specific relay proteins inside the cell. Each such protein binds to a specific phosphorylated tyrosine, undergoing a resulting structural change that activates the bound protein. Each activated protein triggers a transduction pathway, leading to a cellular response.

Continued on next page

Figure 11.7 (continued)
Exploring Membrane Receptors

ION CHANNEL RECEPTORS

A **ligand-gated ion channel** is a type of membrane receptor, a region of which can act as a "gate" when the receptor changes shape. When a signal molecule binds as a ligand to the receptor protein, the gate opens or closes, allowing or blocking the flow of specific ions, such as Na^+ or Ca^{2+}, through a channel in the receptor. Like the other receptors we have discussed, these proteins bind the ligand at a specific site on their extracellular side.

1. Here we show a ligand-gated ion channel receptor that remains closed until a ligand binds to it.

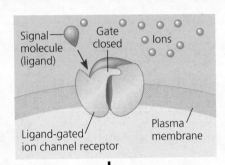

2. When the ligand binds to the receptor and the gate opens, specific ions can flow through the channel and rapidly change the concentration of that particular ion inside the cell. This change may directly affect the activity of the cell in some way.

3. When the ligand dissociates from this receptor, the gate closes and ions no longer enter the cell.

Ligand-gated ion channels are very important in the nervous system. For example, the neurotransmitter molecules released at a synapse between two nerve cells (see Figure 11.4b) bind as ligands to ion channels on the receiving cell, causing the channels to open. Ions flow in and trigger an electrical signal that propagates down the length of the receiving cell. Some gated ion channels are controlled by electrical signals instead of ligands; these voltage-gated ion channels are also crucial to the functioning of the nervous system, as we will discuss in Chapter 48.

Concept 11.3

Transduction: Cascades of molecular interactions relay signals from receptors to target molecules in the cell

When signal receptors are plasma membrane proteins, like most of those we have discussed, the transduction stage of cell signaling is usually a multistep pathway. One benefit of such pathways is the possibility of greatly amplifying a signal. If some of the molecules in a pathway transmit the signal to multiple molecules of the next component in the series, the result can be a large number of activated molecules at the end of the pathway. In other words, a small number of extracellular signal molecules can produce a large cellular response. Moreover, multistep pathways provide more opportunities for coordination and regulation than simpler systems do, as we'll discuss later.

Signal Transduction Pathways

The binding of a specific signal molecule to a receptor in the plasma membrane triggers the first step in the chain of molecular interactions—the signal transduction pathway—that leads to a particular response within the cell. Like falling dominoes, the signal-activated receptor activates another protein, which activates another molecule, and so on, until the protein that produces the final cellular response is activated. The molecules that relay a signal from receptor to response, which we call relay molecules in this book, are mostly proteins. The interaction of proteins is a major theme of cell signaling. Indeed, protein interaction is a unifying theme of all regulation at the cellular level.

Keep in mind that the original signal molecule is not physically passed along a signaling pathway; in most cases, it never even enters the cell. When we say that the signal is relayed along a pathway, we mean that certain information is passed on. At each step, the signal is transduced into a different form, commonly a conformational change in a protein. Very often, the conformational change is brought about by phosphorylation.

Protein Phosphorylation and Dephosphorylation

Previous chapters introduced the concept of activating a protein by adding one or more phosphate groups to it (see Figure 8.11). In Figure 11.7, we have already seen how phosphorylation is involved in the activation of receptor tyrosine kinases. In fact, the phosphorylation and dephosphorylation of proteins is a widespread cellular mechanism for regulating protein activity. The general name for an enzyme that transfers phosphate groups from ATP to a protein is **protein kinase.** Recall that receptor tyrosine kinases phosphorylate other receptor tyrosine kinase monomers. Most cytoplasmic protein kinases, however, act on proteins different from themselves. Another distinction is that most cytoplasmic protein kinases phosphorylate either the amino acid serine or threonine,

rather than tyrosine. Such serine/threonine kinases are widely involved in signaling pathways in animals, plants, and fungi.

Many of the relay molecules in signal transduction pathways are protein kinases, and they often act on other protein kinases in the pathway. **Figure 11.8** depicts a hypothetical pathway containing three different protein kinases, which create a "phosphorylation cascade." The sequence shown is similar to many known pathways, including those triggered in yeast by mating factors and in animal cells by many growth factors. The signal is transmitted by a cascade of protein phosphorylations, each bringing with it a conformational change. Each shape change results from the interaction of the newly added phosphate groups with charged or polar amino acids (see Figure 5.17). The addition of phosphate groups often changes a protein from an inactive form to an active form (although in other cases phosphorylation *decreases* the activity of the protein).

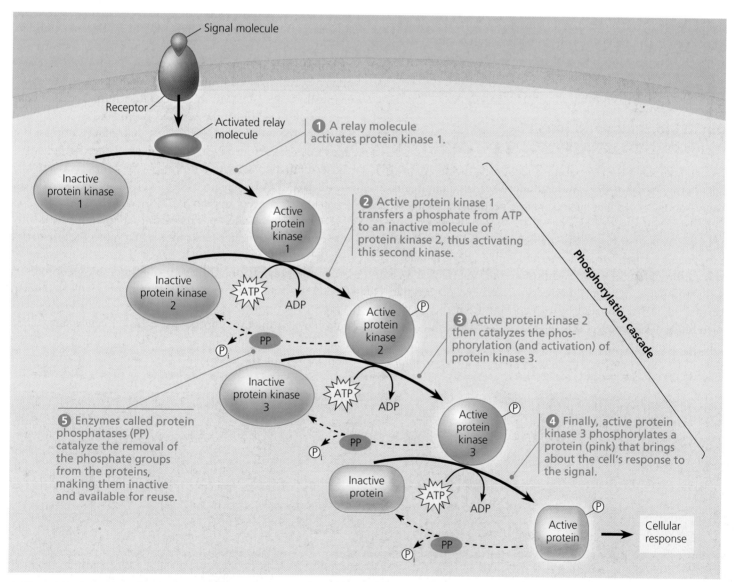

▲ Figure 11.8 **A phosphorylation cascade.** In a phosphorylation cascade, a series of different molecules in a pathway are phosphorylated in turn, each molecule adding a phosphate group to the next one in line. The active and inactive forms of each protein are represented by different shapes to remind you that activation is usually associated with a change in molecular conformation.

The importance of protein kinases can hardly be over-stated. About 2% of our own genes are thought to code for protein kinases. A single cell may have hundreds of different kinds, each specific for a different substrate protein. Together, they probably regulate a large proportion of the thousands of proteins in a cell. Among these are most of the proteins that, in turn, regulate cell reproduction. Abnormal activity of such a kinase can cause abnormal cell growth and contribute to the development of cancer.

Equally important in the phosphorylation cascade are the **protein phosphatases,** enzymes that can rapidly remove phosphate groups from proteins, a process called dephosphorylation. By dephosphorylating and thus inactivating protein kinases, phosphatases provide the mechanism for turning off the signal transduction pathway when the initial signal is no longer present. Phosphatases also make the protein kinases available for reuse, enabling the cell to respond again to an extracellular signal. At any given moment, the activity of a protein regulated by phosphorylation depends on the balance in the cell between active kinase molecules and active phosphatase molecules. The phosphorylation/dephosphorylation system acts as a molecular switch in the cell, turning activities on or off as required.

Small Molecules and Ions as Second Messengers

Not all components of signal transduction pathways are proteins. Many signaling pathways also involve small, nonprotein, water-soluble molecules or ions called **second messengers.** (The extracellular signal molecule that binds to the membrane receptor is a pathway's "first messenger.") Because second messengers are both small and water-soluble, they can readily spread throughout the cell by diffusion. For example, as we'll see shortly, it is a second messenger called cyclic AMP that carries the signal initiated by epinephrine from the plasma membrane of a liver or muscle cell into the cell's interior, where it brings about glycogen breakdown. Second messengers participate in pathways initiated by both G-protein-linked receptors

and receptor tyrosine kinases. The two most widely used second messengers are cyclic AMP and calcium ions, Ca^{2+}. A large variety of relay proteins are sensitive to the cytosolic concentration of one or the other of these second messengers.

Cyclic AMP

Once Earl Sutherland had established that epinephrine somehow causes glycogen breakdown without passing through the plasma membrane, the search began for the second messenger (he coined the term) that transmits the signal from the plasma membrane to the metabolic machinery in the cytoplasm.

Sutherland found that the binding of epinephrine to the plasma membrane of a liver cell elevates the cytosolic concentration of a compound called cyclic adenosine monophosphate, abbreviated **cyclic AMP** or **cAMP** (**Figure 11.9**). An enzyme embedded in the plasma membrane, **adenylyl cyclase,** converts ATP to cAMP in response to an extracellular signal—in this case, epinephrine. But the epinephrine doesn't stimulate the adenylyl cyclase directly. When epinephrine outside the cell binds to a specific receptor protein, the protein activates adenylyl cyclase, which in turn can catalyze the synthesis of many molecules of cAMP. In this way, the normal cellular concentration of cAMP can be boosted twentyfold in a matter of seconds. The cAMP broadcasts the signal to the cytoplasm. It does not persist for long in the absence of the hormone, because another enzyme, called phosphodiesterase, converts the cAMP to AMP. Another surge of epinephrine is needed to boost the cytosolic concentration of cAMP again.

Subsequent research has revealed that epinephrine is only one of many hormones and other signal molecules that trigger the formation of cAMP. It has also brought to light the other components of cAMP pathways, including G proteins, G-protein-linked receptors, and protein kinases (**Figure 11.10**). The immediate effect of cAMP is usually the activation of a serine/threonine kinase called *protein kinase A.* The activated kinase then phosphorylates various other proteins, depending on the cell type. (The complete pathway for

▲ **Figure 11.9 Cyclic AMP.** The second messenger cyclic AMP (cAMP) is made from ATP by adenylyl cyclase, an enzyme embedded in the plasma membrane. Cyclic AMP is inactivated by phosphodiesterase, an enzyme that converts it to AMP.

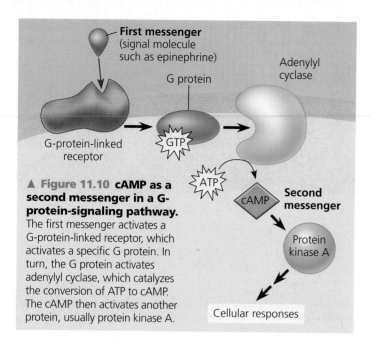

▲ **Figure 11.10 cAMP as a second messenger in a G-protein-signaling pathway.** The first messenger activates a G-protein-linked receptor, which activates a specific G protein. In turn, the G protein activates adenylyl cyclase, which catalyzes the conversion of ATP to cAMP. The cAMP then activates another protein, usually protein kinase A.

epinephrine's stimulation of glycogen breakdown is shown later, in Figure 11.13.)

Further regulation of cell metabolism is provided by other G-protein systems that *inhibit* adenylyl cyclase. In these systems, a different signal molecule activates a different receptor, which activates an *inhibitory* G protein.

Now that we know about the role of cAMP in G-protein-signaling pathways, we can explain in molecular detail how certain microbes cause disease. Consider cholera, a disease that is frequently epidemic in places where the water supply is contaminated with human feces. People acquire the cholera bacterium, *Vibrio cholerae,* by drinking contaminated water. The bacteria colonize the lining of the small intestine and produce a toxin. The cholera toxin is an enzyme that chemically modifies a G protein involved in regulating salt and water secretion. Because the modified G protein is unable to hydrolyze GTP to GDP, it remains stuck in its active form, continuously stimulating adenylyl cyclase to make cAMP. The resulting high concentration of cAMP causes the intestinal cells to secrete large amounts of water and salts into the intestines. An infected person quickly develops profuse diarrhea and if left untreated can soon die from the loss of water and salts.

Our understanding of signaling pathways involving cyclic AMP or related messengers has allowed us to develop treatments for certain conditions in humans. One such pathway uses *cyclic GMP,* or *cGMP,* as a signaling molecule; its effects include relaxation of smooth muscle cells in artery walls. A compound that inhibits the hydrolysis of cGMP to GMP, thus prolonging the signal, was originally prescribed for chest pains because it increased blood flow to the heart muscle. Under the trade name Viagra (see Figure 11.1), this compound is now widely used as a treatment for erectile dysfunction. Viagra causes dilation of blood vessels, which allows increased blood flow to the penis, optimizing physiological conditions for penile erections.

Calcium Ions and Inositol Trisphosphate (IP₃)

Many signal molecules in animals, including neurotransmitters, growth factors, and some hormones, induce responses in their target cells via signal transduction pathways that increase the cytosolic concentration of calcium ions (Ca^{2+}). Calcium is even more widely used than cAMP as a second messenger. Increasing the cytosolic concentration of Ca^{2+} causes many responses in animal cells, including muscle cell contraction, secretion of certain substances, and cell division. In plant cells, a wide range of hormonal and environmental stimuli can cause brief increases in cytosolic Ca^{2+} concentration, triggering various signaling pathways, such as the pathway for greening in response to light (see Figure 39.4). Cells use Ca^{2+} as a second messenger in both G-protein and receptor tyrosine kinase pathways.

Although cells always contain some Ca^{2+}, this ion can function as a second messenger because its concentration in the cytosol is normally much lower than the concentration outside the cell **(Figure 11.11)**. In fact, the level of Ca^{2+} in

▲ **Figure 11.11 The maintenance of calcium ion concentrations in an animal cell.** The Ca^{2+} concentration in the cytosol is usually much lower (light blue) than in the extracellular fluid and ER (darker blue). Protein pumps in the plasma membrane and the ER membrane, driven by ATP, move Ca^{2+} from the cytosol into the extracellular fluid and into the lumen of the ER. Mitochondrial pumps, driven by chemiosmosis (see Chapter 9), move Ca^{2+} into mitochondria when the calcium level in the cytosol rises significantly.

► **Figure 11.12 Calcium and IP$_3$ in signaling pathways.** Calcium ions (Ca^{2+}) and inositol trisphosphate (IP$_3$) function as second messengers in many signal transduction pathways. In this figure, the process is initiated by the binding of a signal molecule to a G-protein-linked receptor. A receptor tyrosine kinase could also initiate this pathway by activating phospholipase C.

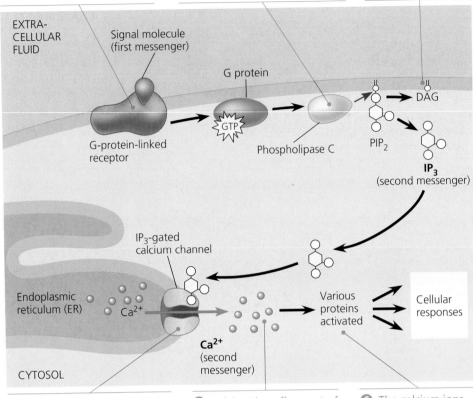

① A signal molecule binds to a receptor, leading to activation of phospholipase C.

② Phospholipase C cleaves a plasma membrane phospholipid called PIP$_2$ into DAG and IP$_3$.

③ DAG functions as a second messenger in other pathways.

EXTRA-CELLULAR FLUID

Signal molecule (first messenger)

G protein

DAG

GTP

G-protein-linked receptor

Phospholipase C

PIP$_2$

IP$_3$ (second messenger)

IP$_3$-gated calcium channel

Endoplasmic reticulum (ER)

Ca^{2+}

Various proteins activated

Cellular responses

Ca^{2+} (second messenger)

CYTOSOL

④ IP$_3$ quickly diffuses through the cytosol and binds to an IP$_3$-gated calcium channel in the ER membrane, causing it to open.

⑤ Calcium ions flow out of the ER (down their concentration gradient), raising the Ca^{2+} level in the cytosol.

⑥ The calcium ions activate the next protein in one or more signaling pathways.

the blood and extracellular fluid of an animal often exceeds that in the cytosol by more than 10,000 times. Calcium ions are actively transported out of the cell and are actively imported from the cytosol into the endoplasmic reticulum (and, under some conditions, into mitochondria and chloroplasts) by various protein pumps (see Figure 11.11). As a result, the calcium concentration in the ER is usually much higher than that in the cytosol. Because the cytosolic calcium level is low, a small change in absolute numbers of ions represents a relatively large percentage change in calcium concentration.

In response to a signal relayed by a signal transduction pathway, the cytosolic calcium level may rise, usually by a mechanism that releases Ca^{2+} from the cell's ER. The pathways leading to calcium release involve still other second messengers, **inositol trisphosphate (IP$_3$)** and **diacylglycerol (DAG)**. These two messengers are produced by cleavage of a certain kind of phospholipid in the plasma membrane. **Figure 11.12** shows how this occurs and how IP$_3$ stimulates the release of calcium from the ER. Because IP$_3$ acts before calcium in these pathways, calcium could be considered a "*third* messenger." However, scientists use the term *second messenger* for all small, nonprotein components of signal transduction pathways.

Concept 11.4

Response: Cell signaling leads to regulation of cytoplasmic activities or transcription

We now take a closer look at the cell's subsequent response to an extracellular signal—what some researchers call the "output response." What is the nature of the final step in a signaling pathway?

Cytoplasmic and Nuclear Responses

Ultimately, a signal transduction pathway leads to the regulation of one or more cellular activities. The response may occur in the cytoplasm or may involve action in the nucleus.

In the cytoplasm, a signal may cause, for example, the opening or closing of an ion channel in the plasma membrane or a change in cell metabolism. As we have discussed already, the response of liver cells to signaling by the hormone epinephrine helps regulate cellular energy metabolism. The final step in the signaling pathway activates the enzyme that catalyzes the breakdown of glycogen. **Figure 11.13** shows the complete pathway leading to the release of glucose-1-phosphate from glycogen. Note that at each step the response is amplified, as we will discuss later.

Many other signaling pathways ultimately regulate not the *activity* of enzymes but the *synthesis* of enzymes or other proteins, usually by turning specific genes on or off in the nucleus. Like an activated steroid receptor (see Figure 11.6), the final activated molecule in a signaling pathway may function as a transcription factor. **Figure 11.14** shows an example in which a signaling pathway activates a transcription factor that turns a gene on: The response to the growth factor signal is the synthesis of mRNA, which will be translated in the cytoplasm into a specific protein. In other cases, the transcription factor might regulate a gene by turning it off. Often a transcription factor regulates several different genes.

All the different kinds of signal receptors and relay molecules introduced in this chapter participate in various gene-regulating pathways, as well as in pathways leading to other kinds of responses. The molecular messengers that produce gene regulation responses include growth factors and certain plant and animal hormones. Malfunctioning of growth factor pathways like the one in Figure 11.14 can contribute to the development of cancer, as we will see in Chapter 19.

Fine-Tuning of the Response

Why are there often so many steps between a signaling event at the cell surface and the cell's response? As mentioned earlier, signaling pathways with a multiplicity of steps have

Reception

Binding of epinephrine to G-protein-linked receptor (1 molecule)

Transduction

Inactive G protein

Active G protein (10^2 molecules)

Inactive adenylyl cyclase

Active adenylyl cyclase (10^2)

ATP

Cyclic AMP (10^4)

Inactive protein kinase A

Active protein kinase A (10^4)

Inactive phosphorylase kinase

Active phosphorylase kinase (10^5)

Inactive glycogen phosphorylase

Active glycogen phosphorylase (10^6)

Response

Glycogen

Glucose-1-phosphate (10^8 molecules)

▲ **Figure 11.13 Cytoplasmic response to a signal: the stimulation of glycogen breakdown by epinephrine.** In this signaling system, the hormone epinephrine acts through a G-protein-linked receptor to activate a succession of relay molecules, including cAMP and two protein kinases (see also Figure 11.10). The final protein to be activated is the enzyme glycogen phosphorylase, which releases glucose-1-phosphate units from glycogen. This pathway amplifies the hormonal signal, because one receptor protein can activate about 100 molecules of G protein, and each enzyme in the pathway can act on many molecules of its substrate, the next molecule in the cascade. The number of activated molecules given for each step is approximate.

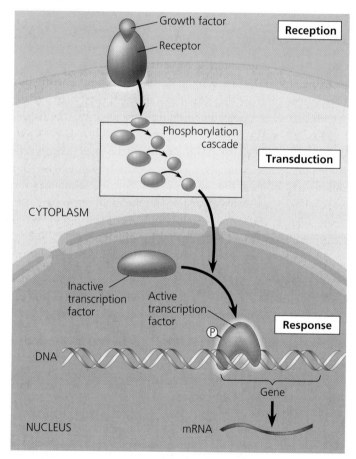

▲ **Figure 11.14 Nuclear responses to a signal: the activation of a specific gene by a growth factor.** This diagram is a simplified representation of a typical signaling pathway that leads to the regulation of gene activity in the cell nucleus. The initial signal molecule, a local regulator called a growth factor, triggers a phosphorylation cascade. (The ATP molecules that serve as sources of phosphate are not shown.) Once phosphorylated, the last kinase in the sequence enters the nucleus and there activates a gene-regulating protein, a transcription factor. This protein stimulates a specific gene so that an mRNA is synthesized, which then directs the synthesis of a particular protein in the cytoplasm.

two important benefits: They amplify the signal (and thus the response), and they contribute to the specificity of response.

Signal Amplification

Elaborate enzyme cascades amplify the cell's response to a signal. At each catalytic step in the cascade, the number of activated products is much greater than in the preceding step. For example, in the epinephrine-triggered pathway in Figure 11.13, each adenylyl cyclase molecule catalyzes the formation of many cAMP molecules, each molecule of protein kinase A phosphorylates many molecules of the next kinase in the pathway, and so on. The amplification effect stems from the fact that these proteins persist in the active form long enough to process numerous molecules of substrate before they become inactive again. As a result of the signal's amplification, a small number of epinephrine molecules binding to receptors on the surface of a liver cell or muscle cell can lead to the release of hundreds of millions of glucose molecules from glycogen.

The Specificity of Cell Signaling

Consider two different cells in your body—a liver cell and a heart muscle cell, for example. Both are in contact with your bloodstream and are therefore constantly exposed to many different hormone molecules, as well as to local regulators secreted by nearby cells. Yet the liver cell responds to some signals but ignores others, and the same is true for the heart cell. And some kinds of signals trigger responses in both cells—but different responses. For instance, epinephrine stimulates the liver cell to break down glycogen, but the main response of the heart cell to epinephrine is contraction, leading to a more rapid heartbeat. How do we account for this difference?

The explanation for the specificity exhibited in cellular responses to signals is the same as the basic explanation for virtually all differences between cells: *Different kinds of cells have different collections of proteins* **(Figure 11.15)**. The response of a particular cell to a signal depends on its particular collection of signal receptor proteins, relay proteins, and proteins needed to carry out the response. A liver cell, for example, is poised to respond appropriately to epinephrine by having the proteins listed in Figure 11.13 as well as those needed to manufacture glycogen.

Thus, two cells that respond differently to the same signal differ in one or more of the proteins that handle and respond to the signal. Notice in Figure 11.15 that different pathways may have some molecules in common. For example, cells A, B, and C all use the same receptor protein for the orange signal molecule; differences in other proteins account for their differing responses. In cell D, a different receptor protein is used for the same signal molecule, leading to yet another response. In cell B, a pathway that is triggered by a single kind of signal diverges to produce two responses; such branched pathways often involve receptor tyrosine kinases (which can

activate multiple relay proteins) or second messengers (which can regulate numerous proteins). In cell C, two pathways triggered by separate signals converge to modulate a single response. Branching of pathways and "cross-talk" (interaction) between pathways are important in regulating and coordinating a cell's responses to information coming in from different sources in the body. Moreover, the use of some of the same proteins in more than one pathway allows the cell to economize on the number of different proteins it must make.

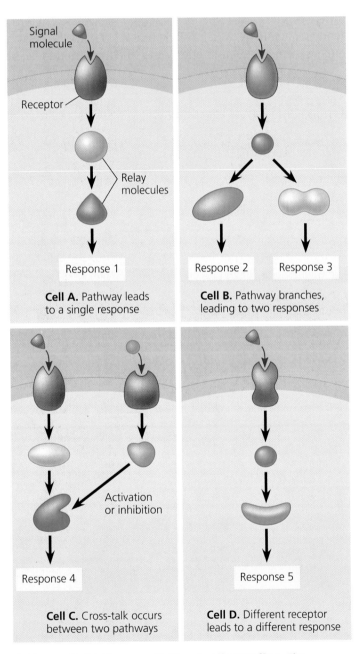

▲ Figure 11.15 **The specificity of cell signaling.** The particular proteins a cell possesses determine what signal molecules it responds to and the nature of the response. The four cells in these diagrams respond to the same signal molecule (orange) in different ways because each has a different set of proteins (purple and teal shapes). Note, however, that the same kinds of molecules can participate in more than one pathway.

Signaling Efficiency: Scaffolding Proteins and Signaling Complexes

The signaling pathways in Figure 11.15 (as well as some of the other pathway depictions in this chapter) are greatly simplified. The diagrams show only a few relay molecules and, for clarity's sake, display these molecules spread out in the cytosol. If this were true in the cell, signaling pathways would operate very inefficiently because most relay molecules are proteins, and proteins are too large to diffuse quickly through the viscous cytosol. How does a particular protein kinase, for instance, find its substrate?

Recent research suggests that the efficiency of signal transduction may in many cases be increased by the presence of **scaffolding proteins**, large relay proteins to which several other relay proteins are simultaneously attached. For example, one scaffolding protein isolated from mouse brain cells holds three protein kinases and carries these kinases with it when it binds to an appropriately activated membrane receptor; it thus facilitates a specific phosphorylation cascade **(Figure 11.16)**. In fact, researchers are finding scaffolding proteins in brain cells that *permanently* hold together networks of signaling-pathway proteins at synapses. This hardwiring enhances the speed and accuracy of signal transfer between cells.

When signaling pathways were first discovered, they were thought to be linear, independent pathways. Our understanding of the processes of cellular communication has benefited from the realization that things are not that simple. In fact, as seen in Figure 11.15, some proteins may participate in more than one pathway, either in different cell types or in the same cell at different times or under different conditions. This view underscores the importance of permanent or transient protein complexes in the functioning of a cell.

The importance of the relay proteins that serve as points of branching or intersection in signaling pathways is highlighted by the problems arising when these proteins are defective or missing. For instance, in an inherited disorder called Wiskott-Aldrich syndrome (WAS), the absence of a single relay protein leads to such diverse effects as abnormal bleeding, eczema, and a predisposition to infections and leukemia. These symptoms are thought to arise primarily from the absence of the protein in cells of the immune system. By studying normal cells, scientists found that the WAS protein is located just beneath the cell surface. The protein interacts both with microfilaments of the cytoskeleton and with several different components of signaling pathways that relay information from the cell surface, including pathways regulating immune cell proliferation. This multifunctional relay protein is thus both a branch point and an important intersection point in a complex signal transduction network that controls immune cell behavior. When the WAS protein is absent, the cytoskeleton is not properly organized and signaling pathways are disrupted, leading to the WAS symptoms.

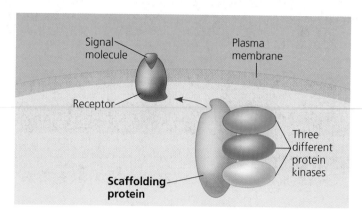

▲ **Figure 11.16 A scaffolding protein.** The scaffolding protein shown here (pink) simultaneously binds to a specific activated membrane receptor and three different protein kinases. This physical arrangement facilitates signal transduction by these molecules.

Termination of the Signal

To keep Figure 11.15 simple, we have not indicated the *inactivation* mechanisms that are an essential aspect of cell signaling. For a cell of a multicellular organism to remain alert and capable of responding to incoming signals, each molecular change in its signaling pathways must last only a short time. As we saw in the cholera example, if a signaling pathway component becomes locked into one state, whether active or inactive, dire consequences for the organism can result.

Thus, a key to a cell's continuing receptiveness to regulation is the reversibility of the changes that signals produce. The binding of signal molecules to receptors is reversible, with the result that the lower the concentration of signal molecules, the fewer will be bound at any given moment. When signal molecules leave the receptor, the receptor reverts to its inactive form. Then, by a variety of means, the relay molecules return to their inactive forms: The GTPase activity intrinsic to a G protein hydrolyzes its bound GTP; the enzyme phosphodiesterase converts cAMP to AMP; protein phosphatases inactivate phosphorylated kinases and other proteins; and so forth. As a result, the cell is soon ready to respond to a fresh signal.

This chapter has introduced you to many of the general mechanisms of cell communication, such as ligand binding, conformational changes, cascades of interactions, and protein phosphorylation. As you continue through the text, you will encounter numerous examples of cell signaling.

Concept Check 11.4

1. How can a target cell's response to a hormone be amplified more than a millionfold?
2. Explain how two cells with different scaffolding proteins could behave differently in response to the same signaling molecule.

For suggested answers, see Appendix A.

Go to the Campbell Biology website (**www.campbellbiology.com**) or CD-ROM to explore Activities, Investigations, and other interactive study aids.

SUMMARY OF KEY CONCEPTS

Concept 11.1

External signals are converted into responses within the cell

▶ **Evolution of Cell Signaling** (**pp. 201–202**) Signaling in microbes has much in common with processes in multicellular organisms, suggesting an early origin.

▶ **Local and Long-Distance Signaling** (**pp. 202–203**) In local signaling, animal cells may communicate by direct contact or by secreting local regulators, such as growth factors or neurotransmitters. For signaling over long distances, both animals and plants use hormones; animals also signal along nerve cells.
Investigation *How Do Cells Communicate with Each Other?*

▶ **The Three Stages of Cell Signaling:** *A Preview* (**pp. 203–204**) Earl Sutherland discovered how the hormone epinephrine acts on cells. The signal molecule epinephrine binds to receptors on a cell's surface (reception), leading to a series of changes in the receptor and other molecules inside the cell (transduction) and finally to the activation of an enzyme that breaks down glycogen (response).
Activity *Overview of Cell Signaling*

Concept 11.2

Reception: A signal molecule binds to a receptor protein, causing it to change shape

▶ The binding between signal molecule (ligand) and receptor is highly specific. A conformational change in a receptor is often the initial transduction of the signal (**pp. 204–205**).

▶ **Intracellular Receptors** (**p. 205**) Intracellular receptors are cytoplasmic or nuclear proteins. Signal molecules that are small or hydrophobic and can readily cross the plasma membrane use these receptors.

▶ **Receptors in the Plasma Membrane** (**pp. 205–208**) A G-protein-linked receptor is a membrane receptor that works with the help of a cytoplasmic G protein. Ligand binding activates the receptor, which then activates a specific G protein, which activates yet another protein, thus propagating the signal along a signal transduction pathway.
Receptor tyrosine kinases react to the binding of signal molecules by forming dimers and then adding phosphate groups to tyrosines on the cytoplasmic side of the other subunit of the receptor. Relay proteins in the cell can then be activated by binding to different phosphorylated tyrosines, allowing this receptor to trigger several pathways at once.
Specific signal molecules cause ligand-gated ion channels in a membrane to open or close, regulating the flow of specific ions.
Activity *Reception*

Concept 11.3

Transduction: Cascades of molecular interactions relay signals from receptors to target molecules in the cell

▶ **Signal Transduction Pathways** (**p. 208**) At each step in a pathway, the signal is transduced into a different form, commonly a conformational change in a protein.

▶ **Protein Phosphorylation and Dephosphorylation** (**pp. 209–210**) Many signal transduction pathways include phosphorylation cascades, in which a series of protein kinases each add a phosphate group to the next one in line, activating it. Phosphatase enzymes soon remove the phosphates.

▶ **Small Molecules and Ions as Second Messengers** (**pp. 210–212**) Second messengers, such as cyclic AMP (cAMP) and Ca^{2+}, diffuse readily through the cytosol and thus help broadcast signals quickly. Many G proteins activate adenylyl cyclase, which makes cAMP from ATP. Cells use Ca^{2+} as a second messenger in both G-protein and tyrosine kinase pathways. The tyrosine kinase pathways can also involve two other second messengers, DAG and IP_3. IP_3 can trigger a subsequent increase in Ca^{2+} levels.
Activity *Signal Transduction Pathways*

Concept 11.4

Response: Cell signaling leads to regulation of cytoplasmic activities or transcription

▶ **Cytoplasmic and Nuclear Responses** (**pp. 212–213**) In the cytoplasm, signaling pathways regulate, for example, enzyme activity and cytoskeleton rearrangement. Other pathways regulate genes by activating transcription factors, proteins that turn specific genes on or off.
Activity *Cellular Responses*
Activity *Build a Signaling Pathway*

▶ **Fine-Tuning of the Response** (**pp. 213–215**) Each catalytic protein in a signaling pathway amplifies the signal by activating multiple copies of the next component of the pathway; for long pathways, the total amplification may be a millionfold or more. The particular combination of proteins in a cell gives the cell great specificity in both the signals it detects and the responses it carries out. Scaffolding proteins can increase signal transduction efficiency. Pathway branching and cross-talk further help the cell coordinate incoming signals. Signal response is terminated quickly by the reversal of ligand binding.

TESTING YOUR KNOWLEDGE

Self-Quiz

1. Phosphorylation cascades involving a series of protein kinases are useful for cellular signal transduction because
   a. they are species specific.
   b. they always lead to the same cellular response.
   c. they amplify the original signal manyfold.
   d. they counter the harmful effects of phosphatases.
   e. the number of molecules used is small and fixed.

2. Binding of a signal molecule to which type of receptor leads directly to a change in the distribution of anions and/or cations on opposite sides of the membrane?
   a. receptor tyrosine kinase
   b. G-protein-linked receptor
   c. phosphorylated receptor tyrosine kinase dimer
   d. ligand-gated ion channel
   e. intracellular receptor

3. The activation of receptor tyrosine kinases is always characterized by
   a. dimerization and phosphorylation.
   b. IP_3 binding.
   c. a phosphorylation cascade.
   d. GTP hydrolysis.
   e. channel protein conformational change.

4. Which of the following provides the best evidence that cell-signaling pathways evolved early in the history of life?
   a. They are seen in "primitive" cells such as yeast.
   b. Yeast cells signal each other for mating.
   c. Signal transduction molecules found in distantly related organisms are similar.
   d. Signals can be sent long distances by cells.
   e. Most signals are received by cell surface receptors.

5. Which observation suggested to Sutherland the involvement of a second messenger in epinephrine's effect on liver cells?
   a. Enzymatic activity was proportional to the amount of calcium added to a cell-free extract.
   b. Receptor studies indicated that epinephrine was a ligand.
   c. Glycogen breakdown was observed only when epinephrine was administered to intact cells.
   d. Glycogen breakdown was observed when epinephrine and glycogen phosphorylase were combined.
   e. Epinephrine was known to have different effects on different types of cells.

6. Protein phosphorylation is commonly involved with all of the following *except*
   a. regulation of transcription by extracellular signal molecules.
   b. enzyme activation.
   c. activation of G-protein-linked receptors.
   d. activation of receptor tyrosine kinases.
   e. activation of protein kinase molecules.

7. Amplification of a chemical signal occurs when
   a. a receptor in the plasma membrane activates several G-protein molecules while a signal molecule is bound to it.
   b. a cAMP molecule activates one protein kinase molecule before being converted to AMP.
   c. phosphorylase and phosphatase activities are balanced.
   d. receptor tyrosine kinases dimerize upon ligand binding.
   e. both a and d occur.

8. Lipid-soluble signal molecules, such as testosterone, cross the membranes of all cells but affect only target cells because
   a. only target cells retain the appropriate DNA segments.
   b. intracellular receptors are present only in target cells.
   c. most cells lack the Y chromosome required.
   d. only target cells possess the cytosolic enzymes that transduce the testosterone.
   e. only in target cells is testosterone able to initiate the phosphorylation cascade leading to activated transcription factor.

9. Signal transduction pathways benefit cells for all of the following reasons *except*
   a. they help cells respond to signal molecules that are too large or too polar to cross the plasma membrane.
   b. they enable different cells to respond appropriately to the same signal.
   c. they help cells use up phosphate generated by ATP breakdown.
   d. they can amplify a signal.
   e. variations in the signal transduction pathways can enhance response specificity.

10. Consider this pathway: epinephrine → G-protein-linked receptor → G protein → adenylyl cyclase → cAMP. Identify the second messenger.
    a. cAMP
    b. G protein
    c. GTP
    d. adenylyl cyclase
    e. G-protein-linked receptor

For Self-Quiz answers, see Appendix A.

Go to the website or CD-ROM for more quiz questions.

Evolution Connection

You learned in this chapter that cell-to-cell signaling is thought to have arisen early in the history of life, because the same mechanisms of signaling are found in distantly related organisms. But why hasn't some "better" mechanism arisen? Is it too difficult to evolve wholly new signaling mechanisms, or are existing mechanisms simply adequate and therefore maintained? Put another way, do superior signaling mechanisms need to evolve if existing mechanisms are adequate and effective? Why or why not?

Scientific Inquiry

Epinephrine initiates a signal transduction pathway that involves production of cyclic AMP (cAMP) and leads to the breakdown of glycogen to glucose, a major energy source for cells. But glycogen breakdown is actually only part of a "fight-or-flight response" that epinephrine brings about; the overall effect on the body includes increased heart rate and alertness, as well as a burst of energy. Given that caffeine blocks the activity of cAMP phosphodiesterase, propose a mechanism by which caffeine ingestion leads to heightened alertness and sleeplessness.

Investigation *How Do Cells Communicate with Each Other?*

Science, Technology, and Society

The aging process is thought to be initiated at the cellular level. Among the changes that can occur after a certain number of cell divisions is the loss of a cell's ability to respond to growth factors and other chemical signals. Much research into aging is aimed at understanding such losses, with the ultimate goal of significantly extending the human life span. Not everyone, however, agrees that this is a desirable goal. If life expectancy were greatly increased, what might be the social and ecological consequences? How might we cope with them?

12

The Cell Cycle

▲ **Figure 12.1** **Chromosomes in a dividing cell.**

Key Concepts

12.1 Cell division results in genetically identical daughter cells

12.2 The mitotic phase alternates with interphase in the cell cycle

12.3 The cell cycle is regulated by a molecular control system

Overview

The Key Roles of Cell Division

The ability of organisms to reproduce their own kind is the one characteristic that best distinguishes living things from nonliving matter. This unique capacity to procreate, like all biological functions, has a cellular basis. Rudolf Virchow, a German physician, put it this way in 1855: "Where a cell exists, there must have been a preexisting cell, just as the animal arises only from an animal and the plant only from a plant." He summarized this concept with the Latin axiom *"Omnis cellula e cellula,"* meaning "Every cell from a cell." The continuity of life is based on the reproduction of cells, or **cell division**. The series of fluorescence micrographs in **Figure 12.1** follows an animal cell's chromosomes, from lower left to lower right, as one cell divides into two.

Cell division plays several important roles in the life of an organism. When a unicellular organism, such as an amoeba, divides and forms duplicate offspring, the division of one cell reproduces an entire organism **(Figure 12.2a)**. Cell division on a larger scale can produce progeny from some multicellular organisms (such as plants that grow from cuttings). Cell division also enables sexually reproducing organisms to develop from a single cell—the fertilized egg, or zygote **(Figure 12.2b)**. And after an organism is fully grown, cell division continues to function in renewal and repair, replacing cells that die from normal wear and tear or accidents. For example, dividing cells in your bone marrow continuously make new blood cells **(Figure 12.2c)**.

100 µm	200 µm	20 µm

(a) Reproduction. An amoeba, a single-celled eukaryote, is dividing into two cells. Each new cell will be an individual organism (LM).

(b) Growth and development. This micrograph shows a sand dollar embryo shortly after the fertilized egg divided, forming two cells (LM).

(c) Tissue renewal. These dividing bone marrow cells (arrow) will give rise to new blood cells (LM).

▲ **Figure 12.2** **The functions of cell division.**

The cell division process is an integral part of the **cell cycle**, the life of a cell from the time it is first formed from a dividing parent cell until its own division into two cells. Passing identical genetic material to cellular offspring is a crucial function of cell division. In this chapter, you will learn how cell division distributes identical genetic material to daughter cells.* After studying the cellular mechanics of cell division, you will learn about the molecular control system that regulates progress through the cell cycle and what happens when the control system malfunctions. Because cell cycle regulation, or a lack thereof, plays a major role in cancer development, this aspect of cell biology is an active area of research.

Concept 12.1

Cell division results in genetically identical daughter cells

The reproduction of an ensemble as complex as a cell cannot occur by a mere pinching in half; a cell is not like a soap bubble that simply enlarges and splits in two. Cell division involves the distribution of identical genetic material—DNA—to two daughter cells. What is most remarkable about cell division is the fidelity with which the DNA is passed along from one generation of cells to the next. A dividing cell duplicates its DNA, allocates the two copies to opposite ends of the cell, and only then splits into daughter cells.

Cellular Organization of the Genetic Material

A cell's endowment of DNA, its genetic information, is called its **genome**. Although a prokaryotic genome is often a single long DNA molecule, eukaryotic genomes usually consist of a number of DNA molecules. The overall length of DNA in a eukaryotic cell is enormous. A typical human cell, for example, has about 2 m of DNA—a length about 250,000 times greater than the cell's diameter. Yet before the cell can divide, all of this DNA must be copied and then the two copies separated so that each daughter cell ends up with a complete genome.

The replication and distribution of so much DNA is manageable because the DNA molecules are packaged into **chromosomes**, so named because they take up certain dyes used in microscopy (from the Greek *chroma*, color, and *soma*, body) **(Figure 12.3)**. Every eukaryotic species has a characteristic number of chromosomes in each cell nucleus. For example, the nuclei of human **somatic cells** (all body cells except the reproductive cells) each contain 46 chromosomes made up of two sets of 23, one set inherited from each parent.

---

* Although the terms *daughter cells* and *sister chromatids* (a term you will encounter later in the chapter) are traditional and will be used throughout this book, the structures they refer to have no gender.

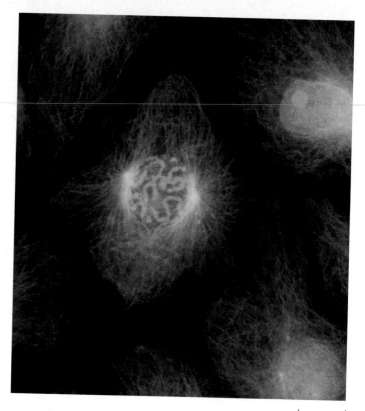

50 μm

▲ **Figure 12.3 Eukaryotic chromosomes.** Chromosomes (stained orange) are visible within the nucleus of the kangaroo rat epithelial cell in the center of this micrograph. The cell is preparing to divide (LM).

Reproductive cells, or **gametes**—sperm cells and egg cells—have half as many chromosomes as somatic cells, or one set of 23 chromosomes in humans.

Eukaryotic chromosomes are made of **chromatin**, a complex of DNA and associated protein molecules. Each single chromosome contains one very long, linear DNA molecule that carries several hundred to a few thousand genes, the units that specify an organism's inherited traits. The associated proteins maintain the structure of the chromosome and help control the activity of the genes.

Distribution of Chromosomes During Cell Division

When a cell is not dividing, and even as it duplicates its DNA in preparation for cell division, each chromosome is in the form of a long, thin chromatin fiber. After DNA duplication, however, the chromosomes condense: Each chromatin fiber becomes densely coiled and folded, making the chromosomes much shorter and so thick that we can see them with a light microscope.

Each duplicated chromosome has two **sister chromatids**. The two chromatids, each containing an identical DNA molecule, are initially attached by adhesive proteins all along their lengths. In its condensed form, the duplicated chromosome

▶ **Figure 12.4 Chromosome duplication and distribution during cell division.** A eukaryotic cell preparing to divide duplicates each of its chromosomes. The micrograph shows a duplicated human chromosome (SEM). The copies of each chromosome are then distributed to two daughter cells during cell division. (Chromosomes normally exist in the highly condensed state shown here only during the process of cell division; the chromosomes in the top and bottom cells are shown in condensed form for illustration purposes only.)

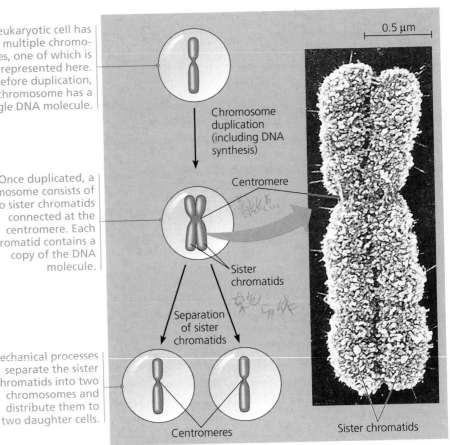

A eukaryotic cell has multiple chromosomes, one of which is represented here. Before duplication, each chromosome has a single DNA molecule.

Chromosome duplication (including DNA synthesis)

Once duplicated, a chromosome consists of two sister chromatids connected at the centromere. Each chromatid contains a copy of the DNA molecule.

Centromere

Sister chromatids

Separation of sister chromatids

Mechanical processes separate the sister chromatids into two chromosomes and distribute them to two daughter cells.

Centromeres

Sister chromatids

0.5 μm

has a narrow "waist" at a specialized region called the **centromere** where the two chromatids are most closely attached **(Figure 12.4)**. Later in the cell division process, the two sister chromatids of each duplicated chromosome separate and move into two new nuclei, one at each end of the cell. Once the sister chromatids separate, they are considered individual chromosomes. Thus, each new nucleus receives a group of chromosomes identical to the original group in the parent cell. **Mitosis,** the division of the nucleus, is usually followed immediately by **cytokinesis,** the division of the cytoplasm. Where there was one cell, there are now two, each the genetic equivalent of the parent cell.

What happens to chromosome number as we follow the human life cycle through the generations? You inherited 46 chromosomes, one set of 23 from each parent. They were combined in the nucleus of a single cell when a sperm cell from your father united with an egg cell from your mother, forming a fertilized egg, or zygote. Mitosis and cytokinesis produced the 200 trillion somatic cells that now make up your body, and the same processes continue to generate new cells to replace dead and damaged ones. In contrast, you produce gametes—eggs or sperm cells—by a variation of cell division called **meiosis,** which yields nonidentical daughter cells that have only one set of chromosomes, thus half as many as the parent cell. Meiosis occurs only in your gonads (ovaries or testes). In each generation of

humans, meiosis reduces the chromosome number from 46 (two sets of chromosomes) to 23 (one set). Fertilization fuses two gametes together and returns the chromosome number to 46, and mitosis conserves that number in every somatic cell nucleus of the new individual. In Chapter 13, we will examine the role of meiosis in reproduction and inheritance in more detail. In the remainder of this chapter, we focus on mitosis and the rest of the cell cycle.

Concept Check 12.1

1. Starting with a fertilized egg (zygote), a series of five cell divisions would produce an early embryo with how many cells?
2. How many chromatids are in a duplicated chromosome?
3. A chicken has 78 chromosomes in its somatic cells; how many chromosomes did the chicken inherit from each parent? How many chromosomes are in each of the chicken's gametes? How many chromosomes will be in each somatic cell of the chicken's offspring? How many chromosomes are in a "set"?

For suggested answers, see Appendix A.

Concept 12.2

The mitotic phase alternates with interphase in the cell cycle

In 1882, a German anatomist named Walther Flemming developed dyes that allowed him to observe, for the first time, the behavior of chromosomes during mitosis and cytokinesis. (In fact, Flemming coined the terms *mitosis* and *chromatin*.) During the period between one cell division and the next, it appeared to Flemming that the cell was simply growing larger. But we now know that many critical events occur during this stage in the life of a cell.

Phases of the Cell Cycle

Mitosis is just one part of the cell cycle **(Figure 12.5)**. In fact, the **mitotic (M) phase,** which includes both mitosis and cytokinesis, is usually the shortest part of the cell cycle. Mitotic cell division alternates with a much longer stage called **interphase,** which often accounts for about 90% of the cycle. It is during interphase that the cell grows and copies its chromosomes in preparation for cell division. Interphase can be divided into subphases: the **G₁ phase** ("first gap"), the **S phase** ("synthesis"), and the **G₂ phase** ("second gap"). During all three subphases, the cell grows by producing proteins and cytoplasmic organelles such as mitochondria and endoplasmic reticulum. However, chromosomes are duplicated only during the S phase (we discuss synthesis of DNA in Chapter 16). Thus, a cell grows (G₁), continues to grow as it copies its chromosomes (S), grows more as it completes preparations for cell division (G₂), and divides (M). The daughter cells may then repeat the cycle.

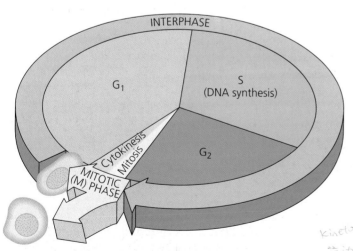

▲ **Figure 12.5 The cell cycle.** In a dividing cell, the mitotic (M) phase alternates with interphase, a growth period. The first part of interphase, called G₁, is followed by the S phase, when the chromosomes replicate; the last part of interphase is called G₂. In the M phase, mitosis divides the nucleus and distributes its chromosomes to the daughter nuclei, and cytokinesis divides the cytoplasm, producing two daughter cells.

A typical human cell might undergo one division in 24 hours. Of this time, the M phase would occupy less than 1 hour, while the S phase might occupy about 10–12 hours, or about half the cycle. The rest of the time would be apportioned between the G₁ and G₂ phases. The G₂ phase usually takes 4–6 hours; in our example, G₁ would occupy about 5–6 hours. G₁ is the most variable in length in different types of cells.

Time-lapse films of living, dividing cells reveal the dynamics of mitosis as a continuum of changes. For purposes of description, however, mitosis is conventionally broken down into five stages: **prophase, prometaphase, metaphase, anaphase,** and **telophase.** Overlapping with the latter stages of mitosis, cytokinesis completes the mitotic phase. **Figure 12.6**, on the next two pages, describes these stages in an animal cell. Be sure to study this figure thoroughly before progressing to the next two sections, which examine mitosis and cytokinesis more closely.

The Mitotic Spindle: *A Closer Look*

Many of the events of mitosis depend on the **mitotic spindle,** which begins to form in the cytoplasm during prophase. This structure consists of fibers made of microtubules and associated proteins. While the mitotic spindle assembles, the other microtubules of the cytoskeleton partially disassemble, probably providing the material used to construct the spindle. The spindle microtubules elongate by incorporating more subunits of the protein tubulin (see Table 6.1).

The assembly of spindle microtubules starts at the **centrosome,** a nonmembranous organelle that functions throughout the cell cycle to organize the cell's microtubules (it is also called the *microtubule-organizing center*). In animal cells, a pair of centrioles is located at the center of the centrosome, but the centrioles are not essential for cell division. In fact, the centrosomes of most plants lack centrioles, and if the centrioles of an animal cell are destroyed with a laser microbeam, a spindle nevertheless forms during mitosis.

During interphase, the single centrosome replicates, forming two centrosomes, which remain together near the nucleus (see Figure 12.6). The two centrosomes move apart from each other during prophase and prometaphase of mitosis, as spindle microtubules grow out from them. By the end of prometaphase, the two centrosomes, one at each pole of the spindle, are at opposite ends of the cell. An **aster,** a radial array of short microtubules, extends from each centrosome. The spindle includes the centrosomes, the spindle microtubules, and the asters.

Each of the two sister chromatids of a chromosome has a **kinetochore,** a structure of proteins associated with specific sections of chromosomal DNA at the centromere. The chromosome's two kinetochores face in opposite directions. During prometaphase, some of the spindle microtubules attach to the kinetochores; these are called kinetochore microtubules. (The number of microtubules attached to a kinetochore varies

Figure 12.6

Exploring The Mitotic Division of an Animal Cell

G₂ OF INTERPHASE	PROPHASE	PROMETAPHASE

Centrosomes (with centriole pairs) — Chromatin (duplicated)

Early mitotic spindle — Aster — Centromere

Fragments of nuclear envelope — Kinetochore — Nonkinetochore microtubules

Nucleolus — Nuclear envelope — Plasma membrane

Chromosome, consisting of two sister chromatids

Kinetochore microtubule

G₂ of Interphase

► A nuclear envelope bounds the nucleus.
► The nucleus contains one or more nucleoli (singular, *nucleolus*).
► Two centrosomes have formed by replication of a single centrosome.
► In animal cells, each centrosome features two centrioles.
► Chromosomes, duplicated during S phase, cannot be seen individually because they have not yet condensed.

The light micrographs show dividing lung cells from a newt, which has 22 chromosomes in its somatic cells (chromosomes appear blue, microtubules green, intermediate filaments red). For simplicity, the drawings show only four chromosomes.

Prophase

► The chromatin fibers become more tightly coiled, condensing into discrete chromosomes observable with a light microscope.
► The nucleoli disappear.
► Each duplicated chromosome appears as two identical sister chromatids joined together.
► The mitotic spindle begins to form. It is composed of the centrosomes and the microtubules that extend from them. The radial arrays of shorter microtubules that extend from the centrosomes are called asters ("stars").
► The centrosomes move away from each other, apparently propelled by the lengthening microtubules between them.

Prometaphase (no nuclear envelope)

► The nuclear envelope fragments.
► The microtubules of the spindle can now invade the nuclear area and interact with the chromosomes, which have become even more condensed.
► Microtubules extend from each centrosome toward the middle of the cell.
► Each of the two chromatids of a chromosome now has a kinetochore, a specialized protein structure located at the centromere.
► Some of the microtubules attach to the kinetochores, becoming "kinetochore microtubules." These kinetochore microtubules jerk the chromosomes back and forth.
► Nonkinetochore microtubules interact with those from the opposite pole of the spindle.

10 μm

| **METAPHASE** | **ANAPHASE** | **TELOPHASE AND CYTOKINESIS** |

Metaphase plate

Spindle

Centrosome at one spindle pole

Daughter chromosomes

Cleavage furrow

Nucleolus forming

Nuclear envelope forming

Metaphase

▶ Metaphase is the longest stage of mitosis, lasting about 20 minutes.

▶ The centrosomes are now at opposite ends of the cell.

▶ The chromosomes convene on the metaphase plate, an imaginary plane that is equidistant between the spindle's two poles. The chromosomes' centromeres lie on the metaphase plate.

▶ For each chromosome, the kinetochores of the sister chromatids are attached to kinetochore microtubules coming from opposite poles.

▶ The entire apparatus of microtubules is called the spindle because of its shape.

Anaphase

▶ Anaphase is the shortest stage of mitosis, lasting only a few minutes.

▶ Anaphase begins when the two sister chromatids of each pair suddenly part. Each chromatid thus becomes a full-fledged chromosome.

▶ The two liberated chromosomes begin moving toward opposite ends of the cell, as their kinetochore microtubules shorten. Because these microtubules are attached at the centromere region, the chromosomes move centromere first (at about 1 μm/min).

▶ The cell elongates as the nonkinetochore microtubules lengthen.

▶ By the end of anaphase, the two ends of the cell have equivalent—and complete—collections of chromosomes.

Telophase

▶ Two daughter nuclei begin to form in the cell.

▶ Nuclear envelopes arise from the fragments of the parent cell's nuclear envelope and other portions of the endomembrane system.

▶ The chromosomes become less condensed.

▶ Mitosis, the division of one nucleus into two genetically identical nuclei, is now complete.

Cytokinesis

▶ The division of the cytoplasm is usually well underway by late telophase, so the two daughter cells appear shortly after the end of mitosis.

▶ In animal cells, cytokinesis involves the formation of a cleavage furrow, which pinches the cell in two.

among species, from one microtubule in yeast cells to 40 or so in some mammalian cells.) When one of a chromosome's kinetochores is "captured" by microtubules, the chromosome begins to move toward the pole from which those microtubules extend. However, this movement is checked as soon as microtubules from the opposite pole attach to the other kinetochore.

▲ **Figure 12.7 The mitotic spindle at metaphase.** The kinetochores of a chromosome's two sister chromatids face in opposite directions. Here, each kinetochore is actually attached to a *cluster* of kinetochore microtubules extending from the nearest centrosome. Nonkinetochore microtubules overlap at the metaphase plate (TEMs).

What happens next is like a tug-of-war that ends in a draw. The chromosome moves first in one direction, then the other, back and forth, finally settling midway between the two ends of the cell. At metaphase, the centromeres of all the duplicated chromosomes are on a plane midway between the spindle's two poles. This imaginary plane is called the **metaphase plate** of the cell **(Figure 12.7)**. Meanwhile, microtubules that do not attach to kinetochores have been growing, and by metaphase they overlap and interact with other nonkinetochore microtubules from the opposite pole of the spindle. (These are sometimes called "polar" microtubules.) By metaphase, the microtubules of the asters have also grown and are in contact with the plasma membrane. The spindle is now complete.

Let's now see how the structure of the completed spindle correlates with its function during anaphase. Anaphase commences suddenly when proteins holding together the sister chromatids of each chromosome are inactivated. Once the chromatids become separate, full-fledged chromosomes, they move toward opposite ends of the cell. How do the kinetochore microtubules function in this poleward movement of chromosomes? One possibility is that the chromosomes are "reeled in" by microtubules that are shortening at the spindle poles. However, experimental evidence supports the hypothesis that the primary mechanism of movement involves motor proteins on the kinetochores that "walk" a chromosome along the attached microtubules toward the nearest pole. Meanwhile, the microtubules shorten by depolymerizing at their kinetochore ends **(Figure 12.8)**. (To review how motor proteins move an object along a microtubule, see Figure 6.21.)

What is the function of the *non*kinetochore microtubules? In a dividing animal cell, these microtubules are responsible for elongating the whole cell during anaphase. Nonkinetochore microtubules from opposite poles overlap each other extensively during metaphase (see Figure 12.7). During anaphase, the region of overlap is reduced as motor proteins attached to the microtubules walk them away from one another, using energy from ATP. As the microtubules push apart from each other, their spindle poles are pushed apart, elongating the cell. At the same time, the microtubules lengthen somewhat by the addition of tubulin subunits to their overlapping ends. As a result, the microtubules continue to overlap.

At the end of anaphase, duplicate groups of chromosomes have arrived at opposite ends of the elongated parent cell. Nuclei re-form during telophase. Cytokinesis generally begins during these later stages of mitosis, and the spindle eventually disassembles.

Cytokinesis: *A Closer Look*

In animal cells, cytokinesis occurs by a process known as **cleavage.** The first sign of cleavage is the appearance of a **cleavage furrow,** a shallow groove in the cell surface near the old metaphase plate **(Figure 12.9a)**. On the cytoplasmic side of

Figure 12.8

Inquiry During anaphase, do kinetochore microtubules shorten at their spindle pole ends or their kinetochore ends?

EXPERIMENT

① The microtubules of a cell in early anaphase were labeled with a fluorescent dye that glows in the microscope (yellow).

② A laser was used to mark the kinetochore microtubules by eliminating the fluorescence in a region between one spindle pole and the chromosomes. As anaphase proceeded, researchers monitored the changes in the lengths of the microtubules on either side of the mark.

RESULTS   As the chromosomes moved toward the poles, the microtubule segments on the kinetochore side of the laser mark shortened, while those on the spindle pole side stayed the same length.

CONCLUSION   This experiment demonstrated that during anaphase, kinetochore microtubules shorten at their kinetochore ends, not at their spindle pole ends. This is just one of the experiments supporting the hypothesis that during anaphase, a chromosome tracks along a microtubule as the microtubule depolymerizes at its kinetochore end, releasing tubulin subunits.

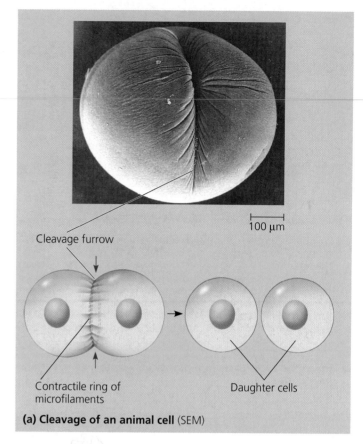

Cleavage furrow

Contractile ring of microfilaments

Daughter cells

(a) Cleavage of an animal cell (SEM)

Vesicles forming cell plate

Wall of parent cell

Cell plate

New cell wall

Daughter cells

(b) Cell plate formation in a plant cell (TEM)

▲ **Figure 12.9 Cytokinesis in animal and plant cells.**

① **Prophase.** The chromatin is condensing. The nucleolus is beginning to disappear. Although not yet visible in the micrograph, the mitotic spindle is starting to form.

② **Prometaphase.** We now see discrete chromosomes; each consists of two identical sister chromatids. Later in prometaphase, the nuclear envelope will fragment.

③ **Metaphase.** The spindle is complete, and the chromosomes, attached to microtubules at their kinetochores, are all at the metaphase plate.

④ **Anaphase.** The chromatids of each chromosome have separated, and the daughter chromosomes are moving to the ends of the cell as their kinetochore micro-tubules shorten.

⑤ **Telophase.** Daughter nuclei are forming. Meanwhile, cytokinesis has started: The cell plate, which will divide the cytoplasm in two, is growing toward the perimeter of the parent cell.

▲ **Figure 12.10 Mitosis in a plant cell.** These light micrographs show mitosis in cells of an onion root.

the furrow is a contractile ring of actin microfilaments associated with molecules of the protein myosin. (Actin and myosin are the same proteins that are responsible for muscle contraction as well as many other kinds of cell movement.) The actin microfilaments interact with the myosin molecules, causing the ring to contract. The contraction of the dividing cell's ring of microfilaments is like the pulling of drawstrings. The cleavage furrow deepens until the parent cell is pinched in two, producing two completely separated cells, each with its own nucleus and share of cytosol and organelles.

Cytokinesis in plant cells, which have cell walls, is markedly different. There is no cleavage furrow. Instead, during telophase, vesicles derived from the Golgi apparatus move along microtubules to the middle of the cell, where they coalesce, producing a **cell plate (Figure 12.9b)**. Cell wall materials carried in the vesicles collect in the cell plate as it grows. The cell plate enlarges until its surrounding membrane fuses with the plasma membrane along the perimeter of the cell. Two daughter cells result, each with its own plasma membrane. Meanwhile, a new cell wall arising from the contents of the cell plate has formed between the daughter cells.

Figure 12.10 is a series of micrographs of a dividing plant cell. Examining this figure will help you review mitosis and cytokinesis.

Binary Fission

Prokaryotes (bacteria) reproduce by a type of cell division called **binary fission**, meaning literally "division in half." Most bacterial genes are carried on a single *bacterial chromosome* that consists of a circular DNA molecule and associated proteins. Although bacteria are smaller and simpler than eukaryotic cells, the problem of replicating their genomes in an orderly fashion and distributing the copies equally to two daughter cells is still formidable. The chromosome of the bacterium *Escherichia coli*, for example, when it is fully stretched out, is about 500 times longer than the length of the cell. Clearly, such a long chromosome must be highly coiled and folded within the cell—and it is.

In *E. coli*, the process of cell division begins when the DNA of the bacterial chromosome begins to replicate at a specific place on the chromosome called the **origin of replication**, producing two origins. As the chromosome continues to replicate, one origin moves rapidly toward the opposite end of the cell **(Figure 12.11)**. While the chromosome is replicating, the cell elongates. When replication is complete and the bacterium has reached about twice its initial size, its plasma membrane grows inward, dividing the parent *E. coli* cell into two daughter cells. Each cell inherits a complete genome.

Using the techniques of modern DNA technology to tag the origins of replication with molecules that glow green in fluorescence microscopy (see Figure 6.3), researchers have directly observed the movement of bacterial chromosomes. This movement is reminiscent of the poleward movements of the centromere regions of eukaryotic chromosomes during anaphase of mitosis, but bacteria don't have visible mitotic spindles or even microtubules. In most bacterial species studied, the two origins of replication end up at opposite ends of the cell or in some other very specific location, possibly anchored there by one or more proteins. How bacterial chromosomes move and how their specific location is established and maintained are

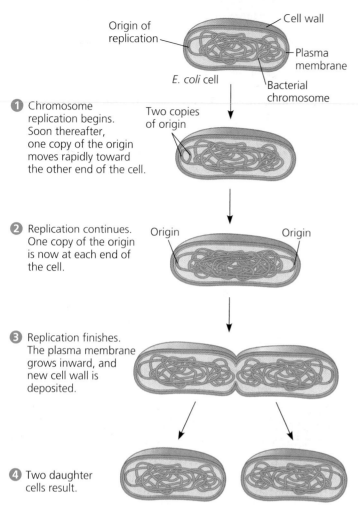

Origin of replication

Cell wall

E. coli cell

Plasma membrane

Bacterial chromosome

Two copies of origin

1 Chromosome replication begins. Soon thereafter, one copy of the origin moves rapidly toward the other end of the cell.

2 Replication continues. One copy of the origin is now at each end of the cell.

Origin

Origin

3 Replication finishes. The plasma membrane grows inward, and new cell wall is deposited.

4 Two daughter cells result.

▲ **Figure 12.11 Bacterial cell division (binary fission).** The example shown here is the bacterium *E. coli*. The single, circular chromosome replicates, and the two copies move apart by an unknown mechanism, so that the two origins of replication (green) end up at opposite ends of the cell. Meanwhile, the cell elongates. When chromosomal replication is complete, the plasma membrane grows inward, dividing the cell in two as a new cell wall is deposited between the daughter cells.

becoming clearer but are still not fully understood. Several proteins have been identified that play important roles.

The Evolution of Mitosis

How did mitosis evolve? Given that prokaryotes preceded eukaryotes on Earth by billions of years, we might hypothesize that mitosis had its origins in simpler bacterial mechanisms of cell reproduction. In fact, some of the proteins involved in bacterial binary fission are related to eukaryotic proteins, strengthening the case for the evolution of mitosis from bacterial cell division. Intriguingly, recent work has shown that two of the proteins involved in binary fission are related to eukaryotic tubulin and actin proteins.

As eukaryotes evolved, along with their larger genomes and nuclear envelopes, the ancestral process of binary fission somehow gave rise to mitosis. **Figure 12.12** traces a

Bacterial chromosome

(a) Prokaryotes. During binary fission, the origins of the daughter chromosomes move to opposite ends of the cell. The mechanism is not fully understood, but proteins may anchor the daughter chromosomes to specific sites on the plasma membrane.

Chromosomes

Microtubules

Intact nuclear envelope

(b) Dinoflagellates. In unicellular protists called dinoflagellates, the nuclear envelope remains intact during cell division, and the chromosomes attach to the nuclear envelope. Microtubules pass through the nucleus inside cytoplasmic tunnels, reinforcing the spatial orientation of the nucleus, which then divides in a fission process reminiscent of bacterial division.

Kinetochore microtubules

Intact nuclear envelope

(c) Diatoms. In another group of unicellular protists, the diatoms, the nuclear envelope also remains intact during cell division. But in these organisms, the microtubules form a spindle *within* the nucleus. Microtubules separate the chromosomes, and the nucleus splits into two daughter nuclei.

Kinetochore microtubules

Centrosome

Fragments of nuclear envelope

(d) Most eukaryotes. In most other eukaryotes, including plants and animals, the spindle forms outside the nucleus, and the nuclear envelope breaks down during mitosis. Microtubules separate the chromosomes, and the nuclear envelope then re-forms.

▲ **Figure 12.12 A hypothetical sequence for the evolution of mitosis.** In modern organisms, researchers have observed mechanisms of cell division that appear to be intermediate between the binary fission of bacteria (a) and mitosis as it occurs in most eukaryotes (d). Except for (a), these schematic diagrams do not show cell walls.

hypothesis for the stepwise evolution of mitosis. Possible intermediate stages are represented by two unusual types of nuclear division found in certain modern unicellular protists. These two examples of nuclear division are thought to be cases where ancestral mechanisms have remained relatively unchanged over evolutionary time. In both types, the nuclear envelope remains intact. In dinoflagellates, replicated chromosomes are attached to the nuclear envelope and separate as the nucleus elongates prior to cell division. In diatoms, a spindle within the nucleus separates the chromosomes. In most eukaryotic cells, the nuclear envelope breaks down and a spindle separates the chromosomes.

Concept Check 12.2

1. During which stages of a cell cycle would a chromosome consist of two identical chromatids?
2. How many chromosomes are shown in the Figure 12.7 diagram? How many chromatids are shown?
3. Compare cytokinesis in animal cells and plant cells.
4. What is a function of nonkinetochore microtubules?
5. Identify three similarities between bacterial chromosomes and eukaryotic chromosomes, considering both structure and behavior during cell division.

For suggested answers, see Appendix A.

Concept 12.3

The cell cycle is regulated by a molecular control system

The timing and rate of cell division in different parts of a plant or animal are crucial to normal growth, development, and maintenance. The frequency of cell division varies with the type of cell. For example, human skin cells divide frequently throughout life, whereas liver cells maintain the ability to divide but keep it in reserve until an appropriate need arises—say, to repair a wound. Some of the most specialized cells, such as mature, fully formed nerve cells and muscle cells, do not divide at all in a mature human. These cell cycle differences result from regulation at the molecular level. The mechanisms of this regulation are of intense interest, not only for understanding the life cycles of normal cells but also for understanding how cancer cells manage to escape the usual controls.

Evidence for Cytoplasmic Signals

What drives the cell cycle? One reasonable hypothesis might be that each event in the cycle triggers the next. According to this hypothesis, for example, the replication of chromosomes

in the S phase might cause cell growth during the G₂ phase, which might in turn directly trigger the onset of mitosis. However, this apparently logical hypothesis is not in fact correct.

In the early 1970s, a variety of experiments suggested an alternative hypothesis: that the cell cycle is driven by specific molecular signals present in the cytoplasm. Some of the first strong evidence for this hypothesis came from experiments with mammalian cells grown in culture. In these experiments, two cells in different phases of the cell cycle were fused to form a single cell with two nuclei. If one of the original cells was in the S phase and the other was in G_1, the G_1 nucleus immediately entered the S phase, as though stimulated by chemicals present in the cytoplasm of the first cell. Similarly, if a cell undergoing mitosis (M phase) was fused with another cell in any stage of its cell cycle, even G_1, the second nucleus immediately entered mitosis, with condensation of the chromatin and formation of a mitotic spindle **(Figure 12.13)**.

Figure 12.13

Inquiry **Are there molecular signals in the cytoplasm that regulate the cell cycle?**

EXPERIMENT In each experiment, cultured mammalian cells at two different phases of the cell cycle were induced to fuse.

Experiment 1   Experiment 2

S G_1 M G_1

RESULTS

S   S   M   M

When a cell in the S phase was fused with a cell in G_1, the G_1 cell immediately entered the S phase—DNA was synthesized.

When a cell in the M phase was fused with a cell in G_1, the G_1 cell immediately began mitosis—a spindle formed and chromatin condensed, even though the chromosome had not been duplicated.

CONCLUSION The results of fusing cells at two different phases of the cell cycle suggest that molecules present in the cytoplasm of cells in the S or M phase control the progression of phases.

The Cell Cycle Control System

The experiment shown in Figure 12.13 and other experiments demonstrated that the sequential events of the cell cycle are directed by a distinct **cell cycle control system,** a cyclically operating set of molecules in the cell that both triggers and coordinates key events in the cell cycle. The cell cycle control system has been compared to the control device of an automatic washing machine **(Figure 12.14)**. Like the washer's timing device, the cell cycle control system proceeds on its own, driven by a built-in clock. However, just as a washer's cycle is subject to both internal control (such as the sensor that detects when the tub is filled with water) and external adjustment (such as activation of the start mechanism), the cell cycle is regulated at certain checkpoints by both internal and external controls.

A **checkpoint** in the cell cycle is a critical control point where stop and go-ahead signals can regulate the cycle. (The signals are transmitted within the cell by the kinds of signal transduction pathways discussed in Chapter 11.) Animal cells generally have built-in stop signals that halt the cell cycle at checkpoints until overridden by go-ahead signals. Many signals registered at checkpoints come from cellular surveillance mechanisms inside the cell; the signals report whether crucial cellular processes up to that point have been completed correctly and thus whether or not the cell cycle should proceed. Checkpoints also register signals from outside the cell, as we will discuss later. Three major checkpoints are found in the G_1, G_2, and M phases (see Figure 12.14).

For many cells, the G_1 checkpoint—dubbed the "restriction point" in mammalian cells—seems to be the most important. If a cell receives a go-ahead signal at the G_1 checkpoint, it will usually complete the S, G_2, and M phases and divide. Alternatively,

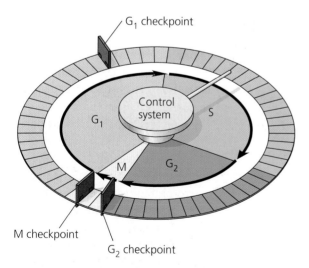

▲ **Figure 12.14 Mechanical analogy for the cell cycle control system.** In this diagram of the cell cycle, the flat "stepping stones" around the perimeter represent sequential events. Like the control device of an automatic washer, the cell cycle control system proceeds on its own, driven by a built-in clock. However, the system is subject to regulation at various checkpoints, of which three are shown (red).

(a) If a cell receives a go-ahead signal at the G_1 checkpoint, the cell continues on in the cell cycle.

(b) If a cell does not receive a go-ahead signal at the G_1 checkpoint, the cell exits the cell cycle and goes into G_0, a nondividing state.

▲ **Figure 12.15 The G_1 checkpoint.**

if it does not receive a go-ahead signal at that point, it will exit the cycle, switching into a nondividing state called the **G_0 phase (Figure 12.15)**. Most cells of the human body are actually in the G_0 phase. As mentioned earlier, fully formed, mature nerve cells and muscle cells never divide. Other cells, such as liver cells, can be "called back" from the G_0 phase to the cell cycle by certain external cues, such as growth factors released during injury.

To understand how cell cycle checkpoints work, we first need to see what kinds of molecules make up the cell cycle control system (the molecular basis for the cell cycle clock) and how a cell progresses forward through the cycle. Then we will consider the internal and external checkpoint signals that can make the clock pause or continue.

The Cell Cycle Clock: Cyclins and Cyclin-Dependent Kinases

Rhythmic fluctuations in the abundance and activity of cell cycle control molecules pace the sequential events of the cell cycle. These regulatory molecules are proteins of two main types: kinases and cyclins. Protein kinases are enzymes that activate or inactivate other proteins by phosphorylating them (see Chapter 11). Particular protein kinases give the go-ahead signals at the G_1 and G_2 checkpoints.

The kinases that drive the cell cycle are actually present at a constant concentration in the growing cell, but much of the time they are in an inactive form. To be active, such a kinase must be attached to a **cyclin,** a protein that gets its name from its cyclically fluctuating concentration in the cell. Because of this requirement, these kinases are called **cyclin-dependent kinases,** or **Cdks.** The activity of a Cdk rises and falls with changes in the concentration of its cyclin partner.

Figure 12.16a shows the fluctuating activity of the cyclin-Cdk complex that was discovered first, called **MPF**. Note that the peaks of MPF activity correspond to the peaks of cyclin concentration. The cyclin level rises during the S and G_2 phases, then falls abruptly during mitosis (M).

The initials MPF stand for "maturation-promoting factor," but we can think of MPF as "M-phase-promoting factor" because it triggers the cell's passage past the G_2 checkpoint into M phase **(Figure 12.16b)**. When cyclins that accumulate during G_2 associate with Cdk molecules, the resulting MPF complex initiates mitosis, phosphorylating a variety of proteins. MPF acts both directly as a kinase and indirectly by activating other kinases. For example, MPF causes phosphorylation of various proteins of the nuclear lamina (see Figure 6.10), which promotes fragmentation of the nuclear envelope during prometaphase of mitosis. There is also evidence that MPF contributes to molecular events required for chromosome condensation and spindle formation during prophase.

During anaphase, MPF helps switch itself off by initiating a process that leads to the destruction of its own cyclin. The noncyclin part of MPF, the Cdk, persists in the cell in inactive form until it associates with new cyclin molecules synthesized during the S and G_2 phases of the next round of the cycle.

What about the G_1 checkpoint? Recent research suggests the involvement of at least three Cdk proteins and several different cyclins at this checkpoint. The fluctuating activities of different cyclin-Cdk complexes seem to control all the stages of the cell cycle.

(a) Fluctuation of MPF activity and cyclin concentration during the cell cycle

5 During G_1, conditions in the cell favor degradation of cyclin, and the Cdk component of MPF is recycled.

1 Synthesis of cyclin begins in late S phase and continues through G_2. Because cyclin is protected from degradation during this stage, it accumulates.

2 Accumulated cyclin molecules combine with recycled Cdk molecules, producing enough molecules of MPF to pass the G_2 checkpoint and initiate the events of mitosis.

4 During anaphase, the cyclin component of MPF is degraded, terminating the M phase. The cell enters the G_1 phase.

3 MPF promotes mitosis by phosphorylating various proteins. MPF's activity peaks during metaphase.

(b) Molecular mechanisms that help regulate the cell cycle

▲ **Figure 12.16 Molecular control of the cell cycle at the G_2 checkpoint.** The steps of the cell cycle are timed by rhythmic fluctuations in the activity of cyclin-dependent kinases (Cdks). Here we focus on a cyclin-Cdk complex called MPF, which acts at the G_2 checkpoint as a go-ahead signal, triggering the events of mitosis.

Stop and Go Signs: Internal and External Signals at the Checkpoints

Research scientists are only in the early stages of working out the signaling pathways that link cyclin-dependent kinases to other molecules and events inside and outside the cell. For example, they know that in general, active Cdks function by phosphorylating substrate proteins that affect particular steps in the cell cycle. In many cases, though, scientists don't yet know what the various Cdks actually do. However, they have identified some steps of the signaling pathways that convey information to the cell cycle machinery.

An example of an internal signal occurs at the M phase checkpoint. Anaphase, the separation of sister chromatids, does not begin until all the chromosomes are properly attached to the spindle at the metaphase plate. Researchers have learned that kinetochores not yet attached to spindle microtubules send a molecular signal that causes the sister chromatids to remain together, delaying anaphase. Only when the kinetochores of all the chromosomes are attached to the spindle will the sister chromatids separate (owing to inactivation of the proteins holding them together). This mechanism ensures that daughter cells do not end up with missing or extra chromosomes.

By growing animal cells in culture, researchers have been able to identify many external factors, both chemical and physical, that can influence cell division. For example, cells fail to divide if an essential nutrient is left out of the culture medium. (This is analogous to trying to run an automatic washing machine without the water supply hooked up.) And even if all other conditions are favorable, most types of mammalian cells divide in culture only if the growth medium includes specific growth factors. As mentioned in Chapter 11, a **growth factor** is a protein released by certain cells that stimulates other cells to divide. While called a growth factor for historical reasons, a protein that promotes mitosis is sometimes more narrowly called a mitogen.

One such growth factor is *platelet-derived growth factor (PDGF)*, which is made by blood cells called platelets. The experiment illustrated in **Figure 12.17** demonstrates that PDGF is required for the division of fibroblasts in culture. Fibroblasts, a type of connective tissue cell, have PDGF receptors on their plasma membranes. The binding of PDGF molecules to these receptors (which are receptor tyrosine kinases; see Chapter 11) triggers a signal transduction pathway that allows the cells to pass the G_1 checkpoint and divide. PDGF stimulates fibroblast division not only in the artificial conditions of cell culture, but in an animal's body as well. When an injury occurs, platelets release PDGF in the vicinity. The resulting proliferation of fibroblasts helps heal the wound. Researchers have discovered at least 50 different growth factors that can trigger cells to divide. Different cell types respond specifically to a certain growth factor or combination of growth factors.

The effect of an external physical factor on cell division is clearly seen in **density-dependent inhibition,** a phenomenon in which crowded cells stop dividing (**Figure 12.18a**, on the next page). As first observed many years ago, cultured cells normally divide until they form a single layer of cells on the inner surface of the culture container, at which point the cells stop dividing. If some cells are removed, those bordering the open space begin dividing again and continue until the vacancy is filled. It was originally thought that a cell's physical contact with neighboring cells signaled it to stop dividing. However, while physical contact may have some influence, it turns out that the amount of required growth factors and nutrients available to each cell has a more important effect: Apparently, when a cell population reaches a certain density, the availability of nutrients becomes insufficient to allow continued cell growth and division.

Most animal cells also exhibit **anchorage dependence** (see Figure 12.18a). To divide, they must be attached to a substratum, such as the inside of a culture jar or the extracellular matrix of a tissue. Experiments suggest that anchorage is signaled to the cell cycle control system via pathways involving plasma membrane proteins and elements of the cytoskeleton linked to them.

Figure 12.17

Inquiry **Does platelet-derived growth factor (PDGF) stimulate the division of human fibroblast cells in culture?**

EXPERIMENT

Scalpels

❶ A sample of connective tissue was cut up into small pieces.

Petri plate

❷ Enzymes were used to digest the extracellular matrix, resulting in a suspension of free fibroblast cells.

❸ Cells were transferred to sterile culture vessels containing a basic growth medium consisting of glucose, amino acids, salts, and antibiotics (as a precaution against bacterial growth). PDGF was added to half the vessels. The culture vessels were incubated at 37°C.

Without PDGF

With PDGF

RESULTS

(a) In a basic growth medium without PDGF (the control), cells failed to divide.

Without PDGF

(b) In a basic growth medium plus PDGF, cells proliferated. The SEM shows cultured fibroblasts.

With PDGF

10 µm

CONCLUSION   This experiment confirmed that PDGF stimulates the division of human fibroblast cells in culture.

Density-dependent inhibition and anchorage dependence appear to function in the body's tissues as well as in cell culture, checking the growth of cells at some optimal density and location. Cancer cells, which we discuss next, exhibit neither density-dependent inhibition nor anchorage dependence (Figure 12.18b).

Cells anchor to dish surface and divide (anchorage dependence).

When cells have formed a complete single layer, they stop dividing (density-dependent inhibition).

If some cells are scraped away, the remaining cells divide to fill the gap and then stop (density-dependent inhibition).

25 μm

(a) Normal mammalian cells. The availability of nutrients, growth factors, and a substratum for attachment limits cell density to a single layer.

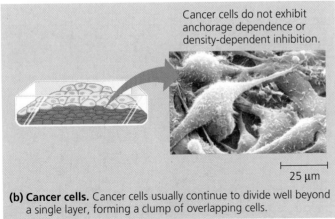

Cancer cells do not exhibit anchorage dependence or density-dependent inhibition.

25 μm

(b) Cancer cells. Cancer cells usually continue to divide well beyond a single layer, forming a clump of overlapping cells.

▲ Figure 12.18 **Density-dependent inhibition and anchorage dependence of cell division.** Individual cells are shown disproportionately large in the drawings.

Loss of Cell Cycle Controls in Cancer Cells

Cancer cells do not respond normally to the body's control mechanisms. They divide excessively and invade other tissues. If unchecked, they can kill the organism.

By studying cells growing in culture, researchers have learned that cancer cells do not heed the normal signals that regulate the cell cycle. For example, as Figure 12.18b shows, cancer cells do not exhibit density-dependent inhibition when growing in culture; they do not stop dividing when growth factors are depleted. A logical hypothesis to explain this behavior is that cancer cells do not need growth factors in their culture medium in order to grow and divide. They may make a required growth factor themselves, or they may have an abnormality in the signaling pathway that conveys the growth factor's signal to the cell cycle control system even in the absence of that factor. Another possibility is an abnormal cell cycle control system. In fact, as you will learn in Chapter 19, these are all conditions that may lead to cancer.

There are other important differences between normal cells and cancer cells that reflect derangements of the cell cycle. If and when they stop dividing, cancer cells do so at random points in the cycle, rather than at the normal checkpoints. Moreover, in culture, cancer cells can go on dividing indefinitely if they are given a continual supply of nutrients; they are said to be "immortal." A striking example is a cell line that has been reproducing in culture since 1951. Cells of this line are called HeLa cells because their original source was a tumor removed from a woman named Henrietta Lacks. By contrast, nearly all normal mammalian cells growing in culture divide only about 20 to 50 times before they stop dividing, age, and die. (We'll see a possible reason for this phenomenon when we discuss chromosome replication in Chapter 16.)

The abnormal behavior of cancer cells can be catastrophic when it occurs in the body. The problem begins when a single cell in a tissue undergoes **transformation,** the process that converts a normal cell to a cancer cell. The body's immune system normally recognizes a transformed cell as an insurgent and destroys it. However, if the cell evades destruction, it may proliferate and form a tumor, a mass of abnormal cells within otherwise normal tissue. If the abnormal cells remain at the original site, the lump is called a **benign tumor.** Most benign tumors do not cause serious problems and can be completely removed by surgery. In contrast, a **malignant tumor** becomes invasive enough to impair the functions of one or more organs (Figure 12.19). An individual with a malignant tumor is said to have cancer.

The cells of malignant tumors are abnormal in many ways besides their excessive proliferation. They may have unusual numbers of chromosomes (whether this is a cause or an effect of transformation is a current topic of debate). Their metabolism may be disabled, and they may cease to function in any constructive way. Also, owing to abnormal changes on the

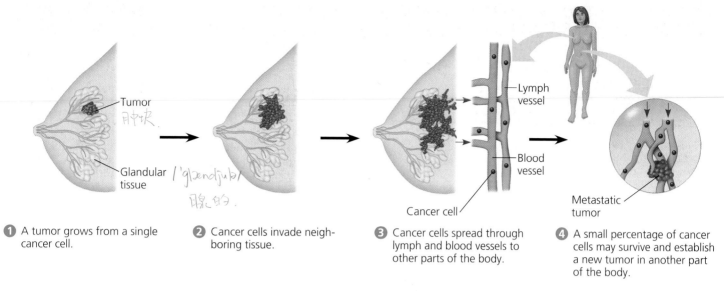

① A tumor grows from a single cancer cell.

② Cancer cells invade neighboring tissue.

③ Cancer cells spread through lymph and blood vessels to other parts of the body.

④ A small percentage of cancer cells may survive and establish a new tumor in another part of the body.

▲ **Figure 12.19 The growth and metastasis of a malignant breast tumor.** The cells of malignant (cancerous) tumors grow in an uncontrolled way and can spread to neighboring tissues and, via lymph and blood vessels, to other parts of the body. The spread of cancer cells beyond their original site is called metastasis.

cells' surfaces, they lose or destroy their attachments to neighboring cells and the extracellular matrix and can spread into nearby tissues. Cancer cells may also secrete signal molecules that cause blood vessels to grow toward the tumor. A few tumor cells may separate from the original tumor, enter blood vessels and lymph vessels, and travel to other parts of the body. There, they may proliferate and form a new tumor. This spread of cancer cells to locations distant from their original site is called **metastasis** (see Figure 12.19).

A tumor that appears to be localized may be treated with high-energy radiation, which damages DNA in cancer cells much more than it does in normal cells, apparently because cancer cells have lost the ability to repair such damage. To treat known or suspected metastatic tumors, chemotherapy is used, in which drugs that are toxic to actively dividing cells are administered through the circulatory system. As you might expect, chemotherapeutic drugs interfere with specific steps in the cell cycle. For example, the drug Taxol freezes the mitotic spindle by preventing microtubule depolymerization, which stops actively dividing cells from proceeding past metaphase. The side effects of chemotherapy are due to the drugs' effects on normal cells. For example, nausea results from chemotherapy's effects on intestinal cells, hair loss from effects on hair follicle cells, and susceptibility to infection from effects on immune system cells.

Researchers are beginning to understand how a normal cell is transformed into a cancer cell. You will learn more about the molecular biology of cancer in Chapter 19. Though the causes of cancer are diverse, cellular transformation always involves the alteration of genes that somehow influence the cell cycle control system. Our knowledge of how changes in the genome lead to the various abnormalities of cancer cells remains rudimentary, however.

Perhaps the reason we have so many unanswered questions about cancer cells is that there is still so much to learn about how normal cells function. The cell, life's basic unit of structure and function, holds enough secrets to engage researchers well into the future.

Concept Check 12.3

1. A researcher treats cells with a chemical that prevents DNA synthesis. This treatment traps the cells in which part of the cell cycle?
2. In Figure 12.13, why do the nuclei resulting from experiment 2 contain different amounts of DNA?
3. What is the go-ahead signal for a cell to pass the G_2 phase checkpoint and enter mitosis? (See Figure 12.16.)
4. What would happen if you performed the experiment in Figure 12.17 with cancer cells?
5. What phase of the cell cycle are most of your body cells in?
6. Compare and contrast a benign tumor and a malignant tumor.

For suggested answers, see Appendix A.

Go to the Campbell Biology website (**www.campbellbiology.com**) or CD-ROM to explore Activities, Investigations, and other interactive study aids.

SUMMARY OF KEY CONCEPTS

▶ Unicellular organisms reproduce by cell division. Multicellular organisms depend on it for development from a fertilized egg, growth, and repair (pp. 218–219).
Activity *Roles of Cell Division*

Concept 12.1

Cell division results in genetically identical daughter cells

▶ Cells duplicate their genetic material before they divide, ensuring that each daughter cell receives an exact copy of the genetic material, DNA (p. 219).

▶ **Cellular Organization of the Genetic Material** (p. 219) DNA is partitioned among chromosomes. Eukaryotic chromosomes consist of chromatin, a complex of DNA and protein that condenses during mitosis. In animals, gametes have one set of chromosomes and somatic cells have two sets.

▶ **Distribution of Chromosomes During Cell Division** (pp. 219–220) In preparation for cell division, chromosomes replicate, each one then consisting of two identical sister chromatids. The chromatids separate during cell division, becoming the chromosomes of the new daughter cells. Eukaryotic cell division consists of mitosis (division of the nucleus) and cytokinesis (division of the cytoplasm).

Concept 12.2

The mitotic phase alternates with interphase in the cell cycle

▶ **Phases of the Cell Cycle** (pp. 221–223) Between divisions, cells are in interphase: the G_1, S, and G_2 phases. The cell grows throughout interphase, but DNA is replicated only during the synthesis (S) phase. Mitosis and cytokinesis make up the mitotic (M) phase of the cell cycle. Mitosis is a continuous process, often described as occurring in five stages: prophase, prometaphase, metaphase, anaphase, and telophase.
Activity *The Cell Cycle*

▶ **The Mitotic Spindle: *A Closer Look*** (pp. 221–225) The mitotic spindle is an apparatus of microtubules that controls chromosome movement during mitosis. The spindle arises from the centrosomes and includes spindle microtubules and asters. Some spindle microtubules attach to the kinetochores of chromosomes and move the chromosomes to the metaphase plate. In anaphase, sister chromatids separate and move along the kinetochore microtubules toward opposite ends of the cell. Meanwhile, nonkinetochore microtubules from opposite poles overlap and push against each other, elongating the cell. In telophase, genetically identical daughter nuclei form at opposite ends of the cell.

▶ **Cytokinesis: *A Closer Look*** (pp. 224–226) Mitosis is usually followed by cytokinesis. Animal cells carry out cytokinesis by cleavage, and plant cells form a cell plate.
Activity *Mitosis and Cytokinesis Animation*
Activity *Mitosis and Cytokinesis Video*
Investigation *How Much Time Do Cells Spend in Each Phase of Mitosis?*

▶ **Binary Fission** (pp. 226–227) During binary fission, the bacterial chromosome replicates and the two daughter chromosomes actively move apart. The specific proteins involved in this movement are a subject of current research.

▶ **The Evolution of Mitosis** (pp. 227–228) Since prokaryotes preceded eukaryotes by billions of years, it is likely that mitosis evolved from bacterial cell division. Certain protists exhibit types of cell division that seem intermediate between bacterial binary fission and the process of mitosis carried out by most eukaryotic cells.

Concept 12.3

The cell cycle is regulated by a molecular control system

▶ **Evidence for Cytoplasmic Signals** (p. 228) Molecules present in the cytoplasm regulate progress through the cell cycle.

▶ **The Cell Cycle Control System** (pp. 229–232) Cyclic changes in regulatory proteins work as a cell cycle clock. The clock has specific checkpoints where the cell cycle stops until a go-ahead signal is received. The key molecules are cyclins and cyclin-dependent kinases (Cdks). Cell culture has enabled researchers to study the molecular details of cell division. Both internal signals and external signals control the cell cycle checkpoints via signal transduction pathways. Most cells exhibit density-dependent inhibition of cell division as well as anchorage dependence.

▶ **Loss of Cell Cycle Controls in Cancer Cells** (pp. 232–233) Cancer cells elude normal regulation and divide out of control, forming tumors. Malignant tumors invade surrounding tissues and can metastasize, exporting cancer cells to other parts of the body, where they may form secondary tumors.
Activity *Causes of Cancer*

TESTING YOUR KNOWLEDGE

Self-Quiz

1. Increases in the enzymatic activity of some protein kinases important for the regulation of the cell cycle are due to
   a. kinase synthesis by ribosomes.
   b. activation of inactive kinases by binding to cyclins.
   c. conversion of inactive cyclins to active kinases by means of phosphorylation.
   d. cleavage of the inactive kinase molecules by cytoplasmic proteases.
   e. a decline in external growth factors to a concentration below the inhibitory threshold.

2. Through a microscope, you can see a cell plate beginning to develop across the middle of the cell and nuclei re-forming on either side of the cell plate. This cell is most likely
   a. an animal cell in the process of cytokinesis.
   b. a plant cell in the process of cytokinesis.
   c. an animal cell in the S phase of the cell cycle.
   d. a bacterial cell dividing.
   e. a plant cell in metaphase.

3. Vinblastine is a standard chemotherapeutic drug used to treat cancer. Because it interferes with the assembly of microtubules, its effectiveness must be related to
   a. disruption of mitotic spindle formation.
   b. inhibition of regulatory protein phosphorylation.
   c. suppression of cyclin production.
   d. myosin denaturation and inhibition of cleavage furrow formation.
   e. inhibition of DNA synthesis.

4. A particular cell has half as much DNA as some of the other cells in a mitotically active tissue. The cell in question is most likely in
   a. G_1.
   b. G_2.
   c. prophase.
   d. metaphase.
   e. anaphase.

5. One difference between a cancer cell and a normal cell is that
   a. the cancer cell is unable to synthesize DNA.
   b. the cell cycle of the cancer cell is arrested at the S phase.
   c. cancer cells continue to divide even when they are tightly packed together.
   d. cancer cells cannot function properly because they suffer from density-dependent inhibition.
   e. cancer cells are always in the M phase of the cell cycle.

6. The decline of MPF activity at the end of mitosis is caused by
   a. the destruction of the protein kinase (Cdk).
   b. decreased synthesis of cyclin.
   c. the degradation of cyclin.
   d. synthesis of DNA.
   e. an increase in the cell's volume-to-genome ratio.

7. A red blood cell (RBC) has a 120-day life span. If an average adult has 5 L of blood, and each microliter (μL) contains 5 million RBCs, how many new cells must be produced each *second* to replace the entire RBC population? (1 μL = 10^{-6} L)
   a. 30,000
   b. 2,400
   c. 2,400,000
   d. 18,000
   e. 30,000,000

8. The drug cytochalasin B blocks the function of actin. Which of the following aspects of the cell cycle would be most disrupted by cytochalasin B?
   a. spindle formation
   b. spindle attachment to kinetochores
   c. DNA synthesis
   d. cell elongation during anaphase
   e. cleavage furrow formation

9. In some organisms, mitosis occurs without cytokinesis occurring. This will result in
   a. cells with more than one nucleus.
   b. cells that are unusually small.
   c. cells lacking nuclei.
   d. destruction of chromosomes.
   e. cell cycles lacking an S phase.

10. Which of the following does *not* occur during mitosis?
    a. condensation of the chromosomes
    b. replication of the DNA
    c. separation of sister chromatids
    d. spindle formation
    e. separation of the centrosomes

11. In the light micrograph below of dividing cells near the tip of an onion root, identify a cell in each of the following stages: interphase, prophase, metaphase, and anaphase. Describe the major events occurring at each stage.

For Self-Quiz answers, see Appendix A.
Go to the website or CD-ROM for more quiz questions.

Evolution Connection

The result of mitosis is that the daughter cells end up with the same number of chromosomes as the parent cell had. Another way to maintain the number of chromosomes would be to carry out cell division first and then duplicate the chromosomes in each daughter cell. What would be the problems with this alternative? Or do you think it would be an equally good way of organizing the cell cycle?

Scientific Inquiry

Microtubules are polar structures in that one end (called the $+$ end) polymerizes and depolymerizes at a much higher rate than the other end (the $-$ end). The experiment shown in Figure 12.8 clearly identifies these two ends.
   a. From the results, identify the $+$ end and explain your reasoning.
   b. If the opposite end were the $+$ end, what would the results be? Make a sketch.
   c. Redesign the model in the conclusion of Figure 12.8 to reflect your new version of the results.

Investigation *How Much Time Do Cells Spend in Each Phase of Mitosis?*

Science, Technology, and Society

Hundreds of millions of dollars are spent each year in the search for effective treatments for cancer; far less money is spent preventing cancer. Why do you think this is true? What kinds of lifestyle changes could we make to help prevent cancer? What kinds of prevention programs could be initiated or strengthened to encourage these changes? What factors might impede such changes and programs?

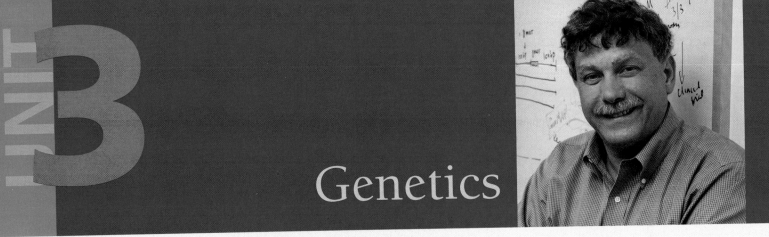

Genetics

AN INTERVIEW WITH
Eric Lander

Genomics, the study of all the genes in an organism and how they function together, is a new field that is bringing about a revolution in biology. Having played a major role in the Human Genome Project, Eric Lander is a leader of this revolution. Dr. Lander is the founding director of the Broad Institute of MIT and Harvard, which uses genomics to develop new tools and approaches to understanding and treating disease. The institute includes the former Whitehead Center for Genome Research, which played a leading role in the sequencing of the human genome.

A graduate of Princeton, Dr. Lander earned a doctorate in mathematics at Oxford University, where he was a Rhodes Scholar. He then taught managerial economics at Harvard Business School until turning full time to biology in 1990. Among his many honors have been a MacArthur Foundation Fellowship and election to the U.S. National Academy of Sciences. Dr. Lander is a professor at both MIT and Harvard, and he has taught MIT's core introductory biology course for a decade.

How did you get into genetics?

In high school, I took biology, but I loved math, and I was a math major in college. I went on to get my Ph.D. in mathematics but decided I didn't want to be a pure mathematician. One day, my brother suggested I might be interested in the coding theory of the brain and sent me some papers on mathematical neurobiology. I realized that, to understand them, I had to learn something about cellular neurobiology. This required me to study cell biology. Next came molecular biology, and finally, I really had to know genetics. So one thing led to another—and here I am still learning genetics!

What was the main purpose of the Human Genome Project?

The ultimate purpose of the Human Genome Project was to read out and make freely available the complete DNA sequence of the human being. This information is fundamental to our biology. It contains the parts list in terms of which all our biological structures and processes must eventually be described.

You can study the detailed properties of individual genes, as biologists did before the Human Genome Project and still do, or you can study how all the components of the system interact. Important discoveries are made at both levels, but there are some things you only see when you step back. Imagine looking at a pointillist painting. Up close, the dots are interesting, but when you step back you can see patterns that weren't evident at first. Until the Human Genome Project, it hadn't been possible to step back and get the big picture of the human genome.

Analysis of the genome is unveiling a comprehensive picture of how the genes are turned on and off in different tissues and at different times, so we can see how genes collaborate in modules or circuits. It's an ensemble picture that we've just never had before.

What were the main challenges of the Human Genome Project?

The biggest challenge was the necessity of a 10,000-fold improvement in our methods for mapping and sequencing DNA—the project was that much more ambitious than anything ever done before! In any realistic sense, the scientific community was crazy to propose it. But realism is much overrated. Once we recognized how important the sequence would be to thousands of scientists, we began to ask why, exactly, we couldn't do it. Then we took on the barriers one at a time. We set intermediate goals, both to obtain some information that would be immediately useful and to show ourselves that we

were on the right track. And one after another, we were able to reach our goals: first, genetic maps we could use to trace the inheritance of diseases, then physical maps of the chromosomal DNA, and, finally, the nucleotide-by-nucleotide sequence of the whole genome.

It was a great experience. Everybody involved in the Human Genome Project knew we were working on something that would still be fundamental to science a hundred years from now. We felt it would be important to our children because the medicine of 50 years from now will be based on this work. And it was the work of no one individual, no one center, no one country. Overall, the project involved several thousand people at 20 centers all over the world—in the United States, the United Kingdom, France, Germany, Japan, and China. It was science at its best, an international collaboration of people working together for something bigger than themselves.

To achieve our goals, we constantly had to invent new methodologies, and we had to figure out how to automate as much as possible. Then we had to figure out how to analyze the data. My own background in mathematics actually turned out to be useful.

The genome sequences are just long chains of A's, C's, T's, and G's. How do you know which sections are genes?

Knowing the three billion letters of the human genome is still a far cry from understanding what they say. It's not easy to identify the genes within a very long sequence. This is particularly so in humans and other multicellular eukaryotes, which generally have huge amounts of noncoding DNA and gene-coding sequences split up into small segments (exons) interrupted by stretches of noncoding DNA (introns). In searching for human genes, we're looking for small signals in a sea of noise.

Computer programs can do a passable job of picking out gene sequences, but only passable. The sequences you can look for include ATG, which starts the coding sequence of all genes, but ATG is so common in the genome that it's not much of a signal. You can also look for places where that start signal is followed by a fairly long stretch of nucleotides before one of the three-nucleotide stop signals appears, but that can easily occur by chance. So, using a computer to look for those kinds of signals alone does a pretty crummy job of identifying genes.

Happily, we have other tricks up our sleeves. One way to identify genes is to compare the genome to copies of messenger RNA molecules from cells (see Figure 5.25). Another powerful approach is to compare the human sequence to those of related species. Because many genes are crucial to an organism's survival, they tend to be conserved (not change very much) during evolution. So if we look at the portions of the human genome that are very similar in other mammals, they tend to contain genes. The task of finding all the genes is a fascinating puzzle that involves computer scientists, evolutionary biologists, molecular biologists, and others.

How many human genes are there?

My best guess today is that there are 20,000–25,000 protein-coding genes. One of the most surprising findings of the Human Genome Project was a gene count much lower than people had expected based on the total size of the human genome; not so many years ago,

textbooks gave 100,000 as the likely number of human genes. When we got the rough draft of the sequence, we thought there might be as many as 40,000 genes, but we soon learned that many of these were actually pseudogenes, which are defective, nonfunctional copies of true genes. The gene count has been falling and falling. Of course, genes for functional RNA molecules, such as rRNA, that are not translated into protein are also present in the genome, but they don't add up to a lot of territory, probably only a few thousand genes—although we're not certain.

How close are we to understanding the human genome?

The extent of our ignorance became clear from comparing the human genome with the mouse genome. When we lined up the two, we found that about 5% of the human genome showed strong similarity to that of the mouse, indicating strong evolutionary conservation since the last common ancestor of mouse and human. Thus, the sequences in this DNA must be functionally very important. But only about a third of the 5% could be accounted for by known genes and regulatory sequences, leaving a lot more that evolution "cares about" than we can explain today.

That's what I love about genomics. We're learning that there are vast tracts of biology we have missed. It's as if we suddenly could look at the whole Earth and see that, golly, there are several continents we hadn't known about. Genomics is revealing huge territories for the next generation of young scientists to explore.

How is genomics affecting the study of evolution?

Evolutionary biology is being transformed by the availability of genomic data. Now we can sit down with the complete sequences of a number of organisms and begin to reconstruct their evolutionary relationships and histories in exquisite detail. We can see the forces at work in different lineages. For instance, we can see that in humans the most actively evolving genes are those involved in reproduction and the immune system. Scientists have long thought that genomes carried such information about evolution, but we're finally getting to see it laid out clearly. Evolution is, so to speak, an experimentalist that has been running experiments for three and a half billion years, since the origin of life on Earth. And, wonderfully, the genomes of today's organisms retain the lab notes of these experiments, so that we can go back and reconstruct the events that took place.

Let's talk about the application of genomics to medicine. What goes on at the Broad Institute?

The key challenge ahead is to understand the molecular basis of common human diseases such as diabetes, lung cancer, psychiatric diseases, and many others. Understanding molecular mechanisms is key to creating therapies. The sequence of the human genome has given us a great foundation for systematic understanding of disease—but it's just a start. We now need a full understanding of all the functional elements encoded in the human genome sequence and how they regulate genes; of all the common genetic variants in the human population and how they correlate with risk of disease; of the gene and protein expression patterns that reflect the activation of cellular pathways; and of all the genetic mutations that underlie cancers. In parallel, we need to develop ways to use this comprehensive picture to identify the right targets for drug development and other therapies.

The Broad Institute's mission is to help drive this next stage of biomedicine. The institute includes many kinds of scientists—biologists, chemists, physicians, mathematicians, and others—from across MIT and Harvard, including the Harvard hospitals. Together, we're developing new ways to generate biological information and new ways to apply it in medical studies. We also feel strongly about making all the data publicly available, so that anyone can use it to ask new questions.

"The Human Genome Project . . . was science at its best, an international collaboration of people working together for something bigger than themselves."

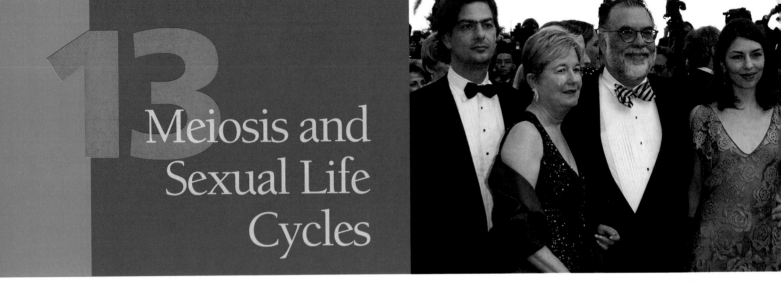

13 Meiosis and Sexual Life Cycles

▲ Figure 13.1 **Francis Ford Coppola and his family.**

Key Concepts

13.1 Offspring acquire genes from parents by inheriting chromosomes

13.2 Fertilization and meiosis alternate in sexual life cycles

13.3 Meiosis reduces the number of chromosome sets from diploid to haploid

13.4 Genetic variation produced in sexual life cycles contributes to evolution

Overview

Hereditary Similarity and Variation

Living organisms are distinguished by their ability to reproduce their own kind. Only oak trees produce oaks, and only elephants can make more elephants. Furthermore, offspring resemble their parents more than they do less closely related individuals of the same species. The transmission of traits from one generation to the next is called inheritance, or **heredity** (from the Latin *heres,* heir). Along with inherited similarity, there is also **variation:** Offspring differ somewhat in appearance from parents and siblings. Farmers have exploited these observations for thousands of years, breeding plants and animals for desired traits. Just as ancient is a curiosity about genetic similarities and differences among people, including family members **(Figure 13.1)**. The mechanisms of heredity and variation, however, eluded biologists until the development of genetics in the 20th century.

Genetics is the scientific study of heredity and hereditary variation. In this unit, you will learn about genetics at the levels of organism, cell, and molecule. On the practical side, you will learn how modern genetics is revolutionizing medicine and agriculture, and you will be asked to consider some social and ethical questions raised by our ability to manipulate DNA, the genetic material. At the end of the unit, you will learn about the contributions geneticists have made to solving the mystery of how multicellular animals and plants arise from a single cell, the fertilized egg. In fact, genetic methods and discoveries are catalyzing progress in all areas of biology—from cell biology to physiology, evolutionary biology, ecology, and even behavior.

We begin our study of genetics in this chapter by examining how chromosomes pass from parents to offspring in sexually reproducing organisms. The processes of meiosis (a special type of cell division) and fertilization (the fusion of sperm and egg) maintain a species' chromosome count during the sexual life cycle. We will describe the cellular mechanics of meiosis and how this process differs from mitosis. Finally, we will consider how both meiosis and fertilization contribute to genetic variation, such as the variation obvious in the Coppola family (see Figure 13.1).

Concept 13.1

Offspring acquire genes from parents by inheriting chromosomes

Family friends may tell you that you have your mother's freckles or your father's eyes. However, parents do not, in any literal sense, give their children freckles, eyes, hair, or any other traits. What, then, *is* actually inherited?

Inheritance of Genes

Parents endow their offspring with coded information in the form of hereditary units called **genes.** The tens of thousands of genes we inherit from our mothers and fathers constitute our genome. This genetic link to our parents accounts for family resemblances such as shared eye color or freckles. Our genes program the specific traits that emerge as we develop from fertilized eggs into adults.

Genes are segments of DNA. You learned in Chapters 1 and 5 that DNA is a polymer of four different kinds of monomers called nucleotides. Inherited information is passed on in the form of each gene's specific sequence of nucleotides, much as printed information is communicated in the form of meaningful sequences of letters. Language is symbolic. The brain translates words and sentences into mental images and ideas; for example, the object you imagine when you read "apple" looks nothing like the word itself. Analogously, cells translate genetic "sentences" into freckles and other features that bear no resemblance to genes. Most genes program cells to synthesize specific enzymes and other proteins whose cumulative action produces an organism's inherited traits. The programming of these traits in the form of DNA is one of the unifying themes of biology.

The transmission of hereditary traits has its molecular basis in the precise replication of DNA, which produces copies of genes that can be passed along from parents to offspring. In animals and plants, reproductive cells called **gametes** are the vehicles that transmit genes from one generation to the next. During fertilization, male and female gametes (sperm and eggs) unite, thereby passing on the genes of both parents to their offspring.

Except for tiny amounts of DNA in mitochondria and chloroplasts, the DNA of a eukaryotic cell is subdivided into chromosomes within the nucleus. Every living species has a characteristic number of chromosomes. For example, humans have 46 chromosomes in almost all of their cells. Each chromosome consists of a single long DNA molecule elaborately coiled in association with various proteins. One chromosome includes several hundred to a few thousand genes, each of which is a specific sequence of nucleotides within the DNA molecule. A gene's specific location along the length of a chromosome is called the gene's **locus** (plural, *loci*). Our genetic endowment consists of the genes carried on the chromosomes we inherited from our parents.

Comparison of Asexual and Sexual Reproduction

Only organisms that reproduce asexually produce offspring that are exact copies of themselves. In **asexual reproduction,** a single individual is the sole parent and passes copies of all its genes to its offspring. For example, single-celled eukaryotic organisms can reproduce asexually by mitotic cell division, in which DNA is copied and allocated equally to two daughter

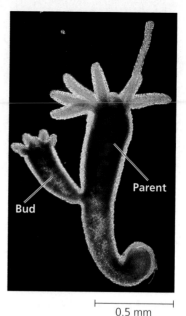

◀ **Figure 13.2 The asexual reproduction of a hydra.** This relatively simple multicellular animal reproduces by budding. The bud, a localized mass of mitotically dividing cells, develops into a small hydra, which detaches from the parent (LM).

Parent

Bud

0.5 mm

cells. The genomes of the offspring are virtually exact copies of the parent's genome. Some multicellular organisms are also capable of reproducing asexually. A hydra, which is related to the jellies (jellyfishes), can reproduce by budding **(Figure 13.2)**. Because the cells of a bud are derived by mitosis in the parent, the "chip off the old block" is usually genetically identical to its parent. An individual that reproduces asexually gives rise to a **clone,** a group of genetically identical individuals. Genetic differences occasionally arise in asexually reproducing organisms as a result of changes in the DNA called mutations, which we will discuss in Chapter 17.

In **sexual reproduction,** two parents give rise to offspring that have unique combinations of genes inherited from the two parents. In contrast to a clone, offspring of sexual reproduction vary genetically from their siblings and both parents: They are variations on a common theme of family resemblance, not exact replicas. Genetic variation like that shown in Figure 13.1 is an important consequence of sexual reproduction. What mechanisms generate this genetic variation? The key is the behavior of chromosomes during the sexual life cycle.

Concept Check 13.1

1. How are the traits of parents (such as hair color) transmitted to their offspring?
2. In the absence of mutation, asexually reproducing organisms produce offspring that are genetically identical to each other and to their parents. Explain.
3. In organisms that reproduce sexually, how similar are the offspring to their parents? Explain.

For suggested answers, see Appendix A.

Concept 13.2

Fertilization and meiosis alternate in sexual life cycles

A **life cycle** is the generation-to-generation sequence of stages in the reproductive history of an organism, from conception to production of its own offspring. In this section, we use humans as an example to track the behavior of chromosomes through sexual life cycles. We begin by considering the chromosome count in human somatic cells and gametes; we will then explore how the behavior of chromosomes relates to the human life cycle and other types of sexual life cycles.

Sets of Chromosomes in Human Cells

In humans, each **somatic cell**—any cell other than a gamete—has 46 chromosomes. During mitosis, the chromosomes become condensed enough to be visible in a light microscope. Because chromosomes differ in size, in the positions of their centromeres, and in the pattern of colored bands produced by certain stains, they can be distinguished from one another by microscopic examination when sufficiently condensed.

Careful examination of a micrograph of the 46 human chromosomes from a single cell in mitosis reveals that there are two chromosomes of each type. This becomes clear when images of the chromosomes are arranged in pairs, starting with the longest chromosomes. The resulting ordered display is called a **karyotype (Figure 13.3)**. The two chromosomes composing a pair have the same length, centromere position, and staining pattern: These are called **homologous chromosomes,** or homologues. Both chromosomes of each pair carry genes controlling the same inherited characters. For example, if a gene for eye color is situated at a particular locus on a certain chromosome, then the homologue of that chromosome will also have a gene specifying eye color at the equivalent locus.

The two distinct chromosomes referred to as X and Y are an important exception to the general pattern of homologous chromosomes in human somatic cells. Human females have a homologous pair of X chromosomes (XX), but males have one X and one Y chromosome (XY). Only small parts of the X and Y are homologous. Most of the genes carried on the X chromosome do not have counterparts on the tiny Y, and the Y chromosome has genes lacking on the X. Because they determine an individual's sex, the X and Y chromosomes are called **sex chromosomes.** The other chromosomes are called **autosomes.**

The occurrence of homologous pairs of chromosomes in each human somatic cell is a consequence of our sexual origins. We inherit one chromosome of each pair from each parent. So the 46 chromosomes in our somatic cells are actually two sets of 23 chromosomes—a maternal set (from our mother) and a paternal set (from our father). The number of chromosomes in a single set is represented by *n*. Any cell with two chromosome

Figure 13.3
Research Method Preparing a Karyotype

APPLICATION A karyotype is a display of condensed chromosomes arranged in pairs. Karyotyping can be used to screen for abnormal numbers of chromosomes or defective chromosomes associated with certain congenital disorders, such as Down syndrome.

TECHNIQUE Karyotypes are prepared from isolated somatic cells, which are treated with a drug to stimulate mitosis and then grown in culture for several days. A slide of cells arrested in metaphase is stained and then viewed with a microscope equipped with a digital camera. A digital photograph of the chromosomes is entered into a computer, and the chromosomes are electronically rearranged into pairs according to size and shape.

RESULTS This karyotype shows the chromosomes from a normal human male. The patterns of stained bands help identify specific chromosomes and parts of chromosomes. Although difficult to discern in the karyotype, each metaphase chromosome consists of two, closely attached sister chromatids (see diagram).

Pair of homologous chromosomes

5 μm

Centromere

Sister chromatids

Key

$2n = 6$ {
◼ Maternal set of chromosomes ($n = 3$)
◼ Paternal set of chromosomes ($n = 3$)
}

Two sister chromatids of one replicated chromosome

Centromere

Two nonsister chromatids in a homologous pair

Pair of homologous chromosomes (one from each set)

▲ **Figure 13.4 Describing chromosomes.** A cell with a diploid number of 6 ($2n = 6$) is depicted here in G_2 of interphase, following chromosome replication. (The chromosomes have been artificially condensed.) Each of the six duplicated chromosomes consists of two sister chromatids joined at the centromere. Each homologous pair is composed of one chromosome from the maternal set (red) and one from the paternal set (blue). Each set is made up of three chromosomes. Nonsister chromatids are any two chromatids in a pair of homologous chromosomes that are not sister chromatids.

sets is called a **diploid cell** and has a diploid number of chromosomes, abbreviated $2n$. For humans, the diploid number is 46 ($2n = 46$), the number of chromosomes in our somatic cells. In a cell in which DNA synthesis has occurred, all the chromosomes are duplicated and thus each consists of two identical sister chromatids. **Figure 13.4** helps clarify the various terms that we use in describing duplicated chromosomes in a diploid cell. Study this figure so that you understand the differences between homologous chromosomes, sister chromatids, nonsister chromatids, and chromosome sets.

Unlike somatic cells, gametes (sperm and egg cells) contain a single chromosome set. Such cells are called **haploid cells**, and each has a haploid number of chromosomes (n). For humans, the haploid number is 23 ($n = 23$), the number of chromosomes found in a gamete. The set of 23 consists of the 22 autosomes plus a single sex chromosome. An unfertilized egg cell (also called an ovum) contains an X chromosome, but a sperm cell may contain an X or a Y chromosome.

Note that each sexually reproducing species has a characteristic haploid number and diploid number. These may be higher than, lower than, or the same as the values for humans. Now let's extend the concepts of haploid and diploid to understand chromosome behavior during the human life cycle.

Behavior of Chromosome Sets in the Human Life Cycle

The human life cycle begins when a haploid sperm cell from the father fuses with a haploid ovum from the mother. This union of gametes, culminating in fusion of their nuclei, is

called **fertilization.** The resulting fertilized egg, or **zygote**, is diploid because it contains two haploid sets of chromosomes bearing genes representing the maternal and paternal family lines. As a human develops from a zygote to a sexually mature adult, mitosis generates all the somatic cells of the body. Both chromosome sets in the zygote and all the genes they carry are passed with precision to our somatic cells.

The only cells of the human body *not* produced by mitosis are the gametes, which develop in the gonads—ovaries in females and testes in males **(Figure 13.5)**. Imagine what would happen if human gametes were made by mitosis: They would be diploid like the somatic cells. At the next round of fertilization, when two gametes fused, the normal chromosome number of 46 would double to 92, and each subsequent generation would double the number of chromosomes yet again. This hypothetical situation of constantly increasing chromosome number in sexually reproducing organisms is avoided through the

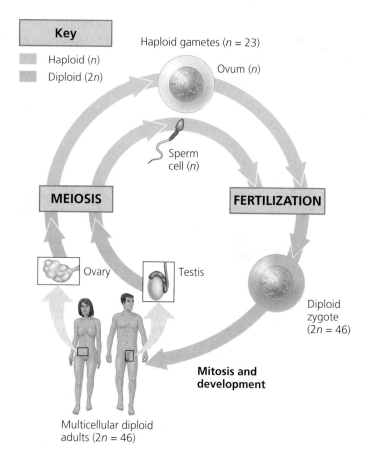

Key

▢ Haploid (n)
▢ Diploid ($2n$)

Haploid gametes ($n = 23$)

Ovum (n)

Sperm cell (n)

MEIOSIS

FERTILIZATION

Ovary

Testis

Diploid zygote ($2n = 46$)

Mitosis and development

Multicellular diploid adults ($2n = 46$)

▲ **Figure 13.5 The human life cycle.** In each generation, the doubling of the number of chromosome sets that results from fertilization is offset by the halving of the number of sets that results from meiosis. For humans, the number of chromosomes in a haploid cell is 23, consisting of one set ($n = 23$); the number of chromosomes in the diploid zygote and all somatic cells arising from it is 46, consisting of two sets ($2n = 46$).

This figure introduces a color code that will be used for other life cycles later in this book. The teal-colored arrows highlight haploid stages of a life cycle, and the beige-colored arrows highlight diploid stages.

process of **meiosis.** This type of cell division reduces the number of sets of chromosomes from two to one in the gametes, compensating for the doubling that occurs at fertilization. In animals, meiosis occurs only in the ovaries or testes. As a result, each human sperm and ovum is haploid ($n = 23$). Fertilization restores the diploid condition by combining two haploid sets of chromosomes, and the human life cycle is repeated, generation after generation (see Figure 13.5). You will learn more about the production of sperm and ova in Chapter 46.

In general, the steps of the human life cycle are typical of many animals. Indeed, the processes of fertilization and meiosis are the unique trademarks of sexual reproduction. Fertilization and meiosis alternate in sexual life cycles, offsetting each other's effects on the chromosome number and thus perpetuating a species' chromosome count.

The Variety of Sexual Life Cycles

Although the alternation of meiosis and fertilization is common to all organisms that reproduce sexually, the timing of these two events in the life cycle varies, depending on the species. These variations can be grouped into three main types of life cycles. In the type of life cycle that occurs in humans and most other animals, gametes are the only haploid cells. Meiosis occurs during the production of gametes, which undergo no further cell division prior to fertilization. The diploid zygote divides by mitosis, producing a multicellular organism that is diploid **(Figure 13.6a).**

Plants and some species of algae exhibit a second type of life cycle called **alternation of generations.** This type of life cycle includes both diploid and haploid multicellular stages. The multicellular diploid stage is called the **sporophyte.** Meiosis in the sporophyte produces haploid cells called **spores.** Unlike a gamete, a spore gives rise to a multicellular individual without fusing with another cell. A spore divides mitotically to generate a multicellular haploid stage called the **gametophyte.** The haploid gametophyte makes gametes by mitosis. Fertilization among the haploid gametes results in a diploid zygote, which develops into the next sporophyte generation. Therefore, in this type of life cycle, the sporophyte generation produces a gametophyte as its offspring, and the gametophyte generation produces the next sporophyte generation **(Figure 13.6b).**

A third type of life cycle occurs in most fungi and some protists, including some algae. After gametes fuse and form a diploid zygote, meiosis occurs without a diploid offspring developing. Meiosis produces not gametes but haploid cells that then divide by mitosis and give rise to a haploid multicellular adult organism. Subsequently, the haploid organism carries out mitosis, producing the cells that develop into gametes. The only diploid stage in these species is the single-celled zygote **(Figure 13.6c).** (Note that *either* haploid or diploid cells can divide by mitosis, depending on the type of life cycle. Only diploid cells, however, can undergo meiosis.)

Though the three types of sexual life cycles differ in the timing of meiosis and fertilization, they share a fundamental

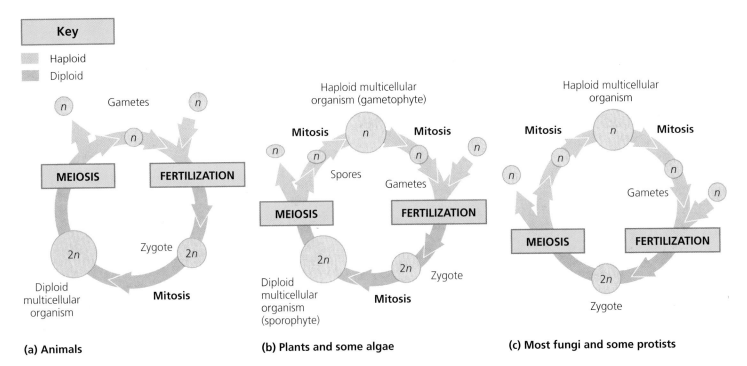

▲ **Figure 13.6 Three types of sexual life cycles.** The common feature of all three cycles is the alternation of meiosis and fertilization, key events that contribute to genetic variation among offspring. The cycles differ in the timing of these two key events.

result: Each cycle of chromosome halving and doubling contributes to genetic variation among offspring. A closer look at meiosis will reveal the sources of this variation.

Concept Check 13.2

1. How does the karyotype of a human female differ from that of a human male?
2. How does the alternation of meiosis and fertilization in the life cycles of sexually reproducing organisms maintain the normal chromosome count for each species?
3. Dog sperm contain 39 chromosomes. What are the haploid number and diploid number for dogs?
4. What process (meiosis or mitosis) is more directly involved in the production of gametes in animals? In plants and most fungi?

For suggested answers, see Appendix A.

Concept 13.3

Meiosis reduces the number of chromosome sets from diploid to haploid

Many of the steps of meiosis closely resemble corresponding steps in mitosis. Meiosis, like mitosis, is preceded by the replication of chromosomes. However, this single replication is followed by two consecutive cell divisions, called **meiosis I** and **meiosis II**. These divisions result in four daughter cells (rather than the two daughter cells of mitosis), each with only half as many chromosomes as the parent cell.

The Stages of Meiosis

The overview of meiosis in **Figure 13.7** shows how both members of a single homologous pair of chromosomes in a diploid cell are replicated and the copies then sorted into four haploid daughter cells. Recall that sister chromatids are two copies of *one* chromosome, attached at the centromere; together they make up one duplicated chromosome (see Figure 13.4). In contrast, the two chromosomes of a homologous pair are individual chromosomes that were inherited from different parents; they are not usually connected to each other. Homologues appear alike in the microscope, but they may have different versions of genes at corresponding loci (for example, a gene for freckles on one chromosome and a gene for the absence of freckles at the same locus on the homologue).

Figure 13.8, on the next two pages, describes in detail the stages of the two divisions of meiosis for an animal cell whose diploid number is 6. Meiosis halves the total number of chro-

▲ **Figure 13.7 Overview of meiosis: how meiosis reduces chromosome number.** After the chromosomes replicate in interphase, the diploid cell divides *twice*, yielding four haploid daughter cells. This overview tracks just one pair of homologous chromosomes, which for the sake of simplicity are drawn in the condensed state throughout (they would not normally be condensed during interphase). The red chromosome was inherited from the female parent, the blue chromosome from the male parent.

mosomes in a very specific way, reducing the number of sets from two to one, with each daughter cell receiving one set of chromosomes. Study Figure 13.8 thoroughly before going on to the next section.

Figure 13.8

Exploring **The Meiotic Division of an Animal Cell**

INTERPHASE	MEIOSIS I: Separates homologous chromosomes		
	PROPHASE I	METAPHASE I	ANAPHASE I

Chromosomes duplicate

Homologous chromosomes (red and blue) pair and exchange segments; 2n = 6 in this example

Tetrads line up

Pairs of homologous chromosomes split up

Interphase

► Chromosomes replicate during S phase but remain uncondensed.

► Each replicated chromosome consists of two genetically identical sister chromatids connected at the centromere.

► The centrosome replicates, forming two centrosomes.

Prophase I

► This phase typically occupies more than 90% of the time required for meiosis.

► Chromosomes begin to condense.

► Homologous chromosomes loosely pair along their lengths, precisely aligned gene by gene.

► In crossing over, the DNA molecules in nonsister chromatids break at corresponding places and then rejoin to the other's DNA.

► In synapsis, a protein structure called the synaptonemal complex forms between homologues, holding them tightly together along their lengths.

► The synaptonemal complex disassembles in late prophase, and each chromosome pair becomes visible in the microscope as a tetrad, a group of four chromatids.

► Each tetrad has one or more chiasmata, criss-crossed regions where crossing over has occurred; these hold the

homologues together until anaphase I.

► The movement of centrosomes, formation of spindle microtubules, breakdown of the nuclear envelope, and dispersal of nucleoli occur as in mitosis.

► In late prophase I (not shown here), the kinetochores of each homologue attach to microtubules from one pole or the other. The homologous pairs then move toward the metaphase plate.

Metaphase I

► The pairs of homologous chromosomes, in the form of tetrads, are now arranged on the metaphase plate, with one

chromosome of each pair facing each pole.

► Both chromatids of a homologue are attached to kinetochore microtubules from one pole; those of the other homologue are attached to microtubules from the opposite pole.

Anaphase I

► The chromosomes move toward the poles, guided by the spindle apparatus.

► Sister chromatids remain attached at the centromere and move as a single unit toward the same pole.

► Homologous chromosomes, each composed of two sister chromatids, move toward opposite poles.

TELOPHASE I AND CYTOKINESIS	PROPHASE II	METAPHASE II	ANAPHASE II	TELOPHASE II AND CYTOKINESIS

Cleavage furrow

Haploid daughter cells forming

Sister chromatids separate

Two haploid cells form; chromosomes are still double

During another round of cell division, the sister chromatids finally separate; four haploid daughter cells result, containing single chromosomes

Telophase I and Cytokinesis

▶ At the beginning of telophase I, each half of the cell has a complete haploid set of chromosomes, but each chromosome is still composed of two sister chromatids.

▶ Cytokinesis (division of the cytoplasm) usually occurs simultaneously with telophase I, forming two haploid daughter cells.

▶ In animal cells, a cleavage furrow forms. (In plant cells, a cell plate forms.)

▶ In some but not all species, the chromosomes decondense and the nuclear envelope and nucleoli re-form.

▶ No chromosome replication occurs between the end of meiosis I and the beginning of meiosis II, as the chromosomes are already replicated.

Prophase II

▶ A spindle apparatus forms.

▶ In late prophase II (not shown here), chromosomes, each still composed of two chromatids, move toward the metaphase II plate.

Metaphase II

▶ The chromosomes are positioned on the metaphase plate as in mitosis.

▶ Because of crossing over in meiosis I, the two sister chromatids of each chromosome are *not* genetically identical.

▶ The kinetochores of sister chromatids are attached to microtubules extending from opposite poles.

Anaphase II

▶ The centromeres of each chromosome finally separate, and the sister chromatids come apart.

▶ The sister chromatids of each chromosome now move as two individual chromosomes toward opposite poles.

Telophase II and Cytokinesis

▶ Nuclei form, the chromosomes begin decondensing, and cytokinesis occurs.

▶ The meiotic division of one parent cell produces four daughter cells, each with a haploid set of (unreplicated) chromosomes.

▶ Each of the four daughter cells is genetically distinct from the other daughter cells and from the parent cell.

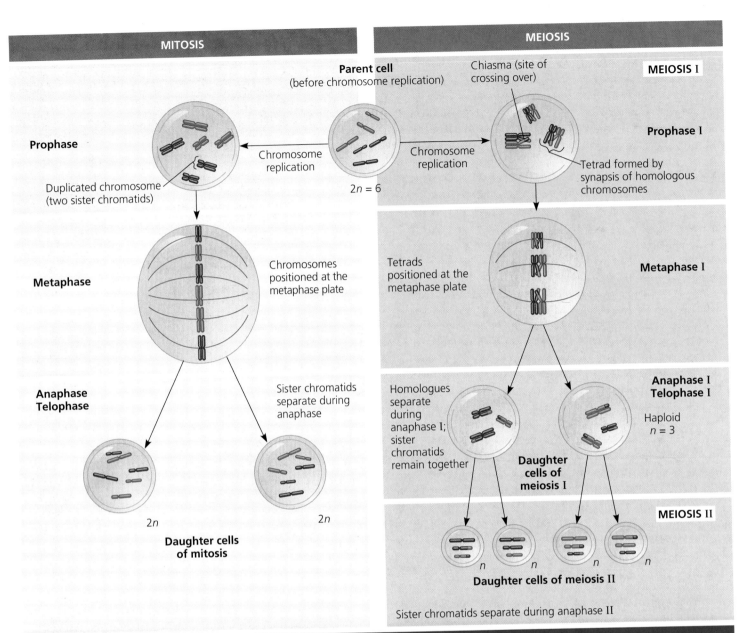

MITOSIS	MEIOSIS

Parent cell (before chromosome replication)

MITOSIS

Prophase

Duplicated chromosome (two sister chromatids)

Chromosome replication

$2n = 6$

Metaphase

Chromosomes positioned at the metaphase plate

Anaphase Telophase

Sister chromatids separate during anaphase

$2n$ $2n$

Daughter cells of mitosis

MEIOSIS

Chiasma (site of crossing over)

MEIOSIS I

Prophase I

Chromosome replication

Tetrad formed by synapsis of homologous chromosomes

Tetrads positioned at the metaphase plate

Metaphase I

Anaphase I Telophase I

Homologues separate during anaphase I; sister chromatids remain together

Haploid $n = 3$

Daughter cells of meiosis I

MEIOSIS II

n n n n

Daughter cells of meiosis II

Sister chromatids separate during anaphase II

SUMMARY

Property	Mitosis	Meiosis
DNA replication	Occurs during interphase before mitosis begins	Occurs during interphase before meiosis I begins
Number of divisions	One, including prophase, metaphase, anaphase, and telophase	Two, each including prophase, metaphase, anaphase, and telophase
Synapsis of homologous chromosomes	Does not occur	Occurs during prophase I, forming tetrads (groups of four chromatids); is associated with crossing over between non-sister chromatids
Number of daughter cells and genetic composition	Two, each diploid ($2n$) and genetically identical to the parent cell	Four, each haploid (n), containing half as many chromosomes as the parent cell; genetically different from the parent cell and from each other
Role in the animal body	Enables multicellular adult to arise from zygote; produces cells for growth and tissue repair	Produces gametes; reduces number of chromosomes by half and introduces genetic variability among the gametes

▲ **Figure 13.9 A comparison of mitosis and meiosis.**

A Comparison of Mitosis and Meiosis

Now let's summarize the key differences between meiosis and mitosis. Meiosis reduces the number of chromosome sets from two (diploid) to one (haploid), whereas mitosis conserves the number of chromosome sets. Therefore, mitosis produces daughter cells genetically identical to their parent cell and to each other, whereas meiosis produces cells that differ genetically from their parent cell and from each other.

Figure 13.9 compares mitosis and meiosis. Three events are unique to meiosis, and all three occur during meiosis I:

1. **Synapsis and crossing over.** During prophase I, duplicated homologous chromosomes line up and become physically connected along their lengths by a zipper-like protein structure, the *synaptonemal complex;* this process is called **synapsis**. Genetic rearrangement between nonsister chromatids, known as **crossing over**, also occurs during prophase I. Following disassembly of the synaptonemal complex in late prophase, the four chromatids of a homologous pair are visible in the light microscope as a **tetrad**. Each tetrad normally contains at least one X-shaped region called a **chiasma** (plural, *chiasmata*), the physical manifestation of crossing over. Synapsis and crossing over normally do not occur during mitosis.

2. **Tetrads on the metaphase plate.** At metaphase I of meiosis, paired homologous chromosomes (tetrads) are positioned on the metaphase plate, rather than individual replicated chromosomes, as in mitosis.

3. **Separation of homologues.** At anaphase I of meiosis, the duplicated chromosomes of each homologous pair move toward opposite poles, but the sister chromatids of each duplicated chromosome remain attached. In mitosis, sister chromatids separate.

Meiosis I is called the *reductional division* because it halves the number of chromosome sets per cell—a reduction from two sets (the diploid state) to one set (the haploid state). The sister chromatids then separate during the second meiotic division, meiosis II, producing haploid daughter cells. The mechanism for separating sister chromatids is virtually identical in meiosis II and mitosis.

Concept Check 13.3

1. Using the concept of chromosome sets, explain briefly how mitosis conserves chromosome number, whereas meiosis reduces the number of chromosomes by half.
2. How are the chromosomes in a cell at metaphase of mitosis similar to and different from the chromosomes in a cell at metaphase of meiosis II?

For suggested answers, see Appendix A.

Concept 13.4

Genetic variation produced in sexual life cycles contributes to evolution

How do we account for the genetic variation illustrated in Figure 13.1? As you will learn in later chapters, mutations are the original source of genetic diversity. These changes in an organism's DNA create different versions of genes. Once these differences arise, reshuffling of the versions during sexual reproduction produces the variation that results in each member of a species having its own unique combination of traits.

Origins of Genetic Variation Among Offspring

In species that reproduce sexually, the behavior of chromosomes during meiosis and fertilization is responsible for most of the variation that arises each generation. Let's examine three mechanisms that contribute to the genetic variation arising from sexual reproduction: independent assortment of chromosomes, crossing over, and random fertilization.

Independent Assortment of Chromosomes

One aspect of sexual reproduction that generates genetic variation is the random orientation of homologous pairs of chromosomes at metaphase of meiosis I. At metaphase I, the homologous pairs, each consisting of one maternal and one paternal chromosome, are situated on the metaphase plate. (Note that the terms *maternal* and *paternal* refer, respectively, to the mother and father of the individual whose cells are undergoing meiosis.) Each pair may orient with either its maternal or paternal homologue closer to a given pole—its orientation is as random as the flip of a coin. Thus, there is a 50% chance that a particular daughter cell of meiosis I will get the maternal chromosome of a certain homologous pair and a 50% chance that it will receive the paternal chromosome.

Because each homologous pair of chromosomes is positioned independently of the other pairs at metaphase I, the first meiotic division results in each pair sorting its maternal and paternal homologues into daughter cells independently of every other pair. This is called *independent assortment*. Each daughter cell represents one outcome of all possible combinations of maternal and paternal chromosomes. As shown in **Figure 13.10** on the next page, the number of combinations possible for daughter cells formed by meiosis of a diploid cell with two homologous pairs of chromosomes ($2n = 4$) is four. Note that only two of the four combinations of daughter cells shown in the figure would result from meiosis of a *single* diploid cell, because a single parent cell would have one or the other possible chromosomal arrangement at metaphase I, but not both. However, the population of daughter cells resulting from meiosis of a large number of diploid cells contains all four types in approximately equal numbers. In the case of $n = 3$, eight combinations of chromosomes are possible for daughter cells. More generally, the number of possible combinations when chromosomes sort independently during meiosis is 2^n, where n is the haploid number of the organism.

In the case of humans, the haploid number (n) in the formula is 23. Thus, the number of possible combinations of maternal and paternal chromosomes in the resulting gametes is 2^{23}, or about 8 million. Each gamete that you produce in your lifetime contains one of roughly 8 million possible combinations of chromosomes inherited from your mother and father.

▲ Figure 13.10 **The independent assortment of homologous chromosomes in meiosis.**

Crossing Over

As a consequence of the independent assortment of chromosomes during meiosis, each of us produces a collection of gametes differing greatly in their combinations of the chromosomes we inherited from our two parents. Figure 13.10 suggests that each individual chromosome in a gamete is exclusively maternal or paternal in origin. In fact, this is *not* the case, because crossing over produces **recombinant chromosomes**, individual chromosomes that carry genes (DNA) derived from two different parents **(Figure 13.11)**.

Crossing over begins very early in prophase I, as homologous chromosomes pair loosely along their lengths. Each gene on one homologue is aligned precisely with the corresponding gene on the other homologue. In a single crossover event, the DNA molecules of two *nonsister* chromatids—one maternal and one paternal chromatid of a homologous pair—are broken at the same place and then rejoined to each other's DNA. That is, the segment of each sister chromatid from the break point to the end is joined to the rest of the other chromatid. In effect, two homologous segments trade places, or cross over, producing chromosomes with new combinations of maternal and paternal genes (see Figure 13.11).

In humans, an average of one to three crossover events occur per chromosome pair, depending on the size of the chromosomes and the position of their centromeres. Recent research indicates that, in some species, crossing over may be essential for synapsis and the proper assortment of chromosomes in meiosis I. However, the exact relationship between crossing over and synapsis is not yet fully understood and seems to vary among species.

At metaphase II, chromosomes that contain one or more recombinant chromatids can be oriented in two alternative, nonequivalent ways with respect to other chromosomes, because their sister chromatids are no longer identical twins. The independent assortment of these nonidentical sister chromatids during meiosis II increases even more the number of genetic types of daughter cells that can result from meiosis.

You will learn more about crossing over in Chapter 15. The important point for now is that crossing over, by combining DNA inherited from two parents into a single chromosome, is an important source of genetic variation in sexual life cycles.

Random Fertilization

The random nature of fertilization adds to the genetic variation arising from meiosis. In humans, for instance, each male and female gamete represents one of approximately 8 million possible chromosome combinations due to independent assortment during meiosis. The fusion of a single male gamete with a single female gamete during fertilization will produce a zygote with any of about 64 trillion (8 million × 8 million) diploid combinations. (If you calculate $2^{23} \times 2^{23}$ exactly, you will find that the total is actually over 70 trillion.) Adding in the variation brought about by crossing over, the number of possibilities is truly astronomical. No wonder brothers and sisters can be so different. You really *are* unique.

Evolutionary Significance of Genetic Variation Within Populations

Now that you've learned how new combinations of genes arise among offspring in a sexually reproducing population, let's see how the genetic variation in a population relates to evolution. Darwin recognized that a population evolves through the differential reproductive success of its variant members. On

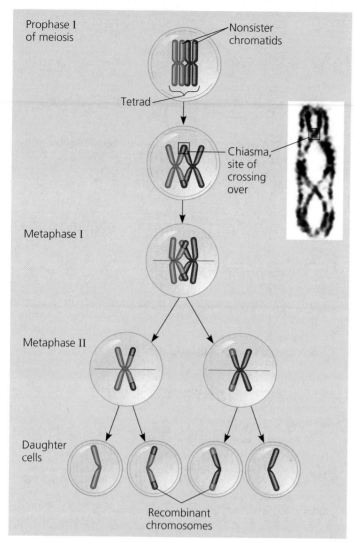

Prophase I of meiosis

Nonsister chromatids

Tetrad

Chiasma, site of crossing over

Metaphase I

Metaphase II

Daughter cells

Recombinant chromosomes

▲ **Figure 13.11** **The results of crossing over during meiosis.**

average, those individuals best suited to the local environment leave the most offspring, thus transmitting their genes. This natural selection results in the accumulation of those genetic variations favored by the environment. As the environment changes, the population may survive if, in each generation, at least some of its members can cope effectively with the new conditions. Different genetic variations may work better than those that previously prevailed. In this chapter, we have seen how sexual reproduction contributes to the genetic variation present in a population, which ultimately results from mutations.

Although Darwin realized that heritable variation is what makes evolution possible, he could not explain why offspring resemble—but are not identical to—their parents. Ironically, Gregor Mendel, a contemporary of Darwin, published a theory of inheritance that helps explain genetic variation, but his discoveries had no impact on biologists until 1900, more than 15 years after Darwin (1809–1882) and Mendel (1822–1884) had died. In the next chapter, you will learn how Mendel discovered the basic rules governing the inheritance of specific traits.

Concept Check 13.4

1. Fruit flies have a diploid number of 8, and honeybees have a diploid number of 32. Assuming no crossing over, is the genetic variation among offspring from the same two parents likely to be greater in fruit flies or honeybees? Explain.
2. Under what circumstances would crossing over during meiosis *not* contribute to genetic variation among daughter cells?

For suggested answers, see Appendix A.

Chapter 13 Review

Go to the Campbell Biology website (**www.campbellbiology.com**) or CD-ROM to explore Activities, Investigations, and other interactive study aids.

SUMMARY OF KEY CONCEPTS

Concept 13.1

Offspring acquire genes from parents by inheriting chromosomes

▶ **Inheritance of Genes** (p. 239) Each gene in an organism's DNA has a specific locus on a certain chromosome. We inherit one set of chromosomes from our mother and one set from our father.

▶ **Comparison of Asexual and Sexual Reproduction** (p. 239) In asexual reproduction, one parent produces genetically identical offspring by mitosis. Sexual reproduction combines sets of genes from two different parents, forming genetically diverse offspring.
Activity Asexual and Sexual Life Cycles

Concept 13.2

Fertilization and meiosis alternate in sexual life cycles

▶ **Sets of Chromosomes in Human Cells** (pp. 240–241) Normal human somatic cells have 46 chromosomes made up of two sets—one set of 23 chromosomes derived from each parent. In diploid cells (2n = 46), each of the 22 maternal autosomes has a homologous paternal chromosome. The 23rd pair, the sex chromosomes, determines whether the person is female (XX) or male (XY).

▶ **Behavior of Chromosome Sets in the Human Life Cycle** (pp. 241–242) At sexual maturity, ovaries and testes (the gonads) produce haploid gametes by meiosis, each gamete containing a single set of 23 chromosomes. During fertilization, an ovum and sperm unite, forming a diploid (2n) single-celled zygote, which develops into a multicellular organism by mitosis.

▶ **The Variety of Sexual Life Cycles** (pp. 242–243) Sexual life cycles differ in the timing of meiosis in relation to fertilization. Multicellular organisms may be diploid or haploid or may alternate between haploid and diploid generations.

Meiosis reduces the number of chromosome sets from diploid to haploid

▶ **The Stages of Meiosis** (pp. 243–245) The two cell divisions of meiosis produce four haploid daughter cells. The number of chromosome sets is reduced from diploid to haploid during meiosis I, the reductional division.

▶ **A Comparison of Mitosis and Meiosis** (pp. 246–247) Meiosis is distinguished from mitosis by three events of meiosis I: synapsis, which is associated with crossing over; positioning of paired homologous chromosomes (tetrads) on the metaphase plate; and movement of the two chromosomes of each homologous pair (not the sister chromatids) to opposite poles during anaphase I. Meiosis II separates the sister chromatids.
Activity *Meiosis Animation*

Concept 13.4

Genetic variation produced in sexual life cycles contributes to evolution

▶ **Origins of Genetic Variation Among Offspring** (pp. 247–249) The events of sexual reproduction that contribute to genetic variation in a population are independent assortment of chromosomes during meiosis, crossing over during meiosis I, and random fertilization of egg cells by sperm.
Activity *Origins of Genetic Variation*
Investigation *How Can the Frequency of Crossing Over Be Estimated?*

▶ **Evolutionary Significance of Genetic Variation Within Populations** (pp. 248–249) Genetic variation is the raw material for evolution by natural selection. Mutations are the original source of this variation; the production of new combinations of variant genes in sexual reproduction generates additional genetic diversity.

TESTING YOUR KNOWLEDGE

Self-Quiz

1. A human cell containing 22 autosomes and a Y chromosome is
   a. a somatic cell of a male.
   b. a zygote.
   c. a somatic cell of a female.
   d. a sperm cell.
   e. an ovum.

2. Homologous chromosomes move toward opposite poles of a dividing cell during
   a. mitosis.
   b. meiosis I.
   c. meiosis II.
   d. fertilization.
   e. binary fission.

3. Meiosis II is similar to mitosis in that
   a. homologous chromosomes synapse.
   b. DNA replicates before the division.
   c. the daughter cells are diploid.
   d. sister chromatids separate during anaphase.
   e. the chromosome number is reduced.

4. If the DNA content of a diploid cell in the G_1 phase of the cell cycle is x, then the DNA content of the same cell at metaphase of meiosis I would be
   a. $0.25x$.   b. $0.5x$.   c. x.   d. $2x$.   e. $4x$.

5. If we continued to follow the cell lineage from question 4, then the DNA content at metaphase of meiosis II would be
   a. $0.25x$.   b. $0.5x$.   c. x.   d. $2x$.   e. $4x$.

6. How many different combinations of maternal and paternal chromosomes can be packaged in gametes made by an organism with a diploid number of 8 ($2n = 8$)?
   a. 2   b. 4   c. 8   d. 16   e. 32

7. The immediate product of meiosis in a plant is a
   a. spore.   c. sporophyte.   e. zygote.
   b. gamete.   d. gametophyte.

8. Multicellular haploid organisms
   a. are typically called sporophytes.
   b. produce new cells for growth by meiosis.
   c. produce gametes by mitosis.
   d. are found only in aquatic environments.
   e. are the direct result of fertilization.

9. Crossing over usually contributes to genetic variation by exchanging chromosomal segments between
   a. sister chromatids of a chromosome.
   b. chromatids of nonhomologues.
   c. nonsister chromatids of homologues.
   d. nonhomologous loci of the genome.
   e. autosomes and sex chromosomes.

10. In comparing the typical life cycles of plants and animals, a stage found in plants but not in animals is a
    a. gamete.   c. multicellular diploid.
    b. zygote.   d. multicellular haploid.

For Self-Quiz answers, see Appendix A.

Go to the website or CD-ROM for more quiz questions.

Evolution Connection

Many species can reproduce either asexually or sexually. Speculate about the evolutionary significance of the switch from asexual to sexual reproduction that occurs in some organisms when the environment becomes unfavorable.

Scientific Inquiry

You prepare a karyotype of an animal you are studying and discover that its somatic cells each have three homologous sets of chromosomes, a condition called triploidy. What might have happened?

Investigation *How Can the Frequency of Crossing Over Be Estimated?*

Science, Technology, and Society

Starting with short pieces of needles from straight, fast-growing pine trees, we can grow thousands of genetically identical trees that are superior producers of lumber. What are the short-term and long-term benefits and drawbacks of this approach?

14

Mendel and the Gene Idea

Key Concepts

14.1 Mendel used the scientific approach to identify two laws of inheritance

14.2 The laws of probability govern Mendelian inheritance

14.3 Inheritance patterns are often more complex than predicted by simple Mendelian genetics

14.4 Many human traits follow Mendelian patterns of inheritance

Overview

Drawing from the Deck of Genes

Eyes of brown, blue, green, or gray; hair of black, brown, blond, or red—these are just a few examples of heritable variations that we may observe among individuals in a population. What genetic principles account for the transmission of such traits from parents to offspring?

One possible explanation of heredity is a "blending" hypothesis, the idea that genetic material contributed by the two parents mixes in a manner analogous to the way blue and yellow paints blend to make green. This hypothesis predicts that over many generations, a freely mating population will give rise to a uniform population of individuals. However, our everyday observations and the results of breeding experiments with animals and plants contradict such a prediction. The blending hypothesis also fails to explain other phenomena of inheritance, such as traits reappearing after skipping a generation.

An alternative to the blending model is a "particulate" hypothesis of inheritance: the gene idea. According to this model, parents pass on discrete heritable units—genes—that retain their separate identities in offspring. An organism's collection of genes is more like a deck of cards or a bucket of marbles than a pail of paint. Like cards and marbles, genes can be sorted and passed along, generation after generation, in undiluted form.

Modern genetics had its genesis in an abbey garden, where a monk named Gregor Mendel documented a particulate mechanism of inheritance. The painting in **Figure 14.1** depicts Mendel working with his experimental organism, garden peas. Mendel developed his theory of inheritance several decades before the behavior of chromosomes was observed in the microscope and their significance understood. So in this chapter, we digress from the study of chromosomes to recount how Mendel arrived at his theory. We will also explore how to predict the inheritance of certain characteristics and consider inheritance patterns more complex than those Mendel observed in garden peas. Finally, we will see how the Mendelian model applies to the inheritance of human variations, including hereditary disorders such as sickle-cell disease.

Concept 14.1

Mendel used the scientific approach to identify two laws of inheritance

Mendel discovered the basic principles of heredity by breeding garden peas in carefully planned experiments. As we retrace his work, the key elements of the scientific process that were introduced in Chapter 1 will be evident.

Mendel's Experimental, Quantitative Approach

Mendel grew up on his parents' small farm in a region of Austria that is now part of the Czech Republic. At school in this agricultural area, Mendel and the other children received agricultural training along with basic education. Later, Mendel overcame financial hardship and illness to excel in high school and at the Olmutz Philosophical Institute.

In 1843, at the age of 21, Mendel entered an Augustinian monastery. After failing an examination to become a teacher, he went to the University of Vienna, where he studied from 1851 to 1853. These were very important years for Mendel's development as a scientist. Two professors were especially influential. One was the physicist Christian Doppler, who encouraged his students to learn science through experimentation and trained Mendel to use mathematics to help explain natural phenomena. The second was a botanist named Franz Unger, who aroused Mendel's interest in the causes of variation in plants. These influences came together in Mendel's subsequent experiments with garden peas.

After attending the university, Mendel was assigned to teach at a school where several other teachers shared his enthusiasm for scientific research. What's more, many university professors and researchers lived at the monastery with Mendel. Most important, the monks had a long-standing interest in the breeding of plants. Around 1857, Mendel began breeding garden peas in the abbey garden in order to study inheritance. In itself, this does not seem extraordinary. What *was* extraordinary was Mendel's fresh approach to very old questions about heredity.

Mendel most likely chose to work with peas because they are available in many varieties. For example, one variety has purple flowers, while another variety has white flowers. A **character** is a heritable feature, such as flower color, that varies among individuals. Each variant for a character, such as purple or white color for flowers, is called a **trait.** (Some geneticists use the terms *character* and *trait* synonymously, but in this book we distinguish between them.)

Another advantage in using peas was that Mendel could strictly control which plants mated with which. The reproductive organs of a pea plant are in its flowers, and each pea flower has both pollen-producing organs (stamens) and an egg-bearing organ (carpel). In nature, pea plants usually self-fertilize: Pollen grains released from the stamens land on the carpel of the same flower, and sperm from the pollen fertilize eggs in the carpel. To achieve cross-pollination (fertilization between different plants), Mendel removed the immature stamens of a plant before they produced pollen and then dusted pollen from another plant onto the altered flowers **(Figure 14.2)**. Each resulting zygote then developed into a plant embryo encased in a seed (pea). Whether ensuring self-pollination or executing artificial cross-pollination, Mendel could always be sure of the parentage of new seeds.

Mendel chose to track only those characters that varied in an "either-or" manner rather than a "more-or-less" manner. For example, his plants had either purple flowers or white flowers; there was nothing intermediate between these two varieties. Had Mendel focused instead on characters that varied in a continuum among individuals—seed weight, for example—he would not have discovered the particulate nature of inheritance (you'll learn why later).

Mendel also made sure that he started his experiments with varieties that were **true-breeding.** When true-breeding plants self-pollinate, all their offspring are of the same variety. For example, a plant with purple flowers is true-breeding if

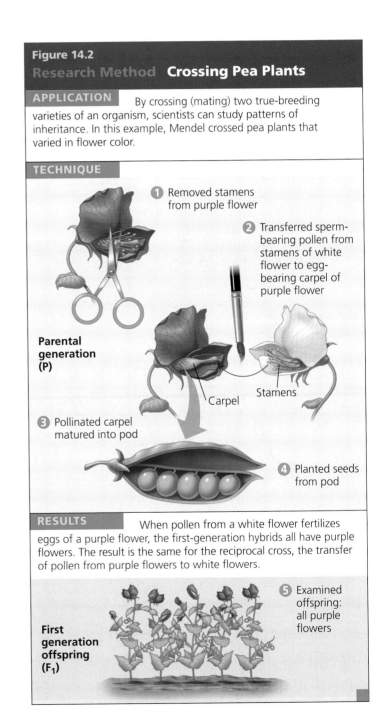

Figure 14.2

Research Method   **Crossing Pea Plants**

APPLICATION   By crossing (mating) two true-breeding varieties of an organism, scientists can study patterns of inheritance. In this example, Mendel crossed pea plants that varied in flower color.

TECHNIQUE

1 Removed stamens from purple flower

2 Transferred sperm-bearing pollen from stamens of white flower to egg-bearing carpel of purple flower

Parental generation (P)

Carpel

Stamens

3 Pollinated carpel matured into pod

4 Planted seeds from pod

RESULTS   When pollen from a white flower fertilizes eggs of a purple flower, the first-generation hybrids all have purple flowers. The result is the same for the reciprocal cross, the transfer of pollen from purple flowers to white flowers.

First generation offspring (F_1)

5 Examined offspring: all purple flowers

the seeds produced by self-pollination all give rise to plants that also have purple flowers.

In a typical breeding experiment, Mendel cross-pollinated two contrasting, true-breeding pea varieties—for example, purple-flowered plants and white-flowered plants (see Figure 14.2). This mating, or crossing, of two true-breeding varieties is called **hybridization.** The true-breeding parents are referred to as the **P generation** (parental generation), and their hybrid offspring are the **F$_1$ generation** (first filial generation, the word *filial* from the Latin word for "son"). Allowing these F$_1$ hybrids to self-pollinate produces an **F$_2$ generation** (second filial generation). Mendel usually followed traits for at least the P, F$_1$, and F$_2$ generations. Had Mendel stopped his experiments with the F$_1$ generation, the basic patterns of inheritance would have eluded him. It was mainly Mendel's quantitative analysis of F$_2$ plants that revealed the two fundamental principles of heredity that are now known as the law of segregation and the law of independent assortment.

The Law of Segregation

If the blending model of inheritance were correct, the F$_1$ hybrids from a cross between purple-flowered and white-flowered pea plants would have pale purple flowers, intermediate between the two varieties of the P generation. Notice in Figure 14.2 that the experiment produced a very different result: All the F$_1$ offspring had flowers just as purple as the purple-flowered parents. What happened to the white-flowered plants' genetic contribution to the hybrids? If it were lost, then the F$_1$ plants could produce only purple-flowered offspring in the F$_2$ generation. But when Mendel allowed the F$_1$ plants to self-pollinate and planted their seeds, the white-flower trait reappeared in the F$_2$ generation.

Mendel used very large sample sizes and kept accurate records of his results: 705 of the F$_2$ plants had purple flowers, and 224 had white flowers. These data fit a ratio of approximately three purple to one white **(Figure 14.3)**. Mendel reasoned that the heritable factor for white flowers did not disappear in the F$_1$ plants, but only the purple-flower factor was affecting flower color in these hybrids. In Mendel's terminology, purple flower color is a *dominant* trait and white flower color is a *recessive* trait. The reappearance of white-flowered plants in the F$_2$ generation was evidence that the heritable factor causing that recessive trait had not been diluted by coexisting with the purple-flower factor in the F$_1$ hybrids.

Mendel observed the same pattern of inheritance in six other characters, each represented by two different traits **(Table 14.1**, on the next page). For example, the parental pea seeds either had a smooth, round shape or were wrinkled. When Mendel crossed his two true-breeding varieties, all the F$_1$ hybrids produced round seeds; this is the dominant trait. In the F$_2$ generation, 75% of the seeds were

round and 25% were wrinkled—a 3:1 ratio, as in Figure 14.3. Now let's see how Mendel deduced the law of segregation from his experimental results. In our discussion, we will use modern terms instead of some of the terms used by Mendel (for example, we'll use "gene" instead of Mendel's "heritable factor").

Mendel's Model

Mendel developed a hypothesis, or model, to explain the 3:1 inheritance pattern that he consistently observed among the F$_2$ offspring in his pea experiments. We describe four related concepts making up this model, the fourth of which is the law of segregation.

First, *alternative versions of genes account for variations in inherited characters.* The gene for flower color in pea plants, for example, exists in two versions, one for purple flowers and the other for white. These alternative versions of a gene are

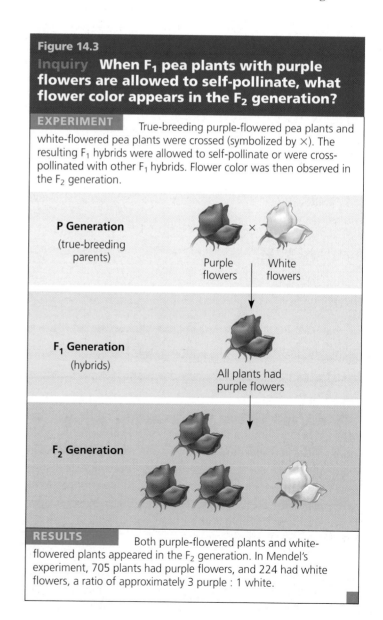

Figure 14.3

Inquiry **When F$_1$ pea plants with purple flowers are allowed to self-pollinate, what flower color appears in the F$_2$ generation?**

EXPERIMENT True-breeding purple-flowered pea plants and white-flowered pea plants were crossed (symbolized by ✕). The resulting F$_1$ hybrids were allowed to self-pollinate or were cross-pollinated with other F$_1$ hybrids. Flower color was then observed in the F$_2$ generation.

P Generation
(true-breeding parents)

Purple flowers ✕ White flowers

F$_1$ Generation
(hybrids)

All plants had purple flowers

F$_2$ Generation

RESULTS Both purple-flowered plants and white-flowered plants appeared in the F$_2$ generation. In Mendel's experiment, 705 plants had purple flowers, and 224 had white flowers, a ratio of approximately 3 purple : 1 white.

Table 14.1 The Results of Mendel's F₁ Crosses for Seven Characters in Pea Plants

Character	Dominant Trait	×	Recessive Trait	F₂ Generation Dominant:Recessive	Ratio
Flower color	Purple	×	White	705:224	3.15:1
Flower position	Axial	×	Terminal	651:207	3.14:1
Seed color	Yellow	×	Green	6022:2001	3.01:1
Seed shape	Round	×	Wrinkled	5474:1850	2.96:1
Pod shape	Inflated	×	Constricted	882:299	2.95:1
Pod color	Green	×	Yellow	428:152	2.82:1
Stem length	Tall	×	Dwarf	787:277	2.84:1

now called **alleles (Figure 14.4)**. Today, we can relate this concept to chromosomes and DNA. As noted in Chapter 13, each gene resides at a specific locus on a specific chromosome. The DNA at that locus, however, can vary somewhat in its sequence of nucleotides and hence in its information content. The purple-flower allele and the white-flower allele are two DNA variations possible at the flower-color locus on one of a pea plant's chromosomes.

Second, *for each character, an organism inherits two alleles, one from each parent.* Remarkably, Mendel made this deduction without knowing about the role of chromosomes. Recall from Chapter 13 that each somatic cell in a diploid

organism has two sets of chromosomes, one set inherited from each parent. Thus, a genetic locus is actually represented twice in a diploid cell. The two alleles at a particular locus may be identical, as in the true-breeding plants of Mendel's P generation. Or the alleles may differ, as in the F₁ hybrids (see Figure 14.4).

Third, *if the two alleles at a locus differ, then one, the **dominant allele**, determines the organism's appearance; the other, the **recessive allele**, has no noticeable effect on the organism's appearance.* Thus, Mendel's F₁ plants had purple flowers because the allele for that trait is dominant and the allele for white flowers is recessive.

The fourth and final part of Mendel's model, now known as the **law of segregation**, states that *the two alleles for a heritable character separate (segregate) during gamete formation and end up in different gametes.* Thus, an egg or a sperm gets only one of the two alleles that are present in the somatic cells of the organism. In terms of chromosomes, this segregation corresponds to the distribution of homologous chromosomes to different gametes in meiosis (see Figure 13.7). Note that if an organism has identical alleles for a particular character—that is, the organism is true-breeding for that character—then that allele is present in all gametes. But if different alleles are present, as in the F₁ hybrids, then 50% of the gametes receive the dominant allele and 50% receive the recessive allele.

Does Mendel's segregation model account for the 3:1 ratio he observed in the F₂ generation of his numerous crosses? For the flower-color character, the model predicts that the two different alleles present in an F₁ individual will segregate into gametes such that half the gametes will have the purple-flower allele and half will have the white-flower allele. During self-pollination, gametes of each class unite randomly. An egg with a purple-flower allele has an equal chance of being fertilized by a sperm with a purple-flower allele or one with a white-flower allele. Since the same is true for an egg with a white-flower allele, there are a total of four equally likely combinations of sperm and egg. **Figure 14.5** illustrates these combinations using a **Punnett square**, a handy diagrammatic device for predicting the allele composition of offspring from a cross between individuals of known genetic makeup. Notice that we use a capital letter to symbolize a dominant allele and a lowercase letter for a recessive allele. In our example, *P* is the purple-flower allele, and *p* is the white-flower allele.

▲ **Figure 14.4 Alleles, alternative versions of a gene.** A somatic cell has two copies of each chromosome (forming a homologous pair) and thus two alleles of each gene, which may be identical or different. This figure depicts an F_1 pea hybrid with an allele for purple flowers, inherited from one parent, and an allele for white flowers, inherited from the other parent.

What will be the physical appearance of these F_2 offspring? One-fourth of the plants have inherited two purple-flower alleles; clearly, these plants will have purple flowers. One-half of the F_2 offspring have inherited one purple-flower allele and one white-flower allele; these plants will also have purple flowers, the dominant trait. Finally, one-fourth of the F_2 plants have inherited two white-flower alleles and will, in fact, express the recessive trait. Thus, Mendel's model accounts for the 3:1 ratio of traits that he observed in the F_2 generation.

Useful Genetic Vocabulary

An organism having a pair of identical alleles for a character is said to be **homozygous** for the gene controlling that character. A pea plant that is true-breeding for purple flowers (*PP*) is an example. Pea plants with white flowers are also homozygous, but for the recessive allele (*pp*). If we cross dominant homozygotes with recessive homozygotes, as in the parental (P generation) cross of Figure 14.5, every offspring will have two different alleles—*Pp* in the case of the F_1 hybrids of our flower-color experiment. An organism that has two different alleles for a gene is said to be **heterozygous** for that gene. Unlike

▶ **Figure 14.5 Mendel's law of segregation.** This diagram shows the genetic makeup of the generations in Figure 14.3. It illustrates Mendel's model for inheritance of the alleles of a single gene. Each plant has two alleles for the gene controlling flower color, one allele inherited from each parent. To construct a Punnett square, list all the possible female gametes along one side of the square and all the possible male gametes along an adjacent side. The boxes represent the offspring resulting from all the possible unions of male and female gametes.

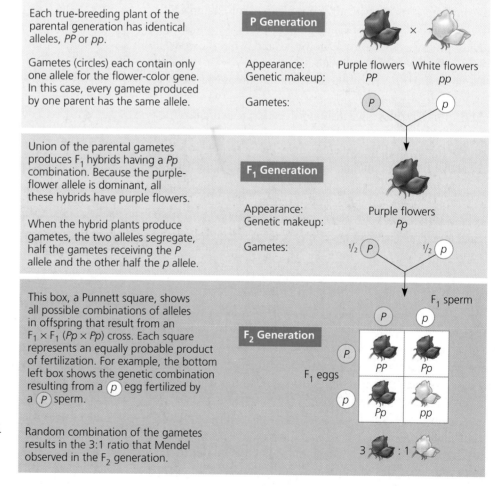

Each true-breeding plant of the parental generation has identical alleles, *PP* or *pp*.

Gametes (circles) each contain only one allele for the flower-color gene. In this case, every gamete produced by one parent has the same allele.

Union of the parental gametes produces F_1 hybrids having a *Pp* combination. Because the purple-flower allele is dominant, all these hybrids have purple flowers.

When the hybrid plants produce gametes, the two alleles segregate, half the gametes receiving the *P* allele and the other half the *p* allele.

This box, a Punnett square, shows all possible combinations of alleles in offspring that result from an $F_1 \times F_1$ (*Pp* × *Pp*) cross. Each square represents an equally probable product of fertilization. For example, the bottom left box shows the genetic combination resulting from a (*p*) egg fertilized by a (*P*) sperm.

Random combination of the gametes results in the 3:1 ratio that Mendel observed in the F_2 generation.

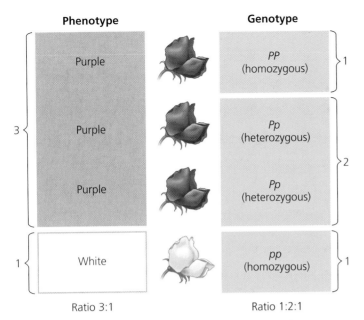

Phenotype | Genotype

3 {
Purple — PP (homozygous) } 1

Purple — Pp (heterozygous)

Purple — Pp (heterozygous) } 2

1 {
White — pp (homozygous) } 1

Ratio 3:1 | Ratio 1:2:1

▲ **Figure 14.6 Phenotype versus genotype.** Grouping F₂ offspring from a cross for flower color according to phenotype results in the typical 3:1 phenotypic ratio. In terms of genotype, however, there are actually two categories of purple-flowered plants, *PP* (homozygous) and *Pp* (heterozygous), giving a 1:2:1 genotypic ratio.

homozygotes, heterozygotes are not true-breeding because they produce gametes with different alleles—for example, *P* and *p* in the F₁ hybrids of Figure 14.5. As a result, those F₁ hybrids produce both purple-flowered and white-flowered offspring when they self-pollinate.

Because of the different effects of dominant and recessive alleles, an organism's traits do not always reveal its genetic composition. Therefore, we distinguish between an organism's traits, called its **phenotype,** and its genetic makeup, its **genotype.** In the case of flower color in pea plants, *PP* and *Pp* plants have the same phenotype (purple) but different genotypes. **Figure 14.6** reviews these terms. Note that phenotype refers to physiological traits as well as traits relating directly to appearance. For example, there is a pea variety that lacks the normal trait of being able to self-pollinate. This physiological variation is a phenotype.

The Testcross

Suppose we have a pea plant that has purple flowers. We cannot tell from its flower color if this plant is homozygous or heterozygous because the genotypes *PP* and *Pp* result in the same phenotype. But if we cross this pea plant with one having white flowers, the appearance of the offspring will reveal the genotype of the purple-flowered parent **(Figure 14.7).** Because white flowers is a recessive trait, the white-flowered parent must be homozygous (*pp*). If all the offspring of the cross have purple flowers, then the other parent must be homozygous for the dominant allele, because a *PP* × *pp*

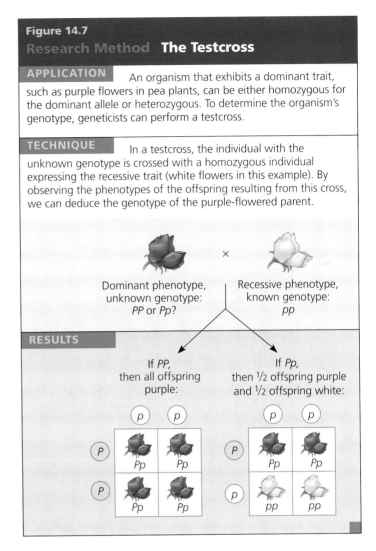

Figure 14.7

Research Method   The Testcross

APPLICATION An organism that exhibits a dominant trait, such as purple flowers in pea plants, can be either homozygous for the dominant allele or heterozygous. To determine the organism's genotype, geneticists can perform a testcross.

TECHNIQUE In a testcross, the individual with the unknown genotype is crossed with a homozygous individual expressing the recessive trait (white flowers in this example). By observing the phenotypes of the offspring resulting from this cross, we can deduce the genotype of the purple-flowered parent.

Dominant phenotype, unknown genotype: *PP* or *Pp*? × Recessive phenotype, known genotype: *pp*

RESULTS

If *PP*, then all offspring purple:

	p	p
P	Pp	Pp
P	Pp	Pp

If *Pp*, then ½ offspring purple and ½ offspring white:

	p	p
P	Pp	Pp
p	pp	pp

cross produces all *Pp* offspring. But if both the purple and the white phenotypes appear among the offspring, then the purple-flowered parent must be heterozygous. The offspring of a *Pp* × *pp* cross will have a 1:1 phenotypic ratio. This breeding of a recessive homozygote with an organism of dominant phenotype but unknown genotype is called a **testcross.** It was devised by Mendel and continues to be an important tool of geneticists.

The Law of Independent Assortment

Mendel derived the law of segregation by performing breeding experiments in which he followed only a *single* character, such as flower color. All the F₁ progeny produced in his crosses of true-breeding parents were **monohybrids,** meaning that they were heterozygous for one character. We refer to a cross between such heterozygotes as a *monohybrid cross.*

Mendel identified his second law of inheritance by following *two* characters at the same time. For instance, two of the seven characters Mendel studied were seed color and seed shape. Seeds may be either yellow or green. They also may be either round (smooth) or wrinkled. From single-character crosses, Mendel knew that the allele for yellow seeds is dominant (Y) and that the allele for green seeds is recessive (y). For the seed-shape character, the allele for round is dominant (R), and the allele for wrinkled is recessive (r).

Imagine crossing two true-breeding pea varieties differing in *both* of these characters—a parental cross between a plant with yellow-round seeds ($YYRR$) and a plant with green-wrinkled seeds ($yyrr$). The F_1 plants will be **dihybrids,** heterozygous for both characters ($YyRr$). But are these two characters, seed color and seed shape, transmitted from parents to offspring as a package? Put another way, will the Y and R alleles always stay together, generation after generation? Or are seed color and seed shape inherited independently of each other? **Figure 14.8** illustrates how a *dihybrid cross*, a cross between F_1 dihybrids, can determine which of these two hypotheses is correct.

The F_1 plants, of genotype $YyRr$, exhibit both dominant phenotypes, yellow seeds with round shapes, no matter which hypothesis is correct. The key step in the experiment is to see what happens when F_1 plants self-pollinate and produce F_2 offspring. If the hybrids must transmit their alleles in the same combinations in which they were inherited from the P generation, then there will only be two classes of gametes: YR and yr. This hypothesis predicts that the phenotypic ratio of the F_2 generation will be 3:1, just as in a monohybrid cross (see Figure 14.8).

The alternative hypothesis is that the two pairs of alleles segregate independently of each other. In other words, genes are packaged into gametes in all possible allelic combinations, as long as each gamete has one allele for each gene. In our example, four classes of gametes would be produced by an F_1 plant in equal quantities: YR, Yr, yR, and yr. If sperm of the four classes are mixed with eggs of the four classes, there will be 16 (4 × 4) equally probable ways in which the alleles can combine in the F_2 generation, as shown in the Punnett square on the right in Figure 14.8. These combinations make up four phenotypic categories with a ratio of 9:3:3:1 (nine yellow-round to three green-round to three yellow-wrinkled to one green-wrinkled). When Mendel did the

experiment and "scored" (classified) the F_2 offspring, his results were close to the predicted 9:3:3:1 phenotypic ratio, supporting the hypothesis that each character—seed color or seed shape—is inherited independently of the other character.

Mendel tested his seven pea characters in various dihybrid combinations and always observed a 9:3:3:1 phenotypic ratio in the F_2 generation. Notice in Figure 14.8, however, that, if you consider the two characters separately, there is a 3:1 phenotypic ratio for each: three yellow to one green; three round to one wrinkled. As far as a single character is concerned, the alleles segregate as if this were a monohybrid cross. The results of Mendel's dihybrid experiments are the basis for what we

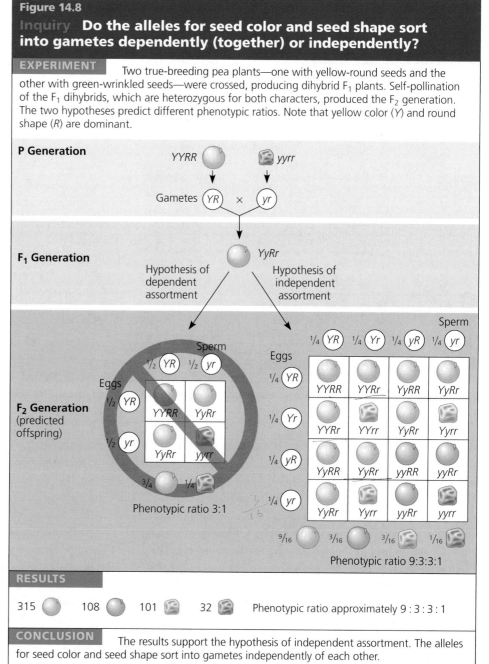

Figure 14.8

Inquiry **Do the alleles for seed color and seed shape sort into gametes dependently (together) or independently?**

EXPERIMENT   Two true-breeding pea plants—one with yellow-round seeds and the other with green-wrinkled seeds—were crossed, producing dihybrid F_1 plants. Self-pollination of the F_1 dihybrids, which are heterozygous for both characters, produced the F_2 generation. The two hypotheses predict different phenotypic ratios. Note that yellow color (Y) and round shape (R) are dominant.

RESULTS   315   108   101   32   Phenotypic ratio approximately 9 : 3 : 3 : 1

CONCLUSION   The results support the hypothesis of independent assortment. The alleles for seed color and seed shape sort into gametes independently of each other.

now call the **law of independent assortment**, which states that *each pair of alleles segregates independently of other pairs of alleles during gamete formation.*

Strictly speaking, this law applies only to genes (allele pairs) located on different chromosomes—that is, on chromosomes that are not homologous. Genes located near each other on the same chromosome tend to be inherited together and have more complex inheritance patterns than predicted by the law of independent assortment. We will describe such inheritance patterns in Chapter 15. All the pea characters studied by Mendel were controlled by genes on different chromosomes (or behaved as though they were); this fortuitous situation greatly simplified interpretation of his multi-character pea crosses. All the examples we consider in the rest of this chapter involve genes located on different chromosomes.

Concept Check 14.1

1. Briefly describe how the experimental results shown in Figure 14.3 support Mendel's "particulate" hypothesis of inheritance.
2. Pea plants heterozygous for flower position and stem length (*AaTt*) are allowed to self-pollinate, and 400 of the resulting seeds are planted. How many offspring would be predicted to be dwarf with terminal flowers? (See Table 14.1.)

For suggested answers, see Appendix A.

Concept 14.2

The laws of probability govern Mendelian inheritance

Mendel's laws of segregation and independent assortment reflect the same rules of probability that apply to tossing coins, rolling dice, and drawing cards from a deck. The probability scale ranges from 0 to 1. An event that is certain to occur has a probability of 1, while an event that is certain *not* to occur has a probability of 0. With a coin that has heads on both sides, the probability of tossing heads is 1, and the probability of tossing tails is 0. With a normal coin, the chance of tossing heads is $\frac{1}{2}$, and the chance of tossing tails is $\frac{1}{2}$. The probability of drawing the ace of spades from a 52-card deck is $\frac{1}{52}$. The probabilities of all possible outcomes for an event must add up to 1. With a deck of cards, the chance of picking a card other than the ace of spades is $\frac{51}{52}$.

Tossing a coin illustrates an important lesson about probability. For every toss, the probability of heads is $\frac{1}{2}$. The outcome of any particular toss is unaffected by what has happened

on previous trials. We refer to phenomena such as coin tosses as independent events. Each toss of a coin, whether done sequentially with one coin or simultaneously with many, is independent of every other toss. And like two separate coin tosses, the alleles of one gene segregate into gametes independently of another gene's alleles (the law of independent assortment). Two basic rules of probability can help us predict the outcome of the fusion of such gametes in simple monohybrid crosses and more complicated crosses.

The Multiplication and Addition Rules Applied to Monohybrid Crosses

How do we determine the probability that two or more independent events will occur together in some specific combination? For example, what is the chance that two coins tossed simultaneously will both land heads up? The *multiplication rule* states that to determine this probability, we multiply the probability of one event (one coin coming up heads) by the probability of the other event (the other coin coming up heads). By the multiplication rule, then, the probability that both coins will land heads up is $\frac{1}{2} \times \frac{1}{2} = \frac{1}{4}$.

We can apply the same reasoning to an F_1 monohybrid cross **(Figure 14.9)**. With seed shape in pea plants as the heritable character, the genotype of F_1 plants is *Rr*. Segregation in a heterozygous plant is like flipping a coin: Each egg produced has a $\frac{1}{2}$ chance of carrying the dominant allele (*R*) and a $\frac{1}{2}$ chance of carrying the recessive allele (*r*). The same odds apply to each sperm cell produced. For a particular F_2 plant to have wrinkled seeds, the recessive trait, both the egg and the sperm that come together must carry the *r* allele. The probability that two *r* alleles will be present in gametes at fertilization is $\frac{1}{2}$ (the probability that the egg will have an *r*) $\times$ $\frac{1}{2}$ (the probability that the sperm will have an *r*). Thus, the multiplication rule tells us that the probability of an F_2 plant with wrinkled seeds (*rr*) is $\frac{1}{4}$ (see the Punnett square in Figure 14.9). Likewise, the probability of an F_2 plant carrying both dominant alleles for seed shape (*RR*) is $\frac{1}{4}$.

To figure out the probability that an F_2 plant from a monohybrid cross will be heterozygous rather than homozygous, we need to invoke a second rule. Notice in Figure 14.9 that the dominant allele can come from the egg and the recessive allele from the sperm, or vice versa. That is, F_1 gametes can combine to produce *Rr* offspring in two independent and mutually exclusive ways: For any particular heterozygous F_2 plant, the dominant allele can come from the egg *or* the sperm, but not from both. According to the *addition rule,* the probability that any one of two or more mutually exclusive events will occur is calculated by adding together their individual probabilities. As we have just seen, the multiplication rule gives us the individual probabilities to add together. The probability for one possible way of obtaining an F_2 heterozygote—the dominant allele from

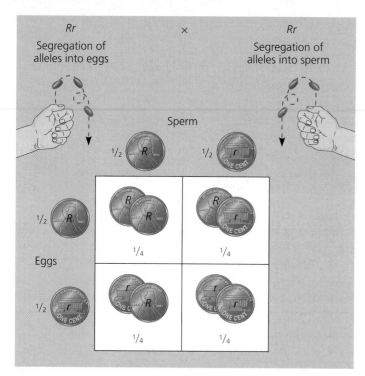

Rr × Rr

Segregation of alleles into eggs

Segregation of alleles into sperm

Sperm

$1/2$ R $1/2$ r

Eggs

$1/2$ R $1/4$ $1/4$

$1/2$ r $1/4$ $1/4$

▲ **Figure 14.9 Segregation of alleles and fertilization as chance events.** When a heterozygote (Rr) forms gametes, segregation of alleles is like the toss of a coin. We can determine the probability for any genotype among the offspring of two heterozygotes by multiplying together the individual probabilities of an egg and sperm having a particular allele (R or r in this example).

the egg and the recessive allele from the sperm—is $1/4$. The probability for the other possible way—the recessive allele from the egg and the dominant allele from the sperm—is also $1/4$ (see Figure 14.9). Using the rule of addition, then, we can calculate the probability of an F_2 heterozygote as $1/4 + 1/4 = 1/2$.

Solving Complex Genetics Problems with the Rules of Probability

We can also apply the rules of probability to predict the outcome of crosses involving multiple characters. Recall that each allelic pair segregates independently during gamete formation (the law of independent assortment). Thus, a dihybrid or other multi-character cross is equivalent to two or more independent monohybrid crosses occurring simultaneously. By applying what we have learned about monohybrid crosses, we can determine the probability of specific genotypes occurring in the F_2 generation without having to construct unwieldy Punnett squares.

Consider the dihybrid cross between $YyRr$ heterozygotes shown in Figure 14.8. We will focus first on the seed-color character. For a monohybrid cross of Yy plants, the probabilities of the offspring genotypes are $1/4$ for YY, $1/2$ for Yy, and $1/4$ for yy. The same probabilities apply to the offspring genotypes for seed shape: $1/4$ RR, $1/2$ Rr, and $1/4$ rr. Knowing these

probabilities, we can simply use the multiplication rule to determine the probability of each of the genotypes in the F_2 generation. For example, the probability of an F_2 plant having the $YYRR$ genotype is $1/4 \times 1/4 = 1/16$. This corresponds to the upper left box in the Punnett square on the right in Figure 14.8. To give another example, the probability of an F_2 plant with the $YyRR$ genotype is $1/2$ (Yy) $\times$ $1/4$ (RR) = $1/8$. If you look closely at the Punnett square on the right in Figure 14.8, you will see that 2 of the 16 boxes ($1/8$) correspond to the $YyRR$ genotype.

Now let's see how we can combine the multiplication and addition rules to solve even more complex problems in Mendelian genetics. For instance, imagine a cross of two pea varieties in which we track the inheritance of three characters. Suppose we cross a trihybrid with purple flowers and yellow, round seeds (heterozygous for all three genes) with a plant with purple flowers and green, wrinkled seeds (heterozygous for flower color but homozygous recessive for the other two characters). Using Mendelian symbols, our cross is $PpYyRr \times Ppyyrr$. What fraction of offspring from this cross would be predicted to exhibit the recessive phenotypes for *at least two* of the three characters?

To answer this question, we can start by listing all genotypes that fulfill this condition: $ppyyRr$, $ppYyrr$, $Ppyyrr$, $PPyyrr$, and $ppyyrr$. (Because the condition is *at least two* recessive traits, the last genotype, which produces all three recessive phenotypes, counts.) Next, we calculate the probability for each of these genotypes resulting from our $PpYyRr \times Ppyyrr$ cross by multiplying together the individual probabilities for the allele pairs, just as we did in our dihybrid example. Note that in a cross involving heterozygous and homozygous allele pairs (for example, $Yy \times yy$), the probability of heterozygous offspring is $1/2$ and the probability of homozygous offspring is $1/2$. Finally, we use the addition rule to add together the probabilities for all the different genotypes that fulfill the condition of at least two recessive traits, as shown below.

$ppyyRr$	$1/4$ (probability of pp) $\times$ $1/2$ (yy) $\times$ $1/2$ (Rr) =	$1/16$
$ppYyrr$	$1/4 \times 1/2 \times 1/2$	$= 1/16$
$Ppyyrr$	$1/2 \times 1/2 \times 1/2$	$= 2/16$
$PPyyrr$	$1/4 \times 1/2 \times 1/2$	$= 1/16$
$ppyyrr$	$1/4 \times 1/2 \times 1/2$	$= 1/16$
Chance of *at least two* recessive traits		$= 6/16$ or $3/8$

With practice, you'll be able to solve genetics problems faster by using the rules of probability than by filling in Punnett squares.

We cannot predict with certainty the exact numbers of progeny of different genotypes resulting from a genetic cross. But the rules of probability give us the *chance* of various outcomes. Usually, the larger the sample size, the closer the results will conform to our predictions. The reason Mendel counted so many offspring from his crosses is that he understood this statistical feature of inheritance and had a keen sense of the rules of chance.

Concept 14.3

Inheritance patterns are often more complex than predicted by simple Mendelian genetics

In the 20th century, geneticists extended Mendelian principles not only to diverse organisms, but also to patterns of inheritance more complex than Mendel actually described. It was brilliant (and lucky) that Mendel chose pea plant characters that turned out to have a relatively simple genetic basis: Each character he studied is determined by one gene, for which there are only two alleles, one completely dominant to the other.* But these conditions are not met by all heritable characters, even in garden peas. The relationship between genotype and phenotype is rarely so simple. This does not diminish the utility of Mendelian genetics (also called Mendelism), however, because the basic principles of segregation and independent assortment apply even to more complex patterns of inheritance. In this section, we will extend Mendelian genetics to hereditary patterns that were not reported by Mendel.

---

* There is one exception: Geneticists have found that Mendel's flower-position character is actually determined by two genes.

Extending Mendelian Genetics for a Single Gene

The inheritance of characters determined by a single gene deviates from simple Mendelian patterns when alleles are not completely dominant or recessive, when a particular gene has more than two alleles, or when a single gene produces multiple phenotypes. We will describe examples of each of these situations in this section.

The Spectrum of Dominance

Alleles can show different degrees of dominance and recessiveness in relation to each other. We refer to this range as the *spectrum of dominance.* One extreme on this spectrum is seen in the F_1 offspring of Mendel's classic pea crosses. These F_1 plants always looked like one of the two parental varieties because of the **complete dominance** of one allele over another. In this situation, the phenotypes of the heterozygote and the dominant homozygote are indistinguishable.

At the other extreme is the **codominance** of both alleles; that is, the two alleles both affect the phenotype in separate, distinguishable ways. For example, the human MN blood group is determined by codominant alleles for two specific molecules located on the surface of red blood cells, the M and N molecules. A single gene locus, at which two allelic variations are possible, determines the phenotype of this blood group. Individuals homozygous for the *M* allele (*MM*) have red blood cells with only M molecules; individuals homozygous for the *N* allele (*NN*) have red blood cells with only N molecules. But *both* M and N molecules are present on the red blood cells of individuals heterozygous for the *M* and *N* alleles (*MN*). Note that the MN phenotype is *not* intermediate between the M and N phenotypes. Rather, both the M and N phenotypes are exhibited by heterozygotes, since both molecules are present.

The alleles for some characters fall in the middle of the spectrum of dominance. In this case, the F_1 hybrids have a phenotype somewhere in between the phenotypes of the two parental varieties. This phenomenon, called the **incomplete dominance** of either allele, is seen when red snapdragons are crossed with white snapdragons: All the F_1 hybrids have pink flowers **(Figure 14.10)**. This third phenotype results from flowers of the heterozygotes having less red pigment than the red homozygotes (unlike the situation in Mendel's pea plants, where the *Pp* heterozygotes make enough pigment for the flowers to be a purple color indistinguishable from those of *PP* plants).

At first glance, incomplete dominance of either allele seems to provide evidence for the blending hypothesis of inheritance, which would predict that the red or white trait could never be retrieved from the pink hybrids. In fact, interbreeding F_1 hybrids produces F_2 offspring with a phenotypic ratio of one red to two pink to one white. (Because

P Generation

Red
$C^R C^R$ × White
$C^W C^W$

Gametes C^R C^W

F₁ Generation

Pink
$C^R C^W$

Gametes ½ C^R ½ C^W

F₂ Generation

Sperm

½ C^R ½ C^W

Eggs

½ C^R

½ C^W

$C^R C^R$ $C^R C^W$

$C^R C^W$ $C^W C^W$

▲ **Figure 14.10 Incomplete dominance in snapdragon color.** When red snapdragons are crossed with white ones, the F₁ hybrids have pink flowers. Segregation of alleles into gametes of the F₁ plants results in an F₂ generation with a 1:2:1 ratio for both genotype and phenotype. Superscripts indicate alleles for flower color: C^R for red and C^W for white.

heterozygotes have a separate phenotype, the genotypic and phenotypic ratios for the F₂ generation are the same, 1:2:1.) The segregation of the red-flower and white-flower alleles in the gametes produced by the pink-flowered plants confirms that the alleles for flower color are heritable factors that maintain their identity in the hybrids; that is, inheritance is particulate.

The Relation Between Dominance and Phenotype. We've now seen that the relative effects of two alleles range from complete dominance of one allele, through incomplete dominance of either allele, to codominance of both alleles. It is important to understand that an allele is not termed *dominant* because it somehow subdues a recessive allele. Recall that alleles are simply variations in a gene's nucleotide sequence. When a dominant allele coexists with a recessive allele in a heterozygote, they do not actually interact at all. It is in the pathway from genotype to phenotype that dominance and recessiveness come into play.

To illustrate the relation between dominance and phenotype, we can use one of Mendel's characters—round versus wrinkled pea seed shape. The dominant allele (round) codes for the synthesis of an enzyme that helps convert sugar to starch in the seed. The recessive allele (wrinkled) codes for a defective form of this enzyme. Thus, in a recessive homozygote, sugar accumulates in the seed because it is not converted to starch. As the seed develops, the high sugar concentration causes the osmotic uptake of water, and the seed swells. Then when the mature seed dries, it develops wrinkles. In contrast, if a dominant allele is present, sugar is converted to starch, the seeds do not take up excess water, and so the seeds do not wrinkle when they dry. One dominant allele results in enough of the enzyme to convert sugar to starch, and thus dominant homozygotes and heterozygotes have the same phenotype: round seeds.

A closer look at the relation between dominance and phenotype reveals an intriguing fact: For any character, the observed dominance/recessiveness relationship of alleles depends on the level at which we examine phenotype. **Tay-Sachs disease,** an inherited disorder in humans, provides an example. The brain cells of a baby with Tay-Sachs disease are unable to metabolize certain lipids because a crucial enzyme does not work properly. As these lipids accumulate in brain cells, an infant begins to suffer seizures, blindness, and degeneration of motor and mental performance. An affected child dies within a few years.

Only children who inherit two copies of the Tay-Sachs allele (homozygotes) have the disease. Thus, at the *organismal* level, the Tay-Sachs allele qualifies as recessive. However, the activity level of the lipid-metabolizing enzyme in heterozygotes is intermediate between that in individuals homozygous for the normal allele and that in individuals with Tay-Sachs disease. The intermediate phenotype observed at the *biochemical* level is characteristic of incomplete dominance of either allele. Fortunately, the heterozygote condition does not lead to disease symptoms, apparently because half the normal enzyme activity is sufficient to prevent lipid accumulation in the brain. Extending our analysis to yet another level, we find that heterozygous individuals produce equal numbers of normal and dysfunctional enzyme molecules. Thus, at the *molecular* level, the normal allele and the Tay-Sachs allele are codominant. As you can see, whether alleles appear to be completely dominant, incompletely dominant, or codominant relative to each other depends on which phenotypic trait is considered.

Frequency of Dominant Alleles. Although you might assume that the dominant allele for a particular character would be more common in a population than the recessive allele for that character, this is not necessarily the case. For example, about one baby out of 400 in the United States is born with extra fingers or toes, a condition known as polydactyly. The allele for the unusual trait of polydactyly is dominant to the allele for the more common trait of five digits per appendage. In other words, 399 out of every 400 people are recessive homozygotes for this character; the recessive allele is far more prevalent than the dominant allele in the population. In Chapter 23, you will learn how the relative frequencies of alleles in a population are affected by natural selection.

Multiple Alleles

Only two alleles exist for the pea characters that Mendel studied, but most genes actually exist in populations in more than two allelic forms. The ABO blood group in humans, for instance, is determined by multiple alleles of a single gene. There are four possible phenotypes for this character: A person's blood group may be either A, B, AB, or O. These letters refer to two carbohydrates—A and B—that may be found on the surface of red blood cells. A person's blood cells may have carbohydrate A (type A blood), carbohydrate B (type B), both (type AB), or neither (type O), as shown schematically in **Table 14.2**.

The four blood groups result from various combinations of three different alleles for the enzyme (I) that attaches the A or B carbohydrate to red blood cells. The enzyme encoded by the I^A allele adds the A carbohydrate, whereas the enzyme encoded by I^B adds the B carbohydrate (the superscripts indicate the carbohydrate). The enzyme encoded by the i allele adds neither A nor B. Because each person carries two alleles, six genotypes are possible, resulting in four phenotypes (see Table 14.2). Both the I^A and the I^B alleles are dominant to the i allele. Thus, $I^A I^A$ and $I^A i$ individuals have type A blood, and $I^B I^B$ and $I^B i$ individuals have type B blood. Recessive homozygotes, ii, have type O blood, because their red blood cells have neither the A nor the B carbohydrate. The I^A and I^B alleles are codominant; both are expressed in the phenotype of $I^A I^B$ heterozygotes, who have type AB blood.

Matching compatible blood groups is critical for safe blood transfusions. For example, if a type A person receives blood from a type B or type AB donor, the recipient's immune system recognizes the "foreign" B substance on the donated blood cells and attacks them. This response causes the donated blood cells to clump together, potentially killing the recipient (see Chapter 43).

Pleiotropy

So far, we have treated Mendelian inheritance as though each gene affects one phenotypic character. Most genes, however, have multiple phenotypic effects, a property called **pleiotropy** (from the Greek *pleion*, more). For example, pleiotropic alleles are responsible for the multiple symptoms associated with certain hereditary diseases in humans, such as cystic fibrosis

Table 14.2 Determination of ABO Blood Group by Multiple Alleles

Genotype	Phenotype (Blood Group)	Red Blood Cells
$I^A I^A$ or $I^A i$	A	
$I^B I^B$ or $I^B i$	B	
$I^A I^B$	AB	
ii	O	

and sickle-cell disease, discussed later in this chapter. Considering the intricate molecular and cellular interactions responsible for an organism's development and physiology, it is not surprising that a single gene can affect a number of characteristics in an organism.

Extending Mendelian Genetics for Two or More Genes

Dominance relationships, multiple alleles, and pleiotropy all have to do with the effects of the alleles of a single gene. We now consider two situations in which two or more genes are involved in determining a particular phenotype.

Epistasis

In **epistasis** (from the Greek for "stopping"), a gene at one locus alters the phenotypic expression of a gene at a second locus. An example will help clarify this concept. In mice and many other mammals, black coat color is dominant to brown. Let's designate *B* and *b* as the two alleles for this character. For a mouse to have brown fur, its genotype must be *bb*. But there is more to the story. A second gene determines whether or not pigment will be deposited in the hair. The dominant allele, symbolized by *C* (for color), results in the deposition of either black or brown pigment, depending on the genotype at the first locus. But if the mouse is homozygous recessive for the second locus (*cc*), then the coat is white (albino), regardless of the genotype at the black/brown locus. The gene for pigment deposition is said to be epistatic to the gene that codes for black or brown pigment.

What happens if we mate black mice that are heterozygous for both genes (*BbCc*)? Although the two genes affect the same phenotypic character (coat color), they follow the law of independent assortment. Thus, our breeding experiment represents an F₁ dihybrid cross, like those that produced a 9:3:3:1 ratio in Mendel's experiments. We can use a Punnett square to represent the genotypes of the F₂ offspring (**Figure 14.11**). As a result of epistasis, the phenotypic ratio among the F₂ offspring is 9 black to 3 brown to 4 (3 + 1) white. Other types of epistatic interactions produce different ratios, but all are modified versions of 9:3:3:1.

Polygenic Inheritance

Mendel studied characters that could be classified on an either-or basis, such as purple versus white flower color. But for many characters, such as human skin color and height, an either-or classification is impossible because the characters vary in the population along a continuum (in gradations). These are called **quantitative characters.** Quantitative variation usually indicates **polygenic inheritance,** an additive effect of two or more genes on a single phenotypic character (the converse of pleiotropy, where a single gene affects several phenotypic characters).

There is evidence, for instance, that skin pigmentation in humans is controlled by at least three separately inherited genes (probably more, but we will simplify). Let's consider three genes, with a dark-skin allele for each gene (*A*, *B*, or *C*) contributing one "unit" of darkness to the phenotype and being incompletely dominant to the other allele (*a*, *b*, or *c*). An *AABBCC* person would be very dark, while an *aabbcc* individual would be very light. An *AaBbCc* person would have skin of an intermediate shade. Because the alleles have a cumulative effect, the genotypes *AaBbCc* and *AABbcc* would make the same genetic contribution (three units) to skin darkness. **Figure 14.12** shows how this polygenic inheritance could result in a bell-shaped curve, called a normal distribution, for skin darkness among the progeny of hypothetical matings between individuals heterozygous for all three genes. (You are probably familiar with the concept of a normal distribution for class curves of test scores.) Environmental factors, such as exposure to the sun, also affect the skin-color phenotype and help make the graph a smooth curve rather than a stair-like histogram.

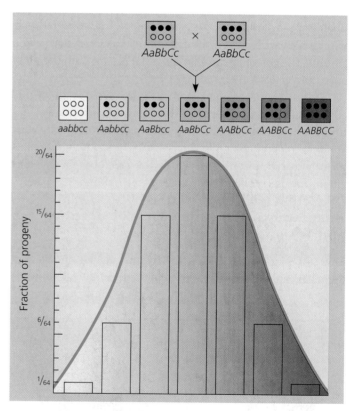

▲ **Figure 14.12 A simplified model for polygenic inheritance of skin color.** According to this model, three separately inherited genes affect the darkness of skin. The heterozygous individuals (*AaBbCc*), represented by the two rectangles at the top of this figure, each carry three dark-skin alleles (black circles) and three light-skin alleles (open circles). The variations in genotype and skin color that can occur among offspring from a large number of hypothetical matings between these heterozygotes are shown above the graph. The y-axis represents the fraction of progeny with each skin color. The resulting histogram is smoothed into a bell-shaped curve by environmental factors that affect skin color.

▲ **Figure 14.11 An example of epistasis.** This Punnett square illustrates the genotypes and phenotypes predicted for offspring of matings between two black mice of genotype *BbCc*. The *C/c* gene, which is epistatic to the *B/b* gene, controls whether or not pigment of any color will be deposited in the hair.

Nature and Nurture: The Environmental Impact on Phenotype

Another departure from simple Mendelian genetics arises when the phenotype for a character depends on environment as well as on genotype. A single tree, locked into its inherited genotype, has leaves that vary in size, shape, and greenness, depending on exposure to wind and sun. For humans, nutrition influences height, exercise alters build, sun-tanning darkens the skin, and experience improves performance on intelligence tests. Even identical twins, who are genetic equals, accumulate phenotypic differences as a result of their unique experiences.

Whether human characteristics are more influenced by genes or the environment—nature or nurture—is a very old and hotly contested debate that we will not attempt to settle here. We can say, however, that a genotype generally is not associated with a rigidly defined phenotype, but rather with a range of phenotypic possibilities due to environmental influences. This phenotypic range is called the **norm of reaction** for a genotype **(Figure 14.13)**. For some characters, such as the ABO blood group, the norm of reaction has no breadth whatsoever; that is, a given genotype mandates a very specific phenotype. In contrast, a person's blood count of red and white cells varies quite a bit, depending on such factors as the altitude, the customary level of physical activity, and the presence of infectious agents.

Generally, norms of reaction are broadest for polygenic characters. Environment contributes to the quantitative nature of these characters, as we have seen in the continuous variation of skin color. Geneticists refer to such characters as **multifactorial,** meaning that many factors, both genetic and environmental, collectively influence phenotype.

Integrating a Mendelian View of Heredity and Variation

Over the past several pages, we have broadened our view of Mendelian inheritance by exploring the spectrum of dominance as well as multiple alleles, pleiotropy, epistasis, polygenic inheritance, and the phenotypic impact of the environment. How can we integrate these refinements into a comprehensive theory of Mendelian genetics? The key is to make the transition from the reductionist emphasis on single genes and phenotypic characters to the emergent properties of the organism as a whole, one of the themes of this book.

The term *phenotype* can refer not only to specific characters, such as flower color and blood group, but also to an organism in its entirety—*all* aspects of its physical appearance, internal anatomy, physiology, and behavior. Similarly, the term *genotype* can refer to an organism's entire genetic makeup, not just its alleles for a single genetic locus. In most cases, a gene's impact on phenotype is affected by other genes and by the environment. In this integrated view of heredity and variation, an organism's phenotype reflects its overall genotype and unique environmental history.

Considering all that can occur in the pathway from genotype to phenotype, it is indeed impressive that Mendel could uncover the fundamental principles governing the transmission of individual genes from parents to offspring. Mendel's two laws, segregation and independent assortment, explain heritable variations in terms of alternative forms of genes (hereditary "particles") that are passed along, generation after generation, according to simple rules of probability. This theory of inheritance is equally valid for peas, flies, fishes, birds, and human beings. Furthermore, by extending the principles of segregation and independent assortment to help explain such hereditary patterns as epistasis and quantitative characters, we begin to see how broadly Mendelism applies. From Mendel's abbey garden came a theory of particulate inheritance that anchors modern genetics. In the last section of this chapter, we will apply Mendelian genetics to human inheritance, with emphasis on the transmission of hereditary diseases.

▲ **Figure 14.13 The effect of environment on phenotype.** The outcome of a genotype lies within its norm of reaction, a phenotypic range that depends on the environment in which the genotype is expressed. For example, hydrangea flowers of the same genetic variety range in color from blue-violet to pink, depending on the acidity of the soil.

Concept Check 14.3

1. A rooster with gray feathers is mated with a hen of the same phenotype. Among their offspring, 15 chicks are gray, 6 are black, and 8 are white. What is the simplest explanation for the inheritance of these colors in chickens? What phenotypes would you expect in the offspring resulting from a cross between a gray rooster and a black hen?
2. In humans, tall parents tend to have tall children, and short parents tend to have short children. Adult heights, however, vary in the population over a wide range, following a normal bell-shaped curve. Explain these observations.

For suggested answers, see Appendix A.

Many human traits follow Mendelian patterns of inheritance

Whereas peas are convenient subjects for genetic research, humans are not. The human generation span is about 20 years, and human parents produce relatively few offspring compared to peas and most other species. Furthermore, breeding experiments like the ones Mendel performed are unacceptable with humans. In spite of these difficulties, the study of human genetics continues to advance, spurred on by the desire to understand our own inheritance. New techniques in molecular biology have led to many breakthrough discoveries, as we will see in Chapter 20, but basic Mendelism endures as the foundation of human genetics.

Pedigree Analysis

Unable to manipulate the mating patterns of people, geneticists must analyze the results of matings that have already occurred. They do so by collecting information about a family's history for a particular trait and assembling this information into a family tree describing the interrelationships of parents and children across the generations—the family **pedigree.**

Figure 14.14a shows a three-generation pedigree that traces the occurrence of a pointed contour of the hairline on the forehead. This trait, called a widow's peak, is due to a dominant allele, W. Because the widow's-peak allele is dominant, all individuals who lack a widow's peak must be homozygous recessive (ww). The two grandparents with widow's peaks must have the Ww genotype, since some of their offspring are homozygous recessive. The offspring in the second generation who *do* have widow's peaks must also be heterozygous, because they are the products of Ww × ww matings. The third generation in this pedigree consists of two sisters. The one who has a widow's peak could be either homozygous (WW) or heterozygous (Ww), given what we know about the genotypes of her parents (both Ww).

Figure 14.14b is a pedigree of the same family, but this time we focus on a recessive trait, attached earlobes. We'll use *f* for the recessive allele and *F* for the dominant allele, which results in free earlobes. As you work your way through the pedigree, notice once again that you can apply what you have learned about Mendelian inheritance to fill in the genotypes for most individuals.

(a) **Dominant trait (widow's peak).** This pedigree traces the trait called widow's peak through three generations of a family. Notice in the third generation that the second-born daughter lacks a widow's peak, although both of her parents had the trait. Such a pattern of inheritance supports the hypothesis that the trait is due to a dominant allele. If the trait were due to a *recessive* allele, and both parents had the recessive phenotype, then *all* of their offspring would also have the recessive phenotype.

(b) **Recessive trait (attached earlobe).** This is the same family, but in this case we are tracing the inheritance of a recessive trait, attached earlobes. Notice that the first-born daughter in the third generation has attached earlobes, although both of her parents lack that trait (they have free earlobes). Such a pattern is easily explained if the attached-lobe phenotype is due to a recessive allele. If it were due to a *dominant* allele, then at least one parent would also have had the trait.

▲ **Figure 14.14 Pedigree analysis.** In these family trees, squares represent males and circles represent females. A horizontal line connecting a male and female (□—O) indicates a mating, with offspring listed below in their order of birth from left to right. Shaded squares and circles represent individuals who exhibit the trait being traced.

An important application of a pedigree is to help us predict the future. Suppose that the couple represented in the second generation of Figure 14.14 decide to have one more child. What is the probability that the child will have a widow's peak? This is equivalent to a Mendelian F_1 monohybrid cross ($Ww \times Ww$), and thus the probability that a child will inherit a dominant allele and have a widow's peak is $\frac{3}{4}$ ($\frac{1}{4}$ WW + $\frac{1}{2}$ Ww). What is the probability that the child will have attached earlobes? Again, we can treat this as a monohybrid cross ($Ff \times Ff$), but this time we want to know the chance that the offspring will be homozygous recessive (ff). That probability is $\frac{1}{4}$. Finally, what is the chance that the child will have a widow's peak *and* attached earlobes? Assuming that the genes for these two characters are on different chromosomes, the two pairs of alleles will assort independently in this dihybrid cross ($WwFf \times WwFf$). Thus, we can use the multiplication rule: $\frac{3}{4}$ (chance of widow's peak) $\times$ $\frac{1}{4}$ (chance of attached earlobes) = $\frac{3}{16}$ (chance of widow's peak and attached earlobes).

Pedigrees are a more serious matter when the alleles in question cause disabling or deadly hereditary diseases instead of innocuous human variations such as hairline or earlobe configuration. However, for disorders inherited as simple Mendelian traits, the same techniques of pedigree analysis apply.

Recessively Inherited Disorders

Thousands of genetic disorders are known to be inherited as simple recessive traits. These disorders range in severity from relatively mild, such as albinism (lack of pigmentation, which results in susceptibility to skin cancers and vision problems), to life-threatening, such as cystic fibrosis.

How can we account for the recessive behavior of the alleles causing these disorders? Recall that genes code for proteins of specific function. An allele that causes a genetic disorder codes either for a malfunctional protein or for no protein at all. In the case of disorders classified as recessive, heterozygotes are normal in phenotype because one copy of the normal allele produces a sufficient amount of the specific protein. Thus, a recessively inherited disorder shows up only in the homozygous individuals who inherit one recessive allele from each parent. We can symbolize the genotype of such individuals as *aa* and the genotypes of individuals with the normal phenotype as either *AA* or *Aa*. Although phenotypically normal with regard to the disorder, heterozygotes (*Aa*) may transmit the recessive allele to their offspring and thus are called **carriers.**

Most people who have recessive disorders are born to parents who are carriers of the disorder but themselves have a normal phenotype. A mating between two carriers corresponds to a Mendelian F_1 monohybrid cross ($Aa \times Aa$); the genotypic ratio for the offspring is 1 *AA* : 2 *Aa* : 1 *aa*. Thus, each child has a $\frac{1}{4}$ chance of inheriting a double dose of the reces-

sive allele and being affected by the disorder. From the genotypic ratio, we also can see that out of three offspring with the *normal* phenotype (one *AA* plus two *Aa*), two are predicted to be heterozygous carriers, a $\frac{2}{3}$ chance. Recessive homozygotes could also result from *Aa* $\times$ *aa* and *aa* $\times$ *aa* matings, but if the disorder is lethal before reproductive age or results in sterility, no *aa* individuals will reproduce. Even if recessive homozygotes are able to reproduce, such individuals will still account for a much smaller percentage of the population than heterozygous carriers (for reasons we will examine in Chapter 23).

In general, a genetic disorder is not evenly distributed among all groups of humans. For example, the incidence of Tay-Sachs disease, which we described earlier in this chapter, is disproportionately high among Ashkenazic Jews, Jewish people whose ancestors lived in central Europe. In that population, Tay-Sachs disease occurs in one out of 3,600 births, about 100 times greater than the incidence among non-Jews or Mediterranean (Sephardic) Jews. Such an uneven distribution results from the different genetic histories of the world's peoples during less technological times, when populations were more geographically (and hence genetically) isolated. We will now examine two other recessively inherited diseases, which are also more prevalent in some groups than others.

Cystic Fibrosis

The most common lethal genetic disease in the United States is **cystic fibrosis,** which strikes one out of every 2,500 people of European descent but is much rarer in other groups. Among people of European descent, one out of 25 (4%) is a carrier of the cystic fibrosis allele. The normal allele for this gene codes for a membrane protein that functions in chloride ion transport between certain cells and the extracellular fluid. These chloride transport channels are defective or absent in the plasma membranes of children who inherit two recessive alleles for cystic fibrosis. The result is an abnormally high concentration of extracellular chloride, which causes the mucus that coats certain cells to become thicker and stickier than normal. The mucus builds up in the pancreas, lungs, digestive tract, and other organs, leading to multiple (pleiotropic) effects, including poor absorption of nutrients from the intestines, chronic bronchitis, foul stools, and recurrent bacterial infections. Recent research indicates that the extracellular chloride also contributes to infection by disabling a natural antibiotic made by some body cells. When immune cells come to the rescue, their remains add to the mucus, creating a vicious cycle.

If untreated, most children with cystic fibrosis die before their fifth birthday. Gentle pounding on the chest to clear mucus from clogged airways, daily doses of antibiotics to prevent infection, and other preventive treatments can prolong life. In the United States, more than half of the people with cystic fibrosis now survive into their late 20s or even 30s and beyond.

Sickle-Cell Disease

The most common inherited disorder among people of African descent is **sickle-cell disease,** which affects one out of 400 African-Americans. Sickle-cell disease is caused by the substitution of a single amino acid in the hemoglobin protein of red blood cells. When the oxygen content of an affected individual's blood is low (at high altitudes or under physical stress, for instance), the sickle-cell hemoglobin molecules aggregate into long rods that deform the red cells into a sickle shape (see Figure 5.21). Sickled cells may clump and clog small blood vessels, often leading to other symptoms throughout the body, including physical weakness, pain, organ damage, and even paralysis. The multiple effects of a double dose of the sickle-cell allele are another example of pleiotropy. Regular blood transfusions can ward off brain damage in children with sickle-cell disease, and new drugs can help prevent or treat other problems, but there is no cure.

Although two sickle-cell alleles are necessary for an individual to manifest full-blown sickle-cell disease, the presence of one sickle-cell allele can affect the phenotype. Thus, at the organismal level, the normal allele is incompletely dominant to the sickle-cell allele. Heterozygotes, said to have *sickle-cell trait,* are usually healthy, but they may suffer some sickle-cell symptoms during prolonged periods of reduced blood oxygen. At the molecular level, the two alleles are codominant; both normal and abnormal (sickle-cell) hemoglobins are made in heterozygotes.

About one out of ten African-Americans has sickle-cell trait, an unusually high frequency of heterozygotes for an allele with severe detrimental effects in homozygotes. One explanation for this is that a single copy of the sickle-cell allele reduces the frequency and severity of malaria attacks, especially among young children. The malaria parasite spends part of its life cycle in red blood cells (see Figure 28.11), and the presence of even heterozygous amounts of sickle-cell hemoglobin results in lower parasite densities and hence reduced malaria symptoms. Thus, in tropical Africa where infection with the malaria parasite is common, the sickle-cell allele is both boon and bane. The relatively high frequency of African-Americans with sickle-cell trait is a vestige of their African roots.

Mating of Close Relatives

When a disease-causing recessive allele is rare, it is relatively unlikely that two carriers of the same harmful allele will meet and mate. However, if the man and woman are close relatives (for example, siblings or first cousins), the probability of passing on recessive traits increases greatly. These are called consanguineous ("same blood") matings, and they are indicated in pedigrees by double lines. Because people with recent common ancestors are more likely to carry the same recessive alleles than are unrelated people, it is more likely that a mating of close relatives will produce offspring homozygous for recessive traits—

including harmful ones. Such effects can be observed in many types of domesticated and zoo animals that have become inbred.

There is debate among geneticists about the extent to which human consanguinity increases the risk of inherited diseases. Many deleterious alleles have such severe effects that a homozygous embryo spontaneously aborts long before birth. Still, most societies and cultures have laws or taboos forbidding marriages between close relatives. These rules may have evolved out of empirical observation that in most populations, stillbirths and birth defects are more common when parents are closely related. Social and economic factors have also influenced the development of customs and laws against consanguineous marriages.

Dominantly Inherited Disorders

Although many harmful alleles are recessive, a number of human disorders are due to dominant alleles. One example is *achondroplasia,* a form of dwarfism with a prevalence of one among every 25,000 people. Heterozygous individuals have the dwarf phenotype **(Figure 14.15).** Therefore, all people who are not achondroplastic dwarfs—99.99% of the population—are homozygous for the recessive allele. Like the presence of extra fingers or toes mentioned earlier, achondroplasia is a trait for which the recessive allele is much more prevalent than the corresponding dominant allele.

▲ **Figure 14.15**
Achondroplasia. The late David Rappaport, an actor, had achondroplasia, a form of dwarfism that is caused by a dominant allele.

Dominant alleles that cause a lethal disease are much less common than recessive alleles that do so. All such lethal alleles arise by mutations (changes to the DNA) in a sperm or egg; presumably, such mutations occur equally often whether the mutant allele is dominant or recessive. However, if a lethal dominant allele causes the death of offspring before they mature and can reproduce, the allele will not be passed on to future generations. In contrast, a lethal recessive allele can be perpetuated from generation to generation by heterozygous carriers who have normal phenotypes. These carriers can reproduce and pass on the recessive allele. Only homozygous recessive offspring will have the lethal disease.

A lethal dominant allele can escape elimination if it causes death only at a relatively advanced age. By the time the symptoms become evident, the individual may have already transmitted the lethal allele to his or her children. For example, **Huntington's disease**, a degenerative disease of the nervous system, is caused by a lethal dominant allele that has no obvious phenotypic effect until the individual is about 35 to 45 years old. Once the deterioration of the nervous system begins, it is irreversible and inevitably fatal. Any child born to a parent who has the allele for Huntington's disease has a 50% chance of inheriting the allele and the disorder. (The mating can be symbolized as *Aa × aa*, with *A* being the dominant allele that causes Huntington's disease.) In the United States, this devastating disease afflicts about one in 10,000 people.

Until relatively recently, the onset of symptoms was the only way to know if a person had inherited the Huntington's allele. This is no longer the case. By analyzing DNA samples from a large family with a high incidence of the disorder, geneticists tracked the Huntington's allele to a locus near the tip of chromosome 4 **(Figure 14.16)**. This information led to development of a test that can detect the presence of the Huntington's allele in an individual's genome. (The methods that make such tests possible are discussed in Chapter 20.) For those with a family history of Huntington's disease, the availability of this test poses an agonizing dilemma: Under what circumstances is it beneficial for a presently healthy person to find out whether he or she has inherited a fatal and not yet curable disease? Some individuals may want to be tested for the disease before planning a family.

▲ **Figure 14.16 Large families as excellent case studies of human genetics.** Here, Nancy Wexler, of Columbia University and the Hereditary Disease Foundation, studies a huge pedigree that traces Huntington's disease through several generations of one large family in Venezuela. Classical Mendelian analysis of this family, coupled with the techniques of molecular biology, enabled scientists to develop a test for the presence of the dominant allele that causes Huntington's disease—a test that can be used before symptoms appear. Dr. Wexler's mother died of Huntington's disease, and thus there is a 50% chance that Dr. Wexler inherited the dominant allele that causes the disease. To date she has shown no symptoms.

Multifactorial Disorders

The hereditary diseases we have discussed so far are sometimes described as simple Mendelian disorders because they result from abnormality of one or both alleles at a single genetic locus. Many more people are susceptible to diseases that have a multifactorial basis—a genetic component plus a significant environmental influence. Heart disease, diabetes, cancer, alcoholism, certain mental illnesses such as schizophrenia and manic-depressive disorder, and many other diseases are multifactorial. In many cases, the hereditary component is polygenic. For example, many genes affect cardiovascular health, making some of us more prone than others to heart attacks and strokes. But our lifestyle intervenes tremendously between genotype and phenotype for cardiovascular health and other multifactorial characters. Exercise, a healthful diet, abstinence from smoking, and an ability to handle stressful situations all reduce our risk of heart disease and some types of cancer.

At present, so little is understood about the genetic contributions to most multifactorial diseases that the best public health strategy is to educate people about the importance of environmental factors and to promote healthful behavior.

Genetic Testing and Counseling

A preventive approach to simple Mendelian disorders is possible when the risk of a particular genetic disorder can be assessed before a child is conceived or during the early stages of the pregnancy. Many hospitals have genetic counselors who can provide information to prospective parents concerned about a family history for a specific disease.

Counseling Based on Mendelian Genetics and Probability Rules

Consider the case of a hypothetical couple, John and Carol. Both had a brother who died from the same recessively inherited lethal disease. Before conceiving their first child, John and Carol seek genetic counseling to determine the risk of having a child with the disease. From the information about their brothers, we know that both parents of John and both parents of Carol must have been carriers of the recessive allele. Thus, John and Carol are both products of *Aa × Aa* crosses, where *a* symbolizes the allele that causes this particular disease. We also know that John and Carol are not homozygous recessive (*aa*), because they do not have the disease. Therefore, their genotypes are either *AA* or *Aa*.

Given a genotypic ratio of $1\,AA : 2\,Aa : 1\,aa$ for offspring of an *Aa × Aa* cross, John and Carol each have a $2/3$ chance of being carriers (*Aa*). According to the rule of multiplication, the overall probability of their firstborn having the disorder is $2/3$ (the chance that John is a carrier) multiplied by $2/3$ (the chance that Carol is a carrier) multiplied by $1/4$ (the chance of two carriers having a child with the disease), which equals $1/9$.

Suppose that Carol and John decide to have a child—after all, there is an 8/9 chance that their baby will not have the disorder. If, despite these odds, their child is born with the disease, then we would know that *both* John and Carol are, in fact, carriers (*Aa* genotype). If both John and Carol are carriers, there is a 1/4 chance that any subsequent child this couple has will have the disease.

When we use Mendel's laws to predict possible outcomes of matings, it is important to remember that each child represents an independent event in the sense that its genotype is unaffected by the genotypes of older siblings. Suppose that John and Carol have three more children, and *all three* have the hypothetical hereditary disease. There is only one chance in 64 (1/4 × 1/4 × 1/4) that such an outcome will occur. Despite this run of misfortune, the chance that still another child of this couple will have the disease remains 1/4.

Tests for Identifying Carriers

Because most children with recessive disorders are born to parents with normal phenotypes, the key to assessing more accurately the genetic risk for a particular disease is determining whether the prospective parents are heterozygous carriers of the recessive allele. For an increasing number of heritable disorders, tests are available that can distinguish individuals of normal phenotype who are dominant homozygotes from those who are heterozygotes. There are now tests that can identify carriers of the alleles for Tay-Sachs disease, sickle-cell disease, and the most common form of cystic fibrosis.

These tests for identifying carriers enable people with family histories of genetic disorders to make informed decisions about having children. But these new methods for genetic screening pose potential problems. If confidentiality is breached, will carriers be stigmatized? Will they be denied health or life insurance, even though they themselves are healthy? Will misinformed employers equate "carrier" with disease? And will sufficient genetic counseling be available to help a large number of individuals understand their test results? New biotechnology offers possibilities for reducing human suffering, but not before key ethical issues are resolved. The dilemmas posed by human genetics reinforce one of this book's themes: the immense social implications of biology.

Fetal Testing

Suppose a couple learns that they are both Tay-Sachs carriers, but they decide to have a child anyway. Tests performed in conjunction with a technique known as **amniocentesis** can determine, beginning at the 14th to 16th week of pregnancy, whether the developing fetus has Tay-Sachs disease (**Figure 14.17a**, on the next page). To perform this procedure, a physician inserts a needle into the uterus and extracts about 10 milliliters of amniotic fluid, the liquid that bathes the fetus. Some genetic disorders can be detected from the presence of certain chemicals in the amniotic fluid itself. Tests for other disorders, including Tay-Sachs disease, are performed on cells grown in the laboratory, descendants of the fetal cells sloughed off into the amniotic fluid. These cultured cells can also be used for karyotyping to identify certain chromosomal defects (see Figure 13.3).

In an alternative technique called **chorionic villus sampling (CVS),** a physician inserts a narrow tube through the cervix into the uterus and suctions out a tiny sample of tissue from the placenta, the organ that transmits nutrients and fetal wastes between the fetus and the mother (**Figure 14.17b**). The cells of the chorionic villi of the placenta, the portion sampled, are derived from the fetus and have the same genotype as the new individual. These cells are proliferating rapidly enough to allow karyotyping to be carried out immediately. This rapid analysis is an advantage over amniocentesis, in which the cells must be cultured for several weeks before karyotyping. Another advantage of CVS is that it can be performed as early as the eighth to tenth week of pregnancy. However, CVS is not suitable for tests requiring amniotic fluid, and it is less widely available than amniocentesis. Recently, medical scientists have developed methods for isolating fetal cells that have escaped into the mother's blood. Although very few in number, these cells can be cultured and then tested.

Imaging techniques allow a physician to examine a fetus directly for major anatomical abnormalities. In the *ultrasound* technique, sound waves are used to produce an image of the fetus by a simple noninvasive procedure. In *fetoscopy*, a needle-thin tube containing a viewing scope and fiber optics (to transmit light) is inserted into the uterus.

Ultrasound has no known risk to either mother or fetus, but amniocentesis and fetoscopy cause complications, such as maternal bleeding or even fetal death, in about 1% of cases. For this reason, these techniques generally are used only when the chance of a genetic disorder or other type of birth defect is relatively great. If the fetal tests reveal a serious disorder, the parents face the difficult choice of terminating the pregnancy or preparing to care for a child with a genetic disorder.

Newborn Screening

Some genetic disorders can be detected at birth by simple tests that are now routinely performed in most hospitals in the United States. One common screening program is for phenylketonuria (PKU), a recessively inherited disorder that occurs in about one out of every 10,000 to 15,000 births in the United States. Children with this disease cannot properly break down the amino acid phenylalanine. This compound and its by-product, phenylpyruvate, can accumulate to toxic levels in the blood, causing mental retardation. However, if the deficiency is detected in the newborn, a special diet low in phenylalanine can usually promote normal development and

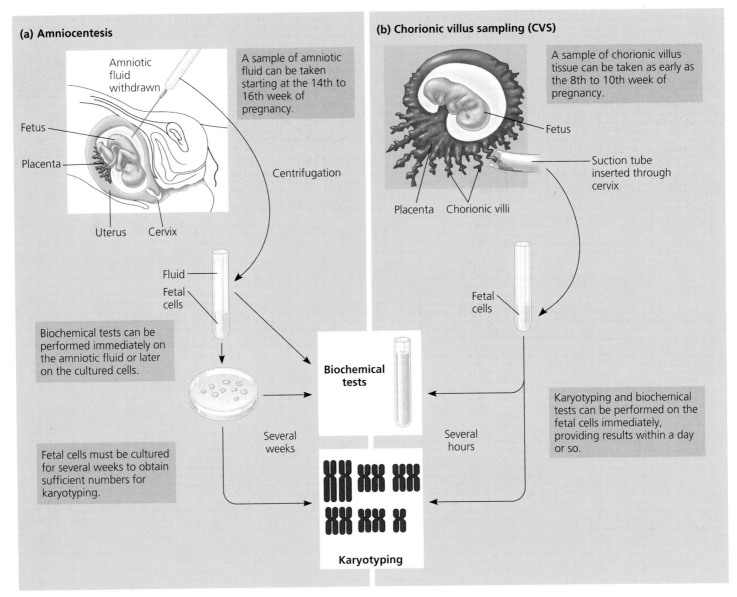

(a) Amniocentesis

Amniotic fluid withdrawn

A sample of amniotic fluid can be taken starting at the 14th to 16th week of pregnancy.

Fetus

Placenta

Uterus   Cervix

Centrifugation

Fluid

Fetal cells

Biochemical tests can be performed immediately on the amniotic fluid or later on the cultured cells.

Biochemical tests

Several weeks

Fetal cells must be cultured for several weeks to obtain sufficient numbers for karyotyping.

Karyotyping

(b) Chorionic villus sampling (CVS)

A sample of chorionic villus tissue can be taken as early as the 8th to 10th week of pregnancy.

Fetus

Suction tube inserted through cervix

Placenta   Chorionic villi

Fetal cells

Several hours

Karyotyping and biochemical tests can be performed on the fetal cells immediately, providing results within a day or so.

▲ **Figure 14.17 Testing a fetus for genetic disorders.** Biochemical tests may detect substances associated with particular disorders. Karyotyping shows whether the chromosomes of the fetus are normal in number and appearance.

prevent retardation. Unfortunately, very few other genetic disorders are treatable at the present time.

Screening of newborns and fetuses for serious inherited diseases, tests for identifying carriers, and genetic counseling—all these tools of modern medicine rely on the Mendelian model of inheritance. We owe the "gene idea"—the concept of particulate heritable factors transmitted according to simple rules of chance—to the elegant quantitative experiments of Gregor Mendel. The importance of his discoveries was overlooked by most biologists until early in the 20th century, several decades after his findings were reported. In the next chapter, you will learn how Mendel's laws have their physical basis in the behavior of chromosomes during sexual life cycles and how the synthesis of Mendelism and a chromosome theory of inheritance catalyzed progress in genetics.

Concept Check 14.4

1. Beth and Tom each have a sibling with cystic fibrosis, but neither Beth nor Tom nor any of their parents have the disease. Calculate the probability that if this couple has a child, the child will have cystic fibrosis. What would be the probability if a test revealed that Tom is a carrier but Beth is not?

2. Joan was born with six toes on each foot, a dominant trait called polydactyly. Two of her five siblings and her mother, but not her father, also have extra digits. What is Joan's genotype for the number-of-digits character? Explain your answer. Use D and d to symbolize the alleles for this character.

For suggested answers, see Appendix A.

Go to the Campbell Biology website (**www.campbellbiology.com**) or CD-ROM to explore Activities, Investigations, and other interactive study aids.

SUMMARY OF KEY CONCEPTS

Concept 14.1

Mendel used the scientific approach to identify two laws of inheritance

▶ **Mendel's Experimental, Quantitative Approach** (pp. 252–253) Gregor Mendel formulated a particulate theory of inheritance based on experiments with garden peas, carried out in the 1860s. He showed that parents pass on to their offspring discrete genes that retain their identity through the generations.

▶ **The Law of Segregation** (pp. 253–256) This law states that the two alleles of a gene separate (segregate) during gamete formation, so that a sperm or an egg carries only one allele of each pair. Mendel proposed this law to explain the 3:1 ratio of F_2 phenotypes he observed when monohybrids self-pollinated. According to Mendel's model, genes have alternative forms (alleles), and each organism inherits one allele for each gene from each parent. If the two alleles of a gene are different, expression of one (the dominant allele) masks the phenotypic effect of the other (the recessive allele). Homozygous individuals have identical alleles of a given gene and are true-breeding. Heterozygous individuals have two different alleles of a given gene.
Activity Monohybrid Cross

▶ **The Law of Independent Assortment** (pp. 256–258) This law states that each pair of alleles segregates into gametes independently of other pairs. Mendel proposed this law based on dihybrid crosses between plants heterozygous for two genes. Alleles of each gene segregate into gametes independently of alleles of other genes. The offspring of a dihybrid cross (the F_2 generation) have four phenotypes in a 9:3:3:1 ratio.
Activity Dihybrid Cross

Concept 14.2

The laws of probability govern Mendelian inheritance

▶ **The Multiplication and Addition Rules Applied to Monohybrid Crosses** (pp. 258–259) The multiplication rule states that the probability of a compound event is equal to the product of the individual probabilities of the independent single events. The addition rule states that the probability of an event that can occur in two or more independent, mutually exclusive ways is the sum of the individual probabilities.
Activity Gregor's Garden

▶ **Solving Complex Genetics Problems with the Rules of Probability** (pp. 259–260) A dihybrid or other multi-character cross is equivalent to two or more independent monohybrid crosses occurring simultaneously. In calculating the chances for the various offspring genotypes from such crosses, each character first is considered separately and then the individual probabilities are multiplied together.

Concept 14.3

Inheritance patterns are often more complex than predicted by simple Mendelian genetics

▶ **Extending Mendelian Genetics for a Single Gene** (pp. 260–262) For a gene with complete dominance of one allele, the heterozygous phenotype is the same as that for the homozygous dominant phenotype. For a gene with codominance of both alleles, both phenotypes are expressed in heterozgotes. For a gene with incomplete dominance of either allele, the heterozygous phenotype is intermediate between the two homozygous phenotypes. Many genes exist in multiple (more than two) alleles in a population. Pleiotropy is the ability of a single gene to affect multiple phenotypic characters.
Activity Incomplete Dominance

▶ **Extending Mendelian Genetics for Two or More Genes** (pp. 262–263) In epistasis, one gene affects the expression of another gene. In polygenic inheritance, a single phenotypic character is affected by two or more genes. Characters influenced by multiple genes are often quantitative, meaning that they vary continuously.

▶ **Nature and Nurture: The Environmental Impact on Phenotype** (p. 264) The expression of a genotype can be affected by environmental influences. The phenotypic range of a particular genotype is called its norm of reaction. Polygenic characters that are also influenced by the environment are called multifactorial characters.

▶ **Integrating a Mendelian View of Heredity and Variation** (p. 264) An organism's overall phenotype, including its physical appearance, internal anatomy, physiology, and behavior, reflects its overall genotype and unique environmental history. Even in more complex inheritance patterns, Mendel's fundamental laws of segregation and independent assortment still apply.

Concept 14.4

Many human traits follow Mendelian patterns of inheritance

▶ **Pedigree Analysis** (pp. 265–266) Family pedigrees can be used to deduce the possible genotypes of individuals and make predictions about future offspring. Predictions are usually statistical probabilities rather than certainties.

▶ **Recessively Inherited Disorders** (pp. 266–267) Tay-Sachs disease, cystic fibrosis, sickle-cell disease, and many other genetic disorders are inherited as simple recessive traits. Most affected individuals (with the homozygous recessive genotype) are children of phenotypically normal, heterozygous carriers.

▶ **Dominantly Inherited Disorders** (pp. 267–268) Lethal dominant alleles are eliminated from the population if affected people die before reproducing. Nonlethal dominant alleles and lethal ones that strike relatively late in life, such as the allele that causes Huntington's disease, are inherited in a Mendelian way.

▶ **Multifactorial Disorders** (p. 268) Many human diseases, such as most forms of cancer and heart disease, have both genetic and environmental components. These do not follow simple Mendelian inheritance patterns.

▶ **Genetic Testing and Counseling** (pp. 268–270) Using family histories, genetic counselors help couples determine the odds that their children will have genetic disorders. For a growing number of diseases, tests that identify carriers define the odds more accurately. Once a child is conceived, amniocentesis and chorionic villus sampling can help determine whether a suspected genetic disorder is present. Further genetic tests can be performed after a child is born.
Investigation How Do You Diagnose a Genetic Disorder?

Genetics Problems

1. In some plants, a true-breeding, red-flowered strain gives all pink flowers when crossed with a white-flowered strain: RR (red) $\times$ rr (white) $\rightarrow$ Rr (pink). If flower position (axial or terminal) is inherited as it is in peas (see Table 14.1), what will be the ratios of genotypes and phenotypes of the F_1 generation resulting from the following cross: axial-red (true-breeding) $\times$ terminal-white? What will be the ratios in the F_2 generation?

2. Flower position, stem length, and seed shape were three characters that Mendel studied. Each is controlled by an independently assorting gene and has dominant and recessive expression as follows:

Character	Dominant	Recessive
Flower position	Axial (A)	Terminal (a)
Stem length	Tall (T)	Dwarf (t)
Seed shape	Round (R)	Wrinkled (r)

If a plant that is heterozygous for all three characters is allowed to self-fertilize, what proportion of the offspring would you expect to be as follows? (*Note:* Use the rules of probability instead of a huge Punnett square.)
   a. homozygous for the three dominant traits
   b. homozygous for the three recessive traits
   c. heterozygous for all three characters
   d. homozygous for axial and tall, heterozygous for seed shape

3. A black guinea pig crossed with an albino guinea pig produces 12 black offspring. When the albino is crossed with a second black one, 7 blacks and 5 albinos are obtained. What is the best explanation for this genetic situation? Write genotypes for the parents, gametes, and offspring.

4. In sesame plants, the one-pod condition (P) is dominant to the three-pod condition (p), and normal leaf (L) is dominant to wrinkled leaf (l). Pod type and leaf type are inherited independently. Determine the genotypes for the two parents for all possible matings producing the following offspring:
   a. 318 one-pod, normal leaf : 98 one-pod, wrinkled leaf
   b. 323 three-pod, normal leaf : 106 three-pod, wrinkled leaf
   c. 401 one-pod, normal leaf
   d. 150 one-pod, normal leaf : 147 one-pod, wrinkled leaf : 51 three-pod, normal leaf : 48 three-pod, wrinkled leaf
   e. 223 one-pod, normal leaf : 72 one-pod, wrinkled leaf : 76 three-pod, normal leaf : 27 three-pod, wrinkled leaf

5. A man with type A blood marries a woman with type B blood. Their child has type O blood. What are the genotypes of these individuals? What other genotypes, and in what frequencies, would you expect in offspring from this marriage?

6. Phenylketonuria (PKU) is an inherited disease caused by a recessive allele. If a woman and her husband, who are both carriers, have three children, what is the probability of each of the following?

   a. All three children are of normal phenotype.
   b. One or more of the three children have the disease.
   c. All three children have the disease.
   d. At least one child is phenotypically normal.

   (*Note:* Remember that the probabilities of all possible outcomes always add up to 1.)

7. The genotype of F_1 individuals in a tetrahybrid cross is $AaBbCcDd$. Assuming independent assortment of these four genes, what are the probabilities that F_2 offspring will have the following genotypes?
   a. $aabbccdd$
   b. $AaBbCcDd$
   c. $AABBCCDD$
   d. $AaBBccDd$
   e. $AaBBCCdd$

8. What is the probability that each of the following pairs of parents will produce the indicated offspring? (Assume independent assortment of all gene pairs.)
   a. $AABBCC \times aabbcc \rightarrow AaBbCc$
   b. $AABbCc \times AaBbCc \rightarrow AAbbCC$
   c. $AaBbCc \times AaBbCc \rightarrow AaBbCc$
   d. $aaBbCC \times AABbcc \rightarrow AaBbCc$

9. Karen and Steve each have a sibling with sickle-cell disease. Neither Karen nor Steve nor any of their parents have the disease, and none of them have been tested to reveal sickle-cell trait. Based on this incomplete information, calculate the probability that if this couple has a child, the child will have sickle-cell disease.

10. In 1981, a stray black cat with unusual rounded, curled-back ears was adopted by a family in California. Hundreds of descendants of the cat have since been born, and cat fanciers hope to develop the curl cat into a show breed. Suppose you owned the first curl cat and wanted to develop a true-breeding variety. How would you determine whether the curl allele is dominant or recessive? How would you obtain true-breeding curl cats? How could you be sure they are true-breeding?

11. Imagine that a newly discovered, recessively inherited disease is expressed only in individuals with type O blood, although the disease and blood group are independently inherited. A normal man with type A blood and a normal woman with type B blood have already had one child with the disease. The woman is now pregnant for a second time. What is the probability that the second child will also have the disease? Assume that both parents are heterozygous for the gene that causes the disease.

12. In tigers, a recessive allele causes an absence of fur pigmentation (a white tiger) and a cross-eyed condition. If two phenotypically normal tigers that are heterozygous at this locus are mated, what percentage of their offspring will be cross-eyed? What percentage will be white?

13. In corn plants, a dominant allele I inhibits kernel color, while the recessive allele i permits color when homozygous.

At a different locus, the dominant allele *P* causes purple kernel color, while the homozygous recessive genotype *pp* causes red kernels. If plants heterozygous at both loci are crossed, what will be the phenotypic ratio of the offspring?

14. The pedigree below traces the inheritance of alkaptonuria, a biochemical disorder. Affected individuals, indicated here by the colored circles and squares, are unable to break down a substance called alkapton, which colors the urine and stains body tissues. Does alkaptonuria appear to be caused by a dominant allele or by a recessive allele? Fill in the genotypes of the individuals whose genotypes can be deduced. What genotypes are possible for each of the other individuals?

15. A man has six fingers on each hand and six toes on each foot. His wife and their daughter have the normal number of digits. Extra digits is a dominant trait. What fraction of this couple's children would be expected to have extra digits?

16. Imagine that you are a genetic counselor, and a couple planning to start a family come to you for information. Charles was married once before, and he and his first wife had a child with cystic fibrosis. The brother of his current wife Elaine died of cystic fibrosis. What is the probability that Charles and Elaine will have a baby with cystic fibrosis? (Neither Charles nor Elaine has cystic fibrosis.)

17. In mice, black color (*B*) is dominant to white (*b*). At a different locus, a dominant allele (*A*) produces a band of yellow just below the tip of each hair in mice with black fur. This gives a frosted appearance known as agouti. Expression of the recessive allele (*a*) results in a solid coat color. If mice that are heterozygous at both loci are crossed, what is the expected phenotypic ratio of their offspring?

For Genetics Problems answers, see Appendix A.

Go to the website or CD-ROM for more quiz questions.

Evolution Connection

Over the past half century, there has been a trend in the United States and other developed countries for people to marry and start families later in life than did their parents and grandparents. Speculate on the effects this trend may have on the incidence (frequency) of late-acting dominant lethal alleles in the population.

Scientific Inquiry

You are handed a mystery pea plant with long stems and axial flowers and asked to determine its genotype as quickly as possible. You know the allele for tall stems (*T*) is dominant to that for dwarf stems (*t*) and that the allele for axial flowers (*A*) is dominant to that for terminal flowers (*a*).

a. What are *all* the possible genotypes for your mystery plant?
b. Describe the *one* cross you would do, out in your garden, to determine the exact genotype of your mystery plant.
c. While waiting for the results of your cross, you predict the results for each possible genotype listed in part a. How do you do this?
d. Make your predictions using the following format: If the genotype of my mystery plant is _____, the plants resulting from my cross will be _____.
e. If ½ of your offspring plants have tall stems with axial flowers and ½ have tall stems with terminal flowers, what must be the genotype of your mystery plant?
f. Explain why the activities you performed in parts c and d were not "doing a cross."

Investigation *How Do You Diagnose a Genetic Disorder?*

Science, Technology, and Society

Imagine that one of your parents had Huntington's disease. What is the probability that you, too, will someday manifest the disease? There is no cure for Huntington's. Would you want to be tested for the Huntington's allele? Why or why not?

15

The Chromosomal Basis of Inheritance

▲ Figure 15.1 **Chromosomes tagged to reveal a specific gene (yellow).**

Key Concepts

15.1 Mendelian inheritance has its physical basis in the behavior of chromosomes

15.2 Linked genes tend to be inherited together because they are located near each other on the same chromosome

15.3 Sex-linked genes exhibit unique patterns of inheritance

15.4 Alterations of chromosome number or structure cause some genetic disorders

15.5 Some inheritance patterns are exceptions to the standard chromosome theory

Overview

Locating Genes on Chromosomes

Today, we can show that genes—Gregor Mendel's "hereditary factors"—are located on chromosomes. We can see the location of a particular gene by tagging isolated chromosomes with a fluorescent dye that highlights that gene. For example, the yellow dots in **Figure 15.1** mark the locus of a specific gene on a homologous pair of human chromosomes. (Because the chromosomes in this light micrograph have already replicated, we see two dots per chromosome, one on each sister chromatid.) A century or so ago, however, the relation of genes and chromosomes was not immediately obvious. Many biologists remained skeptical about Mendel's laws of segregation and independent assortment until evidence accumulated that these principles of heredity had a physical basis in the behavior of chromosomes. In this chapter, which integrates and extends what you learned in the past two chapters, we describe the chromosomal basis for the transmission of genes from parents to offspring, along with some important exceptions.

Mendelian inheritance has its physical basis in the behavior of chromosomes

Using improved techniques of microscopy, cytologists worked out the process of mitosis in 1875 and meiosis in the 1890s. Then, around 1900, cytology and genetics converged as biologists began to see parallels between the behavior of chromosomes and the behavior of Mendel's "factors" during sexual life cycles: Chromosomes and genes are both present in pairs in diploid cells; homologous chromosomes separate and alleles segregate during the process of meiosis; and fertilization restores the paired condition for both chromosomes and genes. Around 1902, Walter S. Sutton, Theodor Boveri, and others independently noted these parallels, and the **chromosome theory of inheritance** began to take form. According to this theory, Mendelian genes have specific loci (positions) on chromosomes, and it is the chromosomes that undergo segregation and independent assortment.

Figure 15.2 shows that the behavior of homologous chromosomes during meiosis can account for the segregation of the alleles at each genetic locus to different gametes. The figure also shows that the behavior of nonhomologous chromosomes can account for the independent assortment of the alleles for two or more genes located on different chromosomes. By carefully studying this figure, which traces the same dihybrid pea cross you learned about in Figure 14.8, you can see how the behavior of chromosomes during meiosis in the F_1 generation and subsequent random fertilization gives rise to the F_2 phenotypic ratio observed by Mendel.

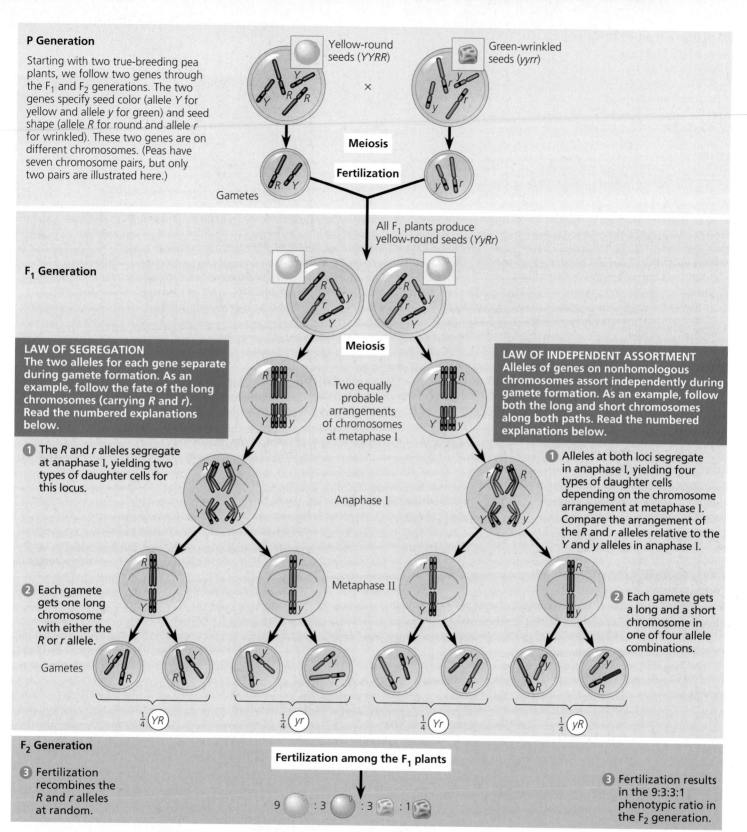

P Generation

Starting with two true-breeding pea plants, we follow two genes through the F_1 and F_2 generations. The two genes specify seed color (allele *Y* for yellow and allele *y* for green) and seed shape (allele *R* for round and allele *r* for wrinkled). These two genes are on different chromosomes. (Peas have seven chromosome pairs, but only two pairs are illustrated here.)

Yellow-round seeds (*YYRR*)

Green-wrinkled seeds (*yyrr*)

×

Meiosis

Fertilization

Gametes

All F_1 plants produce yellow-round seeds (*YyRr*)

F_1 Generation

LAW OF SEGREGATION
The two alleles for each gene separate during gamete formation. As an example, follow the fate of the long chromosomes (carrying *R* and *r*). Read the numbered explanations below.

Meiosis

Two equally probable arrangements of chromosomes at metaphase I

LAW OF INDEPENDENT ASSORTMENT
Alleles of genes on nonhomologous chromosomes assort independently during gamete formation. As an example, follow both the long and short chromosomes along both paths. Read the numbered explanations below.

1 The *R* and *r* alleles segregate at anaphase I, yielding two types of daughter cells for this locus.

Anaphase I

1 Alleles at both loci segregate in anaphase I, yielding four types of daughter cells depending on the chromosome arrangement at metaphase I. Compare the arrangement of the *R* and *r* alleles relative to the *Y* and *y* alleles in anaphase I.

Metaphase II

2 Each gamete gets one long chromosome with either the *R* or *r* allele.

2 Each gamete gets a long and a short chromosome in one of four allele combinations.

Gametes

$\frac{1}{4}$ (YR) $\frac{1}{4}$ (yr) $\frac{1}{4}$ (Yr) $\frac{1}{4}$ (yR)

F_2 Generation

3 Fertilization recombines the *R* and *r* alleles at random.

Fertilization among the F_1 plants

3 Fertilization results in the 9:3:3:1 phenotypic ratio in the F_2 generation.

9 : 3 : 3 : 1

▲ **Figure 15.2 The chromosomal basis of Mendel's laws.** Here we correlate the results of one of Mendel's dihybrid crosses (see Figure 14.8) with the behavior of chromosomes during meiosis (see Figure 13.8). The arrangement of chromosomes at metaphase I of meiosis and their movement during anaphase I account for the segregation and independent assortment of the alleles for seed color and shape. Each cell that undergoes meiosis in an F_1 plant produces two kinds of gametes. Overall, however, F_1 plants produce equal numbers of all four kinds of gametes because the alternative chromosome arrangements at metaphase I are equally likely.

Morgan's Experimental Evidence: *Scientific Inquiry*

The first solid evidence associating a specific gene with a specific chromosome came from the work of Thomas Hunt Morgan, an experimental embryologist at Columbia University early in the 20th century. Although Morgan was initially skeptical about both Mendelism and the chromosome theory, his early experiments provided convincing evidence that chromosomes are indeed the location of Mendel's heritable factors.

Morgan's Choice of Experimental Organism

Many times in the history of biology, important discoveries have come to those insightful enough or lucky enough to choose an experimental organism suitable for the research problem being tackled. Mendel chose the garden pea because a number of distinct varieties were available. For his work, Morgan selected a species of fruit fly, *Drosophila melanogaster,* a common, generally innocuous insect that feeds on the fungi growing on fruit. Fruit flies are prolific breeders; a single mating will produce hundreds of offspring, and a new generation can be bred every two weeks. These characteristics make the fruit fly a convenient organism for genetic studies. Morgan's laboratory soon became known as "the fly room."

Another advantage of the fruit fly is that it has only four pairs of chromosomes, which are easily distinguishable with a light microscope. There are three pairs of autosomes and one pair of sex chromosomes. Female fruit flies have a homologous pair of X chromosomes, and males have one X chromosome and one Y chromosome.

While Mendel could readily obtain different pea varieties, there were no convenient suppliers of fruit fly varieties for Morgan to employ. Indeed, he was probably the first person to want different varieties of this common insect. After a year of breeding flies and looking for variant individuals, Morgan was rewarded with the discovery of a single male fly with white eyes instead of the usual red. The normal phenotype for a character (the phenotype most common in natural populations), such as red eyes in *Drosophila,* is called the **wild type** (Figure 15.3). Traits that are alternatives to the wild type, such as white eyes in *Drosophila,* are called *mutant phenotypes* because they are due to alleles assumed to have originated as changes, or mutations, in the wild-type allele.

Morgan and his students invented a notation for symbolizing alleles in *Drosophila* that is still widely used for fruit flies. For a given character in flies, the gene takes its symbol from the first mutant (non–wild type) discovered. Thus, the allele for white eyes in *Drosophila* is symbolized by *w*. A superscript + identifies the allele for the wild-type trait—w^+ for the allele for red eyes, for example. Over the years, different gene notation systems have been developed for different organisms. For example, human genes are usually written in all capitals, such as *HD* for the allele for Huntington's disease.

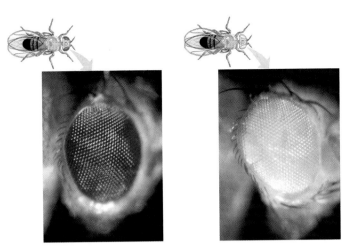

▲ Figure 15.3 **Morgan's first mutant.** Wild-type *Drosophila* flies have red eyes (left). Among his flies, Morgan discovered a mutant male with white eyes (right). This variation made it possible for Morgan to trace a gene for eye color to a specific chromosome (LMs).

Correlating Behavior of a Gene's Alleles with Behavior of a Chromosome Pair

Morgan mated his white-eyed male fly with a red-eyed female. All the F_1 offspring had red eyes, suggesting that the wild-type allele is dominant. When Morgan bred the F_1 flies to each other, he observed the classical 3:1 phenotypic ratio among the F_2 offspring. However, there was a surprising additional result: The white-eye trait showed up only in males. All the F_2 females had red eyes, while half the males had red eyes and half had white eyes. Therefore, Morgan concluded that somehow a fly's eye color was linked to its sex. (If the eye-color gene were unrelated to gender, one would have expected half of the white-eyed flies to be male and half female.)

A female fly has two X chromosomes (XX), while a male fly has an X and a Y (XY). The correlation between the trait of white eye color and the male sex of the affected F_2 flies suggested to Morgan that the gene affected in his white-eyed mutant was located exclusively on the X chromosome, with no corresponding allele present on the Y chromosome. His reasoning can be followed in **Figure 15.4**. For a male, a single copy of the mutant allele would confer white eyes; since a male has only one X chromosome, there can be no wild-type allele (w^+) present to offset the recessive allele. On the other hand, a female could have white eyes only if both her X chromosomes carried the recessive mutant allele (w). This was impossible for the F_2 females in Morgan's experiment because all the F_1 fathers had red eyes.

Morgan's finding of the correlation between a particular trait and an individual's sex provided support for the chromosome theory of inheritance: namely, that a specific gene is carried on a specific chromosome (in this case, the eye-color gene on the X chromosome). In addition, Morgan's work indicated that genes located on a sex chromosome exhibit unique inheritance patterns, which we will discuss later in this chapter. Recognizing the importance of Morgan's early work, many bright students were attracted to his fly room.

Figure 15.4

Inquiry In a cross between a wild-type female fruit fly and a mutant white-eyed male, what color eyes will the F₁ and F₂ offspring have?

EXPERIMENT Morgan mated a wild-type (red-eyed) female with a mutant white-eyed male. The F₁ offspring all had red eyes.

P Generation ♀ × ♂

F₁ Generation

Morgan then bred an F₁ red-eyed female to an F₁ red-eyed male to produce the F₂ generation.

RESULTS The F₂ generation showed a typical Mendelian 3:1 ratio of red eyes to white eyes. However, no females displayed the white-eye trait; they all had red eyes. Half the males had white eyes, and half had red eyes.

F₂ Generation ♀ ♀ ♂ ♂

CONCLUSION Since all F₁ offspring had red eyes, the mutant white-eye trait (*w*) must be recessive to the wild-type red-eye trait (*w⁺*). Since the recessive trait—white eyes—was expressed only in males in the F₂ generation, Morgan hypothesized that the eye-color gene is located on the X chromosome and that there is no corresponding locus on the Y chromosome, as diagrammed here.

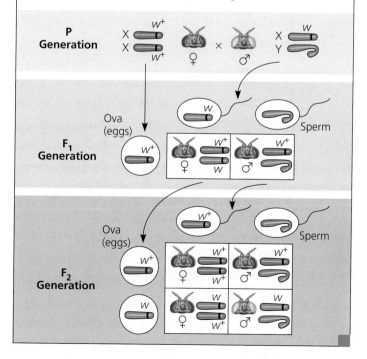

P Generation

F₁ Generation
Ova (eggs) / Sperm

F₂ Generation
Ova (eggs) / Sperm

---

1. Which one of Mendel's laws relates to the inheritance of alleles for a single character? Which law relates to the inheritance of alleles for two characters in a dihybrid cross? What is the physical basis of these laws?
2. If the eye-color locus in *Drosophila* were located on an autosome, what would be the sex and phenotype of all the F₂ offspring produced by the crosses in Figure 15.4?

For suggested answers, see Appendix A.

Concept 15.2

Linked genes tend to be inherited together because they are located near each other on the same chromosome

The number of genes in a cell is far greater than the number of chromosomes; in fact, each chromosome has hundreds or thousands of genes. Genes located on the same chromosome that tend to be inherited together in genetic crosses are said to be **linked genes**. When geneticists follow linked genes in breeding experiments, the results deviate from those expected from Mendel's law of independent assortment.

How Linkage Affects Inheritance:
Scientific Inquiry

To see how linkage between genes affects the inheritance of two different characters, let's examine another of Morgan's *Drosophila* experiments. In this case, the characters are body color and wing size, each with two different phenotypes. Wild-type flies have gray bodies and normal-sized wings. In addition to these flies, Morgan had doubly mutant flies with black bodies and vestigial wings (much smaller than normal wings). The alleles for these traits are represented by the following symbols: b^+ = gray, b = black; vg^+ = normal wings, vg = vestigial wings. The mutant alleles are recessive to the wild-type alleles, and neither gene is on a sex chromosome.

In studying these two genes, Morgan carried out the crosses shown in **Figure 15.5** (p. 279). He first mated true-breeding wild-type flies ($b^+ b^+ vg^+ vg^+$) with black, vestigial-winged ones ($b b vg vg$) to produce heterozygous F₁ dihybrids ($b^+ b vg^+ vg$), all of which were wild-type in appearance. He then crossed female dihybrids with true-breeding males of the double-mutant phenotype ($b b vg vg$). In this second cross, which corresponds to a Mendelian testcross, we know the genotype of the female parent ($b^+ b vg^+ vg$), and we also know which allele combinations are "parental," meaning derived from the parents in the P generation: b^+ with vg^+ and b with vg. We don't know, however, whether the two genes are located on the same or different chromosomes. In the testcross, all the sperm will donate recessive alleles (b and vg); so the phenotypes of the offspring will depend on the ova's alleles. Therefore, from the phenotypes of the offspring, we can determine whether or not the parental allele combinations, b^+ with vg^+ and b with vg, stayed together during formation of the F_1 female's ova.

When Morgan "scored" (classified according to phenotype) 2,300 offspring from the testcross matings, he observed a much higher proportion of parental phenotypes than would be expected if the two genes assorted independently (see Figure 15.5). Based on these results, Morgan reasoned that body color and wing size are usually inherited together in specific combinations (the parental combinations) because the genes for these characters are on the same chromosome:

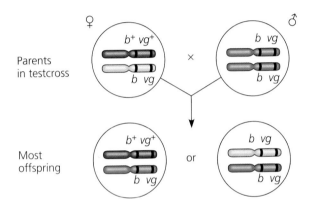

However, if the genes for body color and wing size were always inherited together in those parental combinations, no nonparental phenotypes would have been observed among the offspring of Morgan's testcross. In fact, both of the nonparental phenotypes *were* produced in Morgan's experiments (see Figure 15.5), suggesting that the body-color and wing-size genes are only partially linked genetically. To understand this result, we need to further explore **genetic recombination,** the production of offspring with combinations of traits differing from those found in either parent.

Genetic Recombination and Linkage

In Chapter 13, you learned that meiosis and random fertilization generate genetic variation among offspring of sexually reproducing organisms. Here we will examine the chromosomal basis of recombination in relation to the genetic findings of Mendel and Morgan.

Recombination of Unlinked Genes: Independent Assortment of Chromosomes

Mendel learned from crosses in which he followed two characters that some offspring have combinations of traits that do not match either parent in the parental (P) generation. For example, we can represent the cross between a pea plant with yellow-round seeds that is heterozygous for both seed color and seed shape ($YyRr$) and a plant with green-wrinkled seeds (homozygous for both recessive alleles, $yyrr$) by the following Punnett square:

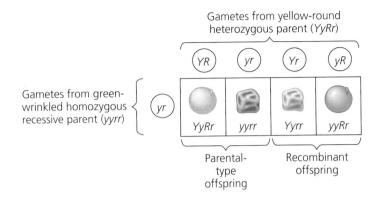

Notice in this Punnett square that one-half of the offspring are expected to inherit a phenotype that matches one of the parental phenotypes. These offspring are called **parental types.** But two nonparental phenotypes are also found among the offspring. Because these offspring have new combinations of seed shape and color, they are called **recombinant types,** or **recombinants** for short. When 50% of all offspring are recombinants, as in this example, geneticists say that there is a 50% frequency of recombination. The predicted phenotypic ratios among the offspring are similar to what Mendel actually found in $YyRr \times yyrr$ crosses.

A 50% frequency of recombination is observed for any two genes that are located on different chromosomes. The physical basis of recombination between unlinked genes is the random orientation of homologous chromosomes at metaphase I of meiosis, which leads to the independent assortment of alleles (see Figures 15.2 and 13.10).

Recombination of Linked Genes: Crossing Over

Now let's return to Morgan's fly room to see how we can explain the results of the *Drosophila* testcross illustrated in Figure 15.5. Recall that most of the offspring from the testcross for body color and wing size had parental phenotypes, suggesting that the two genes were on the same chromosome, but a small number of offspring were recombinants. Although there was linkage, it appeared to be incomplete.

Faced with these results, Morgan proposed that some process must occasionally break the physical connection between genes on the same chromosome. Subsequent experiments demonstrated that this process, now called **crossing over,** accounts for the recombination of linked genes. In crossing over, which occurs while replicated homologous chromosomes are paired during prophase of meiosis I, one maternal

Figure 15.5

Inquiry **Are the genes for body color and wing size in fruit flies located on the same chromosome or different chromosomes?**

EXPERIMENT   Morgan first mated true-breeding wild-type flies with black, vestigial-winged flies to produce heterozygous F_1 dihybrids, all of which are wild-type in appearance. He then mated wild-type F_1 dihybrid females with black, vestigial-winged males, producing 2,300 F_2 offspring, which he classified according to phenotype.

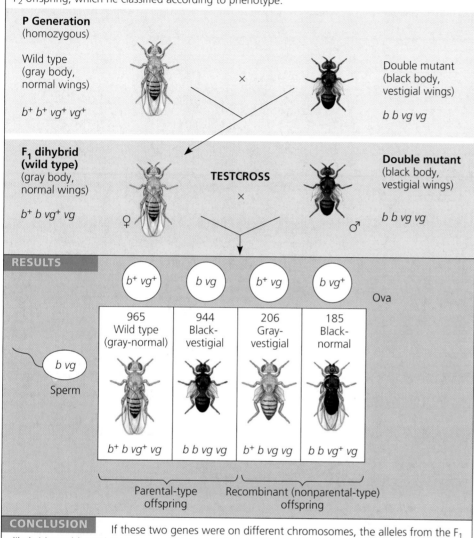

P Generation
(homozygous)

Wild type
(gray body,
normal wings)

$b^+ b^+ vg^+ vg^+$

×

Double mutant
(black body,
vestigial wings)

$b\ b\ vg\ vg$

F_1 dihybrid
(wild type)
(gray body,
normal wings)

$b^+ b\ vg^+ vg$

♀

TESTCROSS

×

Double mutant
(black body,
vestigial wings)

$b\ b\ vg\ vg$

♂

RESULTS

Ova: $b^+ vg^+$ $b\ vg$ $b^+ vg$ $b\ vg^+$

Sperm: $b\ vg$

965 Wild type (gray-normal)	944 Black-vestigial	206 Gray-vestigial	185 Black-normal
$b^+ b\ vg^+ vg$	$b\ b\ vg\ vg$	$b^+ b\ vg\ vg$	$b\ b\ vg^+ vg$

Parental-type offspring   Recombinant (nonparental-type) offspring

CONCLUSION   If these two genes were on different chromosomes, the alleles from the F_1 dihybrid would sort into gametes independently, and we would expect to see equal numbers of the four types of offspring. If these two genes were on the same chromosome, we would expect each allele combination, $b^+ vg^+$ and $b\ vg$, to stay together as gametes formed. In this case, only offspring with parental phenotypes would be produced. Since most offspring had a parental phenotype, Morgan concluded that the genes for body color and wing size are located on the same chromosome. However, the production of a small number of offspring with nonparental phenotypes indicated that some mechanism occasionally breaks the linkage between genes on the same chromosome.

and one paternal chromatid break at corresponding points and then are rejoined to each other (see Figure 13.11). In effect, the end portions of two nonsister chromatids trade places each time a crossover occurs.

The recombinant chromosomes resulting from crossing over may bring alleles together in new combinations, and the subsequent events of meiosis distribute the recombinant chromo-

somes to gametes. **Figure 15.6** (p. 280) shows how crossing over in a dihybrid female fly resulted in recombinant ova and ultimately recombinant offspring in Morgan's testcross. Most of the ova had a chromosome with either the $b^+ vg^+$ or $b\ vg$ parental genotype for body color and wing size, but some ova had a recombinant chromosome ($b^+ vg$ or $b\ vg^+$). Fertilization of these various classes of ova by homozygous recessive sperm ($b\ vg$) produced an offspring population in which 17% exhibited a nonparental, recombinant phenotype (see Figure 15.6). As we discuss next, the percentage of recombinant offspring, the *recombination frequency*, is related to the distance between linked genes.

Linkage Mapping Using Recombination Data: *Scientific Inquiry*

The discovery of linked genes and recombination due to crossing over led one of Morgan's students, Alfred H. Sturtevant, to a method for constructing a **genetic map**, an ordered list of the genetic loci along a particular chromosome.

Sturtevant hypothesized that recombination frequencies calculated from experiments like the one in Figures 15.5 and 15.6 depend on the distances between genes on a chromosome. He assumed that crossing over is a random event, and thus the chance of crossing over is approximately equal at all points along a chromosome. Based on these assumptions, Sturtevant predicted that *the farther apart two genes are, the higher the probability that a crossover will occur between them and therefore the higher the recombination frequency.* His reasoning was simple: The greater the distance between two genes, the more points there are between them where crossing over can occur. Using recombination data from various fruit fly crosses, Sturtevant proceeded to assign relative positions to genes on the same chromosomes—that is, to *map* genes.

A genetic map based on recombination frequencies is specifically called a **linkage map. Figure 15.7** (p. 281) shows Sturtevant's linkage map of three genes: the body-color (b) and wing-size (vg) genes depicted in Figure 15.6 and a third gene, called cinnabar (cn). Cinnabar is one of many *Drosophila* genes affecting eye color. Cinnabar eyes, a mutant phenotype, are a brighter red than the wild-type color. The recombination frequency between *cn* and *b* is 9%; that between *cn* and *vg*, 9.5%; and that between *b* and *vg*, 17%. In other words, crossovers between *cn* and *b* and between *cn* and *vg* are about half as frequent as crossovers between *b* and *vg*. Only a map that locates *cn* about midway between *b* and *vg* is consistent with these data, as you can prove to yourself by drawing alternative maps.

Sturtevant expressed the distances between genes in **map units,** defining one map unit as equivalent to a 1% recombination frequency. Today, map units often are called *centimorgans* in honor of Morgan.

In practice, the interpretation of recombination data is more complicated than this example suggests. For example, some genes on a chromosome are so far from each other that a crossover between them is virtually certain. The observed

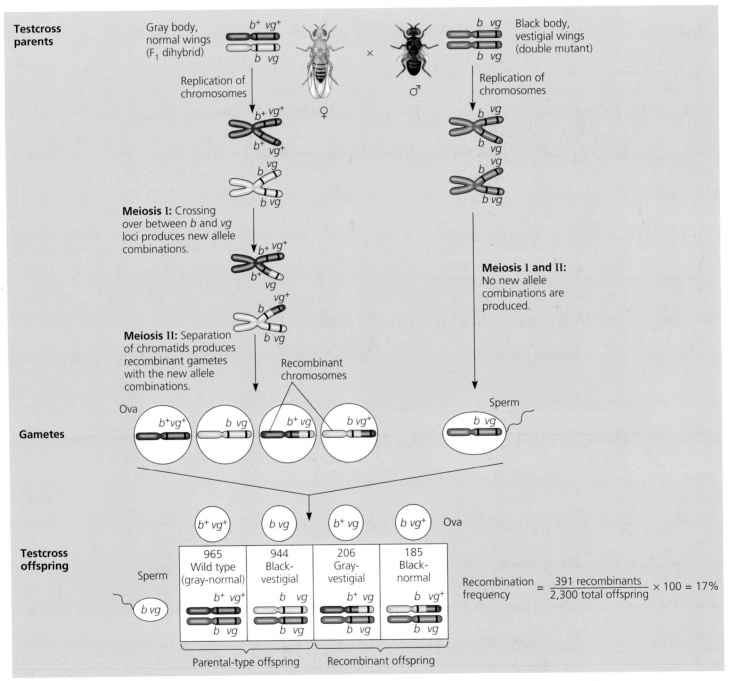

▲ **Figure 15.6 Chromosomal basis for recombination of linked genes.** In these diagrams re-creating the testcross in Figure 15.5, we track chromosomes as well as genes. The maternal chromosomes are color-coded to distinguish one homologue from the other. Because crossing over between the *b* and *vg* loci occurs in some, but not all, ovum-producing cells, more ova with parental-type chromosomes than with recombinant ones are produced in the mating females. Fertilization of the ova by sperm of genotype *b vg* gives rise to some recombinant offspring. The recombination frequency is the percentage of recombinant flies in the total pool of offspring.

Figure 15.7
Research Method **Constructing a Linkage Map**

APPLICATION   A linkage map shows the relative locations of genes along a chromosome.

TECHNIQUE   A linkage map is based on the assumption that the probability of a crossover between two genetic loci is proportional to the distance separating the loci. The recombination frequencies used to construct a linkage map for a particular chromosome are obtained from experimental crosses, such as the cross depicted in Figure 15.6. The distances between genes are expressed as map units (centimorgans), with one map unit equivalent to a 1% recombination frequency. Genes are arranged on the chromosome in the order that best fits the data.

RESULTS   In this example, the observed recombination frequencies between three *Drosophila* gene pairs (*b–cn* 9%, *cn–vg* 9.5%, and *b–vg* 17%) best fit a linear order in which *cn* is positioned about halfway between the other two genes:

Recombination
frequencies

←— 9% —→ ←— 9.5% —→

←——— 17% ———→

Chromosome   *b*   *cn*   *vg*

The *b–vg* recombination frequency is slightly less than the sum of the *b–cn* and *cn–vg* frequencies because double crossovers are fairly likely to occur between *b* and *vg* in matings tracking these two genes. A second crossover would "cancel out" the first and thus reduce the observed *b–vg* recombination frequency.

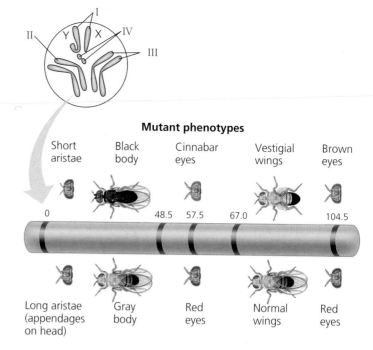

Mutant phenotypes

| Short aristae | Black body | Cinnabar eyes | Vestigial wings | Brown eyes |

0 48.5 57.5 67.0 104.5

Long aristae (appendages on head) | Gray body | Red eyes | Normal wings | Red eyes

Wild-type phenotypes

▲ **Figure 15.8 A partial genetic (linkage) map of a Drosophila chromosome.** This simplified map shows just a few of the genes that have been mapped on *Drosophila* chromosome II. The number at each gene locus indicates the number of map units between that locus and the locus for aristae length (left). Notice that more than one gene can affect a given phenotypic characteristic, such as eye color. Also, note that in contrast to the homologous autosomes (II–IV), the X and Y sex chromosomes (I) have distinct shapes.

frequency of recombination in crosses involving two such genes can have a maximum value of 50%, a result indistinguishable from that for genes on different chromosomes. In this case, the physical connection between genes on the same chromosome is not reflected in the results of genetic crosses. Despite being on the same chromosome and thus being *physically linked*, the genes are *genetically unlinked*; alleles of such genes assort independently as if they were on different chromosomes. In fact, the genes for two of the pea characters that Mendel studied—seed color and flower color—are now known to be on the same chromosome, but the distance between them is so great that linkage is not observed in genetic crosses. Genes located far apart on a chromosome are mapped by adding the recombination frequencies from crosses involving each of the distant genes and a number of genes lying between them.

Using recombination data, Sturtevant and his colleagues were able to map numerous *Drosophila* genes in linear arrays. They found that the genes clustered into four groups of linked genes. Because microscopists had found four pairs of chromosomes in *Drosophila* cells, this clustering of genes was additional evidence that genes are located on chromosomes. Each chromosome has a linear array of specific gene loci **(Figure 15.8)**.

Because a linkage map is based on recombination frequencies, it gives only an approximate picture of a chromosome. The frequency of crossing over is not actually uniform over the length of a chromosome, as Sturtevant assumed, and therefore map units do not correspond to actual physical distances (in nanometers, for instance). A linkage map does portray the order of genes along a chromosome, but it does not accurately portray the precise locations of those genes. Other methods enable geneticists to construct **cytogenetic maps** of chromosomes, which locate genes with respect to chromosomal features, such as stained bands, that can be seen in the microscope. The ultimate maps, which we will discuss in Chapter 20, show the physical distances between gene loci in DNA nucleotides. Comparing a linkage map with such a physical map or with a cytogenetic map of the same chromosome, we find that the linear order of genes is identical in all the maps, but the spacing between genes is not.

Concept Check 15.2

Concept Check 15.2

1. When two genes are located on the same chromosome, what is the physical basis for the production of recombinant offspring in a testcross between a dihybrid parent and a double-mutant parent?
2. For each type of offspring in Figure 15.5, explain the relationship between its phenotype and the alleles contributed by the female parent.
3. Genes *A*, *B*, and *C* are located on the same chromosome. Testcrosses show that the recombination frequency between *A* and *B* is 28% and between *A* and *C* is 12%. Can you determine the linear order of these genes?

For suggested answers, see Appendix A.

Concept 15.3

Sex-linked genes exhibit unique patterns of inheritance

As you learned earlier, Morgan's discovery of a trait (white eyes) that correlated with the sex of flies was a key episode in the development of the chromosome theory of inheritance. In this section, we consider the role of sex chromosomes in inheritance in more detail. We begin by reviewing the chromosomal basis of sex determination in humans and some other animals.

The Chromosomal Basis of Sex

Whether we are male or female is one of our more obvious phenotypic characters. Although the anatomical and physiological differences between women and men are numerous, the chromosomal basis for determining sex is rather simple. In humans and other mammals, there are two varieties of sex chromosomes, designated X and Y. A person who inherits two X chromosomes, one from each parent, usually develops as a female. A male develops from a zygote containing one X chromosome and one Y chromosome **(Figure 15.9a)**. The Y chromosome is much smaller than the X chromosome (see the

micrograph to the left), and only relatively short segments at either end of the Y chromosome are homologous with corresponding regions of the X. These homologous regions allow the X and Y chromosomes in males to pair and behave like homologous chromosomes during meiosis in the testes.

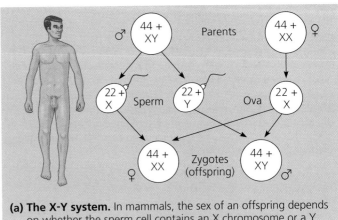

(a) The X-Y system. In mammals, the sex of an offspring depends on whether the sperm cell contains an X chromosome or a Y.

(b) The X-0 system. In grasshoppers, roaches, and some other insects, there is only one type of sex chromosome, the X. Females are XX; males have only one sex chromosome (X0). Sex of the offspring is determined by whether the sperm cell contains an X chromosome or no sex chromosome.

(c) The Z-W system. In birds, some fishes, and some insects, the sex chromosome present in the ovum (not the sperm) determines the sex of offspring. The sex chromosomes are designated Z and W. Females are ZW and males are ZZ.

(d) The haplo-diploid system. There are no sex chromosomes in most species of bees and ants. Females develop from fertilized ova and are thus diploid. Males develop from unfertilized eggs and are haploid; they have no fathers.

▲ **Figure 15.9 Some chromosomal systems of sex determination.** Numerals indicate the number of autosomes. In *Drosophila*, males are XY, but sex depends on the ratio between the number of X chromosomes and the number of autosome sets, not simply on the presence of a Y chromosome.

In both testes and ovaries, the two sex chromosomes segregate during meiosis, and each gamete receives one. Each ovum contains one X chromosome. In contrast, sperm fall into two categories: Half the sperm cells a male produces contain an X chromosome, and half contain a Y chromosome. We can trace the sex of each offspring to the moment of conception: If a sperm cell bearing an X chromosome happens to fertilize an ovum, the zygote is XX, a female; if a sperm cell containing a Y chromosome fertilizes an ovum, the zygote is XY, a male (see Figure 15.9a). Thus sex determination is a matter of chance—a fifty-fifty chance. Besides the mammalian X-Y system, three other chromosomal systems for determining sex are shown in Figure 15.9, in parts b–d.

In humans, the anatomical signs of sex begin to emerge when the embryo is about two months old. Before then, the rudiments of the gonads are generic—they can develop into either ovaries or testes, depending on hormonal conditions within the embryo. Which of these two possibilities occurs depends on whether or not a Y chromosome is present. In 1990, a British research team identified a gene on the Y chromosome required for the development of testes. They named the gene *SRY*, for sex-determining region of Y. In the absence of *SRY*, the gonads develop into ovaries. The researchers emphasized that the presence (or absence) of *SRY* is just a trigger. The biochemical, physiological, and anatomical features that distinguish males and females are complex, and many genes are involved in their development. *SRY* codes for a protein that regulates other genes. Researchers have subsequently identified a number of additional genes on the Y chromosome that are required for normal testis functioning. In the absence of these genes, an XY individual is male but does not produce normal sperm.

Inheritance of Sex-Linked Genes

In addition to their role in determining sex, the sex chromosomes, especially X chromosomes, have genes for many characters unrelated to sex. A gene located on either sex chromosome is called a **sex-linked gene**, although in humans the term has historically referred specifically to a gene on the X chromosome. (Note the distinction between the terms *sex-linked gene*, referring to a gene on a sex chromosome, and *linked genes*, referring to genes on the same chromosome that tend to be inherited together.) Sex-linked genes in humans follow the same pattern of inheritance that Morgan observed for the eye-color locus in *Drosophila* (see Figure 15.4). Fathers pass sex-linked alleles to all of their daughters but to none of their sons. In contrast, mothers can pass sex-linked alleles to both sons and daughters **(Figure 15.10)**.

If a sex-linked trait is due to a recessive allele, a female will express the phenotype only if she is a homozygote. Because males have only one locus, the terms *homozygous* and *heterozygous* lack meaning for describing their sex-linked genes (the term *hemizygous* is used in such cases). Any male receiving the recessive allele from his mother will express the trait. For this reason, far more males than females have sex-linked recessive disorders. However, even though the chance of a female inheriting a double dose of the mutant allele is much less than the probability of a male inheriting a single dose, there *are* females with sex-linked disorders. For instance, color blindness is a mild disorder inherited as a sex-linked trait. A color-blind daughter may be born to a color-blind father whose mate is a carrier (see Figure 15.10c). However, because the sex-linked allele for color blindness is relatively rare, the probability that such a man and woman will mate is low.

A number of human sex-linked disorders are much more serious than color blindness. An example is **Duchenne muscular dystrophy**, which affects about one out of every 3,500 males

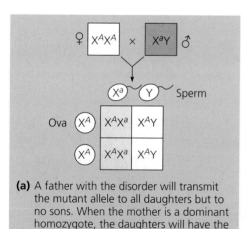

(a) A father with the disorder will transmit the mutant allele to all daughters but to no sons. When the mother is a dominant homozygote, the daughters will have the normal phenotype but will be carriers of the mutation.

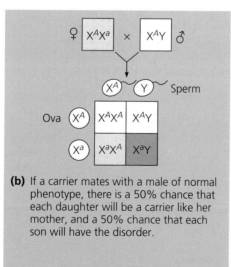

(b) If a carrier mates with a male of normal phenotype, there is a 50% chance that each daughter will be a carrier like her mother, and a 50% chance that each son will have the disorder.

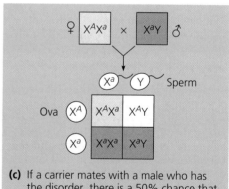

(c) If a carrier mates with a male who has the disorder, there is a 50% chance that each child born to them will have the disorder, regardless of sex. Daughters who do not have the disorder will be carriers, whereas males without the disorder will be completely free of the recessive allele.

▲ **Figure 15.10 The transmission of sex-linked recessive traits.** In this diagram, the superscript *A* represents a dominant allele carried on the X chromosome, and the superscript *a* represents a recessive allele. Imagine that this recessive allele is a mutation that causes a sex-linked disorder, such as color blindness. White boxes indicate unaffected individuals, light-colored boxes indicate carriers, and dark-colored boxes indicate individuals with the sex-linked disorder.

born in the United States. The disease is characterized by a progressive weakening of the muscles and loss of coordination. Affected individuals rarely live past their early 20s. Researchers have traced the disorder to the absence of a key muscle protein called dystrophin and have mapped the gene for this protein to a specific locus on the X chromosome.

Hemophilia is a sex-linked recessive disorder defined by the absence of one or more of the proteins required for blood clotting. When a person with hemophilia is injured, bleeding is prolonged because a firm clot is slow to form. Small cuts in the skin are usually not a problem, but bleeding in the muscles or joints can be painful and can lead to serious damage. Today, people with hemophilia are treated as needed with intravenous injections of the missing protein.

X Inactivation in Female Mammals

Although female mammals, including humans, inherit two X chromosomes, one X chromosome in each cell becomes almost completely inactivated during embryonic development. As a result, the cells of females and males have the same effective dose (one copy) of genes with loci on the X chromosome. The inactive X in each cell of a female condenses into a compact object called a **Barr body,** which lies along the inside of the nuclear envelope. Most of the genes of the X chromosome that forms the Barr body are not expressed. In the ovaries, Barr-body chromosomes are reactivated in the cells that give rise to ova, so every female gamete has an active X.

British geneticist Mary Lyon demonstrated that selection of which X chromosome will form the Barr body occurs randomly and independently in each embryonic cell present at the time of X inactivation. As a consequence, females consist of a *mosaic* of two types of cells: those with the active X derived from the father and those with the active X derived from the mother. After an X chromosome is inactivated in a particular cell, all mitotic descendants of that cell have the same inactive X. Thus, if a female is heterozygous for a sex-linked trait, about half her cells will express one allele, while the others will express the alternate allele. **Figure 15.11** shows how this mosaicism results in the mottled coloration of a tortoiseshell cat. In humans, mosaicism can be observed in a recessive X-linked mutation that prevents the development of sweat glands. A woman who is heterozygous for this trait has patches of normal skin and patches of skin lacking sweat glands.

Inactivation of an X chromosome involves modification of the DNA, such as attachment of methyl groups ($-CH_3$) to one of the nitrogenous bases of DNA nucleotides. (The regulatory role of DNA methylation is discussed further in Chapter 19.) Researchers also have discovered a gene called *XIST* (for X-inactive specific transcript) that is active *only* on the Barr-body chromosome. Multiple copies of the RNA molecule produced from this gene apparently attach to the X chromosome on which they are made, eventually almost covering it. Interaction of this RNA with the chromosome seems to initiate X inactivation. Our understanding of X inactivation is still rudimentary, however.

Concept Check 15.3

1. A white-eyed female *Drosophila* is mated with a red-eyed (wild-type) male, the reciprocal cross of that shown in Figure 15.4. What phenotypes and genotypes do you predict for the offspring?
2. Neither Tim nor Rhoda has Duchenne muscular dystrophy, but their firstborn son does have it. What is the probability that a second child of this couple will have the disease?

For suggested answers, see Appendix A.

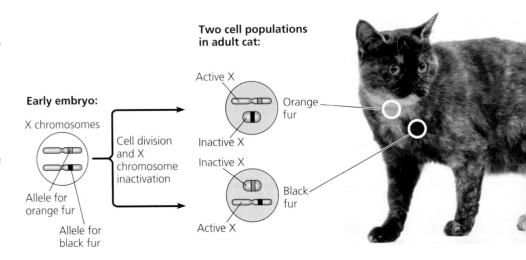

▶ **Figure 15.11 X inactivation and the tortoiseshell cat.** The tortoiseshell gene is on the X chromosome, and the tortoiseshell phenotype requires the presence of two different alleles, one for orange fur and one for black fur. Normally, only females can have both alleles, because only they have two X chromosomes. If a female is heterozygous for the tortoiseshell gene, she is tortoiseshell. Orange patches are formed by populations of cells in which the X chromosome with the orange allele is active; black patches have cells in which the X chromosome with the black allele is active. ("Calico" cats also have white areas, which are determined by yet another gene.)

Early embryo:

X chromosomes

Allele for orange fur

Allele for black fur

Cell division and X chromosome inactivation

Two cell populations in adult cat:

Active X

Inactive X

Orange fur

Inactive X

Active X

Black fur

Concept 15.4

Alterations of chromosome number or structure cause some genetic disorders

Sex-linked traits are not the only notable deviation from the inheritance patterns observed by Mendel, and the gene mutations that generate new alleles are not the only kind of changes to the genome that can affect phenotype. Physical and chemical disturbances, as well as errors during meiosis, can damage chromosomes in major ways or alter their number in a cell. Large-scale chromosomal alterations often lead to spontaneous abortion (miscarriage) of a fetus, and individuals born with these types of genetic defects commonly exhibit various developmental disorders. In plants, such genetic defects may be tolerated to a greater extent than in animals.

Abnormal Chromosome Number

Ideally, the meiotic spindle distributes chromosomes to daughter cells without error. But there is an occasional mishap, called a **nondisjunction**, in which the members of a pair of homologous chromosomes do not move apart properly during meiosis I or sister chromatids fail to separate during meiosis II. In these cases, one gamete receives two of the same type of chromosome and another gamete receives no copy **(Figure 15.12)**. The other chromosomes are usually distributed normally. If either of the aberrant gametes unites with a normal one at fertilization, the offspring will have an abnormal number of a particular chromosome, a condition known as **aneuploidy**.

If a chromosome is present in triplicate in the fertilized egg (so that the cell has a total of 2n + 1 chromosomes), the aneuploid cell is said to be **trisomic** for that chromosome. If a chromosome is missing (so that the cell has 2n − 1 chromosomes), the aneuploid cell is **monosomic** for that chromosome. Mitosis will subsequently transmit the anomaly to all embryonic cells. If the organism survives, it usually has a set of symptoms caused by the abnormal dose of the genes associated with the extra or missing chromosome. Nondisjunction can also occur during mitosis. If such an error takes place early in embryonic development, then the aneuploid condition is passed along by mitosis to a large number of cells and is likely to have a substantial effect on the organism.

Some organisms have more than two complete chromosome sets. The general term for this chromosomal alteration is **polyploidy,** with the specific terms *triploidy* (3n) and *tetraploidy* (4n) indicating three or four chromosomal sets, respectively. One way a triploid cell may be produced is by the fertilization of an abnormal diploid egg produced by nondisjunction of all its chromosomes. An example of an accident that would result in tetraploidy is the failure of a 2n zygote to divide after replicating its chromosomes. Subsequent normal mitotic divisions would then produce a 4n embryo.

Polyploidy is fairly common in the plant kingdom. As we will see in Chapter 24, the spontaneous origin of polyploid individuals plays an important role in the evolution of plants. In the animal kingdom, polyploid species are much less common, although they are known to occur among the fishes and amphibians. Researchers in Chile were the first to identify a

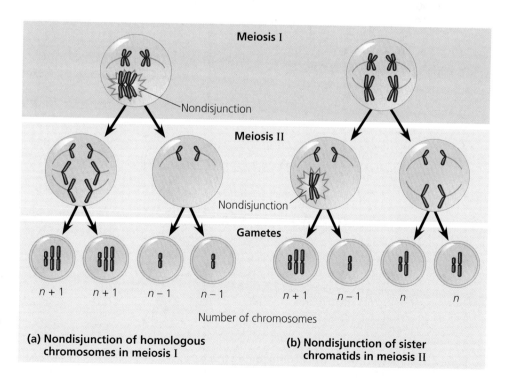

▶ **Figure 15.12 Meiotic nondisjunction.** Gametes with an abnormal chromosome number can arise by nondisjunction in either meiosis I or meiosis II.

(a) Nondisjunction of homologous chromosomes in meiosis I

(b) Nondisjunction of sister chromatids in meiosis II

▲ **Figure 15.13 A tetraploid mammal.** The somatic cells of this burrowing rodent, *Tympanoctomys barrerae*, have about twice as many chromosomes as those of closely related species. Interestingly, its sperm's head is unusually large, presumably a necessity for holding all that genetic material. Scientists think that this tetraploid species may have arisen when an ancestor doubled its chromosome number, presumably by errors in mitosis or meiosis within the animal's reproductive organs.

polyploid mammal, a rodent whose cells are tetraploid **(Figure 15.13)**. Additional research has found that a closely related species also appears to be tetraploid. In general, polyploids are more nearly normal in appearance than aneuploids. One extra (or missing) chromosome apparently disrupts genetic balance more than does an entire extra set of chromosomes.

Alterations of Chromosome Structure

Breakage of a chromosome can lead to four types of changes in chromosome structure, depicted in **Figure 15.14**. A **deletion** occurs when a chromosomal fragment lacking a centromere is lost. The affected chromosome is then missing certain genes. In some cases, if meiosis is in progress, such a "deleted" fragment may become attached as an extra segment to a sister chromatid, producing a **duplication**. Alternatively, a detached fragment could attach to a nonsister chromatid of a homologous chromosome. In that case, though, the "duplicated" segments might not be identical because the homologues could carry different alleles of certain genes. A chromosomal fragment may also reattach to the original chromosome but in the reverse orientation, producing an **inversion**. A fourth possible result of chromosomal breakage is for the fragment to join a nonhomologous chromosome, a rearrangement called a **translocation.**

Deletions and duplications are especially likely to occur during meiosis. In crossing over, nonsister chromatids sometimes break and rejoin at "incorrect" places, so that one partner gives up more genes than it receives. The products of such a *nonreciprocal* crossover are one chromosome with a deletion and one chromosome with a duplication.

A diploid embryo that is homozygous for a large deletion (or has a single X chromosome with a large deletion, in a male) is usually missing a number of essential genes, a condition that is ordinarily lethal. Duplications and translocations also tend to have harmful effects. In reciprocal translocations, in which segments are exchanged between nonhomologous chromosomes, and in inversions, the balance of genes is not abnormal—all genes are present in their normal doses. Never-

(a) A **deletion** removes a chromosomal segment.

(b) A **duplication** repeats a segment.

(c) An **inversion** reverses a segment within a chromosome.

(d) A **translocation** moves a segment from one chromosome to another, nonhomologous one. In a reciprocal translocation, the most common type, nonhomologous chromosomes exchange fragments. Nonreciprocal translocations also occur, in which a chromosome transfers a fragment without receiving a fragment in return.

▲ **Figure 15.14 Alterations of chromosome structure.** Vertical arrows indicate breakage points. Dark purple highlights the chromosomal parts affected by the rearrangements.

theless, translocations and inversions can alter phenotype because a gene's expression can be influenced by its location among neighboring genes.

Human Disorders Due to Chromosomal Alterations

Alterations of chromosome number and structure are associated with a number of serious human disorders. Nondisjunction in meiosis results in aneuploid gametes. If an aneuploid gamete combines with a normal haploid gamete during fertilization, the result is an aneuploid zygote. Although the frequency of aneuploid zygotes may be quite high in humans, most of these chromosomal alterations are so disastrous to development that the embryos are spontaneously aborted long before birth. However, some types of aneuploidy appear to upset the genetic balance less than others, with the result that individuals with certain aneuploid conditions can survive to birth and beyond. These individuals have a set of symptoms—a *syndrome*—characteristic of the type of aneuploidy. Genetic disorders caused by aneuploidy can be diagnosed before birth by fetal testing (see Figure 14.17).

Down Syndrome (Trisomy 21)

One aneuploid condition, **Down syndrome,** affects approximately one out of every 700 children born in the United States **(Figure 15.15)**. Down syndrome is usually the result of an extra chromosome 21, so that each body cell has a total of 47 chromosomes. Because the cells are trisomic for chromosome 21, Down syndrome is often called *trisomy 21.* Down syndrome includes characteristic facial features, short stature, heart defects, susceptibility to respiratory infection, and mental retardation. Furthermore, individuals with Down syndrome are prone to developing leukemia and Alzheimer's disease. Although people with Down syndrome, on average, have a life span shorter than normal, some live to middle age or beyond. Most are sexually underdeveloped and sterile.

The frequency of Down syndrome increases with the age of the mother. While the disorder occurs in just 0.04% of children born to women under age 30, the risk climbs to 1.25% for mothers in their early 30s and is even higher for older mothers. Because of this relatively high risk, pregnant women over 35 are candidates for fetal testing to check for trisomy 21 in the embryo. The correlation of Down syndrome with maternal age has not yet been explained. Most cases result from nondisjunction during meiosis I, and some research points to an age-dependent abnormality in a meiosis checkpoint that normally delays anaphase until all the kinetochores are attached to the spindle (like the M phase checkpoint of the mitotic cell cycle; see Chapter 12). Trisomies of some other chromosomes also increase in incidence with maternal age, although infants with these autosomal trisomies rarely survive for long.

Aneuploidy of Sex Chromosomes

Nondisjunction of sex chromosomes produces a variety of aneuploid conditions. Most of these conditions appear to upset genetic balance less than aneuploid conditions involving autosomes. This may be because the Y chromosome carries relatively few genes and because extra copies of the X chromosome become inactivated as Barr bodies in somatic cells.

An extra X chromosome in a male, producing XXY, occurs approximately once in every 2,000 live births. People with this disorder, called *Klinefelter syndrome,* have male sex organs, but the testes are abnormally small and the man is sterile. Even though the extra X is inactivated, some breast enlargement and other female body characteristics are common. The affected individual is usually of normal intelligence. Males with an extra Y chromosome (XYY) do not exhibit any well-defined syndrome, but they tend to be somewhat taller than average.

Females with trisomy X (XXX), which occurs once in approximately 1,000 live births, are healthy and cannot be distinguished from XX females except by karyotype. Monosomy X, called *Turner syndrome,* occurs about once in every 5,000 births and is the only known viable monosomy in humans. Although these X0 individuals are phenotypically female, they are sterile because their sex organs do not mature. When provided with estrogen replacement therapy, girls with Turner syndrome do develop secondary sex characteristics. Most have normal intelligence.

▲ **Figure 15.15 Down syndrome.** The child exhibits the facial features characteristic of Down syndrome. The karyotype shows trisomy 21, the most common cause of this disorder.

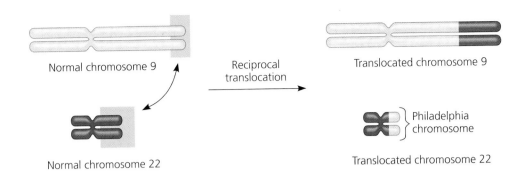

► Figure 15.16 Translocation associated with chronic myelogenous leukemia (CML). The cancerous cells in nearly all CML patients contain an abnormally short chromosome 22, the so-called Philadelphia chromosome, and an abnormally long chromosome 9. These altered chromosomes result from the translocation shown here.

Normal chromosome 9

Reciprocal translocation

Translocated chromosome 9

Normal chromosome 22

Philadelphia chromosome

Translocated chromosome 22

Disorders Caused by Structurally Altered Chromosomes

Many deletions in human chromosomes, even in a heterozygous state, cause severe problems. One such syndrome, known as *cri du chat* ("cry of the cat"), results from a specific deletion in chromosome 5. A child born with this deletion is mentally retarded, has a small head with unusual facial features, and has a cry that sounds like the mewing of a distressed cat. Such individuals usually die in infancy or early childhood.

Another type of chromosomal structural alteration associated with human disorders is translocation, the attachment of a fragment from one chromosome to another, nonhomologous chromosome. Chromosomal translocations have been implicated in certain cancers, including *chronic myelogenous leukemia (CML)*. Leukemia is a cancer affecting the cells that give rise to white blood cells, and in the cancerous cells of CML patients, a reciprocal translocation has occurred. In these cells, the exchange of a large portion of chromosome 22 with a small fragment from a tip of chromosome 9 produces a much shortened, easily recognized chromosome 22, called the *Philadelphia chromosome* **(Figure 15.16)**. We will discuss how such an exchange might cause cancer in Chapter 19.

Concept Check 15.4

1. More common than completely polyploid animals are mosaic polyploids, animals that are diploid except for patches of polyploid cells. How might a mosaic tetraploid—an animal with some cells containing four sets of chromosomes—arise?
2. About 5% of individuals with Down syndrome have a chromosomal translocation in which one copy of chromosome 21 is attached to chromosome 14. How could this translocation in a parent's gonad lead to Down syndrome in a child?
3. Explain how a male cat could have the tortoiseshell phenotype.

For suggested answers, see Appendix A.

Concept 15.5

Some inheritance patterns are exceptions to the standard chromosome theory

In the previous section, you learned about abnormal deviations from the usual patterns of chromosomal inheritance. We conclude this chapter by describing two *normal* exceptions to Mendelian genetics, one involving genes located in the nucleus and the other involving genes located outside of the nucleus.

Genomic Imprinting

Throughout our discussions of Mendelian genetics and the chromosomal basis of inheritance, we have assumed that a specific allele will have the same effect regardless of whether it was inherited from the mother or the father. This is probably a safe assumption most of the time. For example, when Mendel crossed purple-flowered pea plants with white-flowered pea plants, he observed the same results regardless of whether the purple-flowered parent supplied the ova or the pollen. In recent years, however, geneticists have identified two to three dozen traits in mammals that depend on which parent passed along the alleles for those traits. Such variation in phenotype depending on whether an allele is inherited from the male or female parent is called **genomic imprinting.** (Note that the issue here is not sex linkage; most imprinted genes are on autosomes.)

Genomic imprinting occurs during the formation of gametes and results in the silencing of one allele of certain genes. Because these genes are imprinted differently in sperm and ova, a zygote expresses only one allele of an imprinted gene, either the allele inherited from the female parent or the allele inherited from the male parent. The imprints are transmitted to all the body cells during development, so the same allele of a given gene—either the maternally inherited allele or the paternally inherited allele—is expressed in all cells of that organism. In each generation, the old imprints are "erased" in gamete-producing cells, and the chromosomes of the developing gametes are newly imprinted according to the sex of the individual. In a given species, the imprinted genes are always imprinted in the same way. For instance, a gene imprinted for maternal allele expression is always imprinted for maternal allele expression, generation after generation.

Consider, for example, the gene for insulin-like growth factor 2 (*Igf2*), one of the first imprinted genes to be identified. Although this growth factor is required for normal prenatal growth, only the paternal allele is expressed **(Figure 15.17a)**. Evidence that the *Igf2* gene is imprinted initially came from crosses between wild-type mice and dwarf mice homozygous for a recessive mutation in the *Igf2* gene. The phenotypes of heterozygous offspring (one normal allele and one mutant) differed, depending on whether the mutant allele came from the mother or the father **(Figure 15.17b)**.

(a) A wild-type mouse is homozygous for the normal *Igf2* allele.

(b) When a normal *Igf2* allele is inherited from the father, heterozygous mice grow to normal size. But when a mutant allele is inherited from the father, heterozygous mice have the dwarf phenotype.

▲ **Figure 15.17 Genomic imprinting of the mouse *Igf2* gene. (a)** In mice, the paternal *Igf2* allele is expressed and the maternal allele is not. **(b)** Matings between wild-type mice and those homozygous for the recessive mutant *Igf2* allele produce heterozygous offspring that can be either normal size or dwarf, depending on which parent passes on the mutant allele.

What exactly is a genomic imprint? In many cases, it seems to consist of methyl (—CH₃) groups that are added to cytosine nucleotides of one of the alleles. Such methylation may directly silence the allele, an effect consistent with evidence that heavily methylated genes are usually inactive (see Chapter 19). However, for a few genes, methylation has been shown to *activate* expression of the allele. This is the case for the *Igf2* gene: Methylation of a certain DNA sequence on the paternal chromosome leads to expression of the paternal *Igf2* allele.

Genomic imprinting is thought to affect only a small fraction of the genes in mammalian genomes, but most of the known imprinted genes are critical for embryonic development. In experiments with mice, for example, embryos engineered to inherit both copies of certain chromosomes from the same parent inevitably die before birth, whether that parent is male or female. Normal development apparently requires that embryonic cells have exactly one active copy—not zero, not two—of certain genes. The association of aberrant imprinting with abnormal development and certain cancers is stimulating numerous studies on how different genes are imprinted.

Inheritance of Organelle Genes

Although our focus in this chapter has been on the chromosomal basis of inheritance, we end with an important amendment: Not all of a eukaryotic cell's genes are located on nuclear chromosomes, or even in the nucleus. Some genes are located in organelles in the cytoplasm; these genes are sometimes called *extranuclear genes*. Mitochondria, as well as chloroplasts and other plant plastids, contain small circular DNA molecules that carry genes coding for proteins and RNA. These organelles reproduce themselves and transmit their genes to daughter organelles. Because organelle genes are not distributed to offspring according to the same rules that direct the distribution of nuclear chromosomes during meiosis, they do not display Mendelian inheritance.

The first hint that extranuclear genes exist came from studies by Karl Correns on the inheritance of yellow or white patches on the leaves of an otherwise green plant. In 1909, he observed that the coloration of the offspring was determined only by the maternal parent (the source of seeds that germinate to give rise to the offspring) and not by the paternal parent (the pollen source). Subsequent research showed that such coloration patterns, or variegation, are due to mutations in plastid genes that control pigmentation. In most plants, a zygote receives all its plastids from the cytoplasm of the egg and none from pollen, which contributes little more than a haploid set of chromosomes. As the zygote develops, plastids containing wild-type or mutant pigment genes are distributed randomly to daughter cells. The pattern of leaf coloration exhibited by a

► **Figure 15.18 Variegated leaves from *Croton dioicus*.** Variegated (striped or spotted) leaves result from mutations in pigment genes located in plastids, which generally are inherited from the maternal parent.

plant depends on the ratio of wild-type to mutant plastids in its various tissues (**Figure 15.18**).

Similar maternal inheritance is also the rule for mitochondrial genes in most animals and plants, because almost all the mitochondria passed on to a zygote come from the cytoplasm of the egg. The products of most mitochondrial genes help make up the protein complexes of the electron transport chain and ATP synthase (see Chapter 9). Defects in one or more of these proteins, therefore, reduce the amount of ATP the cell can make and have been shown to cause a number of rare human disorders. Because the parts of the body most susceptible to energy deprivation are the nervous system and the muscles, most mitochondrial diseases primarily affect these systems. For example, a person with the disease called *mitochondrial myopathy* suffers weakness, intolerance of exercise, and muscle deterioration.

In addition to the rare diseases clearly caused by defects in mitochondrial DNA, mitochondrial mutations inherited from a person's mother may contribute to at least some cases of diabetes and heart disease, as well as to other disorders that commonly debilitate the elderly, such as Alzheimer's disease. In the course of a lifetime, new mutations gradually accumulate in our mitochondrial DNA, and some researchers think that these mutations play a role in the normal aging process.

Wherever genes are located in the cell—in the nucleus or in cytoplasmic organelles—their inheritance depends on the precise replication of DNA, the genetic material. In the next chapter, you will learn how this molecular reproduction occurs.

Concept Check 15.5

1. Gene dosage, the number of active copies of a gene, is important to proper development. Identify and describe two processes that help establish the proper dosage of certain genes.
2. Reciprocal crosses between two primrose varieties, A and B, produced the following results: A female × B male → offspring with all green (nonvariegated) leaves. B female × A male → offspring with spotted (variegated) leaves. Explain these results.
3. Mitochondrial genes are critical to the energy metabolism of cells, but mitochondrial disorders caused by mutations in these genes are generally not lethal. Why not?

For suggested answers, see Appendix A.

Chapter 15 Review

Go to the Campbell Biology website (**www.campbellbiology.com**) or CD-ROM to explore Activities, Investigations, and other interactive study aids.

SUMMARY OF KEY CONCEPTS

Concept 15.1

Mendelian inheritance has its physical basis in the behavior of chromosomes

► In the early 1900s, several researchers proposed that genes are located on chromosomes and that the behavior of chromosomes during meiosis accounts for Mendel's laws of segregation and independent assortment (pp. 274–275).

► **Morgan's Experimental Evidence: *Scientific Inquiry*** (pp. 276–277) Morgan's discovery that transmission of the X chromosome in *Drosophila* correlates with inheritance of the eye-color trait was the first solid evidence indicating that a specific gene is associated with a specific chromosome.

Concept 15.2

Linked genes tend to be inherited together because they are located near each other on the same chromosome

► **How Linkage Affects Inheritance: *Scientific Inquiry*** (pp. 277–278) Each chromosome has hundreds or thousands of genes. Genes on the same chromosome whose alleles are so close together that they do not assort independently are said to be linked. The alleles of unlinked genes are either on separate chromosomes or so far apart on the same chromosome that they assort independently.

► **Genetic Recombination and Linkage** (pp. 278–280) Recombinant offspring exhibit new combinations of traits inherited from two parents. Because of the independent assortment of chromosomes and random fertilization, unlinked genes exhibit a 50% frequency of recombination. Even with crossing over between nonsister chromatids during the first meiotic division, linked genes exhibit recombination frequencies less than 50%.

▶ **Linkage Mapping Using Recombination Data:** *Scientific Inquiry* (pp. 279–281) Geneticists can deduce the order of genes on a chromosome and the relative distances between them from recombination frequencies observed in genetic crosses. In general, the farther apart genes are on a chromosome, the more likely they are to be separated during crossing over.
Activity Linked Genes and Crossing Over

Concept 15.3
Sex-linked genes exhibit unique patterns of inheritance

▶ **The Chromosomal Basis of Sex** (pp. 282–283) An organism's sex is an inherited phenotypic character usually determined by the presence or absence of certain chromosomes. Humans and other mammals have an X-Y system in which sex normally is determined by the presence or absence of a Y chromosome. Different systems of sex determination are found in birds, fishes, and insects.

▶ **Inheritance of Sex-Linked Genes** (pp. 283–284) The sex chromosomes carry certain genes for traits that are unrelated to maleness or femaleness. For instance, recessive alleles causing color blindness, hemophilia, and Duchenne muscular dystrophy are carried on the X chromosome. Fathers transmit such sex-linked alleles to all daughters but to no sons. Any male who inherits a single sex-linked recessive allele from his mother will express the trait.
Activity Sex-Linked Genes
Investigation What Can Fruit Flies Reveal About Inheritance?
Biology Labs On-Line FlyLab
Biology Labs On-Line PedigreeLab

▶ **X Inactivation in Female Mammals** (p. 284) In mammalian females, one of the two X chromosomes in each cell is randomly inactivated during early embryonic development. If a female is heterozygous for a particular gene located on the X chromosome, she will be mosaic for that character, with about half her cells expressing the maternal allele and about half expressing the paternal allele.

Concept 15.4
Alterations of chromosome number or structure cause some genetic disorders

▶ **Abnormal Chromosome Number** (pp. 285–286) Aneuploidy can arise when a normal gamete unites with one containing two copies or no copies of a particular chromosome as a result of nondisjunction during meiosis. The cells of the resulting zygote have either one extra copy of that chromosome (trisomy) or are missing a copy (monosomy). Polyploidy, in which there are more than two complete sets of chromosomes, can result from complete nondisjunction during gamete formation.
Activity Polyploid Plants

▶ **Alterations of Chromosome Structure** (pp. 286–287) Chromosome breakage can result in various rearrangements. A lost fragment leaves one chromosome with a deletion; the deleted fragment may reattach to the same chromosome in a different orientation, producing an inversion. Or the fragment may attach to a homologous chromosome, producing a duplication, or to a nonhomologous chromosome, producing a translocation.

▶ **Human Disorders Due to Chromosomal Alterations** (pp. 287–288) Changes in the number of chromosomes per cell or in the structure of individual chromosomes can affect phenotype. Such alterations cause Down syndrome (usually due to trisomy of chromosome 21), certain cancers associated with chromosomal translocations, and various other human disorders.

Concept 15.5
Some inheritance patterns are exceptions to the standard chromosome theory

▶ **Genomic Imprinting** (pp. 288–289) In mammals, the phenotypic effects of certain genes depend on which allele is inherited from the mother and which is inherited from the father. Imprints are formed during gamete production, with the result that one allele (either maternal or paternal) is not expressed in offspring. Most imprinted genes now known play a role in embryonic development.

▶ **Inheritance of Organelle Genes** (pp. 289–290) The inheritance of traits controlled by the genes present in mitochondria and chloroplasts depends solely on the maternal parent because the zygote's cytoplasm comes from the egg. Some diseases affecting the nervous and muscular systems are caused by defects in mitochondrial genes that prevent cells from making enough ATP.

TESTING YOUR KNOWLEDGE

Genetics Problems

1. A man with hemophilia (a recessive, sex-linked condition) has a daughter of normal phenotype. She marries a man who is normal for the trait. What is the probability that a daughter of this mating will be a hemophiliac? That a son will be a hemophiliac? If the couple has four sons, what is the probability that all four will be born with hemophilia?

2. Pseudohypertrophic muscular dystrophy is an inherited disorder that causes gradual deterioration of the muscles. It is seen almost exclusively in boys born to apparently normal parents and usually results in death in the early teens. Is this disorder caused by a dominant or a recessive allele? Is its inheritance sex-linked or autosomal? How do you know? Explain why this disorder is almost never seen in girls.

3. Red-green color blindness is caused by a sex-linked recessive allele. A color-blind man marries a woman with normal vision whose father was color-blind. What is the probability that they will have a color-blind daughter? What is the probability that their first son will be color-blind? (*Note:* The two questions are worded a bit differently.)

4. A wild-type fruit fly (heterozygous for gray body color and normal wings) is mated with a black fly with vestigial wings. The offspring have the following phenotypic distribution: wild type, 778; black-vestigial, 785; black-normal, 158; gray-vestigial, 162. What is the recombination frequency between these genes for body color and wing size?

5. In another cross, a wild-type fruit fly (heterozygous for gray body color and red eyes) is mated with a black fruit fly with purple eyes. The offspring are as follows: wild type, 721; black-purple, 751; gray-purple, 49; black-red, 45. What is the recombination frequency between these genes for body color and eye color? Using information from problem 4, what fruit flies (genotypes and phenotypes) would you mate to determine the sequence of the body-color, wing-size, and eye-color genes on the chromosome?

6. What pattern of inheritance would lead a geneticist to suspect that an inherited disorder of cell metabolism is due to a defective mitochondrial gene?

7. Women born with an extra X chromosome (XXX) are healthy and phenotypically indistinguishable from normal XX women. What is a likely explanation for this finding? How could you test this explanation?

8. Determine the sequence of genes along a chromosome based on the following recombination frequencies: A–B, 8 map units; A–C, 28 map units; A–D, 25 map units; B–C, 20 map units; B–D, 33 map units.

9. Assume that genes A and B are linked and are 50 map units apart. An animal heterozygous at both loci is crossed with one that is homozygous recessive at both loci. What percentage of the offspring will show phenotypes resulting from crossovers? If you did not know that genes A and B were linked, how would you interpret the results of this cross?

10. A space probe discovers a planet inhabited by creatures who reproduce with the same hereditary patterns seen in humans. Three phenotypic characters are height (T = tall, t = dwarf), head appendages (A = antennae, a = no antennae), and nose morphology (S = upturned snout, s = downturned snout). Since the creatures are not "intelligent," Earth scientists are able to do some controlled breeding experiments, using various heterozygotes in testcrosses. For tall heterozygotes with antennae, the offspring are: tall-antennae, 46; dwarf-antennae, 7; dwarf-no antennae, 42; tall-no antennae, 5. For heterozygotes with antennae and an upturned snout, the offspring are: antennae-upturned snout, 47; antennae-downturned snout, 2; no antennae-downturned snout, 48; no antennae-upturned snout, 3. Calculate the recombination frequencies for both experiments.

11. Using the information from problem 10, a further testcross is done using a heterozygote for height and nose morphology. The offspring are: tall-upturned snout, 40; dwarf-upturned snout, 9; dwarf-downturned snout, 42; tall-downturned snout, 9. Calculate the recombination frequency from these data; then use your answer from problem 10 to determine the correct sequence of the three linked genes.

12. The ABO blood type locus has been mapped on chromosome 9. A father who has blood type AB and a mother who has blood type O have a child with trisomy 9 and blood type A. Using this information, can you tell in which parent the nondisjunction occurred? Explain your answer.

13. Two genes of a flower, one controlling blue (B) versus white (b) petals and the other controlling round (R) versus oval (r) stamens, are linked and are 10 map units apart. You cross a homozygous blue-oval plant with a homozygous white-round plant. The resulting F_1 progeny are crossed with homozygous white-oval plants, and 1,000 progeny are obtained. How many plants of each of the four phenotypes do you expect?

14. You design *Drosophila* crosses to provide recombination data for gene a, which is located on the same chromosome shown in Figure 15.8. Gene a has recombination frequencies of 14% with the vestigial-wing locus and 26% with the brown-eye locus. Where is a located on the chromosome?

For Genetics Problems answers, see Appendix A.

Go to the website or CD-ROM for more quiz questions.

Evolution Connection

You have seen that crossing over, or recombination, is thought to be evolutionarily advantageous because this process continually shuffles genetic alleles into novel combinations. Some organisms, however, have apparently lost the recombination mechanism, while in others, certain chromosomes do not recombine. What factors do you think may favor reduced levels of recombination?

Scientific Inquiry

Consider Figure 15.5, in which the F_1 dihybrid females resulted from a cross between parental (P) flies with genotypes $b^+ b^+ vg^+ vg^+$ and $b b vg vg$. Now, imagine you make F_1 females by crossing two different P generation flies: $b^+ b^+ vg vg \times b b vg^+ vg^+$.

a. What will be the genotype of your F_1 females? Is this the same as that for the F_1 females in Figure 15.5?

b. Draw the chromosomes for the F_1 females, indicating the position of each allele. Are these the same as for the F_1 females in Figure 15.5?

c. Knowing that the distance between these two genes is 17 map units, predict the phenotypic ratios you will get from a cross. Will they be the same as in Figure 15.5?

d. Draw the chromosomes of the P, F_1, and F_2 generations (as is done in Figure 15.6 for the cross in Figure 15.5), showing how this arrangement of alleles in the P generation leads, via F_1 gametes, to the phenotypic ratios seen in the F_2 flies.

Investigation *What Can Fruit Flies Reveal About Inheritance?*
Biology Labs On-Line *FlyLab*
Biology Labs On-Line *PedigreeLab*

Science, Technology, and Society

About one in every 1,500 boys and one in every 2,500 girls are born with a fragile X chromosome, the tip of which hangs on to the rest of the chromosome by a thin thread of DNA. This abnormality causes mental retardation. Opinions differ about whether children with learning disorders should be tested by karyotyping for the presence of a fragile X chromosome. Some argue that it's always better to know the cause of the problem so that education specialized for that disorder can be prescribed. Others counter that attaching a specific biological cause to a learning disability stigmatizes a child and limits his or her opportunities. What is your evaluation of these arguments?

The Molecular Basis of Inheritance

▲ Figure 16.1 **Watson and Crick with their DNA model.**

Key Concepts

16.1 DNA is the genetic material
16.2 Many proteins work together in DNA replication and repair

Overview

Life's Operating Instructions

In April 1953, James Watson and Francis Crick shook the scientific world with an elegant double-helical model for the structure of deoxyribonucleic acid, or DNA. **Figure 16.1** shows Watson and Crick admiring their DNA model, which they built from tin and wire. Over the past 50 years, their model has evolved from a novel proposition to an icon of modern biology. DNA, the substance of inheritance, is the most celebrated molecule of our time. Mendel's heritable factors and Morgan's genes on chromosomes are, in fact, composed of DNA. Chemically speaking, your genetic endowment is the DNA contained in the 46 chromosomes you inherited from your parents.

Of all nature's molecules, nucleic acids are unique in their ability to direct their own replication from monomers. Indeed, the resemblance of offspring to their parents has its basis in the precise replication of DNA and its transmission from one generation to the next. Hereditary information is encoded in the chemical language of DNA and reproduced in all the cells of your body. It is this DNA program that directs the development of your biochemical, anatomical, physiological, and, to some extent, behavioral traits. In this chapter, you will learn how biologists deduced that DNA is the genetic material, how Watson and Crick discovered its structure, and how cells replicate and repair their DNA—the molecular basis of inheritance.

Concept 16.1

DNA is the genetic material

Today, even schoolchildren have heard of DNA, and scientists routinely manipulate DNA in the laboratory and use it to change the heritable characteristics of cells. Early in the 20th century, however, the identification of the molecules of inheritance loomed as a major challenge to biologists.

The Search for the Genetic Material: *Scientific Inquiry*

Once T. H. Morgan's group showed that genes are located on chromosomes (described in Chapter 15), the two chemical components of chromosomes—DNA and protein—became the candidates for the genetic material. Until the 1940s, the case for proteins seemed stronger, especially since biochemists had identified them as a class of macromolecules with great heterogeneity and specificity of function, essential requirements for the hereditary material. Moreover, little was known about nucleic acids, whose physical and chemical properties seemed far too uniform to account for the multitude of specific inherited traits exhibited by every organism. This view gradually changed as experiments with microorganisms yielded unexpected results. As with the work of Mendel and Morgan, a key factor in determining the identity of the genetic material was the choice of appropriate experimental organisms. The role of DNA in heredity was first worked out by studying bacteria and the viruses that infect them, which are far simpler than pea plants, fruit flies, or humans. In this section, we will trace the search for the genetic material in some detail as a case study in scientific inquiry.

Evidence That DNA Can Transform Bacteria

We can trace the discovery of the genetic role of DNA back to 1928. Frederick Griffith, a British medical officer, was studying *Streptococcus pneumoniae*, a bacterium that causes pneumonia in mammals. Griffith had two strains (varieties) of the bacterium, a pathogenic (disease-causing) one and a nonpathogenic (harmless) strain. He was surprised to find that when he killed the pathogenic bacteria with heat and then mixed the cell remains with living bacteria of the nonpathogenic strain, some of the living cells became pathogenic (**Figure 16.2**). Furthermore, this new trait of pathogenicity was inherited by all the descendants of the transformed bacteria. Clearly, some chemical component of the dead pathogenic cells caused this heritable change, although the identity of the substance was not known. Griffith called the phenomenon **transformation**, now defined as a change in genotype and phenotype due to the assimilation of external DNA by a cell. (This use of the word *transformation* should not be confused with the conversion of a normal animal cell to a cancerous one, discussed in Chapter 12.)

Griffith's work set the stage for a 14-year search for the identity of the transforming substance by American bacteriologist Oswald Avery. Avery purified various types of molecules from the heat-killed pathogenic bacteria, then tried to transform live nonpathogenic bacteria with each type. Only DNA worked. Finally, in 1944, Avery and his colleagues Maclyn McCarty and Colin MacLeod announced that the transforming agent was DNA. Their discovery was greeted with interest but considerable skepticism, in part because of the lingering belief that proteins were better candidates for the genetic material. Moreover, many biologists were not convinced that the genes of bacteria would be similar in composition and function to those of more complex organisms. But the major reason for the continued doubt was that so little was known about DNA.

Evidence That Viral DNA Can Program Cells

Additional evidence for DNA as the genetic material came from studies of a virus that infects bacteria. Viruses are much simpler than cells. A virus is little more than DNA (or sometimes RNA) enclosed by a protective coat, which is often simply protein. To reproduce, a virus must infect a cell and take over the cell's metabolic machinery.

Figure 16.2

Inquiry   Can the genetic trait of pathogenicity be transferred between bacteria?

EXPERIMENT   Bacteria of the "S" (smooth) strain of *Streptococcus pneumoniae* are pathogenic because they have a capsule that protects them from an animal's defense system. Bacteria of the "R" (rough) strain lack a capsule and are nonpathogenic. Frederick Griffith injected mice with the two strains as shown below:

CONCLUSION   Griffith concluded that the living R bacteria had been transformed into pathogenic S bacteria by an unknown, heritable substance from the dead S cells.

Viruses that infect bacteria are widely used as tools by researchers in molecular genetics. These viruses are called **bacteriophages** (meaning "bacteria-eaters"), or just **phages** (**Figure 16.3**). In 1952, Alfred Hershey and Martha Chase performed experiments showing that DNA is the genetic material of a phage known as T2. This is one of many phages that infect *Escherichia coli* (*E. coli*), a bacterium that normally lives in the intestines of mammals. At that time, biologists already knew that T2, like many other viruses, was composed almost entirely of DNA and protein. They also knew that the T2 phage could quickly turn an *E. coli* cell into a T2-producing factory that released many copies when the cell ruptured. Somehow, T2 could reprogram its host cell to produce viruses. But which viral component—protein or DNA—was responsible?

Hershey and Chase answered this question by devising an experiment showing that only one of the two components of T2 actually enters the *E. coli* cell during infection (**Figure 16.4**). In preparation for their experiment, they used different radioactive isotopes to tag phage DNA and protein. First, they grew T2 with *E. coli* in the presence of radioactive sulfur.

▲ **Figure 16.3 Viruses infecting a bacterial cell.** T2 and related phages attach to the host cell and inject their genetic material (colorized TEM).

Phage head

Tail

Tail fiber

DNA

Bacterial cell

100 nm

Because protein, but not DNA, contains sulfur, the radioactive atoms were incorporated only into the protein of the phage. Next, in a similar way, the DNA of a separate batch of T2 was labeled with atoms of radioactive phosphorus; because nearly all the phage's phosphorus is in its DNA, this procedure left the phage protein unlabeled. In the experiment, the protein-labeled and DNA-labeled batches of T2 were each allowed to infect separate samples of nonradioactive *E. coli* cells. Shortly after the onset of infection, the cultures were whirled in a blender to shake loose any parts of the phages that remained outside the bacterial cells. The mixtures were then spun in a centrifuge, forcing the bacterial cells to form a pellet at the bottom of the centrifuge tubes, but allowing free phages and parts of phages, which are lighter, to remain suspended in the liquid, or supernatant. The scientists then measured the radioactivity in the pellet and in the supernatant.

Figure 16.4

Inquiry   Is DNA or protein the genetic material of phage T2?

EXPERIMENT   In their famous 1952 experiment, Alfred Hershey and Martha Chase used radioactive sulfur and phosphorus to trace the fates of the protein and DNA, respectively, of T2 phages that infected bacterial cells.

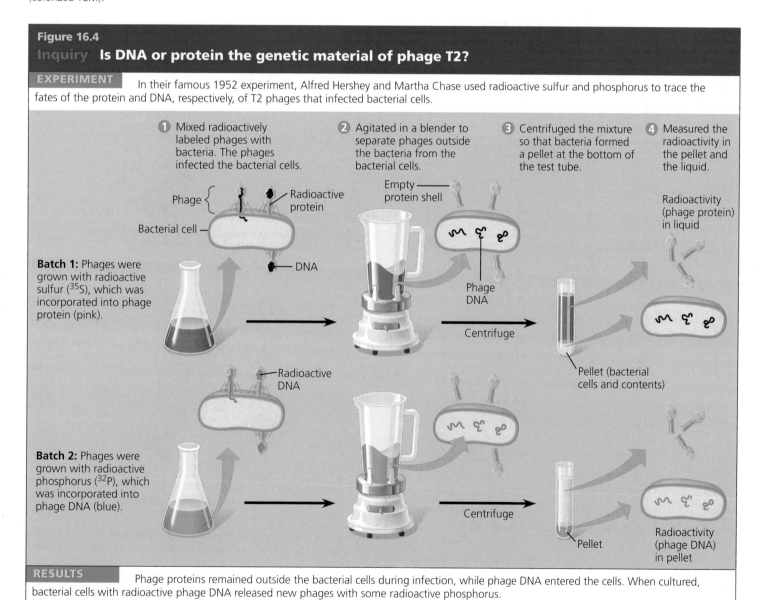

① Mixed radioactively labeled phages with bacteria. The phages infected the bacterial cells.

② Agitated in a blender to separate phages outside the bacteria from the bacterial cells.

③ Centrifuged the mixture so that bacteria formed a pellet at the bottom of the test tube.

④ Measured the radioactivity in the pellet and the liquid.

Phage

Radioactive protein

Bacterial cell

DNA

Empty protein shell

Phage DNA

Radioactivity (phage protein) in liquid

Batch 1: Phages were grown with radioactive sulfur (^{35}S), which was incorporated into phage protein (pink).

Centrifuge

Pellet (bacterial cells and contents)

Radioactive DNA

Batch 2: Phages were grown with radioactive phosphorus (^{32}P), which was incorporated into phage DNA (blue).

Centrifuge

Pellet

Radioactivity (phage DNA) in pellet

RESULTS   Phage proteins remained outside the bacterial cells during infection, while phage DNA entered the cells. When cultured, bacterial cells with radioactive phage DNA released new phages with some radioactive phosphorus.

CONCLUSION   Hershey and Chase concluded that DNA, not protein, functions as the T2 phage's genetic material.

Hershey and Chase found that when the bacteria had been infected with the T2 phage containing radioactively labeled proteins, most of the radioactivity was found in the supernatant, which contained phage particles (but not bacteria). This result suggested that the protein of the phage did not enter the host cells. But when the bacteria had been infected with the T2 phage containing radioactively labeled DNA, most of the radioactivity was found in the pellet, which contained the host bacteria. This result suggested that the phage DNA entered the host cells. Moreover, when these bacteria were returned to a culture medium, the infection ran its course, and the *E. coli* released phages that contained some radioactive phosphorus.

Hershey and Chase concluded that the DNA of the virus is injected into the host cell during infection, leaving the protein outside. The injected DNA provides genetic information that makes the cells produce new viral DNA and proteins, which assemble into new viruses. Thus, the Hershey-Chase experiment provided powerful evidence that nucleic acids, rather than proteins, are the hereditary material, at least for viruses.

Additional Evidence That DNA Is the Genetic Material

Further evidence that DNA is the genetic material came from the laboratory of biochemist Erwin Chargaff. It was already known that DNA is a polymer of nucleotides, each consisting of three components: a nitrogenous (nitrogen-containing) base, a pentose sugar called deoxyribose, and a phosphate group **(Figure 16.5)**. The base can be adenine (A), thymine (T), guanine (G), or cytosine (C). Chargaff analyzed the base composition of DNA from a number of different organisms. In 1947, he reported that DNA composition varies from one species to another. For example, 30.3% of human DNA nucleotides have the base A, whereas DNA from the bacterium *E. coli* has only 26.0% A. This evidence of molecular diversity among species, which had been presumed absent from DNA, made DNA a more credible candidate for the genetic material.

Chargaff also found a peculiar regularity in the ratios of nucleotide bases within a single species. In the DNA of each species he studied, the number of adenines approximately equaled the number of thymines, and the number of guanines approximately equaled the number of cytosines. In human DNA, for example, the four bases are present in these percentages: A = 30.3% and T = 30.3%; G = 19.5% and C = 19.9%. The equivalences for any given species between the number of A and T bases and the number of G and C bases became known as *Chargaff's rules*. The basis for these rules remained unexplained until the discovery of the double helix.

Additional circumstantial evidence was consistent with DNA being the genetic material in eukaryotes. Prior to mitosis, a eukaryotic cell exactly doubles its DNA content, and during mitosis, this DNA is distributed equally to the two daughter cells. Also, in a given species, a diploid set of chromosomes has twice as much DNA as the haploid set.

Building a Structural Model of DNA: *Scientific Inquiry*

Once most biologists were convinced that DNA was the genetic material, the challenge was to determine how the structure of DNA could account for its role in inheritance. By the early 1950s, the arrangement of covalent bonds in a nucleic acid polymer was well established (see Figure 16.5), and researchers focused on discovering the three-dimensional structure of DNA. Among the scientists working on the problem were Linus Pauling, in California, and Maurice Wilkins and Rosalind Franklin, in London. First to come up with the correct answer, however, were two scientists who were relatively unknown at the time— the American James Watson and the Englishman Francis Crick.

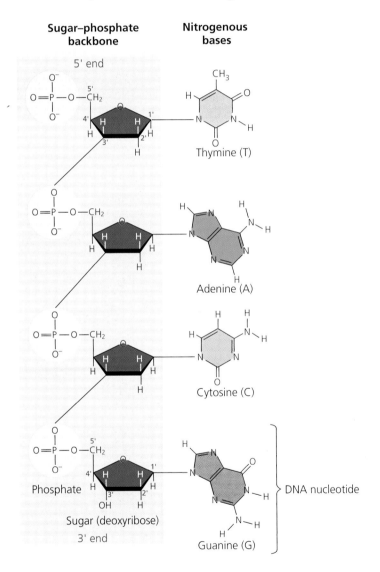

▲ **Figure 16.5 The structure of a DNA strand.** Each nucleotide (monomer) consists of a nitrogenous base (T, A, C, or G), the sugar deoxyribose (blue), and a phosphate group (yellow). The phosphate of one nucleotide is attached to the sugar of the next, resulting in a "backbone" of alternating phosphates and sugars from which the bases project. The polynucleotide strand has directionality, from the 5′ end (with the phosphate group) to the 3′ end (with the —OH group). 5′ and 3′ refer to the numbers assigned to the carbons in the sugar ring.

The brief but celebrated partnership that solved the puzzle of DNA structure began soon after Watson journeyed to Cambridge University, where Crick was studying protein structure with a technique called X-ray crystallography (see Figure 5.24). While visiting the laboratory of Maurice Wilkins at King's College in London, Watson saw an X-ray diffraction image of DNA produced by Wilkins' colleague Rosalind Franklin (**Figure 16.6a**). Images produced by X-ray crystallography are not actually pictures of molecules. The spots and smudges in **Figure 16.6b** were produced by X-rays that were diffracted (deflected) as they passed through aligned fibers of purified DNA. Crystallographers use mathematical equations to translate such patterns into information about the three-dimensional shapes of molecules, and Watson was familiar with the types of patterns that helical molecules produce. Just a glance at Franklin's X-ray diffraction photo of DNA not only told him that DNA was helical in shape, but also enabled him to deduce the width of the helix and the spacing of the nitrogenous bases along it. The width of the helix suggested that it was made up of two strands, contrary to a three-stranded model that Linus Pauling had recently proposed. The presence of two strands accounts for the now-familiar term **double helix** (**Figure 16.7**).

Watson and Crick began building models of a double helix that would conform to the X-ray measurements and what was then known about the chemistry of DNA. Having read an annual report summarizing Franklin's work, they knew she had concluded that the sugar-phosphate backbones were on the outside of the double helix. This arrangement was appealing because it put the relatively hydrophobic nitrogenous bases in the molecule's interior and thus away from the surrounding aqueous solution. Watson constructed a model with the nitrogenous bases facing the interior of the double helix (see

(a) Rosalind Franklin **(b) Franklin's X-ray diffraction photograph of DNA**

▲ **Figure 16.6 Rosalind Franklin and her X-ray diffraction photo of DNA.** Franklin, an X-ray crystallographer, made the photo that Watson and Crick used in deducing the double-helical structure of DNA. Franklin died of cancer in 1958, when she was only 38. Her colleague Maurice Wilkins received the Nobel Prize in 1962 along with Watson and Crick.

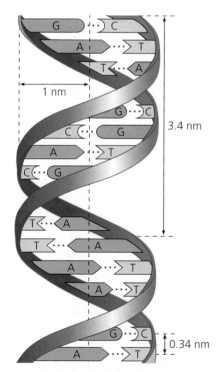

(a) Key features of DNA structure

(b) Partial chemical structure

(c) Space-filling model

▲ **Figure 16.7 The double helix. (a)** The "ribbons" in this diagram represent the sugar-phosphate backbones of the two DNA strands. The helix is "right-handed," curving up to the right. The two strands are held together by hydrogen bonds (dotted lines) between the nitrogenous bases, which are paired in the interior of the double helix. **(b)** For clarity, the two DNA strands are shown untwisted in this partial chemical structure. Notice that the strands are antiparallel, meaning that they are oriented in opposite directions. **(c)** The tight stacking of the base pairs is clear in this computer model. Van der Waals attractions between the stacked pairs play a major role in holding the molecule together.

Figure 16.7). You can imagine this arrangement as a rope ladder with rigid rungs. The side ropes are the equivalent of the sugar-phosphate backbones, and the rungs represent pairs of nitrogenous bases. Now imagine the ladder twisted into a spiral. Franklin's X-ray data indicated that the helix makes one full turn every 3.4 nm along its length. With the bases stacked just 0.34 nm apart, there are ten layers of base pairs, or rungs of the ladder, in each turn of the helix.

The nitrogenous bases of the double helix are paired in specific combinations: adenine (A) with thymine (T), and guanine (G) with cytosine (C). It was mainly by trial and error that Watson and Crick arrived at this key feature of DNA. At first, Watson imagined that the bases paired like with like—for example, A with A and C with C. But this model did not fit the X-ray data, which suggested that the double helix had a uniform diameter. Why is this requirement inconsistent with like-with-like pairing of bases? Adenine and guanine are purines, nitrogenous bases with two organic rings. In contrast, cytosine and thymine belong to the family of nitrogenous bases known as pyrimidines, which have a single ring. Thus, purines (A and G) are about twice as wide as pyrimidines (C and T). A purine-purine pair is too wide and a pyrimidine-pyrimidine pair too narrow to account for the 2-nm diameter of the double helix. Always pairing a purine with a pyrimidine, however, results in a uniform diameter:

Purine + purine: too wide

Pyrimidine + pyrimidine: too narrow

Purine + pyrimidine: width consistent with X-ray data

Watson and Crick reasoned that there must be additional specificity of pairing dictated by the structure of the bases. Each base has chemical side groups that can form hydrogen bonds with its appropriate partner: Adenine can form two hydrogen bonds with thymine and only thymine; guanine forms three hydrogen bonds with cytosine and only cytosine. In shorthand, A pairs with T, and G pairs with C (**Figure 16.8**).

The Watson-Crick model explained the basis for Chargaff's rules. Wherever one strand of a DNA molecule has an A, the partner strand has a T. And a G in one strand is always paired with a C in the complementary strand. Therefore, in the DNA of any organism, the amount of adenine equals the amount of thymine, and the amount of guanine equals the amount of cytosine. Although the base-pairing rules dictate the combinations of nitrogenous bases that form the "rungs" of the double helix, they do not restrict the sequence of nucleotides *along* each DNA strand. The linear sequence of the four bases can be

Adenine (A)   **Thymine (T)**

Guanine (G)   **Cytosine (C)**

▲ **Figure 16.8 Base pairing in DNA.** The pairs of nitrogenous bases in a DNA double helix are held together by hydrogen bonds, as shown here.

varied in countless ways, and each gene has a unique order, or base sequence.

In April 1953, Watson and Crick surprised the scientific world with a succinct, one-page paper in the British journal *Nature*.* The paper reported their molecular model for DNA: the double helix, which has since become the symbol of molecular biology. The beauty of the model was that the structure of DNA suggested the basic mechanism of its replication.

> **Concept Check 16.1**
>
> 1. How did bacterial transformation occur in Griffith's famous experiment (Figure 16.2)?
> 2. In Hershey and Chase's experiment with the bacterial virus T2, what result would you expect if protein were the genetic material?
> 3. A fly has the following percentages of nucleotides in its DNA: 27.3 % A, 27.6% T, 22.5% G, and 22.5% C. How do these numbers demonstrate Chargaff's rules?
> 4. How did Watson and Crick's model explain the basis for Chargaff's rules?
>
> *For suggested answers, see Appendix A.*

*J. D. Watson and F. H. C. Crick, "Molecular Structure of Nucleic Acids: A Structure for Deoxynucleic Acids." *Nature* 171 (1953): 738.

Many proteins work together in DNA replication and repair

The relationship between structure and function is manifest in the double helix. The idea that there is specific pairing of nitrogenous bases in DNA was the flash of inspiration that led Watson and Crick to the correct double helix. At the same time, they saw the functional significance of the base-pairing rules. They ended their classic paper with this wry statement: "It has not escaped our notice that the specific pairing we have postulated immediately suggests a possible copying mechanism for the genetic material." In this section, you will learn about the basic principle of DNA replication, as well as some important details of the process.

The Basic Principle: Base Pairing to a Template Strand

In a second paper, Watson and Crick stated their hypothesis for how DNA replicates:

> Now our model for deoxyribonucleic acid is, in effect, a pair of templates, each of which is complementary to the other. We imagine that prior to duplication the hydrogen bonds are broken, and the two chains unwind and separate. Each chain then acts as a template for the formation onto itself of a new companion chain, so that eventually we shall have two pairs of chains, where we only had one before. Moreover, the sequence of the pairs of bases will have been duplicated exactly.*

---

*F. H. C. Crick and J. D. Watson, "The Complementary Structure of Deoxyribonucleic Acid." *Proc. Roy. Soc.* (A) 223 (1954): 80.

Figure 16.9 illustrates Watson and Crick's basic idea. To make it easier to follow, we show only a short section of double helix in untwisted form. Notice that if you cover one of the two DNA strands of Figure 16.9a, you can still determine its linear sequence of bases by referring to the uncovered strand and applying the base-pairing rules. The two strands are complementary; each stores the information necessary to reconstruct the other. When a cell copies a DNA molecule, each strand serves as a template for ordering nucleotides into a new, complementary strand. As nucleotides line up along the template strand according to the base-pairing rules, they are linked to form the new strands. Where there was one double-stranded DNA molecule at the beginning of the process, there are soon two, each an exact replica of the "parent" molecule. The copying mechanism is analogous to using a photographic negative to make a positive image, which can in turn be used to make another negative, and so on.

This model of DNA replication remained untested for several years following publication of the DNA structure. The requisite experiments were simple in concept but difficult to perform. Watson and Crick's model predicts that when a double helix replicates, each of the two daughter molecules will have one old strand, derived from the parent molecule, and one newly made strand. This **semiconservative model** can be distinguished from a conservative model of replication, in which the parent molecule somehow re-forms after the process (that is, it is conserved). In yet a third model, called the dispersive model, all four strands of DNA following replication have a mixture of old and new DNA (**Figure 16.10**, on the next page). Although mechanisms for conservative or dispersive DNA replication are not easy to devise, these models remained possibilities until they could be ruled out. Finally, in the late 1950s, Matthew Meselson and Franklin Stahl devised experiments that tested the three hypotheses. Their experiments

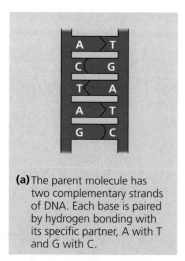

(a) The parent molecule has two complementary strands of DNA. Each base is paired by hydrogen bonding with its specific partner, A with T and G with C.

(b) The first step in replication is separation of the two DNA strands.

(c) Each parental strand now serves as a template that determines the order of nucleotides along a new, complementary strand.

(d) The nucleotides are connected to form the sugar-phosphate backbones of the new strands. Each "daughter" DNA molecule consists of one parental strand and one new strand.

▲ **Figure 16.9 A model for DNA replication: the basic concept.** In this simplification, a short segment of DNA has been untwisted into a structure that resembles a ladder. The rails of the ladder are the sugar-phosphate backbones of the two DNA strands; the rungs are the pairs of nitrogenous bases. Simple shapes symbolize the four kinds of bases. Dark blue represents DNA strands present in the parent molecule; light blue represents free nucleotides and newly synthesized DNA.

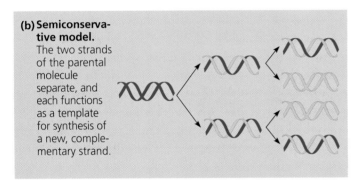

(a) Conservative model. The two parental strands reassociate after acting as templates for new strands, thus restoring the parental double helix.

Parent cell | First replication | Second replication

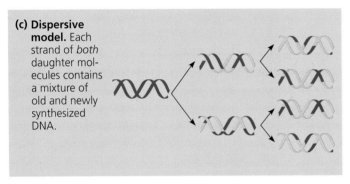

(b) Semiconservative model. The two strands of the parental molecule separate, and each functions as a template for synthesis of a new, complementary strand.

(c) Dispersive model. Each strand of *both* daughter molecules contains a mixture of old and newly synthesized DNA.

▲ **Figure 16.10 Three alternative models of DNA replication.** The short segments of double helix here symbolize the DNA within a cell. Beginning with a parent cell, we follow the DNA for two generations of cells—two rounds of DNA replication. Newly made DNA is light blue.

supported the semiconservative model of DNA replication, as predicted by Watson and Crick (**Figure 16.11**).

The basic principle of DNA replication is elegantly simple. However, the actual process involves some complicated biochemical gymnastics, as we will now see.

DNA Replication: *A Closer Look*

The bacterium *E. coli* has a single chromosome of about 4.6 million nucleotide pairs. In a favorable environment, an *E. coli* cell can copy all this DNA and divide to form two genetically identical daughter cells in less than an hour. Each of *your* cells has 46 DNA molecules in its nucleus, one long double helical molecule per chromosome. In all, that represents about

Figure 16.11

Inquiry   Does DNA replication follow the conservative, semiconservative, or dispersive model?

EXPERIMENT   Matthew Meselson and Franklin Stahl cultured *E. coli* bacteria for several generations on a medium containing nucleotide precursors labeled with a heavy isotope of nitrogen, ^{15}N. The bacteria incorporated the heavy nitrogen into their DNA. The scientists then transferred the bacteria to a medium with only ^{14}N, the lighter, more common isotope of nitrogen. Any new DNA that the bacteria synthesized would be lighter than the parental DNA made in the ^{15}N medium. Meselson and Stahl could distinguish DNA of different densities by centrifuging DNA extracted from the bacteria.

❶ Bacteria cultured in medium containing ^{15}N

❷ Bacteria transferred to medium containing ^{14}N

RESULTS

❸ DNA sample centrifuged after 20 min (after first replication)

❹ DNA sample centrifuged after 40 min (after second replication)

Less dense

More dense

The bands in these two centrifuge tubes represent the results of centrifuging two DNA samples from the flask in step 2, one sample taken after 20 minutes and one after 40 minutes.

CONCLUSION   Meselson and Stahl concluded that DNA replication follows the semiconservative model by comparing their result to the results predicted by each of the three models in Figure 16.10. The first replication in the ^{14}N medium produced a band of hybrid (^{15}N–^{14}N) DNA. This result eliminated the conservative model. A second replication produced both light and hybrid DNA, a result that eliminated the dispersive model and supported the semiconservative model.

First replication | Second replication

Conservative model

Semiconservative model

Dispersive model

6 billion base pairs, or over a thousand times more DNA than is found in a bacterial cell. If we were to print the one-letter symbols for these bases (A, G, C, and T) the size of the letters you are now reading, the 6 billion bases of information in a diploid human cell would fill about 1,200 books as thick as this text. Yet it takes a cell just a few hours to copy all this DNA. This replication of an enormous amount of genetic information is achieved with very few errors—only about one per 10 billion nucleotides. The copying of DNA is remarkable in its speed and accuracy.

More than a dozen enzymes and other proteins participate in DNA replication. Much more is known about how this "replication machine" works in bacteria than in eukaryotes, and we will describe the basic steps of the process for *E. coli*, except where otherwise noted. What scientists have learned about eukaryotic DNA replication suggests, however, that most of the process is fundamentally similar for prokaryotes and eukaryotes.

Getting Started: Origins of Replication

The replication of a DNA molecule begins at special sites called **origins of replication.** The bacterial chromosome, which is circular, has a single origin, a stretch of DNA having a specific sequence of nucleotides. Proteins that initiate DNA replication recognize this sequence and attach to the DNA, separating the two strands and opening up a replication "bubble." Replication of DNA then proceeds in both directions until the entire molecule is copied (see Figure 18.14). In contrast to a bacterial chromosome, a eukaryotic chromosome may have hundreds or even thousands of replication origins. Multiple replication bubbles form and eventually fuse, thus speeding up the copying of the very long DNA molecules **(Figure 16.12).** As in bacteria, eu-

karyotic DNA replication proceeds in both directions from each origin. At each end of a replication bubble is a **replication fork,** a Y-shaped region where the new strands of DNA are elongating.

Elongating a New DNA Strand

Elongation of new DNA at a replication fork is catalyzed by enzymes called **DNA polymerases.** As individual nucleotides align with complementary nucleotides along a template strand of DNA, DNA polymerase adds them, one by one, to the growing end of the new DNA strand. The rate of elongation is about 500 nucleotides per second in bacteria and 50 per second in human cells. In *E. coli*, two different DNA polymerases are involved in replication: DNA polymerase III and DNA polymerase I. The situation in eukaryotes is more complicated, with at least 11 different DNA polymerases discovered so far; however, the general principles are the same.

Each nucleotide that is added to a growing DNA strand is actually a nucleoside triphosphate, which is a nucleoside (a sugar and a base) with three phosphate groups. You have already encountered such a molecule—ATP (adenosine triphosphate; see Figure 8.8). The only difference between the ATP of energy metabolism and the nucleoside triphosphate that supplies adenine to DNA is the sugar component, which is deoxyribose in the building block of DNA, but ribose in ATP. Like ATP, the triphosphate monomers used for DNA synthesis are chemically reactive, partly because their triphosphate tails have an unstable cluster of negative charge. As each monomer joins the growing end of a DNA strand, it loses two phosphate groups as a molecule of pyrophosphate $(P)–(P)_i$. Subsequent hydrolysis of the pyrophosphate to two molecules of inorganic

❶ Replication begins at specific sites where the two parental strands separate and form replication bubbles.

❷ The bubbles expand laterally, as DNA replication proceeds in both directions.

❸ Eventually, the replication bubbles fuse, and synthesis of the daughter strands is complete.

Origin of replication
Parental (template) strand
Daughter (new) strand
0.25 μm

Bubble
Replication fork

Two daughter DNA molecules

(a) In eukaryotes, DNA replication begins at many sites along the giant DNA molecule of each chromosome.

(b) In this micrograph, three replication bubbles are visible along the DNA of a cultured Chinese hamster cell (TEM).

▲ **Figure 16.12 Origins of replication in eukaryotes.** The red arrows indicate the movement of the replication forks and thus the overall directions of DNA replication within each bubble.

► **Figure 16.13 Incorporation of a nucleotide into a DNA strand.** DNA polymerase catalyzes the addition of a nucleoside triphosphate to the 3′ end of a growing DNA strand.

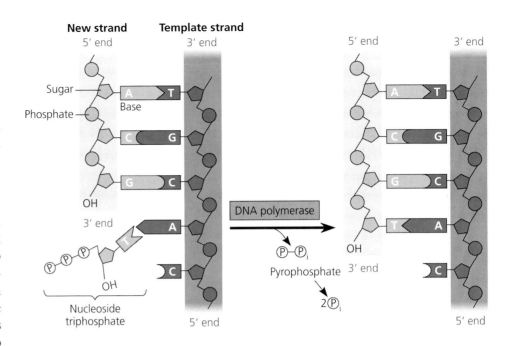

phosphate Ⓟ$_i$ is the exergonic reaction that drives the polymerization reaction **(Figure 16.13)**.

Antiparallel Elongation

As we have noted throughout this chapter, the two ends of a DNA strand are different (see Figure 16.5). In addition, the two strands of DNA in a double helix are antiparallel, meaning that they are oriented in opposite directions to each other (see Figure 16.13). Clearly, the two new strands formed during DNA replication must also be antiparallel to their template strands.

How does the antiparallel structure of the double helix affect replication? DNA polymerases add nucleotides only to the free 3′ end of a growing DNA strand, never to the 5′ end (see Figure 16.13). Thus, a new DNA strand can elongate only in the 5′→3′ direction. With this in mind, let's examine a replication fork **(Figure 16.14)**. Along one template strand, DNA polymerase III (abbreviated DNA pol III) can synthesize a complementary strand continuously by elongating the new DNA in the mandatory 5′→3′ direction. DNA pol III simply nestles in the replication fork on that template strand and continuously adds nucleotides to the complementary strand as the fork progresses. The DNA strand made by this mechanism is called the **leading strand**.

To elongate the other new strand of DNA in the mandatory 5′→3′ direction, DNA pol III must work along the other template strand in the direction *away from* the replication fork. The DNA strand synthesized in this direction is called the **lagging strand**.* In contrast to the leading strand, which elongates continuously, the lagging strand is synthesized as a series of segments. Once a replication bubble opens far enough, a DNA pol III molecule attaches to the lagging strand's template and moves away from the replication fork, synthesizing a short segment of DNA. As the bubble grows, another segment of the lagging strand can be made in a similar way. These segments of the lagging strand are called **Okazaki fragments**, after the Japanese scientist who

① DNA pol III elongates DNA strands only in the 5′ → 3′ direction.

② One new strand, the leading strand, can elongate continuously 5′ → 3′ as the replication fork progresses.

③ The other new strand, the lagging strand, must grow in an overall 3′ → 5′ direction by addition of short segments, Okazaki fragments, that grow 5′ → 3′ (numbered here in the order they were made).

④ DNA ligase joins Okazaki fragments by forming a bond between their free ends. This results in a continuous strand.

▲ **Figure 16.14 Synthesis of leading and lagging strands during DNA replication.** DNA polymerase III (DNA pol III) is closely associated with a protein that encircles the newly synthesized double helix like a doughnut. Note that Okazaki fragments are actually much longer than the ones shown here. In this figure, we depict only five bases per fragment for simplicity.

---

*Synthesis of the leading strand and synthesis of the lagging strand occur concurrently and at the same rate. The lagging strand is so named because its synthesis is slightly delayed relative to synthesis of the leading strand; each new fragment cannot be started until enough template has been exposed at the replication fork.

discovered them. The fragments are about 1,000 to 2,000 nucleotides long in *E. coli* and 100 to 200 nucleotides long in eukaryotes. Another enzyme, **DNA ligase**, eventually joins (ligates) the sugar-phosphate backbones of the Okazaki fragments, forming a single new DNA strand.

Priming DNA Synthesis

DNA polymerases cannot *initiate* the synthesis of a polynucleotide; they can only add nucleotides to the 3' end of an already existing chain that is base-paired with the template strand (see Figure 16.13). The initial nucleotide chain is a short one called a **primer.** Primers may consist of either DNA or RNA (the other class of nucleic acid), and in initiating the replication of cellular DNA, the primer is a short stretch of RNA with an available 3' end. An enzyme called **primase** can start an RNA chain from scratch. Primase joins RNA nucleotides together one at a time, making a primer complementary to the template strand at the location where initiation of the new DNA strand will occur. (Primers are generally 5 to 10 nucleotides long.) DNA pol III then adds a DNA nucleotide to the 3' end of the RNA primer and continues adding DNA nucleotides to the growing DNA strand according to the base-pairing rules.

Only one primer is required for DNA pol III to begin synthesizing the leading strand. For synthesis of the lagging strand, however, each Okazaki fragment must be primed separately **(Figure 16.15)**. Another DNA polymerase, DNA polymerase I (DNA pol I), replaces the RNA nucleotides of the primers with DNA versions, adding them one by one onto the 3' end of the adjacent Okazaki fragment (fragment 2 in Figure 16.15). But DNA pol I cannot join the final nucleotide of this replacement DNA segment to the first DNA nucleotide of the Okazaki fragment whose primer was just replaced (fragment 1 in Figure 16.15). DNA ligase accomplishes this task, joining the sugar-phosphate backbones of all the Okazaki fragments into a continuous DNA strand.

Other Proteins That Assist DNA Replication

You have learned about three kinds of proteins that function in DNA synthesis: DNA polymerases, ligase, and primase. Other kinds of proteins also participate, including helicase, topoisomerase, and single-strand binding proteins. **Helicase** is an enzyme that untwists the double helix at the replication forks, separating the two parental strands and making them available as template strands. This untwisting causes tighter twisting and strain ahead of the replication fork, and **topoisomerase** helps relieve this strain. After helicase separates the two parental strands, molecules of **single-strand binding protein** then bind to the unpaired DNA strands, stabilizing them until they serve as templates for the synthesis of new complementary strands.

Table 16.1 and **Figure 16.16**, on the next page, summarize DNA replication. Study them carefully before proceeding.

1 Primase joins RNA nucleotides into a primer.

Template strand

2 DNA pol III adds DNA nucleotides to the primer, forming an Okazaki fragment.

RNA primer

3 After reaching the next RNA primer (not shown), DNA pol III falls off.

Okazaki fragment

4 After the second fragment is primed, DNA pol III adds DNA nucleotides until it reaches the first primer and falls off.

5 DNA pol I replaces the RNA with DNA, adding to the 3' end of fragment 2.

6 DNA ligase forms a bond between the newest DNA and the adjacent DNA of fragment 1.

7 The lagging strand in this region is now complete.

◄——— Overall direction of replication ———►

▲ **Figure 16.15 Synthesis of the lagging strand.**

Table 16.1 Bacterial DNA replication proteins and their functions

Protein	Function for Leading and Lagging Strands	
Helicase	Unwinds parental double helix at replication forks	
Single-strand binding protein	Binds to and stabilizes single-stranded DNA until it can be used as a template	
Topoisomerase	Corrects "overwinding" ahead of replication forks by breaking, swiveling, and rejoining DNA strands	
	Function for Leading Strand	**Function for Lagging Strand**
Primase	Synthesizes a single RNA primer at the 5′ end of the leading strand	Synthesizes an RNA primer at the 5′ end of each Okazaki fragment
DNA pol III	Continuously synthesizes the leading strand, adding on to the primer	Elongates each Okazaki fragment, adding on to its primer
DNA pol I	Removes primer from the 5′ end of leading strand and replaces it with DNA, adding on to the adjacent 3′ end	Removes the primer from the 5′ end of each fragment and replaces it with DNA, adding on to the 3′ end of the adjacent fragment
DNA Ligase	Joins the 3′ end of the DNA that replaces the primer to the rest of the leading strand	Joins the Okazaki fragments

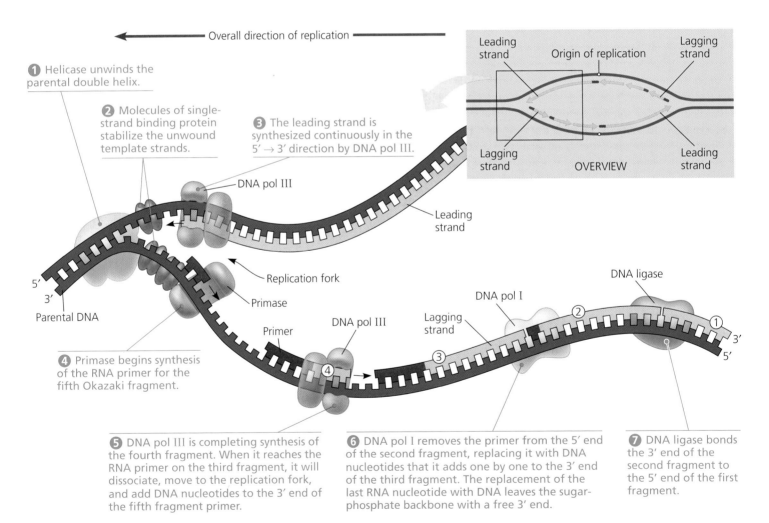

Overall direction of replication

1 Helicase unwinds the parental double helix.

2 Molecules of single-strand binding protein stabilize the unwound template strands.

3 The leading strand is synthesized continuously in the 5′ → 3′ direction by DNA pol III.

DNA pol III

Leading strand

Replication fork

5′
3′
Parental DNA

Primase

Primer

DNA pol III

Leading strand
Origin of replication
Lagging strand

Lagging strand
OVERVIEW
Leading strand

Lagging strand

DNA pol I

DNA ligase

3′
5′

4 Primase begins synthesis of the RNA primer for the fifth Okazaki fragment.

5 DNA pol III is completing synthesis of the fourth fragment. When it reaches the RNA primer on the third fragment, it will dissociate, move to the replication fork, and add DNA nucleotides to the 3′ end of the fifth fragment primer.

6 DNA pol I removes the primer from the 5′ end of the second fragment, replacing it with DNA nucleotides that it adds one by one to the 3′ end of the third fragment. The replacement of the last RNA nucleotide with DNA leaves the sugar-phosphate backbone with a free 3′ end.

7 DNA ligase bonds the 3′ end of the second fragment to the 5′ end of the first fragment.

▲ **Figure 16.16 A summary of bacterial DNA replication.** The detailed diagram shows one replication fork, but as indicated in the overview diagram, replication usually occurs simultaneously at two forks, one at either end of a replication bubble. Notice in the overview diagram that a leading strand is initiated by an RNA primer (red), as is each Okazaki fragment in a lagging strand. Viewing each daughter strand in its entirety in the overview, you can see that half of it is made continuously as a leading strand, while the other half (on the other side of the origin) is synthesized in fragments as a lagging strand.

The DNA Replication Machine as a Stationary Complex

It is traditional—and convenient—to represent DNA polymerase molecules as locomotives moving along a DNA "railroad track," but such a model is inaccurate in two important ways. First, the various proteins that participate in DNA replication actually form a single large complex, a DNA replication "machine." Many protein-protein interactions facilitate the efficiency of this machine; for example, helicase works much more rapidly when it is in contact with primase. Second, the DNA replication machine is probably stationary during the replication process. In eukaryotic cells, multiple copies of the machine, perhaps grouped into "factories," may anchor to the nuclear matrix, a framework of fibers extending through the interior of the nucleus. Recent studies support a model in which DNA polymerase molecules "reel in" the parental DNA and extrude newly made daughter DNA molecules. Additional evidence suggests that the lagging strand is looped through the complex, so that when a DNA polymerase completes synthesis of an Okazaki fragment and dissociates, it doesn't have far to travel to reach the primer for the next fragment, near the replication fork. This looping of the lagging strand enables more Okazaki fragments to be synthesized in less time.

Proofreading and Repairing DNA

We cannot attribute the accuracy of DNA replication solely to the specificity of base pairing. Although errors in the completed DNA molecule amount to only one in 10 billion nucleotides, initial pairing errors between incoming nucleotides and those in the template strand are 100,000 times more common—an error rate of one in 100,000 base pairs. During DNA replication, DNA polymerases proofread each nucleotide against its template as soon as it is added to the growing strand. Upon finding an incorrectly paired nucleotide, the polymerase removes the nucleotide and then resumes synthesis. (This action is similar to fixing a typing error by using the "delete" key and then entering the correct letter.)

Mismatched nucleotides sometimes evade proofreading by a DNA polymerase or arise after DNA synthesis is completed—by damage to an existing nucleotide base, for instance. In **mismatch repair**, cells use special enzymes to fix incorrectly paired nucleotides. Researchers spotlighted the importance of such enzymes when they found that a hereditary defect in one of them is associated with a form of colon cancer. Apparently, this defect allows cancer-causing errors to accumulate in the DNA at a faster rate than normal.

Maintenance of the genetic information encoded in DNA requires frequent repair of various kinds of damage to existing DNA. DNA molecules are constantly subjected to potentially harmful chemical and physical agents, as we'll discuss in Chapter 17. Reactive chemicals (in the environment and occurring naturally in cells), radioactive emissions, X-rays, and ultraviolet light can change nucleotides in ways that can affect encoded genetic information, usually adversely. In addition, DNA bases often undergo spontaneous chemical changes under normal cellular conditions. Fortunately, changes in DNA are usually corrected before they become self-perpetuating mutations. Each cell continuously monitors and repairs its genetic material. Because repair of damaged DNA is so important to the survival of an organism, it is no surprise that many different DNA repair enzymes have evolved. Almost 100 are known in *E. coli*, and about 130 have been identified so far in humans.

Most mechanisms for repairing DNA damage take advantage of the base-paired structure of DNA. Usually, a segment of the strand containing the damage is cut out (excised) by a DNA-cutting enzyme—a **nuclease**—and the resulting gap is filled in with nucleotides properly paired with the nucleotides in the undamaged strand. The enzymes involved in filling the gap are a DNA polymerase and ligase. DNA repair of this type is called **nucleotide excision repair (Figure 16.17)**.

❶ A thymine dimer distorts the DNA molecule.

❷ A nuclease enzyme cuts the damaged DNA strand at two points and the damaged section is removed.

Nuclease

DNA polymerase

❸ Repair synthesis by a DNA polymerase fills in the missing nucleotides.

DNA ligase

❹ DNA ligase seals the free end of the new DNA to the old DNA, making the strand complete.

▲ Figure 16.17 **Nucleotide excision repair of DNA damage.** A team of enzymes detects and repairs damaged DNA. This figure shows DNA containing a thymine dimer, a type of damage often caused by ultraviolet radiation. A nuclease enzyme cuts out the damaged region of DNA, and a DNA polymerase (in bacteria, DNA pol I) replaces it with a normal DNA segment. Ligase completes the process by closing the remaining break in the sugar-phosphate backbone.

One function of the DNA repair enzymes in our skin cells is to repair genetic damage caused by the ultraviolet rays of sunlight. One type of damage, the type shown in Figure 16.17, is the covalent linking of thymine bases that are adjacent on a DNA strand. Such thymine dimers cause the DNA to buckle and interfere with DNA replication. The importance of repairing this kind of damage is underscored by the disorder xeroderma pigmentosum, which in most cases is caused by an inherited defect in a nucleotide excision repair enzyme. Individuals with this disorder are hypersensitive to sunlight; mutations in their skin cells caused by ultraviolet light are left uncorrected and cause skin cancer.

Replicating the Ends of DNA Molecules

In spite of the major role played by DNA polymerases in DNA replication and repair, it turns out that there is a small portion of the cell's DNA that DNA polymerases cannot replicate or repair. For linear DNA, such as the DNA of eukaryotic chromosomes, the fact that a DNA polymerase can only add nucleotides to the 3' end of a preexisting polynucleotide leads to a problem. The usual replication machinery provides no way to complete the 5' ends of daughter DNA strands. Even if an Okazaki fragment can be started with an RNA primer bound to the very end of the template strand, once that primer is removed, it cannot be replaced with DNA, because there is no 3' end onto which DNA polymerase can add DNA nucleotides **(Figure 16.18)**. As a result, repeated rounds of replication produce shorter and shorter DNA molecules.

Prokaryotes do not have this problem because their DNA is circular (with no ends), but what about eukaryotes? Eukaryotic chromosomal DNA molecules have nucleotide sequences called **telomeres** at their ends **(Figure 16.19)**. Telomeres do not contain genes; instead, the DNA typically consists of multiple repetitions of one short nucleotide sequence. The repeated unit in human telomeres, for example, is the six-nucleotide sequence TTAGGG. The number of repetitions in a telomere varies from about 100 to 1,000. Telomeric DNA protects the organism's genes from being eroded through successive rounds of DNA replication. In addition, telomeric DNA and specific proteins associated with it somehow prevent the staggered ends of the daughter molecule from activating the cell's systems for monitoring DNA damage. (The end of a DNA molecule that is "seen" as a double-strand break may otherwise trigger signal transduction pathways leading to cell cycle arrest or cell death.)

Telomeres do not prevent the shortening of DNA molecules due to successive rounds of replication; they just postpone the erosion of genes near the ends of DNA molecules. As shown in Figure 16.18, telomeres become shorter during every round of replication. As we would expect, telomeric DNA does tend to be shorter in dividing somatic cells of older individuals and in cultured cells that have divided many times. It has been proposed that shortening of telomeres is somehow connected

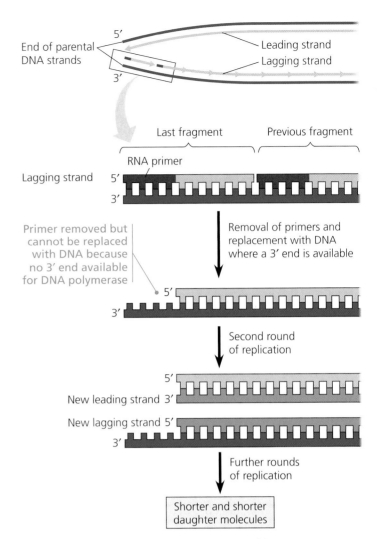

▲ **Figure 16.18 Shortening of the ends of linear DNA molecules.** Here we follow the end of one strand of a DNA molecule through two rounds of replication. After the first round, the new lagging strand is shorter than its template. After a second round, both the leading and lagging strands have become shorter than the original parental DNA. Although not shown here, the other ends of these DNA molecules also become shorter.

▲ **Figure 16.19 Telomeres.** Eukaryotes have repetitive, noncoding sequences called telomeres at the ends of their DNA, marked in these mouse chromosomes by a bright orange stain (LM).

to the aging process of certain tissues and even to aging of the organism as a whole.

But what about the cells whose genomes persist unchanged from an organism to its offspring over many generations? If the chromosomes of germ cells (which give rise to gametes) became shorter in every cell cycle, essential genes would eventually be missing from the gametes they produce. Fortunately, this does not occur: An enzyme called **telomerase** catalyzes the lengthening of telomeres in eukaryotic germ cells, thus restoring their original length and compensating for the shortening that occurs during DNA replication. The lengthening process is made possible by the presence, in telomerase, of a short molecule of RNA that serves as a template for new telomere segments. Telomerase is not active in most somatic cells, but its activity in germ cells results in telomeres of maximum length in the zygote.

Normal shortening of telomeres may protect organisms from cancer by limiting the number of divisions that somatic cells can undergo. Cells from large tumors often have unusually short telomeres, as one would expect for cells that have undergone many cell divisions. Further shortening would presumably lead to self-destruction of the cancer. Intriguingly, researchers have found telomerase activity in cancerous somatic cells, suggesting that its ability to stabilize telomere length may allow these cancer cells to persist. Many cancer cells do seem capable of unlimited cell division, as do immortal strains of cultured cells (see Chapter 12). If telomerase is indeed an important factor in many cancers, it may provide a useful target for both cancer diagnosis and chemotherapy.

In this chapter, you have learned how DNA replication provides the copies of genes that parents pass to offspring. However, it is not enough that genes be copied and transmitted; they must also be expressed. In the next chapter, we will examine how the cell translates genetic information encoded in DNA.

Concept Check 16.2

1. What role does complementary base pairing play in the replication of DNA?
2. Identify two major functions of DNA pol III in DNA replication.
3. Why is DNA pol I necessary to complete synthesis of a leading strand? Point out in the overview box in Figure 16.16 where DNA pol I would function on the top leading strand.
4. How are telomeres important for preserving eukaryotic genes?

For suggested answers, see Appendix A.

Chapter 16 Review

SUMMARY OF KEY CONCEPTS

Concept 16.1
DNA is the genetic material

▶ **The Search for the Genetic Material:** *Scientific Inquiry* (pp. 293–296) Experiments with bacteria and with phages provided the first strong evidence that the genetic material is DNA.
Activity *The Hershey-Chase Experiment*

▶ **Building a Structural Model of DNA:** *Scientific Inquiry* (pp. 296–298) Watson and Crick deduced that DNA is a double helix. Two antiparallel sugar-phosphate chains wind around the outside of the molecule; the nitrogenous bases project into the interior, where they hydrogen-bond in specific pairs, A with T and G with C.
Activity *DNA and RNA Structure*
Activity *DNA Double Helix*

Concept 16.2
Many proteins work together in DNA replication and repair

▶ **The Basic Principle: Base Pairing to a Template Strand** (pp. 299–300) DNA replication is semiconservative: The parent molecule unwinds, and each strand then serves as a template for the synthesis of a new strand according to base-pairing rules.
Activity *DNA Replication: An Overview*
Investigation *What Is the Correct Model for DNA Replication?*

▶ **DNA Replication:** *A Closer Look* (pp. 300–305) DNA replication begins at origins of replication. Y-shaped replication forks form at opposite ends of a replication bubble, where the two DNA strands separate. DNA synthesis starts at the 3′ end of an RNA primer, a short polynucleotide complementary to the template strand. DNA polymerases catalyze the synthesis of new DNA strands, working in the 5′→3′ direction. The leading strand is synthesized continuously, and the lagging strand is synthesized in short segments, called Okazaki fragments. The fragments are joined together by DNA ligase.
Activity *DNA Replication: A Closer Look*
Activity *DNA Replication Review*

▶ **Proofreading and Repairing DNA** (pp. 305–306) DNA polymerases proofread newly made DNA, replacing any incorrect nucleotides. In mismatch repair of DNA, repair enzymes correct errors in base pairing. In nucleotide excision repair, enzymes cut out and replace damaged stretches of DNA.

▶ **Replicating the Ends of DNA Molecules** (pp. 306–307) The ends of eukaryotic chromosomal DNA get shorter with each round of replication. The presence of telomeres, repetitive sequences at the ends of linear DNA molecules, postpones the erosion of genes. Telomerase catalyzes the lengthening of telomeres in germ cells.

Self-Quiz

1. In his work with pneumonia-causing bacteria and mice, Griffith found that
   a. the protein coat from pathogenic cells was able to transform nonpathogenic cells.
   b. heat-killed pathogenic cells caused pneumonia.
   c. some substance from pathogenic cells was transferred to nonpathogenic cells, making them pathogenic.
   d. the polysaccharide coat of bacteria caused pneumonia.
   e. bacteriophages injected DNA into bacteria.

2. *E. coli* cells grown on ^{15}N medium are transferred to ^{14}N medium and allowed to grow for two more generations (two rounds of DNA replication). DNA extracted from these cells is centrifuged. What density distribution of DNA would you expect in this experiment?
   a. one high-density and one low-density band
   b. one intermediate-density band
   c. one high-density and one intermediate-density band
   d. one low-density and one intermediate-density band
   e. one low-density band

3. A biochemist isolates and purifies molecules needed for DNA replication. When she adds some DNA, replication occurs, but each DNA molecule consists of a normal strand paired with numerous segments of DNA a few hundred nucleotides long. What has she probably left out of the mixture?
   a. DNA polymerase   d. Okazaki fragments
   b. DNA ligase   e. primase
   c. nucleotides

4. What is the basis for the difference in how the leading and lagging strands of DNA molecules are synthesized?
   a. The origins of replication occur only at the 5′ end.
   b. Helicases and single-strand binding proteins work at the 5′ end.
   c. DNA polymerase can join new nucleotides only to the 3′ end of a growing strand.
   d. DNA ligase works only in the 3′→5′ direction.
   e. Polymerase can only work on one strand at a time.

5. In analyzing the number of different bases in a DNA sample, which result would be consistent with the base-pairing rules?
   a. A = G   d. A = C
   b. A + G = C + T   e. G = T
   c. A + T = G + T

6. Synthesis of a new DNA strand usually begins with
   a. an RNA primer.   d. DNA ligase.
   b. a DNA primer.   e. a thymine dimer.
   c. an Okazaki fragment.

7. A eukaryotic cell lacking active telomerase would
   a. be unable to take up DNA from the surrounding solution.
   b. be unable to identify and correct mismatched nucleotides.
   c. experience a gradual reduction of chromosome length with each replication cycle.
   d. have a greater potential to become cancerous.
   e. be unable to connect Okazaki fragments.

8. The elongation of the leading strand during DNA synthesis
   a. progresses away from the replication fork.
   b. occurs in the 3′→5′ direction.
   c. produces Okazaki fragments.
   d. depends on the action of DNA polymerase.
   e. does not require a template strand.

9. The spontaneous loss of amino groups from adenine results in hypoxanthine, an unnatural base, opposite thymine. What combination of molecules could the cell use to repair such damage?
   a. nuclease, DNA polymerase, DNA ligase
   b. telomerase, primase, DNA polymerase
   c. telomerase, helicase, single-strand binding protein
   d. DNA ligase, replication fork proteins, adenylyl cyclase
   e. nuclease, telomerase, primase

10. The most reasonable inference from the observation that defects in DNA repair enzymes contribute to some cancers is that
   a. cancer is generally inherited.
   b. uncorrected changes in DNA can lead to cancer.
   c. cancer cannot occur when repair enzymes work properly.
   d. mutations generally lead to cancer.
   e. cancer is caused by environmental factors that damage DNA repair enzymes.

For Self-Quiz answers, see Appendix A.

Go to the website or CD-ROM for more quiz questions.

Evolution Connection

Many bacteria may be able to respond to environmental stress by increasing the rate at which mutations occur during cell division. How might this be accomplished, and what might be an evolutionary advantage of this ability?

Scientific Inquiry

Demonstrate your understanding of the Meselson-Stahl experiment by answering the following questions.

   a. Describe in your own words exactly what each of the centrifugation bands pictured in Figure 16.11 represents.
   b. Imagine that the experiment is done as follows: Bacteria are first grown for several generations in a medium containing the *lighter* isotope of nitrogen, ^{14}N, then switched into a medium containing ^{15}N. The rest of the experiment is identical. Redraw Figure 16.11 to reflect this experiment, predicting what band positions you would expect after one generation and after two generations if each of the three models shown in Figure 16.10 were true.

Investigation *What Is the Correct Model for DNA Replication?*

Science, Technology, and Society

Cooperation and competition are both common in science. What roles did these two social behaviors play in Watson and Crick's discovery of the double helix? How might competition between scientists accelerate progress? How might it slow progress?

17 From Gene to Protein

Key Concepts

17.1 Genes specify proteins via transcription and translation

17.2 Transcription is the DNA-directed synthesis of RNA: *a closer look*

17.3 Eukaryotic cells modify RNA after transcription

17.4 Translation is the RNA-directed synthesis of a polypeptide: *a closer look*

17.5 RNA plays multiple roles in the cell: *a review*

17.6 Comparing gene expression in prokaryotes and eukaryotes reveals key differences

17.7 Point mutations can affect protein structure and function

Overview

The Flow of Genetic Information

The information content of DNA, the genetic material, is in the form of specific sequences of nucleotides along the DNA strands. But how does this information determine an organism's traits? Put another way, what does a gene actually say? And how is its message translated by cells into a specific trait, such as brown hair or type A blood?

Consider, once again, Mendel's peas. One of the characters Mendel studied was stem length (see Table 14.1). Mendel did not know the physiological basis for the difference between the tall and dwarf varieties of pea plants, but plant scientists have since worked out the explanation: Dwarf peas lack growth hormones called gibberellins, which stimulate the normal elongation of stems. A dwarf plant treated with gibberellins from an external source grows to normal height.

Why do dwarf peas fail to make their own gibberellins? They are missing a key protein, an enzyme required for gibberellin synthesis. And they are missing that protein because they do not have a properly functioning gene for that protein.

This example illustrates the main point of this chapter: The DNA inherited by an organism leads to specific traits by dictating the synthesis of proteins. In other words, proteins are the links between genotype and phenotype. The process by which DNA directs protein synthesis, *gene expression*, includes two stages, called transcription and translation. In **Figure 17.1**, you can see a computer model of a ribosome, which is part of the cellular machinery for translation—polypeptide synthesis. This chapter describes the flow of information from gene to protein in detail. By the end, you will understand how genetic mutations, such as the one causing the dwarf trait in pea plants, affect organisms through their proteins.

Concept 17.1

Genes specify proteins via transcription and translation

Before going into the details of how genes direct protein synthesis, let's step back and examine how the fundamental relationship between genes and proteins was discovered.

Evidence from the Study of Metabolic Defects

In 1909, British physician Archibald Garrod was the first to suggest that genes dictate phenotypes through enzymes that catalyze specific chemical reactions in the cell. Garrod postulated that the symptoms of an inherited disease reflect a person's inability to make a particular enzyme. He referred to such diseases as "inborn errors of metabolism." Garrod gave as one example the hereditary condition called alkaptonuria, in which the urine is black because it contains the chemical alkapton, which darkens upon exposure to air. Garrod reasoned that most people have an enzyme that breaks down alkapton, whereas people with alkaptonuria have inherited an inability to make the enzyme that metabolizes alkapton.

Garrod's idea was ahead of its time, but research conducted several decades later supported his hypothesis that a gene dictates the production of a specific enzyme. Biochemists accumulated much evidence that cells synthesize and degrade most organic molecules via metabolic pathways, in which each chemical reaction in a sequence is catalyzed by a specific enzyme. Such metabolic pathways lead, for instance, to the synthesis of the pigments that give fruit flies (*Drosophila*) their eye color (see Figure 15.3). In the 1930s, George Beadle and Boris Ephrussi speculated that in *Drosophila*, each of the various mutations affecting eye color blocks pigment synthesis at a specific step by preventing production of the enzyme that catalyzes that step. However, neither the chemical reactions nor the enzymes that catalyze them were known at the time.

Nutritional Mutants in Neurospora: Scientific Inquiry

A breakthrough in demonstrating the relationship between genes and enzymes came a few years later, when Beadle and Edward Tatum began working with a bread mold, *Neurospora crassa*. They bombarded *Neurospora* with X-rays and then looked among the survivors for mutants that differed in their nutritional needs from the wild-type mold. Wild-type *Neurospora* has modest food requirements. It can survive in the laboratory on agar (a moist support medium) mixed only with inorganic salts, glucose, and the vitamin biotin. From this *minimal medium*, the mold uses its metabolic pathways to produce all the other molecules it needs. Beadle and Tatum identified mutants that could not survive on minimal medium, apparently because they were unable to synthesize certain essential molecules from the minimal ingredients. However, most such nutritional mutants *can* survive on a *complete growth medium*, minimal medium supplemented with all 20 amino acids and a few other nutrients.

To characterize the metabolic defect in each nutritional mutant, Beadle and Tatum took samples from the mutant growing on complete medium and distributed them to a number of different vials. Each vial contained minimal medium plus a single additional nutrient. The particular supplement that allowed growth indicated the metabolic defect. For example, if the only supplemented vial that supported growth of the mutant was the one fortified with the amino acid arginine, the researchers could conclude that the mutant was defective in the biochemical pathway that wild-type cells use to synthesize arginine.

Beadle and Tatum went on to pin down each mutant's defect more specifically. Their work with arginine-requiring mutants was especially instructive. Using genetic crosses, they determined that their mutants fell into three classes, each mutated in a different gene. The researchers then showed that they could distinguish among the classes of mutants nutritionally by additional tests of their growth requirements (**Figure 17.2**). In the synthetic pathway leading to arginine, they suspected, a precursor nutrient is converted to ornithine, which is converted to citrulline, which is converted to arginine. When they tested their arginine mutants for growth on ornithine and citrulline, they found that one class could grow on either compound (or arginine), the second class only on citrulline (or arginine), and the third on neither—it absolutely required arginine. The three classes of mutants, the researchers reasoned, must be blocked at different steps in the pathway that synthesizes arginine, with each mutant class lacking the enzyme that catalyzes the blocked step.

Because each mutant was defective in a single gene, Beadle and Tatum's results provided strong support for the *one gene–one enzyme hypothesis,* as they dubbed it, which states that the function of a gene is to dictate the production of a specific enzyme. The researchers also showed how a combination of genetics and biochemistry could be used to work out the steps in a metabolic pathway. Further support for the one gene–one enzyme hypothesis came with experiments that identified the specific enzymes lacking in the mutants.

The Products of Gene Expression: A Developing Story

As researchers learned more about proteins, they made minor revisions to the one gene–one enzyme hypothesis. First of all, not all proteins are enzymes. Keratin, the structural protein of animal hair, and the hormone insulin are two examples of nonenzyme proteins. Because proteins that are not enzymes are nevertheless gene products, molecular biologists began to think in terms of one gene–one protein. However, many proteins are constructed from two or more different polypeptide chains, and each polypeptide is specified by its own gene. For example, hemoglobin, the oxygen-transporting protein of vertebrate red blood cells, is built from two kinds of polypeptides, and thus two genes code for this protein (see Figure 5.20). Beadle and Tatum's idea has therefore been restated as the **one gene–one polypeptide hypothesis.** Even this statement is not entirely accurate, though. As you will learn later in this chapter, some genes code for RNA molecules that have important functions in cells even though they are never translated into protein. But for now, we will focus on genes that code for polypeptides. (Note that it is common to refer to proteins, rather than polypeptides, as the gene products, a practice you will encounter in this book.)

Figure 17.2

Inquiry Do individual genes specify different enzymes in arginine biosynthesis?

EXPERIMENT Working with the mold *Neurospora crassa*, George Beadle and Edward Tatum had isolated mutants requiring arginine in their growth medium and had shown genetically that these mutants fell into three classes, each defective in a different gene. From other considerations, they suspected that the metabolic pathway of arginine biosynthesis included the precursors ornithine and citrulline. Their most famous experiment, shown here, tested both their one gene–one enzyme hypothesis and their postulated arginine pathway. In this experiment, they grew their three classes of mutants under the four different conditions shown in the Results section below.

RESULTS The wild-type strain required only the minimal medium for growth. The three classes of mutants had different growth requirements.

	Wild type	Class I Mutants	Class II Mutants	Class III Mutants
Minimal medium (MM) (control)				
MM + Ornithine				
MM + Citrulline				
MM + Arginine (control)				

CONCLUSION From the growth patterns of the mutants, Beadle and Tatum deduced that each mutant was unable to carry out one step in the pathway for synthesizing arginine, presumably because it lacked the necessary enzyme. Because each of their mutants was mutated in a single gene, they concluded that each mutated gene must normally dictate the production of one enzyme. Their results supported the one gene–one enzyme hypothesis and also confirmed the arginine pathway. (Notice that a mutant can grow only if supplied with a compound made *after* the defective step.)

	Wild type	Class I Mutants (mutation in gene *A*)	Class II Mutants (mutation in gene *B*)	Class III Mutants (mutation in gene *C*)
Gene A → Enzyme A	Precursor ↓ Ornithine	Precursor ✗ Ornithine	Precursor ↓ Ornithine	Precursor ↓ Ornithine
Gene B → Enzyme B	Ornithine ↓ Citrulline	Ornithine ↓ Citrulline	Ornithine ✗ Citrulline	Ornithine ↓ Citrulline
Gene C → Enzyme C	Citrulline ↓ Arginine	Citrulline ↓ Arginine	Citrulline ↓ Arginine	Citrulline ✗ Arginine

Basic Principles of Transcription and Translation

Genes provide the instructions for making specific proteins. But a gene does not build a protein directly. The bridge between DNA and protein synthesis is the nucleic acid RNA. You learned in Chapter 5 that RNA is chemically similar to DNA, except that it contains ribose instead of deoxyribose as its sugar and has the nitrogenous base uracil rather than thymine (see Figure 5.26). Thus, each nucleotide along a DNA strand has A, G, C, or T as its base, and each nucleotide along an RNA strand has A, G, C, or U as its base. An RNA molecule usually consists of a single strand.

It is customary to describe the flow of information from gene to protein in linguistic terms because both nucleic acids and proteins are polymers with specific sequences of monomers that convey information, much as specific sequences of letters communicate information in a language like English. In DNA or RNA, the monomers are the four types of nucleotides, which differ in their nitrogenous bases. Genes are typically hundreds or thousands of nucleotides long, each gene having a specific sequence of bases. Each polypeptide of a protein also has monomers arranged in a particular linear order (the protein's primary structure), but its monomers are the 20 amino acids. Thus, nucleic acids and proteins contain information written in two different chemical languages. Getting from DNA to protein requires two major stages, transcription and translation.

Transcription is the synthesis of RNA under the direction of DNA. Both nucleic acids use the same language, and the information is simply transcribed, or copied, from one molecule to the other. Just as a DNA strand provides a template for the synthesis of a new complementary strand during DNA replication, it provides a template for assembling a sequence of RNA nucleotides. The resulting RNA molecule is a faithful transcript of the gene's protein-building instructions. In discussing protein-coding genes, this type of RNA molecule is called **messenger RNA (mRNA)**, because it carries a genetic message from the DNA to the protein-synthesizing machinery of the cell. (Transcription is the general term for the synthesis of *any* kind of RNA on a DNA template. Later in this chapter, you will learn about other types of RNA produced by transcription.)

Translation is the actual synthesis of a polypeptide, which occurs under the direction of mRNA. During this stage, there is a change in language: The cell must translate the base sequence of an mRNA molecule into the amino acid sequence of a polypeptide. The sites of translation are **ribosomes**, complex particles that facilitate the orderly linking of amino acids into polypeptide chains.

You might wonder why proteins couldn't simply be translated directly from DNA. There are evolutionary reasons for using an RNA intermediate. First, it provides protection for the DNA and its genetic information. As an analogy, when an architect designs a house, the original specifications (analogous to DNA) are not what the construction workers use at the site. Instead they use *copies* of the originals (analogous to mRNA), keeping the originals pristine and undamaged. Second, using an RNA intermediate allows more copies of a protein to be made simultaneously, since many RNA transcripts can be made from one gene. Also, each RNA transcript can be translated repeatedly.

Although the basic mechanics of transcription and translation are similar for prokaryotes and eukaryotes, there is an important difference in the flow of genetic information within the cells. Because bacteria lack nuclei, their DNA is not segregated from ribosomes and the other protein-synthesizing equipment **(Figure 17.3a)**. As you will see later, this allows translation of an mRNA to begin while its transcription is still in progress (see Figure 17.22). In a eukaryotic cell, by contrast, the nuclear envelope separates transcription from translation in space and time **(Figure 17.3b)**. Transcription occurs in the nucleus, and mRNA is transported to the cytoplasm, where translation occurs. But before they can leave the nucleus, eukaryotic RNA transcripts are modified in various ways to produce the final, functional mRNA. The transcription of a protein-coding eukaryotic gene results in *pre-mRNA*, and **RNA processing** yields the finished mRNA. The initial RNA transcript from any gene, including those coding for RNA that is not translated into protein, is more generally called a **primary transcript**.

Let's summarize: Genes program protein synthesis via genetic messages in the form of messenger RNA. Put another way, cells are governed by a molecular chain of command: DNA → RNA → protein. In the next section, we discuss how the instructions for assembling amino acids into a specific order are encoded in nucleic acids.

The Genetic Code

When biologists began to suspect that the instructions for protein synthesis were encoded in DNA, they recognized a problem: There are only four nucleotide bases to specify 20 amino acids. Thus, the genetic code cannot be a language like Chinese, where each written symbol corresponds to a single word. How many bases, then, correspond to an amino acid?

Codons: Triplets of Bases

If each nucleotide base were translated into an amino acid, only 4 of the 20 amino acids could be specified. Would a language of two-letter code words suffice? The base sequence AG, for example, could specify one amino acid, and GT could specify another. Since there are four bases, this would give us 16 (that is, 4^2) possible arrangements—still not enough to code for all 20 amino acids.

Triplets of nucleotide bases are the smallest units of uniform length that can code for all the amino acids. If each arrangement of three consecutive bases specifies an amino acid, there can be 64 (that is, 4^3) possible code words—more

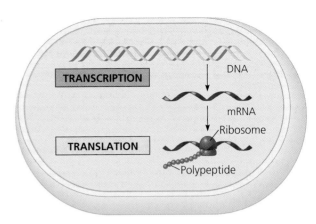

(a) Prokaryotic cell. In a cell lacking a nucleus, mRNA produced by transcription is immediately translated without additional processing.

(b) Eukaryotic cell. The nucleus provides a separate compartment for transcription. The original RNA transcript, called pre-mRNA, is processed in various ways before leaving the nucleus as mRNA.

▲ **Figure 17.3 Overview: the roles of transcription and translation in the flow of genetic information.** In a cell, inherited information flows from DNA to RNA to protein. The two main stages of information flow are transcription and translation. A miniature version of part (a) or (b) accompanies several figures later in the chapter as an orientation diagram to help you see where a particular figure fits into the overall scheme.

than enough to specify all the amino acids. Experiments have verified that the flow of information from gene to protein is based on a **triplet code**: The genetic instructions for a polypeptide chain are written in the DNA as a series of nonoverlapping, three-nucleotide words. For example, the base triplet AGT at a particular position along a DNA strand results in the placement of the amino acid serine at the corresponding position of the polypeptide to be produced.

During transcription, the gene determines the sequence of bases along the length of an mRNA molecule (**Figure 17.4**). For each gene, only one of the two DNA strands is transcribed. This strand is called the **template strand** because it provides the template for ordering the sequence of nucleotides in an RNA transcript. A given DNA strand can be the template strand for some genes along a DNA molecule, while for other genes in other regions, the complementary strand may function as the template. Note, however, that for a given gene, the same strand is used as the template every time it is transcribed.

An mRNA molecule is complementary rather than identical to its DNA template because RNA bases are assembled on the template according to base-pairing rules. The pairs are similar to those that form during DNA replication, except that U, the RNA substitute for T, pairs with A and the mRNA nucleotides contain ribose instead of deoxyribose. Like a new strand of DNA, the RNA molecule is synthesized in an antiparallel direction to the template strand of DNA. (To review what is meant by "antiparallel" and the 5′ and 3′ ends of a nucleic acid chain, see Figure 16.7.) For example, the base triplet ACC along the DNA (written as 3′-ACC-5′) provides a template for 5′-UGG-3′ in the mRNA molecule. The mRNA base triplets are called **codons**, and they are customarily written in the 5′ → 3′ direction. In our example, UGG is the codon for the amino acid tryptophan (abbreviated Trp). The term *codon* is also sometimes used for the DNA base triplets along the *nontemplate* strand. These codons are complementary to the template strand and thus identical in sequence to the mRNA except that they have T instead of U. (For this reason, the nontemplate DNA strand is sometimes called the "coding strand.")

During translation, the sequence of codons along an mRNA molecule is decoded, or translated, into a sequence of amino acids making up a polypeptide chain. The codons are read by the translation machinery in the 5′ → 3′ direction along the mRNA. Each codon specifies which one of the 20 amino acids will be incorporated at the corresponding position along a polypeptide. Because codons are base triplets, the number of nucleotides making up a genetic message must be three times the number of amino acids making up the protein product. For example, it takes 300 nucleotides along an mRNA strand to code for a polypeptide that is 100 amino acids long.

Cracking the Code

Molecular biologists cracked the code of life in the early 1960s, when a series of elegant experiments disclosed the amino acid translations of each of the RNA codons. The first codon was deciphered in 1961 by Marshall Nirenberg, of the National Institutes of Health, and his colleagues. Nirenberg synthesized an artificial mRNA by linking identical RNA nucleotides containing uracil as their base. No matter where this message started or stopped, it could contain only one codon in repetition: UUU. Nirenberg added this "poly-U" to a test-tube mixture containing amino acids, ribosomes, and the other components required for protein synthesis. His artificial system translated the poly-U into a polypeptide containing a single amino acid, phenylalanine (Phe), strung together as a long polyphenylalanine chain. Thus, Nirenberg determined that the mRNA codon UUU specifies the amino acid phenylalanine. Soon, the amino acids specified by the codons AAA, GGG, and CCC were also determined.

Although more elaborate techniques were required to decode mixed triplets such as AUA and CGA, all 64 codons were deciphered by the mid-1960s. As **Figure 17.5** on the next page shows, 61 of the 64 triplets code for amino acids. The three codons that do not designate amino acids are "stop" signals, or termination codons, marking the end of translation. Notice that the codon AUG has a dual function: It codes for the amino acid methionine (Met) and also functions as a "start" signal, or initiation codon. Genetic messages begin with the mRNA codon AUG, which signals the protein-synthesizing machinery to begin translating the mRNA at that location. (Because AUG also stands for methionine, polypeptide chains begin with methionine when they are synthesized. However, an enzyme may subsequently remove this starter amino acid from the chain.)

▲ **Figure 17.4 The triplet code.** For each gene, one DNA strand functions as a template for transcription. The base-pairing rules for DNA synthesis also guide transcription, but uracil (U) takes the place of thymine (T) in RNA. During translation, the mRNA is read as a sequence of base triplets, called codons. Each codon specifies an amino acid to be added to the growing polypeptide chain. The mRNA is read in the 5′ → 3′ direction.

Second mRNA base

	U	C	A	G	
U	UUU ⎤ Phe UUC ⎦ UUA ⎤ Leu UUG ⎦	UCU ⎤ UCC ⎥ Ser UCA ⎥ UCG ⎦	UAU ⎤ Tyr UAC ⎦ UAA Stop UAG Stop	UGU ⎤ Cys UGC ⎦ UGA Stop UGG Trp	U C A G
C	CUU ⎤ CUC ⎥ Leu CUA ⎥ CUG ⎦	CCU ⎤ CCC ⎥ Pro CCA ⎥ CCG ⎦	CAU ⎤ His CAC ⎦ CAA ⎤ Gln CAG ⎦	CGU ⎤ CGC ⎥ Arg CGA ⎥ CGG ⎦	U C A G
A	AUU ⎤ AUC ⎥ Ile AUA ⎦ AUG Met or start	ACU ⎤ ACC ⎥ Thr ACA ⎥ ACG ⎦	AAU ⎤ Asn AAC ⎦ AAA ⎤ Lys AAG ⎦	AGU ⎤ Ser AGC ⎦ AGA ⎤ Arg AGG ⎦	U C A G
G	GUU ⎤ GUC ⎥ Val GUA ⎥ GUG ⎦	GCU ⎤ GCC ⎥ Ala GCA ⎥ GCG ⎦	GAU ⎤ Asp GAC ⎦ GAA ⎤ Glu GAG ⎦	GGU ⎤ GGC ⎥ Gly GGA ⎥ GGG ⎦	U C A G

First mRNA base (5' end) — Third mRNA base (3' end)

▲ **Figure 17.5 The dictionary of the genetic code.** The three bases of an mRNA codon are designated here as the first, second, and third bases, reading in the 5′ → 3′ direction along the mRNA. (Practice using this dictionary by finding the codons in Figure 17.4.) The codon AUG not only stands for the amino acid methionine (Met) but also functions as a "start" signal for ribosomes to begin translating the mRNA at that point. Three of the 64 codons function as "stop" signals, marking the end of a genetic message.

Notice in Figure 17.5 that there is *redundancy* in the genetic code, but no ambiguity. For example, although codons GAA and GAG both specify glutamic acid (redundancy), neither of them ever specifies any other amino acid (no ambiguity). The redundancy in the code is not altogether random. In many cases, codons that are synonyms for a particular amino acid differ only in the third base of the triplet. We will consider a possible benefit for this redundancy later in the chapter.

Our ability to extract the intended message from a written language depends on reading the symbols in the correct groupings—that is, in the correct **reading frame.** Consider this statement: "The red dog ate the cat." Group the letters incorrectly by starting at the wrong point, and the result will probably be gibberish: for example, "her edd oga tet hec at." The reading frame is also important in the molecular language of cells. The short stretch of polypeptide shown in Figure 17.4, for instance, will only be made correctly if the mRNA nucleotides are read from left to right (5′ → 3′) in the groups of three shown in the figure: UGG UUU GGC UCA. Although a genetic message is written with no spaces between the codons, the cell's protein-synthesizing machinery reads the message as a series of nonoverlapping three-letter words. The message is *not* read as a series of overlapping

▶ **Figure 17.6 A tobacco plant expressing a firefly gene.** Because diverse forms of life share a common genetic code, it is possible to program one species to produce proteins characteristic of another species by transplanting DNA. In this experiment, researchers were able to incorporate a gene from a firefly into the DNA of a tobacco plant. The firefly gene codes for an enzyme that catalyzes a chemical reaction that releases light energy.

words—UGGUUU, and so on—which would convey a very different message.

Evolution of the Genetic Code

The genetic code is nearly universal, shared by organisms from the simplest bacteria to the most complex animals. The RNA codon CCG, for instance, is translated as the amino acid proline in all organisms whose genetic code has been examined. In laboratory experiments, genes can be transcribed and translated after being transplanted from one species to another **(Figure 17.6).** Bacteria can be programmed by the insertion of human genes to synthesize certain human proteins for medical use. Such applications have produced many exciting developments in biotechnology (see Chapter 20).

Exceptions to the universality of the genetic code include translation systems where a few codons differ from the standard ones. Slight variations in the genetic code exist in certain unicellular eukaryotes and in the organelle genes of some species. Some prokaryotes can translate stop codons into one of two amino acids not found in most organisms. Despite these exceptions, the evolutionary significance of the code's *near* universality is clear. A language shared by all living things must have been operating very early in the history of life—early enough to be present in the common ancestors of all modern organisms. A shared genetic vocabulary is a reminder of the kinship that bonds all life on Earth.

Concept Check 17.1

1. Draw the nontemplate strand of DNA for the template shown in Figure 17.4. Compare and contrast its base sequence with the mRNA molecule.
2. What protein product would you expect from a poly-G mRNA that is 30 nucleotides long?

For suggested answers, see Appendix A.

Transcription is the DNA-directed synthesis of RNA: *a closer look*

Now that we have considered the linguistic logic and evolutionary significance of the genetic code, we are ready to reexamine transcription, the first stage of gene expression, in more detail.

Molecular Components of Transcription

Messenger RNA, the carrier of information from DNA to the cell's protein-synthesizing machinery, is transcribed from the template strand of a gene. An enzyme called an **RNA polymerase** pries the two strands of DNA apart and hooks together the RNA nucleotides as they base-pair along the DNA template **(Figure 17.7)**. Like the DNA polymerases that function in DNA replication, RNA polymerases can only assemble a polynucleotide in its 5′ → 3′ direction. Unlike DNA polymerases, however, RNA polymerases are able to start a chain from scratch; they don't need a primer.

Specific sequences of nucleotides along the DNA mark where transcription of a gene begins and ends. The DNA sequence where RNA polymerase attaches and initiates transcription is known as the **promoter**; in prokaryotes, the sequence that signals the end of transcription is called the **terminator.** (The termination mechanism is different in eukaryotes, which we'll describe later.) Molecular biologists refer to the direction of transcription as "downstream" and the other direction as "upstream." These terms are also used to describe the positions of nucleotide sequences within the DNA or RNA. Thus, the promoter sequence in DNA is said to be upstream from the terminator. The stretch of DNA that is transcribed into an RNA molecule is called a **transcription unit.**

Bacteria have a single type of RNA polymerase that synthesizes not only mRNA but also other types of RNA that function in

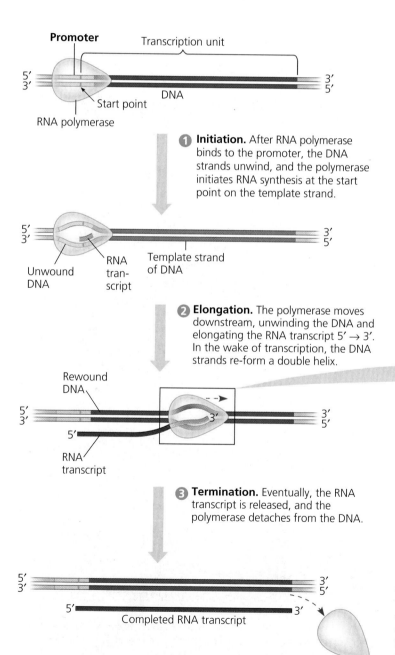

Promoter · Transcription unit

5′
3′

Start point · DNA

RNA polymerase

1 Initiation. After RNA polymerase binds to the promoter, the DNA strands unwind, and the polymerase initiates RNA synthesis at the start point on the template strand.

5′
3′

Unwound DNA · RNA tran-script · Template strand of DNA

2 Elongation. The polymerase moves downstream, unwinding the DNA and elongating the RNA transcript 5′ → 3′. In the wake of transcription, the DNA strands re-form a double helix.

Rewound DNA

5′
3′

5′

RNA transcript

3 Termination. Eventually, the RNA transcript is released, and the polymerase detaches from the DNA.

5′
3′

5′ · Completed RNA transcript · 3′

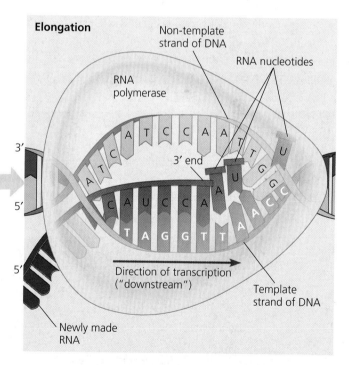

Elongation

Non-template strand of DNA

RNA nucleotides

RNA polymerase

3′

3′ end

5′

Direction of transcription ("downstream")

Template strand of DNA

Newly made RNA

◀ **Figure 17.7 The stages of transcription: initiation, elongation, and termination.** This general depiction of transcription applies to both prokaryotes and eukaryotes, but the details of termination vary for prokaryotes and eukaryotes, as described in the text. Also, in a prokaryote, the RNA transcript is immediately usable as mRNA, whereas in a eukaryote, it must first undergo processing to become mRNA.

protein synthesis. In contrast, eukaryotes have three types of RNA polymerase in their nuclei, numbered I, II, and III. The one used for mRNA synthesis is RNA polymerase II. The other two RNA polymerases transcribe RNA molecules that are not translated into protein. In the discussion of transcription that follows, we start with the features of mRNA synthesis common to both prokaryotes and eukaryotes and then describe some key differences.

Synthesis of an RNA Transcript

The three stages of transcription, as shown in Figure 17.7 and described next, are initiation, elongation, and termination of the RNA chain. Study Figure 17.7 to familiarize yourself with the stages and the terms used to describe them.

RNA Polymerase Binding and Initiation of Transcription

The promoter of a gene includes within it the transcription start point (the nucleotide where RNA synthesis actually begins) and typically extends several dozen nucleotide pairs "upstream" from the start point. In addition to serving as a binding site for RNA polymerase and determining where transcription starts, the promoter determines which of the two strands of the DNA helix is used as the template.

Certain sections of a promoter are especially important for binding RNA polymerase. In prokaryotes, the RNA polymerase itself specifically recognizes and binds to the promoter. In eukaryotes, a collection of proteins called **transcription factors** mediate the binding of RNA polymerase and the initiation of transcription. Only after certain transcription factors are attached to the promoter does RNA polymerase II bind to it. The completed assembly of transcription factors and RNA polymerase II bound to the promoter is called a **transcription initiation complex.** **Figure 17.8** shows the role of transcription factors and a crucial promoter DNA sequence called a **TATA box** in forming the initiation complex in eukaryotes.

The interaction between eukaryotic RNA polymerase II and transcription factors is an example of the importance of protein-protein interactions in controlling eukaryotic transcription (as we will discuss further in Chapter 19). Once the polymerase is firmly attached to the promoter DNA, the two DNA strands unwind there, and the enzyme starts transcribing the template strand.

Elongation of the RNA Strand

As RNA polymerase moves along the DNA, it continues to untwist the double helix, exposing about 10 to 20 DNA bases at a time for pairing with RNA nucleotides (see Figure 17.7). The enzyme adds nucleotides to the 3′ end of the growing RNA molecule as it continues along the double helix. In the wake of this advancing wave of RNA synthesis, the new RNA molecule peels away from its DNA template and the DNA double helix re-forms. Transcription progresses at a rate of about 60 nucleotides per second in eukaryotes.

A single gene can be transcribed simultaneously by several molecules of RNA polymerase following each other like trucks in a convoy. A growing strand of RNA trails off from each polymerase, with the length of each new strand reflecting how far along the template the enzyme has traveled from the start point (see Figure 17.22). The congregation of many polymerase molecules simultaneously transcribing a single gene increases the amount of mRNA transcribed from it, which helps the cell make the encoded protein in large amounts.

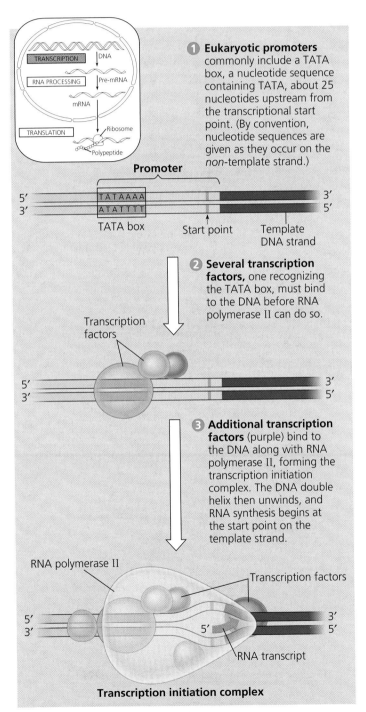

1 **Eukaryotic promoters** commonly include a TATA box, a nucleotide sequence containing TATA, about 25 nucleotides upstream from the transcriptional start point. (By convention, nucleotide sequences are given as they occur on the *non*-template strand.)

2 **Several transcription factors,** one recognizing the TATA box, must bind to the DNA before RNA polymerase II can do so.

3 **Additional transcription factors** (purple) bind to the DNA along with RNA polymerase II, forming the transcription initiation complex. The DNA double helix then unwinds, and RNA synthesis begins at the start point on the template strand.

▲ **Figure 17.8 The initiation of transcription at a eukaryotic promoter.** In eukaryotic cells, proteins called transcription factors mediate the initiation of transcription by RNA polymerase II.

Termination of Transcription

The mechanism of termination differs between prokaryotes and eukaryotes. In prokaryotes, transcription proceeds through a terminator sequence in the DNA. The transcribed terminator (an RNA sequence) functions as the termination signal, causing the polymerase to detach from the DNA and release the transcript, which is available for immediate use as mRNA. In eukaryotes, however, the pre-mRNA is cleaved from the growing RNA chain while RNA polymerase II continues to transcribe the DNA. Specifically, the polymerase transcribes a sequence on the DNA called the polyadenylation signal sequence, which codes for a polyadenylation signal (AAUAAA) in the pre-mRNA. Then, at a point about 10 to 35 nucleotides downstream from the AAUAAA signal, proteins associated with the growing RNA transcript cut it free from the polymerase, releasing the pre-mRNA. The polymerase continues transcribing for hundreds of nucleotides past the site where the pre-mRNA was released. Transcription is terminated when the polymerase eventually falls off the DNA (by a mechanism that is not fully understood). Once the pre-mRNA has been made, it is modified during RNA processing, the topic of our next section.

Concept Check 17.2

1. Compare and contrast the functioning of DNA polymerase and RNA polymerase.
2. Is the promoter at the upstream or downstream end of a transcription unit?
3. In a prokaryote, how does RNA polymerase "know" where to start transcribing a gene? In a eukaryote?
4. How is the primary transcript produced by a prokaryotic cell different from that produced by a eukaryotic cell?

For suggested answers, see Appendix A.

Concept 17.3

Eukaryotic cells modify RNA after transcription

Enzymes in the eukaryotic nucleus modify pre-mRNA in specific ways before the genetic messages are dispatched to the cytoplasm. During this RNA processing, both ends of the primary transcript are usually altered. Also, in most cases, certain interior sections of the molecule are cut out and the remaining parts spliced together. These modifications help form an mRNA molecule that is ready to be translated.

Alteration of mRNA Ends

Each end of a pre-mRNA molecule is modified in a particular way (**Figure 17.9**). The 5′ end, the end transcribed first, is capped off with a modified form of a guanine (G) nucleotide after transcription of the first 20 to 40 nucleotides, forming a **5′ cap**. The 3′ end of the pre-mRNA molecule is also modified before the mRNA exits the nucleus. Recall that the pre-mRNA is released soon after the polyadenylation signal, AAUAAA, is transcribed. At the 3′ end, an enzyme adds 50 to 250 adenine (A) nucleotides, forming a **poly-A tail**. The 5′ cap and poly-A tail share several important functions. First, they seem to facilitate the export of the mature mRNA from the nucleus. Second, they help protect the mRNA from degradation by hydrolytic enzymes. And third, once the mRNA reaches the cytoplasm, both structures help ribosomes attach to the 5′ end of the mRNA. Figure 17.9 shows a diagram of a eukaryotic mRNA molecule with cap and tail. The figure also shows the untranslated regions (UTRs) at the 5′ and 3′ ends of the mRNA (referred to as the *5′ UTR* and *3′ UTR*). The UTRs are parts of the mRNA that will not be translated into protein, but they have other functions, such as ribosome binding.

▲ **Figure 17.9 RNA processing: addition of the 5′ cap and poly-A tail.** Enzymes modify the two ends of a eukaryotic pre-mRNA molecule. The modified ends may promote the export of mRNA from the nucleus and help protect the mRNA from degradation. When the mRNA reaches the cytoplasm, the modified ends, in conjunction with certain cytoplasmic proteins, facilitate ribosome attachment. The 5′ cap and poly-A tail are not translated into protein, nor are the regions called the 5′ untranslated region (5′ UTR) and 3′ untranslated region (3′ UTR).

Split Genes and RNA Splicing

The most remarkable stage of RNA processing in the eukaryotic nucleus is the removal of a large portion of the RNA molecule that is initially synthesized—a cut-and-paste job called **RNA splicing (Figure 17.10)**. The average length of a transcription unit along a eukaryotic DNA molecule is about 8,000 nucleotides, so the primary RNA transcript is also that long. But it takes only about 1,200 nucleotides to code for an average-sized protein of 400 amino acids. (Remember, each amino acid is encoded by a *triplet* of nucleotides.) This means that most eukaryotic genes and their RNA transcripts have long noncoding stretches of nucleotides, regions that are not translated. Even more surprising is that most of these noncoding sequences are interspersed between coding segments of the gene and thus between coding segments of the pre-mRNA. In other words, the sequence of DNA nucleotides that codes for a eukaryotic polypeptide is usually not continuous; it is split into segments. The noncoding segments of nucleic acid that lie between coding regions are called intervening sequences, or **introns** for short. The other regions are called **exons**, because they are eventually expressed, usually by being translated into amino acid sequences. (Exceptions include the UTRs of the exons at the ends of the RNA, which make up part of the mRNA but are not translated into protein. Because of these exceptions, you may find it helpful to think of exons as sequences of RNA that *exit* the nucleus.) The terms *intron* and *exon* are used for both RNA sequences and the DNA sequences that encode them.

In making a primary transcript from a gene, RNA polymerase II transcribes both introns and exons from the DNA, but the mRNA molecule that enters the cytoplasm is an abridged version. The introns are cut out from the molecule and the exons joined together, forming an mRNA molecule with a continuous coding sequence. This is the process of RNA splicing.

How is pre-mRNA splicing carried out? Researchers have learned that the signal for RNA splicing is a short nucleotide sequence at each end of an intron. Particles called *small nuclear ribonucleoproteins,* abbreviated *snRNPs* (pronounced "snurps"), recognize these splice sites. As the name implies, snRNPs are located in the cell nucleus and are composed of RNA and protein molecules. The RNA in a snRNP particle is called a *small nuclear RNA (snRNA);* each molecule is about 150 nucleotides long. Several different snRNPs join with additional proteins to form an even larger assembly called a **spliceosome,** which is almost as big as a ribosome. The spliceosome interacts with certain sites along an intron, releasing the intron and joining together the two exons that flanked the intron **(Figure 17.11)**. There is strong evidence that snRNAs play a major role in these catalytic processes, as well as in spliceosome assembly and splice site recognition.

Ribozymes

The idea of a catalytic role for snRNA arose from the discovery of **ribozymes**, RNA molecules that function as enzymes. In some organisms, RNA splicing can occur without proteins or additional RNA molecules: The intron RNA functions as a ribozyme and catalyzes its own excision! For example, in the protozoan *Tetrahymena,* self-splicing occurs in the production of ribosomal RNA (rRNA), a component of the organism's ribosomes. The pre-rRNA actually removes its own introns.

The fact that RNA is single-stranded plays an important role in allowing certain RNA molecules to function as ribozymes. A region of an RNA molecule may base-pair with a complementary region elsewhere in the same molecule, thus imparting specific structure to the RNA molecule as a whole. Also, some of the bases contain functional groups that may participate in catalysis. Just as the specific shape of an enzymatic protein and the functional groups on its amino acid side chains allow the protein to function as a catalyst, the structure of some RNA molecules allows them to function as catalysts, too. The discovery of ribozymes rendered obsolete the belief that all biological catalysts were proteins.

▲ **Figure 17.10 RNA processing: RNA splicing.** The RNA molecule shown here codes for β-globin, one of the polypeptides of hemoglobin. The numbers under the RNA refer to codons; β-globin is 146 amino acids long. The β-globin gene and its pre-mRNA transcript have three exons, corresponding to sequences that will leave the nucleus as mRNA. (The 5′ UTR and 3′ UTR are parts of exons because they are included in the mRNA; however, they do not code for protein.) During RNA processing, the introns are cut out and the exons spliced together.

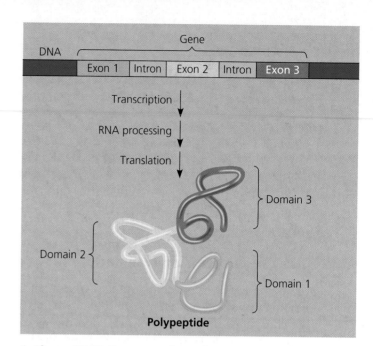

▲ **Figure 17.12 Correspondence between exons and protein domains.** In a large number of genes, different exons encode separate domains of the protein product.

▲ **Figure 17.11 The roles of snRNPs and spliceosomes in pre-mRNA splicing.** The diagram shows only a portion of the pre-mRNA transcript; additional introns and exons lie downstream from the ones pictured here. ❶ Small nuclear ribonucleoproteins (snRNPs) and other proteins form a molecular complex called a spliceosome on a pre-mRNA containing exons and introns. ❷ Within the spliceosome, snRNA base-pairs with nucleotides at specific sites along the intron. ❸ The RNA transcript is cut, releasing the intron and at the same time splicing the exons together. The spliceosome then comes apart, releasing spliced mRNA, which now contains only exons.

The Functional and Evolutionary Importance of Introns

What are the biological functions of introns and RNA splicing? One idea is that introns play regulatory roles in the cell; at least some introns contain sequences that control gene activity in some way. And the splicing process itself is necessary for the passage of mRNA from the nucleus to the cytoplasm.

One established benefit of the presence of exons and introns in genes is to enable a single gene to encode more than one kind of polypeptide. A number of genes are known to give rise to two or more different polypeptides, depending on which segments are treated as exons during RNA processing; this is called **alternative RNA splicing** (see Figure 19.8). For example, sex differences in fruit flies are largely due to differences in how males and females splice the RNA transcribed from certain genes. Early results from the Human Genome Project (discussed in Chapter 20) suggest that alternative RNA splicing may be one reason humans can get along with a

relatively small number of genes—not quite twice as many as a fruit fly. Because of alternative splicing, the number of different protein products an organism can produce is much greater than its number of genes.

Proteins often have a modular architecture consisting of discrete structural and functional regions called **domains.** One domain of an enzymatic protein, for instance, might include the active site, while another might attach the protein to a cellular membrane. In many cases, different exons code for the different domains of a protein **(Figure 17.12).** The presence of introns in a gene may facilitate the evolution of new and potentially useful proteins as a result of a process known as *exon shuffling.* Introns increase the probability of potentially beneficial crossing over between the exons of alleles—simply by providing more terrain for crossovers without interrupting coding sequences. We can also imagine the occasional mixing and matching of exons between completely different (nonallelic) genes. Exon shuffling of either sort could lead to new proteins with novel combinations of functions. While most of the shuffling would result in nonbeneficial changes, occasionally a beneficial variant might arise.

Concept Check 17.3

1. How does alteration of the 5' and 3' ends of pre-mRNA affect the mRNA that exits the nucleus?
2. Describe the role of snRNPs in RNA splicing.
3. How can alternative RNA splicing generate a greater number of polypeptide products than there are genes?

For suggested answers, see Appendix A.

Translation is the RNA-directed synthesis of a polypeptide: *a closer look*

We will now examine in greater detail how genetic information flows from mRNA to protein—the process of translation. As we did for transcription, we'll concentrate on the basic steps of translation that occur in both prokaryotes and eukaryotes while pointing out key differences.

Molecular Components of Translation

In the process of translation, a cell interprets a genetic message and builds a polypeptide accordingly. The message is a series of codons along an mRNA molecule, and the interpreter is called **transfer RNA (tRNA).** The function of tRNA is to transfer amino acids from the cytoplasmic pool of amino acids to a ribosome. A cell keeps its cytoplasm stocked with all 20 amino acids, either by synthesizing them from other compounds or by taking them up from the surrounding solution. The ribosome adds each amino acid brought to it by tRNA to the growing end of a polypeptide chain **(Figure 17.13).**

Molecules of tRNA are not all identical. The key to translating a genetic message into a specific amino acid sequence is that each type of tRNA molecule translates a particular mRNA codon into a particular amino acid. As a tRNA molecule arrives at a ribosome, it bears a specific amino acid at one end. At the other end of the tRNA is a nucleotide triplet called an **anticodon,** which base-pairs with a complementary codon on mRNA. For example, consider the mRNA codon UUU, which is translated as the amino acid phenylalanine. The tRNA that base-pairs with this codon by hydrogen bonding has AAA as its anticodon and carries phenylalanine at its other end (see the middle tRNA in Figure 17.13). As an mRNA molecule is moved through a ribosome, phenylalanine will be added to the polypeptide chain whenever the codon UUU is presented for translation. Codon by codon, the genetic message is translated as tRNAs deposit amino acids in the order prescribed, and the ribosome joins the amino acids into a chain. The tRNA molecule is a translator because it can read a nucleic acid word (the mRNA codon) and interpret it as a protein word (the amino acid).

Translation is simple in principle but complex in its biochemistry and mechanics, especially in the eukaryotic cell. In dissecting translation, we'll concentrate on the slightly less complicated version of the process that occurs in prokaryotes. Let's first look at some of the major players in this cellular drama, then see how they act together to make a polypeptide.

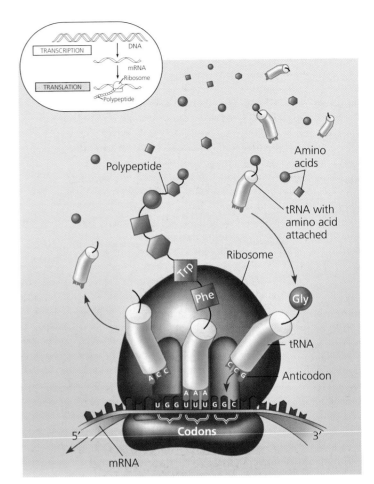

▲ **Figure 17.13 Translation: the basic concept.** As a molecule of mRNA is moved through a ribosome, codons are translated into amino acids, one by one. The interpreters are tRNA molecules, each type with a specific anticodon at one end and a corresponding amino acid at the other end. A tRNA adds its amino acid cargo to a growing polypeptide chain when the anticodon bonds to a complementary codon on the mRNA. The figures that follow show some of the details of translation in the prokaryotic cell.

The Structure and Function of Transfer RNA

Like mRNA and other types of cellular RNA, transfer RNA molecules are transcribed from DNA templates. In a eukaryotic cell, tRNA, like mRNA, is made in the nucleus and must travel from the nucleus to the cytoplasm, where translation occurs. In both prokaryotic and eukaryotic cells, each tRNA molecule is used repeatedly, picking up its designated amino acid in the cytosol, depositing this cargo at the ribosome, and then leaving the ribosome to pick up another amino acid.

As illustrated in **Figure 17.14,** a tRNA molecule consists of a single RNA strand that is only about 80 nucleotides long (compared to hundreds of nucleotides for most mRNA molecules). Because of the presence of complementary stretches of bases that can hydrogen-bond to each other, this single strand can fold back upon itself, forming a molecule with a three-dimensional structure. Flattened into one plane to reveal this base pairing, a tRNA molecule looks like a cloverleaf **(Figure 17.14a).** The tRNA actually twists and folds into a

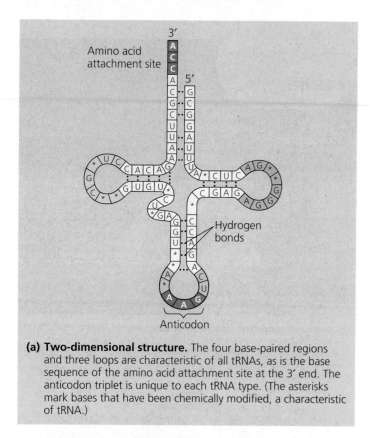

(a) **Two-dimensional structure.** The four base-paired regions and three loops are characteristic of all tRNAs, as is the base sequence of the amino acid attachment site at the 3′ end. The anticodon triplet is unique to each tRNA type. (The asterisks mark bases that have been chemically modified, a characteristic of tRNA.)

(b) **Three-dimensional structure**

(c) **Symbol** used in this book

▲ **Figure 17.14 The structure of transfer RNA (tRNA).** Anticodons are conventionally written 3′ → 5′ to align properly with codons written 5′ → 3′ (see Figure 17.13). For base pairing, RNA strands must be antiparallel, like DNA. For example, anticodon 3′-AAG-5′ pairs with mRNA codon 5′-UUC-3′.

compact three-dimensional structure that is roughly L-shaped **(Figure 17.14b)**. The loop protruding from one end of the L includes the anticodon, the special base triplet that binds to a specific mRNA codon. From the other end of the L-shaped tRNA molecule protrudes its 3′ end, which is the attachment site for an amino acid. Thus, the structure of a tRNA molecule fits its function.

▲ **Figure 17.15 An aminoacyl-tRNA synthetase joins a specific amino acid to a tRNA.** Linkage of the tRNA and amino acid is an endergonic process that occurs at the expense of ATP. The ATP loses two phosphate groups, becoming AMP (adenosine monophosphate).

The accurate translation of a genetic message requires two recognition steps. First, there must be a correct match between a tRNA and an amino acid. A tRNA that binds to an mRNA codon specifying a particular amino acid must carry *only* that amino acid to the ribosome. Each amino acid is joined to the correct tRNA by a specific enzyme called an **aminoacyl-tRNA synthetase (Figure 17.15)**. The active site of each type of aminoacyl-tRNA synthetase fits only a specific combination of amino acid and tRNA. There are 20 different synthetases, one for each amino acid; each synthetase is able to bind all the different tRNAs that code for its specific amino acid. The synthetase catalyzes the covalent attachment of the amino acid to its tRNA in a process driven by the hydrolysis of ATP. The resulting aminoacyl tRNA, also called an activated amino acid, is released from the enzyme and delivers its amino acid to a growing polypeptide chain on a ribosome.

The second recognition step involves a correct match between the tRNA anticodon and an mRNA codon. If one tRNA variety existed for each of the mRNA codons that specifies an amino acid, there would be 61 tRNAs (see Figure 17.5). In fact, there are only about 45, signifying that some tRNAs must be able to bind to more than one codon. Such versatility is possible because the rules for base pairing between the third base of a codon and the corresponding base of a tRNA anticodon are not as strict as those for DNA and mRNA codons. For example, the base U at the 5′ end of a tRNA anticodon can pair with either A or G in the third position (at the 3′ end) of an mRNA codon. This relaxation of the base-pairing rules is called **wobble**. Wobble explains why the synonymous codons for a given amino acid can differ in their third base, but usually not in their other bases.

Ribosomes

Ribosomes facilitate the specific coupling of tRNA anticodons with mRNA codons during protein synthesis. A ribosome, which is large enough to be seen with an electron microscope, is made up of two subunits, called the large and small subunits **(Figure 17.16)**. The ribosomal subunits are constructed of proteins and RNA molecules named **ribosomal RNA, or rRNA.** In eukaryotes, the subunits are made in the nucleolus. Ribosomal RNA genes on the chromosomal DNA are transcribed, and the RNA is processed and assembled with proteins imported from the cytoplasm. The resulting ribosomal subunits are then exported via nuclear pores to the cytoplasm. In both prokaryotes and eukaryotes, large and small subunits join to form a functional ribosome only when they attach to an mRNA molecule. About two-thirds of the mass of a ribosome is rRNA. Because most cells contain thousands of ribosomes, rRNA is the most abundant type of RNA.

Although the ribosomes of prokaryotes and eukaryotes are very similar in structure and function, those of eukaryotes are slightly larger and differ somewhat from prokaryotic ribosomes in their molecular composition. The differences are medically significant. Certain antibiotic drugs can inactivate prokaryotic ribosomes without inhibiting the ability of eukaryotic ribosomes to make proteins. These drugs, including tetracycline and streptomycin, are used to combat bacterial infections.

The structure of a ribosome reflects its function of bringing mRNA together with amino acid-bearing tRNAs. In addition to a binding site for mRNA, each ribosome has three binding sites for tRNA (see Figure 17.16). The **P site** (peptidyl-tRNA site) holds the tRNA carrying the growing polypeptide chain, while the **A site** (aminoacyl-tRNA site) holds the tRNA carrying the next amino acid to be added to the chain. Discharged tRNAs leave the ribosome from the **E site** (exit site). The ribosome holds the tRNA and mRNA in close proximity and

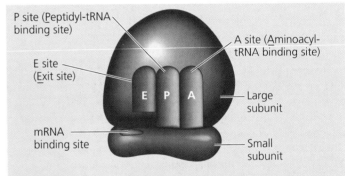

(a) **Computer model of functioning ribosome.** This is a model of a bacterial ribosome, showing its overall shape. The eukaryotic ribosome is roughly similar. A ribosomal subunit is an aggregate of ribosomal RNA molecules and proteins.

(b) **Schematic model showing binding sites.** A ribosome has an mRNA binding site and three tRNA binding sites, known as the A, P, and E sites. This schematic ribosome will appear in later diagrams.

(c) **Schematic model with mRNA and tRNA.** A tRNA fits into a binding site when its anticodon base-pairs with an mRNA codon. The P site holds the tRNA attached to the growing polypeptide. The A site holds the tRNA carrying the next amino acid to be added to the polypeptide chain. Discharged tRNA leaves from the E site.

▲ **Figure 17.16 The anatomy of a functioning ribosome.**

positions the new amino acid for addition to the carboxyl end of the growing polypeptide. It then catalyzes the formation of the peptide bond. As the polypeptide becomes longer, it passes through an *exit tunnel* in the ribosome's large subunit. When the polypeptide is complete, it is released to the cytosol through the exit tunnel.

Four decades of genetic and biochemical research on ribosome structure have culminated in the detailed structure of the bacterial ribosome, which appears as a ribbon model in Figure 17.1. Recent research strongly supports the hypothesis that rRNA, not protein, is primarily responsible for both structure and function of the ribosome. The proteins, which are largely on the exterior, support the conformational changes of the rRNA molecules as they carry out catalysis during translation. RNA is the main constituent of the interface between the two subunits and of the A and P sites, and it is the catalyst of peptide bond formation. Thus, a ribosome can be regarded as one colossal ribozyme!

Building a Polypeptide

We can divide translation, the synthesis of a polypeptide chain, into three stages (analogous to those of transcription): initiation, elongation, and termination. All three stages require protein "factors" that aid mRNA, tRNA, and ribosomes in the translation process. For certain aspects of chain initiation and elongation, energy is also required. It is provided by the hydrolysis of GTP (guanosine triphosphate), a molecule closely related to ATP.

Ribosome Association and Initiation of Translation

The initiation stage of translation brings together mRNA, a tRNA bearing the first amino acid of the polypeptide, and the two subunits of a ribosome (**Figure 17.17**). First, a small ribosomal subunit binds to both mRNA and a specific initiator tRNA, which carries the amino acid methionine. The small subunit then moves, or *scans*, downstream along the mRNA until it reaches the start codon, AUG, which signals the start of translation; this is important because it establishes the codon reading frame for the mRNA. The initiator tRNA, already associated with the complex, then hydrogen-bonds with the start codon.

The union of mRNA, initiator tRNA, and a small ribosomal subunit is followed by the attachment of a large ribosomal subunit, completing a translation initiation

complex. Proteins called *initiation factors* are required to bring all these components together. The cell also spends energy in the form of a GTP molecule to form the initiation complex. At the completion of the initiation process, the initiator tRNA sits in the P site of the ribosome, and the vacant A site is ready for the next aminoacyl tRNA. Note that a polypeptide is always synthesized in one direction, from the initial methionine at the amino end, also called the N-terminus, toward the final amino acid at the carboxyl end, also called the C-terminus (see Figure 5.18).

Elongation of the Polypeptide Chain

In the elongation stage of translation, amino acids are added one by one to the preceding amino acid. Each addition involves the participation of several proteins called *elongation factors* and occurs in a three-step cycle described in **Figure 17.18** on the next page. Energy expenditure occurs in the first and third steps. Codon recognition requires hydrolysis of two molecules of GTP, which increases the accuracy and efficiency of this step. One more GTP is hydrolyzed to provide energy for the translocation step.

The mRNA is moved through the ribosome in one direction only, 5′ end first; this is equivalent to the ribosome moving 5′ → 3′ on the mRNA. The important point is that the ribosome and the mRNA move relative to each other, unidirectionally, codon by codon. The elongation cycle takes less than a tenth of a second in prokaryotes and is repeated as each amino acid is added to the chain until the polypeptide is completed.

1 A small ribosomal subunit binds to a molecule of mRNA. In a prokaryotic cell, the mRNA binding site on this subunit recognizes a specific nucleotide sequence on the mRNA just upstream of the start codon. An initiator tRNA, with the anticodon UAC, base-pairs with the start codon, AUG. This tRNA carries the amino acid methionine (Met).

2 The arrival of a large ribosomal subunit completes the initiation complex. Proteins called initiation factors (not shown) are required to bring all the translation components together. GTP provides the energy for the assembly. The initiator tRNA is in the P site; the A site is available to the tRNA bearing the next amino acid.

▲ Figure 17.17 **The initiation of translation.**

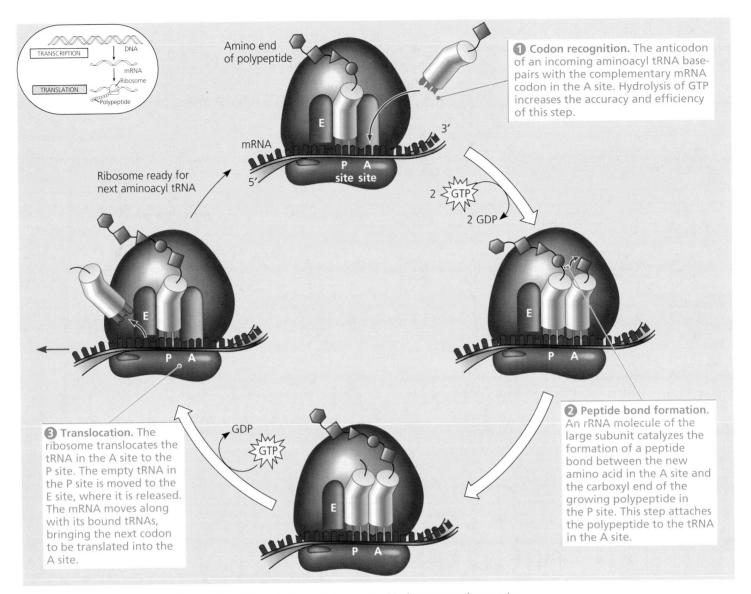

Amino end of polypeptide

mRNA

E P A
site site

Ribosome ready for next aminoacyl tRNA

3'
5'

1 Codon recognition. The anticodon of an incoming aminoacyl tRNA base-pairs with the complementary mRNA codon in the A site. Hydrolysis of GTP increases the accuracy and efficiency of this step.

2 GTP
2 GDP

E P A

2 Peptide bond formation. An rRNA molecule of the large subunit catalyzes the formation of a peptide bond between the new amino acid in the A site and the carboxyl end of the growing polypeptide in the P site. This step attaches the polypeptide to the tRNA in the A site.

3 Translocation. The ribosome translocates the tRNA in the A site to the P site. The empty tRNA in the P site is moved to the E site, where it is released. The mRNA moves along with its bound tRNAs, bringing the next codon to be translated into the A site.

GDP
GTP

E P A

▲ **Figure 17.18 The elongation cycle of translation.** Not shown in this diagram are the proteins called elongation factors. The hydrolysis of GTP plays an important role in the elongation process.

Termination of Translation

The final stage of translation is termination **(Figure 17.19)**. Elongation continues until a stop codon in the mRNA reaches the A site of the ribosome. The base triplets UAG, UAA, and UGA do not code for amino acids but instead act as signals to stop translation. A protein called a *release factor* binds directly to the stop codon in the A site. The release factor causes the addition of a water molecule instead of an amino acid to the polypeptide chain. This reaction hydrolyzes the completed polypeptide from the tRNA in the P site, releasing the polypeptide through the exit tunnel of the ribosome's large subunit (see Figure 17.16a). The remainder of the translation assembly then comes apart.

Polyribosomes

A single ribosome can make an average-sized polypeptide in less than a minute. Typically, however, a single mRNA is used to make many copies of a polypeptide simultaneously because several ribosomes can translate the message from one mRNA at the same time. Once a ribosome moves past the start codon, a second ribosome can attach to the mRNA; thus, a number of ribosomes may trail along one mRNA. Such strings of ribosomes, called **polyribosomes** (or **polysomes**), can be seen with an electron microscope **(Figure 17.20)**. Polyribosomes are found in both prokaryotic and eukaryotic cells. They enable a cell to make many copies of a polypeptide very quickly.

Completing and Targeting the Functional Protein

The process of translation is often not sufficient to make a functional protein. In this section, you will learn about modifications that polypeptide chains undergo after the translation process as well as some of the mechanisms used to target completed proteins to specific sites in the cell.

① When a ribosome reaches a stop codon on mRNA, the A site of the ribosome accepts a protein called a release factor instead of tRNA.

Release factor

Stop codon (UAG, UAA, or UGA)

② The release factor hydrolyzes the bond between the tRNA in the P site and the last amino acid of the polypeptide chain. The polypeptide is thus freed from the ribosome.

Free polypeptide

③ The two ribosomal subunits and the other components of the assembly dissociate.

▲ Figure 17.19 **The termination of translation.**

Protein Folding and Post-Translational Modifications 修改

During its synthesis, a polypeptide chain begins to coil and fold spontaneously, forming a functional protein of specific conformation: a three-dimensional molecule with secondary and tertiary structure (see Figure 5.20). A gene determines primary structure, and primary structure in turn determines conformation. In many cases, a chaperone protein (chaperonin) helps the polypeptide fold correctly (see Figure 5.23).

Additional steps—*post-translational modifications*—may be required before the protein can begin doing its particular job in the cell. Certain amino acids may be chemically modified by the attachment of sugars, lipids, phosphate groups, or other additions. Enzymes may remove one or more amino acids from the leading (amino) end of the polypeptide chain. In some cases, a single polypeptide chain may be enzymatically cleaved into two or more pieces. For example, the protein insulin is first synthesized as a single polypeptide chain but becomes active only after an enzyme cuts out a central part of the chain, leaving a protein made up of two polypeptide chains connected by disulfide bridges. In other cases, two or more polypeptides that are synthesized separately may come together, becoming the subunits of a protein that has quaternary structure.

Targeting Polypeptides to Specific Locations

In electron micrographs of eukaryotic cells active in protein synthesis, two populations of ribosomes (and polyribosomes) are evident: free and bound (see Figure 6.11). Free ribosomes are suspended in the cytosol and mostly synthesize proteins that dissolve in the cytosol and function there. In contrast, bound ribosomes are attached to the cytosolic side of the endoplasmic reticulum (ER), or to the nuclear envelope. Bound

ribosomes make proteins of the endomembrane system (the nuclear envelope, ER, Golgi apparatus, lysosomes, vacuoles, and plasma membrane) as well as proteins secreted from the cell, such as insulin. The ribosomes themselves are identical and can switch their status from free to bound.

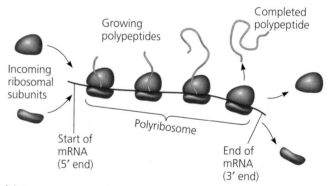

(a) An mRNA molecule is generally translated simultaneously by several ribosomes in clusters called polyribosomes.

(b) This micrograph shows a large polyribosome in a prokaryotic cell (TEM).

▲ Figure 17.20 **Polyribosomes.**

What determines whether a ribosome will be free in the cytosol or bound to rough ER at any particular time? Polypeptide synthesis always begins in the cytosol, when a free ribosome starts to translate an mRNA molecule. There the process continues to completion—*unless* the growing polypeptide itself cues the ribosome to attach to the ER. The polypeptides of proteins destined for the endomembrane system or for secretion are marked by a **signal peptide**, which targets the protein to the ER (**Figure 17.21**). The signal peptide, a sequence of about 20 amino acids at or near the leading (amino) end of the polypeptide, is recognized as it emerges from the ribosome by a protein-RNA complex called a **signal-recognition particle (SRP)**. This particle functions as an adapter that brings the ribosome to a receptor protein built into the ER membrane. This receptor is part of a multiprotein translocation complex. Polypeptide synthesis continues there, and the growing polypeptide snakes across the membrane into the ER lumen via a protein pore. The signal peptide is usually removed by an enzyme. The rest of the completed polypeptide, if it is to be a secretory protein, is released into solution within the ER lumen (as in Figure 17.21). Alternatively, if the polypeptide is to be a membrane protein, it remains partially embedded in the ER membrane.

Other kinds of signal peptides are used to target polypeptides to mitochondria, chloroplasts, the interior of the nucleus, and other organelles that are not part of the endomembrane system. The critical difference in these cases is that translation is completed in the cytosol before the polypeptide is imported into the organelle. The mechanisms of translocation also vary, but in all cases studied to date, the "zip codes" that address proteins for secretion or to cellular locations are signal peptides of some sort. Prokaryotes also employ signal sequences to target proteins for secretion.

Concept Check 17.4

1. Which two processes ensure that the correct amino acid is added to a growing polypeptide chain?
2. Describe how the formation of polyribosomes can benefit the cell.
3. Describe how a polypeptide to be secreted is transported to the endomembrane system.

For suggested answers, see Appendix A.

1 Polypeptide synthesis begins on a free ribosome in the cytosol.

2 An SRP binds to the signal peptide, halting synthesis momentarily.

3 The SRP binds to a receptor protein in the ER membrane. This receptor is part of a protein complex (a translocation complex) that has a membrane pore and a signal-cleaving enzyme.

4 The SRP leaves, and the polypeptide resumes growing, meanwhile translocating across the membrane. (The signal peptide stays attached to the membrane.)

5 The signal-cleaving enzyme cuts off the signal peptide.

6 The rest of the completed polypeptide leaves the ribosome and folds into its final conformation.

Ribosome
mRNA
Signal peptide
Signal-recognition particle (SRP)
SRP receptor protein
CYTOSOL
Translocation complex
ER LUMEN
Signal peptide removed
ER membrane
Protein

▲ **Figure 17.21 The signal mechanism for targeting proteins to the ER.** A polypeptide destined for the endomembrane system or for secretion from the cell begins with a signal peptide, a series of amino acids that targets it for the ER. This figure shows the synthesis of a secretory protein and its simultaneous import into the ER. In the ER and then in the Golgi, the protein is further processed. Finally, a transport vesicle conveys it to the plasma membrane for release from the cell (see Figure 7.9).

RNA plays multiple roles in the cell: *a review*

As we have seen, the cellular machinery of protein synthesis (and ER targeting) is dominated by RNA of various kinds. In addition to mRNA, these include tRNA, rRNA, and, in eukaryotes, snRNA and SRP RNA **(Table 17.1)**. A type of RNA called *small nucleolar RNA (snoRNA)* aids in processing pre-rRNA transcripts in the nucleolus, a process necessary for ribosome formation. The diverse functions of these small RNA molecules range from structural to informational to catalytic. Recent research has also revealed the presence of small, single- and double-stranded RNA molecules that play unexpectedly important roles in regulating which genes get expressed. These types of RNA are called *small interfering RNA (siRNA)* and *microRNA (miRNA)* (see Chapter 19).

The ability of RNA to perform so many different functions is based on three properties. First, RNA can hydrogen-bond to other nucleic acid molecules (DNA or RNA). Second, it can assume a specific three-dimensional shape by forming hydrogen bonds between bases in different parts of its own polynucleotide chain (as seen in tRNA; see Figure 17.14). Third, it has functional groups that allow it to act as a catalyst (ribozyme). These three properties make RNA quite multifunctional.

DNA may be the genetic material of all living cells, but RNA is much more versatile. You will learn in Chapter 18 that many viruses use RNA rather than DNA as their genetic material. In the past few years, scientists have begun to appreciate the diverse functions carried out by RNA molecules. In fact, the journal *Science* bestowed its 2002 "Breakthrough of the Year" award on the discovery of the small regulatory RNA molecules siRNA and miRNA.

Concept Check 17.5

1. Describe three properties of RNA that allow it to perform diverse roles in the cell.

For suggested answers, see Appendix A.

Comparing gene expression in prokaryotes and eukaryotes reveals key differences

Although prokaryotes and eukaryotes carry out transcription and translation in very similar ways, we have noted certain differences in cellular machinery and in details of the processes. Prokaryotic and eukaryotic RNA polymerases are different, and those of eukaryotes depend on a complex set of transcription factors. Transcription is terminated differently in the two kinds of cells. Also, prokaryotic and eukaryotic ribosomes are slightly different. The most important differences, however, arise from the eukaryotic cell's compartmental organization. Like a one-room workshop, a prokaryotic cell ensures a streamlined operation. In the absence of a nucleus, it can simultaneously transcribe and translate the same gene (**Figure 17.22**, on the next page), and the newly made protein can quickly diffuse to its site of function. In contrast, the eukaryotic cell's nuclear envelope segregates transcription from translation and provides a compartment for extensive RNA processing. This processing stage provides additional steps whose regulation can help coordinate the eukaryotic cell's elaborate activities (see Chapter 19). Finally, eukaryotic cells have complicated mechanisms for targeting proteins to the appropriate cellular compartment (organelle).

Where did eukaryotes and prokaryotes get the genes that encode the huge diversity of proteins they synthesize? For the past few billion years, the ultimate source of new genes has been the mutation of preexisting genes, the topic of the next section.

Table 17.1 Types of RNA in a Eukaryotic Cell	
Type of RNA	**Functions**
Messenger RNA (mRNA)	Carries information specifying amino acid sequences of proteins from DNA to ribosomes.
Transfer RNA (tRNA)	Serves as adapter molecule in protein synthesis; translates mRNA codons into amino acids.
Ribosomal RNA (rRNA)	Plays catalytic (ribozyme) roles and structural roles in ribosomes.
Primary transcript	Serves as a precursor to mRNA, rRNA, or tRNA, before being processed by splicing or cleavage. Some intron RNA acts as a ribozyme, catalyzing its own splicing.
Small nuclear RNA (snRNA)	Plays structural and catalytic roles in spliceosomes, the complexes of protein and RNA that splice pre-mRNA.
SRP RNA	Is a component of the signal-recognition particle (SRP), the protein-RNA complex that recognizes the signal peptides of polypeptides targeted to the ER.
Small nucleolar RNA (snoRNA)	Aids in processing of pre-rRNA transcripts for ribosome subunit formation in the nucleolus.
Small interfering RNA (siRNA) and microRNA (miRNA)	Are involved in regulation of gene expression.

RNA polymerase

DNA

Polyribosome

mRNA

Direction of transcription →

0.25 μm

RNA polymerase

DNA

Polyribosome

Polypeptide (amino end)

Ribosome

mRNA (5′ end)

▲ **Figure 17.22 Coupled transcription and translation in bacteria.** In prokaryotic cells, the translation of mRNA can begin as soon as the leading (5′) end of the mRNA molecule peels away from the DNA template. The micrograph (TEM) shows a strand of *E. coli* DNA being transcribed by RNA polymerase molecules. Attached to each RNA polymerase molecule is a growing strand of mRNA, which is already being translated by ribosomes. The newly synthesized polypeptides are not visible in the micrograph but are shown in the diagram.

Concept Check 17.6

1. In Figure 17.22, number the RNA polymerases in order of their initiation of transcription. Then number each mRNA's ribosomes in order of their initiation of translation.
2. Would the arrangement shown in Figure 17.22 be found in a eukaryotic cell? Explain.

For suggested answers, see Appendix A.

Concept 17.7

Point mutations can affect protein structure and function

Mutations are changes in the genetic material of a cell (or virus). In Figure 15.14, we considered large-scale mutations, chromosomal rearrangements that affect long segments of DNA. Now we can examine **point mutations**, chemical changes in just one base pair of a gene.

If a point mutation occurs in a gamete or in a cell that gives rise to gametes, it may be transmitted to offspring and to a succession of future generations. If the mutation has an adverse ef-

fect on the phenotype of an organism, the mutant condition is referred to as a genetic disorder, or hereditary disease. For example, we can trace the genetic basis of sickle-cell disease to a mutation of a single base pair in the gene that codes for one of the polypeptides of hemoglobin. The change of a single nucleotide in the DNA's template strand leads to the production of an abnormal protein (**Figure 17.23**, and see Figure 5.21). In individuals who are homozygous for the mutant allele, the sickling of red blood cells caused by the altered hemoglobin produces the multiple symptoms associated with sickle-cell disease (see Chapter 14). Let's see how different types of point mutations translate into altered proteins.

Types of Point Mutations

Point mutations within a gene can be divided into two general categories: base-pair substitutions and base-pair insertions or deletions. While reading about how these mutations affect proteins, refer to **Figures 17.24** and **17.25**, on the next two pages.

Substitutions

A **base-pair substitution** is the replacement of one nucleotide and its partner with another pair of nucleotides. Some substitutions are called *silent mutations* because, owing to the redundancy of the genetic code, they have no effect on the encoded protein. In other words, a change in a base pair may transform one codon into another that is translated into the same amino acid. For example, if 3′-CCG-5′ on the template strand mutated to 3′-CCA-5′, the mRNA codon that used to be GGC would become GGU, and a glycine would still be inserted at the proper location in the protein (see Figure 17.5). Other substitutions may change an amino acid but have little effect on the protein. The new amino acid may have properties similar to those of the amino acid it replaces, or it may be in a region of the protein where the exact sequence of amino acids is not essential to the protein's function.

However, the base-pair substitutions of greatest interest are those that cause a readily detectable change in a protein. The alteration of a single amino acid in a crucial area of a protein—in the active site of an enzyme, for example—will significantly alter protein activity. Occasionally, such a mutation leads to an improved protein or one with novel capabilities, but much more often such mutations are detrimental, leading to a useless or less active protein that impairs cellular function.

Substitution mutations are usually **missense mutations**; that is, the altered codon still codes for an amino acid and thus makes sense, although not necessarily the *right* sense. But a point mutation can also change a codon for an amino acid into a stop codon. This is called a **nonsense mutation,** and it causes translation to be terminated prematurely; the resulting polypeptide will be shorter than the polypeptide encoded by the normal gene (see Figure 17.24). Nearly all nonsense mutations lead to nonfunctional proteins.

► **Figure 17.23 The molecular basis of sickle-cell disease: a point mutation.** The allele that causes sickle-cell disease differs from the wild-type (normal) allele by a single DNA base pair.

Wild-type hemoglobin DNA

Mutant hemoglobin DNA

In the DNA, the mutant template strand has an A where the wild-type template has a T.

mRNA

mRNA

The mutant mRNA has a U instead of an A in one codon.

Normal hemoglobin — Glu

Sickle-cell hemoglobin — Val

The mutant (sickle-cell) hemoglobin has a valine (Val) instead of a glutamic acid (Glu).

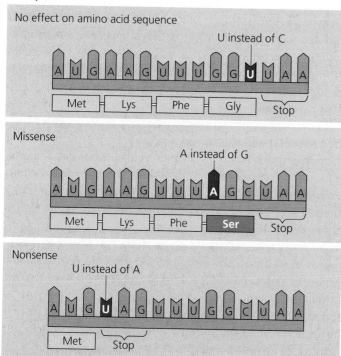

Wild type

mRNA 5′ — A U G A A G U U U G G C U A A — 3′

Protein — Met — Lys — Phe — Gly — Stop

Amino end

Carboxyl end

Base-pair substitution

No effect on amino acid sequence

U instead of C

A U G A A G U U U G G U U A A

Met — Lys — Phe — Gly — Stop

Missense

A instead of G

A U G A A G U U U A G C U A A

Met — Lys — Phe — Ser — Stop

Nonsense

U instead of A

A U G U A G U U U G G C U A A

Met — Stop

▲ **Figure 17.24 Base-pair substitution.** Mutations are changes in DNA, but they are represented here as they are reflected in mRNA and its protein product. Base-pair substitutions may lead to silent, missense, or nonsense mutations.

Insertions and Deletions

Insertions and **deletions** are additions or losses of nucleotide pairs in a gene. These mutations have a disastrous effect on the resulting protein more often than substitutions do. Because mRNA is read as a series of nucleotide triplets during translation, the insertion or deletion of nucleotides may alter the reading frame (triplet grouping) of the genetic message. Such a mutation, called a **frameshift mutation,** will occur whenever the number of nucleotides inserted or deleted is not a multiple of three (see Figure 17.25, on the next page). All the nucleotides that are downstream of the deletion or insertion will be improperly grouped into codons, and the result will be extensive missense probably ending sooner or later in nonsense and premature termination. Unless the frameshift is very near the end of the gene, it will produce a protein that is almost certain to be nonfunctional.

Mutagens

Mutations can arise in a number of ways. Errors during DNA replication, repair, or recombination can lead to base-pair substitutions, insertions, or deletions, as well as to mutations affecting longer stretches of DNA. Mutations resulting from such errors are called *spontaneous mutations*. It is difficult to calculate the rate at which such mutations occur. Rough estimates have been made of the rate of mutation during DNA replication for both *E. coli* and eukaryotes, and the numbers are similar: About 1 nucleotide in every 10^{10} is altered and passed on to the next generation of cells.

A number of physical and chemical agents, called **mutagens,** interact with DNA in ways that cause mutations. In the 1920s, Hermann Muller discovered that X-rays caused genetic changes in fruit flies. With X-rays, he was able to make *Drosophila* mutants that he could use in his genetic studies. But he also recognized an alarming implication of his discovery: X-rays and other forms of high-energy radiation pose hazards to the genetic material of people as well as laboratory

Wild type

Base-pair insertion or deletion

▲ **Figure 17.25 Base-pair insertion or deletion.** Strictly speaking, the example at the bottom is not a point mutation because it involves insertion or deletion of more than one nucleotide.

organisms. Mutagenic radiation, a physical mutagen, includes ultraviolet (UV) light, which can cause disruptive thymine dimers in DNA (see Figure 16.17).

Chemical mutagens fall into several categories. Base analogs are chemicals that are similar to normal DNA bases but that pair incorrectly during DNA replication. Some other chemical mutagens interfere with correct DNA replication by inserting themselves into the DNA and distorting the double helix. Still other mutagens cause chemical changes in bases that change their pairing properties.

Researchers have developed various methods to test the mutagenic activity of different chemicals. A major application of these tests is the preliminary screening of chemicals to identify those that may cause cancer. This approach makes sense because most carcinogens (cancer-causing chemicals) are mutagenic and, conversely, most mutagens are carcinogenic.

What is a gene? *revisiting the question*

Our definition of a gene has evolved over the past few chapters, as it has through the history of genetics. We began with the Mendelian concept of a gene as a discrete unit of inheritance that affects a phenotypic character (Chapter 14). We saw that Morgan and his colleagues assigned such genes to specific loci on chromosomes (Chapter 15). We went on to view a gene as a region of specific nucleotide sequence along the length of a DNA molecule (Chapter 16). Finally, in this chapter, we have considered a functional definition of a gene as a DNA sequence coding for a specific polypeptide chain. All these definitions are useful, depending on the context in which genes are being studied. (**Figure 17.26** summarizes the path from gene to polypeptide in a eukaryotic cell.)

Even the one gene–one polypeptide model must be refined and applied selectively. Most eukaryotic genes contain non-coding segments (introns), so large portions of these genes have no corresponding segments in polypeptides. Molecular biologists also often include promoters and certain other regulatory regions of DNA within the boundaries of a gene. These DNA sequences are not transcribed, but they can be considered part of the functional gene because they must be present for transcription to occur. Our molecular definition of a gene must also be broad enough to include the DNA that is transcribed into rRNA, tRNA, and other RNAs that are not translated. These genes have no polypeptide products. Thus, we arrive at the following definition: *A gene is a region of DNA whose final product is either a polypeptide or an RNA molecule.*

For most genes, however, it is still useful to retain the one gene–one polypeptide idea. In this chapter, you have learned in molecular terms how a typical gene is expressed—by transcription into RNA and then translation into a polypeptide that forms a protein of specific structure and function. Proteins, in turn, bring about an organism's observable phenotype.

Genes are regulated. We will explore the regulation of gene expression in eukaryotes in Chapters 19 and 21. In the next chapter, we begin our discussion of gene regulation by focusing on the simpler molecular biology of bacteria and viruses.

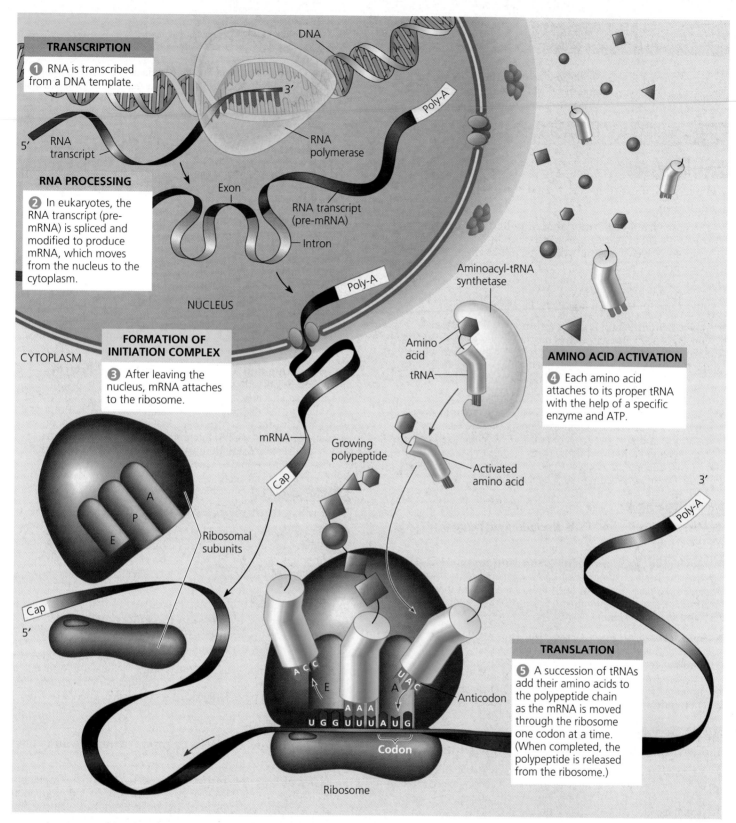

TRANSCRIPTION

1 RNA is transcribed from a DNA template.

DNA

RNA transcript

5'

RNA polymerase

3'

Poly-A

RNA PROCESSING

2 In eukaryotes, the RNA transcript (pre-mRNA) is spliced and modified to produce mRNA, which moves from the nucleus to the cytoplasm.

Exon

Intron

RNA transcript (pre-mRNA)

NUCLEUS

Poly-A

CYTOPLASM

FORMATION OF INITIATION COMPLEX

3 After leaving the nucleus, mRNA attaches to the ribosome.

mRNA

Cap

Growing polypeptide

Ribosomal subunits

A

P

E

Cap

5'

AMINO ACID ACTIVATION

Aminoacyl-tRNA synthetase

Amino acid

tRNA

4 Each amino acid attaches to its proper tRNA with the help of a specific enzyme and ATP.

Activated amino acid

3'

Poly-A

TRANSLATION

5 A succession of tRNAs add their amino acids to the polypeptide chain as the mRNA is moved through the ribosome one codon at a time. (When completed, the polypeptide is released from the ribosome.)

A C C

E

U A C

A

Anticodon

A A A

U G G U U U A U G

Codon

Ribosome

▲ **Figure 17.26 A summary of transcription and translation in a eukaryotic cell.** This diagram shows the path from one gene to one polypeptide. Keep in mind that each gene in the DNA can be transcribed repeatedly into many RNA molecules, and that each mRNA can be translated repeatedly to yield many polypeptide molecules. (Also, remember that the final products of some genes are not polypeptides but RNA molecules, including tRNA and rRNA.) In general, the steps of transcription and translation are similar in prokaryotic and eukaryotic cells. The major difference is the occurrence of RNA processing in the eukaryotic nucleus. Other significant differences are found in the initiation stages of both transcription and translation and in the termination of transcription.

Chapter 17 Review

Go to the Campbell Biology website (**www.campbellbiology.com**) or CD-ROM to explore Activities, Investigations, and other interactive study aids.

SUMMARY OF KEY CONCEPTS

Concept 17.1
Genes specify proteins via transcription and translation

▶ **Evidence from the Study of Metabolic Defects (pp. 309–311)** DNA controls metabolism by directing cells to make specific enzymes and other proteins. Beadle and Tatum's experiments with mutant strains of *Neurospora* supported the one gene–one enzyme hypothesis. Genes code for polypeptide chains or for RNA molecules.
Investigation How Is a Metabolic Pathway Analyzed?

▶ **Basic Principles of Transcription and Translation (pp. 311–312)** Transcription is the nucleotide-to-nucleotide transfer of information from DNA to RNA, while translation is the informational transfer from nucleotide sequence in RNA to amino acid sequence in a polypeptide.
Activity Overview of Protein Synthesis

▶ **The Genetic Code (pp. 312–314)** Genetic information is encoded as a sequence of nonoverlapping base triplets, or codons. A codon in messenger RNA (mRNA) either is translated into an amino acid (61 codons) or serves as a translational stop signal (3 codons). Codons must be read in the correct reading frame for the specified polypeptide to be produced.

Concept 17.2
Transcription is the DNA-directed synthesis of RNA: *a closer look*

▶ **Molecular Components of Transcription (pp. 315–316)** RNA synthesis is catalyzed by RNA polymerase. It follows the same base-pairing rules as DNA replication, except that in RNA, uracil substitutes for thymine.
Activity Transcription

▶ **Synthesis of an RNA Transcript (pp. 316–317)** The three stages of transcription are initiation, elongation, and termination. Promoters signal the initiation of RNA synthesis. Transcription factors help eukaryotic RNA polymerase recognize promoter sequences. The mechanisms of termination are different in prokaryotes and eukaryotes.

Concept 17.3
Eukaryotic cells modify RNA after transcription

▶ **Alteration of mRNA Ends (p. 317)** Eukaryotic mRNA molecules are processed before leaving the nucleus by modification of their ends and by RNA splicing. The 5′ end receives a modified nucleotide cap, and the 3′ end a poly-A tail.
Activity RNA Processing

▶ **Split Genes and RNA Splicing (pp. 318–319)** Most eukaryotic genes have introns interspersed among the coding regions, the exons. In RNA splicing, introns are removed and exons joined. RNA splicing is carried out by spliceosomes, but in some cases, RNA alone catalyzes splicing. Catalytic RNA molecules are called ribozymes. The presence of introns allows for alternative RNA splicing.

Concept 17.4
Translation is the RNA-directed synthesis of a polypeptide: *a closer look*

▶ **Molecular Components of Translation (pp. 320–323)** A cell translates an mRNA message into protein with the help of transfer RNA (tRNA). After binding specific amino acids, tRNA molecules line up by means of their anticodons at complementary codons on mRNA. Ribosomes help facilitate this coupling with binding sites for mRNA and tRNA.

▶ **Building a Polypeptide (pp. 323–325)** Ribosomes coordinate the three stages of translation: initiation, elongation, and termination. The formation of peptide bonds between amino acids is catalyzed by rRNA. A number of ribosomes can translate a single mRNA molecule simultaneously, forming a polyribosome.
Activity Translation
Biology Labs On-Line TranslationLab

▶ **Completing and Targeting the Functional Protein (pp. 324–326)** After translation, proteins may be modified in ways that affect their three-dimensional shape. Free ribosomes in the cytosol initiate the synthesis of all proteins, but proteins destined for the endomembrane system or for secretion must be transported into the ER. Such proteins have signal peptides to which a signal-recognition particle (SRP) binds, enabling the translating ribosome to bind to the ER.

Concept 17.5
RNA plays multiple roles in the cell: *a review*

▶ RNA can hydrogen-bond to other nucleic acid molecules (DNA or RNA). It can assume a specific three-dimensional shape. And it has functional groups that allow it to act as a catalyst, a ribozyme (p. 327).

Concept 17.6
Comparing gene expression in prokaryotes and eukaryotes reveals key differences

▶ Because prokaryotic cells lack a nuclear envelope, translation can begin while transcription is still in progress. In a eukaryotic cell, the nuclear envelope separates transcription from translation, and extensive RNA processing occurs in the nucleus (pp. 327–328).

Concept 17.7
Point mutations can affect protein structure and function

▶ **Types of Point Mutations (pp. 328–330)** A point mutation is a change in one DNA base pair, which may lead to production of a nonfunctional protein or no protein at all. Base-pair substitutions can cause missense or nonsense mutations. Base-pair insertions or deletions may produce frameshift mutations.

▶ **Mutagens (pp. 329–330)** Spontaneous mutations can occur during DNA replication, recombination, or repair. Chemical and physical mutagens can also alter genes.

TESTING YOUR KNOWLEDGE

Self-Quiz

1. Base-pair substitutions involving the third base of a codon are unlikely to result in an error in the polypeptide. This is because
   a. substitutions are corrected before transcription begins.
   b. substitutions are restricted to introns.
   c. the base-pairing rules are less strict for the third base of codons and anticodons.
   d. a signal-recognition particle corrects coding errors.
   e. transcribed errors attract snRNPs, which then stimulate splicing and correction.

2. In eukaryotic cells, transcription cannot begin until
   a. the two DNA strands have completely separated and exposed the promoter.
   b. several transcription factors have bound to the promoter.
   c. the 5′ caps are removed from the mRNA.
   d. the DNA introns are removed from the template.
   e. DNA nucleases have isolated the transcription unit.

3. Which of the following is *not* true of a codon?
   a. It consists of three nucleotides.
   b. It may code for the same amino acid as another codon.
   c. It never codes for more than one amino acid.
   d. It extends from one end of a tRNA molecule.
   e. It is the basic unit of the genetic code.

4. The metabolic pathway of arginine synthesis is as follows:

   Precursor → Ornithine → Citrulline → Arginine
            A   B   C

   Beadle and Tatum discovered several classes of *Neurospora* mutants that were able to grow on minimal medium with arginine added (see Figure 17.2). They were able to conclude that
   a. one gene codes for the entire metabolic pathway.
   b. the genetic code of DNA is a triplet code.
   c. class I mutants have their mutations later in the nucleotide chain than do class II mutants.
   d. class I mutants have a nonfunctional enzyme at step A, and class II mutants have one at step B.
   e. class III mutants have nonfunctional enzymes for all three steps.

5. The anticodon of a particular tRNA molecule is
   a. complementary to the corresponding mRNA codon.
   b. complementary to the corresponding triplet in rRNA.
   c. the part of tRNA that bonds to a specific amino acid.
   d. changeable, depending on the amino acid that attaches to the tRNA.
   e. catalytic, making the tRNA a ribozyme.

6. Which of the following is *not* true of RNA processing?
   a. Exons are cut out before mRNA leaves the nucleus.
   b. Nucleotides may be added at both ends of the RNA.
   c. Ribozymes may function in RNA splicing.
   d. RNA splicing can be catalyzed by spliceosomes.
   e. A primary transcript is often much longer than the final RNA molecule that leaves the nucleus.

7. Which of the following is true of translation in both prokaryotes and eukaryotes?
   a. Translation is coupled to transcription.
   b. The product of transcription is immediately ready for translation.
   c. The codon UUU codes for phenylalanine.
   d. Ribosomes are affected by streptomycin.
   e. The signal-recognition particle (SRP) binds to the first 20 amino acids of certain polypeptides.

8. Using Figure 17.5, identify a 5′ → 3′ sequence of nucleotides in the DNA template strand for an mRNA coding for the polypeptide sequence Phe-Pro-Lys.
   a. UUU-GGG-AAA   d. CTT-CGG-GAA
   b. GAA-CCC-CTT   e. AAA-CCC-UUU
   c. AAA-ACC-TTT

9. Which of the following mutations would be *most* likely to have a harmful effect on an organism?
   a. a base-pair substitution
   b. a deletion of three nucleotides near the middle of a gene
   c. a single nucleotide deletion in the middle of an intron
   d. a single nucleotide deletion near the end of the coding sequence
   e. a single nucleotide insertion downstream of, and close to, the start of the coding sequence

10. Which component is *not* directly involved in translation?
   a. mRNA   b. DNA   c. tRNA   d. ribosomes   e. GTP

For Self-Quiz answers, see Appendix A.

Go to the website or CD-ROM for more quiz questions.

Evolution Connection

The genetic code (see Figure 17.5) is rich with evolutionary implications. For instance, notice that the 20 amino acids are not randomly scattered; most amino acids are coded for by a similar set of codons. What evolutionary explanations can be given for this pattern? (*Hint:* There is one explanation relating to historical ancestry, and some less obvious ones of a "form-fits-function" type.)

Scientific Inquiry

A biologist inserts a gene from a human liver cell into the chromosome of a bacterium. The bacterium then transcribes and translates this gene. The protein produced is useless and is found to contain many more amino acids than does the protein made by the eukaryotic cell. Explain why.
Investigation *How Is a Metabolic Pathway Analyzed?*
Biology Labs On-Line *TranslationLab*

Science, Technology, and Society

Our civilization generates many potentially mutagenic chemicals (pesticides, for example) and modifies the environment in ways that increase exposure to other mutagens, notably UV radiation. What role should government play in identifying mutagens and regulating their release to the environment?

18
The Genetics of Viruses and Bacteria

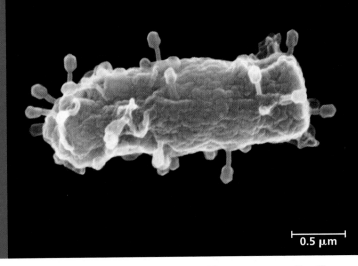

0.5 μm

▲ Figure 18.1 **T4 bacteriophage infecting an *E. coli* cell.**

Key Concepts

18.1 A virus has a genome but can reproduce only within a host cell

18.2 Viruses, viroids, and prions are formidable pathogens in animals and plants

18.3 Rapid reproduction, mutation, and genetic recombination contribute to the genetic diversity of bacteria

18.4 Individual bacteria respond to environmental change by regulating their gene expression

Overview

Microbial Model Systems

The photo in **Figure 18.1** shows a remarkable event: the attack of a bacterial cell by numerous structures that resemble miniature lollipops. These structures, a type of virus called T4 bacteriophage, are seen infecting the bacterium *Escherichia coli* in this colorized SEM. By injecting its DNA into the cell, the virus sets in motion a genetic takeover of the bacterium. Molecular biology was born in the laboratories of microbiologists studying viruses and bacteria. Microbes such as *E. coli* and its viruses are called *model systems* because of their frequent use by researchers in studies that reveal broad biological principles. Experiments with viruses and bacteria provided most of the evidence that genes are made of DNA, and they were critical in working out the molecular mechanisms of the fundamental processes of DNA replication, transcription, and translation.

Beyond their value as model systems, viruses and bacteria have unique genetic mechanisms that are interesting in their own right. These specialized mechanisms have important applications for understanding how viruses and bacteria cause disease. In addition, techniques enabling scientists to manipulate genes and transfer them from one organism to another have emerged from the study of microbes. These techniques are having an important impact on both basic research and biotechnology (see Chapter 20).

In this chapter, we explore the genetics of viruses and bacteria. Recall that bacteria are prokaryotes, with cells much smaller and more simply organized than those of eukaryotes, such as plants and animals. Viruses are smaller and simpler still **(Figure 18.2)**. Lacking the structures and metabolic machinery found in cells, most viruses are little more than genes packaged in protein coats. We will begin with the structure of these simplest of all genetic systems and their role as disease-causing agents, or pathogens. Then we will discuss the genetics of bacteria and regulation of their gene expression.

Concept 18.1

A virus has a genome but can reproduce only within a host cell

Scientists were able to detect viruses indirectly long before they were actually able to see them. The story of how viruses were discovered begins near the end of the 19th century.

The Discovery of Viruses: *Scientific Inquiry*

Tobacco mosaic disease stunts the growth of tobacco plants and gives their leaves a mottled, or mosaic, coloration **(Figure 18.3)**. In 1883, Adolf Mayer, a German scientist, discovered that he could transmit the disease from plant to plant by rubbing sap extracted from diseased leaves onto healthy plants. After

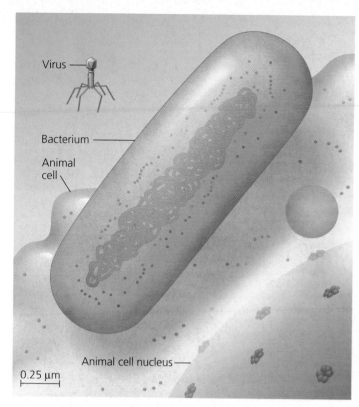

0.25 μm

▲ Figure 18.2 **Comparing the size of a virus, a bacterium, and an animal cell.** Only a portion of a typical animal cell is shown. Its diameter is about ten times greater than the length of *E. coli*.

Virus —
Bacterium —
Animal cell
Animal cell nucleus —

▲ Figure 18.3 **Infection by tobacco mosaic virus (TMV).** A healthy, uninfected tobacco leaf (left) compared with a leaf experimentally infected with TMV (right).

an unsuccessful search for an infectious microbe in the sap, Mayer concluded that the disease was caused by unusually small bacteria that could not be seen with the microscope. This hypothesis was tested a decade later by Dimitri Ivanowsky, a Russian who passed sap from infected tobacco leaves through a filter designed to remove bacteria. After filtering, the sap still produced mosaic disease.

Ivanowsky clung to the hypothesis that bacteria caused tobacco mosaic disease. Perhaps, he reasoned, the bacteria were so small that they passed through the filter or made a filterable toxin that caused the disease. This latter possibility was ruled out when the Dutch botanist Martinus Beijerinck discovered that the infectious agent in the filtered sap could reproduce. He rubbed plants with filtered sap, and after these plants developed mosaic disease, he used their sap to infect more plants, continuing this process through a series of infections. The pathogen must have been reproducing, for its ability to cause disease was undiluted after several transfers from plant to plant.

In fact, the pathogen reproduced only within the host it infected. Unlike bacteria, the mysterious agent of mosaic disease could not be cultivated on nutrient media in test tubes or petri dishes. Beijerinck imagined a reproducing particle much smaller and simpler than bacteria. His suspicions were confirmed in 1935 when the American scientist Wendell Stanley crystallized the infectious particle, now known as

tobacco mosaic virus (TMV). Subsequently, TMV and many other viruses were actually seen with the help of the electron microscope.

Structure of Viruses

The tiniest viruses are only 20 nm in diameter—smaller than a ribosome. Millions could easily fit on a pinhead. Even the largest viruses are barely visible in the light microscope. Stanley's discovery that some viruses could be crystallized was exciting and puzzling news. Not even the simplest of cells can aggregate into regular crystals. But if viruses are not cells, then what are they? They are infectious particles consisting of nucleic acid enclosed in a protein coat and, in some cases, a membranous envelope. Let's examine the structure of viruses more closely and then how they reproduce.

Viral Genomes

We usually think of genes as being made of double-stranded DNA—the conventional double helix—but many viruses defy this convention. Their genomes may consist of double-stranded DNA, single-stranded DNA, double-stranded RNA, or single-stranded RNA, depending on the kind of virus. A virus is called a DNA virus or an RNA virus, according to the kind of nucleic acid that makes up its genome. In either case, the genome is usually organized as a single linear or circular molecule of nucleic acid. The smallest viruses have only four genes, while the largest have several hundred.

Capsids and Envelopes

The protein shell enclosing the viral genome is called a **capsid.** Depending on the type of virus, the capsid may be rod-shaped, polyhedral, or more complex in shape (like T4). Capsids are built from a large number of protein subunits called *capsomeres,* but the number of different *kinds* of proteins is usually small. Tobacco mosaic virus has a rigid, rod-shaped capsid

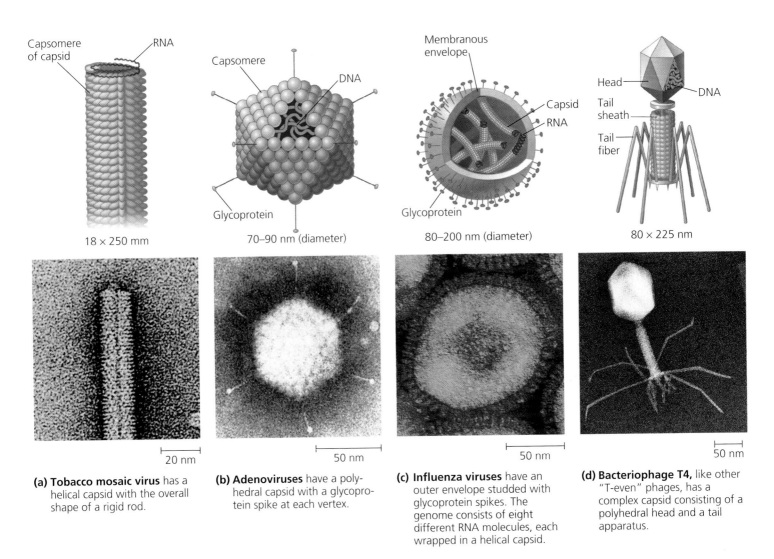

(a) Tobacco mosaic virus has a helical capsid with the overall shape of a rigid rod.

18 × 250 mm

Capsomere of capsid
RNA

(b) Adenoviruses have a polyhedral capsid with a glycoprotein spike at each vertex.

70–90 nm (diameter)

Capsomere
DNA
Glycoprotein

(c) Influenza viruses have an outer envelope studded with glycoprotein spikes. The genome consists of eight different RNA molecules, each wrapped in a helical capsid.

80–200 nm (diameter)

Membranous envelope
Capsid
RNA
Glycoprotein

(d) Bacteriophage T4, like other "T-even" phages, has a complex capsid consisting of a polyhedral head and a tail apparatus.

80 × 225 nm

Head
DNA
Tail sheath
Tail fiber

20 nm   50 nm   50 nm   50 nm

▲ **Figure 18.4 Viral structure.** Viruses are made up of nucleic acid (DNA or RNA) enclosed in a protein coat (the capsid) and sometimes further wrapped in a membranous envelope. The individual protein subunits making up the capsid are called capsomeres. Although diverse in size and shape, viruses have common structural features, most of which appear in the four examples shown here. (All the micrographs are colorized TEMs.)

made from over a thousand molecules of a single type of protein arranged in a helix **(Figure 18.4a)**. Adenoviruses, which infect the respiratory tracts of animals, have 252 identical protein molecules arranged in a polyhedral capsid with 20 triangular facets—an icosahedron **(Figure 18.4b)**.

Some viruses have accessory structures that help them infect their hosts. For instance, a membranous envelope surrounds the capsids of influenza viruses and many other viruses found in animals **(Figure 18.4c)**. These **viral envelopes,** which are derived from the membrane of the host cell, contain host cell phospholipids and membrane proteins. They also contain proteins and glycoproteins of viral origin (glycoproteins are proteins with carbohydrate covalently attached). Some viruses carry a few viral enzyme molecules within their capsids.

The most complex capsids are found among viruses that infect bacteria, called **bacteriophages,** or simply **phages.** The first phages studied included seven that infect *E. coli*. These

seven phages were named type 1 (T1), type 2 (T2), and so forth, in the order of their discovery. The three T-even phages (T2, T4, and T6) turned out to be very similar in structure. Their capsids have elongated icosahedral heads enclosing their DNA. Attached to the head is a protein tail piece with fibers that the phages use to attach to a bacterium **(Figure 18.4d)**.

General Features of Viral Reproductive Cycles

Viruses are obligate intracellular parasites: They can reproduce only within a host cell. An isolated virus is unable to reproduce or do anything else except infect an appropriate host cell. Viruses lack metabolic enzymes, ribosomes, and other equipment for making proteins. Thus, isolated viruses are merely packaged sets of genes in transit from one host cell to another.

Each type of virus can infect only a limited range of host cells, called its **host range.** This host specificity results from the evolution of recognition systems by the virus. Viruses identify their host cells by a "lock-and-key" fit between proteins on the outside of the virus and specific receptor molecules on the surface of cells. (Presumably, the receptors first evolved because they carried out functions of benefit to the organism.) Some viruses have broad host ranges. West Nile virus, for example, can infect mosquitoes, birds, and humans, and equine encephalitis virus can infect mosquitoes, birds, horses, and humans. Other viruses have host ranges so narrow that they infect only a single species. Measles virus and poliovirus, for instance, can infect only humans. Furthermore, infection by viruses of multicellular eukaryotes is usually limited to particular tissues. Human cold viruses infect only the cells lining the upper respiratory tract, and the AIDS virus binds to specific receptors on certain types of white blood cells.

A viral infection begins when the genome of a virus makes its way into a host cell **(Figure 18.5)**. The mechanism by which this nucleic acid enters the cell varies, depending on the type of virus and the type of host cell. For example, the T-even phages use their elaborate tail apparatus to inject DNA into a bacterium (see Figure 18.4d). Once inside, the viral genome can commandeer its host, reprogramming the cell to copy the viral nucleic acid and manufacture viral proteins. The host provides the nucleotides for making viral nucleic acids, as well as enzymes, ribosomes, tRNAs, amino acids, ATP, and other components needed for making the viral proteins dictated by viral genes. Most DNA viruses use the DNA polymerases of the host cell to synthesize new genomes along the templates provided by the viral DNA. In contrast, to replicate their genomes, RNA viruses use special virus-encoded polymerases that can use RNA as a template. (Uninfected cells generally make no enzymes for carrying out this latter process.)

After the viral nucleic acid molecules and capsomeres are produced, their assembly into new viruses is often a spontaneous process of self-assembly. In fact, the RNA and capsomeres of TMV can be separated in the laboratory and then reassembled to form complete viruses simply by mixing the components together under the right conditions. The simplest type of viral reproductive cycle ends with the exit of hundreds or thousands of viruses from the infected host cell, a process that often damages or destroys the cell. Such cellular damage and death, as well as the body's responses to this destruction, cause some of the symptoms associated with viral infections. The viral progeny that exit a cell have the potential to infect additional cells, spreading the viral infection.

There are many variations on the simplified viral reproductive cycle we have traced in this overview. We will now take a closer look at some of these variations in bacterial viruses (phages) and animal viruses; later in the chapter, we will consider plant viruses.

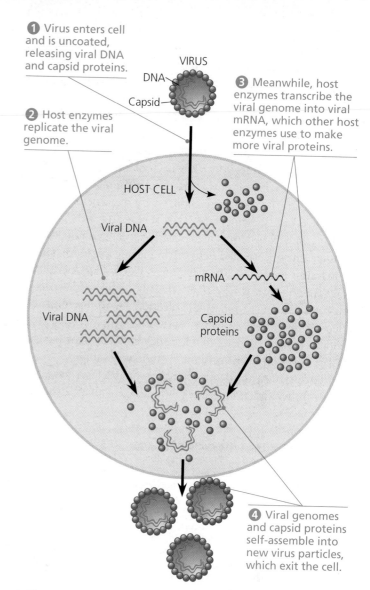

❶ Virus enters cell and is uncoated, releasing viral DNA and capsid proteins.

❷ Host enzymes replicate the viral genome.

❸ Meanwhile, host enzymes transcribe the viral genome into viral mRNA, which other host enzymes use to make more viral proteins.

VIRUS

DNA

Capsid

HOST CELL

Viral DNA

Viral DNA

mRNA

Capsid proteins

❹ Viral genomes and capsid proteins self-assemble into new virus particles, which exit the cell.

▲ **Figure 18.5 A simplified viral reproductive cycle.** A virus is an obligate intracellular parasite that uses the equipment and small precursors of its host cell to reproduce. In this simplest of viral cycles, the parasite is a DNA virus with a capsid consisting of a single type of protein.

Reproductive Cycles of Phages

Phages are the best understood of all viruses, although some of them are also among the most complex. Research on phages led to the discovery that some double-stranded DNA viruses can reproduce by two alternative mechanisms: the lytic cycle and the lysogenic cycle.

The Lytic Cycle

A phage reproductive cycle that culminates in death of the host cell is known as a **lytic cycle.** The term refers to the last stage of infection, during which the bacterium lyses (breaks open) and releases the phages that were produced within the cell. Each of these phages can then infect a healthy cell, and a few successive lytic cycles can destroy an entire bacterial population in just a few hours. A phage that reproduces only by a lytic cycle is a **virulent phage.** **Figure 18.6** illustrates the major steps in the lytic cycle of T4, a typical virulent phage. The figure and legend describe the process, which you should study before proceeding.

After reading about the lytic cycle, you may wonder why phages haven't exterminated all bacteria. In fact, phage treatments have been used medically in some countries to help control bacterial infections. But bacteria are not defenseless. First, natural selection favors bacterial mutants with receptor sites that are no longer recognized by a particular type of phage. Second, when phage DNA successfully enters a bacterium, the DNA often is recognized as foreign and cut up by cellular enzymes called *restriction endonucleases,* or simply **restriction enzymes.** The bacterial cell's own DNA is chemically modified in a way that prevents attack by restriction enzymes. But just as natural selection favors bacteria with effective restriction enzymes, natural selection favors phage mutants that are resistant to these enzymes. Thus, the parasite-host relationship is in constant evolutionary flux.

There is yet a third important reason bacteria have been spared from extinction as a result of phage activity. Instead of lysing their host cells, many phages coexist with them in what is called the lysogenic cycle.

The Lysogenic Cycle

In contrast to the lytic cycle, which kills the host cell, the **lysogenic cycle** replicates the phage genome without destroying the host. Phages capable of using both modes of reproducing within a bacterium are called **temperate phages.** A temperate phage called lambda, written with the Greek letter λ, is widely used in biological research. Phage λ resembles T4, but its tail has only one short tail fiber.

Infection of an *E. coli* cell by phage λ begins when the phage binds to the surface of the cell and injects its DNA **(Figure 18.7).** Within the host, the λ DNA molecule forms a circle. What happens next depends on the reproductive mode: lytic cycle or lysogenic cycle. During a lytic cycle, the viral genes immediately turn the host cell into a λ-producing factory, and the cell soon lyses and releases its viral products. During a lysogenic cycle, however, the λ DNA molecule is incorporated by genetic recombination (crossing over) into a specific site on the host cell's chromosome. When integrated into the bacterial chromosome in this way, the viral DNA is

▶ **Figure 18.6 The lytic cycle of phage T4, a virulent phage.** Phage T4 has about 100 genes, which are transcribed and translated using the host cell's machinery. One of the first phage genes translated after the viral DNA enters the host cell codes for an enzyme that degrades the host cell's DNA (step 2); the phage DNA is protected from breakdown because it contains a modified form of cytosine that is not recognized by the enzyme. The entire lytic cycle, from the phage's first contact with the cell surface to cell lysis, takes only 20–30 minutes at 37°C.

Phage assembly

Head   Tails   Tail fibers

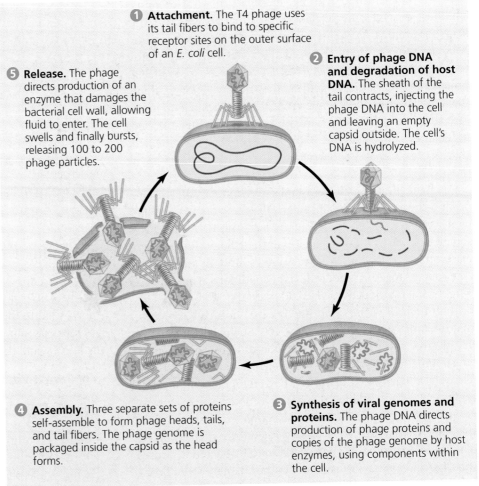

1 Attachment. The T4 phage uses its tail fibers to bind to specific receptor sites on the outer surface of an *E. coli* cell.

2 Entry of phage DNA and degradation of host DNA. The sheath of the tail contracts, injecting the phage DNA into the cell and leaving an empty capsid outside. The cell's DNA is hydrolyzed.

3 Synthesis of viral genomes and proteins. The phage DNA directs production of phage proteins and copies of the phage genome by host enzymes, using components within the cell.

4 Assembly. Three separate sets of proteins self-assemble to form phage heads, tails, and tail fibers. The phage genome is packaged inside the capsid as the head forms.

5 Release. The phage directs production of an enzyme that damages the bacterial cell wall, allowing fluid to enter. The cell swells and finally bursts, releasing 100 to 200 phage particles.

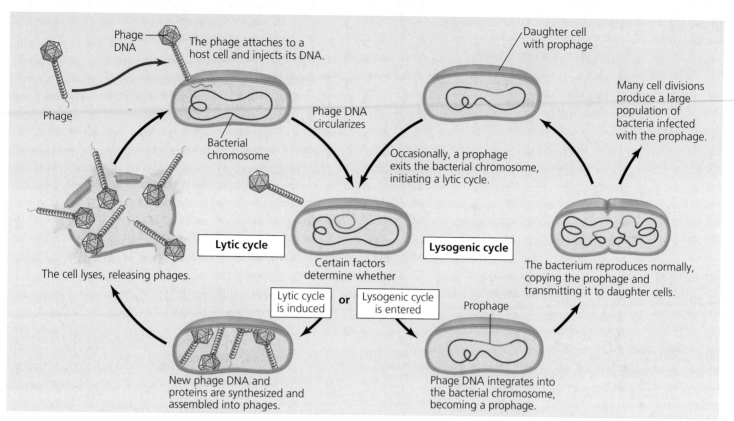

▲ **Figure 18.7 The lytic and lysogenic cycles of phage λ, a temperate phage.** After entering the bacterial cell and circularizing, the λ DNA can immediately initiate the production of a large number of progeny phages (lytic cycle) or integrate into the bacterial chromosome (lysogenic cycle). In most cases, phage λ follows the lytic pathway, which is similar to that detailed in Figure 18.6. However, once a lysogenic cycle begins, the prophage may be carried in the host cell's chromosome for many generations. Phage λ has one main tail fiber, which is short.

The phage attaches to a host cell and injects its DNA.

Phage DNA circularizes

Occasionally, a prophage exits the bacterial chromosome, initiating a lytic cycle.

Many cell divisions produce a large population of bacteria infected with the prophage.

Daughter cell with prophage

Lysogenic cycle

The bacterium reproduces normally, copying the prophage and transmitting it to daughter cells.

Prophage

Phage DNA integrates into the bacterial chromosome, becoming a prophage.

Certain factors determine whether

Lytic cycle is induced **or** Lysogenic cycle is entered

Lytic cycle

The cell lyses, releasing phages.

New phage DNA and proteins are synthesized and assembled into phages.

Phage DNA

Phage

Bacterial chromosome

known as a **prophage.** One prophage gene codes for a protein that prevents transcription of most of the other prophage genes. Thus, the phage genome is mostly silent within the bacterium. Every time the *E. coli* cell prepares to divide, it replicates the phage DNA along with its own and passes the copies on to daughter cells. A single infected cell can quickly give rise to a large population of bacteria carrying the virus in prophage form. This mechanism enables viruses to propagate without killing the host cells on which they depend.

The term *lysogenic* implies that prophages are capable of giving rise to active phages that lyse their host cells. This occurs when the λ genome exits the bacterial chromosome and initiates a lytic cycle. What triggers the switchover from the lysogenic to the lytic mode is usually an environmental signal, such as radiation or the presence of certain chemicals.

In addition to the gene for the transcription-preventing protein, a few other prophage genes may also be expressed during lysogenic cycles. Expression of these genes may alter the host's phenotype, a phenomenon that can have important medical significance. For example, the bacteria that cause the human diseases diphtheria, botulism, and scarlet fever would be harmless to humans if it were not for certain prophage genes that cause the host bacteria to make toxins.

Reproductive Cycles of Animal Viruses

Everyone has suffered from viral infections, whether cold sores, influenza, or the common cold. Like all viruses, those that cause illness in humans and other animals can reproduce only inside host cells. Many variations on the basic scheme of viral infection and reproduction are represented among the animal viruses. One key variable is the nature of the viral genome: Is it composed of DNA or RNA? Is it double-stranded or single-stranded? The nature of the genome is the basis for the common classification of viruses shown in **Table 18.1** on the next page. Single-stranded RNA viruses are further classified into three classes (IV–VI) according to how the RNA genome functions in a host cell.

Another important characteristic of a virus is the presence or absence of a membranous envelope derived from host cell membrane. Rather than consider all the mechanisms of viral infection and reproduction, we will focus on the roles of viral envelopes and on the functioning of RNA as the genetic material of many animal viruses. Whereas few bacteriophages have an envelope or RNA genome, nearly all the animal viruses with RNA genomes have an envelope, as do some with DNA genomes (see Table 18.1).

Table 18.1 Classes of Animal Viruses

Class/Family	Envelope	Examples/Disease
I. Double-stranded DNA (dsDNA)		
Adenovirus (see Figure 18.4b)	No	Respiratory diseases; animal tumors
Papovavirus	No	Papillomavirus (warts, cervical cancer); polyomavirus (animal tumors)
Herpesvirus	Yes	Herpes simplex I and II (cold sores, genital sores); varicella zoster (shingles, chicken pox); Epstein-Barr virus (mononucleosis, Burkitt's lymphoma)
Poxvirus	Yes	Smallpox virus; cowpox virus
II. Single-stranded DNA (ssDNA)		
Parvovirus	No	B19 parvovirus (mild rash)
III. Double-stranded RNA (dsRNA)		
Reovirus	No	Rotavirus (diarrhea); Colorado tick fever virus
IV. Single-stranded RNA (ssRNA); serves as mRNA		
Picornavirus	No	Rhinovirus (common cold); poliovirus, hepatitis A virus, and other enteric (intestinal) viruses
Coronavirus (see Figure 18.11b)	Yes	Severe acute respiratory syndrome (SARS)
Flavivirus	Yes	Yellow fever virus; West Nile virus; hepatitis C virus
Togavirus	Yes	Rubella virus; equine encephalitis viruses
V. ssRNA; template for mRNA synthesis		
Filovirus	Yes	Ebola virus (hemorrhagic fever)
Orthomyxovirus (see Figure 18.4c)	Yes	Influenza virus
Paramyxovirus	Yes	Measles virus; mumps virus
Rhabdovirus	Yes	Rabies virus
VI. ssRNA; template for DNA synthesis		
Retrovirus (see Figure 18.9)	Yes	HIV, human immuno-deficiency virus (AIDS); RNA tumor viruses (leukemia)

Viral Envelopes

An animal virus equipped with an outer membrane, or viral envelope, uses it to enter the host cell. Protruding from the outer surface of this envelope are viral glycoproteins that bind to specific receptor molecules on the surface of a host cell. **Figure 18.8** outlines the events in the reproductive cycle of an enveloped virus with an RNA genome. You can see that viral glycoproteins for new envelopes are made by cellular enzymes in the endoplasmic reticulum (ER) of the host cell. These glycoproteins, embedded in ER membrane, are transported to the cell surface. In a process much like exocytosis, new virus capsids wrap themselves in membrane as they bud from the cell. In other words, the viral envelope is derived from the host cell's plasma membrane, although some of the molecules of this membrane are specified by viral genes. The enveloped viruses are now free to infect other cells. This reproductive cycle does not necessarily kill the host cell, in contrast to the lytic cycles of phages.

Some viruses have envelopes that are not derived from plasma membrane. The envelopes of herpesviruses, for example, are derived from the nuclear membrane of the host. These viruses have a double-stranded DNA genome and reproduce within the host cell nucleus, using a combination of viral and cellular enzymes to replicate and transcribe their DNA. In some cases, copies of the herpesvirus DNA remain behind as minichromosomes in the nuclei of certain nerve cells. There they remain latent until some sort of physical or emotional stress triggers a new round of active virus production. The infection of other cells by these new viruses causes the blisters characteristic of herpes, such as cold sores or genital sores. Once someone acquires a herpesvirus infection, flare-ups may recur throughout the person's life.

RNA as Viral Genetic Material

Although some phages and most plant viruses are RNA viruses, the broadest variety of RNA genomes is found among the viruses that infect animals. Among the three types of single-stranded RNA genomes found in animal viruses, the genome of class IV viruses can directly serve as mRNA and thus can be translated into viral protein immediately after infection. Figure 18.8 shows a virus of class V, in which the RNA genome serves as a *template* for mRNA synthesis. The RNA genome is transcribed into complementary RNA strands, which function both as mRNA and as templates for the synthesis of additional copies of genome RNA. Like all viruses that require RNA → RNA synthesis to make mRNA, this one uses a viral enzyme that is packaged with the genome inside the capsid.

The RNA animal viruses with the most complicated reproductive cycles are the **retroviruses** (class VI). These viruses are

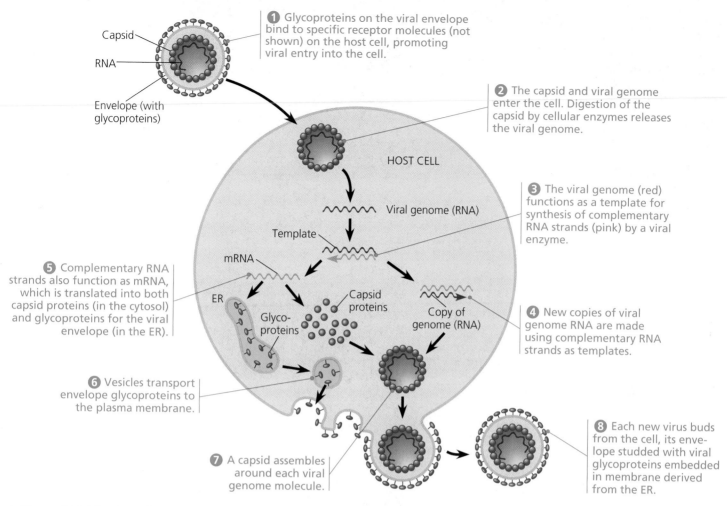

1 Glycoproteins on the viral envelope bind to specific receptor molecules (not shown) on the host cell, promoting viral entry into the cell.

2 The capsid and viral genome enter the cell. Digestion of the capsid by cellular enzymes releases the viral genome.

3 The viral genome (red) functions as a template for synthesis of complementary RNA strands (pink) by a viral enzyme.

4 New copies of viral genome RNA are made using complementary RNA strands as templates.

5 Complementary RNA strands also function as mRNA, which is translated into both capsid proteins (in the cytosol) and glycoproteins for the viral envelope (in the ER).

6 Vesicles transport envelope glycoproteins to the plasma membrane.

7 A capsid assembles around each viral genome molecule.

8 Each new virus buds from the cell, its envelope studded with viral glycoproteins embedded in membrane derived from the ER.

Capsid

RNA

Envelope (with glycoproteins)

HOST CELL

Viral genome (RNA)

Template

mRNA

ER

Glyco-proteins

Capsid proteins

Copy of genome (RNA)

▲ **Figure 18.8 The reproductive cycle of an enveloped RNA virus.** Shown here is a virus with a single-stranded RNA genome that functions as a template for synthesis of mRNA. Some enveloped viruses enter the host cell by fusion of the envelope with the cell's plasma membrane; others enter by endocytosis. For all enveloped RNA viruses, the formation of new envelopes for progeny viruses occurs by the mechanism depicted in this figure.

equipped with an enzyme called **reverse transcriptase**, which transcribes an RNA template into DNA, providing an RNA → DNA information flow, the opposite of the usual direction. This unusual phenomenon gave rise to the name retroviruses (*retro* means "backward"). Of particular medical importance is **HIV (human immunodeficiency virus)**, the retrovirus that causes **AIDS (acquired immunodeficiency syndrome)**. HIV and other retroviruses are enveloped viruses that contain two identical molecules of single-stranded RNA and two molecules of reverse transcriptase **(Figure 18.9)**.

After HIV enters a host cell, its reverse transcriptase molecules are released into the cytoplasm and catalyze synthesis of viral DNA. The newly made viral DNA then enters the cell's nucleus and integrates into the DNA of a chromosome. The integrated viral DNA, called a **provirus**, never leaves the host's genome, remaining a permanent resident of the cell. (Unlike a prophage, a provirus never leaves.) The host's RNA polymerase transcribes the proviral DNA into RNA molecules, which can

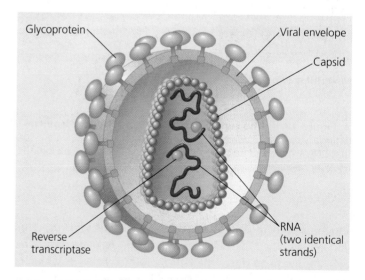

Glycoprotein

Viral envelope

Capsid

Reverse transcriptase

RNA (two identical strands)

▲ **Figure 18.9 The structure of HIV, the retrovirus that causes AIDS.** The envelope glycoproteins enable the virus to bind to specific receptors on certain white blood cells.

HIV
Membrane of white blood cell

0.25 μm

HIV entering a cell

New HIV leaving a cell

1 The virus fuses with the cell's plasma membrane. The capsid proteins are removed, releasing the viral proteins and RNA.

2 Reverse transcriptase catalyzes the synthesis of a DNA strand complementary to the viral RNA.

3 Reverse transcriptase catalyzes the synthesis of a second DNA strand complementary to the first.

4 The double-stranded DNA is incorporated as a provirus into the cell's DNA.

5 Proviral genes are transcribed into RNA molecules, which serve as genomes for the next viral generation and as mRNAs for translation into viral proteins.

6 The viral proteins include capsid proteins and reverse transcriptase (made in the cytosol) and envelope glycoproteins (made in the ER).

7 Vesicles transport the glycoproteins from the ER to the cell's plasma membrane.

8 Capsids are assembled around viral genomes and reverse transcriptase molecules.

9 New viruses bud off from the host cell.

HOST CELL

Reverse transcriptase

Viral RNA

RNA-DNA hybrid

DNA

NUCLEUS
Provirus

Chromosomal DNA

RNA genome for the next viral generation

mRNA

▲ **Figure 18.10 The reproductive cycle of HIV, a retrovirus.** The photos on the left (artificially colored TEMs) reveal HIV entering and leaving a human white blood cell. Note in step 4 that DNA synthesized from the viral RNA genome is integrated into the host cell chromosomal DNA, a characteristic unique to retroviruses.

function both as mRNA for the synthesis of viral proteins and as genomes for new virus particles released from the cell. **Figure 18.10** traces the HIV reproductive cycle, which is typical of a retrovirus. In Chapter 43, we will describe how HIV causes the deterioration of the immune system that occurs in AIDS.

Evolution of Viruses

Viruses do not really fit our definition of living organisms. An isolated virus is biologically inert, unable to replicate its genes or regenerate its own supply of ATP. Yet it has a genetic program written in the universal language of life. Do we think of viruses as nature's most complex molecules or as the simplest forms of life? Either way, we must bend our usual definitions. Although viruses are obligate intracellular parasites that cannot reproduce independently, their use of the genetic code makes it hard to deny their evolutionary connection to the living world.

How did viruses originate? Because they depend on cells for their own propagation, viruses most likely are not the descendants of precellular forms of life, but evolved *after* the first cells appeared, possibly multiple times. Most molecular biologists favor the hypothesis that viruses originated from fragments of cellular nucleic acids that could move from one cell to another. Consistent with this idea is the observation that a viral genome usually has more in common with the genome of its host than with the genomes of viruses infecting other hosts. Indeed, some viral genes are essentially identical to genes of the host. On the other hand, recent sequencing of many viral genomes has found that the genetic sequences of some viruses are quite similar to those of seemingly distantly related viruses (such as an animal virus and a plant virus that share similar sequences). This genetic similarity may reflect the persistence of groups of viral genes that were evolutionarily successful during the early evolution of viruses and the eukaryotic cells serving as their hosts. The origin of viruses is still a topic of much debate.

Perhaps the earliest viruses were naked bits of nucleic acid that made it from one cell to another via injured cell surfaces. The evolution of genes coding for capsid proteins may have facilitated the infection of undamaged cells. Candidates for the original sources of viral genomes include plasmids and transposons, genetic elements that we will discuss in more detail later in the chapter. Plasmids are small, circular DNA molecules, found in bacteria and also in yeasts, which are unicellular eukaryotes. Plasmids exist apart from the cell's genome, can replicate independently of the genome, and are occasionally transferred between cells. Transposons are DNA segments that can move from one location to another within a cell's genome. Thus, plasmids, transposons, and viruses all share an important feature: They are mobile genetic elements.

The ongoing evolutionary relationship between viruses and the genomes of their host cells is an association that makes viruses very useful model systems in molecular biology. Knowledge about viruses also has many practical applications, since viruses have a tremendous impact on all living organisms through their ability to cause disease.

Concept Check 18.1

1. Compare the effect on the host cell of a lytic (virulent) phage and a lysogenic (temperate) phage.
2. How do some viruses reproduce without possessing or ever synthesizing DNA?
3. Why is HIV called a retrovirus?

For suggested answers, see Appendix A.

Concept 18.2

Viruses, viroids, and prions are formidable pathogens in animals and plants

Diseases caused by viral infections afflict humans, agricultural crops, and livestock worldwide. Other smaller, less complex entities known as viroids and prions also cause disease in plants and animals.

Viral Diseases in Animals

The link between a viral infection and the symptoms it produces is often obscure. Viruses may damage or kill cells by causing the release of hydrolytic enzymes from lysosomes. Some viruses cause infected cells to produce toxins that lead to disease symptoms, and some have molecular components that are toxic, such as envelope proteins. How much damage a virus causes depends partly on the ability of the infected tissue to regenerate by cell division. People usually recover completely from colds because the epithelium of the respiratory tract, which the viruses infect, can efficiently repair itself. In contrast, damage inflicted by poliovirus to mature nerve cells is permanent, because these cells do not divide and usually cannot be replaced. Many of the temporary symptoms associated with viral infections, such as fever and aches, actually result from the body's own efforts at defending itself against infection.

The immune system is a complex and critical part of the body's natural defenses (see Chapter 43). The immune system is also the basis for the major medical tool for preventing viral infections—vaccines. **Vaccines** are harmless variants or derivatives of pathogenic microbes that stimulate the immune system to mount defenses against the actual pathogen. Vaccination has eradicated smallpox, at one time a devastating scourge in many parts of the world. The viruses that cause smallpox, polio, and measles infect only humans. This very narrow host range was critical to the successful effort of the World Health Organization to eradicate smallpox; similar worldwide vaccination campaigns currently are under way to eradicate the other two viruses as well. Effective vaccines are also available against rubella, mumps, hepatitis B, and a number of other viral diseases.

Although vaccines can prevent certain viral illnesses, medical technology can do little, at present, to cure most viral infections once they occur. The antibiotics that help us recover from bacterial infections are powerless against viruses. Antibiotics kill bacteria by inhibiting enzyme-catalyzed processes specific to the pathogens, but viruses have few or no enzymes of their own. However, a few drugs effectively combat certain viruses. Most antiviral drugs resemble nucleosides and as a result interfere with viral nucleic acid synthesis. One such drug is acyclovir, which impedes herpesvirus reproduction by inhibiting the viral polymerase that synthesizes viral DNA. Similarly, azidothymidine (AZT) curbs HIV reproduction by interfering with the synthesis of DNA by reverse transcriptase. In the past ten years, much effort has gone into developing drugs against HIV. Currently, multidrug treatments, sometimes called "cocktails," have been found to be most effective. Such a regimen commonly includes a combination of two nucleoside mimics and a protease inhibitor, which interferes with an enzyme required for assembly of virus particles.

Emerging Viruses

Viruses that appear suddenly or that suddenly come to the attention of medical scientists are often referred to as *emerging viruses*. HIV, the AIDS virus, is a classic example: This virus appeared in San Francisco in the early 1980s, seemingly out of nowhere. The deadly Ebola virus, recognized initially in 1976 in central Africa, is one of several emerging viruses that cause *hemorrhagic fever,* an often fatal syndrome characterized by fever, vomiting, massive bleeding, and circulatory system collapse. A number of other dangerous new viruses cause encephalitis, inflammation of the brain. One example is the West Nile virus, which appeared for the first time in North America in 1999 and has spread to all 48 contiguous states in the U.S.

An even more recent viral disease to emerge is *severe acute respiratory syndrome (SARS)*, which first appeared in southern China in November 2002 **(Figure 18.11a)**. During a global outbreak from November 2002 to July 2003, about 8,000 people were known to be infected, of whom more than 700 subsequently died. Researchers quickly identified the agent causing SARS as a *coronavirus,* a virus with a single-stranded RNA genome (class IV) that was not previously known to cause disease in humans **(Figure 18.11b)**.

From where and how do such viruses burst on the human scene, giving rise to previously rare or unknown diseases? Three processes contribute to the emergence of viral diseases. First, the mutation of existing viruses is a major source of these new diseases. RNA viruses tend to have an unusually high rate of mutation because errors in replicating their RNA genomes are not corrected by proofreading. Some mutations enable existing viruses to evolve into new genetic varieties (strains) that can cause disease in individuals who had developed immunity to the ancestral virus. Flu epidemics, for instance, are caused by new strains of influenza virus genetically different enough from earlier strains that people have little immunity to them.

Another source of new viral diseases is the spread of existing viruses from one host species to another. Scientists estimate that about three-quarters of new human diseases originate in other animals. For example, hantavirus is common in rodents, especially deer mice. The population of deer mice in the south-

30 nm

(a) Young ballet students in Hong Kong wear face masks to protect themselves from the virus causing SARS.

(b) The SARS-causing agent is a coronavirus like this one (colorized TEM), so named for the "corona" of glycoprotein spikes protruding from the envelope.

▲ **Figure 18.11 SARS (severe acute respiratory syndrome), a recently emerging viral disease.**

western United States exploded in 1993 after unusually wet weather increased the rodents' food supply. Many people who inhaled dust containing traces of urine and feces from infected mice became infected with hantavirus, and dozens died. The source of the SARS-causing virus was still undetermined as of spring 2004, although candidates include the exotic animals found in food markets in China. And early 2004 brought reports of the first cases of people in southeast Asia infected with a flu virus previously seen only in birds. If this virus evolves so that it can spread easily from person to person, the potential for a major human outbreak is significant. Indeed, evidence is strong that the flu pandemic of 1918–1919, which killed about 40 million people, originated in birds.

Finally, the dissemination of a viral disease from a small, isolated population can lead to widespread epidemics. For instance, AIDS went unnamed and virtually unnoticed for decades before it began to spread around the world. In this case, technological and social factors, including affordable international travel, blood transfusions, sexual promiscuity, and the abuse of intravenous drugs, allowed a previously rare human disease to become a global scourge.

Thus, emerging viruses are generally not new; rather, they are existing viruses that mutate, spread to new host species, or disseminate more widely in the current host species. Changes in host behavior or environmental changes can increase the viral traffic responsible for emerging diseases. For example, new roads through remote areas can allow viruses to spread between previously isolated human populations. Another problem is the destruction of forests to expand cropland, an environmental disturbance that brings humans into contact with other animals that may host viruses capable of infecting humans.

Viral Diseases in Plants

More than 2,000 types of viral diseases of plants are known, and together they account for an estimated loss of $15 billion annually worldwide due to agricultural and horticultural crop destruction. Common symptoms of viral infection include bleached or brown spots on leaves and fruits, stunted growth, and damaged flowers or roots, all tending to diminish the yield and quality of crops (Figure 18.12).

Plant viruses have the same basic structure and mode of replication as animal viruses. Most plant viruses discovered thus far, including tobacco mosaic virus (TMV), have an RNA genome. Many have a rod-shaped capsid, like TMV (see Figure 18.4a); others have a polyhedral capsid.

Plant viral diseases spread by two major routes. In the first route, called *horizontal transmission,* a plant is infected from an external source of the virus. Because the invading virus must get past the plant's outer protective layer of cells (the epidermis), the plant becomes more susceptible to viral infections if it has been damaged by wind, injury, or insects. Insects pose a double threat, because they can also act as carriers of viruses, transmitting disease from plant to plant. Farmers and gardeners may transmit plant viruses inadvertently on pruning shears and other tools. The other route of viral infection is *vertical transmission,* in which a plant inherits a viral infection from a parent. Vertical transmission can occur in

asexual propagation (for example, by taking cuttings) or in sexual reproduction via infected seeds.

Once a virus enters a plant cell and begins reproducing, viral components can spread throughout the plant by passing through plasmodesmata, the cytoplasmic connections that penetrate the walls between adjacent plant cells (see Figure 6.28). Proteins encoded by viral genes are capable of altering the diameter of plasmodesmata to allow passage of viral proteins or genomes. Scientists have not yet devised cures for most viral plant diseases. So their efforts are focused largely on reducing the incidence and transmission of such diseases and on breeding varieties of crop plants that are relatively resistant to certain viruses.

Viroids and Prions: The Simplest Infectious Agents

As small and simple as viruses are, they dwarf another class of pathogens: **viroids.** These are circular RNA molecules, only several hundred nucleotides long, that infect plants. One viroid disease has killed over 10 million coconut palms in the Philippines. Viroids do not encode proteins but can replicate in host plant cells, apparently using cellular enzymes. These small RNA molecules seem to cause errors in the regulatory systems that control plant growth, and the symptoms typically associated with viroid diseases are abnormal development and stunted growth.

An important lesson from viroids is that a single molecule can be an infectious agent that spreads a disease. But viroids are nucleic acid, whose ability to be replicated is well known. Even more surprising is the evidence for infectious *proteins,* called **prions,** which appear to cause a number of degenerative brain diseases in various animal species. These diseases include scrapie in sheep; mad cow disease, which has plagued the European beef industry in recent years; and Creutzfeldt-Jakob disease in humans, which has caused the death of some 125 British people in the past decade. Prions are most likely transmitted in food, as in the consumption by people of prion-laden beef from cattle with mad cow disease. Two characteristics of prions are especially alarming. First, prions are very slow-acting agents; the incubation period until symptoms appear is around ten years. Second, prions are virtually indestructible; they are not destroyed or deactivated by heating to normal cooking temperatures. To date, there is no known cure for prion diseases, and the only hope for developing effective treatments lies in understanding the mechanism of infection.

How can a protein, which cannot replicate itself, be a transmissible pathogen? According to the leading hypothesis, a prion is a misfolded form of a protein normally present in brain cells. When the prion gets into a cell containing the normal form of the protein, the prion

▲ Figure 18.12 **Viral infection of plants.** Infection with particular viruses causes "breaking" or streaking of tulip flower color (top), irregular brown patches on tomatoes (left center), and black blotching on squash (bottom).

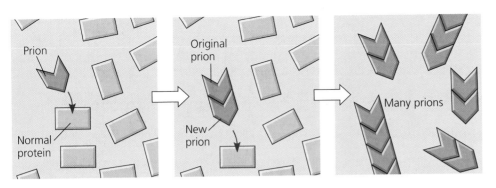

◄ **Figure 18.13 Model for how prions propagate.** Prions are misfolded versions of normal brain proteins. When a prion contacts a normal "twin," it may induce the normal protein to assume the abnormal shape. The resulting chain reaction may continue until prions accumulate in aggregates to dangerous levels, causing cellular malfunction and eventual degeneration of the brain.

converts the normal protein to the prion version **(Figure 18.13)**. In this way, prions may repeatedly trigger chain reactions that increase their numbers. This model, first proposed in the early 1980s, is now widely accepted.

Concept Check 18.2

1. Describe two ways a preexisting virus can become an emerging virus.
2. Compare horizontal versus vertical transmission of viruses in plants.
3. Why does the long incubation period of prions increase their danger as a cause of human disease?

For suggested answers, see Appendix A.

Concept 18.3

Rapid reproduction, mutation, and genetic recombination contribute to the genetic diversity of bacteria

By studying the mechanisms by which viruses are replicated, researchers also learn about the mechanisms that regulate DNA replication and gene expression in cells. Bacteria are equally valuable as microbial models in genetics research, but for different reasons. As prokaryotic cells, bacteria allow researchers to investigate molecular genetics in the simplest true organisms. Information about numerous prokaryotic species has accumulated recently with the advent of large-scale genome sequencing. However, except where otherwise noted, we will focus on what has been learned from the well-studied intestinal bacterium *Escherichia coli*, sometimes called "the laboratory rat of molecular biology."

The Bacterial Genome and Its Replication

The main component of the genome in most bacteria is one double-stranded, circular DNA molecule that is associated with a small amount of protein. Although we will refer to this

structure as the *bacterial chromosome*, it is very different from eukaryotic chromosomes, which have linear DNA molecules associated with a large amount of protein. In *E. coli*, the chromosomal DNA consists of about 4.6 million nucleotide pairs, representing about 4,400 genes. This is 100 times more DNA than is found in a typical virus, but only about one-thousandth as much DNA as in an average human cell. Still, this is a lot of DNA to be packaged in such a small container.

Stretched out, the DNA of an *E. coli* cell would measure about a millimeter in length, 500 times longer than the cell. Within a bacterium, however, certain proteins cause the chromosome to tightly coil and "supercoil," densely packing it so that it fills only part of the cell. This dense region of DNA, called the **nucleoid,** is not bounded by membrane like the nucleus of a eukaryotic cell. In addition to the chromosome, many bacteria also have plasmids, much smaller circles of DNA. Each plasmid has only a small number of genes, from just a few to several dozen. You will learn more about plasmids later in this section.

Bacterial cells divide by binary fission, which is preceded by replication of the bacterial chromosome (see Figure 12.11). From a single origin of replication, DNA synthesis progresses in both directions around the circular chromosome **(Figure 18.14)**. Bacteria can proliferate very rapidly in a favorable environment, whether in a natural habitat or in a laboratory culture. For example, *E. coli* growing under optimal conditions can divide every 20 minutes. A laboratory culture started with a single cell on an agar plate containing nutrients can produce a mass, or *colony,* of 10^7 to 10^8 bacteria within 12 hours. Reproductive rates in the organism's natural habitat, the large intestine (colon) of mammals, can be much slower. One doubling in the human colon takes about 12 hours, for instance, but this is enough to replace the 2×10^{10} bacteria lost each day in feces.

Mutation and Genetic Recombination as Sources of Genetic Variation

Binary fission is an asexual process—the production of offspring from a single parent. Thus, most of the bacteria in a colony are genetically identical to the parent cell. Mutation, however, can cause some of the offspring to differ slightly in genetic makeup. The probability of a spontaneous mutation

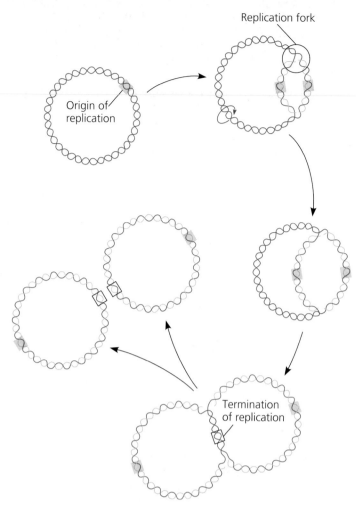

▲ **Figure 18.14 Replication of a bacterial chromosome.** From one origin, DNA replication progresses in both directions around the circular chromosome until the entire chromosome has been reproduced. Enzymes that cut, twirl (red arrow), and reseal the double helix prevent the DNA from tangling. Keep in mind that although the *overall* direction of DNA replication is outward from the origin in both directions, one new strand at each replication fork is made discontinuously in the direction back toward the origin (see Figure 16.16).

occurring in a given *E. coli* gene averages about 1×10^{-7} per cell division, only one in 10 million. But among the 2×10^{10} new *E. coli* cells that arise each day in a single human colon, there will be approximately $(2 \times 10^{10})(1 \times 10^{-7}) = 2,000$ bacteria that have a mutation in that gene. The total number of mutations when all 4,300 *E. coli* genes are considered is about $4,300 \times 2,000 = 9$ million per day per human host. The important point is that new mutations, though individually rare, can significantly increase genetic diversity when reproductive rates are very high because of short generation spans. This diversity, in turn, affects the evolution of bacterial populations: Bacterial populations composed of individuals that are genetically well equipped for the local environment will reproduce more prolifically than populations with less fit individuals.

In contrast, new mutations make a relatively small contribution to genetic variation in a population of slowly reproducing organisms, such as humans. Most of the heritable variation we observe in a human population is due not to the creation of novel alleles by *new* mutations, but to the recombination of existing alleles during sexual reproduction (see Chapter 15). Even in bacteria, where new mutations are a major source of individual variation, additional diversity arises from genetic recombination, defined as the combining of DNA from two sources. In most of the cases we will discuss here, the two sources of DNA are the genomes of two separate bacterial cells, with genomic DNA from one cell ending up in the genome of the other cell.

Figure 18.15 shows one type of experiment providing evidence that genetic recombination occurs in bacteria. This experiment made use of two mutant *E. coli* strains, each unable to synthesize a required amino acid, either tryptophan

---

Figure 18.15

Inquiry Can a bacterial cell acquire genes from another bacterial cell?

EXPERIMENT Researchers had two mutant strains, one that could make arginine but not tryptophan (*arg*⁺ *trp*⁻) and one that could make tryptophan but not arginine (*arg*⁻ *trp*⁺). Each mutant strain and a mixture of both strains were grown in a liquid medium containing all the required amino acids. Samples from each liquid culture were spread on plates containing a solution of glucose and inorganic salts (minimal medium), solidified with agar.

Mixture

Mutant strain *arg*⁺ *trp*⁻   Mutant strain *arg*⁻ *trp*⁺

RESULTS Only the samples from the mixed culture, contained cells that gave rise to colonies on minimal medium, which lacks amino acids.

Mixture

Mutant strain *arg*⁺ *trp*⁻ — No colonies (control)

Colonies grew

Mutant strain *arg*⁻ *trp*⁺ — No colonies (control)

CONCLUSION Because only cells that can make both arginine and tryptophan (*arg*⁺ *trp*⁺ cells) can grow into colonies on minimal medium, the lack of colonies on the two control plates showed that no further mutations had occurred restoring this ability to cells of the mutant strains. Thus, each cell from the mixture that formed a colony on the minimal medium must have acquired one or more genes from a cell of the other strain by genetic recombination.

or arginine. As a result, the mutant strains were unable to grow on a minimal medium containing only glucose (as a source of organic carbon) and salts. When bacteria from the two strains were incubated together, however, cells emerged that could grow on minimal medium, indicating that they made *both* tryptophan and arginine. The number of such cells far exceeded what could be accounted for by mutation. Most of the cells that could synthesize both amino acids must have acquired one or more genes from the other strain, presumably by genetic recombination.

Mechanisms of Gene Transfer and Genetic Recombination in Bacteria

Bacteria differ from eukaryotes in the mechanisms used to bring DNA from two individuals together in one cell. In eukaryotes, the sexual processes of meiosis and fertilization combine DNA from two individuals in a single zygote (see Chapter 13). But meiosis and fertilization do not occur in prokaryotes. Instead, three other processes—transformation, transduction, and conjugation—bring together bacterial DNA from different individuals.

Transformation

In the context of bacterial genetics, the process of **transformation** is the alteration of a bacterial cell's genotype and phenotype by the uptake of naked, foreign DNA from the surrounding environment. For example, bacteria of a harmless strain of *Streptococcus pneumoniae* can be transformed to pneumonia-causing cells by the uptake of DNA from a medium containing dead, broken-open cells of the pathogenic strain (see Figure 16.2). This transformation occurs when a live nonpathogenic cell takes up a piece of DNA carrying the allele for pathogenicity, which codes for a cell coat that protects the bacterium from a host's immune system. The foreign allele is then incorporated into the chromosome of the nonpathogenic cell, replacing the allele for the "coatless" condition by genetic recombination—an exchange of DNA segments by crossing over. The cell is now a recombinant: Its chromosome contains DNA derived from two different cells.

For many years after transformation was discovered in laboratory cultures, most biologists believed the process to be too rare and haphazard to play an important role in natural bacterial populations. But researchers have since learned that many bacteria possess cell-surface proteins that recognize and transport DNA from closely related species into the cell, which can then incorporate the foreign DNA into the genome. *E. coli* and some other bacteria appear to lack this transformation mechanism. However, placing *E. coli* in a culture medium containing a relatively high concentration of calcium ions will artificially stimulate the cells to take up small pieces of DNA. In biotechnology, this technique is applied to introduce foreign genes into the *E. coli* genome—

genes coding for valuable proteins, such as human insulin and growth hormone.

Transduction

In the process known as **transduction**, phages (the viruses that infect bacteria) carry bacterial genes from one host cell to another as a result of aberrations in the phage reproductive cycle.

Figure 18.16 depicts the events in *generalized transduction*, a process by which bacterial genes are randomly transferred from one bacterial cell to another. Recall that near the end of a phage's lytic cycle, viral nucleic acid molecules are packaged within capsids, and the completed phages are released when

1. Phage infects a bacterial cell that has alleles A^+ and B^+.

Phage DNA

$A^+ B^+$

2. Host DNA (brown) is fragmented, and phage DNA and proteins are made. This is the donor cell.

A^+ B^+

Donor cell

3. A bacterial DNA fragment (in this case a fragment with the A^+ allele) may be packaged in a phage capsid.

A^+

4. Phage with the A^+ allele from the donor cell infects a recipient A^-B^- cell, and crossing over (recombination) between donor DNA (brown) and recipient DNA (green) occurs at two places (dotted lines).

Crossing over

A^+
A^- B^-

Recipient cell

5. The genotype of the resulting recombinant cell (A^+B^-) differs from the genotypes of both the donor (A^+B^+) and the recipient (A^-B^-).

A^+ B^-

Recombinant cell

▲ **Figure 18.16 Generalized transduction.** Phages occasionally carry random pieces of the host chromosome containing bacterial genes from one cell (the donor) to another (the recipient). The transferred DNA may recombine with the genome of the recipient, bringing about a recombinant cell.

the host cell lyses. Occasionally, a small piece of the host cell's degraded DNA is accidentally packaged within a phage capsid in place of the phage genome. Such a virus is defective because it lacks its own genetic material. However, after its release from the lysed host, the phage can attach to another bacterium (the recipient) and inject the piece of bacterial DNA acquired from the first cell (the donor). Some of this DNA can subsequently replace the homologous region of the recipient cell's chromosome, if a crossover takes place at each end of the piece. In this case, the recipient cell's chromosome becomes a combination of DNA derived from two cells; genetic recombination has occurred.

Temperate phages, those able to integrate their genome into the bacterial chromosome as a prophage (see Figure 18.7), can carry out *specialized transduction*. In this process, a prophage picks up just a few adjacent bacterial genes as it exits the chromosome and transfers them to a new host cell. This process can result in efficient transfer, but only of genes adjacent to the prophage site.

Conjugation and Plasmids

Sometimes referred to as bacterial "sex," **conjugation** is the direct transfer of genetic material between two bacterial cells that are temporarily joined. The DNA transfer is one-way: One cell donates DNA, and its "mate" receives the DNA. The donor, sometimes called the "male," uses appendages called sex pili (singular, sex pilus) to attach to the recipient, sometimes called the "female" **(Figure 18.17)**. After contacting a recipient cell, a sex pilus retracts, pulling the two cells together, much like a grappling hook. A temporary cytoplasmic *mating bridge* then forms between the two cells, providing an avenue for DNA transfer.

Sex pilus   1 μm

▲ **Figure 18.17 Bacterial conjugation.** The *E. coli* donor cell (left) extends sex pili, one of which is attached to a recipient cell. The two cells will be drawn close together, allowing a cytoplasmic mating bridge to form between them. Through this bridge, the donor will transfer DNA to the recipient (colorized TEM).

In most cases, the ability to form sex pili and donate DNA during conjugation results from the presence of a special piece of DNA called an **F factor** (F for fertility). An F factor can exist either as a segment of DNA within the bacterial chromosome or as a plasmid. A **plasmid** is a small, circular, self-replicating DNA molecule separate from the bacterial chromosome. Certain plasmids, such as F plasmids, can undergo reversible integration into the cell's chromosome. A genetic element that can replicate either as part of the bacterial chromosome or independently of it is called an **episome**. In addition to some plasmids, temperate viruses, such as phage λ, qualify as episomes.

A plasmid has only a small number of genes, and these genes are not required for the survival and reproduction of the bacterium under normal conditions. However, the genes of plasmids can confer advantages on bacteria living in stressful environments. For example, the F plasmid facilitates genetic recombination, which may be advantageous in a changing environment that no longer favors existing strains in a bacterial population.

The F Plasmid and Conjugation. The F factor and its plasmid form, the **F plasmid**, consist of about 25 genes, most required for the production of sex pili. Cells containing the F plasmid, designated F⁺ cells, function as DNA donors during conjugation. The F plasmid replicates in synchrony with the chromosomal DNA, and division of an F⁺ cell usually gives rise to two offspring that are both F⁺. Cells lacking the F factor in either form, designated F⁻, function as DNA recipients during conjugation. The F⁺ condition is transferable in the sense that an F⁺ cell converts an F⁻ cell to F⁺ when the two cells conjugate, as shown in **Figure 18.18a**, on the next page. The original cell remains F⁺ because the process of transfer involves a special type of DNA replication: One parental strand of F factor DNA is transferred across the mating bridge, and each parental strand acts as a template for synthesis of the second strand in its respective cell. In a mating of F⁺ and F⁻ cells, only F plasmid DNA is transferred.

Chromosomal genes can be transferred during conjugation when the donor cell's F factor is integrated into the chromosome **(Figure 18.18b, top)**. A cell with the F factor built into its chromosome is called an *Hfr cell* (for *High frequency of recombination*). Like an F⁺ cell, an Hfr cell functions as a donor during conjugation: DNA replication is initiated at a specific point on the integrated F factor DNA; from that point, a single strand of the F factor DNA moves into the F⁻ partner, dragging along adjacent chromosomal DNA **(Figure 18.18b, center)**. Random movements of the bacteria almost always disrupt conjugation long before an entire strand of the Hfr chromosome can be passed to the F⁻ cell. The single strand in each cell serves as a template for synthesis of a second strand. Thus, the Hfr cell's DNA remains the same, while the F⁻ cell acquires new DNA, some of it chromosomal. Temporarily, the recipient cell is a partial diploid, containing its own complete

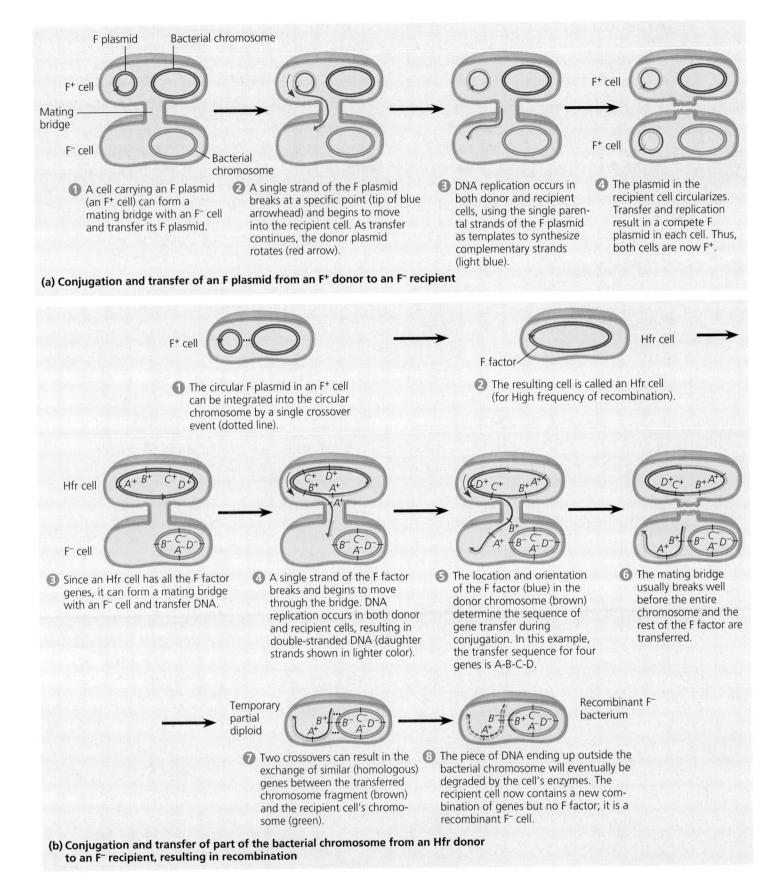

① A cell carrying an F plasmid (an F⁺ cell) can form a mating bridge with an F⁻ cell and transfer its F plasmid.

② A single strand of the F plasmid breaks at a specific point (tip of blue arrowhead) and begins to move into the recipient cell. As transfer continues, the donor plasmid rotates (red arrow).

③ DNA replication occurs in both donor and recipient cells, using the single parental strands of the F plasmid as templates to synthesize complementary strands (light blue).

④ The plasmid in the recipient cell circularizes. Transfer and replication result in a compete F plasmid in each cell. Thus, both cells are now F⁺.

(a) Conjugation and transfer of an F plasmid from an F⁺ donor to an F⁻ recipient

① The circular F plasmid in an F⁺ cell can be integrated into the circular chromosome by a single crossover event (dotted line).

② The resulting cell is called an Hfr cell (for High frequency of recombination).

③ Since an Hfr cell has all the F factor genes, it can form a mating bridge with an F⁻ cell and transfer DNA.

④ A single strand of the F factor breaks and begins to move through the bridge. DNA replication occurs in both donor and recipient cells, resulting in double-stranded DNA (daughter strands shown in lighter color).

⑤ The location and orientation of the F factor (blue) in the donor chromosome (brown) determine the sequence of gene transfer during conjugation. In this example, the transfer sequence for four genes is A-B-C-D.

⑥ The mating bridge usually breaks well before the entire chromosome and the rest of the F factor are transferred.

⑦ Two crossovers can result in the exchange of similar (homologous) genes between the transferred chromosome fragment (brown) and the recipient cell's chromosome (green).

⑧ The piece of DNA ending up outside the bacterial chromosome will eventually be degraded by the cell's enzymes. The recipient cell now contains a new combination of genes but no F factor; it is a recombinant F⁻ cell.

(b) Conjugation and transfer of part of the bacterial chromosome from an Hfr donor to an F⁻ recipient, resulting in recombination

▲ **Figure 18.18 Conjugation and recombination in *E. coli*.** The DNA replication that accompanies transfer of an F plasmid or part of an Hfr bacterial chromosome is called *rolling circle replication*. This is sometimes referred to as the "toilet paper" model because of the way the single strand rolls off the donor cell DNA and moves into the recipient cell.

F⁻ chromosome plus transferred chromosomal DNA from the Hfr donor. If part of the newly acquired DNA aligns with the homologous region of the F⁻ chromosome, segments of DNA can be exchanged (**Figure 18.18b, bottom**). Reproduction of this cell gives rise to a population of recombinant bacteria with genes derived from two different cells. This process of conjugation and recombination accounts for the results of the experiment shown in Figure 18.15, in which one of the bacterial strains was Hfr and the other F⁻.

R Plasmids and Antibiotic Resistance. In the 1950s, Japanese physicians began to notice that some hospital patients suffering from bacterial dysentery, which produces severe diarrhea, did not respond to antibiotics that had generally been effective in the past. Apparently, resistance to these antibiotics had evolved in certain strains of *Shigella,* the pathogen. Eventually, researchers began to identify the specific genes that confer antibiotic resistance in *Shigella* and other pathogenic bacteria. Sometimes, mutation in a chromosomal gene of the pathogen can cause resistance. For example, a mutation in one gene may reduce the pathogen's ability to transport a particular antibiotic into the cell. Mutation in a different gene may alter the intracellular target protein for an antibiotic molecule, reducing its inhibitory effect. Some bacteria have resistance genes coding for enzymes that specifically destroy certain antibiotics, such as tetracycline or ampicillin. Genes conferring this type of resistance are generally carried by plasmids known as **R plasmids** (R for resistance).

Exposure of a bacterial population to a specific antibiotic, whether in a laboratory culture or within a host organism, will kill antibiotic-sensitive bacteria but not those that happen to have R plasmids with genes that counter the antibiotic. The theory of natural selection predicts that under these circumstances, the fraction of the bacterial population carrying genes for antibiotic resistance will increase, and that is exactly what happens. The medical consequences are also predictable: Resistant strains of pathogens are becoming more common, making the treatment of certain bacterial infections more difficult. The problem is compounded by the fact that many R plasmids, like F plasmids, have genes that encode sex pili and enable plasmid transfer from one bacterial cell to another by conjugation. Making the problem still worse, some R plasmids carry as many as ten genes for resistance to that many antibiotics. How do so many antibiotic resistance genes become part of a single plasmid? The answer involves another type of mobile genetic element, which we investigate next.

Transposition of Genetic Elements

In the previous section, you learned how DNA from one bacterial cell can be transferred to another cell and recombined into the genome of the recipient. The DNA of a single cell can also undergo recombination owing to movement of so-called *transposable genetic elements,* or simply **transposable elements,**

within the cell's genome. Unlike a plasmid or prophage, transposable elements never exist independently but are always part of chromosomal or plasmid DNA. During the movement of these elements, called *transposition,* the transposable element moves from one site in a cell's DNA to another site—a target site—by a type of recombination process. In a bacterial cell, a transposable element may move within the chromosome, from a plasmid to the chromosome (or vice versa), or from one plasmid to another.

Transposable elements are sometimes called "jumping genes," but the phrase is misleading because they never completely detach from the cell's DNA. (The original and new DNA sites are brought together by DNA folding.) Some transposable elements move from one DNA location to another by a "cut-and-paste" mechanism. Others move by a "copy-and-paste" mechanism, in which the transposable element replicates at its original site, and a copy inserts elsewhere. In other words, the transposable element is added at a new site without being lost from the old site.

Although transposable elements vary in their selectivity for target sites, most can move to many alternative locations in the DNA. This ability to scatter certain genes throughout the genome makes transposition fundamentally different from other mechanisms of genetic shuffling. During bacterial transformation, generalized transduction, and conjugation (and during meiosis in eukaryotes as well), recombination occurs between homologous regions of DNA, regions of identical or very similar base sequence that can undergo base pairing. In contrast, the insertion of a transposable element in a new site does not depend on complementary base sequences. A transposable element can move genes to a site where genes of that sort have never before existed.

Insertion Sequences

The simplest transposable elements, called **insertion sequences,** exist only in bacteria. An insertion sequence contains a single gene, which codes for transposase, an enzyme that catalyzes movement of the insertion sequence from one site to another within the genome. The transposase gene is bracketed by a pair of noncoding DNA sequences about 20 to 40 nucleotides long. These sequences are called *inverted repeats* because the base sequence at one end of the insertion sequence is repeated upside down and backward (inverted) at the other end (**Figure 18.19a,** on the next page). Transposase recognizes these inverted repeats as the boundaries of the insertion sequence. During transposition, molecules of the enzyme bind to the inverted repeats and to a target site elsewhere in the genome and catalyze the necessary DNA cutting and resealing.

An insertion sequence can cause mutations if it transposes into the coding sequence of a gene or into a DNA region that regulates gene expression. This mechanism of mutation is intrinsic to the cell, in contrast to mutagenesis by extrinsic factors such as environmental radiation and chemicals. Insertion sequences account for about 1.5% of the *E. coli* genome.

Insertion sequence

```
5' [=== ATCCGGT...          ...ACCGGAT ===] 3'
3' [=== TAGGCCA...          ...TGGCCTA ===] 5'
      Inverted    Transposase gene   Inverted
      repeat                         repeat
```

(a) Insertion sequences, the simplest transposable elements in bacteria, contain a single gene that encodes transposase, which catalyzes movement within the genome. The inverted repeats are backward, upside-down versions of each other; only a portion is shown. The inverted repeat sequence varies from one type of insertion sequence to another.

Transposon

```
      Insertion    Antibiotic      Insertion
      sequence    resistance gene  sequence
5' [======================================] 3'
3' [======================================] 5'
      Inverted repeats          Transposase gene
```

(b) Transposons contain one or more genes in addition to the transposase gene. In the transposon shown here, a gene for resistance to an antibiotic is located between twin insertion sequences. The gene for antibiotic resistance is carried along as part of the transposon when the transposon is inserted at a new site in the genome.

▲ **Figure 18.19 Transposable genetic elements in bacteria.** These diagrams are not to scale; most transposons are considerably longer than insertion sequences.

However, mutation of a given gene by transposition occurs only rarely—about once in every 10 million generations. This is about the same as the spontaneous mutation rate due to other factors.

Transposons

Transposable elements longer and more complex than insertion sequences, called **transposons**, also move about in the bacterial genome. In addition to the DNA required for transposition, transposons include extra genes that go along for the ride, such as genes for antibiotic resistance. In some bacterial transposons, the extra genes are sandwiched between two insertion sequences **(Figure 18.19b)**. It is as though two insertion sequences happened to land relatively close together in the genome and now travel together, along with all the DNA between them, as a single transposable element. Other bacterial transposons do not contain insertion sequences; these have different inverted repeats at their ends.

In contrast to insertion sequences, which are not known to benefit bacteria in any specific way, transposons may help bacteria adapt to new environments. We mentioned earlier that a single R plasmid can carry several genes for resistance

to different antibiotics. This is explained by transposons, which can add a gene for antibiotic resistance to a plasmid already carrying genes for resistance to other antibiotics. The transmission of this composite plasmid to other bacterial cells by cell division or conjugation can then spread resistance to a variety of antibiotics throughout a bacterial population. In an antibiotic-rich environment, natural selection favors bacteria that have built up R plasmids with multiple antibiotic resistance genes through a series of transpositions.

Transposons are not unique to bacteria and are important components of eukaryotic genomes as well. You will learn about transposable elements in eukaryotes in Chapter 19.

Concept Check 18.3

1. Distinguish between the three mechanisms of transferring DNA from one bacterial cell to another.
2. What are the similarities and differences between lysogenic phage DNA and a plasmid?
3. Explain why the process of conjugation can lead to genetic recombination of chromosomal DNA in an Hfr $\times$ F$^-$ mating, but not in an F$^+$ $\times$ F$^-$ mating.

For suggested answers, see Appendix A.

Concept 18.4

Individual bacteria respond to environmental change by regulating their gene expression

Mutations and various types of gene transfer generate the genetic variation that makes natural selection possible. And natural selection, acting over many generations, can increase the proportion of individuals in a bacterial population that are adapted to some new environmental condition. But how can an individual bacterium, locked into the genome it has inherited, cope with environmental fluctuation?

Consider, for instance, an individual *E. coli* cell living in the erratic environment of a human colon, dependent for its nutrients on the whimsical eating habits of its host. If the environment is lacking in the amino acid tryptophan, which the bacterium needs to survive, the cell responds by activating a metabolic pathway that makes tryptophan from another compound. Later, if the human host eats a tryptophan-rich meal, the bacterial cell stops producing tryptophan, thus saving itself from squandering its resources to produce a substance that is available from the surrounding solution in prefabricated form. This is just one example of how bacteria tune their metabolism to changing environments.

Metabolic control occurs on two levels (**Figure 18.20**). First, cells can adjust the activity of enzymes already present. This is a fairly fast response, which relies on the sensitivity of many enzymes to chemical cues that increase or decrease their catalytic activity (see Chapter 8). For example, the activity of the first enzyme in the tryptophan synthesis pathway is inhibited by the pathway's end product. Thus, if tryptophan accumulates in a cell, it shuts down the synthesis of more tryptophan by inhibiting enzyme activity. Such *feedback inhibition*, typical of anabolic (biosynthetic) pathways, allows a cell to adapt to short-term fluctuations in the supply of a substance it needs.

Second, cells can adjust the amount being made of certain enzymes; that is, they can regulate the expression of the genes encoding the enzymes. If, in our example, the environment continues to provide all the tryptophan the cell needs, the cell stops making the enzymes that work in the tryptophan pathway. This control of enzyme production occurs at the level of transcription, the synthesis of messenger RNA coding for these enzymes. More generally, many genes of the bacterial genome are switched on or off by changes in the metabolic status of the cell. The basic mechanism for this control of gene expression in bacteria, described as the *operon model*, was discovered in 1961 by François Jacob and Jacques Monod at the Pasteur Institute in Paris. Let's see what an operon is and

how it works, using the control of tryptophan synthesis as our first example.

Operons: The Basic Concept

E. coli synthesizes tryptophan from a precursor molecule in a series of steps, each reaction catalyzed by a specific enzyme (see Figure 18.20). The five genes coding for these enzymes are clustered together on the bacterial chromosome. A single promoter serves all five genes, which constitute a transcription unit. (Recall from Chapter 17 that a promoter is a site where RNA polymerase can bind to DNA and begin transcription.) Thus, transcription gives rise to one long mRNA molecule that codes for all five enzymes in the tryptophan pathway. The cell can translate this mRNA into five separate polypeptides because the mRNA is punctuated with start and stop codons that signal where the coding sequence for each polypeptide begins and ends.

A key advantage of grouping genes of related function into one transcription unit is that a single on-off "switch" can control the whole cluster of functionally related genes. When an *E. coli* cell must make tryptophan for itself because the nutrient medium lacks this amino acid, all the enzymes for the metabolic pathway are synthesized at one time. The switch is a segment of DNA called an **operator**. Both its location and name suit its function: Positioned within the promoter or between the promoter and the enzyme-coding genes, the operator controls the access of RNA polymerase to the genes. All together, the operator, the promoter, and the genes they control—the entire stretch of DNA required for enzyme production for the tryptophan pathway—constitute an **operon**. Here we are dissecting the *trp* operon (*trp* for tryptophan), one of many operons in the *E. coli* genome (**Figure 18.21**, on the next page).

If the operator is the switch for controlling transcription, how does this switch work? By itself, the *trp* operon is turned on; that is, RNA polymerase can bind to the promoter and transcribe the genes of the operon. The operon can be switched off by a protein called the *trp* **repressor**. The repressor binds to the operator and blocks attachment of RNA polymerase to the promoter, preventing transcription of the genes. A repressor protein is specific; that is, it recognizes and binds only to the operator of a particular operon. The repressor that switches off the *trp* operon by binding to the *trp* operator has no effect on other operons in the *E. coli* genome.

The *trp* repressor is the product of a **regulatory gene** called *trpR*, which is located some distance away from the operon it controls and has its own promoter. Regulatory genes are expressed continuously, although at a low rate, and a few *trp* repressor molecules are always present in *E. coli* cells. Why, then, is the *trp* operon not switched off permanently? First, the binding of repressors to operators is reversible. An operator vacillates between two states: one

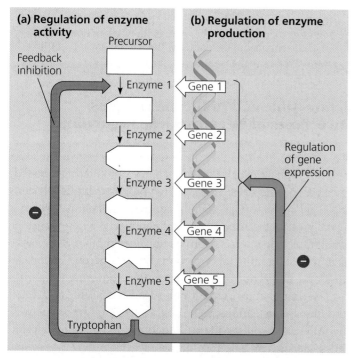

(a) Regulation of enzyme activity

Feedback inhibition

Precursor

Enzyme 1 — Gene 1
Enzyme 2 — Gene 2
Enzyme 3 — Gene 3
Enzyme 4 — Gene 4
Enzyme 5 — Gene 5

Tryptophan

(b) Regulation of enzyme production

Regulation of gene expression

▲ **Figure 18.20 Regulation of a metabolic pathway.** In the pathway for tryptophan synthesis, an abundance of tryptophan can both **(a)** inhibit the activity of the first enzyme in the pathway (feedback inhibition), a rapid response, and **(b)** repress expression of the genes for all the enzymes needed for the pathway, a longer-term response. The ⊝ symbol stands for inhibition.

(a) **Tryptophan absent, repressor inactive, operon on.** RNA polymerase attaches to the DNA at the promoter and transcribes the operon's genes.

(b) **Tryptophan present, repressor active, operon off.** As tryptophan accumulates, it inhibits its own production by activating the repressor protein.

◀ **Figure 18.21 The *trp* operon: regulated synthesis of repressible enzymes.** Tryptophan is an amino acid produced by an anabolic pathway catalyzed by repressible enzymes. **(a)** Five genes encoding the polypeptides that make up the enzymes of this pathway are grouped, along with a promoter and an operator, into the *trp* operon. The *trp* operator is located within the *trp* promoter. **(b)** Accumulation of tryptophan, the end product of the pathway, represses transcription of the *trp* operon, thus blocking synthesis of all the enzymes in the pathway. The mechanism in *E. coli* is shown here.

without the repressor bound and one with the repressor bound. The relative duration of each state depends on the number of active repressor molecules around. Second, the *trp* repressor, like most regulatory proteins, is an allosteric protein, with two alternative shapes, active and inactive (see Figure 8.20). The *trp* repressor is synthesized in an inactive form with little affinity for the *trp* operator. Only if tryptophan binds to the *trp* repressor at an allosteric site does the repressor protein change to the active form that can attach to the operator, turning the operon off.

Tryptophan functions in this system as a **corepressor,** a small molecule that cooperates with a repressor protein to switch an operon off. As tryptophan accumulates, more tryptophan molecules associate with *trp* repressor molecules, which can then bind to the *trp* operator and shut down production of the tryptophan pathway enzymes. If the cell's tryptophan level drops, transcription of the operon's genes resumes. This is one example of how gene expression responds rapidly to changes in the cell's internal and external environment.

Repressible and Inducible Operons: Two Types of Negative Gene Regulation

The *trp* operon is said to be a *repressible operon* because its transcription is usually on but can be inhibited (repressed) when a specific small molecule (tryptophan) binds allosterically to a regulatory protein. In contrast, an *inducible operon* is usually off but can be stimulated (induced) when a specific small molecule interacts with a regulatory protein. The classic example of an inducible operon is the *lac* operon (*lac* for lactose), the subject of Jacob and Monod's pioneering research.

The disaccharide lactose (milk sugar) is available to *E. coli* if the human host drinks milk. Lactose metabolism begins with hydrolysis of the disaccharide into its component monosaccharides, glucose and galactose, a reaction catalyzed by the enzyme β-galactosidase. Only a few molecules of this enzyme are present in an *E. coli* cell growing in the absence of lactose. But if lactose is added to the bacterium's environment, the number of β-galactosidase molecules in the cell increases a thousandfold within about 15 minutes.

The gene for β-galactosidase is part of the *lac* operon, which includes two other genes coding for enzymes that function in lactose metabolism. The entire transcription unit is under the command of a single operator and promoter. The regulatory gene, *lacI*, located outside the operon, codes for an allosteric repressor protein that can switch off the *lac* operon by binding to the operator. So far, this sounds just like regulation of the *trp* operon, but there is one important difference. Recall that the *trp* repressor is inactive by itself and requires tryptophan as a corepressor in order to bind to the operator. The *lac* repressor, in contrast, is active all by itself, binding to the operator and switching the *lac* operon off. In this case, a specific small molecule, called an **inducer**, *inactivates* the repressor.

For the *lac* operon, the inducer is allolactose, an isomer of lactose formed in small amounts from lactose that enters the cell. In the absence of lactose (and hence allolactose), the *lac* repressor is in its active configuration, and the genes of the *lac* operon are silenced **(Figure 18.22a)**. If lactose is added to the cell's sur-

roundings, allolactose binds to the *lac* repressor and alters its conformation, nullifying the repressor's ability to attach to the operator. Without bound repressor, the *lac* operon is transcribed into mRNA for the lactose-utilizing enzymes **(Figure 18.22b)**.

In the context of gene regulation, the enzymes of the lactose pathway are referred to as *inducible enzymes*, because their synthesis is induced by a chemical signal (allolactose, in this case). Analogously, the enzymes for tryptophan synthesis are said to be repressible. *Repressible enzymes* generally function in anabolic pathways, which synthesize essential end products from raw materials (precursors). By suspending production of an end product when it is already present in sufficient quantity, the cell can allocate its organic precursors and energy for other uses. In contrast, inducible enzymes usually function in catabolic pathways, which break down a nutrient to simpler molecules. By producing the appropriate enzymes only when the nutrient is available, the cell avoids wasting energy and precursors making proteins that are not needed.

(a) **Lactose absent, repressor active, operon off.** The *lac* repressor is innately active, and in the absence of lactose it switches off the operon by binding to the operator.

◀ **Figure 18.22 The *lac* operon: regulated synthesis of inducible enzymes.** *E. coli* uses three enzymes to take up and metabolize lactose. The genes for these three enzymes are clustered in the *lac* operon. One gene, *lacZ*, codes for β-galactosidase, which hydrolyzes lactose to glucose and galactose. The second gene, *lacY*, codes for a permease, the membrane protein that transports lactose into the cell. The third gene, *lacA*, codes for an enzyme called transacetylase, whose function in lactose metabolism is still unclear. The gene for the *lac* repressor, *lacI*, happens to be adjacent to the *lac* operon, an unusual situation. The function of the darker green region at the upstream (left) end of the promoter is revealed in Figure 18.23.

(b) **Lactose present, repressor inactive, operon on.** Allolactose, an isomer of lactose, derepresses the operon by inactivating the repressor. In this way, the enzymes for lactose utilization are induced.

Regulation of both the *trp* and *lac* operons involves the *negative* control of genes, because the operons are switched off by the active form of the repressor protein. It may be easier to see this for the *trp* operon, but it is also true for the *lac* operon. Allolactose induces enzyme synthesis not by acting directly on the genome, but by freeing the *lac* operon from the negative effect of the repressor. Gene regulation is said to be *positive* only when a regulatory protein interacts directly with the genome to switch transcription on. Let's look at an example of positive control of genes, again involving the *lac* operon.

Positive Gene Regulation

For the lactose-utilizing enzymes to be synthesized in appreciable quantity, it is not sufficient for lactose to be present in the bacterial cell. The other requirement is that the simple sugar glucose be in short supply. Given a choice of substrates for glycolysis and other catabolic pathways, *E. coli* preferentially uses glucose. The enzymes for glucose breakdown (glycolysis; see Figure 9.9) are continually present.

How does the *E. coli* cell sense the glucose concentration, and how is this information relayed to the genome? Again, the mechanism depends on the interaction of an allosteric regulatory protein with a small organic molecule, in this case **cyclic AMP (cAMP)**, which accumulates when glucose is scarce (see Figure 11.9 for the structure of cAMP). The regulatory protein, called *catabolite activator protein (CAP)*, is an **activator** of transcription. When cAMP binds to CAP, the regulatory protein (CAP) assumes its active shape and can bind to a specific site at the upstream end of the *lac* promoter **(Figure 18.23a)**. The attachment of CAP to the promoter directly stimulates gene expression. Thus, this mechanism qualifies as positive regulation.

If the amount of glucose in the cell increases, the cAMP concentration falls, and without it, CAP detaches from the operon. Because CAP is inactive, transcription of the *lac* operon proceeds at only a low level, even in the presence of lactose **(Figure 18.23b)**. Thus, the *lac* operon is under dual control: negative control by the *lac* repressor and positive control by CAP. The state of the *lac* repressor (with or without bound allolactose) determines whether or not transcription of the *lac* operon's genes occurs at all; the state of CAP (with or without bound cAMP) controls the *rate* of transcription if the operon is repressor-free. It is as though the operon has both an on-off switch and a volume control.

In addition to the *lac* operon, CAP helps regulate several other operons that encode enzymes used in catabolic pathways. When glucose is plentiful and CAP is inactive, the synthesis of enzymes that catabolize compounds other than glucose generally slows down. The cell's ability to catabolize other compounds, such as lactose, enables a cell deprived of glucose to survive. The specific compounds present at the moment determine which operons are switched on. These multiple contingency mechanisms suit an organism that cannot control what its host eats. Bacteria are remarkable in their

(a) **Lactose present, glucose scarce (cAMP level high): abundant *lac* mRNA synthesized.** If glucose is scarce, the high level of cAMP activates CAP, and the *lac* operon produces large amounts of mRNA for the lactose pathway.

(b) **Lactose present, glucose present (cAMP level low): little *lac* mRNA synthesized.** When glucose is present, cAMP is scarce, and CAP is unable to stimulate transcription.

▲ **Figure 18.23 Positive control of the *lac* operon by catabolite activator protein (CAP).** RNA polymerase has high affinity for the *lac* promoter only when catabolite activator protein (CAP) is bound to a DNA site at the upstream end of the promoter. CAP attaches to its DNA site only when associated with cyclic AMP (cAMP), whose concentration in the cell rises when the glucose concentration falls. Thus, when glucose is present, even if lactose also is available, the cell preferentially catabolizes glucose and does not make the lactose-utilizing enzymes.

ability to adapt—over the long term by evolutionary changes in their genetic makeup and over the short term by the control of gene expression in individual cells. Of course, the various control mechanisms are also evolutionary products that exist because they have been favored by natural selection.

Concept Check 18.4

1. A certain mutation in *E. coli* changes the *lac* operator so that the active repressor cannot bind. How would this affect the cell's production of β-galactosidase?

2. How does binding of the *trp* corepressor and the *lac* inducer to their respective repressor proteins alter repressor function and transcription in each case?

For suggested answers, see Appendix A.

Go to the Campbell Biology website (**www.campbellbiology.com**) or CD-ROM to explore Activities, Investigations, and other interactive study aids.

SUMMARY OF KEY CONCEPTS

Concept 18.1

A virus has a genome but can reproduce only within a host cell

▶ **The Discovery of Viruses:** *Scientific Inquiry* (pp. 334–335) Researchers discovered viruses in the late 1800s by studying a plant disease, tobacco mosaic disease.

▶ **Structure of Viruses** (pp. 335–336) A virus is a small nucleic acid genome enclosed in a protein capsid and sometimes a membranous envelope containing viral proteins that help viruses enter cells. The genome may be single- or double-stranded DNA or RNA.

▶ **General Features of Viral Reproductive Cycles** (pp. 336–337) Viruses use enzymes, ribosomes, and small molecules of host cells to synthesize progeny viruses. Each type of virus has a characteristic host range.
Activity *Simplified Viral Reproductive Cycle*

▶ **Reproductive Cycles of Phages** (pp. 337–339) In the lytic cycle, entry of the viral genome into a bacterium programs destruction of host DNA, production of new phages, and digestion of the host's cell wall, releasing the progeny phages. In the lysogenic cycle, the genome of a temperate phage inserts into the bacterial chromosome as a prophage, which is passed on to host daughter cells until it is induced to leave the chromosome and initiate a lytic cycle.
Activity *Phage Lytic Cycle*
Activity *Phage Lysogenic and Lytic Cycles*

▶ **Reproductive Cycles of Animal Viruses** (pp. 339–342) Many animal viruses have an envelope. Retroviruses (such as HIV) use the enzyme reverse transcriptase to copy their RNA genome into DNA, which can be integrated into the host genome as a provirus.
Activity *Retrovirus (HIV) Reproductive Cycle*

▶ **Evolution of Viruses** (pp. 342–343) Since viruses can reproduce only within cells, they probably evolved after the first cells appeared, perhaps as packaged fragments of cellular nucleic acid.

Concept 18.2

Viruses, viroids, and prions are formidable pathogens in animals and plants

▶ **Viral Diseases in Animals** (pp. 343–344) Symptoms may be caused by direct viral harm to cells or by the body's immune response. Vaccines stimulate the immune system to defend the host against specific viruses.

▶ **Emerging Viruses** (p. 344) Outbreaks of "new" viral diseases in humans are usually caused by existing viruses that expand their host territory.
Investigation *What Causes Infections in AIDS Patients?*
Investigation *Why Do AIDS Rates Differ Across the U.S.?*

▶ **Viral Diseases in Plants** (p. 345) Viruses enter plant cells through damaged cell walls (horizontal transmission) or are inherited from a parent (vertical transmission).

▶ **Viroids and Prions: The Simplest Infectious Agents** (pp. 345–346) Viroids are naked RNA molecules that infect plants and disrupt their growth. Prions are slow-acting, virtually indestructible infectious proteins that cause brain diseases in mammals.

Concept 18.3

Rapid reproduction, mutation, and genetic recombination contribute to the genetic diversity of bacteria

▶ **The Bacterial Genome and Its Replication** (p. 346) The bacterial chromosome is usually a circular DNA molecule with few associated proteins. Plasmids are smaller circular DNA molecules that can replicate independently of the chromosome.

▶ **Mutation and Genetic Recombination as Sources of Genetic Variation** (pp. 346–348) Because bacteria can proliferate rapidly, new mutations can quickly increase a population's genetic variation. Further diversity can arise by recombination of the DNA from two different bacterial cells.

▶ **Mechanisms of Gene Transfer and Genetic Recombination in Bacteria** (pp. 348–351) New bacterial strains can arise by the transfer of DNA from one cell to another cell. In transformation, naked DNA enters the cell from the surroundings. In transduction, bacterial DNA is carried from one cell to another by phages. In conjugation, an F^+ donor cell, which contains the F plasmid, transfers plasmid DNA to an F^- recipient cell. The F factor of an Hfr cell, which is integrated into the bacterial chromosome, brings some chromosomal DNA along with it when it is transferred to an F^- cell. R plasmids confer resistance to various antibiotics.
Investigation *What Are the Patterns of Antibiotic Resistance?*

▶ **Transposition of Genetic Elements** (pp. 351–352) DNA segments that can insert at multiple sites in a cell's DNA contribute to genetic shuffling in bacteria. Insertion sequences, the simplest bacterial transposable elements, consist of inverted repeats of DNA flanking a gene for transposase. Bacterial transposons have additional genes, such as those for antibiotic resistance.

Concept 18.4

Individual bacteria respond to environmental change by regulating their gene expression

▶ **Operons: The Basic Concept** (pp. 353–354) Cells control metabolism by regulating enzyme activity or the expression of genes coding for enzymes. In bacteria, genes are often clustered into operons, with one promoter serving several adjacent genes. An operator site on the DNA switches the operon on or off.

▶ **Repressible and Inducible Operons: Two Types of Negative Gene Regulation** (pp. 354–356) In a repressible operon, binding of a specific repressor protein to the operator shuts off transcription. The repressor is active when bound to a corepressor, usually the end product of an anabolic pathway. In an inducible operon, binding of an inducer to an innately active repressor inactivates the repressor and turns on transcription. Inducible enzymes usually function in catabolic pathways.

▶ **Positive Gene Regulation** (p. 356) Some operons are also subject to positive control via a stimulatory activator protein, such as catabolite activator protein (CAP), which promotes transcription when bound to a site within the promoter.
Activity *The lac Operon in E. coli*

Self-Quiz

1. A bacterium is infected with an experimentally constructed bacteriophage composed of the T2 phage protein coat and T4 phage DNA. The new phages produced would have
   a. T2 protein and T4 DNA.
   b. T2 protein and T2 DNA.
   c. a mixture of the DNA and proteins of both phages.
   d. T4 protein and T4 DNA.
   e. T4 protein and T2 DNA.

2. RNA viruses require their own supply of certain enzymes because
   a. host cells rapidly destroy the viruses.
   b. host cells lack enzymes that can replicate the viral genome.
   c. these enzymes translate viral mRNA into proteins.
   d. these enzymes penetrate host cell membranes.
   e. these enzymes cannot be made in host cells.

3. Which of the following is descriptive of an R plasmid?
   a. Its transfer converts an F^- cell into an F^+ cell.
   b. It has genes for antibiotic resistance and maybe for sex pili.
   c. It is transferred between bacteria by transduction.
   d. It is a good example of a composite transposon.
   e. It makes bacteria resistant to phage.

4. Transposition differs from other mechanisms of genetic recombination because it
   a. occurs only in bacteria.
   b. moves genes between homologous regions of the DNA.
   c. plays little or no role in evolution.
   d. occurs only in eukaryotes.
   e. scatters genes to new loci in the genome.

5. If a particular operon encodes enzymes for making an essential amino acid and is regulated like the *trp* operon, then
   a. the amino acid inactivates the repressor.
   b. the enzymes produced are called inducible enzymes.
   c. the repressor is active in the absence of the amino acid.
   d. the amino acid acts as a corepressor.
   e. the amino acid turns on transcription of the operon.

6. What would occur if the repressor of an inducible operon were mutated so it could not bind the operator?
   a. continuous transcription of the operon's genes
   b. reduced transcription of the operon's genes
   c. buildup of a substrate for the pathway controlled by the operon
   d. irreversible binding of the repressor to the promoter
   e. overproduction of catabolite activator protein (CAP)

7. During conjugation between an Hfr cell and an F^- cell,
   a. the F^- cell becomes an F^+ cell.
   b. the F^- cell becomes an Hfr cell.
   c. the chromosome of the F^- cell is degraded.
   d. genes from the Hfr cell may replace genes of the F^- cell by recombination.
   e. DNA from the F^- cell transfers to the Hfr cell, and DNA from the Hfr cell transfers to the F^- cell.

8. Genetic variation in bacterial populations never results from
   a. transduction.
   b. transformation.
   c. conjugation.
   d. mutation.
   e. meiosis.

9. Which of the following characteristics or processes is common to *both* bacteria and viruses?
   a. binary fission
   b. ribosomes
   c. genetic material of nucleic acid
   d. mitosis
   e. conjugation

10. Emerging viruses arise by
    a. mutation of existing viruses.
    b. the spread of existing viruses to new host species.
    c. the spread of existing viruses more widely within their host species.
    d. all of the above
    e. none of the above

For Self-Quiz answers, see Appendix A.

Go to the website or CD-ROM for more quiz questions.

Evolution Connection

The success of some viruses lies in their ability to evolve within the host. Such a virus evades the host's defenses by rapidly mutating and producing many altered progeny viruses before the body can mount an attack. Thus, the viruses present late in infection differ from those that initially infected the body. Discuss this as an example of evolution in microcosm. Which viral lineages tend to survive?

Scientific Inquiry

When bacteria infect an animal, the number of bacteria in the body increases in an exponential fashion (graph A). After infection by a virulent animal virus with a lytic reproductive cycle, there is no evidence of infection for a while. Then, the number of viruses rises suddenly and subsequently increases in a series of steps (graph B). Explain the difference in the growth curves.

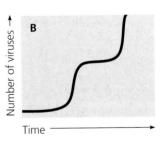

Biological Inquiry: A Workbook of Investigative Cases
Explore West Nile virus in the case "The Donor's Dilemma."
Investigation *What Causes Infections in AIDS Patients?*
Investigation *Why Do AIDS Rates Differ Across the U.S.?*
Investigation *What Are the Patterns of Antibiotic Resistance?*

Science, Technology, and Society

Explain how the excessive or inappropriate use of antibiotics poses a health hazard for a human population.

19 Eukaryotic Genomes
Organization, Regulation, and Evolution

▲ Figure 19.1 **DNA in a eukaryotic chromosome from a developing salamander egg.**

Key Concepts

19.1 Chromatin structure is based on successive levels of DNA packing

19.2 Gene expression can be regulated at any stage, but the key step is transcription

19.3 Cancer results from genetic changes that affect cell cycle control

19.4 Eukaryotic genomes can have many noncoding DNA sequences in addition to genes

19.5 Duplications, rearrangements, and mutations of DNA contribute to genome evolution

Overview

How Eukaryotic Genomes Work and Evolve

Eukaryotic cells face the same challenges as prokaryotic cells in expressing their genes. However, the typical eukaryotic genome is much larger, and, in multicellular eukaryotes, cell specialization is crucial. These two features present a formidable information-processing task for the eukaryotic cell.

The human genome, for instance, has an estimated 25,000 genes—more than five times that of a typical prokaryote. It also includes an enormous amount of DNA that does not code for RNA or protein. Managing so much DNA requires that the genome be elaborately organized. In all organisms, DNA associates with proteins that condense it. In eukaryotes, the DNA-protein complex, called **chromatin,** is ordered into higher structural levels than the DNA-protein complex in prokaryotes. The fluorescence micrograph in **Figure 19.1**

gives a sense of the complex organization of the chromatin in a eukaryotic chromosome. Part of the chromatin is packed into the main axis (white) of the chromosome, while those parts that are being actively transcribed are spread out in loops (red).

Both prokaryotes and eukaryotes must alter their patterns of gene expression in response to changes in environmental conditions. Multicellular eukaryotes, in addition, must develop and maintain multiple cell types. Each of these cell types contains the same genome but expresses a different subset of genes, a significant challenge in gene regulation.

In this chapter, you will first learn about the structure of chromatin and how changes in chromatin structure affect gene expression. Then we will discuss other mechanisms for regulating expression of eukaryotic genes. As in prokaryotes, eukaryotic gene expression is most often regulated at the stage of transcription. Next, we will describe how disruptions in gene regulation can lead to cancer. In the remainder of the chapter, we will consider the various types of nucleotide sequences in eukaryotic genomes and explain how they arose and changed during genome evolution. Being aware of the forces that have shaped—and continue to shape—genomes will help you understand how biological diversity has evolved.

Concept 19.1

Chromatin structure is based on successive levels of DNA packing

Eukaryotic DNA is precisely combined with a large amount of protein, and the resulting chromatin undergoes striking changes in the course of the cell cycle (see Figure 12.6). In interphase cells stained for light microscopy, the chromatin usually appears as a diffuse mass within the nucleus, suggesting that the chromatin is highly extended. As a cell prepares for mitosis, its chromatin coils and folds up (condenses), eventually forming a characteristic number of short, thick chromosomes that are distinguishable from each other with the light microscope.

Eukaryotic chromosomes contain an enormous amount of DNA relative to their condensed length. Each chromosome contains a single linear DNA double helix that, in humans, averages about 1.5×10^8 nucleotide pairs. If completely stretched out, such a DNA molecule would be about 4 cm long, thousands of times longer than the diameter of a cell nucleus. All this DNA—as well as the DNA of the other 45 human chromosomes—fits into the nucleus through the elaborate, multilevel system of DNA packing outlined in **Figure 19.2**.

Nucleosomes, or "Beads on a String"

Proteins called **histones** are responsible for the first level of DNA packing in chromatin. The mass of histone in chromatin is approximately equal to the mass of DNA. Histones have a high proportion of positively charged amino acids (lysine and arginine), and they bind tightly to the negatively charged DNA. (Recall that the phosphate groups of DNA give it a negative charge all along its length; see Figure 16.7.) Histones are very similar from one eukaryote to another, and similar proteins are found even in prokaryotes. The apparent conservation of histone genes during evolution probably reflects the pivotal role of histones in organizing DNA within cells.

In electron micrographs, unfolded chromatin has the appearance of beads on a string, as shown in **Figure 19.2a**. In this configuration, a chromatin fiber is 10 nm in diameter (the *10-nm fiber*). Each "bead" is a **nucleosome**, the basic unit of DNA packing; the "string" between the beads is called *linker DNA*. A nucleosome consists of DNA wound around a protein core composed of two molecules each of four types of histone: H2A, H2B, H3, and H4. The amino end (N-terminus) of each histone protein (the *histone tail*) extends outward from the nucleosome. A molecule of a fifth histone, called H1, attaches to the DNA near the nucleosome when a 10-nm chromatin fiber undergoes the next level of packing.

The association of DNA and histones in nucleosomes seems to remain essentially intact throughout the cell cycle. The histones leave the DNA only transiently during DNA replication, and, with very few exceptions, they stay with the DNA during transcription. How can DNA be transcribed when it is wrapped around histones in a nucleosome? Researchers have learned that changes in the shapes and positions of nucleosomes can allow RNA-synthesizing polymerases to move along the DNA. Later in this chapter, we'll discuss some recent discoveries about the roles of histone tails and nucleosomes in the regulation of gene expression.

Higher Levels of DNA Packing

The next level of packing is due to interactions between the histone tails of one nucleosome and the linker DNA and nucleosomes to either side. With the aid of histone H1, these interactions cause the extended 10-nm fiber to coil or fold, forming a chromatin fiber roughly 30 nm in thickness, the *30-nm fiber* (**Figure 19.2b**). The 30-nm fiber, in turn, forms loops called *looped domains* attached to a chromosome scaffold made of nonhistone proteins, thus making up a *300-nm fiber* (**Figure 19.2c**). In a mitotic chromosome, the looped domains themselves coil and fold, further compacting all the chromatin to produce the characteristic metaphase chromosome shown in the micrograph at the bottom of **Figure 19.2d**. Particular genes always end up located at the same places in metaphase chromosomes, indicating that the packing steps are highly specific and precise.

Though interphase chromatin is generally much less condensed than the chromatin of mitotic chromosomes, it shows several of the same levels of higher-order packing. Much of the chromatin comprising a chromosome is present as a 10-nm fiber, but some is compacted into a 30-nm fiber, which in some regions is further folded into looped domains. Although an interphase chromosome lacks an obvious scaffold, its looped domains seem to be attached to the nuclear lamina, on the inside of the nuclear envelope, and perhaps also to fibers of the nuclear matrix. These attachments may help organize regions of active transcription. The chromatin of each chromosome occupies a specific restricted area within the interphase nucleus, and the chromatin fibers of different chromosomes do not become entangled.

Even during interphase, the centromeres and telomeres of chromosomes, as well as other chromosomal regions in some cells, exist in the highly condensed state represented in Figure 19.2d. This type of interphase chromatin, visible as irregular clumps with a light microscope, is called **heterochromatin,** to distinguish it from the less compacted **euchromatin** ("true chromatin"). Because of its compaction, heterochromatin DNA is largely inaccessible to transcription enzymes and thus generally is not transcribed. In contrast, the looser packing of euchromatin makes its DNA accessible to enzymes and available for transcription. In the next section, we will consider how changes in chromatin and other mechanisms allow a cell to regulate which of its genes are expressed.

Concept Check 19.1

1. Describe the structure of a nucleosome, the basic unit of DNA packing in eukaryotic cells.
2. What chemical properties of histones and DNA enable these molecules to bind tightly together?
3. In general, how does dense packing of DNA in chromosomes prevent gene expression?

For suggested answers, see Appendix A.

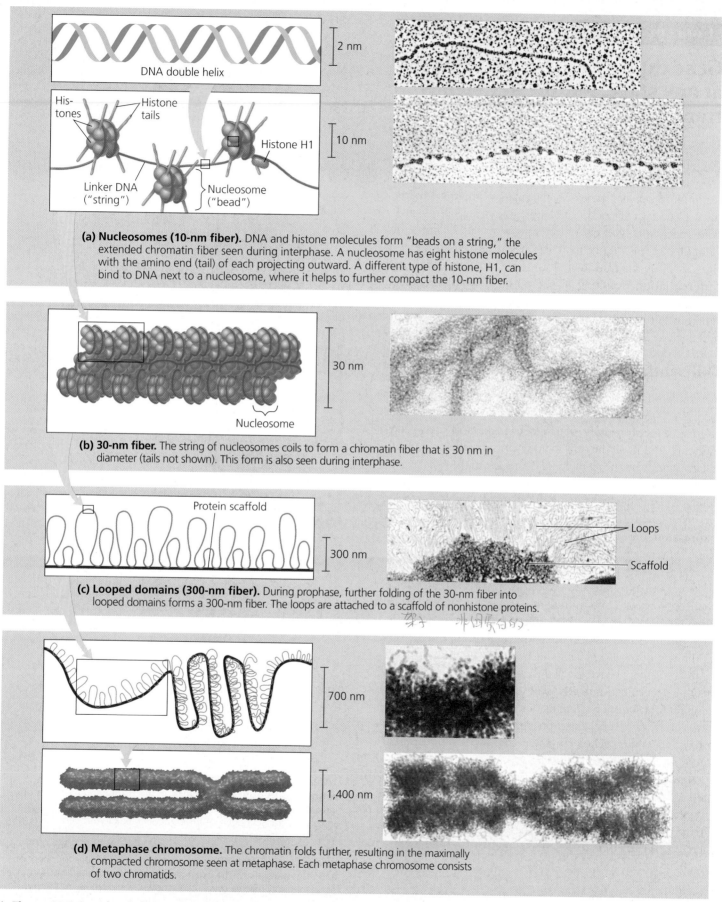

(a) Nucleosomes (10-nm fiber). DNA and histone molecules form "beads on a string," the extended chromatin fiber seen during interphase. A nucleosome has eight histone molecules with the amino end (tail) of each projecting outward. A different type of histone, H1, can bind to DNA next to a nucleosome, where it helps to further compact the 10-nm fiber.

(b) 30-nm fiber. The string of nucleosomes coils to form a chromatin fiber that is 30 nm in diameter (tails not shown). This form is also seen during interphase.

(c) Looped domains (300-nm fiber). During prophase, further folding of the 30-nm fiber into looped domains forms a 300-nm fiber. The loops are attached to a scaffold of nonhistone proteins.

(d) Metaphase chromosome. The chromatin folds further, resulting in the maximally compacted chromosome seen at metaphase. Each metaphase chromosome consists of two chromatids.

▲ **Figure 19.2 Levels of chromatin packing.** This series of diagrams and transmission electron micrographs depicts a current model for the progressive stages of DNA coiling and folding.

Gene expression can be regulated at any stage, but the key step is transcription

All organisms must regulate which genes are expressed at any given time. Both unicellular organisms and the cells of multicellular organisms must continually turn genes on and off in response to signals from their external and internal environments. The cells of a multicellular organism must also regulate their gene expression on a more long-term basis. During development of a multicellular organism, its cells undergo a process of specialization in form and function called **cell differentiation**, resulting in several or many differentiated cell types. The mature human body, for instance, is composed of about 200 different cell types. Examples are muscle cells and nerve cells.

Differential Gene Expression

A typical human cell probably expresses about 20% of its genes at any given time. Highly differentiated cells, such as muscle cells, express an even smaller fraction of their genes. Although almost all the cells in an organism contain an identical genome,* the subset of genes expressed in the cells of each type is unique, allowing these cells to carry out their specific function. The differences between cell types, therefore, are due not to different genes being present, but to **differential gene expression**, the expression of different genes by cells with the same genome.

The genomes of eukaryotes may contain tens of thousands of genes, but for quite a few species, only a small amount of the DNA—about 1.5% in humans—codes for protein. Of the remaining DNA, a very small fraction consists of genes for RNA products such as ribosomal RNA and transfer RNA. Most of the rest of the DNA seems to be noncoding, although recently researchers have learned that a significant amount of it may be transcribed into RNAs of unknown function. In any case, the transcription proteins of a cell must locate the right genes at the right time, a task on a par with finding a needle in a haystack. When gene expression goes awry, serious imbalances and diseases, including cancer, can arise.

Figure 19.3 summarizes the entire process of gene expression in a eukaryotic cell, highlighting key stages in the expression of a protein-coding gene. Each stage depicted in Figure 19.3 is a potential control point at which gene expression can be turned on or off, accelerated, or slowed down.

---

*Cells of the immune system are an exception. During their differentiation, rearrangement of the immunoglobulin genes results in a change in the genome, which will be discussed in Chapter 43.

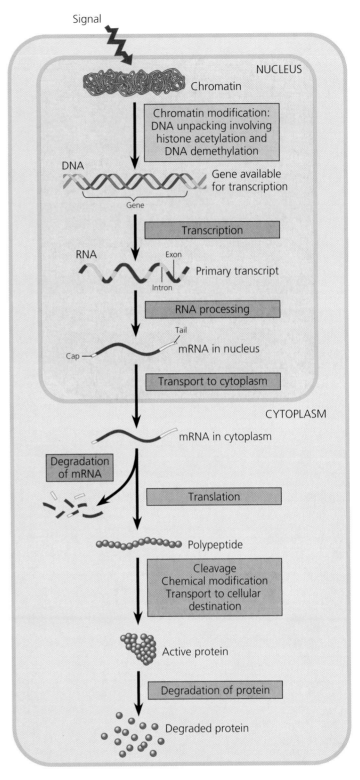

▲ **Figure 19.3 Stages in gene expression that can be regulated in eukaryotic cells.** In this diagram, the colored boxes indicate the processes most often regulated. The nuclear envelope separating transcription from translation in eukaryotic cells offers an opportunity for post-transcriptional control in the form of RNA processing that is absent in prokaryotes. In addition, eukaryotes have a greater variety of control mechanisms operating before transcription and after translation. The expression of any given gene, however, does not necessarily involve every stage shown; for example, not every polypeptide is cleaved. As in prokaryotes, transcription initiation is the most important control point.

Only 40 years ago, an understanding of the mechanisms that control gene expression in eukaryotes seemed almost hopelessly out of reach. Since then, new research methods, including advances in DNA technology (see Chapter 20), have empowered molecular biologists to uncover many of the details of eukaryotic gene regulation. In all organisms, the expression of specific genes is most commonly regulated at transcription, often in response to signals coming from outside the cell. For that reason, the term *gene expression* is often equated with transcription for both prokaryotes and eukaryotes. However, the greater complexity of eukaryotic cell structure and function provides opportunities for regulating gene expression at additional stages. In the following three sections, we'll examine some of the important control points of eukaryotic gene expression more closely.

Regulation of Chromatin Structure

As mentioned earlier, the structural organization of chromatin not only packs a cell's DNA into a compact form that fits inside the nucleus but also is important in helping regulate gene expression. Genes within heterochromatin, which is highly condensed, are usually not expressed. The repressive effect of heterochromatin has been seen in experiments in which a transcriptionally active gene was inserted into a region of heterochromatin in yeast cells; the inserted gene was no longer expressed. In addition, the location of a gene's promoter relative to nucleosomes and to the sites where the DNA attaches to the chromosome scaffold or nuclear lamina can also affect whether it is transcribed. A flurry of recent research indicates that certain chemical modifications to the histones and DNA of chromatin influence both chromatin structure and gene expression. Here we examine the effects of these modifications, which are catalyzed by specific enzymes.

Histone Modifications

There is mounting evidence that chemical modifications to histones play a direct role in the regulation of gene transcription. The N-terminus of each histone molecule in a nucleosome protrudes outward from the nucleosome (**Figure 19.4a**). These histone tails are accessible to various modifying enzymes, which catalyze the addition or removal of specific chemical groups.

In **histone acetylation**, acetyl groups ($-COCH_3$) are attached to positively charged lysines in histone tails; deacetylation is the removal of acetyl groups. When the histone tails of a nucleosome are acetylated, their positive charges are neutralized and they no longer bind to neighboring nucleosomes (**Figure 19.4b**). Recall that such binding promotes the folding of chromatin into a more compact structure; when this binding does not occur, chromatin has a looser structure. As a result, transcription proteins have easier access to genes in an acetylated region. Researchers have shown that some enzymes that acetylate or deacetylate histones are closely associated with or even components of the transcription factors that bind to promoters (see Figure 17.8). In other words, histone acetylation enzymes may promote the initiation of transcription not only by modifying chromatin structure, but also by binding to, and thus "recruiting," components of the transcription machinery.

Several other chemical groups can be reversibly attached to amino acids in histone tails. For example, the addition of methyl groups ($-CH_3$) to histone tails (methylation) can lead

(a) Histone tails protrude outward from a nucleosome. In this end view of a nucleosome, each type of histone is shown in a different color. The amino acids in the N-terminus tails are accessible for chemical modification.

Unacetylated histones   Acetylated histones

(b) Acetylation of histone tails promotes loose chromatin structure that permits transcription. A region of chromatin in which nucleosomes are unacetylated forms a compact structure (left) in which the DNA is not transcribed. When nucleosomes are highly acetylated (right), the chromatin becomes less compact, and the DNA is accessible for transcription.

▲ **Figure 19.4 A simple model of histone tails and the effect of histone acetylation.** In addition to acetylation, histones can undergo several other types of modifications that also help determine the chromatin configuration in a region.

to condensation of the chromatin. The recent discovery that this and many other modifications to histone tails can affect chromatin structure and gene expression has led to the *histone code hypothesis*. According to this model, specific combinations of modifications, rather than the overall level of histone acetylation, help determine the chromatin configuration, which in turn influences transcription.

DNA Methylation

Distinct from methylation of histone tails is the addition of methyl groups to certain bases in DNA after DNA is synthesized. In fact, the DNA of most plants and animals has methylated bases, usually cytosine. Inactive DNA, such as that of inactivated mammalian X chromosomes (see Figure 15.11), is generally highly methylated compared with DNA that is actively transcribed, although there are exceptions.

Comparison of the same genes in different tissues shows that the genes are usually more heavily methylated in cells in which they are not expressed. Removal of the extra methyl groups can turn on certain of these genes. Moreover, researchers have discovered that certain proteins that bind to methylated DNA recruit histone deacetylation enzymes. Thus, a dual mechanism, involving both DNA methylation and histone deacetylation, can repress transcription.

At least in some species, DNA methylation seems to be essential for the long-term inactivation of certain genes that occurs during normal cell differentiation in the embryo. For instance, experiments have shown that deficient DNA methylation due to lack of a methylating enzyme leads to abnormal embryonic development in organisms as different as mice and *Arabidopsis* (a plant). Once methylated, genes usually stay that way through successive cell divisions. At DNA sites where one strand is already methylated, methylation enzymes correctly methylate the daughter strand after each round of DNA replication. Methylation patterns are thus passed on, and cells forming specialized tissues keep a chemical record of what occurred during embryonic development. A methylation pattern maintained in this way also accounts for **genomic imprinting** in mammals, where methylation permanently regulates expression of either the maternal or paternal allele of certain genes at the start of development (see Chapter 15).

Epigenetic Inheritance

The chromatin modifications that we have just discussed do not involve a change in the DNA sequence, and yet they may be passed along to future generations of cells. Inheritance of traits transmitted by mechanisms not directly involving the nucleotide sequence is called **epigenetic inheritance.** Researchers are amassing more and more evidence for the importance of epigenetic information in regulation of gene expression. Clearly, enzymes that modify chromatin structure appear to be integral parts of the cell's machinery for regulating transcription.

Regulation of Transcription Initiation

Chromatin-modifying enzymes provide initial control of gene expression by making a region of DNA either more or less able to bind the transcription machinery. Once a gene is optimally modified for expression, the initiation of transcription is the most important and universally used stage at which gene expression is regulated. Before looking at how cells control their transcription, let's review the structure of a typical eukaryotic gene and its transcript.

Organization of a Typical Eukaryotic Gene

A eukaryotic gene and the DNA elements (segments) that control it are typically organized as shown in **Figure 19.5**, which extends what you learned about eukaryotic genes in Chapter 17. Recall that a cluster of proteins called a *transcription initiation complex* assembles on the promoter sequence at the "upstream" end of the gene. One of these proteins, RNA polymerase II, then proceeds to transcribe the gene, synthesizing a primary RNA transcript (pre-mRNA). RNA processing includes enzymatic addition of a 5′ cap and a poly-A tail, as well as splicing out of introns, to yield a mature mRNA. Associated with most eukaryotic genes are multiple **control elements,** segments of noncoding DNA that help regulate transcription by binding certain proteins. These control elements and the proteins they bind are critical to the precise regulation of gene expression seen in different cell types.

The Roles of Transcription Factors

To initiate transcription, eukaryotic RNA polymerase requires the assistance of proteins called **transcription factors** (see Figure 17.8). Because the transcription factors mentioned in Chapter 17 are essential for the transcription of *all* protein-coding genes, they are sometimes called *general* transcription factors. Only a few general transcription factors independently bind a DNA sequence, such as the TATA box within the promoter; the others primarily bind proteins, including each other and RNA polymerase II. Protein-protein interactions are crucial to the initiation of eukaryotic transcription. Only when the complete initiation complex has assembled can the polymerase begin to move along the DNA template strand, producing a complementary strand of RNA.

The interaction of general transcription factors and RNA polymerase II with a promoter usually leads to only a low rate of initiation and production of few RNA transcripts. In eukaryotes, high levels of transcription of particular genes at the appropriate time and place depend on the interaction of control elements with other proteins that can be thought of as *specific* transcription factors.

Enhancers and Specific Transcription Factors. As you can see in Figure 19.5, some control elements, named *proximal*

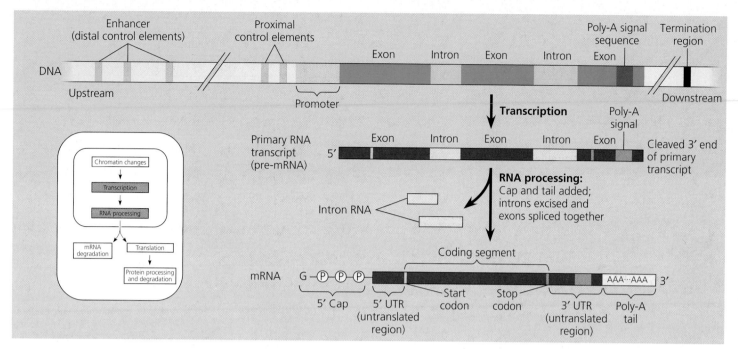

▲ Figure 19.5 A eukaryotic gene and its transcript. Each eukaryotic gene has a promoter, a DNA sequence where RNA polymerase binds and starts transcription, proceeding "downstream." A number of control elements (gold) are involved in regulating the initiation of transcription; these are DNA sequences located near (proximal to) or far from (distal to) the promoter. Distal control elements can be grouped together as enhancers. A polyadenylation (poly-A) signal in the last exon of the gene is transcribed into an RNA sequence that determines where the transcript is cleaved and the poly-A tail added. Transcription may continue for hundreds of nucleotides beyond the poly-A signal before terminating. RNA processing of the primary transcript into a functional mRNA involves three steps: addition of the 5' cap, addition of the poly-A tail, and splicing. In the cell, the 5' cap is added soon after transcription is initiated; splicing and poly-A tail addition may also occur while transcription is still under way (see Figure 17.9).

control elements, are located close to the promoter. (Although some biologists consider proximal control elements part of the promoter, we do not.) The more distant *distal control elements,* groups of which are called **enhancers,** may be thousands of nucleotides upstream or downstream of a gene or even within an intron. A given gene may have multiple enhancers, each active at a different time or in a different cell type or location in the organism.

The interactions between enhancers and specific transcription factors called activators or repressors are particularly important in controlling gene expression. An **activator** is a protein that binds to an enhancer and stimulates transcription of a gene. **Figure 19.6**, on the next page, shows a current model for how binding of activators to enhancers located far from the promoter can influence transcription. Protein-mediated bending of the DNA is thought to bring the bound activators in contact with a group of so-called *mediator proteins,* which in turn interact with proteins at the promoter. These multiple protein-protein interactions help assemble and position the initiation complex on the promoter.

Hundreds of transcription activators have been discovered in eukaryotes. Researchers have identified two common structural elements in a large number of activator proteins: a DNA-binding domain—a part of the protein's three-dimensional structure that binds to DNA—and one or more activation domains. Activation domains bind other regulatory proteins or components of the transcription machinery, allowing a sequence of protein-protein interactions that result in transcription of a given gene.

Some specific transcription factors function as **repressors** to inhibit expression of a particular gene. Eukaryotic repressors can cause inhibition of gene expression in several different ways. Certain repressors block the binding of activators either to their control elements or to components of the transcription machinery. Other repressors bind directly to their own control elements in an enhancer and act to turn off transcription even in the presence of activators.

In addition to affecting assembly of the transcription machinery directly, some activators and repressors act indirectly by influencing chromatin structure. Recall that a gene present in a region of chromatin with high levels of histone acetylation is able to bind the transcription machinery, whereas a gene in a region of chromatin with low levels of histone acetylation is not (see Figure 19.4). Studies in yeast and mammals show that some activators recruit proteins that acetylate histones near the promoters of specific genes, thus promoting transcription. In contrast, other repressors recruit proteins that deacetylate histones, leading to reduced transcription, a phenomenon referred to as *silencing.* Indeed, recruitment of chromatin-modifying proteins seems to be the most common mechanism of repression in eukaryotes.

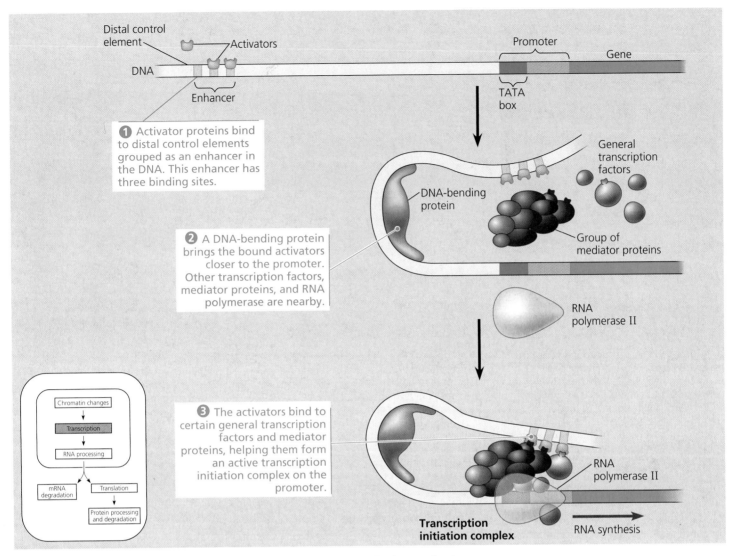

▲ **Figure 19.6 A model for the action of enhancers and transcription activators.**
Bending of the DNA by a protein enables enhancers to influence a promoter hundreds or even thousands of nucleotides away. Specific transcription factors called activators bind to the enhancer DNA sequences and then to a group of mediator proteins, which in turn bind to general transcription factors assembling the transcription initiation complex. These protein-protein interactions facilitate the correct positioning of the complex on the promoter and the initiation of RNA synthesis. Only one enhancer is shown in this figure, but a gene may have several that act at different times or in different cell types.

Combinatorial Control of Gene Activation. In eukaryotes, the precise control of transcription depends largely on the binding of activators to DNA control elements. Considering the very large number of genes that must be regulated in a typical animal or plant cell, the number of completely different nucleotide sequences found in control elements is surprisingly small. A dozen or so short nucleotide sequences appear again and again in the control elements for different genes. On average, each enhancer is composed of about ten control elements, each of which can bind only one or two specific transcription factors. The particular *combination* of control elements in an enhancer associated

with a gene turns out to be more important than the presence of a single unique control element in regulating transcription of the gene.

Even with only a dozen control element sequences available, a large number of combinations are possible. A particular combination of control elements will be able to activate transcription only when the appropriate activator proteins are present, such as at a precise time during development or in a particular cell type. The example in **Figure 19.7** illustrates how the use of different combinations of control elements to activate transcription allows exquisite regulation of transcription with a small set of control elements.

(a) Liver cell. The albumin gene is expressed, and the crystallin gene is not.

(b) Lens cell. The crystallin gene is expressed, and the albumin gene is not.

▲ **Figure 19.7 Cell type–specific transcription.** Both liver cells and lens cells have the genes for making the proteins albumin and crystallin, but only liver cells make albumin (a blood protein) and only lens cells make crystallin (the main component of the lens of the eye). The specific transcription factors (activators and repressors) made in a particular type of cell determine which genes are expressed. In this example, the genes for albumin and crystallin are shown at the top, each with an enhancer made up of three different control elements. Although the enhancers for the two genes share one control element, each enhancer has a unique combination of elements. All the activators required for high-level expression of the albumin gene are present only in liver cells (a), whereas the activators needed for expression of the crystallin gene are present only in lens cells (b). For simplicity, we consider only the role of activators here, although the presence or absence of repressors may also influence transcription in certain cell types.

Coordinately Controlled Genes

How does the eukaryotic cell deal with genes of related function that need to be turned on or off at the same time? In Chapter 18, you learned that in prokaryotes, such coordinately controlled genes are often clustered into an operon, which is regulated by a single promoter and transcribed into a single mRNA molecule. Thus, the genes are expressed together, and the encoded proteins are produced concurrently. With rare exceptions, operons that work in this way have not been found in eukaryotic cells.

Recent studies of the genomes of several eukaryotic species have found that some co-expressed genes are clustered near one another on the same chromosome. Examples include certain genes in the testis of the fruit fly and muscle-related genes in a small worm called a nematode. Unlike genes in prokaryotic operons, however, each eukaryotic gene in these clusters has its own promoter and is individually transcribed. The coordinate regulation of clustered genes in eukaryotic cells is thought to involve changes in the chromatin structure that make the entire group of genes either available or unavailable for transcription.

More commonly, co-expressed eukaryotic genes, such as genes coding for the enzymes of a metabolic pathway, are found scattered over different chromosomes. In these cases, coordinate gene expression seems to depend on the association of a specific control element or combination of elements with every gene of a dispersed group. Copies of the activators that recognize these control elements bind to them, promoting simultaneous transcription of the genes, no matter where they are in the genome.

Coordinate control of dispersed genes in a eukaryotic cell often occurs in response to external chemical signals. A steroid hormone, for example, enters a cell and binds to a specific intracellular receptor protein, forming a hormone-receptor complex that serves as a transcription activator (see Figure 11.6). Every gene whose transcription is stimulated by a particular steroid hormone, regardless of its chromosomal location, has a control element recognized by that hormone-receptor complex.

Many signal molecules, such as nonsteroid hormones and growth factors, bind to receptors on a cell's surface and never actually enter the cell. This kind of signal can control gene expression indirectly by triggering signal transduction pathways that lead to activation of particular transcription activators or repressors (see Figure 11.14). The principle of coordinate regulation is the same as in the case of steroid hormones: Genes with the same control elements are activated by the same chemical signals. Systems for coordinating gene regulation probably arose early in evolutionary history and evolved by the duplication and distribution of control elements within the genome.

Mechanisms of Post-Transcriptional Regulation

Transcription alone does not constitute gene expression. The expression of a protein-coding gene is ultimately measured by the amount of functional protein a cell makes, and much happens between the synthesis of the RNA transcript and the activity of the protein in the cell. An increasing number of examples are being found of regulatory mechanisms that operate at various stages after transcription (see Figure 19.3). These mechanisms allow a cell to fine-tune gene expression rapidly in response to environmental changes without altering its transcription patterns. Here we discuss how cells can regulate gene expression once a gene has been transcribed.

RNA Processing

RNA processing in the nucleus and the export of mature RNA to the cytoplasm provide several opportunities for regulating gene expression that are not available in prokaryotes. One example of regulation at the RNA-processing level is **alternative RNA splicing**, in which different mRNA molecules are produced from the same primary transcript, depending on which RNA segments are treated as exons and which as introns **(Figure 19.8)**. Regulatory proteins specific to a cell type control intron-exon choices by binding to regulatory sequences within the primary transcript.

▲ **Figure 19.8 Alternative RNA splicing.** The primary transcripts of some genes can be spliced in more than one way, generating different mRNA molecules. Notice in this example that one mRNA molecule has ended up with the green exon and the other with the purple exon. With alternative splicing, an organism can produce more than one type of polypeptide from a single gene.

mRNA Degradation

The life span of mRNA molecules in the cytoplasm is an important factor in determining the pattern of protein synthesis in a cell. Prokaryotic mRNA molecules typically are degraded by enzymes within a few minutes of their synthesis. This short life span of prokaryotic mRNAs is one reason prokaryotes can vary their patterns of protein synthesis so quickly in response to environmental changes. In contrast, mRNAs in multicellular eukaryotes typically survive for hours, days, or even weeks. For instance, the mRNAs for the hemoglobin polypeptides (α-globin and β-globin) in developing red blood cells are unusually stable, and these long-lived mRNAs are translated repeatedly in these cells.

Research on yeasts suggests that a common pathway of mRNA breakdown begins with the enzymatic shortening of the poly-A tail (see Figure 19.5). This helps trigger the action of enzymes that remove the 5′ cap (the two ends of the mRNA may be briefly held together by the proteins involved). Removal of the cap, a critical step, is also regulated by particular nucleotide sequences in the mRNA. Once the cap is removed, nuclease enzymes rapidly chew up the mRNA.

Nucleotide sequences that affect the length of time an mRNA remains intact are often found in the untranslated region (UTR) at the 3′ end of the molecule (see Figure 19.5). In one experiment, researchers transferred such a sequence from the short-lived mRNA for a growth factor to the 3′ end of a normally stable globin mRNA. The globin mRNA was quickly degraded.

During the past few years, another mechanism that blocks expression of specific mRNA molecules has come to light. Researchers have found small single-stranded RNA molecules, called **microRNAs (miRNAs)**, that can bind to complementary sequences in mRNA molecules. The miRNAs are formed from longer RNA precursors that fold back on themselves, forming a long, double-stranded hairpin structure held together by hydrogen bonds **(Figure 19.9)**. An enzyme, fittingly called Dicer, then cuts the double-stranded RNA molecule into short fragments. One of the two strands is degraded, and the other strand (miRNA) associates with a large protein complex and acts as a homing device, directing the complex to any mRNA molecules that have the complementary sequence. Depending on various factors, the miRNA-protein complex then either degrades the target mRNA or blocks its translation.

Inhibition of gene expression by RNA molecules was first observed by biologists who noticed that injecting double-stranded RNA molecules into a cell somehow turned off a gene with the same sequence. They called this experimental phenomenon **RNA interference (or RNAi)**. It was later shown to be due to **small interfering RNAs (siRNAs)**, RNAs of similar size and function as miRNAs. In fact, subsequent research showed that the cellular machinery that generates siRNAs is the very same as that responsible for producing miRNAs naturally in the cell. The mechanisms by which these small RNAs function appear to be similar as well.

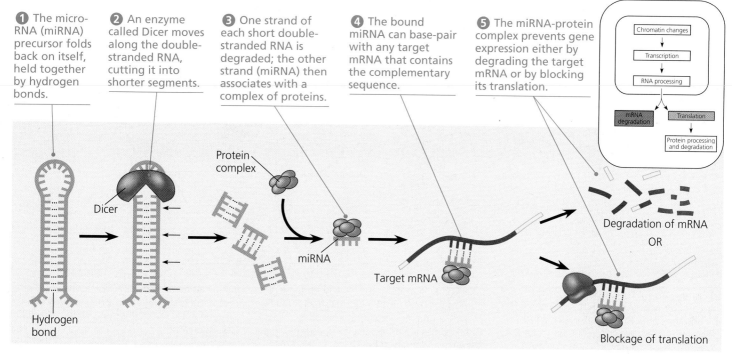

① The micro-RNA (miRNA) precursor folds back on itself, held together by hydrogen bonds.

② An enzyme called Dicer moves along the double-stranded RNA, cutting it into shorter segments.

③ One strand of each short double-stranded RNA is degraded; the other strand (miRNA) then associates with a complex of proteins.

④ The bound miRNA can base-pair with any target mRNA that contains the complementary sequence.

⑤ The miRNA-protein complex prevents gene expression either by degrading the target mRNA or by blocking its translation.

Chromatin changes
↓
Transcription
↓
RNA processing
↓
mRNA degradation | Translation
↓
Protein processing and degradation

Dicer

Protein complex

miRNA

Hydrogen bond

Target mRNA

Degradation of mRNA

OR

Blockage of translation

▲ **Figure 19.9 Regulation of gene expression by microRNAs (miRNAs).** RNA transcripts from miRNA-encoding genes are processed into miRNAs, which prevent expression of complementary mRNAs (siRNAs are believed to be generated and to function in a similar way).

Because the cellular RNAi pathway can lead to the destruction of RNAs with sequences complementary to those found in double-stranded RNA molecules, it is commonly believed to have originated as a natural defense against infection by RNA viruses. However, the fact that the RNAi pathway can affect expression of cellular genes also supports alternative models. In any case, it is clear that RNAi plays an important role in regulating gene expression in the cell.

Initiation of Translation

Translation presents another opportunity for regulating gene expression; such regulation occurs most commonly at the initiation stage (see Figure 17.17). The initiation of translation of selected mRNAs can be blocked by regulatory proteins that bind to specific sequences or structures within the untranslated region at the 5′ end (5′ UTR) of the mRNA, preventing the attachment of ribosomes. A different mechanism for blocking translation is seen in a variety of mRNAs present in the egg cells of many organisms: These stored mRNAs lack poly-A tails of sufficient size to allow translation initiation. At the appropriate time during embryonic development, a cytoplasmic enzyme adds more A residues, allowing translation to begin.

Alternatively, translation of *all* the mRNAs in a cell may be regulated simultaneously. In a eukaryotic cell, such "global" control usually involves the activation or inactivation of one or more of the protein factors required to initiate translation. This mechanism also plays a role in starting translation of mRNAs that are stored in egg cells. Just after fertilization,

translation is triggered by the sudden activation of translation initiation factors. The response is a burst of synthesis of the proteins encoded by the stored mRNAs. Some plants and algae store mRNAs during periods of darkness; light then triggers the reactivation of the translational apparatus.

Protein Processing and Degradation

The final opportunities for controlling gene expression occur after translation. Often, eukaryotic polypeptides must be processed to yield functional protein molecules. For instance, cleavage of the initial insulin polypeptide (pro-insulin) forms the active hormone. In addition, many proteins undergo chemical modifications that make them functional. Regulatory proteins are commonly activated or inactivated by the reversible addition of phosphate groups, and proteins destined for the surface of animal cells acquire sugars. Cell-surface proteins and many others must also be transported to target destinations in the cell in order to function. Regulation might occur at any of the steps involved in modifying or transporting a protein.

Finally, the length of time each protein functions in the cell is strictly regulated by means of selective degradation. Many proteins, such as the cyclins involved in regulating the cell cycle, must be relatively short-lived if the cell is to function appropriately (see Figure 12.16). To mark a particular protein for destruction, the cell commonly attaches molecules of a small protein called ubiquitin to the protein. Giant protein complexes called **proteasomes** then recognize the ubiquitin-tagged

1 Multiple ubiquitin molecules are attached to a protein by enzymes in the cytosol.

2 The ubiquitin-tagged protein is recognized by a proteasome, which unfolds the protein and sequesters it within a central cavity.

3 Enzymatic components of the proteasome cut the protein into small peptides, which can be further degraded by other enzymes in the cytosol.

Chromatin changes → Transcription → RNA processing →→ mRNA degradation / Translation → Protein processing and degradation

Ubiquitin

Proteasome

Proteasome and ubiquitin to be recycled

Protein to be degraded

Ubiquinated protein

Protein entering a proteasome

Protein fragments (peptides)

▲ **Figure 19.10 Degradation of a protein by a proteasome.** A proteasome, an enormous protein complex with a shape suggesting a trash can, chops up unneeded proteins in the cell. In most cases, the proteins attacked by a proteasome have been tagged with short chains of ubiquitin, a small protein. Steps 1 and 3 require ATP. Eukaryotic proteasomes are as massive as ribosomal subunits and are distributed throughout the cell. Their barrel-like shape somewhat resembles that of chaperone proteins, which protect protein structure rather than destroy it (see Figure 5.23).

protein molecules and degrade them **(Figure 19.10)**. The importance of proteasomes is underscored by the finding that mutations making cell cycle proteins impervious to proteasome degradation can lead to cancer.

Concept 19.3

Cancer results from genetic changes that affect cell cycle control

In Chapter 12, we considered cancer as a set of diseases in which cells escape from the control mechanisms normally limiting their growth. Now that we have discussed the molecular basis of gene expression and its regulation, we are ready to look at cancer more closely. The gene regulation systems that go wrong during cancer turn out to be the very same systems that play important roles in embryonic development, the immune response, and many other biological processes. Thus, research into the molecular basis of cancer has both benefited from and informed many other fields of biology.

Types of Genes Associated with Cancer

The genes that normally regulate cell growth and division during the cell cycle include genes for growth factors, their receptors, and the intracellular molecules of signaling pathways. (To review the cell cycle, see Chapter 12.) Mutations that alter any of these genes in somatic cells can lead to cancer. The agent of such change can be random spontaneous mutation. However, it is likely that many cancer-causing mutations result from environmental influences, such as chemical carcinogens, X-rays, and certain viruses.

An early breakthrough in understanding cancer came in 1911, when Peyton Rous discovered a virus that causes cancer in chickens. Since then, scientists have recognized a number of *tumor viruses* that cause cancer in various animals, including humans (see Table 18.1). The Epstein-Barr virus, a herpesvirus that causes infectious mononucleosis, has been linked to several types of cancer, notably Burkitt's lymphoma. Papilloma viruses (of the papovavirus group) are associated with cancer of the cervix. Among the retroviruses, one called HTLV-1 causes a type of adult leukemia. All tumor viruses transform cells into cancer cells through the integration of viral nucleic acid into host cell DNA.

Oncogenes and Proto-Oncogenes

Research on tumor viruses led to the discovery of cancer-causing genes called **oncogenes** (from the Greek *onco,* tumor) in certain retroviruses. Subsequently, close counterparts of these oncogenes were found in the genomes of humans and other animals. The normal cellular genes, called **proto-oncogenes,** code for proteins that stimulate normal cell growth and division.

How might a proto-oncogene—a gene that has an essential function in normal cells—become an oncogene, a cancer-causing gene? In general, an oncogene arises from a genetic change that leads to an increase either in the amount of the proto-oncogene's protein product or in the intrinsic activity of each protein molecule. The genetic changes that convert proto-oncogenes to oncogenes fall into three main categories: movement of DNA within the genome, amplification of a proto-oncogene, and point mutations in a control element or in the proto-oncogene itself **(Figure 19.11)**.

Cancer cells are frequently found to contain chromosomes that have broken and rejoined incorrectly, translocating fragments from one chromosome to another (see Figure 15.14). If a translocated proto-oncogene ends up near an especially active promoter (or other control element), its transcription may increase, making it an oncogene. Movement of transposable elements also may place a more active promoter near a proto-oncogene, increasing its expression. (Eukaryotic transposable elements are described later in the chapter.) The second main type of genetic change, amplification, increases the number of copies of the proto-oncogene in the cell. The third possibility is a point mutation either (1) in the promoter or an enhancer that controls a proto-oncogene, causing an increase in its expression, or (2) in the coding sequence, changing the gene's product to a protein that is more active or more resistant to degradation than the normal protein. All these mechanisms can lead to abnormal stimulation of the cell cycle and put the cell on the path to malignancy.

Tumor-Suppressor Genes

In addition to genes whose products normally promote cell division, cells contain genes whose normal products *inhibit* cell division. Such genes are called **tumor-suppressor genes** because the proteins they encode help prevent uncontrolled cell growth. Any mutation that decreases the normal activity of a tumor-suppressor protein may contribute to the onset of cancer, in effect stimulating growth through the absence of suppression.

The protein products of tumor-suppressor genes have various functions. Some tumor-suppressor proteins normally repair damaged DNA, a function that prevents the cell from accumulating cancer-causing mutations. Other tumor-suppressor proteins control the adhesion of cells to each other or to the extracellular matrix; proper cell anchorage is crucial in normal tissues—and often absent in cancers. Still other tumor-suppressor proteins are components of cell-signaling pathways that inhibit the cell cycle.

Interference with Normal Cell-Signaling Pathways

The proteins encoded by many proto-oncogenes and tumor-suppressor genes are components of cell-signaling pathways. Let's take a closer look at how such proteins function in normal cells and what goes wrong with their function in cancer cells. We will focus on the products of two key genes, the *ras* proto-oncogene and the *p53* tumor-suppressor gene. Mutations in *ras* occur in about 30% of human cancers; mutations in *p53* in more than 50%.

The Ras protein, encoded by the **ras gene,** is a G protein that relays a signal from a growth factor receptor on the plasma membrane to a cascade of protein kinases. The cellular response at the end of the pathway is the synthesis of a protein that stimulates the cell cycle (**Figure 19.12a**, on the next page). Normally, such a pathway will not operate unless triggered by

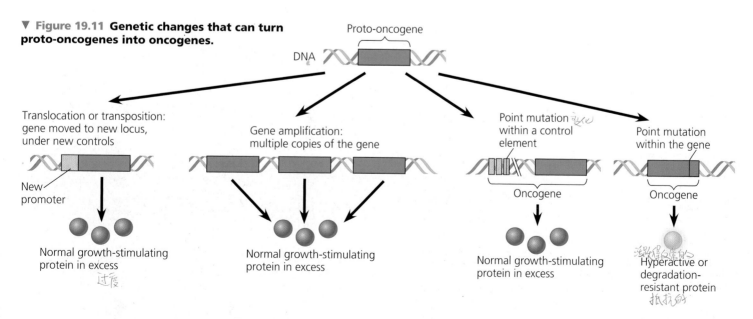

▼ **Figure 19.11 Genetic changes that can turn proto-oncogenes into oncogenes.**

(a) Cell cycle–stimulating pathway.
This pathway is triggered by ① a growth factor that binds to ② its receptor in the plasma membrane. The signal is relayed to ③ a G protein called Ras. Like all G proteins, Ras is active when GTP is bound to it. Ras passes the signal to ④ a series of protein kinases. The last kinase activates ⑤ a transcription activator that turns on one or more genes for proteins that stimulate the cell cycle. If a mutation makes Ras or any other pathway component abnormally active, excessive cell division and cancer may result.

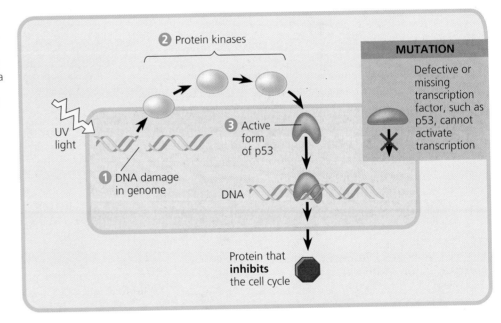

(b) Cell cycle–inhibiting pathway. In this pathway, ① DNA damage is an intracellular signal that is passed via ② protein kinases and leads to activation of ③ p53. Activated p53 promotes transcription of the gene for a protein that inhibits the cell cycle. The resulting suppression of cell division ensures that the damaged DNA is not replicated. Mutations causing deficiencies in any pathway component can contribute to the development of cancer.

(c) Effects of mutations. Increased cell division, possibly leading to cancer, can result if the cell cycle is overstimulated, as in (a), or not inhibited when it normally would be, as in (b).

▲ **Figure 19.12 Signaling pathways that regulate cell division.** Both stimulatory and inhibitory pathways regulate the cell cycle, commonly by influencing transcription. Cancer can result from aberrations in such pathways, in combination with other factors.

the appropriate growth factor. But certain mutations in the *ras* gene can lead to production of a hyperactive Ras protein that triggers the kinase cascade, resulting in increased cell division even in the absence of growth factor. In fact, hyperactive versions or excess amounts of any of the pathway's components can have the same outcome: excessive cell division.

Figure 19.12b shows a pathway in which a signal leads to the synthesis of a protein that suppresses the cell cycle. In this case, the signal is damage to the cell's DNA, perhaps as the result of exposure to ultraviolet light. Operation of this signaling pathway blocks the cell cycle until the damage has been repaired. Otherwise, the damage might contribute to tumor formation by causing mutations or chromosomal abnormalities. Thus, the genes for the components of the pathway act as tumor-suppressor genes. The tumor-suppressor protein encoded by the wild-type *p53* gene is a specific transcription factor that promotes the synthesis of cell cycle–inhibiting proteins. That is why a mutation knocking out the *p53* gene, like a mutation that leads to a hyperactive Ras protein, can lead to excessive cell growth and cancer **(Figure 19.12c)**.

The **p53 gene**, named for the 53,000-dalton molecular weight of its protein product, has been called the "guardian angel of the genome." Once activated, for example by DNA damage, the p53 protein functions as an activator for several genes. Often it activates a gene called *p21*, whose product halts the cell cycle by binding to cyclin-dependent kinases, allowing time for the cell to repair the DNA; the p53 protein can also turn on genes directly involved in DNA repair. When DNA damage is irreparable, p53 activates "suicide" genes, whose protein products cause cell death by a process called apoptosis (see Figure 21.18). Thus, in at least three ways, p53 prevents a cell from passing on mutations due to DNA damage. If mutations do accumulate and the cell survives through many divisions—as is more likely if the *p53* tumor-suppressor gene is defective or missing—cancer may ensue.

The Multistep Model of Cancer Development

More than one somatic mutation is generally needed to produce all the changes characteristic of a full-fledged cancer cell. This may help explain why the incidence of cancer increases greatly with age. If cancer results from an accumulation of mutations and if mutations occur throughout life, then the longer we live, the more likely we are to develop cancer.

The model of a multistep path to cancer is well supported by studies of one of the best understood types of human cancer, colorectal cancer. About 135,000 new cases of colorectal cancer are diagnosed each year in the United States, and the disease causes 60,000 deaths per year. Like most cancers, colorectal cancer develops gradually **(Figure 19.13)**. The first sign is often a polyp, a small, benign growth in the colon lining. The cells of the polyp look normal, although they divide unusually frequently. The tumor grows and may eventually become malignant, invading other tissues. The development of a malignant tumor is paralleled by a gradual accumulation of mutations that convert proto-oncogenes to oncogenes and knock out tumor-suppressor genes. A *ras* oncogene and a mutated *p53* tumor-suppressor gene are often involved.

About a half dozen changes must occur at the DNA level for a cell to become fully cancerous. These usually include the appearance of at least one active oncogene and the mutation or loss of several tumor-suppressor genes. Furthermore, since mutant tumor-suppressor alleles are usually recessive, in most cases mutations must knock out *both* alleles in a cell's genome to block tumor suppression. (Most oncogenes, on the other hand, behave as dominant alleles.) Finally, in many malignant tumors, the gene for telomerase is activated. This enzyme prevents the shortening of chromosome ends during DNA replication (see Figure 16.19). Production of telomerase in cancer cells removes a natural limit on the number of times the cells can divide.

▼ **Figure 19.13 A multistep model for the development of colorectal cancer.** Affecting the colon and/or rectum, this type of cancer is one of the best understood. Changes in a tumor parallel a series of genetic changes, including mutations affecting several tumor-suppressor genes (such as *p53*) and the *ras* proto-oncogene. Mutations of tumor-suppressor genes often entail loss (deletion) of the gene. *APC* stands for "adenomatous polyposis coli," and *DCC* stands for "deleted in colorectal cancer." Other mutation sequences can also lead to cancer.

Colon

Colon wall

1 Loss of tumor-suppressor gene *APC* (or other)

2 Activation of *ras* oncogene

3 Loss of tumor-suppressor gene *DCC*

4 Loss of tumor-suppressor gene *p53*

5 Additional mutations

Normal colon epithelial cells

Small benign growth (polyp)

Larger benign growth (adenoma)

Malignant tumor (carcinoma)

Viruses seem to play a role in about 15% of human cancer cases worldwide. Viruses contribute to cancer development by integrating their genetic material into the DNA of infected cells. By this process, a retrovirus may donate an oncogene to the cell. Alternatively, integrated viral DNA may disrupt a tumor-suppressor gene or convert a proto-oncogene to an oncogene. Finally, some viruses produce proteins that inactivate p53 and other tumor-suppressor proteins, thus making the cell more prone to becoming cancerous.

Inherited Predisposition to Cancer

The fact that multiple genetic changes are required to produce a cancer cell helps explain the observation that certain cancers run in some families. An individual inheriting an oncogene or a mutant allele of a tumor-suppressor gene is one step closer to accumulating the necessary mutations for cancer to develop than is an individual without any such mutations.

Geneticists are devoting much effort to identifying inherited cancer alleles so that predisposition to certain cancers can be detected early in life. About 15% of colorectal cancers, for example, involve inherited mutations. Many of these affect the tumor-suppressor gene called *adenomatous polyposis coli,* or *APC* (see Figure 19.13). This gene has multiple functions in the cell, including regulation of cell migration and adhesion. Even in patients with no family history of the disease, the *APC* gene is mutated in 60% of colorectal cancers. In these individuals, new mutations must occur in both *APC* alleles before the gene's function is lost. Since only 15% of colorectal cancers are associated with known inherited mutations, researchers continue in their efforts to identify "markers" that could predict the risk of developing this type of cancer.

There is evidence of a strong inherited predisposition in 5–10% of patients with breast cancer. This is the second most common type of cancer in the United States, striking over 180,000 women (and some men) annually and killing 40,000 each year. Mutations in the *BRCA1* or *BRCA2* gene are found in at least half of inherited breast cancers (*BRCA* stands for BReast CAncer). A woman who inherits one mutant *BRCA1* allele has a 60% probability of developing breast cancer before the age of 50, compared with only a 2% probability for an individual homozygous for the normal allele. Both *BRCA1* and *BRCA2* are considered to be tumor-suppressor genes because their wild-type alleles protect against breast cancer and their mutant alleles are recessive. Researchers have not yet determined what the normal products of these genes actually do in the cell. However, recent evidence suggests that the BRCA2 protein is directly involved in repairing breaks that occur in both strands of DNA.

The study of these and other genes associated with inherited cancer may lead to new methods for early diagnosis and treatment of all cancers. Studying these genes also increases our understanding of the normal processes of regulation of the genome.

1. Compare the usual functions of proteins encoded by proto-oncogenes with those encoded by tumor-suppressor genes.
2. Explain how the types of mutations that lead to cancer are different for a proto-oncogene and a tumor-suppressor gene.
3. Under what circumstances do we consider cancer to have a hereditary component?

For suggested answers, see Appendix A.

Concept 19.4

Eukaryotic genomes can have many noncoding DNA sequences in addition to genes

We have spent most of this chapter, and indeed this unit, focusing on genes that code for proteins. Yet the coding regions of these genes and the genes for RNA products such as rRNA and tRNA make up only a tiny portion of the genomes of most multicellular eukaryotes. The bulk of most eukaryotic genomes consists of noncoding DNA sequences, often described in the past as "junk DNA." However, much evidence is accumulating that noncoding DNA plays important roles in the cell, an idea supported by its persistence in diverse genomes over many hundreds of generations. In this section, we examine how genes and noncoding DNA sequences are organized within eukaryotic genomes, using the human genome as our prime example. Genome organization tells us much about how genomes have evolved and continue to evolve, the subject of the final section of the chapter.

The Relationship Between Genomic Composition and Organismal Complexity

Several trends are evident when we compare the genomes of prokaryotes and those of eukaryotes, including more complex groups such as mammals. Although there are exceptions, we find a general progression from smaller to larger genomes, but with fewer genes in a given length of DNA. For example, humans have 500 to 1,500 times as many base pairs in their genome as most prokaryotes, but on average only 5 to 15 times as many genes—thus many fewer genes in any given length of DNA.

In prokaryotic genomes, most of the DNA codes for protein, tRNA, or rRNA; the small amount of noncoding DNA consists mainly of regulatory sequences, such as promoters. The coding sequence of nucleotides along a prokaryotic gene proceeds from start to finish without interruption by noncoding sequences (introns). In eukaryotic genomes, by contrast, most of the DNA does *not* encode protein or RNA, and it includes more complex regulatory sequences. In fact, humans have 10,000 times as much noncoding DNA as prokaryotes. Some of the noncoding DNA in multicellular eukaryotes is present as introns within genes. Indeed, introns account for most of the difference in average length between human genes (27,000 base pairs) and prokaryotic genes (1,000 base pairs).

Now that the complete sequence of the human genome is available, we know what makes up most of the 98.5% that does not code for proteins, rRNAs, or tRNAs (**Figure 19.14**). Gene-related regulatory sequences and introns account for 24% of the human genome. The remaining sequences, located between functional genes, include some unique noncoding DNA, such as gene fragments and mutated genes that are non-functional. Most intergenic DNA, however, is **repetitive DNA,** sequences that are present in multiple copies in the genome. Somewhat surprisingly, about three-fourths of this repetitive DNA (44% of the entire human genome) is made up of transposable elements and sequences related to them.

Transposable Elements and Related Sequences

All organisms seem to have stretches of DNA that can move from one location to another within the genome. In Chapter 18, we described transposable elements in prokaryotes, which may have been an evolutionary source of viruses. However, the first evidence for wandering DNA segments did not come from experiments with prokaryotes, but from American geneticist Barbara McClintock's breeding experiments with Indian corn (maize) in the 1940s and 1950s (**Figure 19.15**). McClintock identified changes in the color of corn kernels that made sense only if she postulated the existence of genetic elements capable of moving from other locations in the genome into the genes for kernel color. McClintock's discovery received little attention until transposable elements were discovered in bacteria many years later and microbial geneticists learned more about the molecular basis of transposition.

Movement of Transposons and Retrotransposons

Eukaryotic transposable elements are of two types: **transposons,** which move within a genome by means of a DNA intermediate, and **retrotransposons,** which move by means of an RNA intermediate, a transcript of the retrotransposon DNA. Transposons can move by a "cut-and-paste" mechanism, which removes the element from the original site, or by

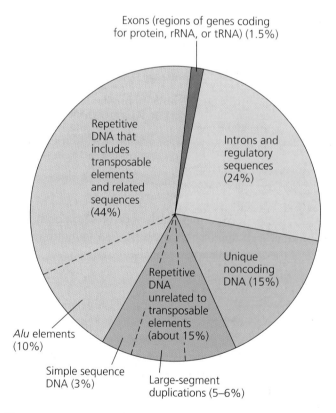

▲ **Figure 19.14 Types of DNA sequences in the human genome.** The coding sequences in genes (dark purple) make up only about 1.5% of the human genome, while introns and regulatory sequences associated with genes (light purple) make up about a quarter. The vast majority of the human genome does not code for human proteins or RNAs, and much of it is repetitive DNA (dark and light green). Because repetitive DNA is the most difficult to sequence and analyze, classification of some portions is tentative, and the percentages given here may shift slightly as genome analysis continues.

▲ **Figure 19.15 The effect of transposable elements on corn kernel color.** Barbara McClintock first proposed the idea of mobile genetic elements after observing variegations in corn kernel color. Although her idea was met with skepticism when she proposed it in the 1940s, it was later validated. She received the Nobel Prize in 1983, at the age of 81, for her pioneering research.

a "copy-and-paste" mechanism, which leaves a copy behind (**Figure 19.16a**).

Retrotransposons always leave a copy at the original site during transposition, since they are initially transcribed into an RNA intermediate (**Figure 19.16b**). To insert at another site, the RNA intermediate is first converted back to DNA by reverse transcriptase, an enzyme encoded in the retrotransposon itself. Thus, reverse transcriptase can be present in cells not infected with retroviruses. (In fact, retroviruses may have evolved from retrotransposons.) A cellular enzyme catalyzes insertion of the reverse-transcribed DNA at a new site. Most transposable elements in eukaryotic genomes are retrotransposons.

Sequences Related to Transposable Elements

Multiple copies of transposable elements and sequences related to them are scattered throughout eukaryotic genomes. A single unit is usually hundreds to thousands of base pairs long, and the dispersed "copies" are similar but usually not identical to each other. Some of these are transposable elements that move using enzymes encoded either by themselves or by other transposable elements, and some are related sequences that have lost the ability to move altogether. Transposable elements and related sequences make up 25–50% of most mammalian genomes and even higher percentages in amphibians and higher plants (see Figure 19.14).

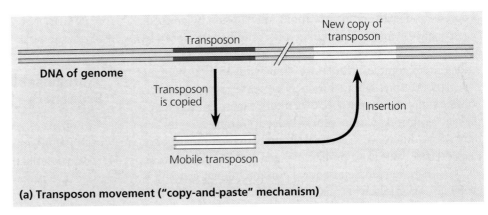

(a) Transposon movement ("copy-and-paste" mechanism)

(b) Retrotransposon movement

▲ **Figure 19.16 Movement of eukaryotic transposable elements. (a)** Movement of transposons by either the cut-and-paste mechanism or the copy-and-paste mechanism (shown here) involves a double-stranded DNA intermediate that is inserted into the genome. **(b)** Movement of retrotransposons begins with formation of a single-stranded RNA intermediate. The remaining steps are essentially identical to part of the retrovirus reproductive cycle (see Figure 18.10). In movement of transposons by the copy-and-paste mechanism and in movement of retrotransposons, the DNA sequence remains in the original site as well as appearing in a new site.

In humans and other primates, a large portion of transposable element–related DNA consists of a family of similar sequences called *Alu elements*. These sequences alone account for approximately 10% of the human genome. *Alu* elements are about 300 nucleotides long, much shorter than most functional transposable elements, and they do not code for any protein. However, many *Alu* elements are transcribed into RNA molecules; their cellular function, if any, is unknown.

Although many transposable elements encode proteins, these proteins do not carry out normal cellular functions. Thus, these elements often are described as "noncoding" DNA, along with other repetitive sequences.

Other Repetitive DNA, Including Simple Sequence DNA

Repetitive DNA that is not related to transposable elements probably arose by mistakes that occurred during DNA replication or recombination. It accounts for about 15% of the human genome (see Figure 19.14). About a third of this (5% of the human genome) consists of large-segment duplications, in which a long stretch of DNA, between 10,000 and 300,000 nucleotide pairs, seems to have been copied from one chromosomal location to another, on the same or a different chromosome.

In contrast to single duplications of long sequences, *simple sequence DNA* contains many copies of tandemly repeated short sequences, as in the following example (showing one DNA strand only):

. . . GTTACGTTACGTTACGTTACGTTACGTTAC . . .

In this case, the repeated unit consists of five nucleotides (GTTAC). Repeated units often contain fewer than 15 nucleotides, but they may include as many as 500 nucleotides. The number of repeated units at a particular site in the genome varies as well. For example, there could be as many as several hundred thousand repetitions of the GTTAC unit at one site. Altogether, simple sequence DNA makes up 3% of the human genome.

The nucleotide composition of simple sequence DNA is often different enough from the rest of the cell's DNA to have an intrinsically different density. If genomic DNA is cut into pieces and centrifuged at high speed, segments of different density migrate to different positions in the centrifuge tube. Repetitive DNA isolated in this way was originally called *satellite DNA* because it appeared as a "satellite" band in the centrifuge tube, separate from the rest of the DNA. Now the term is often used interchangeably with *simple sequence DNA*.

Much of a genome's simple sequence DNA is located at chromosomal telomeres and centromeres, suggesting that this DNA plays a structural role for chromosomes. The DNA at centromeres is essential for the separation of chromatids in cell division (see Chapter 12). Centromeric DNA, along with simple sequence DNA located elsewhere, also may help organize the chromatin within the interphase nucleus. The simple sequence DNA located at telomeres, at the tips of chromosomes, prevents genes from being lost as the DNA shortens with each round of replication (see Chapter 16). Telomeric DNA also binds proteins that protect the ends of a chromosome from degradation and from joining to other chromosomes.

Genes and Multigene Families

We finish our discussion of the various types of DNA sequences in eukaryotic genomes with a closer look at genes. Recall that sequences coding for proteins and structural RNAs compose a mere 1.5% of the human genome (see Figure 19.14). If we include introns and regulatory sequences associated with genes, the total amount of gene-related DNA—coding and noncoding—constitutes about 25% of the human genome.

As in prokaryotes, most eukaryotic genes are present as unique sequences, with only one copy per haploid set of chromosomes. But in the human genome, such solitary genes make up only about half of the total coding DNA. The rest occurs in **multigene families,** collections of identical or very similar genes.

Some multigene families consist of *identical* DNA sequences, usually clustered tandemly. With the notable exception of the genes for histone proteins, multigene families of identical genes code for RNA products. An example is the family of identical sequences encoding the three largest ribosomal RNA (rRNA) molecules **(Figure 19.17a)**. These rRNA molecules are encoded in a single transcription unit that is repeated tandemly hundreds to thousands of times in one or several clusters in the genome of a multicellular eukaryote. The many copies of this rRNA transcription unit help cells to quickly make the millions of ribosomes needed for active protein synthesis. The primary transcript is cleaved to yield the three rRNA molecules. These are then

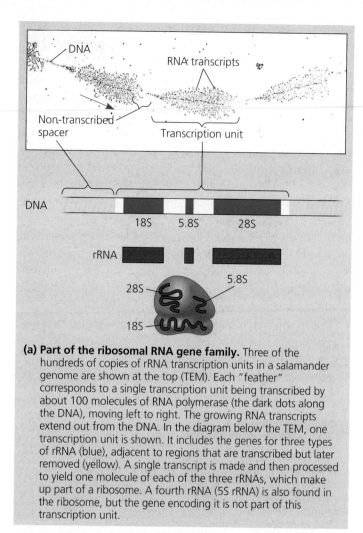

(a) Part of the ribosomal RNA gene family. Three of the hundreds of copies of rRNA transcription units in a salamander genome are shown at the top (TEM). Each "feather" corresponds to a single transcription unit being transcribed by about 100 molecules of RNA polymerase (the dark dots along the DNA), moving left to right. The growing RNA transcripts extend out from the DNA. In the diagram below the TEM, one transcription unit is shown. It includes the genes for three types of rRNA (blue), adjacent to regions that are transcribed but later removed (yellow). A single transcript is made and then processed to yield one molecule of each of the three rRNAs, which make up part of a ribosome. A fourth rRNA (5S rRNA) is also found in the ribosome, but the gene encoding it is not part of this transcription unit.

(b) The human α-globin and β-globin gene families. Hemoglobin is composed of two α-globin and two β-globin polypeptide subunits. The genes (dark blue) encoding α- and β-globins are found in two families, organized as shown here. The noncoding DNA separating the functional genes within each family cluster includes pseudogenes (green), nonfunctional versions of the functional genes. Genes and pseudogenes are named with Greek letters.

▲ **Figure 19.17 Gene families.**

combined with proteins and one other kind of rRNA (5S rRNA) to form ribosomal subunits.

The classic examples of multigene families of *nonidentical* genes are two related families of genes that encode globins, a group of proteins that include the α and β polypeptide subunits of hemoglobin. One family, located on chromosome 16 in humans, encodes various forms of α-globin; the other, on chromosome 11, encodes forms of β-globin (**Figure 19.17b**). The different forms of each globin subunit are expressed at different times in development, allowing hemoglobin to function effectively in the changing environment of the developing animal. In humans, for example, the embryonic and fetal forms of hemoglobin have a higher affinity for oxygen than the adult forms, ensuring the efficient transfer of oxygen from mother to developing fetus. Also found in the globin gene family clusters are several **pseudogenes,** nonfunctional nucleotide sequences quite similar to the functional genes.

The arrangement of the genes in gene families has provided insight into the evolution of genomes. We will consider some of the processes that have shaped the genomes of different species over evolutionary time in the next section.

Concept Check 19.4

1. Discuss the characteristics that make mammalian genomes larger than prokaryotic genomes.
2. How do introns, transposable elements, and simple sequence DNA differ in their distribution in the genome?
3. Discuss the differences in the organization of the rRNA gene family and the globin gene families. How do these gene families benefit the organism?

For suggested answers, see Appendix A.

Concept 19.5

Duplications, rearrangements, and mutations of DNA contribute to genome evolution

The basis of change at the genomic level is mutation, which underlies much of genome evolution. It seems likely that the earliest forms of life had a minimal number of genes—those necessary for survival and reproduction. If this was indeed the case, one aspect of evolution must have been an increase in the size of the genome, with the extra genetic material providing the raw material for gene diversification. In this section, we will first describe how extra copies of all or part of a genome can arise and then consider subsequent processes that

can lead to the evolution of proteins (or RNA products) with related or entirely new functions.

Duplication of Chromosome Sets

An accident in meiosis can result in one or more extra sets of chromosomes, a condition known as polyploidy. In a polyploid organism, one complete set of genes can provide essential functions for the organism. The genes in the one or more extra sets can diverge by accumulating mutations; these variations may persist if the organism carrying them survives and reproduces. In this way, genes with novel functions can evolve. As long as one copy of a crucial gene is expressed, the divergence of another copy can lead to its encoded protein acting in a novel way, thereby changing the organism's phenotype. The accumulation of mutations in many (or even a few) genes may lead to the branching off of a new species, as happens often in plants (see Chapter 24). Although polyploid animals exist, they are rare.

Duplication and Divergence of DNA Segments

Errors during meiosis can also lead to the duplication of individual genes. Unequal crossing over during prophase I of meiosis, for instance, can result in one chromosome with a deletion and another with a duplication of a particular region. As illustrated in **Figure 19.18**, transposable elements in the

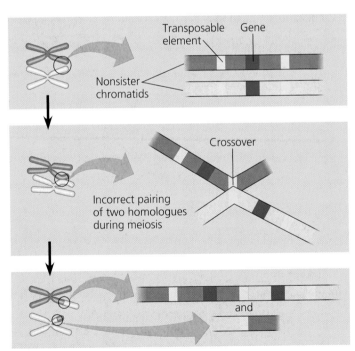

▲ **Figure 19.18 Gene duplication due to unequal crossing over.** One mechanism by which a gene (or other DNA segment) can be duplicated is recombination during meiosis between copies of a transposable element flanking the gene. Such recombination between misaligned nonsister chromatids of homologous chromosomes produces one chromatid with two copies of the gene and one chromatid with no copy.

genome can provide sites where nonsister chromatids can cross over, even when their homologous gene sequences are not correctly aligned.

Also, slippage can occur during DNA replication, such that the template shifts with respect to the new complementary strand, and one region of the template strand is either not copied or copied twice. As a result, a region of DNA is deleted or duplicated. It is easy to imagine how such errors could occur in regions of repeats, such as the simple sequence DNA described previously. The variability in numbers of repeated units of simple sequence DNA at the same site is probably due to errors like these. Evidence that molecular events such as unequal crossing over and slippage lead to duplication of genes is found in the existence of multigene families.

▲ **Figure 19.19 Evolution of the human α-globin and β-globin gene families.** Shown here is a model for evolution of the modern α-globin and β-globin gene families from a single ancestral globin gene.

Evolution of Genes with Related Functions: The Human Globin Genes

Duplication events can lead to the evolution of genes with related functions, such as those of the α-globin and β-globin gene families (see Figure 19.17b). A comparison of gene sequences within a multigene family can suggest the order in which the genes arose. This approach to re-creating the evolutionary history of the various globin genes indicates that they all evolved from one common ancestral globin gene, which was duplicated and diverged into α-globin and β-globin ancestral genes about 450–500 million years ago (Figure 19.19). Each of these genes was later duplicated several times, and the copies then diverged from each other in sequence, yielding the current family members. In fact, the common ancestral globin gene also gave rise to the oxygen-binding muscle protein myoglobin and to the plant protein leghemoglobin. The latter two proteins function as monomers, and their genes are included in a "globin superfamily."

After the duplication events, the differences between the genes in the globin families undoubtedly arose from mutations that accumulated in the gene copies over many generations. The current model is that the necessary function provided by an α-globin protein, for example, was fulfilled by one gene, while other copies of the α-globin gene accumulated random mutations. Some mutations may have had an adverse affect on the organ-

ism and some may have had no effect, but some mutations may have altered the function of the protein product in a way that was advantageous to the organism at a particular life stage without substantially changing its oxygen-carrying function. Presumably, natural selection acted on these altered genes to maintain them in the population, leading to production of alternative forms of α-globin protein.

The similarity in the amino acid sequences of the various α-globin and β-globin proteins supports this model of gene duplication and mutation **(Table 19.1)**. The amino acid sequences of the β-globins, for instance, are much more similar to each other than to the α-globin sequences. The existence of several pseudogenes among the functional globin genes provides additional evidence for this model (see Figure 19.17b). That is, random mutations in these "genes" over evolutionary time have destroyed their function.

Table 19.1 Percentage of Similarity in Amino Acid Sequence Between Human Globin Proteins

		α-Globins		β-Globins		
		α	ζ	β	γ	ε
α-Globins	α	100	58	42	39	37
	ζ	58	100	34	38	37
β-Globins	β	42	34	100	73	75
	γ	39	38	73	100	80
	ε	37	37	75	80	100

Evolution of Genes with Novel Functions

In the evolution of the globin gene families, gene duplication and subsequent divergence produced family members whose protein products performed related functions. Alternatively, one copy of a duplicated gene can undergo alterations that lead to a completely new function for the protein product. The genes for lysozyme and α-lactalbumin are good examples.

Lysozyme is an enzyme that helps prevent infection by hydrolyzing the cell walls of bacteria; α-lactalbumin is a nonenzymatic protein that plays a role in milk production in mammals. The two proteins are quite similar in their amino acid sequences and three-dimensional structures. Both genes are found in mammals, whereas only the lysozyme gene is present in birds. These findings suggest that at some time after the lineages leading to mammals and birds had separated, the lysozyme gene underwent a duplication event in the mammalian lineage but not in the avian lineage. Subsequently, one copy of the duplicated lysozyme gene evolved into a gene encoding α-lactalbumin, a protein with a completely different function.

Rearrangements of Parts of Genes: Exon Duplication and Exon Shuffling

Rearrangement of existing DNA sequences has also contributed to genome evolution. The presence of introns in most eukaryotic genes may have promoted the evolution of new and potentially useful proteins by facilitating the duplication or repositioning of exons in the genome. Recall from Chapter 17 that an exon often codes for a domain, a distinct structural or functional region of a protein.

We've already seen that unequal crossing over during meiosis can lead to duplication of a gene on one chromosome and its loss from the homologous chromosome (see Figure 19.18). By a similar process, a particular exon within a gene could be duplicated on one chromosome and deleted from the homologous chromosome. The gene with the duplicated exon would code for a protein containing a second copy of the encoded domain. This change in the protein's structure could augment its function by increasing its stability, enhancing its ability to bind a particular ligand, or altering some other property. Quite a few protein-coding genes have multiple copies of related exons, which presumably arose by duplication and then diverged. The gene encoding the extracellular matrix protein collagen is a good example. Collagen is a structural protein with a highly repetitive amino acid sequence, which is reflected in the repetitive pattern of exons in the collagen gene.

Alternatively, we can imagine the occasional mixing and matching of different exons either within a gene or between two nonallelic genes owing to errors in meiotic recombination. This process, termed *exon shuffling*, could lead to new

proteins with novel combinations of functions. As an example, let's consider the gene for tissue plasminogen activator (TPA). The TPA protein is an extracellular protein involved in limiting blood clotting. It has four domains of three types, each encoded by an exon; one exon is present in two copies. Because each type of exon is also found in other proteins, the gene for TPA is believed to have arisen by several instances of exon shuffling and duplication (Figure 19.20). The TPA protein slows the clotting reaction and therefore limits the damage that can result from heart attacks and some types of stroke, as long as it is administered immediately to victims.

How Transposable Elements Contribute to Genome Evolution

The persistence of transposable elements as a large fraction of some eukaryotic genomes is consistent with the idea that they can play an important role in shaping a genome over evolutionary time. These elements can contribute to the evolution of the genome in several ways. They can promote recombination, disrupt cellular genes or control elements, and carry entire genes or individual exons to new locations.

The presence of homologous transposable element sequences scattered throughout the genome allows recombination to take place between different chromosomes. Most such alterations are probably detrimental, causing chromosomal translocations and other changes in the genome that may be lethal to the organism. But over the course of evolutionary time, an occasional recombination like this may be advantageous to the organism.

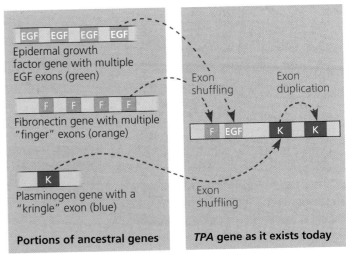

▲ Figure 19.20 **Evolution of a new gene by exon shuffling.** Exon shuffling could have moved exons from ancestral forms of the genes for epidermal growth factor, fibronectin, and plasminogen (left) into the evolving gene for tissue plasminogen activator, TPA (right). The order in which these events might have occurred is unknown. Duplication of the "kringle" exon from plasminogen after its movement could account for the two copies of this exon in the *TPA* gene. Each type of exon encodes a particular domain in the TPA protein.

The movement of transposable elements around the genome can have several direct consequences. For instance, if a transposable element "jumps" into the middle of a coding sequence of a protein-coding gene, it prevents the normal functioning of the interrupted gene. If a transposable element inserts within a regulatory sequence, the transposition may lead to increased or decreased production of one or more proteins. Transposition caused both types of effects on the genes coding for pigment-synthesizing enzymes in McClintock's corn kernels. Again, while such changes may usually be harmful, in the long run some may prove beneficial.

During transposition, a transposable element may carry along a gene or group of genes to a new position in the genome. This mechanism probably accounts for the location of the α-globin and β-globin gene families on different human chromosomes, as well as the dispersion of the genes of certain other gene families. By a similar tag-along process, an exon from one gene may be inserted into another gene in a mechanism similar to that of exon shuffling during recombination. For example, an exon may be inserted by transposition into the intron of a protein-coding gene. If the inserted exon is retained in the RNA transcript during RNA splicing, the protein that is synthesized will have an additional domain, which may confer a new function on the protein.

Recent research reveals yet another way that transposable elements can lead to new coding sequences. This work shows that an *Alu* element may hop into introns in a way that creates a weak alternative splice site in the RNA transcript. During processing of the transcript, the regular splice sites are used more often, so that the original protein is made. On occasion, however, splicing occurs at the new weak site, with the result that some of the *Alu* element ends up in the mRNA, coding for a new portion of the protein. In this way, alternative genetic combinations can be "tried out" while the function of the original gene product is retained.

Clearly, these processes produce either no effect or harmful effects in most individual cases. However, over long periods of time, the generation of genetic diversity provides more raw material for natural selection to work on during evolution. Recent advances in DNA technology have allowed researchers to sequence and compare the genomes of many different species, increasing our understanding of how genomes evolve. You will learn more about these topics in the next chapter.

Concept Check 19.5

1. Describe three examples of errors in cellular processes that lead to DNA duplications.
2. What processes are thought to have led to the evolution of the globin gene families?
3. Look at the portions of the fibronectin and EGF genes shown in Figure 19.20 (left). How might they have arisen?
4. What are three ways transposable elements are thought to contribute to the evolution of the genome?

For suggested answers, see Appendix A.

Chapter 19 Review

Go to the Campbell Biology website (**www.campbellbiology.com**) or CD-ROM to explore Activities, Investigations, and other interactive study aids.

SUMMARY OF KEY CONCEPTS

Concept 19.1

Chromatin structure is based on successive levels of DNA packing

▶ **Nucleosomes, or "Beads on a String" (pp. 360–361)** Eukaryotic chromatin is composed mostly of DNA and histone proteins that bind to each other and to the DNA to form nucleosomes, the most basic units of DNA packing. Histone tails extend outward from each bead-like nucleosome core.

▶ **Higher Levels of DNA Packing (pp. 360–361)** Additional folding leads ultimately to highly compacted heterochromatin, the form of chromatin in a metaphase chromosome. In interphase cells, most chromatin is in the highly extended form called euchromatin.
Activity DNA Packing

Concept 19.2

Gene expression can be regulated at any stage, but the key step is transcription

▶ **Differential Gene Expression (pp. 362–363)** Each cell of a multicellular eukaryote expresses only a fraction of its genes. In each type of differentiated cell, a unique subset of genes is expressed. Key stages at which gene expression may be regulated include changes in chromatin structure, initiation of transcription, RNA processing, mRNA degradation, translation, and protein processing and degradation.
Activity Overview: Control of Gene Expression

▶ **Regulation of Chromatin Structure (pp. 363–364)** Genes in highly compacted chromatin are generally not transcribed. Chemical modification of histone tails can affect the configuration of chromatin and thus gene expression. Histone acetylation seems to loosen chromatin structure and thereby enhance transcription. DNA methylation is associated with reduced transcription.

▶ **Regulation of Transcription Initiation (pp. 364–367)** Multiple DNA control elements distant from the promoter (in one or more enhancers) bind specific transcription factors (activators or repressors) that regulate transcription initiation for specific genes within the genome. Bending of DNA enables activators bound to enhancers to contact proteins at the promoter. Unlike the genes of a prokaryotic operon, coordinately controlled eukaryotic genes each have a promoter and control elements. The same regulatory sequences are common to all the genes of a group, enabling recognition by the same specific transcription factors.

Activity Control of Transcription
Investigation How Do You Design a Gene Expression System?

▶ **Mechanisms of Post-Transcriptional Regulation (pp. 368–370)** Regulation at the RNA-processing level is exemplified by alternative RNA splicing. Also, each mRNA has a characteristic life span, determined in part by sequences in the leader and trailer regions. RNA interference by single-stranded micro-RNAs can lead to degradation of an mRNA or block its translation. The initiation of translation can be controlled via regulation of initiation factors. After translation, various types of protein processing (such as cleavage and the addition of chemical groups) are subject to control, as is the degradation of proteins by proteasomes.

Activity Post-Transcriptional Control Mechanisms
Activity Review: Control of Gene Expression

Concept 19.3

Cancer results from genetic changes that affect cell cycle control

▶ **Types of Genes Associated with Cancer (pp. 370–371)** The products of proto-oncogenes and tumor-suppressor genes control cell division. A DNA change that makes a proto-oncogene excessively active converts it to an oncogene, which may promote excessive cell division and cancer. A tumor-suppressor gene encodes a protein that inhibits abnormal cell division. A mutation in such a gene that reduces the activity of its protein product may also lead to excessive cell division and possibly to cancer.

▶ **Interference with Normal Cell-Signaling Pathways (pp. 371–373)** Many proto-oncogenes and tumor-suppressor genes encode components of growth-stimulating and growth-inhibiting signaling pathways, respectively. A hyperactive version of a protein in a stimulatory pathway, such as Ras (a G protein), functions as an oncogene protein. A defective version of a protein in an inhibitory pathway, such as p53 (a transcription activator), fails to function as a tumor suppressor.

▶ **The Multistep Model of Cancer Development (pp. 373–374)** Normal cells are converted to cancer cells by the accumulation of multiple mutations affecting proto-oncogenes and tumor-suppressor genes. Certain viruses promote cancer by integration of viral DNA into a cell's genome.

▶ **Inherited Predisposition to Cancer (p. 374)** Individuals who inherit a mutant oncogene or tumor-suppressor allele have an increased risk of developing certain types of cancer.

Activity Causes of Cancer

Concept 19.4

Eukaryotic genomes can have many noncoding DNA sequences in addition to genes

▶ **The Relationship Between Genomic Composition and Organismal Complexity (pp. 374–375)** Compared with prokaryotic genomes, the genomes of eukaryotes generally are larger, have longer genes, and contain a much greater amount of noncoding DNA both associated with genes (introns, regulatory sequences) and between genes (much of it repetitive sequences).

▶ **Transposable Elements and Related Sequences (pp. 375–376)** The most abundant type of repetitive DNA in higher eukaryotes consists of transposable elements and related sequences. Two types of transposable elements occur in eukaryotes: transposons, which move via a DNA intermediate, and retrotransposons, which are the most prevalent and move via an RNA intermediate. Each element may be hundreds or thousands of base pairs long, and similar but usually not identical copies are dispersed throughout the genome.

▶ **Other Repetitive DNA, Including Simple Sequence DNA (pp. 376–377)** Short noncoding sequences that are tandemly repeated thousands of times (simple sequence DNA) are especially prominent in centromeres and telomeres, where they probably play structural roles in the chromosome.

▶ **Genes and Multigene Families (pp. 377–378)** Most eukaryotic genes are present in one copy per haploid set of chromosomes. However, the transcription unit encoding the three largest rRNAs is tandemly repeated hundreds to thousands of times at one or several chromosomal sites, enabling the cell to make the rRNA for millions of ribosomes quickly. The multiple, slightly different genes in the two globin gene families encode polypeptides used at different developmental stages of an animal.

Concept 19.5

Duplications, rearrangements, and mutations of DNA contribute to genome evolution

▶ **Duplication of Chromosome Sets (p. 378)** Accidents in cell division can lead to extra copies of all or part of a genome, which may then diverge if one set accumulates sequence changes.

▶ **Duplication and Divergence of DNA Segments (pp. 378–380)** The genes encoding the various globin proteins evolved from one common ancestral globin gene, which duplicated and diverged into α-globin and β-globin ancestral genes. Subsequent duplications of these genes and random mutations gave rise to the present globin genes, all of which code for oxygen-binding proteins. The copies of some duplicated genes have diverged so much during evolutionary time that the functions of their encoded proteins are now substantially different.

▶ **Rearrangements of Parts of Genes: Exon Duplication and Exon Shuffling (p. 380)** Rearrangement of exons within and between genes during evolution has led to genes containing multiple copies of similar exons and/or several different exons derived from other genes.

▶ **How Transposable Elements Contribute to Genome Evolution (pp. 380–381)** Movement of transposable elements or recombination between copies of the same element occasionally generates new sequence combinations that are beneficial to the organism. Such mechanisms can alter the functions of genes or their patterns of expression and regulation.

TESTING YOUR KNOWLEDGE

Self-Quiz

1. In a nucleosome, the DNA is wrapped around
   a. polymerase molecules.
   b. ribosomes.
   c. histones.
   d. the nucleolus.
   e. satellite DNA.

2. Muscle cells differ from nerve cells mainly because
   a. they express different genes.
   b. they contain different genes.
   c. they use different genetic codes.
   d. they have unique ribosomes.
   e. they have different chromosomes.

3. One of the characteristics of retrotransposons is that
   a. they code for an enzyme that synthesizes DNA using an RNA template.
   b. they are found only in animal cells.
   c. they generally move by a cut-and-paste mechanism.
   d. they contribute a significant portion of the genetic variability seen within a population of gametes.
   e. their amplification is dependent on a retrovirus.

4. The functioning of enhancers is an example of
   a. transcriptional control of gene expression.
   b. a post-transcriptional mechanism for editing mRNA.
   c. the stimulation of translation by initiation factors.
   d. post-translational control that activates certain proteins.
   e. a eukaryotic equivalent of prokaryotic promoter functioning.

5. Multigene families are
   a. groups of enhancers that control transcription.
   b. usually clustered at the telomeres.
   c. equivalent to the operons of prokaryotes.
   d. sets of genes that are coordinately controlled.
   e. identical or similar genes that have evolved by gene duplication.

6. Which of the following statements about the DNA in one of your brain cells is true?
   a. Some DNA sequences are present in multiple copies.
   b. Most of the DNA codes for protein.
   c. The majority of genes are likely to be transcribed.
   d. Each gene lies immediately adjacent to an enhancer.
   e. Many genes are grouped into operon-like clusters.

7. Two eukaryotic proteins have one domain in common but are otherwise very different. Which of the following processes is most likely to have contributed to this phenomenon?
   a. gene duplication
   b. RNA splicing
   c. exon shuffling
   d. histone modification
   e. random point mutations

8. Which of the following is an example of a possible step in the post-transcriptional control of gene expression?
   a. the addition of methyl groups to cytosine bases of DNA
   b. the binding of transcription factors to a promoter
   c. the removal of introns and splicing together of exons
   d. gene amplification during a stage in development
   e. the folding of DNA to form heterochromatin

9. Within a cell, the amount of protein made using a given mRNA molecule depends partly on
   a. the degree of DNA methylation.
   b. the rate at which the mRNA is degraded.
   c. the presence of certain transcription factors.
   d. the number of introns present in the mRNA.
   e. the types of ribosomes present in the cytoplasm.

10. Proto-oncogenes can change into oncogenes that cause cancer. Which of the following best explains the presence of these potential time bombs in eukaryotic cells?
    a. Proto-oncogenes first arose from viral infections.
    b. Proto-oncogenes normally help regulate cell division.
    c. Proto-oncogenes are genetic "junk."
    d. Proto-oncogenes are mutant versions of normal genes.
    e. Cells produce proto-oncogenes as they age.

For Self-Quiz answers, see Appendix A.

Go to the website or CD-ROM for more quiz questions.

Evolution Connection

One of the revelations of the human genome sequence was the presence of relict prokaryotic sequences—genes of prokaryotes incorporated into our genome but now defunct molecular fossils. What may have occurred to maroon prokaryotic genes in our genome?

Scientific Inquiry

Prostate cells usually require testosterone and other androgens to survive. But some prostate cancer cells thrive despite treatments that eliminate androgens. One hypothesis is that estrogen, often considered a female hormone, may be activating genes normally controlled by an androgen in these cancer cells. Describe one or more experiments to test this hypothesis. (See Figure 11.6 to review the action of these steroid hormones.)

Investigation *How Do You Design a Gene Expression System?*

Science, Technology, and Society

Trace amounts of dioxin were present in Agent Orange, a defoliant sprayed on vegetation during the Vietnam War. Animal tests suggest that dioxin can cause birth defects, cancer, liver and thymus damage, and immune system suppression, sometimes leading to death. But the animal tests are equivocal; a hamster is not affected by a dose that can kill a guinea pig. Dioxin acts somewhat like a steroid hormone, entering a cell and binding to a receptor protein that then attaches to the cell's DNA. How might this mechanism help explain the variety of dioxin's effects on different body systems and in different animals? How might you determine whether a type of illness is related to dioxin exposure? How might you determine whether a particular individual became ill as a result of exposure to dioxin? Which would be more difficult to demonstrate? Why?

20
DNA Technology
and Genomics

▲ **Figure 20.1 DNA microarray that reveals expression levels of 2,400 human genes (enlarged photo).**

Key Concepts

20.1 DNA cloning permits production of multiple copies of a specific gene or other DNA segment

20.2 Restriction fragment analysis detects DNA differences that affect restriction sites

20.3 Entire genomes can be mapped at the DNA level

20.4 Genome sequences provide clues to important biological questions

20.5 The practical applications of DNA technology affect our lives in many ways

Overview

Understanding and Manipulating Genomes

One of the great achievements of modern science has been the sequencing of the human genome, which was largely completed by 2003. The sequencing of the first complete genome, that of a bacterium, had been carried out a mere eight years previously. During the intervening years, researchers accelerated the pace of DNA sequencing, while working on other genomes, aided by the development of faster and faster sequencing machines. These sequencing accomplishments have all depended on advances in DNA technology, starting with the invention of methods for making **recombinant DNA.** This is DNA in which nucleotide sequences from two different sources—often different species—are combined *in vitro* into the same DNA molecule.

The methods for making recombinant DNA are central to **genetic engineering,** the direct manipulation of genes for practical purposes. Applications of genetic engineering include the manufacture of hundreds of protein products, such as hormones and blood-clotting factors. Using DNA technology, scientists can make recombinant DNA and then introduce it into cultured cells that replicate the DNA and express its genes, yielding a desired protein.

DNA technology has launched a revolution in the area of **biotechnology,** the manipulation of organisms or their components to make useful products. Practices that go back centuries are forms of biotechnology: for example, the use of microbes to make wine and cheese and the selective breeding of livestock, which exploits naturally occurring mutations and genetic recombination. Modern biotechnology based on the manipulation of DNA *in vitro* differs from earlier practices by enabling scientists to modify specific genes and move them between organisms as distinct as bacteria, plants, and animals.

DNA technology is now applied in areas ranging from agriculture to criminal law. More important, its use allows researchers in virtually all fields of biology to tackle age-old questions in a more comprehensive way. For instance, the level of expression of thousands of different genes can now be measured at the same time, as shown in the DNA microarray in **Figure 20.1**. In the photograph, the color of each spot represents the relative expression of one of 2,400 human genes in a particular tissue. With this technique, researchers can compare gene expression in particular tissues or under different conditions. The knowledge gained from such global expression studies was largely inaccessible only a few decades ago.

In this chapter, we first describe the main techniques for manipulating DNA and then discuss how genomes are analyzed and compared at the DNA level. In the last section, we survey the practical applications of DNA technology, concluding the chapter by considering some of the social and ethical issues that arise as DNA technology becomes more pervasive in our lives.

DNA cloning permits production of multiple copies of a specific gene or other DNA segment

The molecular biologist studying a particular gene faces a challenge. Naturally occurring DNA molecules are very long, and a single molecule usually carries many genes. Moreover, genes may occupy only a small proportion of the chromosomal DNA, the rest being noncoding nucleotide sequences. A single human gene, for example, might constitute only $\frac{1}{100,000}$ of a chromosomal DNA molecule. As a further complication, the distinctions between a gene and the surrounding DNA are subtle, consisting only of differences in nucleotide sequence. To work directly with specific genes, scientists have developed methods for preparing well-defined, gene-sized pieces of DNA in multiple identical copies, a process called **gene cloning**.

DNA Cloning and Its Applications: *A Preview*

Most methods for cloning pieces of DNA in the laboratory share certain general features. One common approach uses bacteria (most often, *Escherichia coli*) and their plasmids. Recall from Chapter 18 that bacterial plasmids are relatively small, circular DNA molecules that replicate separate from a bacterial chromosome. For cloning genes or other pieces of DNA in the laboratory, a plasmid is first isolated from a bacterial cell, and then the foreign DNA is inserted into it **(Figure 20.2)**. The resulting plasmid is now a recombinant DNA molecule, combining DNA from two sources. The plasmid is returned to a bacterial cell, producing a *recombinant bacterium*, which reproduces to form a **clone** of identical cells. Because the dividing bacteria replicate the recombinant plasmid and pass it on to their descendants, the foreign gene is "cloned" at the same time; that is, the clone of cells contains multiple copies of the gene.

Cloned genes are useful for two basic purposes: to make many copies of a particular gene and to produce a protein product. Researchers can isolate copies of a cloned gene from bacteria for use in basic research or to endow an organism with a new metabolic capability, such as pest resistance. For example, a resistance gene present in one crop species might be cloned and transferred into plants of another species. Alternatively, a protein with medical uses, such as human growth hormone, can be harvested in large quantities from bacterial cultures carrying the cloned gene for the protein.

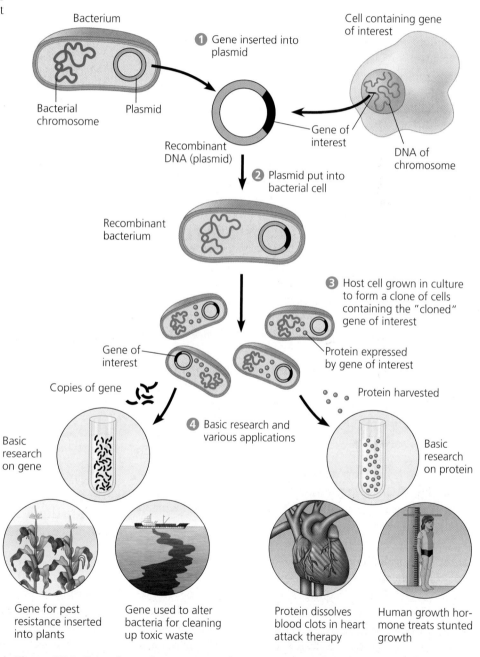

① Gene inserted into plasmid

Bacterium
Bacterial chromosome
Plasmid

Cell containing gene of interest
DNA of chromosome

Recombinant DNA (plasmid)
Gene of interest

② Plasmid put into bacterial cell

Recombinant bacterium

③ Host cell grown in culture to form a clone of cells containing the "cloned" gene of interest

Protein expressed by gene of interest

Gene of interest

Copies of gene

Protein harvested

④ Basic research and various applications

Basic research on gene

Basic research on protein

Gene for pest resistance inserted into plants

Gene used to alter bacteria for cleaning up toxic waste

Protein dissolves blood clots in heart attack therapy

Human growth hormone treats stunted growth

▲ **Figure 20.2 Overview of gene cloning with a bacterial plasmid, showing various uses of cloned genes.** In this simplified diagram of gene cloning in the laboratory, we start with a plasmid isolated from a bacterial cell and a gene of interest from another organism. Only one copy of the plasmid and one copy of the gene of interest are shown at the top of the figure, but the starting materials would include many copies of each.

Most protein-coding genes exist in only one copy per genome—something on the order of one part per million of DNA—so the ability to clone such rare DNA fragments is extremely valuable. In the remainder of this chapter, you will learn more about the techniques outlined in Figure 20.2 and related methods.

Using Restriction Enzymes to Make Recombinant DNA

Gene cloning and genetic engineering were made possible by the discovery of enzymes that cut DNA molecules at a limited number of specific locations. These enzymes, called restriction endonucleases, or **restriction enzymes,** were discovered in the late 1960s by researchers studying bacteria. In nature, these enzymes protect the bacterial cell against intruding DNA from other organisms, such as phages or other species of bacteria. They work by cutting up the foreign DNA, a process called *restriction.*

Hundreds of different restriction enzymes have been identified and isolated. Each restriction enzyme is very specific, recognizing a particular short DNA sequence, or **restriction site,** and cutting both DNA strands at specific points within this restriction site. The DNA of a bacterial cell is protected from the cell's own restriction enzymes by the addition of methyl groups ($-CH_3$) to adenines or cytosines within the sequences recognized by the enzymes.

The top of **Figure 20.3** illustrates a restriction site recognized by a particular restriction enzyme from *E. coli.* As shown in this example, most restriction sites are symmetrical: That is, the sequence of nucleotides is the same on both strands when read in the $5' \rightarrow 3'$ direction. Most restriction enzymes recognize sequences containing four to eight nucleotides. Because any sequence this short usually occurs (by chance) many times in a long DNA molecule, a restriction enzyme will make many cuts in a DNA molecule, yielding a set of **restriction fragments.** All copies of a particular DNA molecule always yield the same set of restriction fragments when exposed to the same restriction enzyme. In other words, a restriction enzyme cuts a DNA molecule in a reproducible way. (Later you will learn how the different fragments can be separated.)

The most useful restriction enzymes cleave the sugar-phosphate backbones in both DNA strands in a staggered way, as indicated in Figure 20.3. The resulting double-stranded restriction fragments have at least one single-stranded end, called a **sticky end.** These short extensions can form hydrogen-bonded base pairs with complementary sticky ends on any other DNA molecules cut with the same enzyme. The associations formed in this way are only temporary, but the associations between fragments can be made permanent by the enzyme **DNA ligase.** This enzyme catalyzes the formation of covalent bonds that close up the sugar-phosphate

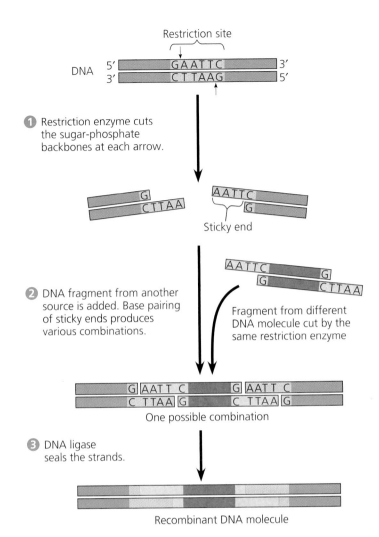

▲ **Figure 20.3 Using a restriction enzyme and DNA ligase to make recombinant DNA.** The restriction enzyme in this example (called *Eco*RI) recognizes a specific six-base-pair sequence, the restriction site, and makes staggered cuts in the sugar-phosphate backbones within this sequence, producing fragments with sticky ends. Any fragments with complementary sticky ends can base-pair; if they come from different DNA molecules, recombinant DNA is the product.

backbones. As you can see at the bottom of Figure 20.3, the ligase-catalyzed joining of DNA from two different sources produces a stable recombinant DNA molecule.

Cloning a Eukaryotic Gene in a Bacterial Plasmid

Now that you've learned about restriction enzymes and DNA ligase, we can take a closer look at how genes are cloned in plasmids. The original plasmid is called a **cloning vector,** defined as a DNA molecule that can carry foreign DNA into a cell and replicate there. Bacterial plasmids are widely used as cloning vectors for several reasons. They can be easily isolated from bacteria, manipulated to form recombinant plasmids by insertion of foreign DNA *in vitro,* and then reintroduced into bacterial cells. Moreover, bacterial cells reproduce rapidly and in the process multiply any foreign DNA they carry.

Producing Clones of Cells

Figure 20.4 details one method for cloning a particular gene from humans or other eukaryotic species using a bacterial plasmid as the cloning vector. The step numbers in the text that follows correspond to those in the figure.

❶ We begin by isolating the bacterial plasmid from *E. coli* cells and DNA containing the gene of interest from human cells grown in laboratory culture. The plasmid has been engineered to carry two genes that will later prove useful: *amp^R*, which makes *E. coli* cells resistant to the antibiotic ampicillin, and *lacZ*, which encodes β-galactosidase. This enzyme hydrolyzes the sugar lactose, as well as a synthetic molecular mimic called X-gal. Within the *lacZ* gene is a single copy of the restriction site recognized by the restriction enzyme used in the next step.

❷ Both the plasmid and the human DNA are digested with the same restriction enzyme, one that produces sticky ends. The enzyme cuts the plasmid DNA at its single restriction site within the *lacZ* gene, but cuts the human DNA at multiple sites, generating many thousands of fragments. One of the human DNA fragments carries the gene of interest.

❸ Next we mix the human DNA fragments with the cut plasmids, allowing base pairing between their complementary sticky ends. We then add DNA ligase, which permanently joins each base-paired plasmid and human DNA fragment. Some of the resulting recombinant plasmids contain human DNA fragments like the three shown in Figure 20.4. This step may also generate other products, such as a plasmid containing several human DNA fragments, a combination of two plasmids, or a rejoined, nonrecombinant version of the original plasmid.

❹ The DNA prepared in step 3 is mixed with bacteria that have a mutation in their own *lacZ* gene, making them unable to hydrolyze lactose. Under

---

Figure 20.4

Research Method   **Cloning a Human Gene in a Bacterial Plasmid**

APPLICATION   Cloning is used to prepare many copies of a gene of interest for use in sequencing the gene, in producing its encoded protein, in gene therapy, or in basic research.

TECHNIQUE   In this example, a human gene is inserted into a plasmid from *E. coli*. The plasmid contains the *amp^R* gene, which makes *E. coli* cells resistant to the antibiotic ampicillin. It also contains the *lacZ* gene, which encodes β-galactosidase. This enzyme hydrolyzes a molecular mimic of lactose (X-gal) to form a blue product. Only three plasmids and three human DNA fragments are shown, but millions of copies of the plasmid and a mixture of millions of different human DNA fragments would be present in the samples.

❶ Isolate plasmid DNA from bacterial cells and DNA from human cells containing the gene of interest.

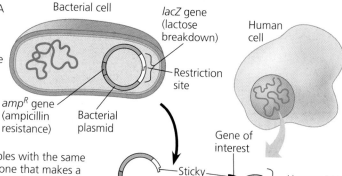

❷ Cut both DNA samples with the same restriction enzyme, one that makes a single cut within the *lacZ* gene and many cuts within the human DNA.

❸ Mix the cut plasmids and DNA fragments. Some join by base pairing; add DNA ligase to seal them together. The products are recombinant plasmids (shown here) and many nonrecombinant plasmids.

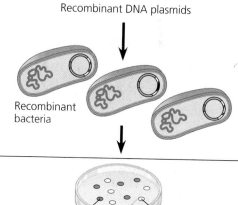

Recombinant DNA plasmids

❹ Introduce the DNA into bacterial cells that have a mutation in their own *lacZ* gene. Under suitable conditions, some cells will take up a recombinant plasmid or other DNA molecule by transformation.

Recombinant bacteria

❺ Plate the bacteria on agar containing ampicillin and X-gal. Incubate until colonies grow.

RESULTS   Only a cell that took up a plasmid, which has the *ampR* gene, will reproduce and form a colony. Colonies with nonrecombinant plasmids will be blue, because they can hydrolyze X-gal. Colonies with recombinant plasmids, in which *lacZ* is disrupted, will be white, because they cannot hydrolyze X-gal. By screening the white colonies with a nucleic acid probe (see Figure 20.5), researchers can identify clones of bacterial cells carrying the gene of interest.

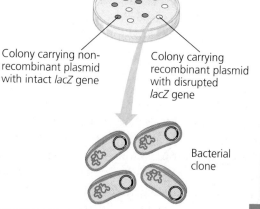

Colony carrying non-recombinant plasmid with intact *lacZ* gene

Colony carrying recombinant plasmid with disrupted *lacZ* gene

Bacterial clone

suitable experimental conditions, the cells take up foreign DNA by transformation (see p. 348). Some cells acquire a recombinant plasmid carrying the gene of interest. Many other cells, however, take up a recombinant plasmid carrying a different gene, a nonrecombinant plasmid, or a human DNA fragment. These different possibilities will be sorted out later.

⑤ In the actual cloning step, the bacteria are plated out on solid nutrient medium (agar) containing ampicillin and X-gal, the molecular mimic of lactose. Use of this medium allows us to identify clones of cells transformed with a recombinant plasmid.

How do we recognize the cell clones carrying recombinant plasmids? First, only cells with a plasmid will reproduce, for only they have the amp^R gene conferring resistance to the ampicillin in the medium. Each reproducing bacterium forms a clone by repeated cell divisions, generating a large group of cells that have all descended from the parent cell. Once the clone contains about 10^5 cells, it is visible as a mass, or *colony*, on the agar. As cells reproduce, any foreign genes carried by recombinant plasmids also are copied, or cloned.

Second, the color of the colonies allows us to distinguish colonies of bacteria with recombinant plasmids from those with nonrecombinant plasmids. Colonies containing nonrecombinant plasmids with the intact *lacZ* gene will be blue because they produce functional β-galactosidase, which hydrolyzes the X-gal in the medium, forming a blue product. In contrast, no functional β-galactosidase is produced in colonies containing recombinant plasmids with foreign DNA inserted into the *lacZ* gene; thus, these colonies will be white.

The procedure to this point will have cloned many different human DNA fragments, not just the one that interests us. The final and most difficult part of cloning a particular gene is identifying a colony containing that gene among the many thousands of colonies carrying other pieces of human DNA.

Identifying Clones Carrying a Gene of Interest

To screen all the colonies with recombinant plasmids (the white colonies in the above method) for a clone of cells containing a gene of interest, we can look either for the gene itself or for its protein product. In the first approach, which we describe here, the DNA of the gene is detected by its ability to base-pair with a complementary sequence on another nucleic acid molecule, a process called **nucleic acid hybridization.** The complementary molecule, a short, single-stranded nucleic acid that can be either RNA or DNA, is called a **nucleic acid probe.** If we know at least part of the nucleotide sequence of the gene of interest (perhaps from knowing the protein it encodes or its sequence in the genome of a closely related species), we can synthesize a probe complementary to

it. For example, if part of the sequence on one strand of the desired gene is

5′ ···GGCTAACTTAGC··· 3′

then we would synthesize this probe:

3′ CCGATTGAATCG 5′

Each probe molecule, which will hydrogen-bond specifically to a complementary strand in the desired gene, is labeled with a radioactive isotope or a fluorescent tag so we can track it.

For example, we could transfer a few cells from each white colony in Figure 20.4 (step 5) to a spot on a new agar plate and allow each to grow into a new colony. **Figure 20.5** shows how a number of such bacterial clones can be simultaneously screened for the presence of DNA complementary to a DNA probe. An essential step in this method is the **denaturation** of the cells' DNA—that is, the separation of its two strands. As with protein denaturation, DNA denaturation is routinely accomplished with chemicals or heat.

Once we've identified the location of a colony carrying the desired gene, we can grow some cells from that colony in liquid culture in a large tank and then easily isolate large amounts of the gene. Also, we can use the cloned gene itself as a probe to identify similar or identical genes in DNA from other sources, such as DNA from other species.

Storing Cloned Genes in DNA Libraries

The cloning procedure in Figure 20.4, which starts with a mixture of fragments from the entire genome of an organism, is called a "shotgun" approach; no single gene is targeted for cloning. Thousands of different recombinant plasmids are produced in step 3, and a clone of each ends up as a (white) colony in step 5. The complete set of plasmid clones, each carrying copies of a particular segment from the initial genome, is referred to as a **genomic library (Figure 20.6a)**. Scientists often obtain such libraries (or even particular cloned genes) from another researcher or a commercial source (sometimes referred to as "cloning by phone"!).

Certain bacteriophages are also common cloning vectors for making genomic libraries. Fragments of foreign DNA can be spliced into a phage genome, as into a plasmid, by using a restriction enzyme and DNA ligase. An advantage of using phages as vectors is that a phage can carry a larger DNA insert than a bacterial plasmid. The recombinant phage DNA is packaged into capsids *in vitro* and introduced into a bacterial cell through the normal infection process. Inside the cell, the phage DNA replicates and produces new phage particles, each carrying the foreign DNA. A genomic library made using phage is stored as a collection of phage clones **(Figure 20.6b)**. Since restriction enzymes do not recognize gene boundaries,

Figure 20.5

Nucleic Acid Probe Hybridization

APPLICATION Hybridization with a complementary nucleic acid probe detects a specific DNA within a mixture of DNA molecules. In this example, a collection of bacterial clones (colonies) are screened to identify those carrying a plasmid with a gene of interest.

TECHNIQUE Cells from each colony known to contain recombinant plasmids (white colonies in Figure 20.4) are transferred to separate locations on a new agar plate and allowed to grow into visible colonies. This collection of bacterial colonies is the master plate.

1 A special filter paper is pressed against the master plate, transferring cells to the bottom side of the filter. Marks (Xs) are placed on the filter paper and agar to establish the position of each individual colony in reference to the marks.

2 The filter is treated to break open the cells and denature their DNA; the resulting single-stranded DNA molecules are treated so that they stick to the filter. Radioactive probe molecules complementary to part of the gene of interest are incubated with the filter. The single-stranded probe base-pairs with any complementary DNA on the filter; excess DNA is rinsed off. (Colonies with radioactive probe–DNA hybrids are shown here in orange but would not be visible yet.)

3 The filter is laid under photographic film, allowing any radioactive areas to expose the film (autoradiography). Black spots on the film correspond to the locations on the filter of DNA that has hybridized to the probe.

4 After the developed film is flipped over, the reference marks on the film and master plate are aligned, so that colonies carrying the gene of interest can be located.

RESULTS Colonies of cells containing the gene of interest have been identified by nucleic acid hybridization. Cells from colonies tagged with the probe can be grown in large tanks of liquid growth medium. Large amounts of the DNA containing the gene of interest can be isolated from these cultures. By using probes with different nucleotide sequences, the collection of bacterial clones can be screened for different genes.

▶ **Figure 20.6 Genomic libraries.** A genomic library is a collection of many bacterial or phage clones, each containing copies of a particular DNA segment from a foreign genome. In a complete genomic library, the foreign DNA segments cover the entire genome of an organism. **(a)** Shown are three of the thousands of "books" in a plasmid library. Each "book" is a clone of bacterial cells, each containing copies of a particular foreign genome fragment (pink, yellow, black segments) in its recombinant plasmid. **(b)** The same three foreign genome segments are shown in three "books" of a phage library.

(a) Plasmid library

(b) Phage library

some genes in either type of genomic library will be cut and divided up among two or more clones.

Researchers can make another kind of DNA library starting with mRNA extracted from cells. The enzyme reverse transcriptase (obtained from retroviruses) is used *in vitro* to make single-stranded DNA transcripts of the mRNA molecules. Following enzymatic degradation of the mRNA, a second DNA strand, complementary to the first, is synthesized by DNA polymerase. This double-stranded DNA, called **complementary DNA (cDNA),** is then modified by addition of restriction enzyme recognition sequences at each end. Finally, the cDNA is inserted into vector DNA in a manner similar to the insertion of genomic DNA fragments. The isolated mRNA was a mixture of all the mRNA molecules in the cells used, transcribed from many different genes. Therefore, the cDNAs that are cloned make up a library containing a collection of genes. However, a **cDNA library** represents only part of the genome—only the subset of genes that were transcribed into mRNA in the original cells.

Genomic and cDNA libraries each have advantages, depending on what is being studied. If you want to clone a gene but are unsure in what cell type it is expressed or are unable to obtain that cell type, a genomic library is almost certain to contain the gene. Also, if you are interested in the regulatory sequences or introns associated with a gene, a genomic library is required because these sequences are absent from the fully processed mRNAs used in making a cDNA library. For this very reason, if you are only interested in the coding sequence of a gene, you can obtain a stripped-down version of the gene from a cDNA library. A cDNA library is also useful for studying genes responsible for the specialized functions of a particular cell type, such as brain or liver cells. Finally, changes in patterns of gene expression during development can be traced by making cDNA from cells of the same type at different times in the life of an organism.

Cloning and Expressing Eukaryotic Genes

As an alternative to screening a DNA library for a particular nucleotide sequence, the clones can sometimes be screened for a desired gene based on detection of its encoded protein. For example, if the protein is an enzyme, its activity can be measured; alternatively, the protein can be detected using antibodies that bind specifically to it. And once a particular gene has been cloned in host cells, its protein product can be produced in larger amounts for research purposes or valuable practical applications.

Bacterial Expression Systems

Getting a cloned eukaryotic gene to function in bacterial host cells can be difficult because certain aspects of gene expression are different in eukaryotes and prokaryotes. To overcome differences in promoters and other DNA control sequences, scientists usually employ an **expression vector,** a cloning vector that contains a highly active prokaryotic promoter just upstream of a restriction site where the eukaryotic gene can be inserted in the correct reading frame. The bacterial host cell will recognize the promoter and proceed to express the foreign gene now linked to that promoter. Such expression vectors allow the synthesis of many eukaryotic proteins in bacterial cells.

Another problem with expressing cloned eukaryotic genes in bacteria is the presence of noncoding regions (introns) in most eukaryotic genes. Introns can make a eukaryotic gene very long and unwieldy, and they prevent correct expression of the gene by bacterial cells, which do not have RNA-splicing machinery. This problem can be surmounted by using a cDNA form of the gene, which includes only the exons. Bacteria can express a eukaryotic cDNA gene if the vector contains a bacterial promoter and any other control elements necessary for the gene's transcription and translation.

Eukaryotic Cloning and Expression Systems

Molecular biologists can avoid eukaryotic-prokaryotic incompatibility by using eukaryotic cells such as yeasts, rather than bacteria, as hosts for cloning and/or expressing eukaryotic genes of interest. Yeast cells, single-celled fungi, offer two advantages: They are as easy to grow as bacteria, and they have plasmids, a rarity among eukaryotes. Scientists have even constructed recombinant plasmids that combine yeast and bacterial DNA and can replicate in either type of cell. Another useful tool for cloning eukaryotic genes are **yeast artificial chromosomes (YACs),** which combine the essentials of a eukaryotic chromosome—an origin for DNA replication, a centromere, and two telomeres—with foreign DNA. These chromosome-like vectors behave normally in mitosis, cloning the foreign DNA as the yeast cell divides. Because a YAC can carry a much longer DNA segment than can a plasmid vector, a cloned fragment is more likely to contain an entire gene rather than just a portion of it.

Another reason to use eukaryotic host cells for expressing a cloned eukaryotic gene is that many eukaryotic proteins will not function unless they are modified after translation, for example by the addition of carbohydrate or lipid groups. Bacterial cells cannot carry out these modifications, and if the gene product requiring such processing is from a mammal, even yeast cells will not be able to modify the protein correctly. The use of host cells from an animal cell culture may therefore be necessary.

Scientists have developed a variety of methods for introducing recombinant DNA into eukaryotic cells. In **electroporation,** a brief electrical pulse applied to a solution containing cells creates temporary holes in their plasma membranes, through which DNA can enter. (This technique is now commonly used for bacteria as well.) Alternatively, scientists can inject DNA directly into single eukaryotic cells using microscopically thin needles. To get DNA into plant cells, the soil bacterium *Agrobacterium* can be used, as you will learn later. If the introduced DNA is incorporated into a cell's genome by genetic recombination, then it may be expressed by the cell.

Amplifying DNA *in Vitro*: The Polymerase Chain Reaction (PCR)

DNA cloning in cells remains the best method for preparing large quantities of a particular gene or other DNA sequence. However, when the source of DNA is scanty or impure, the **polymerase chain reaction,** or **PCR,** is quicker and more selective. In this technique, any specific target segment within one or many DNA molecules can be quickly amplified (copied many times) in a test tube. With automation, PCR can make billions of copies of a target segment of DNA in a few hours, significantly faster than the days it would take to obtain the same number of copies by screening a DNA library for a clone with the desired gene and letting it replicate within host cells.

In the PCR procedure **(Figure 20.7),** a three-step cycle brings about a chain reaction that produces an exponentially growing population of identical DNA molecules. During each cycle, the reaction mixture is heated to denature (separate) the DNA strands and then cooled to allow annealing (hydrogen bonding) of short, single-stranded DNA primers complementary to sequences on opposite strands at each end of the target sequence; finally, a heat-stable DNA polymerase extends the primers in the 5′ → 3′ direction. If a standard DNA polymerase were used, the protein would be denatured along with the DNA during the first heating step and would have to be replaced after each cycle. The key to automating PCR was the discovery of an unusual heat-stable DNA polymerase, first isolated from prokaryotes living in hot springs, that could withstand the heat at the start of each cycle.

Just as impressive as the speed of PCR is its specificity. Only minute amounts of DNA need be present in the starting material, and this DNA can be in a partially degraded state. The key to this high

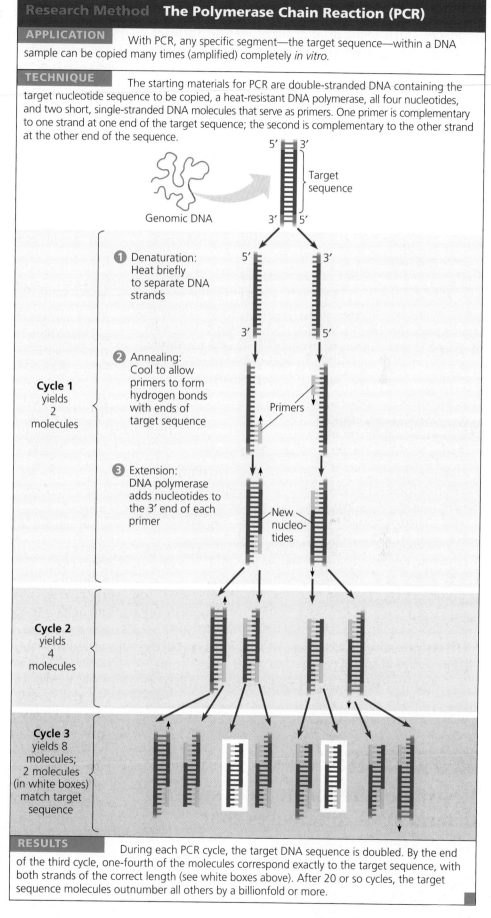

Figure 20.7

Research Method   **The Polymerase Chain Reaction (PCR)**

APPLICATION   With PCR, any specific segment—the target sequence—within a DNA sample can be copied many times (amplified) completely *in vitro*.

TECHNIQUE   The starting materials for PCR are double-stranded DNA containing the target nucleotide sequence to be copied, a heat-resistant DNA polymerase, all four nucleotides, and two short, single-stranded DNA molecules that serve as primers. One primer is complementary to one strand at one end of the target sequence; the second is complementary to the other strand at the other end of the sequence.

Genomic DNA

Target sequence

Cycle 1 yields 2 molecules

1 Denaturation: Heat briefly to separate DNA strands

2 Annealing: Cool to allow primers to form hydrogen bonds with ends of target sequence

Primers

3 Extension: DNA polymerase adds nucleotides to the 3′ end of each primer

New nucleotides

Cycle 2 yields 4 molecules

Cycle 3 yields 8 molecules; 2 molecules (in white boxes) match target sequence

RESULTS   During each PCR cycle, the target DNA sequence is doubled. By the end of the third cycle, one-fourth of the molecules correspond exactly to the target sequence, with both strands of the correct length (see white boxes above). After 20 or so cycles, the target sequence molecules outnumber all others by a billionfold or more.

specificity is the primers, which hydrogen-bond *only* to sequences at opposite ends of the target segment. By the end of the third cycle, one-fourth of the molecules are identical to the target segment, with both strands the appropriate length. With each successive cycle, the number of target segment molecules of the correct length doubles, soon greatly outnumbering all other DNA molecules in the reaction.

Despite its speed and specificity, PCR amplification cannot substitute for gene cloning in cells when large amounts of a gene are desired. Occasional errors during PCR replication impose limits on the number of good copies that can be made by this method. Increasingly, however, PCR is used to make enough of a specific DNA fragment to clone it merely by inserting it into a vector.

Devised in 1985, PCR has had a major impact on biological research and biotechnology. PCR has been used to amplify DNA from a wide variety of sources: fragments of ancient DNA from a 40,000-year-old frozen woolly mammoth; DNA from fingerprints or from tiny amounts of blood, tissue, or semen found at crime scenes; DNA from single embryonic cells for rapid prenatal diagnosis of genetic disorders; and DNA of viral genes from cells infected with viruses that are difficult to detect, such as HIV. We'll return to applications of PCR later in the chapter.

Concept Check 20.1

1. If the medium used for plating cells in step 5 of Figure 20.4 did not contain ampicillin, cells containing no plasmid would be able to grow into colonies. What color would those colonies be and why?

2. Imagine you want to study human β-globin, a protein present in red blood cells. To obtain sufficient amounts of the protein, you decide to clone the β-globin gene. Would you construct a genomic library or a cDNA library? What material would you use as a source of DNA or RNA?

3. What are two potential difficulties in using plasmid vectors and bacterial host cells for production of large quantities of human proteins from cloned genes?

For suggested answers, see Appendix A.

Concept 20.2

Restriction fragment analysis detects DNA differences that affect restriction sites

With techniques available for making homogeneous preparations of large numbers of identical DNA segments, we can begin to tackle interesting questions about specific genes and their functions. Does a particular gene differ from person to person, and are there certain alleles associated with a hereditary disorder? Where in the body and when is the gene expressed? Where is the gene located within the genome? Is expression of the gene related to expression of other genes? We can also ask how the gene differs from species to species and begin to unravel its evolutionary history.

To answer such questions, we need to know the complete nucleotide sequence of the gene and its counterparts in various individuals and species, as well as its expression pattern. These topics are covered in the next two sections. In this section, we discuss a more indirect approach, called *restriction fragment analysis*, that detects certain differences in the nucleotide sequences of DNA molecules. This type of analysis can rapidly provide useful comparative information about DNA sequences.

Gel Electrophoresis and Southern Blotting

Many approaches for studying DNA molecules make use of **gel electrophoresis.** This technique uses a gel as a molecular sieve to separate nucleic acids or proteins on the basis of size, electrical charge, and other physical properties **(Figure 20.8)**. Because nucleic acid molecules carry negative charges on their phosphate groups, they all travel toward the positive electrode in an electric field. As they move, the thicket of polymer fibers impedes longer molecules more than it does shorter ones, separating them by length. Thus, gel electrophoresis separates a mixture of linear DNA molecules into bands, each consisting of DNA molecules of the same length.

In restriction fragment analysis, the DNA fragments produced by restriction enzyme digestion of a DNA molecule are sorted by gel electrophoresis. When the mixture of restriction fragments from a particular DNA molecule undergoes electrophoresis, it yields a band pattern characteristic of the starting molecule and the restriction enzyme used. In fact, the relatively small DNA molecules of viruses and plasmids can be identified simply by their restriction fragment patterns. (Larger DNA molecules, such as those of eukaryotic chromosomes, yield so many fragments that they appear as a smear, rather than as distinct bands.) Because DNA can be recovered undamaged from gels, the procedure also provides a way to prepare pure samples of individual fragments.

Restriction fragment analysis is also useful for comparing two different DNA molecules—for example, two alleles of a gene. A restriction enzyme recognizes a specific sequence of nucleotides, and a change in even one base pair will prevent it from cutting at a particular site. Thus, if the nucleotide differences between the alleles occur within a restriction enzyme recognition sequence, digestion with that enzyme will produce a different mixture of fragments from each allele. And each mixture will give its own band pattern in gel electrophoresis. For example, sickle-cell disease is caused by a mutation in a

Figure 20.8

APPLICATION Gel electrophoresis is used for separating nucleic acids or proteins that differ in size, electrical charge, or other physical properties. DNA molecules are separated by gel electrophoresis in restriction fragment analysis of both cloned genes (see Figure 20.9) and genomic DNA (see Figure 20.10).

TECHNIQUE Gel electrophoresis separates macromolecules on the basis of their rate of movement through a gel in an electric field. How far a DNA molecule travels while the current is on is inversely proportional to its length. A mixture of DNA molecules, usually fragments produced by restriction enzyme digestion, is separated into "bands"; each band contains thousands of molecules of the same length.

❶ Each sample, a mixture of DNA molecules, is placed in a separate well near one end of a thin slab of gel. The gel is supported by glass plates, bathed in an aqueous solution, and has electrodes attached to each end.

❷ When the current is turned on, the negatively charged DNA molecules move toward the positive electrode, with shorter molecules moving faster than longer ones. Bands are shown here in blue, but on an actual gel, DNA bands are not visible until a DNA-binding dye is added. The shortest molecules, having traveled farthest, end up in bands at the bottom of the gel.

RESULTS After the current is turned off, a DNA-binding dye is added. This dye fluoresces pink in ultraviolet light, revealing the separated bands to which it binds. In this actual gel, the pink bands correspond to DNA fragments of different lengths separated by electrophoresis. If all the samples were initially cut with the same restriction enzyme, then the different band patterns indicate that they came from different sources.

single nucleotide that is located within a restriction sequence in the β-globin gene (see Figure 17.23 and p. 267). As shown in **Figure 20.9**, restriction fragment analysis by electrophoresis can distinguish the normal and sickle-cell alleles of the β-globin gene.

The starting materials in Figure 20.9 are samples of the cloned and purified β-globin alleles. Suppose, however, we wanted to compare genomic DNA samples from three individuals: a person homozygous for the normal β-globin allele; a person with sickle-cell disease, homozygous for the mutant allele; and a heterozygous carrier. Electrophoresis of genomic DNA digested with a restriction enzyme yields too many bands to distinguish them

(a) *Dde*I **restriction sites in normal and sickle-cell alleles of β-globin gene.** Shown here are the cloned alleles, separated from the vector DNA but including some DNA next to the coding sequence. The normal allele contains two sites within the coding sequence recognized by the *Dde*I restriction enzyme. The sickle-cell allele lacks one of these sites.

(b) **Electrophoresis of restriction fragments from normal and sickle-cell alleles.** Samples of each purified allele were cut with the *Dde*I enzyme and then subjected to gel electrophoresis, resulting in three bands for the normal allele and two bands for the sickle-cell allele. (The tiny fragments on the ends of both initial DNA molecules are identical and are not seen here.)

▲ **Figure 20.9** **Using restriction fragment analysis to distinguish the normal and sickle-cell alleles of the β-globin gene. (a)** The sickle-cell mutation destroys one of the *Dde*I restriction sites within the β-globin gene. **(b)** As a result, digestion with the *Dde*I enzyme generates different fragments from the normal and sickle-cell alleles.

individually. But with a method called **Southern blotting**, which combines gel electrophoresis and nucleic acid hybridization, we can detect just those bands that include parts of the β-globin gene. The principle is the same as in nucleic acid hybridization for screening bacterial clones (see Figure 20.5). In this case, the probe is a radioactive single-stranded DNA molecule that is complementary to the β-globin gene. **Figure 20.10** outlines the entire procedure and demonstrates how it can be used to compare DNA samples from the three individuals mentioned above. Southern blotting reveals not only whether a particular sequence is present in a sample of DNA but also the size of the restriction fragments that contain the sequence. One of its many applications, as in our β-globin example, is to identify heterozygote carriers of mutant alleles associated with genetic diseases.

Restriction Fragment Length Differences as Genetic Markers

Restriction fragment analysis proved invaluable when biologists turned their attention to *noncoding* DNA, which comprises most of the DNA of animal and plant genomes (see Figure 19.14). When researchers subjected cloned segments of noncoding DNA from different individuals to procedures like that shown in Figure 20.8, they were excited to discover many differences in band patterns. Like different alleles of a gene, noncoding DNA sequences on homologous chromosomes may exhibit small nucleotide differences.

Differences in the restriction sites on homologous chromosomes that result in different restriction fragment patterns are called **restriction fragment length polymorphisms** (**RFLPs**, pronounced "Rif-lips"). RFLPs are scattered abundantly throughout genomes, including the human genome. This type of sequence difference in noncoding DNA is conceptually the same as a difference in coding sequence. Analogous to the single base-pair difference that identifies the sickle-cell allele, a RFLP can serve as a genetic marker for a particular location (locus) in the genome. A given RFLP may occur in numerous variants in a population. (The word *polymorphisms* comes from the Greek for "many forms.")

RFLPs are detected and analyzed by Southern blotting, with the probe complementary to the sequence under consideration. The example shown in Figure 20.10 could as easily represent the detection of a RFLP in noncoding DNA as one in the coding sequences of two alleles. Because of the sensitivity of DNA hybridization, the entire genome can be used as the DNA starting material. (Samples of human DNA are typically obtained from white blood cells.)

Because RFLP markers are inherited in a Mendelian fashion, they can serve as genetic markers for making linkage maps. The geneticist uses the same reasoning illustrated in Figure 15.6: The frequency with which two RFLP markers—or a RFLP marker and a certain allele for a gene—are inherited together is a measure of the closeness of the two loci on a chromosome. The discovery of RFLPs greatly increased the number of markers available for mapping the human genome. No longer were geneticists limited to genetic variations that lead to obvious phenotypic differences (such as genetic diseases) or even to differences in protein products.

Concept Check 20.2

1. Suppose you carry out electrophoresis on a sample of genomic DNA isolated from an individual and treated with a restriction enzyme. After staining the gel with a DNA-binding dye, what would you see? Explain.
2. Explain why restriction fragment length polymorphisms (RFLPs) can serve as genetic markers even though they produce no visible phenotypic differences.

For suggested answers, see Appendix A.

Concept 20.3

Entire genomes can be mapped at the DNA level

As early as 1980, molecular biologist David Botstein and colleagues proposed that the DNA variations reflected in RFLPs could serve as the basis for an extremely detailed map of the entire human genome. Since then, researchers have used such markers in conjunction with the tools and techniques of DNA technology to develop more and more detailed maps of the genomes of a number of species.

The most ambitious mapping project to date has been sequencing of the human genome, officially begun as the **Human Genome Project** in 1990. This effort was largely completed in 2003 when the nucleotide sequence of the vast majority of DNA in each human chromosome (the 22 autosomes and the pair of sex chromosomes) was obtained. Organized by an international, publicly funded consortium of researchers at universities and research institutes, the project proceeded through three stages that provided progressively more detailed views of the human genome: genetic (or linkage) mapping, physical mapping, and DNA sequencing. (The interview with Eric Lander on pp. 236–237 gives a personal view of the project.)

In addition to mapping human DNA, researchers with the Human Genome Project are also working on the genomes of other species important in biological research. They have completed sequences for *E. coli* and numerous other prokaryotes, *Saccharomyces cerevisiae* (yeast), *Caenorhabditis elegans* (nematode), *Drosophila melanogaster* (fruit fly), *Mus musculus* (mouse), and quite a few others. These genomes are of great

Figure 20.10

Research Method   **Southern Blotting of DNA Fragments**

APPLICATION   Researchers can detect specific nucleotide sequences within a DNA sample with this method. In particular, Southern blotting is useful for comparing the restriction fragments produced from different samples of genomic DNA.

TECHNIQUE   In this example, we compare genomic DNA samples from three individuals: a homozygote for the normal β-globin allele (I), a homozygote for the mutant sickle-cell allele (II), and a heterozygote (III).

1 Preparation of restriction fragments. Each DNA sample is mixed with the same restriction enzyme, in this case *Dde*I. Digestion of each sample yields a mixture of thousands of restriction fragments.

2 Gel electrophoresis. The restriction fragments in each sample are separated by electrophoresis, forming a characteristic pattern of bands. (In reality, there would be many more bands than shown here, and they would be invisible unless stained.)

3 Blotting. With the gel arranged as shown above, capillary action pulls the alkaline solution upward through the gel, transferring the DNA to a sheet of nitrocellulose paper (the blot) and denaturing it in the process. The single strands of DNA stuck to the paper blot are positioned in bands corresponding to those on the gel.

4 Hybridization with radioactive probe. The paper blot is exposed to a solution containing a radioactively labeled probe. In this example, the probe is single-stranded DNA complementary to the β-globin gene. Probe molecules attach by base-pairing to any restriction fragments containing a part of the β-globin gene. (The bands would not be visible yet.)

5 Autoradiography. A sheet of photographic film is laid over the paper blot. The radioactivity in the bound probe exposes the film to form an image corresponding to those bands containing DNA that base-pairs with the probe.

RESULTS   Because the band patterns for the three samples are clearly different, this method can be used to identify heterozygous carriers of the sickle-cell allele (III), as well as those with the disease, who have two mutant alleles (II), and unaffected individuals, who have two normal alleles (I). The band patterns for samples I and II resemble those observed for the purified normal and mutant alleles, respectively, seen in Figure 20.9b. The band pattern for the sample from the heterozygote (III) is a combination of the patterns for the two homozygotes (I and II).

interest in their own right and are also providing important insights of general biological significance, as we'll discuss later. In addition, the early mapping efforts on these genomes were useful for developing the strategies, methods, and new technologies necessary for deciphering the human genome, which is much larger.

Genetic (Linkage) Mapping: Relative Ordering of Markers

Even before the Human Genome Project began, earlier research had painted a rough picture of the organization of the genomes of many organisms. For instance, the karyotype of a species reveals the number of chromosomes and their overall banding pattern (see Figure 13.3). And some genes had already been located on a particular region of a whole chromosome by fluorescence *in situ* hybridization (FISH), a method in which fluorescently labeled probes are allowed to hybridize to an immobilized array of whole chromosomes (see Figure 15.1). Cytogenetic maps based on this type of information provided the starting point for more detailed mapping.

With cytogenetic maps of the chromosomes in hand, the initial stage in mapping a large genome is to construct a **linkage map** of several thousand genetic markers spaced throughout each of the chromosomes (**Figure 20.11**, stage ❶). The order of the markers and the relative distances between them on such a map are based on recombination frequencies (see Chapter 15). The markers can be genes or any other identifiable sequences in the DNA, such as RFLPs or the simple sequence DNA discussed in Chapter 19. Relying primarily on simple sequence DNA, which is abundant in the human genome and has various "alleles" differing in length, researchers compiled a human genetic map with some 5,000 markers. Such a map enabled them to locate other markers, including genes, by testing for genetic linkage to the known markers. It was also valuable as a framework for organizing more detailed maps of particular regions.

Physical Mapping: Ordering DNA Fragments

In a **physical map**, the distances between markers are expressed in some physical measure, usually the number of base pairs along the DNA. For whole-genome mapping, a physical map is made by cutting the DNA of each chromosome into a number of restriction fragments and then determining the original order of the fragments in the chromosomal DNA. The key is to make fragments that overlap and then use probes or automated nucleotide sequencing of the ends to find the overlaps (Figure 20.11, stage ❷). In this way, more and more fragments can be assigned to a sequential order that corresponds to their order in a chromosome.

Supplies of the DNA fragments used for physical mapping are prepared by cloning. In working with large genomes,

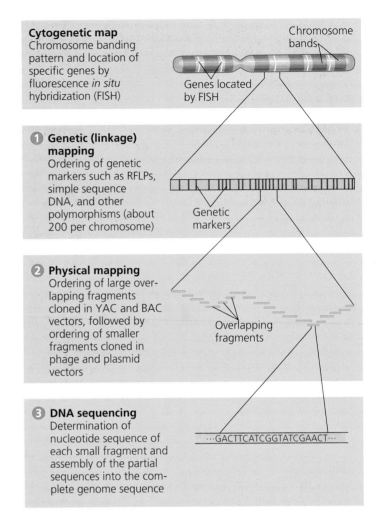

▲ **Figure 20.11 Three-stage approach to mapping an entire genome.** Starting with a cytogenetic map of each chromosome, researchers with the Human Genome Project proceeded through three stages of mapping to reach the ultimate goal, the nearly complete nucleotide sequence of every chromosome.

researchers carry out several rounds of DNA cutting, cloning, and physical mapping. The first cloning vector is often a yeast artificial chromosome (YAC), which can carry inserted fragments a million base pairs long, or a **bacterial artificial chromosome (BAC)**, an artificial version of a bacterial chromosome that can carry inserts of 100,000 to 500,000 base pairs. After such long fragments are ordered, each fragment is cut into smaller pieces, which are cloned in plasmids or phages, ordered in turn, and finally sequenced.

DNA Sequencing

The ultimate goal in mapping a genome is to determine the complete nucleotide sequence of each chromosome (Figure 20.11, stage ❸). If a pure preparation of many copies of a DNA fragment up to about 800 base pairs in length is available, the sequence of the fragment can be determined by a sequencing machine. The usual sequencing technique, described in **Figure 20.12**, was developed by British scientist Frederick Sanger; it is

Figure 20.12

Research Method   **Dideoxy Chain-Termination Method for Sequencing DNA**

APPLICATION   The sequence of nucleotides in any cloned DNA fragment up to about 800 base pairs in length can be determined rapidly with specialized machines that carry out sequencing reactions and separate the labeled reaction products by length.

TECHNIQUE   This method synthesizes a nested set of DNA strands complementary to the original DNA fragment. Each strand starts with the same primer and ends with a dideoxyribonucleotide (ddNTP), a modified nucleotide. Incorporation of a ddNTP terminates a growing DNA strand because it lacks a 3′ —OH group, the site for attachment of the next nucleotide (see Figure 16.13). In the set of strands synthesized, each nucleotide position along the original sequence is represented by strands ending at that point with the complementary ddNTP. Because each type of ddNTP is tagged with a distinct fluorescent label, the identity of the ending nucleotides of the new strands, and ultimately the entire original sequence, can be determined.

1 The fragment of DNA to be sequenced is denatured into single strands and incubated in a test tube with the necessary ingredients for DNA synthesis: a primer designed to base pair with the known 3′ end of the template strand, DNA polymerase, the four deoxyribonucleotides, and the four dideoxyribonucleotides, each tagged with a specific fluorescent molecule.

2 Synthesis of each new strand starts at the 3′ end of the primer and continues until a dideoxyribonucleotide is inserted, at random, instead of the normal equivalent deoxyribonucleotide. This prevents further elongation of the strand. Eventually, a set of labeled strands of various lengths is generated, with the color of the tag representing the last nucleotide in the sequence.

3 The labeled strands in the mixture are separated by passage through a polyacrylamide gel in a capillary tube, with shorter strands moving through faster. A fluorescence detector senses the color of each fluorescent tag as the strands come through. Strands differing by as little as one nucleotide in length can be distinguished.

RESULTS   The color of the fluorescent tag on each strand indicates the identity of the nucleotide at its end. The results can be printed out as a spectrogram, and the sequence, which is complementary to the template strand, can then be read from bottom to top. (Notice that the sequence here begins after the primer.)

CHAPTER 20   DNA Technology and Genomics   **397**

often called the *dideoxyribonucleotide* (or *dideoxy*, for short) *chain-termination method*. Even with automation, the sequencing of all 2.9 billion base pairs in a haploid set of human chromosomes presented a formidable challenge. In fact, as discussed in the interview on pp. 236–237, a major thrust of the Human Genome Project was the development of technology for faster sequencing, along with more sophisticated computer software for analyzing and assembling the partial sequences.

In practice, the three stages shown in Figure 20.11 overlap in a way that our simplified version does not portray, but they accurately represent the overarching strategy employed in the Human Genome Project. In 1992, emboldened by advances in sequencing and computer technology, molecular biologist J. Craig Venter devised an alternative approach to the sequencing of whole genomes. His idea was essentially to skip the genetic mapping and physical mapping stages and start directly with the sequencing of random DNA fragments. Powerful computer programs would then assemble the resulting very large number of overlapping short sequences into a single continuous sequence **(Figure 20.13)**.

Despite the skepticism of many scientists, the value of Venter's approach became clear in 1995 when he and colleagues reported the first complete genome sequence of an organism, the bacterium *Hemophilus influenzae*. In May 1998, he set up a company, Celera Genomics, and promised a completed human sequence in three years. His whole-genome shotgun approach was further validated in March 2000 with completion of the *Drosophila melanogaster* genome sequence. As promised, in February 2001, Celera announced the sequencing of over 90% of the human genome simultaneously with a similar announcement by the public Human Genome Project.

Representatives of the public consortium point out that Celera made much use of the consortium's maps and sequence data, which are immediately made freely available to all researchers, unlike Celera's data. They further assert that the infrastructure established by their approach greatly facilitated Celera's efforts. Venter, on the other hand, argues for the efficiency and economy of Celera's methods, and indeed, the public consortium has made some use of them. Clearly, both approaches are valuable and have contributed to the rapid completion of genome sequencing for quite a few species.

Sequencing of the human genome is now virtually complete, although some gaps remain to be mapped. Because of the presence of repetitive DNA and for other poorly understood reasons, certain parts of the chromosomes of multicellular organisms resist detailed mapping by the usual methods.

On one level, genome sequences of humans and other organisms are simply dry lists of nucleotide bases—millions of A's, T's, C's, and G's in mind-numbing succession. But on another level, analyses of these sequences for various species and comparisons between species are leading to exciting discoveries, which we discuss next.

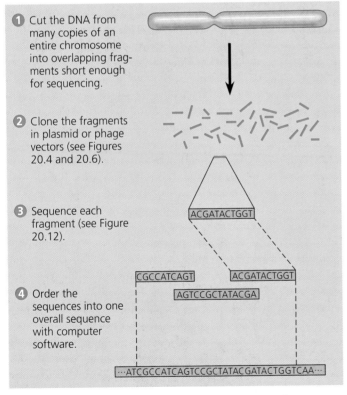

1. Cut the DNA from many copies of an entire chromosome into overlapping fragments short enough for sequencing.

2. Clone the fragments in plasmid or phage vectors (see Figures 20.4 and 20.6).

3. Sequence each fragment (see Figure 20.12).

ACGATACTGGT

4. Order the sequences into one overall sequence with computer software.

CGCCATCAGT   ACGATACTGGT
AGTCCGCTATACGA

···ATCGCCATCAGTCCGCTATACGATACTGGTCAA···

▲ **Figure 20.13 Whole-genome shotgun approach to sequencing.** In this approach, developed by Celera Genomics, random DNA fragments are sequenced and then ordered relative to each other. Compare this approach with the hierarchical, three-stage approach shown in Figure 20.11.

Concept Check 20.3

1. What is the major difference between a genetic (linkage) map and a physical map of a chromosome?
2. In general, how does the approach to genome mapping used in the Human Genome Project differ from the shotgun approach?

For suggested answers, see Appendix A.

Concept 20.4

Genome sequences provide clues to important biological questions

Now that the sequences of entire genomes are available, scientists can study whole sets of genes and their interactions, an approach called **genomics**. Genomics is yielding new insights into fundamental questions about genome organization, regulation of gene expression, growth and development, and evolution. Using the methods of DNA technology, geneticists can study genes directly, without having to infer genotype from phenotype, as in classical genetics. But the newer approach poses the opposite problem, determining the phenotype from the genotype. Starting with a long DNA sequence, how does one recognize genes and determine their function?

Identifying Protein-Coding Genes in DNA Sequences

DNA sequences are collected in computer data banks available via the Internet to researchers all over the world. To identify as-yet unknown protein-coding genes, scientists use software to scan these stored sequences for transcriptional and translational start and stop signals, for RNA-splicing sites, and for other telltale signs of protein-coding genes. The software also looks for certain short coding sequences similar to those present in known genes. Thousands of such sequences, called *expressed sequence tags,* or *ESTs,* are cataloged in computer databases. This type of analysis identifies sequences that may be "new" protein-coding genes, so-called putative genes or gene candidates.

Although genome size generally increases from prokaryotes to eukaryotes, it does not always correlate with biological complexity among eukaryotes. For instance, the genome of *Fritillaria assyriaca,* a flowering plant, contains 120×10^9 base pairs, about 40 times the size of the human genome. Moreover, the number of genes an organism has is often lower than expected from the size of its genome. In particular, the current estimated number of human genes—about 25,000 or less—is much lower than the 50,000 to 100,000 expected and only about one and a half times the number found in the fruit fly and the nematode worm **(Table 20.1)**. This initially seemed surprising, given the larger diversity of cell types in humans and other vertebrates and their generally greater biological complexity. Relative to the other organisms studied so far, genes account for a much smaller fraction of the human genome. Much of the enormous amount of noncoding DNA in the human genome is repetitive DNA, but unusually long introns also contribute significantly.

So what makes humans and other vertebrates apparently more complex than flies or worms? For one thing, gene expression is regulated in more subtle and complicated ways in vertebrates than in other organisms. Some of the large amount of noncoding DNA in vertebrates may function in these regulatory mechanisms. Also, vertebrate genomes tend to "get more bang for the buck" from their coding sequences because of alternative splicing of RNA transcripts. Recall that this process generates more than one functional protein from a single gene (see Figure 19.8). For instance, nearly all human genes contain multiple exons, and an estimated 75% of these multi-exon genes are alternatively spliced. If we assume that each alternatively spliced human gene on average specifies three different polypeptides, then the total number of different human polypeptides would be about 75,000. Additional polypeptide diversity could result from variations in post-translational cleavage or addition of carbohydrate groups in different cell types or at different developmental stages. Another likely contribution to the biological complexity of vertebrates is the much larger number of possible interactions between gene products that result from greater polypeptide diversity. Later we will examine experimental methods for uncovering these interactions.

The identities of about half of the human genes were known before the Human Genome Project began. But what about the others, the new genes revealed by analysis of DNA sequences? Clues about their identities can come from comparing the sequences of new gene candidates with those of known genes from various organisms. In some cases, a newly identified gene sequence will match, at least partially, the sequence of a gene whose function is well known. For example, part of a new gene may match a known gene that encodes a protein kinase, suggesting that the new gene does, too. In other cases, however, the new gene sequence will be similar to a previously encountered sequence whose function is still unknown. In still other cases, the sequence may be entirely unlike anything ever seen before. In the organisms that have been sequenced so far, many of the gene candidate sequences are entirely new to science. For example, about a third of the genes of *E. coli,* the best studied of research organisms, are new to us.

Table 20.1 Genome Sizes and Estimated Numbers of Genes*

Organism	Haploid Genome Size (Mb)	Number of Genes	Genes per Mb
Hemophilus influenzae (bacterium)	1.8	1,700	940
Escherichia coli (bacterium)	4.6	4,400	950
Saccharomyces cerevisiae (yeast)	12	5,800	480
Caenorhabditis elegans (nematode)	97	19,000	200
Arabidopsis thaliana (plant)	118	25,500	215
Drosophila melanogaster (fruit fly)	180	13,700	76
Oryza sativa (rice)	430	60,000	140
Danio rerio (zebrafish)	1,700	22,000	13
Mus musculus (house mouse)	2,600	25,000	11
Homo sapiens (human)	2,900	25,000	10
Fritillaria assyriaca (plant)	120,000	ND	ND

*Strictly defined, "genome" refers to the *haploid* genome of an organism. Some values given here are likely to be revised as genome analysis continues. Mb = million base pairs. ND = not determined.

Determining Gene Function

So how do scientists determine the function of a new gene identified by genome sequencing and comparative analysis? Perhaps the most common approach is to disable the gene and then observe the consequences in the cell or organism. In one application of this approach, called *in vitro* mutagenesis, specific mutations are introduced into the sequence of a cloned gene, after which the mutated gene is returned to a cell. If the introduced mutations alter or destroy the function of the gene product, the phenotype of the mutant cell may help reveal the function of the missing normal protein. Researchers can even put such a mutated gene into cells from the early embryo of a multicellular organism (such as a mouse) to study the role of the gene in the development and functioning of the whole organism.

A simpler and faster method for silencing expression of selected genes exploits the phenomenon of **RNA interference (RNAi),** described in Chapter 19. This experimental approach uses synthetic double-stranded RNA molecules matching the sequence of a particular gene to trigger breakdown or to block translation of the gene's messenger RNA. To date, the RNAi technique has had some limited success in mammalian cells, including human cells in culture. But in other organisms, such as the nematode and the fruit fly, RNAi is already proving valuable for analyzing the functions of genes on a large scale. In one study, RNAi was used to prevent expression of 86% of the genes in early nematode embryos, one gene at a time. Analysis of the phenotypes of the worms that developed from these embryos allowed the researchers to group most of the genes into a small number of functional groups. This type of genome-wide analysis of gene function is sure to become more common as research focuses on the importance of interactions between genes in the system as a whole—the basis of systems biology (see Chapter 1).

Studying Expression of Interacting Groups of Genes

A major goal of genomics is to learn how genes act together to produce and maintain a functioning organism. As mentioned earlier, part of the explanation for how humans get along with so few genes probably lies in the complexity of networks of interactions among genes and their products. Once the sequences of entire genomes of several organisms neared completion, some researchers began using these sequences to investigate which genes are transcribed in different situations, such as in different tissues or at different stages of development. They also consider whether groups of genes are expressed in a coordinated manner, with the aim of identifying global patterns or networks of expression. The results of such studies will begin to reveal how genes act together as a functional network in an organism.

The basic strategy in global expression studies is to isolate the mRNAs made in particular cells, use these molecules as templates for making the corresponding cDNAs by reverse transcription, and then compare this set of cDNAs with collections of genomic DNA fragments. DNA technology makes such studies possible; with automation, they are easily performed on a large scale. Scientists can now measure the expression of thousands of genes at one time.

Currently, the main approach for genome-wide expression studies uses **DNA microarray assays.** A DNA microarray consists of tiny amounts of a large number of single-stranded DNA fragments representing different genes fixed to a glass slide in a tightly spaced array (grid). (The array is also called a *DNA chip* by analogy to a computer chip.) Ideally, these fragments represent all the genes of an organism, as is already possible for organisms whose genomes have been completely sequenced. **Figure 20.14** outlines how the DNA fragments on a microarray are tested for hybridization with samples of cDNA molecules prepared from the mRNAs in particular cells of interest and labeled with fluorescent dyes.

For example, in one study, researchers performed microarray assays of more than 90% of the genes of *C. elegans* during every stage of its life cycle. The results showed that expression of nearly 60% of the genes changed dramatically during development, and many were expressed in a sex-specific pattern. Such studies illustrate the value of DNA microarrays to reveal general profiles of gene expression over the lifetime of an organism.

In addition to uncovering gene interactions and providing clues to gene function, DNA microarray assays may contribute to a better understanding of certain diseases and suggest new diagnostic techniques or therapies. For example, comparing patterns of gene expression in breast cancer tumors and noncancerous breast tissue has already resulted in more informed and effective treatment protocols. Ultimately, information from DNA microarray assays should provide us a grander view—of how ensembles of genes interact to form a living organism.

Comparing Genomes of Different Species

The genomes of about 150 species had been completely or almost completely sequenced by the spring of 2004, with many more in progress. Of these, the vast majority are genomes of prokaryotes, including about 20 archaean genomes. Among the 20 or so eukaryotic species in the group are vertebrates, invertebrates, and plants. The first eukaryotic genome to be completed was that of the yeast *Saccharomyces cerevisiae*, a single-celled organism; the nematode *Caenorhabditis elegans*, a simple worm, was the first multicellular organism whose genome was sequenced. The plant *Arabidopsis thaliana*, another important research organism, has also been completed. Other species whose genomes have been or are currently being sequenced include the honey bee, the dog, the rat, the chicken, and the frog.

Figure 20.14

DNA Microarray Assay of Gene Expression Levels

APPLICATION With this method, researchers can test thousands of genes simultaneously to determine which ones are expressed in a particular tissue, under different environmental conditions in various disease states, or at different developmental stages. They can also look for coordinated gene expression.

TECHNIQUE

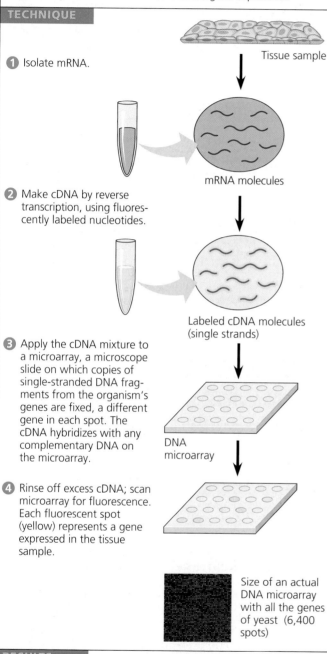

Tissue sample

1 Isolate mRNA.

mRNA molecules

2 Make cDNA by reverse transcription, using fluorescently labeled nucleotides.

Labeled cDNA molecules (single strands)

3 Apply the cDNA mixture to a microarray, a microscope slide on which copies of single-stranded DNA fragments from the organism's genes are fixed, a different gene in each spot. The cDNA hybridizes with any complementary DNA on the microarray.

DNA microarray

4 Rinse off excess cDNA; scan microarray for fluorescence. Each fluorescent spot (yellow) represents a gene expressed in the tissue sample.

Size of an actual DNA microarray with all the genes of yeast (6,400 spots)

RESULTS The intensity of fluorescence at each spot is a measure of the expression of the gene represented by that spot in the tissue sample. Commonly, two different samples are tested together by labeling the cDNAs prepared from each sample with a differently colored fluorescence label. The resulting color at a spot reveals the relative levels of expression of a particular gene in the two samples, which may be from different tissues or the same tissue under different conditions.

Comparisons of genome sequences from different species allow us to determine evolutionary relationships between those species. The more similar in sequence a gene is in two species, the more closely related those species are in their evolutionary history. Likewise, comparing multiple genes between species can shed light on higher groupings of species, which reflect their evolutionary history. Indeed, comparisons of the complete genome sequences of bacteria, archaea, and eukarya strongly support the theory that these are the three fundamental domains of life.

In addition to their value in evolutionary biology, comparative genome studies confirm the relevance of research on simpler organisms to our understanding of biology in general and human biology in particular. The similarities between genes of disparate organisms can be surprising, to the point that one researcher now views fruit flies as "little people with wings." The yeast genome also is proving quite useful in helping us to understand the human genome. For example, the large amount of noncoding DNA in the human genome initially hindered the search for regulatory control elements. But comparisons of noncoding sequences in the human genome with those in the much smaller yeast genome revealed regions with highly conserved sequences; these turned out to be important regulatory sequences in both organisms. In another example, several yeast protein-coding genes are so similar to certain human disease genes that researchers have figured out the functions of the disease genes by studying their normal yeast counterparts.

Comparing the genomes of two closely related species can also be quite useful, because their genomes are likely to be organized similarly. Once the sequence and organization of one genome is known, it can serve as a scaffold for organizing the DNA sequences from a closely related species as they are determined, greatly accelerating mapping of the second genome. For instance, the mouse genome, which is similar in size to the human genome, was mapped at a rapid pace, with the human genome sequence serving as a guide. This approach is particularly helpful when one of two related species has a much shorter genome than the other. An example is the tsetse fly, *Glossina palpalis*, which transmits the parasite causing African sleeping sickness. The tsetse fly genome contains 7×10^9 base pairs (more than twice the size of the human genome), but the genome of a closely related fly is only one-tenth as large. Researchers are sequencing the smaller genome first. Then they will set their sights on the much larger tsetse fly genome, focusing on the coding sequences the two species are expected to share.

The small number of gene differences between closely related species also makes it is easier to correlate phenotypic differences between the species with particular genetic differences. For example, one gene that is clearly different in humans and chimpanzees appears to function in speech, a characteristic that obviously distinguishes the two species. And the genetic similarity between mice and humans, which share 80% of their genes, can be exploited in studying certain human genetic diseases. If researchers know or can hypothesize the organ or tissue in which a defective gene causes a particular disease, they can look for genes that are expressed in these locations in experiments with mice. This approach has revealed several human genes of interest, including one that may be involved in Down syndrome.

Other research efforts are under way to extend genomic studies to many more microbial species and to neglected species from diverse branches of the tree of life. These studies will advance our understanding of all aspects of biology, including health, ecology, and evolution.

Future Directions in Genomics

The success in sequencing genomes and studying entire sets of genes is encouraging scientists to attempt similar systematic study of the full protein sets (*proteomes*) encoded by genomes, an approach called **proteomics.** For reasons already mentioned, the number of proteins in humans and our close relatives undoubtedly exceeds the number of genes. Because proteins, not genes, actually carry out the activities of the cell, we must study when and where they are produced in an organism, and also how they interact, if we are to understand the functioning of cells and organisms. Assembling and analyzing proteomes pose many experimental challenges, but ongoing technical advances are providing the necessary tools to meet those challenges.

Genomics and proteomics are enabling biologists to approach the study of life from an increasingly global perspective. Biologists are now in a position to compile catalogs of genes and proteins—a listing of all the "parts" that contribute to the operation of cells, tissues, and organisms. With such catalogs in hand, researchers are shifting their attention from the individual parts to their functional integration in biological systems. A first step in this systems biology approach is defining gene circuits and protein interaction networks (see Figure 1.10). With the use of computer science and mathematics to process and integrate vast amounts of biological data, researchers can detect and quantify the many combinations of interactions.

Another exciting prospect is our increasing understanding of the spectrum of genetic variation in humans. Because the history of the human species is so short, the amount of DNA variation among humans is small compared to that of many other species. Most of our diversity seems to be in the form of **single nucleotide polymorphisms** (**SNPs,** pronounced "snips"), which are single base-pair variations in the genome, usually detected by sequencing. In the human genome, SNPs occur on average about once in 1,000 base pairs. In other words, if you could compare your personal DNA sequence with that of a person of the same gender—either sitting next to you or on the other side of the world—you would find them to be 99.9% identical.

Scientists are already well on their way to identifying the locations of the several million SNP sites in the human genome. These will be useful genetic markers for studying human evolution, the differences between human populations, and the migratory routes of human populations throughout history. SNPs and other polymorphisms in noncoding (and coding) DNA will also be valuable markers for identifying disease genes and genes that affect our health in more subtle ways. This is likely to change the practice of medicine later in the 21st century. However, applications of DNA research and technology are already affecting our lives in many ways, as we discuss in the final section of the chapter.

Concept Check 20.4

1. Current estimates are that the human genome contains about 25,000 genes, but there is evidence for many more different human polypeptides. What processes might explain this discrepancy?
2. What is the major value of DNA microarray analysis for studying gene expression?
3. Why is the genetic variation among people so much less than it is among individuals of many other species?

For suggested answers, see Appendix A.

Concept 20.5

The practical applications of DNA technology affect our lives in many ways

DNA technology is in the news almost every day. Most often, the topic of the story is a new and promising application in medicine, but this is just one of numerous fields benefiting from DNA technology and genetic engineering.

Medical Applications

One obvious benefit of DNA technology is the identification of human genes whose mutation plays a role in genetic diseases. These discoveries may lead to ways of diagnosing, treating, and even preventing such conditions. DNA technology is also contributing to our understanding of "nongenetic" diseases, from arthritis to AIDS, since a person's genes influence susceptibility to these diseases. Furthermore, diseases of all sorts involve changes in gene expression within the affected cells and often within the patient's immune system. By using DNA microarray assays or other techniques to compare gene expression in healthy and diseased tissues, researchers hope to find many of the genes that are turned on or off in particular diseases. These genes and their products are potential targets for prevention or therapy.

Diagnosis of Diseases

A new chapter in the diagnosis of infectious diseases has been opened by DNA technology, in particular the use of PCR and labeled nucleic acid probes to track down certain pathogens. For example, because the sequence of the HIV genetic material (RNA) is known, PCR can be used to amplify, and thus detect, HIV RNA in blood or tissue samples. RNA cannot be directly amplified by PCR, but the RNA genome is first converted to double-stranded cDNA with reverse transcriptase (RT). PCR is then performed on the cDNA, using a probe specific for one of the HIV genes. This technique, called *RT-PCR,* is often the best way to detect an otherwise elusive infection.

Medical scientists can now diagnose hundreds of human genetic disorders by using PCR and primers corresponding to cloned disease genes, then sequencing the amplified product to look for the disease-causing mutation. Among the genes for human diseases that have been cloned are those for sickle-cell disease, hemophilia, cystic fibrosis, Huntington's disease, and Duchenne muscular dystrophy. Affected individuals with such diseases often can be identified before the onset of symptoms, even before birth. It is also possible to identify symptomless carriers of potentially harmful recessive alleles (see Figure 20.10).

Even when a disease gene has not yet been cloned, the presence of an abnormal allele can be diagnosed with reasonable accuracy if a closely linked RFLP marker has been found (**Figure 20.15**). Alleles for Huntington's disease and a number of other genetic diseases were first detected in this indirect way. If the marker and the gene itself are close enough, crossing over between the marker and the gene is very unlikely to

occur during gamete formation. Therefore, the marker and gene will almost always be inherited together, even though the RFLP marker is not part of the gene. The same principle applies to all kinds of markers, including SNPs.

Human Gene Therapy

Gene therapy—the alteration of an afflicted individual's genes—holds great potential for treating disorders traceable to a single defective gene. In theory, a normal allele of the defective gene could be inserted into the somatic cells of the tissue affected by the disorder.

For gene therapy of somatic cells to be permanent, the cells that receive the normal allele must be ones that multiply throughout the patient's life. Bone marrow cells, which include the stem cells that give rise to all the cells of the blood and immune system, are prime candidates. **Figure 20.16** outlines one possible procedure for gene therapy of an individual

Cloned gene (normal allele, absent from patient's cells)

Retrovirus capsid

Viral RNA

1 Insert RNA version of normal allele into retrovirus.

2 Let retrovirus infect bone marrow cells that have been removed from the patient and cultured.

Bone marrow cell from patient

3 Viral DNA carrying the normal allele inserts into chromosome.

4 Inject engineered cells into patient.

Bone marrow

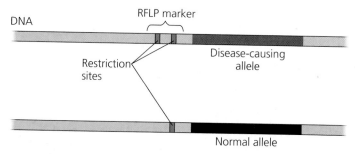

DNA

RFLP marker

Restriction sites

Disease-causing allele

Normal allele

▲ Figure 20.15 **RFLPs as markers for disease-causing alleles.** This diagram depicts homologous segments of DNA from a family in which some members have a genetic disease. In this family, different versions of a RFLP marker are found in unaffected family members and in those who exhibit the disease. If a family member has inherited the version of the RFLP marker with two restriction sites near the gene (rather than one), there is a high probability that the individual has also inherited the disease-causing allele.

▲ Figure 20.16 **Gene therapy using a retroviral vector.** A retrovirus that has been rendered harmless is used as a vector in this procedure, which exploits the ability of a retrovirus to insert a DNA transcript of its RNA genome into the chromosomal DNA of its host cell (see Figure 18.10). If the foreign gene carried by the retroviral vector is expressed, the cell and its descendants will possess the gene product, and the patient may be cured. Cells that reproduce throughout life, such as bone marrow cells, are ideal candidates for gene therapy.

whose bone marrow cells do not produce a vital enzyme because of a single defective gene. One type of severe combined immunodeficiency (SCID) is caused by just this kind of defect. If the treatment is successful, the patient's bone marrow cells will begin producing the missing protein, and the patient will be cured.

The procedure shown in Figure 20.16 was used in the first gene therapy trial for SCID, which began in 1990. But the clinical results from this and succeeding studies during the 1990s did not convincingly demonstrate the effectiveness of the treatment. In another trial that started in 2000, ten young children with SCID were treated by the same procedure. Nine of these patients showed significant, definitive improvement after two years, the first indisputable success of gene therapy. However, two of the patients subsequently developed leukemia, a type of blood cell cancer. Researchers discovered that in both cases, the retroviral vector used to carry the normal allele into bone marrow cells had inserted near a gene involved in the proliferation and development of blood cells, causing leukemia. This and other trials of retrovirus-based gene therapy were temporarily suspended in several countries. By learning more about the behavior of retroviruses, researchers may be able to control the insertion of retroviral vectors to a location that might avoid such problems.

Several other technical questions are also posed by gene therapy. For example, how can the activity of the transferred gene be controlled so that cells make appropriate amounts of the gene product at the right time and in the right place? How can we be sure that the insertion of the therapeutic gene does not harm some other necessary cell function? As more is learned about DNA control elements and gene interactions, researchers may be able to answer such questions.

In addition to technical challenges, gene therapy raises difficult ethical questions. Some critics suggest that tampering with human genes in any way will inevitably lead to the practice of eugenics, a deliberate effort to control the genetic makeup of human populations. Other observers see no fundamental difference between the transplantation of genes into somatic cells and the transplantation of organs.

Treatment of human germ-line cells in the hope of correcting a defect in future generations raises further ethical issues. Such genetic engineering is routinely done in laboratory mice, and the technical problems relating to similar genetic engineering in humans will eventually be solved. Under what circumstances, if any, should we alter the genomes of human germ lines or embryos? In a way, this could be thought of as interfering with evolution. From a biological perspective, the elimination of unwanted alleles from the gene pool could backfire. Genetic variation is a necessary ingredient for the survival of a species as environmental conditions change with time. Genes that are damaging under some conditions may be advantageous under other conditions (one example is the sickle-cell allele, discussed in Chapter 14). Are we willing to risk making genetic changes that could be detrimental to the survival of our species in the future? We may have to face this question soon.

Pharmaceutical Products

You learned earlier in the chapter about DNA cloning and expression systems for producing large quantities of proteins that are present naturally in only minute amounts. The host cells used in such expression systems can even be engineered to secrete a protein as it is made, thereby simplifying the task of purifying it by traditional biochemical methods.

Among the first pharmaceutical products "manufactured" in this way were human insulin and human growth hormone (HGH). Some 2 million people with diabetes in the United States depend on insulin treatment to control their disease. Human growth hormone has been a boon to children born with a form of dwarfism caused by inadequate amounts of HGH. Another important pharmaceutical product produced by genetic engineering is tissue plasminogen activator (TPA). If administered shortly after a heart attack, this protein helps dissolve blood clots and reduces the risk of subsequent heart attacks.

The most recent developments in pharmaceutical products involve truly novel ways to fight certain diseases that do not respond to traditional drug treatments. One approach is the use of genetically engineered proteins that either block or mimic surface receptors on cell membranes. One such experimental drug mimics a receptor protein that HIV binds to while entering white blood cells. The HIV binds to the drug molecules instead and fails to enter the blood cells.

DNA technology also can be used to produce vaccines, which stimulate the immune system to defend against specific pathogens (see Chapter 43). Traditional vaccines are of two types: inactivated (killed) microbes and viable but weakened (attenuated) microbes that generally do not cause illness. Most pathogens have one or more specific proteins on their surface that trigger an immune response against it. This type of protein, produced by recombinant DNA techniques, can be used as a vaccine against the pathogen. Alternatively, genetic engineering methods can be used to modify the genome of the pathogen to attenuate it.

Forensic Evidence

In violent crimes, body fluids or small pieces of tissue may be left at the scene or on the clothes or other possessions of the victim or assailant. If enough blood, semen, or tissue is available, forensic laboratories can determine the blood type or tissue type by using antibodies to detect specific cell-surface proteins. However, such tests require fairly fresh samples in relatively large amounts. Also, because many people have the same blood or tissue type, this approach can only exclude a suspect; it cannot provide strong evidence of guilt.

DNA testing, on the other hand, can identify the guilty individual with a high degree of certainty, because the DNA sequence of every person is unique (except for identical twins). RFLP analysis by Southern blotting is a powerful method for detecting similarities and differences in DNA samples and requires only tiny amounts of blood or other tissue (about 1,000 cells). In a murder case, for example, this method can be used to compare DNA samples from the suspect, the victim, and a small amount of blood found at the crime scene. The forensic scientist usually tests for about five RFLP markers; in other words, only a few selected portions of the DNA are tested. However, even such a small set of markers from an individual can provide a **DNA fingerprint,** or specific pattern of bands, that is of forensic use, because the probability that two people (who are not identical twins) would have the exact same set of RFLP markers is very small. The autoradiograph in **Figure 20.17** resembles the type of evidence presented to juries in murder trials.

DNA fingerprinting can also be used to establish paternity. A comparison of the DNA of a mother, her child, and the purported father can conclusively settle a question of paternity. Sometimes paternity is of historical interest: DNA fingerprinting has provided strong evidence that Thomas Jefferson or one of his close male relatives fathered at least one of the children of his slave Sally Hemings.

Today, instead of RFLPs, variations in the lengths of certain repeated base sequences in simple sequence DNA within the genome are increasingly used as markers for DNA fingerprinting. These repetitive DNA sequences are highly variable from person to person, providing even more markers than RFLPs. For example, one individual may have the repeat unit ACA repeated 65 times at one genome locus, 118 times at a second locus, and so on, whereas another individual is likely to have different numbers of repeats at these loci. Such polymorphic genetic loci are sometimes called *simple tandem repeats (STRs).* The greater the number of markers examined in a DNA sample, the more likely it is that the DNA fingerprint is unique to one individual. PCR is often used to amplify particular STRs or other markers before electrophoresis. PCR is especially valuable when the DNA is in poor condition or available only in minute quantities. A tissue sample as small as 20 cells can be sufficient for PCR amplification.

Just how reliable is DNA fingerprinting? In most forensic cases, the probability of two people having identical DNA fingerprints is between one chance in 100,000 and one in a billion. The exact figure depends on the number of markers compared and on the frequency of those markers in the general population. Information on how common various markers are in different ethnic groups is critical because these marker frequencies may vary considerably among ethnic groups and between a particular ethnic group and the population as a whole. With the increasing availability of frequency data, forensic scientists can make extremely accurate statistical

▲ **Figure 20.17 DNA fingerprints from a murder case.** This autoradiograph shows that DNA in blood from the defendant's clothes matches the DNA fingerprint of the victim but differs from the DNA fingerprint of the defendant. This is evidence that the blood on the defendant's clothes came from the victim, not the defendant. The three DNA samples were subjected to Southern blotting using radioactive probes (see Figure 20.10). The DNA bands resulting from electrophoresis were exposed to probes for several different RFLP markers in succession, with the previous probe washed off before the next one was applied.

calculations. Thus, despite problems that can still arise from insufficient data, human error, or flawed evidence, DNA fingerprints are now accepted as compelling evidence by legal experts and scientists alike. In fact, DNA analysis on stored forensic samples has provided the evidence needed to solve many "cold cases" in recent years.

Environmental Cleanup

Increasingly, the remarkable ability of certain microorganisms to transform chemicals is being exploited for environmental cleanup. Scientists are now engineering these metabolic capabilities into other microorganisms, which are then used to help treat some environmental problems. For example, many bacteria can extract heavy metals, such as copper, lead, and nickel, from their environments and incorporate the metals into compounds such as copper sulfate or lead sulfate, which are readily recoverable. Genetically engineered microbes may become important in both mining minerals (especially as ore reserves are depleted) and cleaning up highly toxic mining wastes. Biotechnologists are also trying to engineer microbes that can degrade chlorinated hydrocarbons and other harmful compounds. These microbes could be used in wastewater treatment plants or by manufacturers before the compounds are ever released into the environment.

A related research area is the identification and engineering of microbes capable of detoxifying specific toxic wastes found in spills and waste dumps. For example, bacterial strains have been developed that can degrade some of the chemicals released during oil spills. By moving the genes responsible for these transformations into different organisms, bioengineers may be able to develop strains that can survive the harsh conditions of environmental disasters and help detoxify the wastes.

Agricultural Applications

Scientists are working to learn more about the genomes of agriculturally important plants and animals, and for a number of years they have been using DNA technology in an effort to improve agricultural productivity.

Animal Husbandry and "Pharm" Animals

DNA technology is now routinely used to make vaccines and growth hormones for treating farm animals. On a still largely experimental basis, scientists can also introduce a gene from one animal into the genome of another animal, which is then called a **transgenic** animal. To do this, they first remove egg cells from a female and fertilize them *in vitro*. Meanwhile, they have cloned the desired gene from another organism. They then inject the cloned DNA directly into the nuclei of the fertilized eggs. Some of the cells integrate the foreign DNA, the *transgene*, into their genomes and are able to express the foreign gene. The engineered embryos are then surgically implanted in a surrogate mother. If an embryo develops successfully, the result is a transgenic animal, containing a gene from a third "parent" that may even be of another species.

The goals of creating a transgenic animal are often the same as the goals of traditional breeding—for instance, to make a sheep with better quality wool, a pig with leaner meat, or a cow that will mature in a shorter time. Scientists might, for example, identify and clone a gene that causes the development of larger muscles (muscles make up most of the meat we eat) in one variety of cattle and transfer it to other cattle or even to sheep.

Transgenic animals also have been engineered to be pharmaceutical "factories"—producers of a large amount of an otherwise rare biological substance for medical use. For example, a transgene for a desired human protein, such as a hormone or blood-clotting factor, can be inserted into the genome of a farm mammal in such a way that the transgene's product is secreted in the animal's milk **(Figure 20.18)**. The protein can then be purified from the milk, usually more easily than from a cell culture. Recently, researchers have engineered transgenic chickens that express large amounts of the transgene's product in eggs. Their success suggests that transgenic chickens may emerge as relatively inexpensive pharmaceutical factories in the near future.

▲ **Figure 20.18 "Pharm" animals.** These transgenic sheep carry a gene for a human blood protein, which they secrete in their milk. This protein inhibits an enzyme that contributes to lung damage in patients with cystic fibrosis and some other chronic respiratory diseases. Easily purified from the sheep's milk, the protein is currently under evaluation as a treatment for cystic fibrosis.

Human proteins produced by farm animals may differ in some ways from the corresponding natural human proteins. Thus, these proteins must be tested very carefully to ensure that they will not cause allergic reactions or other adverse effects in patients receiving them. Also, the health and welfare of farm animals carrying genes from humans and other foreign species are important issues; problems such as low fertility or increased susceptibility to disease are not uncommon.

Genetic Engineering in Plants

Agricultural scientists have already endowed a number of crop plants with genes for desirable traits, such as delayed ripening and resistance to spoilage and disease. In one striking way, plants are easier to genetically engineer than most animals. For many plant species, a single tissue cell grown in culture can give rise to an adult plant (see Figure 21.5). Thus, genetic manipulations can be performed on a single cell and the cell then used to generate an organism with new traits.

The most commonly used vector for introducing new genes into plant cells is a plasmid, called the **Ti plasmid**, from the soil bacterium *Agrobacterium tumefaciens*. This plasmid integrates a segment of its DNA, known as T DNA, into the chromosomal DNA of its host plant cells. For vector purposes, researchers work with a version of the plasmid that does not cause disease, as the wild-type version does. **Figure 20.19** outlines one method for using the Ti plasmid to produce transgenic plants. Scientists can introduce recombinant Ti plasmids into plant cells by electroporation. Alternatively, the recombinant plasmid can be put back into *Agrobacterium*; susceptible plants or plant cells growing in culture are then infected with bacteria that contain the recombinant plasmid.

Figure 20.19

Using the Ti Plasmid to Produce Transgenic Plants

APPLICATION Genes conferring useful traits, such as pest resistance, herbicide resistance, delayed ripening, and increased nutritional value, can be transferred from one plant variety or species to another using the Ti plasmid as a vector.

TECHNIQUE

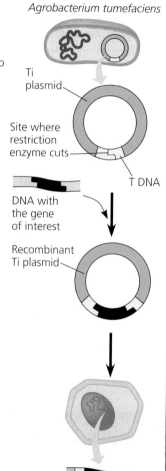

Agrobacterium tumefaciens

Ti plasmid

❶ The Ti plasmid is isolated from the bacterium *Agrobacterium tumefaciens*. The segment of the plasmid that integrates into the genome of host cells is called T DNA.

Site where restriction enzyme cuts

T DNA

❷ Isolated plasmids and foreign DNA containing a gene of interest are incubated with a restriction enzyme that cuts in the middle of T DNA. After base pairing occurs between the sticky ends of the plasmids and foreign DNA fragments, DNA ligase is added. Some of the resulting stable recombinant plasmids contain the gene of interest.

DNA with the gene of interest

Recombinant Ti plasmid

❸ Recombinant plasmids can be introduced into cultured plant cells by electroporation. Or plasmids can be returned to *Agrobacterium*, which is then applied as a liquid suspension to the leaves of susceptible plants, infecting them. Once a plasmid is taken into a plant cell, its T DNA integrates into the cell's chromosomal DNA.

RESULTS

Transformed cells carrying the transgene of interest can regenerate complete plants that exhibit the new trait conferred by the transgene.

Plant with new trait

Genetic engineering is rapidly replacing traditional plant-breeding programs, especially for useful traits, such as herbicide or pest resistance, determined by one or a few genes. For example, crops engineered with a bacterial gene making the plants resistant to herbicides can grow while weeds are destroyed. Similarly, genetically engineered crops that can resist destructive microbes and insects have reduced the need for chemical insecticides.

Genetic engineering also has great potential for improving the nutritional value of crop plants. For instance, scientists have developed transgenic rice plants that produce yellow rice grains containing beta-carotene, which our body uses to make vitamin A (see Figure 38.16). This "golden" rice could help prevent vitamin A deficiency in the half of the world's population that depends on rice as a staple food. Currently, large numbers of young children in Southeast Asia suffer from vitamin A deficiency, which leads to vision impairment and increases susceptibility to disease.

In a novel twist, the pharmaceutical industry is beginning to develop "pharm" plants, analogous to "pharm" animals. Although natural plants have long been sources of drugs, researchers are now creating plants that make human proteins for medical use and viral proteins for use as vaccines. Several such products are being tested in clinical trials, including vaccines for hepatitis B and an antibody produced in transgenic tobacco plants that interferes with the bacteria that cause tooth decay. Large amounts of these proteins might be produced more economically by plants than by cultured cells.

Safety and Ethical Questions Raised by DNA Technology

Early concerns about potential dangers associated with recombinant DNA technology focused on the possibility that hazardous new pathogens might be created. What might happen, for instance, if cancer cell genes were transferred into bacteria or viruses? To guard against such rogue microbes, scientists developed a set of guidelines that were adopted as formal government regulations in the United States and some other countries. One safety measure is a set of strict laboratory procedures designed to protect researchers from infection by engineered microbes and to prevent the microbes from accidentally leaving the laboratory. In addition, strains of microorganisms to be used in recombinant DNA experiments are genetically crippled to ensure that they cannot survive outside the laboratory. Finally, certain obviously dangerous experiments have been banned.

Today, most public concern about possible hazards centers not on recombinant microbes but on **genetically modified (GM) organisms** used as food. In common language, a GM organism is one that has acquired by artificial means one or more genes from the same or another species. Salmon, for example, have been genetically modified by addition of a more active salmon growth hormone gene. However, the majority of the GM organisms that contribute to our food supply are not animals, but crop plants.

Some countries have been wary of the GM revolution, with the safety of GM foods and possible environmental consequences of growing GM plants being the major concerns. In

1999, for instance, the European Union suspended the introduction of new GM crops pending new legislation. Early in 2000, negotiators from 130 countries (including the United States) agreed on a Biosafety Protocol that requires exporters to identify GM organisms present in bulk food shipments and allows importing countries to decide whether the products pose environmental or health risks.

Advocates of a cautious approach toward GM crops fear that transgenic plants might pass their new genes to close relatives in nearby wild areas. We know that lawn and crop grasses, for example, commonly exchange genes with wild relatives via pollen transfer. If crop plants carrying genes for resistance to herbicides, diseases, or insect pests pollinated wild ones, the offspring might become "super weeds" that are very difficult to control. Another possible hazard, suggested by one laboratory-based study, is that a transgene encoding a pesticide-type protein might cause plants to produce pollen toxic to butterflies. However, scientists with the Agricultural Research Service concluded from a two-year study that butterflies were unlikely to be exposed to toxic levels of pollen.

As for the risks to human health from GM foods, some people fear that the protein products of transgenes might lead to allergic reactions. Although there is some evidence that this could happen, advocates claim that these proteins could be tested for their ability to cause allergic reactions.

Today, governments and regulatory agencies throughout the world are grappling with how to facilitate the use of biotechnology in agriculture, industry, and medicine while ensuring that new products and procedures are safe. In the United States, such applications of biotechnology are evaluated for potential risks by various regulatory agencies, including the Food and Drug Administration, Environmental Protection Agency, National Institutes of Health, and Department of Agriculture. These agencies are under increasing pressure from some consumer groups. Meanwhile, these same agencies and the public must consider the ethical implications of biotechnology.

Completion of the mapping of the human genome, for instance, raises significant ethical questions. Who should have the right to examine someone else's genes? How should that information be used? Should a person's genome be a factor in suitability for a job or eligibility for insurance? Ethical considerations, as well as concerns about potential environmental and health hazards, will likely slow some applications of biotechnology. There is always a danger that too much regulation will stifle basic research and its potential benefits. However, the power of DNA technology and genetic engineering—our ability to profoundly and rapidly alter species that have been evolving for millennia—demands that we proceed with humility and caution.

Concept Check 20.5

1. What is the advantage of using stem cells for gene therapy?
2. List at least three different properties that have been acquired by crop plants via genetic engineering.

For suggested answers, see Appendix A.

Chapter 20 Review

Go to the Campbell Biology website (**www.campbellbiology.com**) or CD-ROM to explore Activities, Investigations, and other interactive study aids.

SUMMARY OF KEY CONCEPTS

Concept 20.1

DNA cloning permits production of multiple copies of a specific gene or other DNA segment

▶ **DNA Cloning and Its Applications:** *A Preview* **(pp. 385–386)** DNA cloning and other techniques, collectively termed DNA technology, can be used to manipulate and analyze DNA and to produce useful new products and organisms.
Activity *Applications of DNA Technology*

▶ **Using Restriction Enzymes to Make Recombinant DNA (p. 386)** Bacterial restriction enzymes cut DNA molecules within short, specific nucleotide sequences to yield a set of double-stranded DNA fragments with single-stranded sticky ends. The sticky ends on fragments from one DNA source can base-pair with complementary sticky ends on fragments from other DNA molecules; sealing of the base-paired fragments with DNA ligase produces recombinant DNA molecules.
Activity *Restriction Enzymes*

▶ **Cloning a Eukaryotic Gene in a Bacterial Plasmid (pp. 386–388)** A recombinant plasmid is made by inserting restriction fragments from DNA containing a gene of interest into a plasmid vector that has been cut open by the same enzyme. Gene cloning results when the recombinant plasmid is introduced into a host bacterial cell and the foreign genes are replicated along with the bacterial chromosome as the host cell reproduces. A clone of cells carrying the gene of interest can be identified with a radioactively labeled nucleic acid probe that has a sequence complementary to the gene.
Activity *Cloning a Gene in Bacteria*
Investigation *How Can Antibiotic-Resistant Plasmids Transform* E. coli?

▶ **Storing Cloned Genes in DNA Libraries (pp. 388–390)** A genomic library is the collection of recombinant vector clones produced by cloning DNA fragments derived from an entire genome. A cDNA (complementary DNA) library is made by cloning DNA made *in vitro* by reverse transcription of all the mRNA produced by a particular kind of cell.

- **Cloning and Expressing Eukaryotic Genes** (pp. 390–391) Several technical difficulties hinder the expression of cloned eukaryotic genes in bacterial host cells. The use of cultured eukaryotic cells as host cells and yeast artificial chromosomes (YACs) as vectors helps avoid these problems.

- **Amplifying DNA *in Vitro*: The Polymerase Chain Reaction (PCR)** (pp. 391–392) PCR can produce many copies of a specific target segment of DNA, using primers that bracket the desired sequence and a heat-resistant DNA polymerase.

Concept 20.2

Restriction fragment analysis detects DNA differences that affect restriction sites

- **Gel Electrophoresis and Southern Blotting** (pp. 392–394) DNA restriction fragments of different lengths can be separated by gel electrophoresis. Specific fragments can be identified by Southern blotting, using labeled probes that hybridize to the DNA immobilized on a "blot" of the gel.
  Activity *Gel Electrophoresis of DNA*

- **Restriction Fragment Length Differences as Genetic Markers** (p. 394) Restriction fragment length polymorphisms (RFLPs) are differences in DNA sequence on homologous chromosomes that result in restriction fragments of different lengths, which can be detected by Southern blotting. The thousands of RFLPs present throughout eukaryotic DNA can serve as genetic markers.
  Activity *Analyzing DNA Fragments Using Gel Electrophoresis*
  Investigation *How Can Gel Electrophoresis Be Used to Analyze DNA?*

Concept 20.3

Entire genomes can be mapped at the DNA level

- **Genetic (Linkage) Mapping: Relative Ordering of Markers** (p. 396) The order of genes and other inherited markers in the genome and the relative distances between them can be determined from recombination frequencies.

- **Physical Mapping: Ordering DNA Fragments** (p. 396) A physical map is constructed by cutting a DNA molecule into many short fragments and arranging them in order by identifying overlaps. A physical map gives the actual distance in base pairs between markers.

- **DNA Sequencing** (pp. 396–398) Relatively short DNA fragments can be sequenced by the dideoxy chain-termination method, which can be performed in automated sequencing machines.
  Activity *The Human Genome Project: Genes on Human Chromosome 17*

Concept 20.4

Genome sequences provide clues to important biological questions

- **Identifying Protein-Coding Genes in DNA Sequences** (p. 399) Computer analysis of genome sequences helps researchers identify sequences that are likely to encode proteins. Current estimates are that the human genome contains about 25,000 genes, but the number of human proteins is much larger. Comparison of the sequences of "new" genes with those of known genes in other species may help identify new genes.

- **Determining Gene Function** (p. 400) For a gene of unknown function, experimental inactivation of the gene and observation of the resulting phenotypic effects can provide clues to its function.

- **Studying Expression of Interacting Groups of Genes** (p. 400) DNA microarray assays allow researchers to compare patterns of gene expression in different tissues, at different times, or under different conditions.

- **Comparing Genomes of Different Species** (pp. 400–402) Comparative studies of genomes from related and widely divergent species are providing valuable information in many fields of biology.

- **Future Directions in Genomics** (p. 402) Genomics is the systematic study of entire genomes; proteomics is the systematic study of all the proteins encoded by a genome. Single nucleotide polymorphisms (SNPs) provide useful markers for studying human genetic variation.

Concept 20.5

The practical applications of DNA technology affect our lives in many ways

- **Medical Applications** (pp. 402–404) DNA technology is increasingly being used in the diagnosis of genetic and other diseases and offers potential for better treatment of certain genetic disorders or even permanent cures.

- **Pharmaceutical Products** (p. 404) Large-scale production of human hormones and other proteins with therapeutic uses, including safer vaccines, are possible with DNA technology.

- **Forensic Evidence** (pp. 404–405) DNA "fingerprints" obtained by analysis of tissue or body fluids found at crime scenes can provide definitive evidence that a suspect is guilty or not. Such fingerprints are also useful in parenthood disputes.
  Activity *DNA Fingerprinting*

- **Environmental Cleanup** (pp. 405–406) Genetic engineering can be used to modify the metabolism of microorganisms so that they can be used to extract minerals from the environment or degrade various types of potentially toxic waste materials.

- **Agricultural Applications** (pp. 406–407) The aim of developing transgenic plants and animals is to improve agricultural productivity and food quality.

- **Safety and Ethical Questions Raised by DNA Technology** (pp. 407–408) The potential benefits of genetic engineering must be carefully weighed against the potential hazards of creating products or developing procedures that are harmful to humans or the environment.
  Activity *Making Decisions About DNA Technology: Golden Rice*

TESTING YOUR KNOWLEDGE

Self-Quiz

1. Which of the following tools of recombinant DNA technology is *incorrectly* paired with its use?
   a. restriction enzyme—production of RFLPs
   b. DNA ligase—enzyme that cuts DNA, creating the sticky ends of restriction fragments
   c. DNA polymerase—used in a polymerase chain reaction to amplify sections of DNA
   d. reverse transcriptase—production of cDNA from mRNA
   e. electrophoresis—separation of DNA fragments

2. Which of the following would *not* be true of cDNA produced using human brain tissue as the starting material?
   a. It could be amplified by the polymerase chain reaction.
   b. It could be used to create a complete genomic library.
   c. It is produced from mRNA using reverse transcriptase.
   d. It could be used as a probe to locate genes expressed in the brain.
   e. It lacks the introns of the human genes and thus can probably be introduced into phage vectors.

3. Plants are more readily manipulated by genetic engineering than are animals because
   a. plant genes do not contain introns.
   b. more vectors are available for transferring recombinant DNA into plant cells.
   c. a somatic plant cell can often give rise to a complete plant.
   d. genes can be inserted into plant cells by microinjection.
   e. plant cells have larger nuclei.

4. A paleontologist has recovered a bit of tissue from the 400-year-old preserved skin of an extinct dodo (a bird). The researcher would like to compare DNA from the sample with DNA from living birds. Which of the following would be most useful for increasing the amount of dodo DNA available for testing?
   a. RFLP analysis
   b. polymerase chain reaction (PCR)
   c. electroporation
   d. gel electrophoresis
   e. Southern hybridization

5. Expression of a cloned eukaryotic gene in a prokaryotic cell involves many difficulties. The use of mRNA and reverse transcriptase is part of a strategy to solve the problem of
   a. post-transcriptional processing.
   b. electroporation.
   c. post-translational processing.
   d. nucleic acid hybridization.
   e. restriction fragment ligation.

6. DNA technology has many medical applications. Which of the following is *not* done routinely at present?
   a. production of hormones for treating diabetes and dwarfism
   b. production of viral subunits for vaccines
   c. introduction of genetically engineered genes into human gametes
   d. prenatal identification of genetic disease genes
   e. genetic testing for carriers of harmful alleles

7. Which of the following has the largest genome size and the smallest number of genes per million base pairs?
   a. *Hemophilus influenzae* (bacterium)
   b. *Saccharomyces cerevisiae* (yeast)
   c. *Arabidopsis thaliana* (plant)
   d. *Drosophila melanogaster* (fruit fly)
   e. *Homo sapiens* (human)

8. Which of the following sequences in double-stranded DNA is most likely to be recognized as a cutting site for a restriction enzyme?

a. AAGG	b. AGTC	c. GGCC	d. ACCA	e. AAAA
TTCC	TCAG	CCGG	TGGT	TTTT

9. In recombinant DNA methods, the term *vector* can refer to
   a. the enzyme that cuts DNA into restriction fragments.
   b. the sticky end of a DNA fragment.
   c. a RFLP marker.
   d. a plasmid used to transfer DNA into a living cell.
   e. a DNA probe used to identify a particular gene.

10. When using the shotgun approach to genome mapping, researchers carry out
    a. linkage mapping of each chromosome.
    b. extensive physical mapping of each chromosome, starting with large chromosomal fragments.
    c. DNA sequencing of small fragments and then ordering of the fragments to determine the overall nucleotide sequence.
    d. a and b.
    e. a, b, and c.

For Self-Quiz answers, see Appendix A.

Go to the website or CD-ROM for more quiz questions.

Evolution Connection

If DNA-based technologies become widely used, how might they change the way evolution proceeds, as compared with the natural evolutionary mechanisms of the past 4 billion years?

Scientific Inquiry

You hope to study a gene that codes for a neurotransmitter protein in human brain cells. You know the amino acid sequence of the protein. Explain how you might (a) identify the genes expressed in a specific type of brain cell, (b) identify the gene for the neurotransmitter, (c) produce multiple copies of the gene for study, and (d) produce a quantity of the neurotransmitter for evaluation as a potential medication.

Investigation *How Can Antibiotic-Resistant Plasmids Transform E. coli?*
Investigation *How Can Gel Electrophoresis Be Used to Analyze DNA?*

Science, Technology, and Society

Is there danger of discrimination based on testing for "harmful" genes? What policies can you suggest that would prevent such abuses?

21 The Genetic Basis of Development

▲ **Figure 21.1 Mutant *Drosophila* with an extra small eye on its antenna.**

Key Concepts

21.1 Embryonic development involves cell division, cell differentiation, and morphogenesis

21.2 Different cell types result from differential gene expression in cells with the same DNA

21.3 Pattern formation in animals and plants results from similar genetic and cellular mechanisms

21.4 Comparative studies help explain how the evolution of development leads to morphological diversity

Overview

From Single Cell to Multicellular Organism

This chapter applies much of what you've learned about molecules, cells, and genes to one of biology's most important questions—how a complex multi-cellular organism develops from a single cell. The application of genetic analysis and DNA technology to the study of development has revolutionized the field. In much the same way that researchers have used mutations to deduce pathways of cellular metabolism, they now use mutations to dissect developmental pathways. In one striking example, Swiss researchers demonstrated in 1995 that a particular gene functions as a master switch that triggers development of the eye in *Drosophila*. The scanning electron micrograph in **Figure 21.1** shows part of the head of an abnormal fly that has a small extra eye on each antenna. In this fly, the

master gene triggering eye development was expressed in an abnormal body location, causing extra eyes. A similar gene activates eye development in mice and other mammals. In fact, developmental biologists are discovering remarkable similarities in the mechanisms that form diverse organisms.

The scientific study of development got under way about 130 years ago, around the same time as genetics. But for decades, the two disciplines proceeded along mostly separate paths. Developmental biologists focused on embryology, the study of the stages of development leading from a fertilized egg to a fully formed organism. They studied animals that lay their eggs in water, including marine invertebrates and fresh-water vertebrate amphibians, such as frogs. By studying these and other animals, as well as plants, biologists worked out a description of animal development (see Chapter 47) and plant development (see Chapter 35) at the macroscopic and micro-scopic levels.

In recent years, scientists have applied the concepts and tools of molecular genetics to the study of developmental biology with remarkably fruitful results. In this chapter, we introduce some of the basic mechanisms that control development in animals and plants, focusing on what has been learned from molecular and genetic studies. After introducing the basic cellular processes underlying development, we consider how cells become different from each other and the factors that establish the spatial pattern of these different types of cells in the embryo. Next, we examine in more detail the molecular basis of several specific developmental phenomena as examples of some general principles of development. Finally, we discuss what researchers can learn about evolution from comparing developmental processes in different species.

Figure 21.2

Exploring Model Organisms for Genetic Studies of Development

DROSOPHILA MELANOGASTER
(FRUIT FLY)

CAENORHABDITIS ELEGANS
(NEMATODE)

Researchers can draw on a wealth of information about the fruit fly *Drosophila melanogaster* (often referred to simply as *Drosophila*), one of the most important model organisms in developmental genetics. First chosen as a model organism by the pioneering geneticist T. H. Morgan in the early 20th century, *Drosophila* has been studied intensively by generations of geneticists since then. Small and easily grown in the laboratory, *Drosophila* has a generation time of only two weeks. It produces many offspring and the embryos develop outside the mother's body—both assets for developmental studies. Sequencing of the *Drosophila* genome was completed in 2000; it has 180×10^6 base pairs (180 million bases, Mb) and contains about 13,700 genes. Although early development of fruit flies is at least superficially quite different from that of many other animals, research on *Drosophila* development has yielded deep insights into basic principles of animal development.

The soil-dwelling nematode *Caenorhabditis elegans* (or *C. elegans*) is easily grown in the laboratory in petri dishes. It is about 1 mm long, has a simple, transparent body with only a few types of cells, and grows from zygote to mature adult in only three and a half days. The nematode genome is 97 Mb long and contains an estimated 19,000 genes. Most individuals are hermaphrodites, producing both eggs and sperm. Hermaphrodites are convenient for genetic studies because recessive mutations are easy to detect. If a worm with the wild-type phenotype self-fertilizes and one-fourth of its offspring have a mutant phenotype (homozygous for a recessive allele), then the parent must be heterozygous for the recessive mutant allele. Even if homozygotes with the recessive mutation do not reproduce, the mutation can be maintained in the heterozygotes. Another advantage of *C. elegans* is that every adult hermaphrodite has exactly 959 somatic cells, which arise from the zygote in virtually the same way for every individual. Using a microscope to follow all the cell divisions starting immediately after a zygote forms, biologists have been able to reconstruct the entire ancestry of every cell in the adult body.

0.25 mm

When the primary research goal is to understand broad biological principles, the organism chosen for study is called a **model organism.** Researchers select model organisms that lend themselves to the study of a particular question, are representative of a larger group, and are easy to grow in the lab. For research aimed at uncovering the connections between genes and development, biologists have turned to organisms which have relatively short generation times and small genomes and about which much is already known. Organisms with these attributes are particularly convenient for genetic analysis. Among the favorite model organisms in developmental genetics are the fruit fly *Drosophila melanogaster,* the nematode *Caenorhabditis elegans,* the mouse *Mus musculus,* the zebrafish *Danio rerio,* and the plant *Arabidopsis thaliana.* Before proceeding, acquaint yourself with these model organisms in **Figure 21.2**. Developmental principles we have learned from studying these organisms will be presented throughout this chapter.

Concept 21.1

Embryonic development involves cell division, cell differentiation, and morphogenesis

In the embryonic development of most organisms, a single-celled zygote (fertilized egg) gives rise to cells of many different types, each type with a different structure and corresponding function. For example, an animal will have muscle cells that enable it to move and nerve cells that transmit signals to the muscle cells; a plant will have mesophyll cells that carry out photosynthesis and guard cells around stomata (pores) that regulate the passage of gases into and out of leaves. Within a multicellular organism, cells of different types are organized into tissues, tissues into organs, organs into organ systems, and

MUS MUSCULUS
(MOUSE)

DANIO RERIO
(ZEBRAFISH)

ARABIDOPSIS THALIANA
(COMMON WALL CRESS)

Among vertebrates, two in particular lend themselves to the genetic analysis of development, the mouse and the zebrafish. The mouse *Mus musculus* has a long history as a mammalian model, and much is known about its biology. The mouse genome is about 2,600 Mb long with about 25,000 genes, roughly the same as the human genome. Researchers are now adept at manipulating mouse genes to make transgenic mice and mice in which particular genes are "knocked out" by mutation. However, mice have a generation time of about nine weeks, and their embryos develop in the mother's uterus, hidden from view, both disadvantages for developmental studies.

Many of the disadvantages of the mouse as a vertebrate model are absent in the zebrafish *Danio rerio*. These small fish (2–4 cm long) are easy to breed in the laboratory, and the transparent embryos develop outside the mother's body. Although the generation time is relatively long (two to four months), early development proceeds quickly: By 24 hours after fertilization, most of the tissues and rudiments of the organs have formed, and by two days, a tiny fish hatches out of the egg case. The zebrafish genome (estimated to be 1,700 Mb long) is still being mapped and sequenced, but researchers have already identified many genes involved in this animal's development.

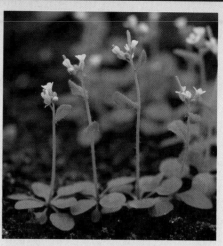

For studying the molecular genetics of plant development, researchers often use a small flowering plant in the mustard family called *Arabidopsis thaliana* (or simply *Arabidopsis*). One of these plants can grow in a test tube and produce thousands of progeny after eight to ten weeks; as in Mendel's pea plants, each flower makes both eggs and sperm. For research on gene function, scientists can make transgenic *Arabidopsis* plants (see Figure 20.19). Compared with some other plant species, *Arabidopsis* has a relatively small genome, about 118 Mb, which contains an estimated 25,500 genes.

organ systems into the whole organism. Thus, the process of embryonic development must give rise not only to cells of different types but to higher-level structures arranged in a particular way in three dimensions.

The photos in **Figure 21.3** illustrate the dramatic transformation of a zygote into an organism. This transformation results from three interrelated processes: cell division, cell differentiation, and morphogenesis. Through a succession of mitotic cell divisions, the zygote gives rise to a large number of cells. Cell division alone, however, would produce only a great ball of identical cells, nothing like an animal or plant. During embryonic development, cells not only increase in number, but also undergo **cell differentiation,** the process by which cells become specialized in structure and function. Moreover, the different kinds of cells are not randomly distributed but are organized into tissues and organs. The physical processes that give an organism its shape constitute **morphogenesis,** meaning "creation of form."

(a) Fertilized eggs of a frog   **(b) Tadpole hatching from egg**

▲ **Figure 21.3 From fertilized egg to animal: what a difference a week makes.** It takes just one week for cell division, differentiation, and morphogenesis to transform each of the fertilized frog eggs shown in (a) into a hatching tadpole like the one in (b). A protective jelly coat surrounds the eggs and tadpole.

The processes of cell division, differentiation, and morphogenesis overlap in time **(Figure 21.4)**. Morphogenetic events lay out the basic body plan very early in embryonic development, establishing, for example, which end of an animal embryo will be the head or which end of a plant embryo will become the roots. These early events determine the body axes of the organism, such as the anterior-posterior (head-to-tail) axis and the dorsal-ventral (back-to-belly) axis. Later morphogenetic events establish relative locations of structures within smaller regions of the embryo, such as the appendages on a fly's body, the fins on a fish, or the digits on a vertebrate limb—and then within regions still smaller.

Cell division and differentiation play important roles in morphogenesis in all organisms, as does the appropriately timed programmed death of certain cells. However, the overall schemes of morphogenesis in animals and plants exhibit significant differences. In addition to many shared developmental mechanisms, the development of animals and plants differs in two major ways:

▶ In animals, but not in plants, *movements* of cells and tissues are necessary to transform the early embryo into the characteristic three-dimensional form of the organism.

▶ In plants, but not in animals, morphogenesis and growth in overall size are not limited to embryonic and juvenile periods but occur throughout the life of the plant.

The structures responsible for a plant's continual growth and formation of new organs are **apical meristems,** perpetually embryonic regions in the tips of shoots and roots. In animals, ongoing development in adults is normally restricted to the generation of cells that must be continually replenished throughout the animal's lifetime. Examples are blood cells, skin cells, and the cells lining the intestines.

During differentiation and morphogenesis, embryonic cells behave and function in different ways from each other, even though all of them have arisen from the same cell—the zygote. In the next section, you will learn about the principal way in which this occurs.

(a) Animal development. Most animals go through some variation of the blastula and gastrula stages. The blastula is a sphere of cells surrounding a fluid-filled cavity. The gastrula forms when a region of the blastula folds inward, creating a tube—a rudimentary gut. Once the animal is mature, differentiation occurs in only a limited way—for the replacement of damaged or lost cells.

(b) Plant development. In plants with seeds, a complete embryo develops within the seed. Morphogenesis, which involves cell division and cell wall expansion rather than cell or tissue movement, occurs throughout the plant's lifetime. Apical meristems (purple) continuously arise and develop into the various plant organs as the plant grows to an indeterminate size.

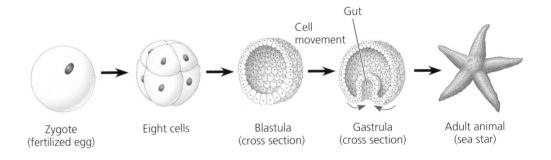

▲ **Figure 21.4 Some key stages of development in animals and plants.** Cell division, morphogenesis, and cell differentiation occur in both animal development and plant development. Molecular events leading to cell differentiation begin as early as the two-cell stage, but observable differences among cells are not evident until much later.

Concept Check 21.1

1. As you learned in Chapter 12, mitosis gives rise to two daughter cells that are genetically identical to the parent cell. Yet you, the product of many mitotic divisions, are not just a ball of identical cells. Why?
2. What are the fundamental differences between plants and animals in their mechanisms of development?

For suggested answers, see Appendix A.

Concept 21.2

Different cell types result from differential gene expression in cells with the same DNA

In earlier chapters, we have stated that differences between cells in a multicellular organism come almost entirely from differences in gene *expression*, not from differences in the cells' genomes. (There are a few exceptions, such as antibody-producing cells; see Figure 43.11.) Furthermore, we have mentioned that these differences arise during development as regulatory mechanisms turn specific genes on and off. Let's now look at some of the evidence for this assertion.

Evidence for Genomic Equivalence

The results of many experiments support the conclusion that nearly all the cells of an organism have *genomic equivalence*—that is, they all have the same genes. What happens to these genes as a cell begins to differentiate? We can shed some light on this question by asking whether genes are irreversibly inactivated during differentiation. For example, does an epidermal cell in your finger contain a functional gene specifying eye color, or has the eye-color gene been destroyed or permanently inactivated there?

Totipotency in Plants

One experimental approach for testing genomic equivalence is to see whether a differentiated cell can generate a whole organism. Such experiments were performed during the 1950s by F. C. Steward and his students at Cornell University, working with carrot plants **(Figure 21.5)**. They found that differentiated cells taken from the root (the carrot) and placed in culture medium could grow into normal adult plants, each genetically identical to the "parent" plant. These results show that differentiation does not necessarily involve irreversible changes in the DNA. In plants, at least, mature cells can dedifferentiate and then give rise to all the specialized cell types of the mature organism. Any cell with this potential is said to be **totipotent.**

Figure 21.5

Inquiry   Can a differentiated plant cell develop into a whole plant?

EXPERIMENT

Transverse section of carrot root

2-mg fragments

Fragments cultured in nutrient medium; stirring causes single cells to shear off into liquid.

Single cells free in suspension begin to divide.

Embryonic plant develops from a cultured single cell.

Plantlet is cultured on agar medium. Later it is planted in soil.

RESULTS A single somatic (nonreproductive) carrot cell developed into a mature carrot plant. The new plant was a genetic duplicate (clone) of the parent plant.

Adult plant

CONCLUSION At least some differentiated (somatic) cells in plants are totipotent, able to reverse their differentiation and then give rise to all the cell types in a mature plant.

Using one or more somatic cells from a multicellular organism to make another genetically identical individual is called **cloning,** and each new individual made in this way can be called a **clone** (from the Greek *klon,* twig). Plant cloning is now used extensively in agriculture. Indeed, if you have ever grown a new plant from a cutting, you have practiced cloning.

Nuclear Transplantation in Animals

Differentiated cells from animals generally do not divide in culture, much less develop into the multiple cell types of a new organism. Therefore, animal researchers had to use a different approach to the question of whether differentiated animal cells can be totipotent. Their approach was to remove the nucleus of an unfertilized egg cell or zygote and replace it with the nucleus of a differentiated cell, a method called *nuclear transplantation.* If the nucleus from the differentiated donor cell retains its full genetic capability, then it should be able to direct development of the recipient egg into all the proper tissues and organs of an organism.

Such experiments were conducted on frogs by Robert Briggs and Thomas King in the 1950s and extended by John Gurdon in the 1980s. These researchers transplanted a nucleus from an embryonic or tadpole cell into an enucleated egg of the same species. The transplanted nucleus was often able to support normal development of the egg into a tadpole **(Figure 21.6)**. However, the "potency" of transplanted nuclei in directing normal development was inversely related to the age of the donor: the older the donor nucleus, the lower the percentage of normally developing tadpoles.

From these results, we can conclude that something in the nucleus *does* change as animal cells differentiate. In frogs and most other animals, nuclear potency tends to be restricted more and more as embryonic development and cell differentiation progress. Research has shown that although the base sequence of the DNA usually does not change, the chromatin structure is altered in specific ways, usually involving chemical modifications of histones or DNA methylation (see Chapter 19). However, these chromatin changes are sometimes reversible, and biologists agree that the nuclei of most differentiated animal cells have all the genes required for making the entire organism. In other words, the various cell types in the body of an animal differ in structure and function not because they contain different genes, but because they express different sets of genes from a common genome.

Reproductive Cloning of Mammals. Evidence that all cells in an organism have the same DNA also comes from experiments with mammals. Researchers have long been able to clone mammals using nuclei or cells from a variety of early embryos. But it was not known whether a nucleus from a fully differentiated cell could be "reprogrammed" to be totipotent. However, in 1997, Scottish researchers captured newspaper headlines when they announced the birth of Dolly, a lamb cloned from an adult sheep by nuclear transplantation from a differentiated cell **(Figure 21.7)**. These researchers achieved the necessary dedifferentiation of donor nuclei by culturing mammary cells in nutrient-poor medium. The researchers then fused these cells with sheep egg cells whose nuclei had been removed. The resulting diploid cells divided to form early embryos, which were implanted into surrogate mothers. One of several hundred implanted embryos successfully completed normal development, and Dolly was born.

Later analyses showed that Dolly's chromosomal DNA was indeed identical to that of the nucleus donor. (Her mitochondrial DNA came from the egg cell donor, as expected.)

Figure 21.6
Inquiry **Can the nucleus from a differentiated animal cell direct development of an organism?**

EXPERIMENT Researchers enucleated frog egg cells by exposing them to ultraviolet light, which destroyed the nucleus. Nuclei from cells of embryos up to the tadpole stage were transplanted into the enucleated egg cells.

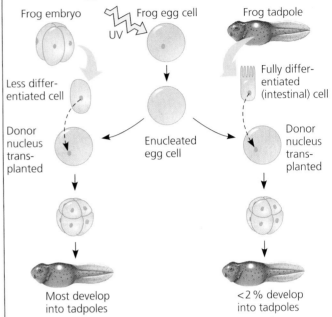

RESULTS Most of the recipient eggs developed into tadpoles when the transplanted nuclei came from cells of an early embryo, which are relatively undifferentiated cells. But with nuclei from the fully differentiated intestinal cells of a tadpole, fewer than 2% of the eggs developed into normal tadpoles, and most of the embryos died at a much earlier developmental stage.

CONCLUSION The nucleus from a differentiated frog cell can direct development of a tadpole. However, its ability to do so decreases as the donor cell becomes more differentiated, presumably because of changes in the nucleus.

In 2003, at age 6, Dolly suffered complications from a lung disease usually seen in much older sheep and was euthanized. Dolly's premature death, as well as her arthritic condition, led to speculation that her cells were "older" than those of a normal sheep, possibly reflecting incomplete reprogramming of the original transplanted nucleus.

Since 1997, cloning has also been demonstrated in numerous other mammals, including mice, cats, cows, horses, and pigs. In most cases, the goal has been to produce new individuals; this is known as *reproductive cloning*. We have already learned much of interest from such experiments. For example, cloned animals of the same species do *not* always look or behave identically. In a herd of cows cloned from the same cell line, certain cows are dominant and others are more submissive. Another example is the first cloned

Figure 21.7

Reproductive Cloning of a Mammal by Nuclear Transplantation

APPLICATION This method is used to produce cloned animals whose nuclear genes are identical to the donor animal supplying the nucleus.

TECHNIQUE Shown here is the procedure used to produce Dolly, the first reported case of a mammal cloned using the nucleus of a differentiated cell.

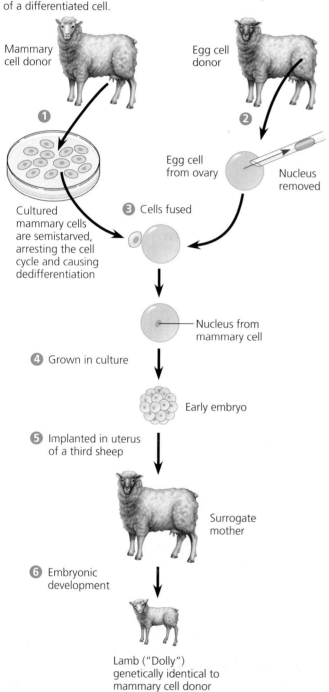

Mammary cell donor

Egg cell donor

❶

❷

Egg cell from ovary

Nucleus removed

Cultured mammary cells are semistarved, arresting the cell cycle and causing dedifferentiation

❸ Cells fused

Nucleus from mammary cell

❹ Grown in culture

Early embryo

❺ Implanted in uterus of a third sheep

Surrogate mother

❻ Embryonic development

Lamb ("Dolly") genetically identical to mammary cell donor

RESULTS The cloned animal is identical in appearance and genetic makeup to the donor animal supplying the nucleus, but differs from the egg cell donor and surrogate mother.

cat, named Copy Cat (**Figure 21.8**). She has a calico coat, like her single female parent, but the color and pattern are different due to random X chromosome inactivation, which is a normal occurrence during embryonic development (see Figure 15.10). Clearly, environmental influences and random phenomena can play a significant role during development.

▲ **Figure 21.8 Copy Cat, the first cloned cat.**

The successful cloning of various mammals has heightened speculation about the cloning of humans. In early 2004, South Korean researchers reported success in the first step of reproductive cloning of humans. In this work, nuclei from differentiated human cells were transplanted into unfertilized eggs from which the nuclei had been removed. These eggs were stimulated to divide, and some reached the blastocyst stage, an early embryonic stage similar to the blastula stage in Figure 21.4. Although the embryos were not allowed to develop beyond the blastocyst stage, the work of these researchers brings us one step closer to the possibility of human reproductive cloning, which raises unprecedented ethical issues. However, problems associated with the cloning process have bought us a little more time for thought.

Problems Associated with Animal Cloning. In most nuclear transplantation studies thus far, only a small percentage of cloned embryos develop normally to birth. And like Dolly, many cloned animals exhibit various defects. Cloned mice, for instance, are prone to obesity, pneumonia, liver failure, and premature death. Scientists believe that even cloned animals that appear normal are likely to have subtle defects.

In recent years, we have begun to learn possible reasons underlying the low efficiency of cloning and the high incidence of abnormalities. In the nuclei of fully differentiated cells, a small subset of genes is turned on and expression of the rest is repressed. This regulation often is the result of epigenetic changes in chromatin, such as acetylation of histones or methylation of DNA (see Figure 19.4). Many of these changes must be reversed in the nucleus from a donor animal in order for genes to be expressed or repressed appropriately for early stages of development. Researchers have found that the DNA in embryonic cells from cloned embryos, like that of differentiated cells, often has more methyl groups than does the DNA in equivalent cells from uncloned embryos of the same species. This finding suggests that the reprogramming of donor nuclei is not always complete. Because DNA methylation helps regulate gene expression, misplaced methyl groups in the DNA of donor nuclei may interfere with the pattern of gene expression necessary for normal embryonic development.

The Stem Cells of Animals

Further support for the idea that cells become different by expressing different sets of genes from the same genome comes from the study of a group of cells called stem cells. A **stem cell** is a relatively unspecialized cell that can both reproduce itself indefinitely and, under appropriate conditions, differentiate into specialized cells of one or more types. Thus, stem cells are able both to replenish their own population and to generate cells that travel down various differentiation pathways.

Many early animal embryos contain totipotent stem cells, which can give rise to differentiated cells of any type. Stem cells can be isolated from early embryos at the blastula stage or its human equivalent, the blastocyst stage **(Figure 21.9)**. In culture, these *embryonic stem cells* reproduce indefinitely; and depending on culture conditions, they can differentiate into various specialized cells, including even eggs and sperm.

The adult body also has a variety of stem cells, which serve to replace nonreproducing specialized cells as needed. In contrast to totipotent embryonic stem cells, adult stem cells are said to be **pluripotent**, able to give rise to multiple but not all cell types. For example, stem cells in the bone marrow give rise to all the different kinds of blood cells (see Figure 21.9), and those in the intestinal wall regenerate the various cells forming the lining of the intestine. To the surprise of many, we have recently discovered that the adult brain contains stem cells that continue to produce certain kinds of nerve cells there. Although adult animals have only tiny numbers of stem cells, scientists are learning to identify and isolate these cells from various tissues and, in some cases, to grow them in culture. Taking this research further, scientists have found that with the right culture conditions (for instance, the addition of specific growth factors), cultured stem cells from adult animals can differentiate into multiple types of specialized cells.

Research with embryonic or adult stem cells is providing valuable information about differentiation and has enormous potential for medical applications. The ultimate aim is to supply cells for the repair of damaged or diseased organs: for example, insulin-producing pancreatic cells for people with diabetes or certain kinds of brain cells for people with Parkinson's disease or Huntington's disease. Currently, embryonic stem cells are more promising than adult stem cells for such applications, but because the cells are derived from human embryos, their use raises ethical and political issues.

Embryonic stem cells are currently obtained from embryos donated by patients undergoing infertility treatment or from long-term cell cultures originally established with cells isolated from donated embryos. With the recent cloning of human embryos to the blastocyst stage, scientists might be able to use such clones as the source of embryonic stem cells in the future. When the major aim of cloning is to produce embryonic stem cells to treat disease, the process is called *therapeutic cloning*. Although most people believe that reproductive cloning of

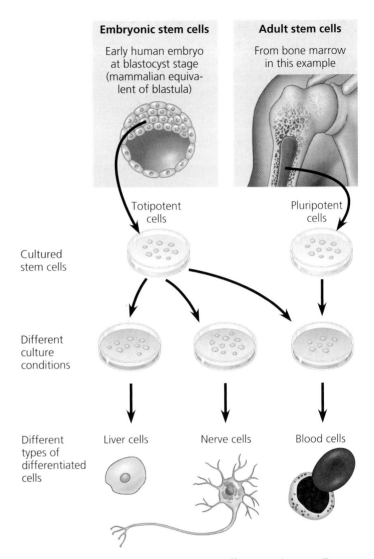

▲ **Figure 21.9 Working with stem cells.** Animal stem cells, which can be isolated from early embryos or adult tissues and grown in culture, are self-perpetuating, relatively undifferentiated cells. Embryonic stem cells are easier to grow than adult stem cells and can theoretically give rise to *all* types of cells. The range of cell types that can arise from adult stem cells is not yet fully understood.

humans is unethical, opinions vary about the morality of therapeutic cloning. Some believe that it is wrong to create embryos that will be destroyed, whereas others, in the words of the researcher who created Dolly, believe that "cloning promises such great benefits that it would be immoral not to do it."

The evidence we've discussed shows that nearly all the cells in a plant or animal contain the same set of genes. Next we look at the main processes that give rise to different cell types—that is, the molecular basis of cell differentiation.

Transcriptional Regulation of Gene Expression During Development

As the tissues and organs of an embryo take shape, the cells become visibly different in structure and function. These observable changes are actually the outcome of a cell's developmental history extending back to the first mitotic divisions of the zygote. However, the earliest changes that set a cell on a path to specialization are subtle ones, showing up only at the molecular level. Before biologists knew much about the molecular changes occurring in embryos, they coined the term **determination** to refer to the events that lead to the observable differentiation of a cell. At the end of this process, an embryonic cell is irreversibly committed to its final fate, and it is said to be determined. If a committed cell is experimentally placed in another location in the embryo, it will still differentiate into the cell type that is its normal fate.

Today we understand determination in terms of molecular changes. The outcome of determination—observable cell differentiation—is marked by the expression of genes for *tissue-specific proteins*. These proteins are found only in a specific cell type and give the cell its characteristic structure and function. The first evidence of differentiation is the appearance of mRNAs for these proteins. Eventually, differentiation is observable with a microscope as changes in cellular structure. In most cases, the pattern of gene expression in a differentiated cell is controlled at the level of transcription.

Differentiated cells are specialists at making tissue-specific proteins. For example, as the result of transcriptional regulation, liver cells specialize in making albumin, and lens cells specialize in making crystallins (see Figure 19.7). Indeed, lens cells devote 80% of their capacity for protein synthesis to making crystallin proteins, which enable the lens to transmit and focus light. Skeletal muscle cells are another instructive example. The "cells" of skeletal muscle are long fibers containing many nuclei within a single plasma membrane. They contain high concentrations of muscle-specific versions of the contractile proteins myosin and actin, as well as membrane receptor proteins that detect signals from nerve cells.

Muscle cells develop from embryonic precursor cells that have the potential to develop into a number of alternative cell types, including cartilage cells or fat cells, but particular conditions commit them to becoming muscle cells. Although the committed cells appear unchanged under the microscope, determination has occurred, and they are now *myoblasts*. Eventually, myoblasts start to churn out large amounts of muscle-specific proteins and fuse to form mature, elongated, multinucleate skeletal muscle cells (**Figure 21.10**, left).

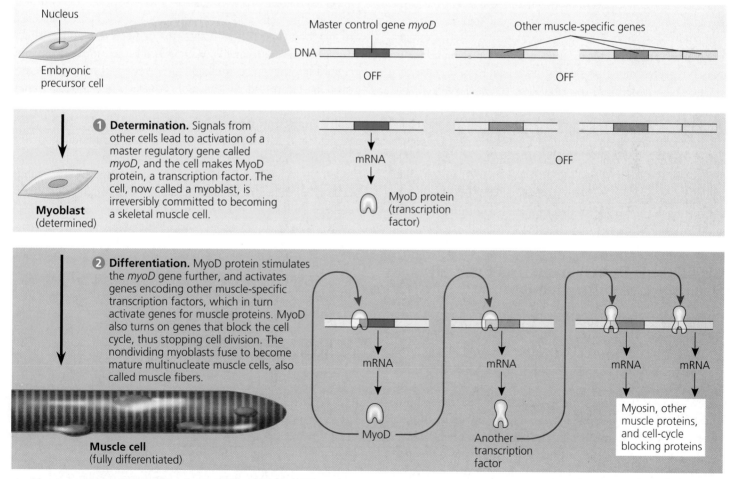

▲ **Figure 21.10 Determination and differentiation of muscle cells.** This figure depicts a simplified version of how skeletal muscle cells arise from embryonic cells. These precursor cells resemble fibroblasts (see the photo in Figure 12.15).

Researchers have worked out what happens at the molecular level during muscle cell determination by growing myoblasts in culture and applying some of the techniques you learned about in Chapter 20. They first produced a cDNA library containing all the genes that are expressed in cultured myoblasts. The researchers then inserted each of the cloned genes into a separate embryonic precursor cell and looked for differentiation into myoblasts and muscle cells. In this way, they identified several so-called "master regulatory genes" whose protein products commit the cells to becoming skeletal muscle. Thus, in the case of muscle cells, the molecular basis of determination is the expression of one or more of these master regulatory genes.

To understand more about how commitment occurs in muscle cell differentiation, let's focus on the master regulatory gene called *myoD* (see Figure 21.10, right). This gene encodes MyoD protein, a transcription factor that binds to specific control elements in the enhancers of various target genes and stimulates their expression (see Figure 19.6). Some target genes for MyoD encode still other muscle-specific transcription factors. MyoD also stimulates expression of the *myoD* gene itself, thus perpetuating its effect in maintaining the cell's differentiated state. Presumably, all the genes activated by MyoD have enhancers recognized by MyoD and are thus coordinately controlled. Finally, the secondary transcription factors activate the genes for proteins, such as myosin and actin, that confer the unique properties of skeletal muscle cells.

The MyoD protein is powerful. Researchers have been able to use it to change some kinds of fully differentiated nonmuscle cells, such as fat cells and liver cells, into muscle cells. Why doesn't it work on *all* kinds of cells? One likely explanation is that activation of the muscle-specific genes is not solely dependent on MyoD but requires a particular *combination* of regulatory proteins, some of which are lacking in cells that do not respond to MyoD. The determination and differentiation of other kinds of tissues may play out in a similar fashion.

Cytoplasmic Determinants and Cell-Cell Signals in Cell Differentiation

Explaining the role of *myoD* in muscle cell differentiation is a long way from explaining the development of an organism. The *myoD* story immediately raises the question of what triggers the expression of *that* gene and then raises a series of similar questions leading back to the zygote. What generates the *first* differences that arise among the cells in an early embryo? And what controls morphogenesis and the differentiation of all the different cell types as development proceeds? As we saw in the case of muscle cells, this question comes down to which genes are transcribed in the cells of a developing organism. Two sources of information, used to varying extents in different species, "tell" a cell which genes to express at any given time during embryonic development.

One important source of information early in development is the egg cell's cytoplasm, which contains both RNA and protein molecules encoded by the mother's DNA. The cytoplasm of an unfertilized egg cell is not homogeneous. Messenger RNA, proteins, other substances, and organelles are distributed unevenly in the unfertilized egg; and this heterogeneity has a profound impact on the development of the future embryo in many species. Maternal substances in the egg that influence the course of early development are called **cytoplasmic determinants.** After fertilization, early mitotic divisions distribute the zygote's cytoplasm into separate cells. The nuclei of many of these cells are thus exposed to different cytoplasmic determinants, depending on which portions of the zygotic cytoplasm a cell received **(Figure 21.11a)**. The set of cytoplasmic determinants a particular cell receives helps determine its developmental fate by regulating expression of the cell's genes during the course of cell differentiation.

The other important source of developmental information, which becomes increasingly important as the number of embryonic cells increases, is the environment around a particular cell. Most important are the signals impinging on an embryonic cell from other embryonic cells in the vicinity. In animals, these include contact with cell-surface molecules on neighboring cells and the binding of growth factors secreted by neighboring cells. In plants, the cell-cell junctions known as plasmodesmata can allow signal molecules to pass from one cell to another. The molecules conveying these signals are proteins expressed by the embryo's own genes. The signal molecules cause changes in nearby target cells, a process called **induction (Figure 21.11b)**. In general, the signal molecules send a cell down a specific developmental path by causing a change in its gene expression that results in observable cellular changes. Thus, interactions between embryonic cells eventually induce differentiation of the many specialized cell types making up a new organism.

You'll learn more about cytoplasmic determinants and induction in the next section, where we take a closer look at some important genetic and cellular mechanisms of development in three model organisms: *Drosophila, C. elegans,* and *Arabidopsis.*

Concept Check 21.2

1. Why can't a single embryonic stem cell develop into an embryo?
2. If you clone a carrot, will all the progeny plants ("clones") look identical? Why or why not?
3. The signal molecules released by an embryonic cell can induce changes in a neighboring cell without entering the cell. How?

For suggested answers, see Appendix A.

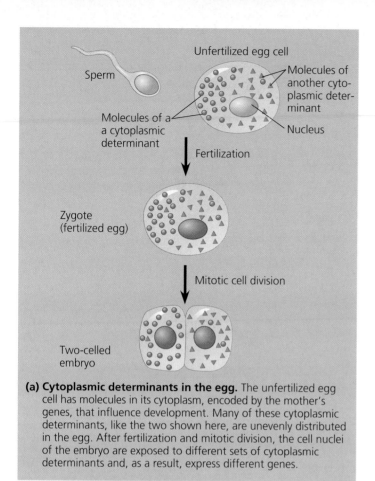

(a) Cytoplasmic determinants in the egg. The unfertilized egg cell has molecules in its cytoplasm, encoded by the mother's genes, that influence development. Many of these cytoplasmic determinants, like the two shown here, are unevenly distributed in the egg. After fertilization and mitotic division, the cell nuclei of the embryo are exposed to different sets of cytoplasmic determinants and, as a result, express different genes.

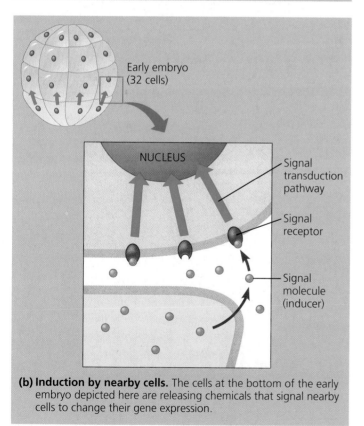

(b) Induction by nearby cells. The cells at the bottom of the early embryo depicted here are releasing chemicals that signal nearby cells to change their gene expression.

▲ **Figure 21.11 Sources of developmental information for the early embryo.**

Pattern formation in animals and plants results from similar genetic and cellular mechanisms

Before morphogenesis can shape an animal or plant, the organism's *body plan*—its overall three-dimensional arrangement—must be established. Cytoplasmic determinants and inductive signals contribute to this process, but what roles do they play? We'll explore this question in the context of **pattern formation**, the development of a spatial organization in which the tissues and organs of an organism are all in their characteristic places. In the life of a plant, pattern formation occurs continually in the apical meristems (see Figure 21.4b). In animals, pattern formation is mostly limited to embryos and juveniles, except in those species where lost parts can be regenerated.

Pattern formation in animals begins in the early embryo, when the major axes of an animal are established. Before construction begins on a new building, the location of the front, back, and sides are determined. In the same way, before specialized tissues or organs of an animal appear, the relative positions of the animal's head and tail, right and left sides, and back and front are set up, thus establishing the three major body axes. In plants, the root-shoot axis is determined at a similarly early stage of development. The molecular cues that control pattern formation, collectively called **positional information**, are provided by cytoplasmic determinants and inductive signals (see Figure 21.11). These cues tell a cell its location relative to the body axes and to neighboring cells and determine how the cell and its progeny will respond to future molecular signals.

Drosophila Development: A Cascade of Gene Activations

Pattern formation has been most extensively studied in *Drosophila melanogaster*, where genetic approaches have had spectacular success. These studies have established that genes control development and have led to an understanding of the key roles that specific molecules play in defining position and directing differentiation. Combining anatomical, genetic, and biochemical approaches to the study of *Drosophila* development, researchers have discovered developmental principles common to many other species, including humans.

The Life Cycle of *Drosophila*

Fruit flies and other arthropods have a modular construction, an ordered series of segments. These segments make up the body's three major parts: the head, the thorax (midbody, from which the wings and legs extend), and the abdomen. Like other bilaterally symmetrical animals, *Drosophila* has an anterior-posterior (head-to-tail) axis and a dorsal-ventral (back-to-belly) axis. In *Drosophila*, cytoplasmic determinants that are localized in the unfertilized egg provide positional information for the placement of these two axes even before fertilization. After fertilization, positional information operating on a finer and finer scale establishes a specific number of correctly oriented segments and finally triggers the formation of each segment's characteristic structures.

The *Drosophila* egg cell develops in the female's ovary, surrounded by ovarian cells called nurse cells and follicle cells (**Figure 21.12**, top). These supply the egg cell with nutrients, mRNAs, and other substances needed for development and make the egg shell. After fertilization and laying of the egg, the following events ensue (see key numbers in Figure 21.12):

1 The first ten mitotic divisions have two notable features. First, these early divisions, which occur very quickly, consist of S and M phases only, with no growth, so the amount of cytoplasm does not change. Second, cytokinesis does not occur. As a result, the early *Drosophila* embryo is one big multinucleate cell (in contrast to vertebrate embryos; see Figure 21.4).

2 At the tenth nuclear division, the nuclei begin to migrate to the periphery of the embryo, forming an early blastula-like stage called the blastoderm.

3 At division 13, plasma membranes finally partition the 6,000 or so nuclei into separate cells of the late blastoderm. Although not yet apparent under the microscope, the basic body plan—including body axes and segment boundaries—has already been determined by this time. A centrally placed yolk nourishes the embryo, and the egg shell continues to protect it.

4 Subsequent events in the embryo create clearly visible segments, which at first look very much alike.

5 Then, some cells move to new positions, organs form, and a wormlike larva (juvenile form) hatches out of the shell. *Drosophila* goes through three larval stages, during which the larva eats, grows, and molts (sheds its tough outer layer).

6 The third larval stage becomes enclosed in a case, forming a pupa.

7 Metamorphosis, the change from larva to adult fly, occurs inside the pupa, and the fly emerges.

▶ **Figure 21.12 Key developmental events in the life cycle of *Drosophila*.** The yellow egg cell (top) is surrounded by other cells, which form a structure called the follicle within one of the mother's ovaries. The nurse cells shrink and eventually disappear; the egg cell grows and matures, eventually filling the egg shell that is secreted by the follicle cells. The egg is fertilized within the mother and then laid. See text for description of steps 1–7, which generate the segmented adult fly, each segment bearing a characteristic appendage.

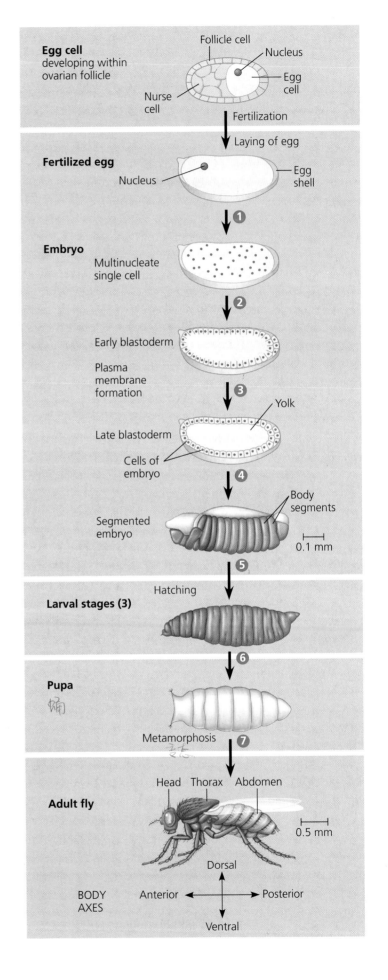

In the adult fly, each segment is anatomically distinct, with characteristic appendages (see Figure 21.12, bottom). For example, the first thoracic segment bears a pair of legs; the second thoracic segment has a pair of legs plus a pair of wings; and the third thoracic segment bears a pair of legs plus a pair of balancing organs called halteres.

Genetic Analysis of Early Development: Scientific Inquiry

During the first half of the 20th century, classical embryologists made detailed anatomical observations of embryonic development in a number of species and performed experiments in which they manipulated embryonic tissues. Although this research laid the groundwork for understanding the mechanisms of development, it did not reveal the specific molecules that guide development or determine how patterns are established. Then, in the 1940s, a visionary American biologist, Edward B. Lewis, showed that a genetic approach—the study of mutants—could be used to investigate *Drosophila* development.

Lewis studied bizarre mutant flies with developmental defects that led to extra wings or legs in the wrong places (**Figure 21.13**). He located the mutations on the fly's genetic map, thus connecting the developmental abnormalities to specific genes. This research supplied the first concrete evidence that genes somehow direct the developmental processes studied by embryologists. The genes Lewis discovered control pattern formation in the late embryo; we'll return to them shortly.

Insight into pattern formation during early development did not come for another 30 years or so, when two researchers in Germany, Christiane Nüsslein-Volhard and Eric Wieschaus, set out to identify *all* the genes that affect segment formation in *Drosophila*. The project was daunting for three reasons. The first was the sheer number of *Drosophila* genes, now known to total about 13,700. The genes affecting segmentation might be just a few needles in a haystack or might be so numerous and varied that the scientists would be unable to make sense of them. Second, mutations affecting a process as fundamental as segmentation would surely be **embryonic lethals**, mutations with phenotypes causing death at the embryonic or larval stage. Because organisms with embryonic lethal mutations never reproduce, they cannot be bred for study. Third, cytoplasmic determinants in the egg were known to play a role in axis formation, and thus the researchers knew they would have to study the mother's genes as well as those of the embryo.

To get around the problem of embryonic lethality, Nüsslein-Volhard and Wieschaus looked for recessive mutations, which can be propagated in heterozygous flies. Their basic strategy was to expose flies to a mutagenic chemical to create mutations in the flies' gametes and then look among the flies' descendants for dead embryos (or larvae) with abnormal segmentation. By doing the appropriate crosses, they would be able to identify living heterozygotes carrying an embryonic lethal mutant allele and a normal allele of the same gene. The researchers hoped that the abnormalities visible in the dead homozygous embryos would suggest how the affected genes normally functioned.

Nüsslein-Volhard and Wieschaus eventually identified about 1,200 genes essential for embryonic development. Of these, about 120 were essential for pattern formation leading to normal segmentation. Over several years, the researchers were able to group these segmentation genes by general function, to map them, and to clone many of them. The result was a detailed molecular understanding of the early steps in pattern formation in *Drosophila*.

When the results of Nüsslein-Volhard and Wieschaus were combined with Lewis's earlier work, a coherent picture of *Drosophila* development emerged. In recognition of their discoveries, the three researchers were awarded a Nobel Prize in 1995. Before we discuss how the segmentation genes function, we need to back up and look at the cytoplasmic determinants deposited in the egg by the mother, for these control the expression of the segmentation genes.

Axis Establishment

As previously mentioned, cytoplasmic determinants in the egg are the substances that initially establish the axes of the *Drosophila* body. These substances are encoded by genes of the

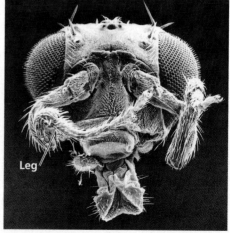

Wild type   Mutant

▲ **Figure 21.13 Abnormal pattern formation in *Drosophila*.** Mutations in certain genes, called homeotic mutations, cause a misplacement of structures in an animal. These micrographs contrast the head of a wild-type fly, bearing a pair of small antennae, with that of a homeotic mutant, bearing a pair of legs in place of antennae (SEMs).

mother, fittingly called maternal effect genes. A **maternal effect gene** is a gene that, when mutant in the mother, results in a mutant phenotype in the offspring, regardless of their own genotype. In fruit fly development, the mRNA or protein products of maternal effect genes are placed in the egg while it is still in the mother's ovary. When the mother has a mutation in such a gene, she makes a defective gene product (or none at all), and her eggs are defective; when these eggs are fertilized, they fail to develop properly.

Because they control the orientation (polarity) of the egg and consequently of the fly, maternal effect genes are also called **egg-polarity genes.** One group of these genes sets up the anterior-posterior axis of the embryo, while a second group establishes the dorsal-ventral axis. Like mutations in segmentation genes, mutations in maternal effect genes are generally embryonic lethals.

To see how maternal effect genes determine the body axes of the offspring, we focus on one such gene called *bicoid,* a term meaning "two-tailed." An embryo whose mother has a mutant *bicoid* gene lacks the front half of its body and has posterior structures at both ends **(Figure 21.14a)**. This phenotype suggested to researchers that the product of the mother's *bicoid* gene is essential for setting up the anterior end of the fly and might be concentrated at the future anterior end. This hypothesis is a specific example of the gradient hypothesis first proposed by embryologists a century ago. According to this idea, gradients of substances called **morphogens** establish an embryo's axes and other features of its form.

DNA technology and other modern biochemical methods enabled researchers to test whether the *bicoid* product is in fact a morphogen that determines the anterior end of the fly. The researchers cloned the *bicoid* gene and used a nucleic acid probe derived from the gene to reveal the location of *bicoid* mRNA in the eggs produced by wild-type female flies. As predicted by the hypothesis, the *bicoid* mRNA is highly concentrated at the extreme anterior end of the mature egg cell **(Figure 21.14b)**. After the egg is fertilized, the mRNA is translated into protein. The Bicoid protein then diffuses from the anterior end toward the posterior, resulting in a gradient of protein within the early embryo, with the highest concentration at the anterior end. These results are consistent with the hypothesis that Bicoid protein is responsible for specifying the fly's anterior end. To test the hypothesis more specifically, scientists injected pure *bicoid* mRNA into various regions of early embryos. The protein that resulted from its translation caused anterior structures to form at the injection sites.

The *bicoid* research is important for several reasons. First, it led to the identification of a specific protein required for some of the earliest steps in pattern formation. Second, it increased our understanding of the mother's critical role in the initial phases of embryonic development. (As one developmental biologist has put it, "Mom tells Junior which way is up.") Finally, the principle that a gradient of molecules can determine

(a) *Drosophila* **larvae with wild-type and** *bicoid* **mutant phenotypes.** A mutation in the mother's *bicoid* gene leads to tail structures at both ends (bottom larva). The numbers refer to the thoracic and abdominal segments that are present.

(b) Gradients of *bicoid* **mRNA and Bicoid protein in normal egg and early embryo.** ❶ Transcribed from the maternal *bicoid* gene in nurse cells, *bicoid* mRNA reaches the egg cell via cytoplasmic bridges. It becomes anchored to the cytoskeleton at the anterior end of the egg as the egg grows and the nurse cells disappear. ❷ Labeled *bicoid* DNA (dark blue) was used as a probe to locate *bicoid* mRNA at the anterior end of the egg. ❸ After fertilization, the mRNA is translated. In this early embryo, the gradient of color (brown) reveals a gradient of Bicoid protein. Bicoid protein is only one of several morphogens involved in axis specification.

▲ **Figure 21.14 The effect of the** *bicoid* **gene, a maternal effect (egg-polarity) gene in** *Drosophila.*

polarity and position has proved to be a key developmental concept for a number of species, just as early embryologists had thought. In *Drosophila*, gradients of specific proteins determine the posterior end as well as the anterior and also are responsible for establishing the dorsal-ventral axis.

Segmentation Pattern

The Bicoid protein and other proteins encoded by egg-polarity genes regulate the expression of some of the embryo's own genes. Gradients of these proteins bring about regional differences in the expression of **segmentation genes,** the genes of the embryo whose products direct formation of segments after the embryo's major body axes are defined.

In a cascade of gene activations, sequential activation of three sets of segmentation genes provides the positional information for increasingly fine details of the animal's modular body plan. The three sets are called the *gap genes,* the *pair-rule genes,* and the *segment polarity genes.*

The products of many segmentation genes, like those of egg-polarity genes, are transcription factors that directly activate the next set of genes in the hierarchical scheme of pattern formation. Other segmentation genes operate more indirectly, supporting the functioning of the transcription factors in various ways. For example, some are components of cell-signaling pathways, including signal molecules used in cell-cell communication and the membrane receptors that recognize them (see Chapter 11). Cell-signaling molecules are critically important once plasma membranes have divided the embryo into separate cellular compartments.

Working together, the products of egg-polarity genes like *bicoid* regulate the regional expression of gap genes, which control the localized expression of pair-rule genes, which in turn activate specific segment polarity genes in different parts of each segment. The boundaries and axes of the segments are now set. In the hierarchy of gene activations responsible for pattern formation, the next genes to be expressed determine the specific anatomy of each segment along the length of the embryo.

Identity of Body Parts

In a normal fly, structures such as antennae, legs, and wings develop on the appropriate segments. The anatomical identity of the segments is set by master regulatory genes called **homeotic genes.** These are the genes discovered by Edward Lewis. Once the segmentation genes have staked out the fly's segments, homeotic genes specify the types of appendages and other structures that each segment will form. Mutations in homeotic genes can cause an entire structure characteristic of a particular segment of the animal to arise in the wrong segment, as Lewis observed in flies (see Figure 21.13).

Like many of the egg-polarity and segmentation genes, the homeotic genes encode specific transcription factors. These regulatory proteins are gene activators or repressors, control-

ling expression of genes responsible for particular anatomical structures. For example, a homeotic protein made in the cells of a particular head segment specifies antenna development. In contrast, a homeotic protein active in a certain thoracic segment selectively activates genes that bring about leg development. A mutant version of the gene encoding the thoracic homeotic protein causes the protein to be expressed also in the head segment. There it overrides the normal antennal gene-activating protein, labeling the segment as "thoracic" instead of "head" and causing legs to develop in place of antennae.

Scientists are now busy identifying the genes activated by the homeotic proteins—the genes specifying the proteins that actually build the fly structures. The following flowchart summarizes the cascade of gene activity in the *Drosophila* embryo:

Hierarchy of Gene Activity in Early *Drosophila* Development

Maternal effect genes (egg-polarity genes)

↓

Gap genes

↓

Pair-rule genes

↓

Segment polarity genes

} Segmentation genes of the embryo

↓

Homeotic genes of the embryo

↓

Other genes of the embryo

Although this simplified summary suggests a strictly sequential series of gene actions, the reality is more complicated. For instance, the genes in each set not only activate the next set of genes but also maintain their own expression in most cases.

Amazingly, many of the molecules and mechanisms revealed by research on fly pattern formation have turned out to have close counterparts throughout the animal kingdom. The homeotic genes and their products exhibit these similarities in a most striking way. We will return to this point later in the chapter when we consider the evolution of development.

C. elegans: The Role of Cell Signaling

The development of a multicellular organism requires close communication between cells. Indeed, even before fertilization in *Drosophila*, molecules made in neighboring nurse cells cause localization of *bicoid* mRNA at one end of the egg, thus helping to establish the anterior end of the future embryo. Once the embryo is truly multicellular, with membranes enclosing each individual nucleus and accompanying cytoplasm, inductive signaling among the embryo's own cells becomes increasingly important. As we've seen, the ultimate basis for the differences between cells is transcriptional regulation—the turning on and off of specific genes. It is induction, signaling from one group of cells to an adjacent group, that brings about differentiation. In some cases, cell signaling also leads to the programmed death of specific cells, a phenomenon that is also crucial to normal embryonic development.

The nematode *C. elegans* has proved to be a very useful model organism for investigating the roles of cell signaling, induction, and programmed cell death in development (see Figure 21.2). Researchers know the entire ancestry of every cell in the body of an adult *C. elegans*, the organism's complete **cell lineage.** This information can be represented in a cell lineage diagram, somewhat like a pedigree, that shows the fates of all the cells in the developing embryo **(Figure 21.15).**

Because the lineage of each *C. elegans* cell is so reproducible, scientists at first thought that it must be determined from the start, suggesting that cytoplasmic determinants are the most important means of establishing cell fate in nematodes. However, although cytoplasmic determinants do play a key role very early in *C. elegans* development, a combination of genetic, biochemical, and embryological approaches have revealed important contributions of inductive events as well.

Induction

As early as the four-cell stage in *C. elegans*, cell signaling helps direct daughter cells down the appropriate pathways. For instance, as shown in **Figure 21.16a**, a signal from cell 4 acts on cell 3 so that one of the daughter cells of cell 3 eventually gives rise to the intestine. The signal is a cell-surface protein, made by cell 4, that can be recognized and bound by a cell-surface receptor protein on cell 3. This interaction triggers events inside cell 3 that result in one end of the cell (the posterior end) becoming different from the other. When cell 3 divides, the posterior daughter cell will go on to make the intestine, whereas the anterior daughter cell has a different fate. If cell 4 is experimentally removed early in the four-cell stage, no intestine forms, but if an isolated cell 3 and cell 4 are recombined, the intestine develops as normal. These results helped researchers recognize the role of induction in early nematode development.

Induction is also critical later in nematode development as the embryo passes through three larval stages prior to becoming an adult. The vulva, the tiny opening through which a worm lays its eggs, arises from six cells that are present on the ventral surface at the second larval stage **(Figure 21.16b).** A single cell of the embryonic gonad, the *anchor cell*, initiates a cascade of inductive signals that establishes the fates of the six

▶ **Figure 21.15 Cell lineage in *C. elegans*.** The *Caenorhabditis elegans* embryo is transparent, making it possible for researchers to trace the lineage of every cell, from the zygote to the adult worm (LM). The diagram shows a detailed lineage only for the intestine (gold), which is derived exclusively from one of the first four cells formed from the zygote. The intestinal cell lineage does not happen to include any programmed cell death, an important aspect of the lineages for some other parts of the animal. The large white cells are eggs, which will be fertilized internally and released through the vulva.

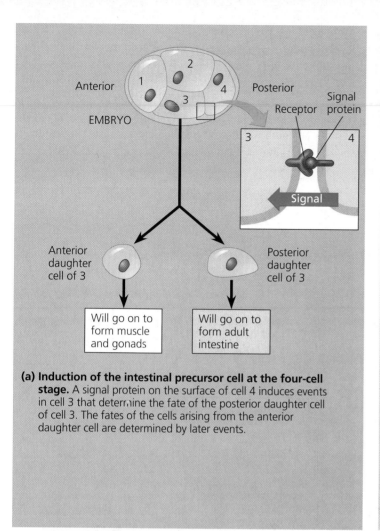

(a) Induction of the intestinal precursor cell at the four-cell stage. A signal protein on the surface of cell 4 induces events in cell 3 that determine the fate of the posterior daughter cell of cell 3. The fates of the cells arising from the anterior daughter cell are determined by later events.

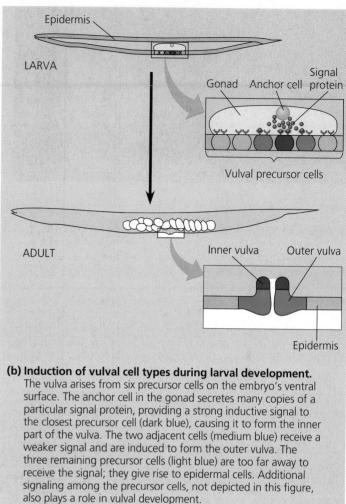

(b) Induction of vulval cell types during larval development. The vulva arises from six precursor cells on the embryo's ventral surface. The anchor cell in the gonad secretes many copies of a particular signal protein, providing a strong inductive signal to the closest precursor cell (dark blue), causing it to form the inner part of the vulva. The two adjacent cells (medium blue) receive a weaker signal and are induced to form the outer vulva. The three remaining precursor cells (light blue) are too far away to receive the signal; they give rise to epidermal cells. Additional signaling among the precursor cells, not depicted in this figure, also plays a role in vulval development.

▲ **Figure 21.16 Cell signaling and induction during development of the nematode.** In both examples, a protein on the surface of or secreted from one cell signals one or more nearby target cells, inducing differentiation of the target cells.

vulval precursor cells. If an experimenter destroys the anchor cell with a laser beam, the vulva fails to form, and the precursor cells simply become part of the worm's epidermis.

The signaling mechanisms in both of these examples are similar to those discussed in Chapter 11. Secreted growth factors or cell-surface proteins bind to a receptor on the recipient cell, initiating intracellular signal transduction pathways. Transcriptional regulation and differential gene expression in the induced cell are the usual results.

These two examples of induction during nematode development illustrate a number of important concepts that apply elsewhere in the development of *C. elegans* and many other animals:

▶ In the developing embryo, sequential inductions drive the formation of organs.
▶ The effect of an inducer can depend on its concentration (just as we saw with cytoplasmic determinants in *Drosophila*).
▶ Inducers produce their effects via signal transduction pathways similar to those operating in adult cells.

▶ The induced cell's response is often the activation (or inactivation) of genes—transcriptional regulation—which in turn establishes the pattern of gene activity characteristic of a particular kind of differentiated cell.

Programmed Cell Death (Apoptosis)

Lineage analysis of *C. elegans* has underscored another outcome of cell signaling that is crucial in animal development: programmed cell death, or **apoptosis.** The timely suicide of cells occurs exactly 131 times in the course of normal development in *C. elegans*, at precisely the same points in the cell lineage of each worm. In worms and other species, apoptosis is triggered by signals that activate a cascade of "suicide" proteins in the cells destined to die. During apoptosis, a cell shrinks and becomes lobed (called "blebbing"), the nucleus condenses, and the DNA is fragmented (**Figure 21.17**, p. 428). Neighboring cells quickly engulf and digest the membrane-bound remains, leaving no trace.

Genetic screening of *C. elegans* has revealed two key apoptosis genes, *ced-3* and *ced-4* (*ced* stands for "cell death"), which

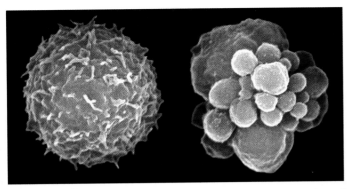

▲ Figure 21.17 Apoptosis of human white blood cells.
A normal white blood cell (left) is compared with a white blood cell undergoing apoptosis (right). The apoptotic cell is shrinking and forming lobes ("blebs"), which eventually are shed as membrane-bound cell fragments.

encode proteins essential for apoptosis. The proteins are called Ced-3 and Ced-4, respectively. These and most other proteins involved in apoptosis are continually present in cells, but in inactive form; thus, protein *activity* is regulated in this case, not transcription or translation. In *C. elegans*, a protein in the outer mitochondrial membrane, called Ced-9 (the product of gene *ced-9*), serves as a master regulator of apoptosis, acting as a brake in the absence of a signal promoting apoptosis **(Figure 21.18)**. When a death signal is received by the cell, the apoptosis pathway activates proteases and nucleases, enzymes that cut up the proteins and DNA of the cell. The main proteases of apoptosis are called *caspases*; in the nematode, the chief caspase is Ced-3.

In humans and other mammals, several different pathways, involving about 15 different caspases, can lead to apoptosis. The pathway that is used depends on the type of cell and on the particular signal that triggers apoptosis. One important pathway involves mitochondrial proteins. Apoptosis pathway proteins or other signals somehow cause the mitochondrial outer membrane to leak, releasing proteins that promote apoptosis. Surprisingly, these include cytochrome *c*, which functions in mitochondrial electron transport in healthy cells (see Figure 9.15), but acts as a cell death factor when released from mitochondria. The mitochondrial apoptosis of mammals uses proteins homologous to the worm proteins Ced-3, Ced-4, and Ced-9. Mammalian cells make life-or-death "decisions" by somehow integrating the signals they receive, both "death" signals and "life" signals such as growth factors.

A built-in cell suicide mechanism is essential to development in all animals. The similarities between apoptosis genes in nematodes and mammals, as well as the observation that apoptosis occurs in multicellular fungi and single-cell yeasts, indicate that the basic mechanism evolved early in animal evolution. In vertebrates, apoptosis is essential for normal development of the nervous system, for normal operation of the immune system, and for normal morphogenesis of hands and feet in humans and paws in other mammals **(Figure 21.19)**. A lower level of apoptosis in developing limbs accounts for the webbed feet of ducks and other water birds, in contrast to chickens and other land birds with nonwebbed feet. In the case of humans, the failure of appropriate apoptosis can result in webbed fingers and toes. Also, researchers are investigating the possibility that certain degenerative diseases of the nervous system result from the inappropriate activation of apoptosis genes and that some

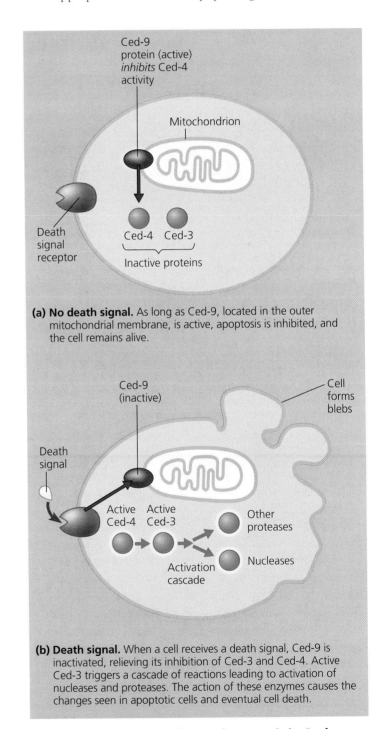

(a) No death signal. As long as Ced-9, located in the outer mitochondrial membrane, is active, apoptosis is inhibited, and the cell remains alive.

(b) Death signal. When a cell receives a death signal, Ced-9 is inactivated, relieving its inhibition of Ced-3 and Ced-4. Active Ced-3 triggers a cascade of reactions leading to activation of nucleases and proteases. The action of these enzymes causes the changes seen in apoptotic cells and eventual cell death.

▲ Figure 21.18 Molecular basis of apoptosis in *C. elegans*.
Three proteins, Ced-3, Ced-4, and Ced-9, are critical to apoptosis and its regulation in the nematode. Apoptosis is more complicated in mammals but involves proteins similar to those in the nematode.

Interdigital tissue

▲ **Figure 21.19 Effect of apoptosis during paw development in the mouse.** In mice, humans, and other mammals, as well as land birds, the embryonic region that develops into feet or hands initially has a solid, platelike structure. Apoptosis eliminates the cells in the interdigital regions, thus forming the digits. The embryonic mouse paws shown here are stained so that cells undergoing apoptosis appear bright green. Apoptosis of cells begins at the margin of each interdigital region (left), peaks as the tissue in these regions is reduced (middle), and is no longer visible when the interdigital tissue has been eliminated.

1 mm

cancers result from a failure of cell suicide. Cells that have suffered irreparable damage, including DNA damage that could lead to cancer, normally generate *internal* signals that trigger apoptosis.

Studies on the roles of induction and apoptosis during development of *C. elegans* were begun less than 30 years ago by Sydney Brenner, John E. Sulston, and H. Robert Horvitz. The importance of their studies was highlighted in 2003, when the Nobel Prize for Medicine was awarded to these researchers for significantly advancing our understanding of how genes regulate organ growth (such as the nematode vulva) and the process of programmed cell death.

Plant Development: Cell Signaling and Transcriptional Regulation

The genetic analysis of plant development, using model organisms such as *Arabidopsis* (see Figure 21.2), has lagged behind that of animal models simply because there are fewer researchers working on plants. For example, in 2000, when the *Arabidopsis* DNA sequence was completed, fewer than 5% of its genes had been defined by mutational analysis, whereas over 25% of the genes in both *Drosophila* and *C. elegans* had been identified in that way. We are just beginning to understand the molecular basis of plant development in detail. Thanks to DNA technology and clues from animal research, plant research is now progressing rapidly.

Mechanisms of Plant Development

In general, cell lineage is much less important for pattern formation in plants than in animals. As mentioned previously, many plant cells are totipotent, and their fates depend more on positional information than on cell lineage. Therefore, the major mechanisms regulating development are cell-signaling (induction) and transcriptional regulation.

The embryonic development of most plants occurs inside the seed and thus is relatively inaccessible to study (a mature seed already contains a fully formed embryo). However, other important aspects of plant development are observable throughout a plant's life in its meristems, particularly the apical meristems at the tips of shoots. It is there that cell division, morphogenesis, and differentiation give rise to new organs, such as leaves or the petals of flowers. We'll discuss two aspects of pattern formation in floral meristems, the apical meristems that produce flowers.

Pattern Formation in Flowers

Environmental signals, such as day length and temperature, trigger signal transduction pathways that convert ordinary shoot meristems to floral meristems, causing a plant to flower. Researchers have combined a genetic approach with tissue transplantation to study induction in the development of tomato flowers. As shown in **Figure 21.20**, a floral meristem is a bump consisting of three layers of cells (L1–L3). All three layers participate in the formation of a flower, a reproductive

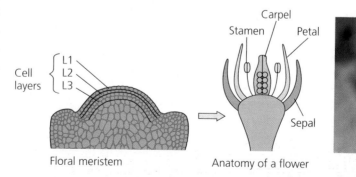

Cell layers { L1 L2 L3

Floral meristem

Carpel
Stamen   Petal

Sepal

Anatomy of a flower

Tomato flower

▲ **Figure 21.20 Flower development.** A flower develops from three cell layers (L1–L3) in a floral meristem. A specific pattern of cell division, differentiation, and enlargement produces a flower. The four types of organs (carpels, stamens, petals, and sepals) that make up a flower are arranged in concentric circles (whorls). Each species has a characteristic number of organs in each whorl. The tomato has six sepals, six petals, six stamens, and four carpels.

structure with four types of organs: *carpels* (containing egg cells), *stamens* (containing sperm-bearing pollen), *petals,* and *sepals* (leaflike structures outside the petals). In a mature plant, the four types of organs are arranged radially, rather than linearly like the body structures in *Drosophila.*

Tomato plants homozygous for a mutant allele called *fasciated (f)* produce flowers with an abnormally large number of organs. To study what controls the number of organs, researchers performed the grafting experiment outlined in **Figure 21.21**. They grafted stems from fasciated plants onto those of wild-type plants (*FF,* homozygous for normal allele) and then grew new plants from the shoots that sprouted near the graft sites. Many of the new plants were **chimeras,** organisms with a mixture of genetically different cells. Some chimeras produced floral meristems in which the three cell layers did not all come from the same "parent." The researchers identified the parental sources of the meristem layers by monitoring other genetic markers, such as an unrelated mutation causing yellow leaves. The results showed that whether the number of floral organs was normal or abnormally high depended on whether the L3 layer arose from wild-type or mutant cells. Thus, the L3 cell layer induces the overlying L2 and L1 layers to form a particular number of organs. The mechanism of cell-cell signaling leading to this induction is not yet known, but is currently under study.

In contrast to genes controlling organ number in flowers are genes controlling organ identity. An **organ identity gene** determines the type of structure that will grow from a meristem—for instance, whether a particular outgrowth from a floral meristem becomes a petal or a stamen. Most of what we know about such organ identity genes comes from research on flower development in *Arabidopsis.*

Organ identity genes are analogous to homeotic genes in animals and are often referred to as plant homeotic genes. Just as a mutation in a fruit fly homeotic gene can cause legs to grow in place of antennae, a mutation in an organ identity gene can cause carpels to grow in place of sepals. By collecting and studying mutants with abnormal flowers, researchers have been able to identify and clone a number of floral organ identity genes. In plants with a "homeotic" mutation, specific organs are missing or repeated **(Figure 21.22)**. Some of these mutant phenotypes are reminiscent of those caused by *bicoid* or other pattern formation mutations in *Drosophila.* Like the homeotic genes of animals, the organ identity genes of plants encode transcription factors that regulate specific target genes by binding to their enhancers in the DNA. In Chapter 35, you will learn about a current model of how these genes control organ development.

Clearly, the developmental mechanisms used by plants are similar to those used by the two animal species we discussed earlier. In the next section, we will see what can be learned from comparing developmental strategies and molecular mechanisms across all multicellular organisms.

Figure 21.21

Inquiry **Which cell layers in the floral meristem determine the number of floral organs?**

EXPERIMENT Tomato plants with the *fasciated (ff)* mutation develop extra floral organs.

Researchers grafted stems from mutant plants onto wild-type plants. They then planted the shoots that emerged near the graft site, many of which were chimeras.

For each chimera, researchers recorded the flower phenotype: wild-type or fasciated. Analysis using other genetic markers identified the parental source for each of the three cell layers of the floral meristem (L1–L3) in the chimeras.

RESULTS The flowers of the chimeric plants had the fasciated phenotype only when the L3 layer came from the fasciated parent.

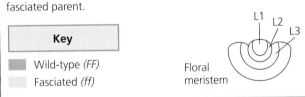

Plant	Flower	Phenotype	Floral Meristem
Wild-type parent		Wild-type	
Fasciated (ff) parent		Fasciated	
Chimera 1		Fasciated	
Chimera 2		Fasciated	
Chimera 3		Wild-type	

CONCLUSION Cells in the L3 layer induce the L1 and L2 layers to form flowers with a particular number of organs. (The nature of the inductive signal from L3 is not entirely understood.)

Wild type   Mutant

▲ **Figure 21.22 Mutations in floral organ identity genes.**
Wild-type *Arabidopsis* has four sepals, four petals, six stamens, and
two carpels. If an organ identity gene called *apetala2* is mutated, the
identities of the organs in the four whorls are carpels, stamens,
stamens, and carpels (there are no petals or sepals).

Concept Check 21.3

1. Why are fruit fly maternal effect genes also called
   egg-polarity genes?
2. If a researcher removes the anchor cell from a
   C. elegans embryo, the vulva does not form, even
   though all the cells that would have made the vulva
   are present. Explain why.
3. Explain why cutting and rooting a shoot from a
   plant, then planting it successfully, provides evidence that plant cells are totipotent.

For suggested answers, see Appendix A.

Concept 21.4

Comparative studies help explain how the evolution of development leads to morphological diversity

Biologists in the field of evolutionary developmental biology,
or "evo-devo" as it is often called, compare developmental
processes of different multicellular organisms. Their aim is to
understand how developmental processes have evolved and
how changes in these processes can modify existing organismal features or lead to new ones. With the advent of molecular
techniques and the recent flood of genomic information, we
are beginning to realize that the genomes of related species
with strikingly different forms may have only minor differences in gene sequence or regulation. Discovering the molecular basis underlying these differences, in turn, helps us
understand how the myriad of diverse forms that cohabit this
planet have arisen, thus informing the study of evolution.

Widespread Conservation of Developmental Genes Among Animals

Molecular analysis of the homeotic genes in *Drosophila* has
shown that they all include a 180-nucleotide sequence called
a **homeobox**, which specifies a 60-amino-acid *homeodomain*
in the protein. An identical or very similar nucleotide sequence
has been discovered in the homeotic genes of many invertebrates and vertebrates. In fact, the vertebrate genes homologous to the homeotic genes of fruit flies have even kept their
chromosomal arrangement **(Figure 21.23)**. (Homeotic genes in

Adult
fruit fly

Fruit fly embryo
(10 hours)

Fly
chromosome

Mouse
chromosomes

Mouse embryo
(12 days)

Adult mouse

▲ **Figure 21.23 Conservation of homeotic genes in a fruit
fly and a mouse.** Homeotic genes that control the form of anterior
and posterior structures of the body occur in the same linear sequence
on chromosomes in *Drosophila* and mice. Each colored band on the
chromosomes shown here represents a homeotic gene. In fruit flies, all
homeotic genes are found on one chromosome. The mouse and other
mammals have the same or similar sets of genes on four chromosomes.
The color code indicates the parts of the embryos in which these genes
are expressed and the adult body regions that result. All of these genes
are essentially identical in flies and mice, except for those represented
by black bands, which are less similar in the two animals.

animals are often called *Hox* genes.) Furthermore, related sequences have been found in regulatory genes of much more distantly related eukaryotes, including plants and yeasts, and even in prokaryotes. From these similarities, we can deduce that the homeobox DNA sequence evolved very early in the history of life and was sufficiently valuable to organisms to have been conserved in animals and plants virtually unchanged for hundreds of millions of years.

Not all homeobox-containing genes are homeotic genes; that is, some do not directly control the identity of body parts. However, most of these genes, in animals at least, are associated with development, suggesting their ancient and fundamental importance in that process. In *Drosophila*, for example, homeoboxes are present not only in the homeotic genes but also in the egg-polarity gene *bicoid*, in several of the segmentation genes, and in the master regulatory gene for eye development.

Researchers have found that the homeobox-encoded homeodomain is the part of a protein that binds to DNA when the protein functions as a transcriptional regulator. However, the shape of the homeodomain allows it to bind to any DNA segment; by itself it cannot select a specific sequence. Rather, more variable domains in a homeodomain-containing protein determine which genes the protein regulates. Interaction of these latter domains with still other transcription factors helps a homeodomain-containing protein recognize specific enhancers in the DNA. Proteins with homeodomains probably regulate development by coordinating the transcription of batteries of developmental genes, switching them on or off. In embryos of *Drosophila* and other animal species, different combinations of homeobox genes are active in different parts of the embryo. This selective expression of regulatory genes, varying over time and space, is central to pattern formation.

Developmental biologists have found that in addition to homeotic genes, many other genes involved in development are highly conserved from species to species. These include numerous genes encoding components of signaling pathways. The extraordinary similarity among particular developmental genes in different animal species raises the question, How can the same genes be involved in the development of animals whose forms are so very different from each other?

Current studies are suggesting likely answers to this question. In some cases, small changes in regulatory sequences of particular genes can lead to major changes in body form. For example, the differing patterns of expression of the *Hox* genes along the body axis in insects and crustaceans can explain the different number of leg-bearing segments among these segmented animals **(Figure 21.24)**. In other cases, similar genes direct different developmental processes in different organisms, resulting in different body shapes. Several *Hox* genes, for instance, are expressed in the embryonic and larval stages of the sea urchin, nonsegmented animals that have a body plan quite different from insects and mice. Sea urchin adults make the pincushion-shaped shells you may have seen on the beach. They are among the organisms long used in classical embryological studies (see Chapter 47).

Sequencing of the *Arabidopsis* genome has revealed that plants do have some homeobox-containing genes. However, these apparently do not function as master regulatory switches as do the homeobox-containing homeotic genes in animals. Other genes appear to carry out basic processes of pattern formation in plants.

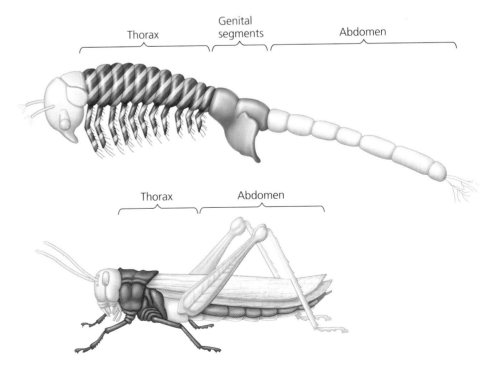

▶ **Figure 21.24 Effect of differences in *Hox* gene expression during development in crustaceans and insects.** Changes in the expression patterns of four *Hox* genes have occurred over evolutionary time. These changes account in part for the different body plans of the brine shrimp *Artemia*, a crustacean (top), and the grasshopper, an insect. Shown here are regions of the adult body color-coded for expression of the *Hox* genes that determine formation of particular body parts during embryonic development.

Comparison of Animal and Plant Development

The last common ancestor of plants and animals was probably a single-celled microbe living hundreds of millions of years ago, so the processes of development must have evolved independently in the two lineages of organisms. Plants evolved with rigid cell walls that make the movement of cells and tissue layers virtually impossible, ruling out the morphogenetic movements of cells and tissues that are important in animals. Instead, morphogenesis in plants relies more heavily on differing planes of cell division and on selective cell enlargement. (You will learn about these processes in Chapter 35.) But despite the differences between plants and animals, there are some basic similarities in the actual mechanisms of development—legacies of their shared cellular origins.

In both plants and animals, development relies on a cascade of transcriptional regulators turning on or turning off genes in a finely tuned series—for example, setting up the head-to-tail axis in *Drosophila* and establishing the organ identities in a radial pattern in the *Arabidopsis* flower. But the genes that direct these processes differ considerably in plants and animals. While quite a few of the master regulatory switches in *Drosophila* are homeobox-containing *Hox* genes, those in *Arabidopsis* belong to a completely different family of genes, called the *Mads-box* genes. And although homeobox-containing genes can be found in plants and *Mads-box* genes in animals, in neither case do they perform the same major roles in development that they do in the other group.

In this final chapter of the genetics unit, you have learned how genetic studies can reveal much about the molecular and cellular mechanisms underlying development. The unity of life is reflected in the similarity of biological mechanisms used to establish body pattern, although the genes directing development may differ among organisms. The similarities reflect the common ancestry of life on Earth. But the differences are also crucial, for they have created the huge diversity of organisms that have evolved. In the remainder of the book, we expand our perspective beyond the level of molecules, cells, and genes to explore this diversity on the organismal level.

Concept Check 21.4

1. The DNA sequences called homeoboxes, which help homeotic genes in animals direct development, are common to flies and mice. Given this similarity, explain why these animals are so different.

For suggested answers, see Appendix A.

Chapter 21 Review

Go to the Campbell Biology website (**www.campbellbiology.com**) or CD-ROM to explore Activities, Investigations, and other interactive study aids.

SUMMARY OF KEY CONCEPTS

Concept 21.1

Embryonic development involves cell division, cell differentiation, and morphogenesis

▶ In addition to mitosis, embryonic cells undergo differentiation, becoming specialized in structure and function. Morphogenesis encompasses the processes that give shape to the organism and its various parts. Several model organisms are commonly used to study different aspects of the genetic basis of development (pp. 412–415).

Concept 21.2

Different cell types result from differential gene expression in cells with the same DNA

▶ **Evidence for Genomic Equivalence** (pp. 415–418) Cells differ in structure and function not because they contain different genes but because they express different portions of a common genome; they have genomic equivalence. Differentiated cells from mature plants are often totipotent, capable of generating a complete new plant. The nucleus from a differentiated animal cell can sometimes give rise to a new animal if transplanted to an enucleated egg cell. Pluripotent stem cells from animal embryos or adult tissues can reproduce and differentiate *in vitro* as well as *in vivo*, offering the potential for medical use.

▶ **Transcriptional Regulation of Gene Expression During Development** (pp. 418–420) Differentiation is heralded by the appearance of tissue-specific proteins. These proteins enable differentiated cells to carry out their specialized roles.

▶ **Cytoplasmic Determinants and Cell-Cell Signals in Cell Differentiation** (p. 420) Cytoplasmic determinants in the cytoplasm of the unfertilized egg regulate the expression of genes in the zygote that affect the developmental fate of embryonic cells. In the process called induction, signal molecules from embryonic cells cause transcriptional changes in nearby target cells.
Activity *Signal Transduction Pathways*

Concept 21.3

Pattern formation in animals and plants results from similar genetic and cellular mechanisms

▶ Pattern formation, the development of a spatial organization of tissues and organs, occurs continually in plants, but is mostly limited to embryos and juveniles in animals. Positional information, the molecular cues that control pattern formation, tell a cell its location relative to the body's axes and to other cells (p. 421).

▶ ***Drosophila* Development: A Cascade of Gene Activations** (pp. 421–425) After fertilization, positional information on an increasingly fine scale specifies the segments in *Drosophila* and finally triggers the formation of each segment's characteristic structures. Gradients of morphogens encoded by maternal effect genes, such as *bicoid*, produce regional differences in the sequential expression of three sets of segmentation genes, the products of which direct the actual formation of segments. Finally, master regulatory genes, called homeotic genes, specify the type of appendages and other structures that form on each segment. Transcription factors encoded by the homeotic genes are regulatory proteins that control the expression of genes responsible for specific anatomical structures.

Activity *Role of* bicoid *Gene in* Drosophila *Development*
Investigation *How Do* bicoid *Mutations Alter Development?*

▶ **C. elegans: The Role of Cell Signaling** (pp. 425–429)
The complete lineage of each cell in *C. elegans* is known. Cell signaling and induction are critical in determining worm cell fates, including apoptosis (programmed cell death). An inducing signal produced by one cell in the embryo can initiate a chain of inductions that results in the formation of a particular organ, such as the intestine or vulva. In apoptosis, precisely timed signals trigger the activation of a cascade of "suicide" proteins in the cells destined to die.

▶ **Plant Development: Cell Signaling and Transcriptional Regulation** (pp. 429–431) Induction by cell-cell signaling helps determine the numbers of floral organs that develop from a floral meristem. Organ identity genes determine the type of structure (stamen, carpal, sepal, or petal) that grows from each whorl of a floral meristem. The organ identity genes apparently act as master regulatory genes, each controlling the activity of other genes that more directly bring about an organ's structure and function.

Concept 21.4

Comparative studies help explain how the evolution of development leads to morphological diversity

▶ **Widespread Conservation of Developmental Genes Among Animals** (pp. 431–432) Homeotic genes and some other genes associated with animal development contain a homeobox region, whose sequence is identical or similar in diverse species. Related sequences are present in the genes of yeasts, plants, and even prokaryotes. Other developmental genes also are highly conserved among animal species. In many cases, genes with conserved sequences play different roles in the development of different species. In plants, for instance, homeobox-containing genes do not function in pattern formation as they do in many animals.

▶ **Comparison of Animal and Plant Development** (p. 433)
During embryonic development in both plants and animals, a cascade of transcription regulators turns genes on or off in a carefully regulated sequence. But the genes that direct analogous developmental processes differ considerably in sequence in plants and animals, as a result of their remote ancestry.

TESTING YOUR KNOWLEDGE

Self-Quiz

1. Which of the following processes is most directly responsible for the lack of webbing between the fingers of most humans?
   a. pattern formation.
   b. transcriptional regulation.
   c. apoptosis.
   d. cell division.
   e. induction.

2. The criteria for a good model organism for studying development would probably include all of the following *except*
   a. observable embryonic development.
   b. short generation time.
   c. a relatively small genome.
   d. preexisting knowledge of the organism's life history.
   e. a rare pattern of development when compared to most organisms.

3. Totipotency is demonstrated when
   a. mutations in homeotic genes result in the development of misplaced appendages.
   b. a cell isolated from a plant leaf grows into a normal adult plant.
   c. an embryonic cell divides and differentiates.
   d. replacing the nucleus of an unfertilized egg with that of an intestinal cell converts the egg to an intestinal cell.
   e. segment-specific organs develop along the anterior-posterior axis of a *Drosophila* embryo.

4. Cell differentiation always involves
   a. the production of tissue-specific proteins, such as muscle actin.
   b. the movement of cells.
   c. the transcription of the *myoD* gene.
   d. the selective loss of certain genes from the genome.
   e. the cell's sensitivity to environmental cues such as light or heat.

5. The development of *Drosophila* is somewhat unusual in that
   a. the early mitotic divisions proceed without cytokinesis.
   b. metamorphosis occurs during the larval stage rather than the pupal stage, as with other insects.
   c. homeotic genes are mutated.
   d. cell migration within the embryo does not occur.
   e. the initial cell divisions have lengthy G_1 phases.

6. In *Drosophila*, which genes initiate a cascade of gene activation that includes all other genes in the list?
   a. homeotic genes
   b. gap genes
   c. pair-rule genes
   d. egg-polarity genes
   e. segment polarity genes

7. Absence of *bicoid* mRNA from a *Drosophila* egg leads to the absence of anterior larval body parts and mirror-image duplication of posterior parts. This is evidence that the product of the *bicoid* gene
   a. is transcribed in the early embryo.
   b. normally leads to formation of tail structures.
   c. normally leads to formation of head structures.
   d. is a protein present in all head structures.
   e. leads to programmed cell death.

8. Homeotic genes
   a. encode transcription factors that control the expression of genes responsible for specific anatomical structures.
   b. are found only in *Drosophila* and other arthropods.
   c. specify the anterior-posterior axis for each fruit fly segment.
   d. create the basic subdivisions of the anterior-posterior axis of the fly embryo.
   e. are responsible for the programmed cell death occurring during morphogenesis.

9. The embryonic development of *C. elegans* illustrates all of the following developmental concepts *except*:
   a. An inducer's effect can depend on its concentration gradient.
   b. The response of an induced cell involves the establishment of a unique pattern of gene activity.
   c. The signal transduction pathways activated by inducers are unique to embryonic cells.
   d. Sequential inductions direct the formation of complex structures in the developing embryo.
   e. Inducers bring about their effects via the activation or inactivation of genes that code for transcriptional regulators.

10. Although quite different in structure, plants and animals share some basic similarities in their development, such as
    a. the importance of cell and tissue movements.
    b. the importance of selective cell enlargement.
    c. the importance of homeobox-containing homeotic genes.
    d. the retention of meristematic tissues in the adult.
    e. master regulatory genes that encode DNA-binding proteins.

For Self-Quiz answers, see Appendix A.

Go to the website or CD-ROM for more quiz questions.

Evolution Connection

Genes important in the embryonic development of animals, such as homeobox-containing genes, have been relatively well conserved during evolution; that is, they are more similar among different species than are many other genes. Why is this?

Scientific Inquiry

Stem cells in an adult organism can divide to form two daughter stem cells, thus maintaining a population of relatively undifferentiated cells. Alternatively, a given mitotic division may yield one daughter cell that remains a stem cell and a second daughter cell that initiates a differentiation pathway. Propose one or more hypotheses to explain how this can happen. (*Note:* There is no easy answer to this question, but it is worth considering. For a hint, look at Figure 21.16a.)

Investigation *How Do bicoid Mutations Alter Development?*

Science, Technology, and Society

Government funding of embryonic stem cell research has been a contentious political issue. Why has this debate been so heated? Summarize the arguments for and against embryonic stem cell research, and explain your own position on the issue.

Mechanisms of Evolution

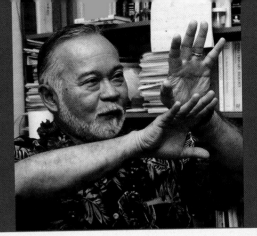

AN INTERVIEW WITH
Kenneth Kaneshiro

The Hawaiian Islands are one of Earth's greatest natural laboratories for understanding mechanisms of evolution. Dr. Kenneth Kaneshiro has contributed much to that understanding through his research on the diverse species of Hawaiian *Drosophila* flies. Professor Kaneshiro is the director of the Hawaiian Evolutionary Biology Program at the University of Hawaii, Manoa, where he is also the director of the Center for Conservation Research and Training. I first met Dr. Kaneshiro in 2003, when I was a visiting scholar at Iolani School in Honolulu, where Kaneshiro began his education. It was a joy returning to Hawaii a year later to conduct this interview. I love this job!

How did the Hawaiian Islands form?
Geologically, the islands are very young, with the oldest island, Kauai, being only about 5 to 6 million years old. The islands popped up in chronological fashion as the Pacific Plate moved northwest over a volcanic hotspot on the seafloor. The youngest island, the Big Island of Hawaii, is over the hotspot now, and there is a new island, Loihi, beginning to form as an undersea mountain to the southeast of the Big Island.

And what makes the Hawaiian Islands such a compelling place to study evolution?
First, they're the most isolated landmass in the world, sitting out in the middle of the Pacific nearly 2,000 miles away from continents in any direction. So for any species of organism that arrived here—by blowing across the ocean on the wind, for example—the founding population would have then been isolated from gene flow from other populations of that species.

And some of the organisms that made it here radiated profusely into new species by colonizing other islands. Since the islands formed in single file, from Kauai to the Big Island, you also have a chronological sequence in the origin of species as founders went from older islands to newer ones. In the case of *Drosophila*, the evidence points to a single founder (a fertilized female) that arrived several million years ago and whose progeny eventually radiated into the more than 500 described species of Hawaiian *Drosophila* flies. That's about a quarter of all known *Drosophila* species in the world.

Obviously, that's far more *Drosophila* species than there are islands. Did environmental variation on each island contribute to that radiation of species?
Yes, differences in elevation, rainfall, and other factors make each island very environmentally diverse. And each island also has what are called *kipukas*, "islands" of vegetation surrounded by lava. So, there are islands within islands, with the lava forming barriers between the kipukas. For example, we have studied two kipukas on the Big Island that used to be connected before a lava flow separated them just 100 years ago. And we're already detecting significant genetic differences between *Drosophila* populations that live in these two kipukas. They're still the same species, but they've started to diverge. Speciation is still a very dynamic process on the Hawaiian Islands.

How did your interest in biology develop?
It probably started when I was a child growing up here in Hawaii. When my dad took us fishing around Oahu, it was very scientific, though it didn't seem that way to me at the time. My dad considered the tides and wind, and he matched the colors of his fishing lures to the kinds of baitfish that might be out there. When I fish today, I

still apply those lessons from my dad. I think it was that sort of scientific approach to fishing that first got me interested in biology.

When did that interest turn to evolutionary biology?
When I was a freshman here at the University of Hawaii, I wanted to go into marine biology. But because of family pressures, I enrolled in the pre-med program instead. To help pay my way, I took a job with The Hawaiian *Drosophila* Project, starting as a dishwasher in the lab and learning how to prepare the nutrient media for breeding the flies. Within a few months, I was involved in actual research, dissecting genitalia and looking at other morphological characters that give us clues about the evolutionary history of the Hawaiian *Drosophila* species. I also had the opportunity to go into the field. So ecology also became part of my undergraduate education, not so much from the classroom, but by being involved in the *Drosophila* research. Every summer, 10 or 12 top scientists with different research specialties would visit to work on various *Drosophila* projects. Looking over the shoulders of these eminent scientists when I was an undergraduate really got me hooked. After I graduated, I switched to entomology for my graduate work so I could continue studying the Hawaiian *Drosophila*.

And that work included your research on mating behavior in *Drosophila*. I think many students will be surprised to learn that these flies court their mates.
The courtship between males and females is very elaborate. And the mating behavior also includes competition between males. A male will defend a territory to which females are attracted for mating. In one *Drosophila* species, for example, the males have very wide heads, and two males will butt their heads together—like rams—and then push each other back and forth as they joust for territory. In another species, the

competition is more like sumo wrestling; the males get up "tippy-toe" on their hind legs, grappling with their middle and forelegs, and lock heads. But being a good fighter doesn't mean that you're also a good lover. For a male fly, being able to fight off other males and defend a territory gives him the most opportunity to encounter females, but he still has to be able to perform the very complex behavior that satisfies the courtship requirements of a female.

Such as?

In one species, the male hoists his abdomen up and over his head, in a scorpion-like pose. This displays to the female a row of specialized bristles that are on the underside of the abdomen. Each bristle is flattened like a fan. Then the male vibrates his abdomen, and the bristles waft a sex-attractant vapor called a pheromone secreted from an abdominal gland. At the same time, the male spreads his wings and rocks back and forth, emitting a sound. While dancing and singing, the male extends his mouthparts from a very white face. In response, the female actually kisses the male. Mating only occurs if the male can perform this elaborate display.

According to a model now known as the "Kaneshiro Hypothesis," changes in such mating behavior played a key role in the origin of Hawaiian Drosophila species, especially in the early stages of speciation. What's the basic idea?

Shifts in mating behavior can occur in a small population after a founding event. Say you have

a population of flies on Kauai, the oldest island. Then Oahu pops up, and a fertilized female happens to make it there. She may found a new population on Oahu by producing a few hundred offspring. The males will vary in their ability to perform the species' original courtship rituals. But in such a small population, females who are very choosy will have less opportunity to reproduce than less choosy females, who will encounter more mates they are willing to accept. So selection favors fresh combinations of genes that combine adaptations to the new environment along with less rigid mating behavior than in the "parent" species back on Kauai. That would explain why mating behavior is typically the most complex in the oldest Drosophila species. I think such shifts in mating behavior have been very important in the evolution of the Hawaiian Drosophila, and probably in many other groups of organisms as well.

At the same time that biologists are studying the evolution of such a diversity of species on the Hawaiian islands, the islands have been designated a biodiversity hotspot, meaning that many species are endangered. What are the biggest threats to biodiversity in Hawaii?

There is the destruction of habitat, but the impact of invasive species—nonnative species that are accidentally or purposefully brought to the islands—is probably the biggest threat. And ants may be the number one problem. Hawaii doesn't have any native ants; they're all alien.

Their foraging in native forest ecosystems has severely impacted the native arthropod fauna. Invasive rats threaten the native birds by getting into nests and eating the eggs and young. Wild pigs are also a serious problem. They descended from hybridization between pigs the native Hawaiians brought to the islands and the pigs brought by Europeans. The wild pigs root in the forests, which creates puddles in which mosquitoes breed. The mosquitoes carry pathogens that cause malaria in birds. Also, invasive plants are crowding out many of the native plant species. Unfortunately, in spite of its small size, Hawaii is the extinction capital of the United States, if not the world.

One of your many hats is your role as director of the Center for Conservation Research and Training here at the University of Hawaii. What kind of work does the Center conduct?

Our research interest in conservation biology mainly takes an ecosystem and ecoregional approach: What happens on the mountaintops affects ecosystems all the way down to the coral reefs and beyond. I think we have to understand such relationships between ecosystems in order to protect the islands' biodiversity. The Center also has a major commitment to education. We have a National Science Foundation grant that supports outreach programs where our graduate students work with schoolchildren and mentor their teachers. We get these K-12 students out into the field participating in research: They are collecting valid scientific data, discovering new species, and helping us understand how to eradicate some of the alien species. The sheer numbers of these young scientists enable us to make certain kinds of measurements that would be impossible otherwise. For example, researchers would usually monitor contaminants in a stream by collecting water samples at a few points along the stream. But our graduate students worked with 320 seventh graders to sample the water all the way from a mountain waterfall to where the stream drains into the ocean. To me, this kind of environmental education, beginning at a young age, will eventually increase public awareness and make us all more effective in protecting our water resources and our native ecosystems.

Aloha and mahalo, Dr. Kaneshiro!

In the case of Drosophila, *the evidence points to a single founder (a fertilized female) that arrived several million years ago and whose progeny eventually radiated into the more than 500 described species of Hawaiian* Drosophila *flies.*

22 Descent with Modification
A Darwinian View of Life

▲ Figure 22.1 **A marine iguana, well-suited to its rocky habitat in the Galápagos Islands.**

Key Concepts

22.1 The Darwinian revolution challenged traditional views of a young Earth inhabited by unchanging species

22.2 In *The Origin of Species,* Darwin proposed that species change through natural selection

22.3 Darwin's theory explains a wide range of observations

Overview

Darwin Introduces a Revolutionary Theory

A new era of biology began on November 24, 1859, the day Charles Darwin published *On the Origin of Species by Means of Natural Selection.* Darwin's book drew a cohesive picture of life by connecting the dots among what had once seemed a bewildering array of unrelated observations. *The Origin of Species* focused biologists' attention on the great diversity of organisms—their origins and relationships, their similarities and differences, their geographic distribution, and their adaptations to surrounding environments **(Figure 22.1)**.

Darwin made two major points in *The Origin of Species.* First, he presented evidence that the many species of organisms presently inhabiting Earth are descendants of ancestral species that were different from the modern species. Second, he proposed a mechanism for this evolutionary process, which he termed **natural selection.** The basic idea of natural selection is that a population can change over generations if individuals that possess certain heritable traits leave more offspring than other individuals. The result of natural selection is

evolutionary adaptation, an accumulation of inherited characteristics that enhance organisms' ability to survive and reproduce in specific environments. In modern terms, we can define **evolution** as a change over time in the genetic composition of a population. Eventually, a population may accumulate enough change that it constitutes a new species—a new life-form. Thus we can also use the term *evolution* on a grand scale to mean the gradual appearance of all of biological diversity, from the earliest microbes to the enormous variety of organisms alive today.

Evolution is such a fundamental concept that its study illuminates biology at every level from molecules to ecosystems, and it continues to transform medicine, agriculture, biotechnology, and conservation biology. You have already encountered evolution as the main thematic thread woven throughout this book. In this chapter, you will learn about the historical development of the Darwinian view of life.

Concept 22.1

The Darwinian revolution challenged traditional views of a young Earth inhabited by unchanging species

The impact of an intellectual revolution such as Darwinism depends on timing as well as logic. To understand why Darwin's ideas were revolutionary, we need to examine his views in the context of other Western ideas about Earth and its life **(Figure 22.2)**.

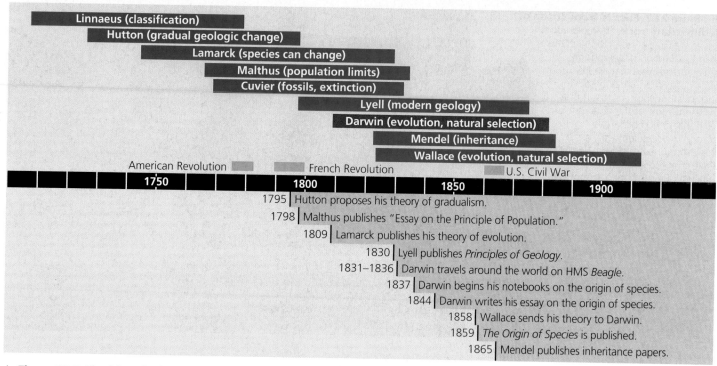

▲ **Figure 22.2 The historical context of Darwin's life and ideas.** The dark blue bars above the timeline represent the lives of some individuals whose ideas have contributed to our modern understanding of evolution.

Resistance to the Idea of Evolution

The Origin of Species not only challenged prevailing scientific views but also shook the deepest roots of Western culture. Darwin's view of life contrasted sharply with traditional beliefs of an Earth only a few thousand years old, populated by forms of life that had been created at the beginning and remained unchanged ever since. Darwin's book challenged a worldview that had been prevalent for centuries.

The Scale of Nature and Classification of Species

Although several Greek philosophers suggested that life might have evolved gradually, one philosopher who greatly influenced early Western science, Aristotle (384–322 B.C.), viewed species as fixed (unchanging). Through his observations of nature, Aristotle recognized certain "affinities" among living things, leading him to conclude that life-forms could be arranged on a ladder, or scale, of increasing complexity, later called the *scala naturae* ("scale of nature"). Each form of life, perfect and permanent, had its allotted rung on this ladder.

These ideas coincided with the Old Testament account of creation, which holds that species were individually designed by God and therefore perfect. In the 1700s, many scientists interpreted the superb adaptations of organisms to their environments as evidence that the Creator had designed each species for a particular purpose.

One such scientist was Carolus Linnaeus (1707–1778), a Swedish physician and botanist who sought to classify life's diversity "for the greater glory of God." Linnaeus was a founder of **taxonomy,** the branch of biology concerned with naming and classifying organisms. He developed the two-part, or binomial, system of naming organisms according to genus and species that is still used today. In contrast to the linear hierarchy of the *scala naturae*, Linnaeus adopted a nested classification system, grouping similar species into increasingly general categories. For example, similar species are grouped in the same genus, similar genera (plural of genus) are grouped in the same family, and so on (see Figure 1.14).

To Linnaeus, the observation that some species resemble each other did not imply evolutionary kinship, but rather the pattern of their creation. However, a century later his taxonomic system would play a role in Darwin's arguments for evolution.

Fossils, Cuvier, and Catastrophism

The study of fossils also helped to lay the groundwork for Darwin's ideas. **Fossils** are remains or traces of organisms from the past. Most fossils are found in **sedimentary rocks** formed from the sand and mud that settle to the bottom of seas, lakes, and marshes. New layers of sediment cover older ones and compress them into superimposed layers of rock called strata (singular, *stratum*). Later, erosion may carve

▶ **Figure 22.3 Fossils from strata of sedimentary rock.** The Colorado River carved the Grand Canyon through more than 2,000 m of rock, exposing sedimentary layers that are like huge pages from the book of life. Each stratum entombs fossils that represent some of the organisms from that period of Earth's history. The seed fern leaf fossil (top) is from the shallower Hermit Shale layer (265 million years old), and the trilobite fossil (bottom) is from the deeper Bright Angel Shale layer (530 million years old).

through upper (younger) strata and reveal older strata that had been buried. Fossils in each layer provide a glimpse of some of the organisms that populated Earth at the time that layer formed (Figure 22.3).

Paleontology, the study of fossils, was largely developed by French scientist Georges Cuvier (1769–1832). In examining rock layers in the region around Paris, Cuvier noted that the deeper (older) the strata, the more dissimilar the fossils are from current life. He also observed that from one stratum to the next, some new species appear while others disappear. He inferred that extinctions must have been a common occurrence in the history of life. Yet Cuvier staunchly opposed the idea of gradual evolutionary change. Instead, he advocated **catastrophism,** speculating that each boundary between strata represents a catastrophe, such as a flood or drought, that destroyed many of the species living at that time. He proposed that these periodic catastrophes were usually confined to local geographic regions, which were repopulated by species immigrating from other areas.

Theories of Gradualism

In contrast to catastrophism, the work of other scientists promoted the concept of **gradualism**—the idea that profound change can take place through the cumulative effect of slow but continuous processes. In 1795, Scottish geologist James Hutton (1726–1797) proposed that Earth's geologic features could be explained by gradual mechanisms *currently* operating in the world. He suggested that valleys were formed by rivers wearing through rocks and that sedimentary rocks containing marine fossils were formed from particles that had eroded from the land and been carried by rivers to the sea.

The leading geologist of Darwin's time, Charles Lyell (1797–1875), incorporated Hutton's thinking into a more comprehensive theory known as **uniformitarianism.** Lyell proposed that the same geologic processes are operating today as in the past, and at the same rate.

Hutton and Lyell's ideas exerted a strong influence on Darwin's thinking. Darwin agreed that if geologic change results from slow, continuous actions rather than sudden events, then Earth must be much older than the 6,000 years that theologians estimated. He later reasoned that perhaps similarly slow and subtle processes could act on living organisms over a long period of time, producing substantial change. Darwin was not the first to apply the principle of gradualism to biological evolution, however.

Lamarck's Theory of Evolution

During the 18th century, several naturalists (including Darwin's grandfather, Erasmus Darwin) suggested that life evolves as environments change. But only one of Charles Darwin's predecessors developed a comprehensive model for *how* life evolves: French biologist Jean-Baptiste de Lamarck (1744–1829). Alas, Lamarck is primarily remembered today not for his visionary recognition that evolutionary change explains the fossil record and organisms' adaptations to their environments, but for the incorrect mechanism he proposed to explain how evolution occurs.

Lamarck published his theory in 1809, the year Darwin was born. By comparing current species with fossil forms, Lamarck had found what appeared to be several lines of descent, each a chronological series of older to younger fossils leading to a living species. He explained this with two principles that

▲ **Figure 22.4 Acquired traits cannot be inherited.** This bonsai tree was "trained" to grow as a dwarf by pruning and shaping. However, seeds from this tree would produce offspring of normal size.

were commonly accepted at that time. The first was *use and disuse*, the idea that parts of the body that are used extensively become larger and stronger, while those that are not used deteriorate. As an example, he cited a giraffe stretching its neck to reach leaves on high branches. The second principle, *inheritance of acquired characteristics*, stated that an organism could pass these modifications to its offspring. Lamarck reasoned that the long, muscular neck of the living giraffe had evolved over many generations as giraffes stretched their necks ever higher. Lamarck also thought that evolution happens because organisms have an innate drive to become more complex. Darwin rejected this idea in favor of natural selection, but he too thought that variation was introduced into the evolutionary process through inheritance of acquired characteristics. However, our modern understanding of genetics refutes this principle; there is no evidence that acquired characteristics can be inherited **(Figure 22.4)**.

Lamarck was vilified in his own time, especially by Cuvier, who denied that species ever evolve. In retrospect, however, Lamarck deserves credit for his insightful observations of nature and recognition of gradual evolutionary change as the best explanation for those observations.

Concept Check 22.1

1. Which of the individuals discussed in this section viewed species as fixed, and which viewed species as being able to change over time?
2. What was Lamarck's theory of evolution? Explain its significance.

For suggested answers, see Appendix A.

Concept 22.2

In *The Origin of Species*, Darwin proposed that species change through natural selection

As the 19th century dawned, it was generally believed that species had remained unchanged since their creation. A few clouds of doubt about the permanence of species were beginning to gather, but no one could have forecast the thundering storm just over the horizon.

Darwin's Research

Charles Darwin (1809–1882) was born in Shrewsbury in western England. Even as a boy, he had a consuming interest in nature. When he was not reading nature books, he was fishing, hunting, and collecting insects. Darwin's father, an eminent physician, could see no future for his 16-year-old son as a naturalist and sent him to the University of Edinburgh to study medicine. But Charles found medical school boring and surgery before the days of anesthesia horrifying. He left Edinburgh without a degree and enrolled at Cambridge University with the intention of becoming a clergyman. At that time in England, many scholars of science belonged to the clergy.

At Cambridge, Darwin became the protégé of the Reverend John Henslow, a professor of botany. Soon after Darwin received his B.A. degree, Henslow recommended the young graduate to Captain Robert FitzRoy, who was preparing the survey ship HMS *Beagle* for a voyage around the world. FitzRoy accepted Darwin on board because of his education and because of his age and social class, which were similar to FitzRoy's.

The Voyage of the Beagle

In 1831, the 22-year-old Darwin left England aboard the *Beagle*. The primary mission of the voyage was to chart poorly known stretches of the South American coastline. While the ship's crew surveyed the coast, Darwin spent most of his time on shore, observing and collecting thousands of South American plants and animals. He observed the various adaptations of plants and animals that inhabited such diverse environments as the Brazilian jungles, the expansive grasslands of the Argentine pampas, the desolate lands of Tierra del Fuego near Antarctica, and the towering heights of the Andes Mountains.

Darwin noted that the plants and animals in temperate regions of South America more closely resembled species living in the South American tropics than species in temperate regions of Europe. Furthermore, the fossils he found, though clearly different from living species, were distinctly South American in their resemblance to the living organisms of that continent.

▲ Figure 22.5 **The voyage of HMS *Beagle*.**

Geologic observations also impressed Darwin during the voyage. Despite bouts of seasickness, he read Lyell's *Principles of Geology* while aboard the *Beagle*. He experienced geologic change firsthand when a violent earthquake rocked the coast of Chile, and he observed afterward that the coastline had risen by several feet. Finding fossils of ocean organisms high in the Andes Mountains, he inferred that the rocks containing the fossils must have been raised there by a long series of similar earthquakes. These observations reinforced what he had learned from Lyell—the physical evidence did not support the traditional view of a static Earth only a few thousand years old.

Darwin's interest in the geographic distribution of species was further kindled by the *Beagle*'s stop at the Galápagos, a group of geologically young volcanic islands located near the equator about 900 km (540 miles) west of South America **(Figure 22.5)**. Darwin was fascinated by the unusual organisms he found there. Among the birds he collected on the Galápagos were several kinds of finches that, although quite similar, seemed to be different species. Some were unique to individual islands, while others were distributed on two or more adjacent islands. But Darwin did not fully grasp the significance of these observations until after his return to England in 1836. He and others found that although the animals on the Galápagos resemble species living on the South American mainland, most of the Galápagos animals live nowhere else in the world. He hypothesized that the Galápagos had been colonized by organ-

isms that had strayed from South America and had then diversified on the various islands.

Darwin's Focus on Adaptation

As Darwin reassessed all that he had observed during the voyage, he began to perceive adaptation to the environment and the origin of new species as closely related processes. Could a new species arise from an ancestral form by the gradual accumulation of adaptations to a different environment? From studies made years after Darwin's voyage, biologists have concluded that this is indeed what happened to the Galápagos finches. Their beaks and behaviors are adapted to the specific foods available on their home islands **(Figure 22.6)**. Darwin realized that an explanation for such adaptations was essential to understanding evolution.

By the early 1840s, Darwin had worked out the major features of his theory of natural selection as the mechanism of evolution. However, he had not yet published his ideas. He was in poor health, and he rarely left his home near London. Despite his reclusiveness, Darwin was not isolated. Already famous as a naturalist because of the letters and specimens he had sent to England during the voyage of the *Beagle*, Darwin corresponded extensively with scientists around the world and was often visited by Lyell, Henslow, and others.

In 1844, Darwin wrote a long essay on the origin of species and natural selection. However, he was reluctant to introduce

► **Figure 22.6 Beak variation in Galápagos finches.** The Galápagos Islands are home to more than a dozen species of closely related finches, some found only on a single island. The most striking differences among them are their beaks, which are adapted for specific diets.

(a) Cactus eater. The long, sharp beak of the cactus ground finch (*Geospiza scandens*) helps it tear and eat cactus flowers and pulp.

(b) Insect eater. The green warbler finch (*Certhidea olivacea*) uses its narrow, pointed beak to grasp insects.

(c) Seed eater. The large ground finch (*Geospiza magnirostris*) has a large beak adapted for cracking seeds that fall from plants to the ground.

his theory publicly, apparently because he anticipated the uproar it would cause. Darwin asked his wife to publish his essay if he were to die before finishing a more thorough dissertation. Even as he procrastinated, he continued to compile evidence in support of his theory. Lyell, not yet himself convinced of evolution, nevertheless urged Darwin to publish on the subject before someone else came to the same conclusions and published first.

In June 1858, Lyell's prediction came true. Darwin received a manuscript from Alfred Russel Wallace (1823–1913), a young British naturalist working in the East Indies who had developed a theory of natural selection similar to Darwin's. Wallace asked Darwin to evaluate his paper and forward it to Lyell if it merited publication. Darwin complied, writing to Lyell: "Your words have come true with a vengeance. . . . I never saw a more striking coincidence . . . so all my originality, whatever it may amount to, will be smashed." Lyell and a colleague then presented Wallace's paper, along with extracts from Darwin's unpublished 1844 essay, to the Linnean Society of London on July 1, 1858. Darwin quickly finished *The Origin of Species* and published it the next year. Although Wallace had written up his ideas for publication first, he was a great admirer of Darwin and agreed that Darwin had developed the theory of natural selection so extensively that he should be known as its main architect.

Within a decade, Darwin's book and its proponents had convinced most biologists that biological diversity was the product of evolution. Darwin succeeded where previous evolutionists had failed, mainly because he presented his reasoning with immaculate logic and an avalanche of sup-porting evidence. He soon followed up his first book with other pioneering work, in particular an exploration of the type of natural selection known as sexual selection (see Chapter 23).

The Origin of Species

In publishing his theory, Darwin developed two main ideas: that evolution explains life's unity and diversity and that natural selection is a cause of adaptive evolution.

Descent with Modification

In the first edition of *The Origin of Species,* Darwin did not use the word *evolution* until the very end. Instead, he referred to **descent with modification,** a phrase that summarized his view of life. Darwin perceived unity in life, with all organisms related through descent from an ancestor that lived in the remote past. As the descendants of that ancestral organism spilled into various habitats over millions of years, they accumulated diverse modifications, or adaptations, that fit them to specific ways of life.

In the Darwinian view, the history of life is like a tree, with multiple branchings from a common trunk to the tips of the youngest twigs that represent the diversity of living organisms. Each fork of the tree represents an ancestor of all the lines of evolution that subsequently branched from that point. Closely related species, such as the Asian elephant and African elephants, are very similar because they shared the same line of descent until a relatively recent divergence

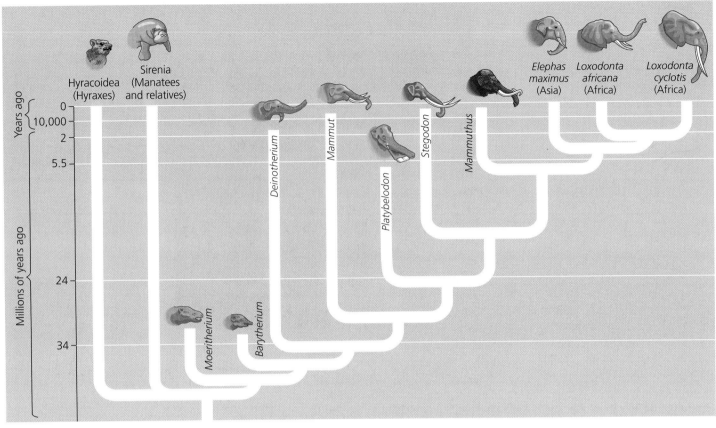

▲ Figure 22.7 **Descent with modification.** This evolutionary tree of the elephants is based mainly on fossils—their anatomy, order of appearance in strata, and geographic distribution. Note that most branches of descent ended in extinction. Despite their very different appearances, the manatees and hyraxes are the elephants' closest living relatives. (Timeline not to scale.)

from their common ancestor **(Figure 22.7)**. Most branches of evolution, even some major ones, are dead ends; about 99% of all species that have ever lived are now extinct. Thus, there are no living animals that fill the gap between the elephants and their nearest relatives today, the manatees and hyraxes, though some fossils have been found.

Linnaeus had realized that some organisms resemble each other more closely than others, but he had not linked these resemblances to evolution. Nonetheless, because he had recognized that the great diversity of organisms could be organized into "groups subordinate to groups" (Darwin's phrase), his taxonomic scheme largely fit with Darwin's theory. To Darwin, the Linnaean hierarchy reflected the branching history of the tree of life, with organisms at the various taxonomic levels related through descent from common ancestors.

Natural Selection and Adaptation

How does natural selection work, and how does it explain adaptation? Evolutionary biologist Ernst Mayr has dissected the logic of Darwin's theory of natural selection into three inferences based on five observations:*

OBSERVATION #1: For any species, population sizes would increase exponentially if all individuals that are born reproduced successfully **(Figure 22.8)**.

OBSERVATION #2: Nonetheless, populations tend to remain stable in size, except for seasonal fluctuations.

OBSERVATION #3: Resources are limited.

INFERENCE #1: Production of more individuals than the environment can support leads to a struggle for existence among individuals of a population, with only a fraction of their offspring surviving each generation.

OBSERVATION #4: Members of a population vary extensively in their characteristics; no two individuals are exactly alike **(Figure 22.9)**.

OBSERVATION #5: Much of this variation is heritable.

INFERENCE #2: Survival depends in part on inherited traits. Individuals whose inherited traits give them a high probability of surviving and reproducing in a given environment have higher fitness and are likely to leave more offspring than less fit individuals.

INFERENCE #3: This unequal ability of individuals to survive and reproduce will lead to a gradual change in a population, with favorable characteristics accumulating over generations.

_____

* Adapted from E. Mayr, *The Growth of Biological Thought: Diversity, Evolution and Inheritance* (Cambridge, MA: Harvard University Press, 1982).

► **Figure 22.8 Overproduction of offspring.** Just one branch of a maple tree bears dozens of winged seeds. If all the tree's offspring survived, we would quickly be overwhelmed by maple forests.

▲ **Figure 22.9 Variation in a population.** To the extent that the variation in color and dot patterns among the members of this population of ladybird beetles is heritable, it can be acted on by natural selection.

Darwin perceived an important connection between natural selection, which results from what he called the struggle for existence, and the capacity of organisms to "overreproduce." Apparently, this insight came after he read a 1798 essay on population growth by Thomas Malthus. Malthus contended that much of human suffering—disease, famine, homelessness, and war—was the inescapable consequence of the human population's potential to increase faster than food and other resources. The capacity to overreproduce seems to be characteristic of all species (see Figure 22.8). Of the many eggs laid, young born, and seeds spread, only a tiny fraction complete their development and leave offspring of their own. The rest are eaten, starved, diseased, unmated, or unable to reproduce for some other reason.

In each generation, environmental factors filter heritable variations, favoring some over others. Organisms with traits favored by the environment tend to produce more offspring than do organisms without those traits. This differential re-

productive success results in favored traits being disproportionately represented in the next generation. Increases in the frequencies of favored traits in a population, which are always taking place regardless of whether the environment is changing, are an important source of evolutionary modification.

Artificial Selection. Darwin derived another piece of his theory from the many familiar examples of selective breeding of domesticated plants and animals. Humans have modified other species over many generations by selecting and breeding individuals that possess desired traits—a process called **artificial selection.** As a result of artificial selection, crop plants and animals bred as livestock or pets often bear little resemblance to their wild ancestors **(Figure 22.10).**

If artificial selection can achieve so much change in a relatively short period of time, Darwin reasoned, then what he termed "natural selection" should be capable of considerable modification of species over hundreds or thousands of generations. Even if the advantages of some heritable traits over others are slight, the advantageous variations will gradually accumulate in the population, and less favorable variations will diminish.

Summary of Natural Selection. Let's once more state the main ideas of natural selection:

► Natural selection is the differential success in reproduction (the unequal ability of individuals to survive and reproduce) that results from the interaction between individuals that vary in heritable traits and their environment.

▲ **Figure 22.10 Artificial selection.** These vegetables have all been selected from one species of wild mustard. By selecting variations in different parts of the plant, breeders have obtained these divergent results.

(a) A flower mantid in Malaysia

(b) A stick mantid in Africa

▲ **Figure 22.11 Camouflage as an example of evolutionary adaptation.** Related species of the insects called mantids have diverse shapes and colors that evolved in different environments.

▶ Over time, natural selection can increase the adaptation of organisms to their environment **(Figure 22.11)**.

▶ If an environment changes over time, or if individuals of a particular species move to a new environment, natural selection may result in adaptation to these new conditions, sometimes giving rise to new species in the process.

Before continuing, we need to emphasize three subtle but important points about evolution by natural selection. The first is that although natural selection occurs through interactions between individual organisms and their environment, individuals do not evolve. A population is the smallest unit that can evolve. (For now, we will define a population as a group of interbreeding individuals belonging to a particular species and sharing a common geographic area.) Evolution can be measured only as changes in relative proportions of heritable variations in a population over a succession of generations.

Another key point is that natural selection can amplify or diminish *only* heritable traits—that is, traits that are passed from organisms to their offspring. Though an organism may become modified through its own interactions with the environment during its lifetime, and these acquired characteristics may even adapt the organism to its environment, there is no evidence that such acquired characteristics can be inherited by offspring. We must distinguish between adaptations that an organism acquires during its lifetime and inherited adaptations that accumulate in a population over many generations as a result of natural selection.

Also, remember that environmental factors vary from place to place and from time to time. A trait that is favorable in one situation may be useless—or even detrimental—in different circumstances. Natural selection is always operating, but which traits are favored depends on the environment.

Thus, Darwin envisioned life as evolving through this gradual accumulation of small changes. He postulated that natural selection, operating in varying contexts over vast spans of time as revealed by the emerging science of geology, could account for the entire diversity of life.

Concept Check 22.2

1. Describe how the following concepts relate to Darwin's theory of evolution by natural selection: overreproduction of populations, limited resources, and heritable variation.
2. Explain why an individual organism cannot be said to evolve.

For suggested answers, see Appendix A.

Concept 22.3

Darwin's theory explains a wide range of observations

Scientific inquiry seeks *natural* causes for natural phenomena (see Chapter 1). The power of evolution as a unifying theory is its versatility as a natural explanation for a diversity of data from biology's many subfields. And like all general theories in science, Darwin's theory of evolution continues to be tested by how effectively it can account for additional observations and experimental outcomes. Perhaps the most direct validations of Darwin's theory are provided by the many cases where scientists can actually observe natural selection at work.

Natural Selection in Action

Let's look at two examples of natural selection as a mechanism of evolution in populations.

Differential Predation and Guppy Populations

Guppies (*Poecilia reticulata*) are small freshwater fish that you may know as aquarium pets. For many years, John Endler, of the University of California, Santa Barbara, and David Reznick, of the University of California, Riverside, have studied wild guppy populations living in pools in the Aripo River system on the Caribbean island Trinidad.

The researchers observed significant differences between populations in the average age and size at which the guppies reached sexual maturity. These variations were correlated to the type of predator most active on that population. In some pools, the main predator is the small killifish, which preys predominantly on juvenile guppies. In other pools, the major predator is the pike-cichlid, a larger fish that primarily eats sexually mature individuals. Guppies in populations preyed on by pike-cichlids begin reproducing at a younger age and are smaller at maturity, on average, than guppies that are preyed on by killifish.

But although correlation with type of predator was suggestive, it does not necessarily indicate cause and effect. To test whether these differences are due to natural selection, Reznick and Endler introduced guppies from "pike-cichlid pools" to new pools that contained killifish but no guppies (**Figure 22.12**). Over the next 11 years, the researchers compared the age and size at maturity of the transplanted guppies with the original population. After periods of 30 to 60 generations, the transplanted guppies were an average of 14% heavier at maturity than the nontransplanted individuals. Their average age at maturity had also risen. This result supports the hypothesis that natural selection caused the difference in the populations. The conclusion is that because pike-cichlids prey mainly on reproductively mature adults, the chance that a guppy will survive to reproduce several times is relatively low. The guppies with greatest reproductive success in these ponds are those that mature at a young age and small size, enabling them to produce at least one brood before growing to a size preferred by the pike-cichlids. But in ponds with killifish the guppies that survive early predation can grow slowly and still produce many broods of young. This research by Reznick and Endler is one of many documented examples of evolution in natural settings over relatively short time periods.

The Evolution of Drug-Resistant HIV

An unsettling example of ongoing natural selection that directly affects our own lives is the evolution of drug-resistant pathogens. This is a particular problem in bacteria and viruses with rapid rates of reproduction, because a variation that makes individuals resistant to a particular drug can increase in frequency very quickly in the population.

Consider the example of HIV (human immunodeficiency virus), which causes AIDS (see Chapter 18 and Chapter 43). Researchers have developed numerous drugs to combat this pathogen, but using these medications selects for viruses resistant to the drugs. A few drug-resistant viruses may be present by chance at the beginning of treatment. Those that survive the early doses pass on the genes that enable them to

---

Figure 22.12

Inquiry **Can predation pressure select for size and age at maturity in guppies?**

EXPERIMENT Reznick and Endler transplanted guppies from pike-cichlid pools to killifish pools and measured the average age and size of guppies at maturity over an 11-year period (30 to 60 generations).

Pools with killifish, but no guppies prior to transplant

Experimental transplant of guppies

Predator: Killifish; preys mainly on small guppies

Guppies: Larger at sexual maturity than those in "pike-cichlid pools"

Predator: Pike-cichlid; preys mainly on large guppies

Guppies: Smaller at sexual maturity than those in "killifish pools"

RESULTS After 11 years, the average size and age at maturity of guppies in the transplanted populations increased compared to those of guppies in control populations.

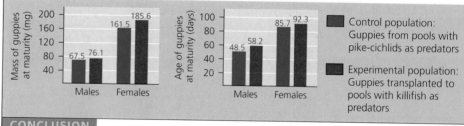

Control population: Guppies from pools with pike-cichlids as predators

Experimental population: Guppies transplanted to pools with killifish as predators

CONCLUSION Reznick and Endler concluded that the change in predator resulted in different variations in the population (larger size and faster maturation) being favored. Over a relatively short time, this altered selection pressure resulted in an observable evolutionary change in the experimental population.

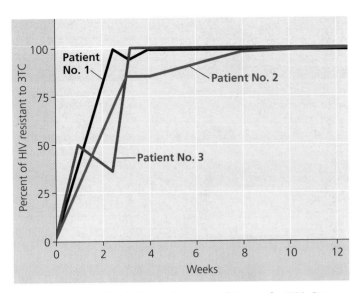

▲ **Figure 22.13 Evolution of drug resistance in HIV.** Rare resistant viruses multiply quickly when each of these patients is treated with the anti-HIV drug 3TC. Within just a few weeks, 3TC-resistant organisms comprise 100% of the virus population in each case.

resist the drug to their progeny, rapidly increasing the frequency of resistant viruses.

Figure 22.13 illustrates the evolution of HIV resistance to the drug 3TC. Scientists designed 3TC to interfere with reverse transcriptase, the enzyme HIV uses to copy its RNA genome into the DNA of the human host cell (see Figure 18.10). Because the 3TC molecule is similar in shape to the C (cytosine) nucleotide of DNA, the HIV's reverse transcriptase picks up a 3TC molecule instead of C and inserts it into a growing DNA chain. This error terminates further elongation of the DNA and thus blocks reproduction of the HIV.

The 3TC-resistant varieties of HIV carry slightly different versions of reverse transcriptase that are able to discriminate between the drug and the normal C nucleotide. The viruses that carry these genes have no advantage in the absence of 3TC; in fact, they replicate more slowly than those that carry the more common form. But once 3TC is added to their environment it becomes a powerful selecting force, favoring reproduction of resistant individuals.

These examples highlight two key points about natural selection. First, natural selection is more a process of editing than a creative mechanism. A drug does not *create* resistant pathogens; it *selects for* resistant individuals that were already present in the population. Second, natural selection depends on time and place. It favors those characteristics in a genetically variable population that increase fitness in the current, local environment. What is adaptive in one situation may be useless or even harmful in another. In the guppy example, individuals that mature at an early age and small size are at an advantage in a pool with pike-cichlids, but at a disadvantage in a pool with killifish.

Homology, Biogeography, and the Fossil Record

The two examples you just read about show that natural selection can bring about change rapidly enough to be observed directly. In addition, Darwin's theory provides a cohesive explanation for observations made by researchers in the fields of anatomy, embryology, molecular biology, biogeography, and paleontology.

Homology

Darwin's concept of descent with modification can explain why certain characteristics in related species have an underlying similarity even though they may have very different functions. Such similarity resulting from common ancestry is known as **homology**.

Anatomical Homologies. The view of evolution as a remodeling process accounts for the findings of comparative anatomy, the comparison of body structures between species. The forelimbs of all mammals, including humans, cats, whales, and bats, show the same arrangement of bones from the shoulder to the tips of the digits, even though these appendages can have very different functions—lifting, walking, swimming, and flying **(Figure 22.14)**. Such striking anatomical resemblances would not exist if these structures had arisen anew in each species. The arms, forelegs, flippers, and wings of different mammals are **homologous structures** that represent variations on a structural theme that was present in their common ancestor.

Comparative embryology, the comparison of early stages of animal development, reveals additional anatomical homologies not visible in adult organisms. For example, at some point in their development, all vertebrate embryos have tails posterior to the anus, as well as structures called pharyngeal (throat) pouches **(Figure 22.15)**. These embryonic structures develop into homologous structures with very different functions, such as gills in fishes and parts of the ears and throat in humans.

Some of the most intriguing homologous structures are **vestigial organs,** structures of marginal, if any, importance to the organism. Vestigial organs are remnants of structures that served important functions in the organism's ancestors. For instance, the skeletons of some snakes retain vestiges of the pelvis and leg bones of walking ancestors. Because limbs are a hindrance to a snake's way of life, natural selection has favored snake ancestors with successively smaller limbs. We would not expect to see these vestigial structures if snakes had an origin separate from other vertebrate animals.

Because evolution can only modify existing structures and functions, it often produces less than perfect results. For example, the human knee joint and spine derive from ancestral structures that supported four-legged mammals. Few people

Human   Cat   Whale   Bat

▲ **Figure 22.14 Mammalian forelimbs: homologous structures.** Even though they have become adapted for different functions, the forelimbs of all mammals are constructed from the same basic skeletal elements: one large bone (gray), attached to two smaller bones (dark and light orange), attached to several small bones (yellow), attached to approximately five digits, or phalanges (brown).

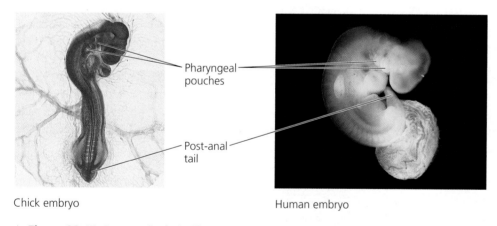

Pharyngeal pouches

Post-anal tail

Chick embryo   Human embryo

▲ **Figure 22.15 Anatomical similarities in vertebrate embryos.** At some stage in their embryonic development, all vertebrates have a tail located posterior to the anus, as well as pharyngeal (throat) pouches. Descent from a common ancestor can explain such similarities.

reach old age without experiencing knee or back problems. If these structures had originally evolved to support our bipedal posture, we would expect them to be less subject to injury. The anatomical remodeling that enabled our ancestors to stand upright was apparently constrained by our evolutionary history.

Molecular Homologies. Biologists also observe similarities among organisms at the molecular level. All forms of life use the same genetic machinery of DNA and RNA, and the genetic code is essentially universal (see Chapter 17). Because the genetic code is shared by all organisms, it is likely that all species descended from a common ancestor. Molecular homologies also go beyond a shared code. Organisms as dissimilar as humans and bacteria share many genes that have been inherited from a distant common ancestor. Like the forelimbs of humans and whales, these genes have often acquired different functions.

Homologies and the Tree of Life. The Darwinian concept of an evolutionary tree of life can explain the homologies that researchers have observed. Some homologies, such as the genetic code, are shared by all species because they date to the deep ancestral past. Homologies that evolved more recently are shared only within smaller branches of the tree. For example, all tetrapods (from the Greek *tetra*, four, and *pod*, foot), the vertebrate branch consisting of amphibians, reptiles (including birds), and mammals, possess the same basic five-digit limb structure illustrated in Figure 22.14. Thus, homologies result in a nested pattern, with all life sharing the deepest layer and each smaller group adding homologies to those they share with larger groups. This nested pattern is exactly what we would expect if life evolved and diversified from a common ancestor.

Anatomical resemblances among species are generally reflected in their molecules—in their genes (DNA) and gene products (proteins). **Figure 22.16**, on the next page, compares the amino acid sequence of human hemoglobin, the protein that transports oxygen in blood, with the hemoglobin of other vertebrates. The data show the same pattern of evolutionary relationships that researchers find when they compare other proteins or assess relationships based on nonmolecular methods such as comparative anatomy. The Darwinian view of life predicts that different kinds of homologies in a group of organisms will all tend to show the same branching pattern through evolutionary history.

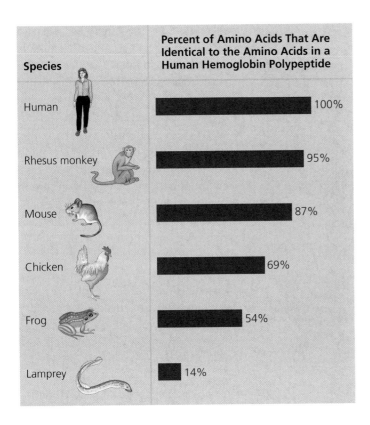

Species	Percent of Amino Acids That Are Identical to the Amino Acids in a Human Hemoglobin Polypeptide
Human	100%
Rhesus monkey	95%
Mouse	87%
Chicken	69%
Frog	54%
Lamprey	14%

▲ **Figure 22.16 Comparison of a protein found in diverse vertebrates.**

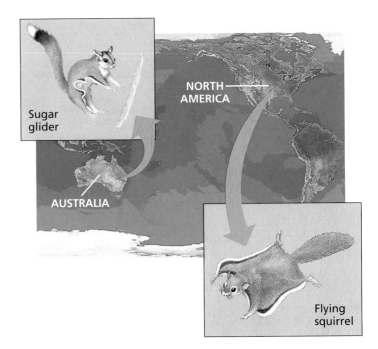

▲ **Figure 22.17 Different geographic regions, different mammalian "brands."** The sugar glider is an example of the diverse marsupial life that evolved in isolation on the island continent of Australia. While sugar gliders superficially resemble the eutherian flying squirrels of North America, the ability to glide through the air evolved independently in these two distantly related groups of mammals.

Biogeography

Darwin's observations of the geographic distribution of species—or **biogeography**—formed an important part of his theory of evolution. Closely related species tend to be found in the same geographic region, whereas the same ecological niches in distant regions are occupied by very different (though sometimes similar-looking) species. Consider Australia, which is home to a group of mammals—the marsupials—that are distinct from another group of mammals—the eutherians—that live elsewhere on Earth. (Eutherians are mammals that complete their embryonic development in the uterus, whereas marsupials are born as embryos and complete their development in an external pouch.) Some Australian marsupials have eutherian look-alikes with similar adaptations living on other continents. For instance, a forest-dwelling Australian marsupial called the sugar glider is superficially very similar to "flying" squirrels, gliding eutherians that live in North American forests **(Figure 22.17)**. But the sugar glider has many other characteristics that define it as distinctly marsupial, much more closely related to kangaroos and other Australian marsupials than to flying squirrels or other eutherians. Once again Darwin's theory can explain these observations. Although these two mammals have adapted to similar environments in similar ways, they evolved independently from different ancestors. The sugar glider is a marsupial not because that is a requirement for its gliding lifestyle, but simply because

its ancestors were marsupials. The unique fauna of Australia diversified after that island continent became isolated from the landmasses on which eutherians diversified. The resemblance between sugar gliders and flying squirrels is not homologous; rather, it is an example of what biologists call convergent evolution (we'll take a closer look at convergence in Chapter 25).

It's no wonder that Darwin's experiences in the Galápagos were so pivotal to his thinking, since islands are showcases of the influence of geography on evolution. They generally have many species of plants and animals that are **endemic**, which means they are found nowhere else in the world. And yet, as Darwin observed when he reassessed his collections from the voyage, most island species are closely related to species from the nearest mainland or neighboring island. This explains why two islands with similar environments in different parts of the world are populated not by closely related species but rather by species close to those of the nearest mainland, where the environment is often quite different. Island chains like the Galápagos, or archipelagos, are especially interesting in their biogeography. If a species that disperses from a mainland to an island succeeds in its new environment, it may give rise to several new species as populations spread to other islands in the archipelago. The finches of the Galápagos archipelago are an example of this process (see Figure 1.23), as are the hundreds of Hawaiian *Drosophila* species studied by Kenneth Kaneshiro (see interview on pages 436–437).

The Fossil Record

The succession of forms observed in the fossil record is consistent with other inferences about the major branches of descent in the tree of life. For instance, comparative data from biochemistry, molecular biology, and cell biology suggest that prokaryotes are the ancestors of all life and predict that prokaryotes should precede all eukaryotic life in the fossil record. Indeed, the oldest known fossils are prokaryotes (see Chapter 26).

The Darwinian view of life predicts that evolutionary transitions should leave signs in the fossil record. Paleontologists have discovered fossils of many such transitional forms that link ancient organisms to modern species. For example, researchers have found fossil evidence that birds descended from one branch of dinosaurs, and they have also found fossilized whales linking these aquatic mammals to their terrestrial ancestors **(Figure 22.18)**.

Darwin's theory endures in biology because it explains so many different kinds of observations: anatomical and molecular homologies that match patterns in space (biogeography) and time (the fossil record). Natural selection can also explain how similar adaptations can evolve independently among distantly related species, such as sugar gliders and flying squirrels.

▲ **Figure 22.18 A transitional fossil linking past and present.** The hypothesis that whales evolved from terrestrial (land-dwelling) ancestors predicts a four-limbed beginning for whales. Paleontologists digging in Egypt and Pakistan have identified extinct whales that had hind limbs. Shown here are the fossilized leg bones of *Basilosaurus,* one of those ancient whales. Other fossil whales have been found with larger or smaller limbs, and all are related to still older animals that spent only part of their time in the water.

What Is Theoretical about the Darwinian View of Life?

Some people dismiss the Darwinian view of life as "just a theory." However, as we have seen, Darwin's explanation makes sense of massive amounts of data, and the effects of natural selection can be observed in nature.

What, then, is theoretical about evolution? The term *theory* has a very different meaning in science than in everyday use. The colloquial use of the word *theory* comes close to what scientists mean by a hypothesis. In science, a theory is more comprehensive than a hypothesis. A theory, such as Newton's theory of gravitation or Darwin's theory of evolution by natural selection, accounts for many observations and data and attempts to explain and integrate a great variety of phenomena. Such a unifying theory does not become widely accepted unless its predictions stand up to thorough and continual testing by experiment and additional observation (see Chapter 1). As the next three chapters demonstrate, this has certainly been the case with the theory of evolution by natural selection.

The skepticism of scientists as they continue to test theories prevents these ideas from becoming dogma. For example, many evolutionary biologists now question whether natural selection is the only evolutionary mechanism responsible for the evolutionary history inferred from the fossil and molecular data. As we'll explore further in this unit, other factors have also played an important role, particularly in the evolution of genes and proteins. The study of evolution is livelier than ever as scientists find more ways to test the predictions of Darwin's theory.

By attributing the diversity of life to natural processes, Darwin gave biology a sound, scientific basis. Nevertheless, the diverse products of evolution remain elegant and inspiring. As Darwin said in the closing paragraph of *The Origin of Species,* "There is grandeur in this view of life. . . ."

Concept Check 22.3

1. Explain why the following statement is inaccurate: "Anti-HIV drugs have created drug resistance in the virus."
2. How does Darwin's theory account for both the similar mammalian forelimbs with different functions shown in Figure 22.14 and the similar lifestyle of the two distantly related mammals shown in Figure 22.17?
3. Explain how the fossil record can be used to test predictions of evolutionary theory.

For suggested answers, see Appendix A.

Go to the Campbell Biology website (www.campbellbiology.com) or CD-ROM to explore Activities, Investigations, and other interactive study aids.

SUMMARY OF KEY CONCEPTS

Concept 22.1

The Darwinian revolution challenged traditional views of a young Earth inhabited by unchanging species

▶ **Resistance to the Idea of Evolution (pp. 439–440)** Darwin's theory that life's diversity has arisen from fewer ancestral species through natural selection was a radical departure from the prevailing views of Western culture.

▶ **Theories of Gradualism (p. 440)** Geologists Hutton and Lyell perceived that changes in Earth's surface can result from slow, continuous actions still operating at the present time.

▶ **Lamarck's Theory of Evolution (pp. 440–441)** Lamarck hypothesized that species evolve, but the mechanisms he proposed are unsupported by evidence.

Concept 22.2

In *The Origin of Species*, Darwin proposed that species change through natural selection

▶ **Darwin's Research (pp. 441–443)** Darwin's experiences during the voyage of HMS *Beagle* provided much of the background for his idea that new species originate from ancestral forms through the gradual accumulation of adaptations. After returning to England, he refined his theory and finally published it in 1859 after learning that Wallace had the same idea.
Activity *Darwin and the Galápagos Islands*
Activity *The Voyage of the* Beagle: *Darwin's Trip Around the World*
Biology Labs On-Line *EvolutionLab*

▶ ***The Origin of Species* (pp. 443–446)** In his book describing his theory of descent with modification, Darwin recognized that there are heritable variations in populations and that some of those variations are better suited than others to a particular environment. Because organisms tend to produce many more offspring than the environment can support, there is a struggle for existence, and those that are better suited to the environment tend to have greater success in surviving and reproducing. Thus, these better-suited individuals leave more offspring than other individuals. Over time, this process of natural selection can result in adaptation of organisms to their environment.

Concept 22.3

Darwin's theory explains a wide range of observations

▶ **Natural Selection in Action (pp. 446–448)** Researchers have observed natural selection leading to adaptive evolution in wild guppy populations. In humans, the use of drugs selects for pathogens that through chance mutations are resistant to the drugs' effects. The ability of bacteria and viruses to evolve rapidly poses a challenge to our society.
Investigation *How Do Environmental Changes Affect a Population?*
Investigation *What Are the Patterns of Antibiotic Resistance?*

▶ **Homology, Biogeography, and the Fossil Record (pp. 448–451)** Evolutionary theory explains many kinds of observations, including structural and molecular similarities, geographic distribution of organisms, and the fossil record.
Activity *Reconstructing Forelimbs*

▶ **What Is Theoretical about the Darwinian View of Life? (p. 451)** Darwin's theory of evolution by natural selection integrates diverse areas of biological study and stimulates many new research questions.

TESTING YOUR KNOWLEDGE

Self-Quiz

1. Which of the following reflect aspects of Hutton and Lyell's ideas of gradualism that were incorporated into Darwin's theory of evolution?
   a. There is a struggle in populations for survival and reproduction.
   b. Natural selection acts on heritable variation.
   c. Small changes accumulated over vast spans of time can produce dramatic results.
   d. Characteristics acquired gradually over an organism's lifetime can lead to changes in the characteristics of the next generation.
   e. Homologous structures are found in organisms with a common ancestor.

2. Which of the following is *not* an observation or inference on which natural selection is based?
   a. There is heritable variation among individuals.
   b. Poorly adapted individuals never produce offspring.
   c. There is a struggle for limited resources, and only a fraction of offspring survive.
   d. Individuals whose characteristics are best suited to the environment generally leave more offspring than those whose characteristics are less well suited.
   e. Organisms interact with their environments.

3. Analysis of forelimb anatomy of humans, bats, and whales shows that humans and bats have fairly similar skeletal structures, while whales have diverged considerably in the shapes and proportions of their bones. However, analysis of several genes in these species suggests that all three diverged from a common ancestor at about the same time. Which of the following is the best explanation for these data?
   a. Humans and bats evolved by natural selection, and whales evolved by Lamarckian mechanisms.
   b. Evolution of human and bat forelimbs was adaptive, but not for whales.
   c. Natural selection in an aquatic environment resulted in significant changes to whale forelimb anatomy.
   d. Genes mutate more rapidly in whales than in humans or bats.
   e. Whales are not properly defined as mammals.

4. Which of the following observations helped Darwin shape his concept of descent with modification?
   a. Species diversity declines as distance from the equator increases.
   b. Fewer species are found living on islands than on the nearest continents.
   c. Birds can be found on islands that are farther from the mainland than the birds' maximum nonstop flight distance.
   d. South American temperate plants are more similar to the tropical plants of South America than to the temperate plants of Europe.
   e. Earthquakes reshape life by causing mass extinctions.

5. Darwin synthesized information from several sources in developing his theory of evolution by natural selection. Which of the following did *not* influence his thinking?
   a. Linnaeus' hierarchical classification of species
   b. Lyell's *Principles of Geology*
   c. observations of molecular homologies
   d. examples of major changes in domesticated species produced by artificial selection
   e. the distribution of species that he observed on the Galápagos Islands and during his journey around South America

6. In science, the term *theory* generally applies to an idea that
   a. is a speculation lacking supportive observations or experiments.
   b. attempts to explain many related phenomena.
   c. is synonymous with what biologists mean by a hypothesis.
   d. is considered a law of nature.
   e. all of the above.

7. Within a few weeks of treatment with the drug 3TC, a patient's HIV population consists entirely of 3TC-resistant viruses. How can this result best be explained?
   a. HIV has the ability to change its surface proteins and resist vaccines.
   b. The patient must have become reinfected with 3TC-resistant viruses.
   c. HIV began making drug-resistant versions of reverse transcriptase in response to the drug.
   d. A few drug-resistant viruses were present at the start of treatment, and natural selection increased their frequency.
   e. The drug caused the HIV RNA to change.

8. The smallest biological unit that can evolve over time is
   a. a cell.
   b. an individual organism.
   c. a population.
   d. a species.
   e. an ecosystem.

9. Which of the following ideas is common to both Darwin's and Lamarck's theories of evolution?
   a. Adaptation results from differential reproductive success.
   b. Evolution drives organisms to greater and greater complexity.
   c. Evolutionary adaptation results from interactions between organisms and their environments.
   d. Adaptation results from the use and disuse of anatomical structures.
   e. The fossil record supports the view that species are fixed.

10. Which of the following pairs of structures is *least* likely to represent homology?
   a. the wings of a bat and the forelimbs of a human
   b. the hemoglobin of a baboon and that of a gorilla
   c. the mitochondria of a plant and those of an animal
   d. the wings of a bird and those of an insect
   e. the brain of a cat and that of a dog

For Self-Quiz answers, see Appendix A.

Go to the website or CD-ROM for more quiz questions.

Evolution Connection

Explain why anatomical and molecular homologies generally fit a similar nested pattern.

Scientific Inquiry

Darwin's argument for the idea that evolution has occurred is largely inductive, while his argument for the mechanism of natural selection is essentially deductive. Summarize in your own words the inductive and deductive components of Darwin's theory. (You can review induction and deduction in Chapter 1.)

Investigation *How Do Environmental Changes Affect a Population?*
Investigation *What Are the Patterns of Antibiotic Resistance?*
Biology Labs On-Line *EvolutionLab*

Science, Technology, and Society

Is the concept of natural selection relevant in an economic or political context? In other words, if a particular corporation or nation achieves success or dominance, does this mean that it is fitter than its competitors and that dominance is justified? Why or why not?

23

The Evolution of Populations

Key Concepts

23.1 Population genetics provides a foundation for studying evolution

23.2 Mutation and sexual recombination produce the variation that makes evolution possible

23.3 Natural selection, genetic drift, and gene flow can alter a population's genetic composition

23.4 Natural selection is the primary mechanism of adaptive evolution

Overview

The Smallest Unit of Evolution

One common misconception about evolution is that individual organisms evolve, in the Darwinian sense, during their lifetimes. It is true that natural selection acts on individuals; each organism's combination of traits affects its survival and reproductive success compared to other individuals. But the evolutionary impact of natural selection is only apparent in the changes in a population of organisms over time. Consider, for example, the collection of shells from a population of Cuban tree snails (*Polymita picta*) shown in **Figure 23.1**. Their different patterns and colors are largely the result of genetic differences among the individuals. Suppose that predators are less likely to feed on snails with a particular coloration, perhaps because these snails are better camouflaged against their surroundings. The proportion of snails of that color will tend to increase from one generation to the next. Thus, the population, not its individual members, evolves; some traits become more common within the population, while other traits become less common.

Concept 23.1

Population genetics provides a foundation for studying evolution

Today we can define evolutionary change on its smallest scale, or **microevolution,** as change in the genetic makeup of a population from generation to generation **(Figure 23.2).** But Darwin did not define evolution in this way. In natural selection, Darwin had found a mechanism for change in species

▲ **Figure 23.2 Individuals are selected; populations evolve.** The bent grass (*Agrostis tenuis*) in the foreground is growing on the tailings of an abandoned mine. These plants tolerate concentrations of heavy metals that are toxic to other plants of the same species in the pasture beyond the fence. Many seeds from the pasture drift onto the tailings, but only those with genes that enable them to tolerate metallic soil survive and reproduce.

over time. However, he did not have a satisfactory explanation for how the heritable variations required for natural selection appear in populations or how organisms transmit these variations to their offspring. Ideas about inheritance from Darwin's time could not explain how inherited variations are maintained in populations. For instance, the widely accepted blending hypothesis proposed that the traits of parents are blended in the offspring. But Darwin and others realized that over time, blending would eliminate the differences between individuals. Although breeding experiments and observations of nature refuted this prediction, Darwin lacked an alternate model of inheritance that could support his hypothesis.

Just a few years after Darwin published *On the Origin of Species*, Gregor Mendel proposed just such a model: the particulate hypothesis of inheritance, which stated that parents pass on discrete heritable units (genes) that retain their identities in offspring. But Darwin never saw Mendel's paper, and its implications were not understood by the few scientists who read it at the time. Mendel's contribution to evolutionary theory was not appreciated until half a century later.

The Modern Synthesis

Ironically, when Mendel's work was reconsidered in the early 20th century, many geneticists thought that his laws of inheritance were at odds with Darwin's theory. Darwin considered the raw material for natural selection to be "quantitative" characters—those characteristics in a population that vary along a continuum, such as fur length in mammals or the running speed of animals fleeing from predators. But Mendel and other early geneticists worked only with discrete "either-or" traits, such as purple or white flowers in pea plants. It was therefore not obvious that there was a genetic basis to the more subtle variations that were central to Darwin's theory. Within a few decades, however, geneticists determined that quantitative characters are influenced by multiple genetic loci and that the alleles at each of these loci follow Mendelian patterns of inheritance (see Chapter 14). These discoveries helped reconcile Darwin's and Mendel's ideas and led to the formal founding of **population genetics,** the study of how populations change genetically over time.

By the mid-20th century, population genetics also gave rise to what is called the **modern synthesis,** a comprehensive theory of evolution that integrated ideas from many other fields. The first architects of the modern synthesis included statistician R. A. Fisher (1890–1962), who demonstrated the rules by which Mendelian characters are inherited, and biologist J. B. S. Haldane (1892–1964), who studied the rules of natural selection. Later contributors included geneticists Theodosius Dobzhansky (1900–1975) and Sewall Wright (1889–1988), biogeographer Ernst Mayr (1904–), paleontologist George Gaylord Simpson (1902–1984), and botanist G. Ledyard Stebbins (1906–2000).

Of course, scientific paradigms rarely endure without modification. The modern synthesis is still expanding to integrate, for example, the discovery of genetic changes in populations caused by mechanisms other than natural selection. Although the modern synthesis itself continues to evolve, its focus on populations has shaped much of our current thinking about evolutionary processes.

Gene Pools and Allele Frequencies

Before continuing our discussion of population genetics, we need to define what we mean by a population. A **population** is a localized group of individuals that are capable of interbreeding and producing fertile offspring. Populations of the same species may be isolated from one another, thus exchanging genetic material only rarely. Such isolation is common for populations confined to different, widely separated islands or lakes. But not all populations are isolated, nor must they have sharp boundaries **(Figure 23.3)**. Still, individuals near the population center are more likely to breed with members of their own population than other populations and thus on average are more closely related to one another than to members of other populations.

The total aggregate of genes in a population at any one time is called the population's **gene pool.** It consists of all

▲ **Figure 23.3 One species, two populations.** These two caribou populations in the Yukon are not totally isolated—they sometimes share the same area. Nonetheless, members of either population are more likely to breed with members of their own population than with members of the other population.

alleles at all gene loci in all individuals of the population. If only one allele exists at a particular locus in a population, that allele is said to be *fixed* in the gene pool, and all individuals are homozygous for that allele. (Recall that homozygous individuals have two identical alleles for a given locus, while heterozygous individuals have two different alleles at that locus.) But if there are two or more alleles for a particular locus in a population, individuals may be either homozygous or heterozygous.

Each allele has a frequency (proportion) in the population. For example, imagine a population of 500 wildflower plants with two alleles, C^R and C^W, at a locus that codes for flower pigment. Plants homozygous for the C^R allele ($C^R C^R$) produce red pigment and have red flowers; plants homozygous for the C^W allele ($C^W C^W$) produce no red pigment and have white flowers; and heterozygotes ($C^R C^W$) produce some red pigment and have pink flowers. In our population there are 320 plants with red flowers, 160 with pink flowers, and 20 with white flowers. These alleles show incomplete dominance (see Chapter 14). Because these are diploid organisms, there are a total of 1,000 copies of genes for flower color in the population of 500 individuals. The C^R allele accounts for 800 of these genes ($320 \times 2 = 640$ for $C^R C^R$ plants, plus $160 \times 1 = 160$ for $C^R C^W$ plants).

When there are two alleles at a particular locus, the convention is to use p to represent the frequency of one allele and q to represent the frequency of the other allele. Thus, p, the frequency of the C^R allele in the gene pool of this population, is $800/1,000 = 0.8 = 80\%$. And because there are only two allelic forms of this gene, then the frequency of the C^W allele, represented by q, must be 0.2, or 20%. At loci that have more than two alleles, the sum of all allele frequencies must still equal 1 (100%).

We can easily measure genetic variability at this flower-color locus because each genotype has a distinct phenotype. Although many loci in gene pools have more than one allele, this variability is usually less easy to quantify than in our flower example, because one allele may be completely dominant or the alleles may not have obvious effects on phenotypes.

The Hardy-Weinberg Theorem

In a moment we will explore how genes and allele frequencies can change over time, representing evolutionary change. But first, to provide a benchmark against which to measure such changes, we'll investigate the properties of gene pools that are *not* evolving. Such gene pools are described by the **Hardy-Weinberg theorem**, named for the two scientists who independently derived the principle in 1908. The theorem states that the frequencies of alleles and genotypes in a population's gene pool remain constant from generation to generation, provided that only Mendelian segregation and recombination of alleles are at work **(Figure 23.4)**.

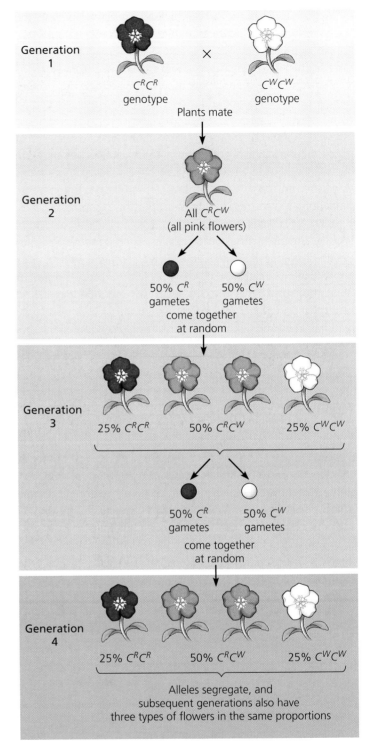

▲ **Figure 23.4 Mendelian inheritance preserves genetic variation from one generation to the next.**

Preservation of Allele Frequencies

The Hardy-Weinberg theorem describes how Mendelian inheritance preserves genetic variation from one generation to the next in populations that are not evolving. But it does more than this. We will see that the theorem lays the groundwork for understanding long-term evolutionary changes that Darwin, lacking knowledge of genetics, could not have envisioned. The preservation of genetic variation provides the opportunity for natural selection to act over many generations.

Let's apply the Hardy-Weinberg theorem to our hypothetical wildflower population. Recall that 80% (0.8) of the flower-color alleles in the gene pool are C^R and 20% (0.2) are C^W. Because each gamete produced by the flowers is haploid, it carries only one allele for flower color. The chance that a gamete will carry a C^R allele is 0.8, and the chance that it will carry a C^W allele is 0.2. The allele frequencies in all the gametes produced by the population will be the same as in the original population. Provided that gametes are contributed to the next generation at random, allele frequencies will be unchanged.

Hardy-Weinberg Equilibrium

Suppose that the individuals in a population not only donate gametes to the next generation at random but also mate at random—that is, all male-female matings are equally likely. Not only will this population have the same allele frequencies from one generation to the next, but its genotype frequencies can be predicted from the allele frequencies. Such populations are in a state of **Hardy-Weinberg equilibrium.**

It turns out that our wildflower population is in Hardy-Weinberg equilibrium (**Figure 23.5**). Using the rule of multiplication (see Chapter 14), we can calculate the frequencies of the three possible genotypes assuming random unions of sperm and ova. The probability that two C^R alleles will come together is $0.8 \times 0.8 = p \times p = p^2 = 0.64$. Thus, about 64% of the plants in the next generation will have the genotype $C^R C^R$. The frequency of $C^W C^W$ individuals will be about $0.2 \times 0.2 = q^2 = 0.04$, or 4%. $C^R C^W$ heterozygotes can arise in two different ways. If the sperm provides the C^R allele and the ovum provides the C^W allele, the resulting heterozygotes will be $0.8 \times 0.2 = 16\%$ of the total. If the ovum provides the C^R allele and the sperm the C^W allele, the heterozygous offspring will make up another $0.8 \times 0.2 = 16\%$. We can summarize these unions of gametes in an algebraic equation:

$$(p + q) \quad \times \quad (p + q) \quad = \quad p^2 + 2pq + q^2$$

Allele frequencies of male gametes	Allele frequencies of female gametes	Genotype frequencies in the next generation

As with allele frequencies, all of these genotype frequencies sum to 1. Thus, the equation for Hardy-Weinberg equilibrium states that at a locus with two alleles, the three genotypes will appear in the following proportions:

$$p^2 + 2pq + q^2 = 1$$

If a population were in Hardy-Weinberg equilibrium and its members continued to mate randomly generation after generation, allele and genotype frequencies would remain constant. The system operates somewhat like a deck of cards: No matter how many times the deck is reshuffled to deal out new hands, the deck itself remains the same. Aces do not grow more numerous than jacks. And the repeated shuffling of a population's

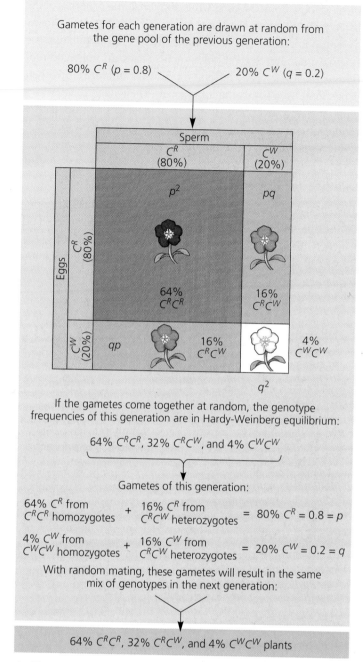

▲ **Figure 23.5 The Hardy-Weinberg theorem.** In our wildflower population, the gene pool remains constant from one generation to the next. Mendelian processes alone do not alter frequencies of alleles or genotypes.

gene pool over the generations cannot, in itself, change the frequency of one allele relative to another.

Note that a population does not need to be in Hardy-Weinberg equilibrium for its allele frequencies to remain constant. Many species, such as the peas that Mendel used in his experiments, do not mate randomly. Since pea pollen normally matures before the flower opens, it fertilizes the same flower that contains it. (In fact, Mendel could cross plants only by artificial fertilization.) Because of self-fertilization, pea populations are far from Hardy-Weinberg equilibrium. All the homozygous plants produce only homozygotes, while about half the offspring of the heterozygous plants are homozygous. It does not take many generations before almost all the plants in the population are homozygous. But even though such species do not mate randomly, they still produce their gametes at random from their gene pools. Without other influences, their allele frequencies will not change over time. Just as in populations that do mate at random, genetic variation—the raw material for evolutionary change—is preserved even in the self-fertilizing peas.

Conditions for Hardy-Weinberg Equilibrium

The Hardy-Weinberg theorem describes a hypothetical population that is not evolving. But in real populations, allele and genotype frequencies *do* change over time. This is because the following five conditions for non-evolving populations are rarely met for long in nature:

1. *Extremely large population size.* The smaller the population, the greater the role played by chance fluctuations in allele frequencies from one generation to the next, known as genetic drift.
2. *No gene flow.* Gene flow, the transfer of alleles between populations, can alter allele frequencies.
3. *No mutations.* By introducing or removing genes from chromosomes or by changing one allele into another, mutations modify the gene pool.
4. *Random mating.* If individuals preferentially choose mates with certain genotypes, including close relatives (inbreeding), random mixing of gametes does not occur.
5. *No natural selection.* Differential survival and reproductive success of individuals carrying different genotypes will alter allele frequencies.

Departure from these conditions usually results in evolution. While natural populations rarely if ever are in true Hardy-Weinberg equilibrium, in many populations the rate of evolutionary change is so slow that these populations *appear* to be close to equilibrium. This enables us to obtain approximate estimates of allele and genotype frequencies, as the following example shows.

Population Genetics and Human Health

The Hardy-Weinberg equation can be used to estimate the percentage of the population carrying the allele for an inherited disease. For example, about one out of every 10,000 babies in the United States is born with phenylketonuria (PKU), a metabolic disorder that results from homozygosity for a recessive allele. Left untreated, PKU results in mental retardation and other problems. (Newborns are now tested for PKU,

and their symptoms can be lessened with a phenylalanine-free diet.)

To use the Hardy-Weinberg equation, we must assume that people do not choose their mates because of whether or not they carry this gene and do not generally mate with close relatives (inbreeding). We must also neglect any effects of gene flow from other populations into the United States, introduction of new PKU mutations, and differential survival and reproductive success among PKU genotypes. These assumptions are reasonable, since inbreeding in the United States is not common, populations outside the United States have PKU allele frequencies similar to those seen in the United States, the mutation rate for the PKU gene is low, and selection occurs only against the rare homozygotes.

If all these assumptions hold, then the frequency of individuals in the population born with PKU will correspond to q^2 in the Hardy-Weinberg equation (q^2 = frequency of the homozygotes for this allele). Because the allele is recessive, we must estimate the number of heterozygotes rather than counting them directly as we did with the pink flowers. Since we know there is one PKU occurrence per 10,000 births (q^2 = 0.0001), the frequency of the recessive allele for PKU is

$$q = \sqrt{0.0001} = 0.01$$

and the frequency of the dominant allele is

$$p = 1 - q = 1 - 0.01 = 0.99$$

The frequency of carriers, heterozygous people who do not have PKU but may pass the PKU allele to offspring, is

$$2pq = 2 \times 0.99 \times 0.01 = 0.0198 \text{ (approximately 2\% of the U.S. population)}$$

Remember, the assumption of Hardy-Weinberg equilibrium results in only an approximation; the real number of carriers may be somewhat different. Nevertheless, we can conclude that many harmful recessive alleles at this and other loci are concealed in the human population because they are carried by healthy heterozygotes.

Concept Check 23.1

1. What did Mendel's findings about genetics add to Darwin's theory of evolution by natural selection?
2. Suppose a population of organisms with 500 gene loci is fixed at half of these loci, and has two alleles at each of the other loci. How many alleles are found in its gene pool? Explain.
3. Which term in the Hardy-Weinberg equation ($p^2 + 2pq + q^2 = 1$) corresponds to the frequency of individuals with PKU alleles?

For suggested answers, see Appendix A.

Mutation and sexual recombination produce the variation that makes evolution possible

As you have learned, natural selection operates on the heritable differences, often slight ones, among individuals in a population. Two processes, mutation and sexual recombination, produce the variation in gene pools that contributes to these individual differences.

Mutation

New genes and new alleles originate only by **mutations** (**Figure 23.6**), which are changes in the nucleotide sequence of DNA. A mutation is like a shot in the dark—it is not possible to predict how it will alter DNA and what its effects will be. Most mutations occur in somatic cells and are lost when the individual dies. Only mutations in cell lines that produce gametes can be passed to offspring, and only a small fraction of these spread through populations.

Point Mutations

A change of as little as one base in a gene—a "point mutation"—can have a significant impact on phenotype, as in sickle-cell disease (see Figure 5.21). But most point mutations are probably harmless. One reason is that much of the DNA in eukaryotic genomes does not code for protein products. And because the genetic code is redundant, even point mutations in genes that code for protein may have little effect because they do not alter the protein's amino acid composition (see

▲ **Figure 23.6 Mutations are the source of all heritable variation.** The diverse coat colors of these wild mustangs are the products of past mutations over many generations.

Figure 17.24). However, some noncoding regions of DNA *do* regulate the expression of genes. Changes in these regulatory regions of DNA can have profound effects.

Organisms reflect thousands of generations of past selection, and a single mutational change is about as likely to improve the genome as blindly firing a gunshot through the hood of a car is likely to improve engine performance. On rare occasions, however, a mutant allele may actually make its bearer better suited to the environment, enhancing reproductive success. This is more likely when the environment is changing and mutations that were once selected against become favorable. For example, as you read in Chapter 22, certain mutations that make HIV resistant to particular drugs also slow its reproductive rate. Only after the drugs were introduced were these mutant alleles favored, and natural selection increased their frequency as a result.

Mutations that Alter Gene Number or Sequence

Chromosomal mutations that delete, disrupt, or rearrange many loci at once are almost certain to be harmful. However, when such mutations leave genes intact, their effects on organisms may be neutral. In rare cases, chromosomal rearrangements may even be beneficial. For example, the translocation of part of one chromosome to a different chromosome could link genes that together have some heightened positive effect.

Gene **duplication** is an important source of variation. Duplications of chromosome segments, like other chromosomal mutations, are nearly always harmful. But smaller pieces of DNA are often introduced into a genome through the activity of transposable elements (see Chapter 19). If such a duplicated segment does not have severe effects, it can persist over generations, providing an expanded genome with new loci that may take on new functions by further mutations and subsequent selection. New genes may also arise when the coding portions of genes (exons) are shuffled within the genome.

Such beneficial increases in gene number appear to have played a major role in evolution. For example, the remote ancestors of mammals carried a single gene for detecting odors that has been duplicated through a variety of mutational mechanisms. As a result, modern humans have close to 1,000 olfactory receptor genes, and mice have 1,300. About 60% of human olfactory receptor genes have been inactivated by subsequent mutations, whereas mice have lost only 20% of theirs—a remarkable demonstration that a versatile sense of smell is more important to mice than it is to us!

Mutation Rates

Mutation rates tend to be low in animals and plants, averaging about one mutation in every 100,000 genes per generation. But in microorganisms and viruses with short generation spans, mutations can rapidly generate genetic variation. For instance, the HIV virus has a generation span of about two days and an RNA genome, which has a much higher mutation rate than a typical

DNA genome. For this reason, single-drug treatments will probably never be effective against HIV—mutant forms of the virus that are resistant to a particular drug are likely to appear in relatively short order. Even double-drug treatments rarely work for long, because viruses with double mutations conferring resistance to *both* drugs arise daily. This explains why the most effective AIDS treatments at this time are drug "cocktails" combining several medications. It is less likely that multiple mutations against *all* the drugs will occur in a short time period.

Sexual Recombination

In sexually reproducing populations, sexual recombination is far more important than mutation on a generation-to-generation time scale in producing the variations that make adaptation possible. Nearly all phenotypic variations based on genetic differences result from recombinational shuffling of the existing alleles in the gene pool. (Of course, this allelic variation originated from past mutations.) A population contains myriad possible mating combinations, and fertilization brings together the gametes of individuals that are likely to have different genetic backgrounds. Sexual reproduction rearranges alleles into fresh combinations every generation.

Bacteria and many viruses can also undergo recombination, but they do so less regularly than animals and plants and often in ways that allow them to cross species barriers (see Chapter 18). Many of the genes of the *Escherichia coli* bacterium O157:H7, a frequent culprit in food poisoning cases, are actually "mosaics" of genes from different types of bacteria. The ability of pathogens to evolve rapidly through such extensive recombination, combined with their high mutation rates, makes them especially dangerous adversaries.

Concept Check 23.2

1. Of all the mutations that occur, why do only a small fraction become widespread in a gene pool?
2. How does sexual recombination produce variation?

For suggested answers, see Appendix A.

Concept 23.3

Natural selection, genetic drift, and gene flow can alter a population's genetic composition

Note again on page 458 the five conditions required for a population to be in Hardy-Weinberg equilibrium. A deviation from any of these conditions is a potential cause of evolution. However, although new mutations can modify allele frequencies, the change from one generation to the next is likely to be small. Recombination reshuffles alleles, but does not change their frequencies. Nonrandom mating can affect the relative frequencies of homozygous and heterozygous genotypes but usually has no effect on allele frequencies. The three major factors that alter allele frequencies and bring about most evolutionary change are natural selection, genetic drift, and gene flow.

Natural Selection

As you read in Chapter 22, Darwin's concept of natural selection is based on differential success in reproduction: Individuals in a population exhibit variations in their heritable traits, and those with variations that are better suited to their environment tend to produce more offspring than those with variations that are less well suited.

We now know that selection results in alleles being passed to the next generation in proportions different from their relative frequencies in the present generation. For example, in our imaginary wildflower population, white flowers ($C^W C^W$) might be more visible to plant-eating insects, resulting in more white flowers being eaten. And perhaps red flowers ($C^R C^R$) are more attractive to pollinators, increasing the opportunity for red flowers to produce offspring. These differences in survival and reproductive success would disturb Hardy-Weinberg equilibrium: The frequency of the C^W allele would decline in the gene pool, and the frequency of the C^R allele would increase. Later in the chapter, we'll examine the process of natural selection more closely.

Genetic Drift

Flip a coin 1,000 times, and a result of 700 heads and 300 tails would make you suspicious about that coin. But flip a coin 10 times, and an outcome of 7 heads and 3 tails would not be surprising. The smaller the sample, the greater the chance of deviation from the predicted result—in this case, an equal number of heads and tails.

Similar deviations from the expected result—which occur because real populations are finite in size rather than infinite—explain how allele frequencies can fluctuate unpredictably from one generation to the next. Such fluctuations are called **genetic drift**. Consider the example in **Figure 23.7**. Note that in this example, one of the alleles has been lost by an indiscriminant event; that is, it was a matter of likelihood that the C^W allele rather than the C^R allele was lost. Over time, drift tends to reduce genetic variation through such losses of alleles from the gene pool.

Two situations that can increase the likelihood that genetic drift will have a large impact on a population are referred to as the bottleneck effect and the founder effect.

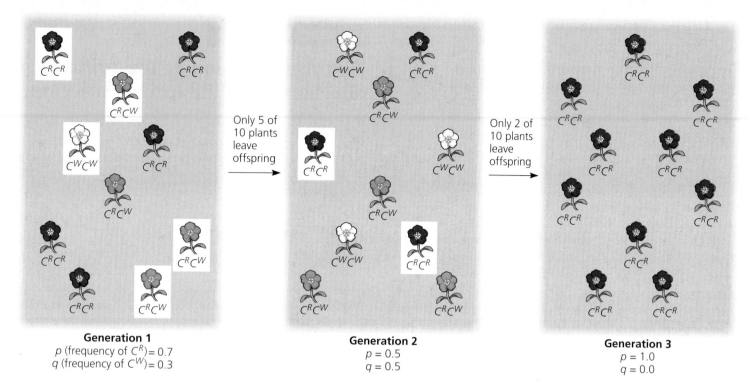

Generation 1
p (frequency of C^R) = 0.7
q (frequency of C^W) = 0.3

Generation 2
p = 0.5
q = 0.5

Generation 3
p = 1.0
q = 0.0

▲ **Figure 23.7 Genetic drift.** This small wildflower population has a stable size of ten plants. Only five plants (those in white boxes) of generation 1 produce fertile offspring. By chance, only two plants of generation 2 manage to leave fertile offspring. The C^W allele first increases in generation 2, then falls to zero in generation 3.

The Bottleneck Effect

A disaster caused by a sudden change in the environment may drastically reduce the size of a population. In effect, the few survivors have passed through a restrictive "bottleneck," and their gene pool may no longer be reflective of the original population's gene pool; this is called the **bottleneck effect** **(Figure 23.8a)**. By chance, certain alleles may be overrepresented among the survivors, others may be underrepresented, and some may be eliminated altogether. Genetic drift may continue to substantially change the gene pool for many generations until the population is large enough that chance fluctuations have less effect.

One reason that understanding the bottleneck effect is important is that human actions can sometimes create severe bottlenecks for other species. For example, in the 1890s, hunters reduced the population of northern elephant seals in California to about 20 individuals. Since then, this mammal has become a protected species, and the population has rebounded to over 30,000 **(Figure 23.8b)**. However, in examining 24 gene loci in a representative sample of the seals, researchers found *no* variation: For each of the 24 genes, there was only one allele. In contrast, populations of the southern elephant seal, a closely related species that was not bottlenecked, show abundant genetic variation.

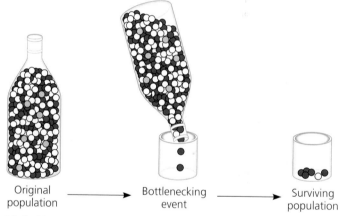

(a) Shaking just a few marbles through the narrow neck of a bottle is analogous to a drastic reduction in the size of a population after some environmental disaster. By chance, blue marbles are overrepresented in the new population and gold marbles are absent.

Original population → Bottlenecking event → Surviving population

(b) Similarly, bottlenecking a population of organisms tends to reduce genetic variation, as in these northern elephant seals in California that were once hunted nearly to extinction.

▲ **Figure 23.8 The bottleneck effect.**

The Founder Effect

When a few individuals become isolated from a larger population, this smaller group may establish a new population whose gene pool is not reflective of the source population; this is called the **founder effect.** For example, the founder effect can occur when a few members of a population colonize a new location. These founders pass through an "isolation bottleneck" and represent a distinct gene pool with different allele frequencies from those of the parent population.

The founder effect probably accounts for the relatively high frequency of certain inherited disorders among isolated human populations. For example, in 1814, 15 colonists founded a British settlement on Tristan da Cunha, a group of small islands in the Atlantic Ocean midway between Africa and South America. Apparently, one of the colonists carried a recessive allele for retinitis pigmentosa, a progressive form of blindness that afflicts homozygous individuals. Of the 240 descendants living on the island in the late 1960s, four had the disease. The frequency of this allele remains ten times higher on Tristan da Cunha than in the populations from which the founders came.

Gene Flow

A population may gain or lose alleles by **gene flow,** genetic additions to and/or subtractions from a population resulting from the movement of fertile individuals or gametes. Suppose, for example, that near our original hypothetical wildflower population there is a newly established wildflower population consisting primarily of white-flowered individuals ($C^W C^W$). Insects carrying pollen from these plants may fly to and pollinate plants in our original population. The introduced C^W alleles will modify our original population's allele frequencies in the next generation.

Gene flow tends to reduce differences between populations. If it is extensive enough, gene flow can amalgamate neighboring populations into a single population with a common gene pool. For example, humans today move much more freely about the world than in the past, and gene flow has become an important agent of evolutionary change in human populations that were previously quite isolated.

Concept Check 23.3

1. In what sense is natural selection more "predictable" than genetic drift?
2. Distinguish genetic drift and gene flow in terms of (a) how they occur and (b) their implications for future genetic variation in a population.

For suggested answers, see Appendix A.

Concept 23.4

Natural selection is the primary mechanism of adaptive evolution

Of all the factors that can change a gene pool, only natural selection is likely to adapt a population to its environment. Natural selection accumulates and maintains favorable genotypes in a population. As you have read, the process of selection depends on the existence of genetic variation.

Genetic Variation

You probably have no trouble recognizing your friends in a crowd. Each person has a unique genome, reflected in individual phenotypic variations such as appearance, voice, and temperament. Individual variation occurs in populations of all species. Although most people are very conscious of human diversity, we are generally less sensitive to individuality in other organisms. But variations are always present, and as Darwin realized, variations that are heritable are the raw material for natural selection. In addition to the differences that we can see or hear, populations have extensive genetic variation that can only be observed at the molecular level. For example, you cannot identify a person's blood group (A, B, AB, or O) from his or her appearance.

Not all phenotypic variation is heritable **(Figure 23.9)**. Phenotype is the cumulative product of an inherited genotype and a multitude of environmental influences. For example, bodybuilders alter their phenotypes dramatically but do not pass their huge muscles on to the next generation. It is important to remember that only the genetic component of variation can have evolutionary consequences as a result of natural selection.

(a) Map butterflies that emerge in spring: orange and brown

(b) Map butterflies that emerge in late summer: black and white

▲ **Figure 23.9 Nonheritable variation within a population.** These European map butterflies are seasonal forms of the same species (*Araschnia levana*). Owing to seasonal differences in hormones, **(a)** individuals that emerge in the spring are orange and brown, while **(b)** individuals that emerge in the late summer are black and white. These two forms are genetically identical at the loci for coloration. Therefore, if these two forms differ in reproductive success, that in itself would not lead to any change in the ability of the butterflies to develop in these two different ways.

Variation Within a Population

Both discrete and quantitative characters contribute to variation *within* a population. *Discrete characters,* such as the red, pink, and white colors of our hypothetical wildflower population, can be classified on an either-or basis (each plant has flowers that are all either red or pink or white). Discrete characters often are determined by a single gene locus with different alleles that produce distinct phenotypes. However, as discussed in Chapter 22, most heritable variation consists of *quantitative characters* that vary along a continuum within a population. Heritable quantitative variation results from the influence of two or more genes on a single phenotypic character.

Polymorphism. When individuals differ in a discrete character, the different forms are called *morphs*. A population is said to display **phenotypic polymorphism** for a character if two or more distinct morphs are each represented in high enough frequencies to be readily noticeable. (Obviously, the definition of "readily noticeable" is somewhat subjective, but a population is not considered polymorphic if it consists primarily of a single morph and other morphs are extremely rare.)

In contrast, height variation in the human population does not show phenotypic polymorphism because it does not consist of distinct and separate morphs—heights vary along a continuum. Nonetheless, polymorphisms play a role in such characters at the genetic level. The heritable component of height is the result of such **genetic polymorphisms** for alleles at the several loci that influence height.

Measuring Genetic Variation. Population geneticists measure the number of polymorphisms in a population by determining the amount of heterozygosity at both the level of whole genes (gene variability) and the molecular level of DNA (nucleotide variability). To see how this works, consider a population of fruit flies (*Drosophila*). The genome of a fruit fly has about 13,000 loci. The **average heterozygosity** of *Drosophila* is measured as the average percent of these loci that are heterozygous. On average, a fruit fly is heterozygous (has two different alleles) at about 14% of its loci. You can therefore say that the fly population has an average heterozygosity of 14%, meaning that a typical fruit fly is heterozygous at about 1,800 of its 13,000 gene loci and homozygous at all the rest.

Nucleotide variability is measured by comparing the nucleotide sequences of DNA samples from two individuals and then averaging the data from many such comparisons. The fruit fly genome has about 180 million nucleotides, and the sequences of any two flies differ on average by approximately 1%.

Why does average heterozygosity tend to be greater than nucleotide variability? This occurs because a gene can consist of thousands of bases of DNA. A difference at only one of these bases is sufficient to make two alleles of that gene different and count toward average heterozygosity.

Based on measurements of nucleotide variability, humans have relatively little genetic variation compared to most species. Two humans differ by only about 0.1% of their bases, a tenth of the nucleotide variability found within *Drosophila* populations. Clearly, we humans are all far more genetically alike than we are different. Still, this 0.1% nucleotide variability encompasses the entire heritable component of the many different ways that people look, sound, and act, along with their biochemical differences, such as ABO blood group, that are not outwardly visible.

Variation Between Populations

Most species exhibit **geographic variation,** differences between the gene pools of separate populations or population subgroups. **Figure 23.10** illustrates an example of geographic variation observed in isolated populations of house mice (*Mus musculus*) that were inadvertently introduced to the Atlantic island of Madeira by Portuguese settlers in the 15th century.

▲ **Figure 23.10 Geographic variation in chromosomal mutations.** Separated by mountains, several populations of house mice on the island of Madeira have evolved in isolation from one another. Researchers have observed differences in the karyotypes (chromosome sets) of these isolated populations. In some of the populations, the original chromosomes have become fused. For example, "2.4" indicates fusion of chromosome 2 and chromosome 4. However, the patterns of fused chromosomes differ from one mouse population to another. Mice in the areas indicated by the gold dots have the set of fused chromosomes in the gold box; mice in the locales with the red dots have the different pattern of fusions in the red box. Because these mutations leave genes intact, their effects on the mice appear to be neutral.

Because environmental factors are likely to differ from one place to another, natural selection can contribute to geographic variation. For example, one population of our hypothetical wildflower species might have a higher frequency of C^W alleles than other populations because local pollinators prefer white flowers. Genetic drift can also produce allele frequency differences between populations through the cumulative effect of random fluctuations in frequencies rather than natural selection.

Some examples of geographic variation occur as a **cline**, a graded change in a trait along a geographic axis. In some cases, a cline may represent a graded region of overlap where individuals of neighboring populations are interbreeding. In other cases, a gradation in some environmental variable may produce a cline. For example, the average body size of many North American species of birds and mammals increases gradually with increasing latitude. Presumably, the reduced ratio of surface area to volume that accompanies larger size is an adaptation that helps animals conserve body heat in cold environments. Experimental studies of many clines have confirmed that both genetic variation and environment play a role in the geographic differences of phenotype **(Figure 23.11)**.

A Closer Look at Natural Selection

From the range of available variations in a population, natural selection increases the frequencies of certain genotypes, fitting organisms to their environment over generations. This section takes a closer look at natural selection as a mechanism of evolutionary adaptation.

Evolutionary Fitness

The phrases "struggle for existence" and "survival of the fittest" are commonly used to describe natural selection, yet these expressions are misleading if taken to mean direct competitive contests among individuals. There *are* animal species in which individuals, usually the males, lock horns or otherwise do combat to determine mating privilege. But reproductive success is generally subtler and depends on many factors besides outright battles for mates. For example, a barnacle may produce more eggs than its neighbors because it is more efficient at collecting food from the water. A moth may have more offspring than other moths in the same population because its body colors more effectively conceal it from predators. Wildflowers may differ in reproductive success because some attract more pollinators owing to slight variations in color, shape, or fragrance. These are all examples of adaptive advantage, and they are all components of what we call **fitness**: the contribution an individual makes to the gene pool of the next generation, relative to the contributions of other individuals.

In a more quantitative approach to natural selection, population geneticists define **relative fitness** as the contribution of a genotype to the next generation compared to the contributions of alternative genotypes for the same locus. Consider our wildflower population once again. Let's assume that, on average, individuals with red flowers produce fewer offspring than those with white or pink flowers, which produce equal numbers of offspring. The relative fitness of the most reproductively successful variants is set at 1 as a basis for comparison, so the relative fitness of a white-flowered or pink-flowered plant is 1. If plants with red flowers average only 80% as many offspring, their relative fitness is 0.8.

Although population geneticists often refer to the relative fitness of a genotype, it is important to remember that natural selection acts on phenotypes, not genotypes. The entity that is subjected to natural selection is the whole organism. Thus, the relative fitness of a particular allele depends on the entire genetic and environmental context in which it is expressed. For example, alleles that enhance the growth of a tree's trunk and limbs may be useless or even detrimental in the absence of alleles at other loci that enhance the growth of roots necessary

Figure 23.11

Inquiry **Does geographic variation in yarrow plants have a genetic component?**

EXPERIMENT Researchers observed that the average size of yarrow plants *(Achillea)* growing on the slopes of the Sierra Nevada mountains gradually decreases with increasing elevation. To eliminate the effect of environmental differences at different elevations, researchers collected seeds from various altitudes and planted them in a common garden. They then measured the heights of the resulting plants.

RESULTS The average plant sizes in the common garden were inversely correlated with the altitudes at which the seeds were collected, although the height differences were less than in the plants' natural environments.

Heights of yarrow plants grown in common garden

CONCLUSION The lesser but still measurable clinal variation in yarrow plants grown at a common elevation demonstrates the role of genetic as well as environmental differences.

to support the tree. On the other hand, alleles or other pieces of DNA that contribute nothing to an organism's success (or that may even be slightly maladaptive) may be perpetuated in individuals whose overall fitness is high. In this way, thousands of pieces of old retroviruses and transposable elements have accumulated and continue to accumulate in our genomes. These functionless bits of DNA are carried along from one generation to the next because they do no harm.

Survival alone does not guarantee reproductive success. Relative fitness is zero for a sterile plant or animal, even if it is robust and outlives other members of the population. But survival is necessary for reproduction, and longevity increases fitness if it means that long-lived individuals leave more descendants than those that die sooner. On the other hand, an individual that matures quickly and becomes fertile at an early age, even if it only lives for a short time, may have more offspring than an individual that lives longer but matures late. Thus, many factors affect both survival and fertility and contribute to evolutionary fitness.

Directional, Disruptive, and Stabilizing Selection

Natural selection can alter the frequency distribution of heritable traits in three ways, depending on which phenotypes in a population are favored. These three modes of selection are called directional selection, disruptive selection, and stabilizing selection.

Directional selection (Figure 23.12a) is most common when a population's environment changes or when members of a population migrate to a new habitat with different environmental conditions than their former one. Directional selection shifts the frequency curve for some phenotypic character in one direction or the other by favoring individuals that deviate from the average. For instance, fossil evidence indicates that the average size of black bears in Europe increased with each glacial period, only to decrease again during the warmer interglacial periods. Larger bears, with a smaller surface-to-volume ratio, are better at conserving body heat and surviving periods of extreme cold.

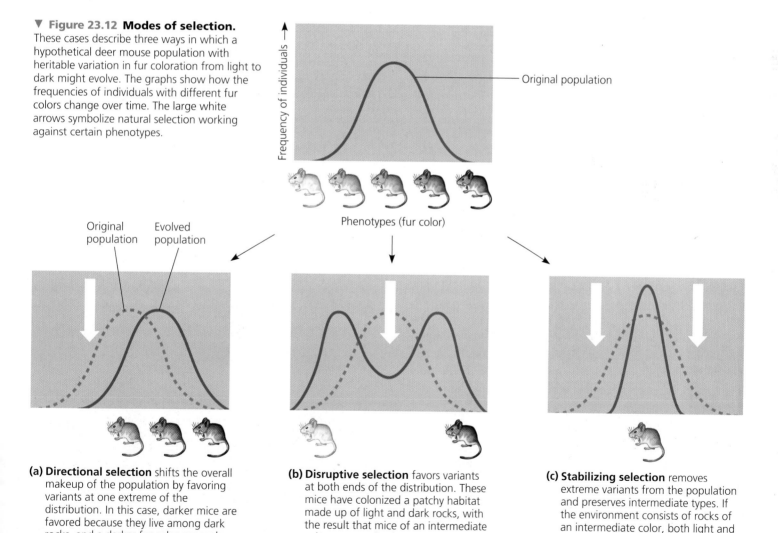

▼ **Figure 23.12 Modes of selection.** These cases describe three ways in which a hypothetical deer mouse population with heritable variation in fur coloration from light to dark might evolve. The graphs show how the frequencies of individuals with different fur colors change over time. The large white arrows symbolize natural selection working against certain phenotypes.

Frequency of individuals →

Original population

Phenotypes (fur color)

Original population   Evolved population

(a) Directional selection shifts the overall makeup of the population by favoring variants at one extreme of the distribution. In this case, darker mice are favored because they live among dark rocks, and a darker fur color conceals them from predators.

(b) Disruptive selection favors variants at both ends of the distribution. These mice have colonized a patchy habitat made up of light and dark rocks, with the result that mice of an intermediate color are at a disadvantage.

(c) Stabilizing selection removes extreme variants from the population and preserves intermediate types. If the environment consists of rocks of an intermediate color, both light and dark mice will be selected against.

Disruptive selection (Figure 23.12b) occurs when environmental conditions favor individuals on both extremes of a phenotypic range over intermediate phenotypes. For example, a population of black-bellied seedcracker finches in Cameroon displays two distinctly different beak sizes. Small-billed individuals feed mainly on soft seeds, whereas large-billed birds specialize in cracking hard seeds. It appears that birds with intermediate-sized bills are relatively inefficient at cracking both types of seeds, and thus have lower relative fitness. As you will read in the next chapter, disruptive selection can be important in the early stages of speciation.

Stabilizing selection (Figure 23.12c) acts against extreme phenotypes and favors intermediate variants. This mode of selection reduces variation and maintains the status quo for a particular phenotypic character. For example, the birth weights of most human babies lie in the range of 3–4 kg; babies who are much smaller or larger suffer higher rates of mortality.

Regardless of the mode of selection, however, the basic mechanism remains the same. Selection favors certain heritable traits through differential reproductive success.

The Preservation of Genetic Variation

What prevents natural selection from reducing genetic variation by culling all unfavorable genotypes? The tendency for directional and stabilizing selection to reduce variation is countered by mechanisms that preserve or restore it.

Diploidy

Because most eukaryotes are diploid, a considerable amount of genetic variation is hidden from selection in the form of recessive alleles. Recessive alleles that are less favorable than their dominant counterparts, or even harmful in the current environment, can persist because they are propagated in heterozygous individuals. This latent variation is exposed to natural selection only when both parents carry the same recessive allele and combine two copies in one zygote. This happens only rarely if the frequency of the recessive allele is very low. The rarer the recessive allele, the greater the degree of protection from natural selection. Heterozygote protection maintains a huge pool of alleles that might not be favored under present conditions but some of which could bring new benefits when the environment changes.

Balancing Selection

Selection itself may preserve variation at some gene loci. **Balancing selection** occurs when natural selection maintains stable frequencies of two or more phenotypic forms in a population, a state called **balanced polymorphism**. This type of selection includes heterozygote advantage and frequency-dependent selection.

Heterozygote Advantage. If individuals who are heterozygous at a particular gene locus have greater fitness than the homozygotes, natural selection will tend to maintain two or more alleles at that locus. An example of this **heterozygote advantage** occurs at the locus in humans that codes for one of the peptide subunits in hemoglobin, the oxygen-carrying protein of red blood cells. In homozygous individuals, a recessive allele at that locus causes sickle-cell disease (see Figures 5.21 and 17.23). However, heterozygotes are protected against the severest effects of malaria (although they are not resistant to malarial infection). This protection is an important advantage in tropical regions where malaria is a major killer. The environment in these areas favors heterozygotes over homozygous dominant individuals, who are more susceptible to malaria, and also over homozygous recessive individuals, who develop sickle-cell disease. The frequency of the sickle-cell allele in Africa is generally highest in areas where the malaria parasite is most common (Figure 23.13). In some tribes, it accounts for 20% of the hemoglobin alleles in the gene pool, a very high frequency for such a harmful allele. But even at this high frequency ($q = 0.2$), only 4% of the population suffers from sickle-cell disease ($q^2 = 0.04$). There are far more heterozygotes who are resistant to malaria ($2pq = 2 \times 0.8 \times 0.2 = 0.32$). Although the fitness advantage to the heterozygotes is much smaller than the disadvantage to the homozygotes, there are so many more heterozygotes than homozygotes that the aggregate benefit of the allele in the population *balances* its aggregate harm.

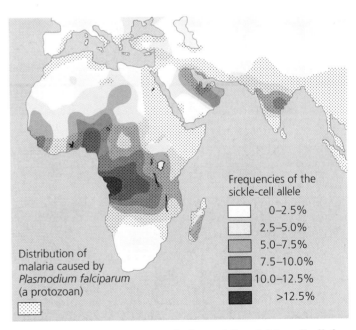

Frequencies of the sickle-cell allele

☐	0–2.5%
☐	2.5–5.0%
☐	5.0–7.5%
☐	7.5–10.0%
☐	10.0–12.5%
☐	>12.5%

Distribution of malaria caused by *Plasmodium falciparum* (a protozoan)

▲ **Figure 23.13 Mapping malaria and the sickle-cell allele.** The sickle-cell allele is most common in Africa, but it is not the only balanced polymorphism that confers protection against malaria. Different balanced polymorphisms are found in populations in other parts of the world, such as around the Mediterranean Sea and in Southeast Asia, where malaria is widespread.

Figure 23.14
Research Method **Using a Virtual Population to Study the Effects of Selection**

APPLICATION   Using virtual organisms that can "reproduce" and pass on characteristics to their offspring, biologists can model the effects of selection over many generations in a compressed period of time. This method also enables researchers to isolate the effect of the study variable by controlling for other influences on the population's evolution—a nearly impossible goal in nature.

TECHNIQUE   Studies involving virtual populations are most meaningful when based on a natural system. For example, Alan Bond and Alan Kamil of the University of Nebraska created a "virtual ecology" based on the well-studied predator-prey relationship between the North American blue jay and the woodland moth. First, the researchers converted gray-scale photographs of moths into digital moths. The wing patterns were determined by a complex computerized genome based on real moth genetics, including polygenic inheritance, crossing-over events, and mutation. These moths can be "mated" and the genotypes and phenotypes of the offspring determined by various mathematical models.

Bond and Kamil trained captive blue jays to "hunt" digital moths displayed against patterned backgrounds, as the birds would hunt moths hidden on tree trunks in the wild. To model the effects of blue jay predation on the moth population, the researchers presented each moth to a jay and measured the detection time (or lack of detection). The researchers used a statistical model to calculate each moth's likelihood of breeding, producing the next generation of potential prey. They repeated this process for 100 generations each for the experimental group (exposed to frequency-dependent selection by jays) and two control groups. In one control (no selection by jays), the researchers randomly recombined the genotypes in each generation. In the other control (frequency-independent selection), jays selected moths, but a computer program eliminated the "search image" effect.

On pecking a moth image the blue jay receives a food reward. If the bird does not detect a moth on either screen, it pecks the green circle to continue to a new set of images (a new feeding opportunity).

RESULTS   Using a virtual prey population enabled the researchers to model the long-term evolutionary impact of selection by real predators. In this study, the experimental moth population became more difficult to detect against the patterned backgrounds compared to the nonselected control (as did the frequency-independent control). But as shown in the graph below, in three trials, the experimental group (colored lines) showed much greater phenotypic variation than the frequency-independent control group (black line). This result supports Bond and Kamil's hypothesis that frequency-dependent selection by visual predators promotes polymorphism in a prey population.

Parental population sample

Experimental group sample

Plain background   Patterned background

Frequency-Dependent Selection. In **frequency-dependent selection,** the fitness of any one morph declines if it becomes too common in the population. **Figure 23.14** illustrates an experiment that simulates frequency-dependent selection. In the wild, blue jays locate and eat moths that sit motionless on tree trunks during the day. Captive jays can be trained to find virtual prey on a computer screen. These jays were presented with a series of screens that showed a speckled background, sometimes including an image of a moth. When a jay pecked at a moth image, it was rewarded with a small piece of food. The jays soon learned a "search image"—a quick way to recognize the most common type of moth. As their skill grew, the computer program adjusted the frequencies of the virtual prey, making the common type rare and formerly rare types common, just as natural selection would do. The researchers also programmed "mutations" that introduced new moth patterns.

Whenever a type of moth became common, the jays rapidly learned a new search image and targeted it. Frequency-dependent selection preserved polymorphism in this population: Rare moths of any pattern were at an advantage and common moths of any pattern were at a disadvantage because the jays learned to find the common moths more easily than the rare ones. Similar frequency-dependent selection has been observed in a number of predator-prey interactions in the wild.

Neutral Variation

Some of the genetic variation in populations probably has little or no impact on reproductive success, and thus natural selection does not affect these alleles. For example, most of the DNA base differences between humans that are found in untranslated parts of the genome appear to confer no selective advantage and therefore are considered **neutral variation.** And in **pseudogenes,** genes that have become inactivated by mutations, genetic "noise" is free to accumulate in all parts of the gene. The relative frequencies of neutral variations are not affected by natural selection; over time, some neutral alleles increase in frequency and others decrease through genetic drift. Even mutational changes that alter proteins can be neutral. For example, data from *Drosophila* suggest that roughly half of the amino-acid-changing mutations that arise and subsequently become fixed have no selective effect—that is, they do not affect protein function.

Of course, it is possible that genetic differences that appear to be neutral may actually influence survival and reproductive success in ways that are difficult to measure. Furthermore, a variant allele may be neutral in one environment but not in another. The debate over the extent of neutral variation continues (as you will read further in Chapter 25), but one thing is clear: Even if only a fraction of the extensive variation in a gene pool significantly affects fitness, that is still an enormous reservoir of raw material for natural selection and adaptive evolution.

Sexual Selection

Charles Darwin was the first to explore the implications of **sexual selection,** which is natural selection for mating success. This type of selection can result in **sexual dimorphism,** marked differences between the sexes in secondary sexual characteristics, which are not directly associated with reproduction **(Figure 23.15).** These distinctions include differences in size, color, and ornamentation. In vertebrates, males are usually the showier sex.

It is important to distinguish between *intra*sexual and *inter*sexual selection. **Intrasexual selection,** meaning selection "within the same sex," is a direct competition among individuals of one sex for mates of the opposite sex. Intrasexual selection is usually most obvious in males. For example, in many species a single male patrols a group of females and prevents other males from mating with them. The patrolling male may defend his status by defeating smaller, weaker, or less fierce males in combat; more often, he is the psychological

▲ **Figure 23.15 Sexual dimorphism and sexual selection.** Peacocks and peahens show extreme sexual dimorphism. There is intrasexual selection between competing males followed by intersexual selection when the females choose among the showiest males.

victor in ritualized displays that discourage would-be competitors but do not risk injury that would reduce his own fitness (see Chapter 51). But evidence is growing that intrasexual selection can take place between females as well. In ring-tailed lemurs, for example, females dominate males and also establish hierarchies of dominance among themselves.

In **intersexual selection,** also called mate choice, individuals of one sex (usually females) are choosy in selecting their mates from the other sex. In many cases, the female's choice depends on the showiness of the male's appearance or behavior (see Figure 23.15). However, because females have fewer chances to mate than males, a female only gains an advantage over other females if she chooses a mate that enables her to produce more fit offspring.

What intrigued Darwin about mate choice is that some of the male showiness does not seem to be adaptive in any other way and may in fact pose some risk. For example, bright plumage may make male birds more visible to predators. But if such secondary sexual characteristics help a male gain a mate, and this benefit outweighs the risk from predation, then both the bright plumage and the female preference for it will be reinforced for the most Darwinian of reasons—because they enhance reproductive success. Every time a female chooses a mate based on a certain appearance or behavior, she perpetuates the alleles that influenced her to make that choice, allowing a male with an especially showy phenotype to pass on his alleles to offspring.

How do female preferences for certain male characteristics evolve? Could there be fitness benefits to showy traits? Several researchers are testing the hypothesis that these sexual advertisements reflect overall health. For example, male birds with serious parasitic infections may have dull, disheveled plumage. They don't usually win many females. If the female chooses a showy male, she may be choosing a healthy one as well, and the benefit will be a greater chance of healthy offspring.

The Evolutionary Enigma of Sexual Reproduction

Even as biologists study the mechanisms of sexual selection, they continue to wonder about the evolution of sex itself. As a mechanism of rapid population expansion, it is far inferior to asexual reproduction. Consider, for example, a population of insects in which half the females reproduce only sexually and half reproduce only asexually. Even if both types of females produced the same number of offspring each generation, the asexual condition would increase in frequency because all of the females' offspring would be daughters that are able to give birth to more reproductive daughters in turn. In contrast, half of the sexual females' offspring would be males, which would be required for reproduction but would themselves be unable to give birth. **Figure 23.16** diagrams this "reproductive handicap" of sex.

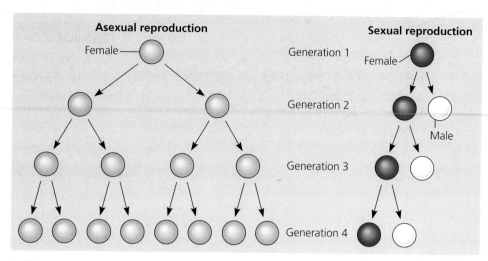

▲ **Figure 23.16 The "reproductive handicap" of sex.** These diagrams contrast the reproductive output of females (blue circles) over four generations for asexual versus sexual reproduction. The scenarios assume two surviving offspring per female. The asexual population rapidly outgrows the sexual one.

Nonetheless, sex is maintained in the vast majority of eukaryotic species, even in those that can also reproduce asexually. It must enhance reproductive success somehow, for otherwise natural selection would act in favor of alleles that promote asexual reproduction. But what advantage does sex provide?

One explanation is that the processes of meiotic recombination and fertilization generate the genetic variation on which natural selection acts. The assumption is that natural selection sustains sex, in spite of its reproductive drawbacks, because genetic variation enables *future* adaptation to an ever-changing environment. But this assumption is difficult to defend. Natural selection always acts in the here and now, favoring the success of those individuals that reproduce best in the current environment.

So instead, consider how the genetic variation that results from sex might benefit sexually reproducing individuals over the short term—on a generation-to-generation time scale. One hypothesis emphasizes the importance of genetic variation in resistance to disease. Many bacterial and viral pathogens recognize and infect a host by attaching to receptor molecules on the host's cells. There should be an advantage in producing offspring that vary in their resistance to different diseases. For example, one offspring may have cellular markers that make it resistant to virus A, while another may be resistant to virus B. This hypothesis predicts that gene loci that code for the receptors to which pathogens attach should have many alleles. And that seems to be the case. In humans, for example, there are hundreds of alleles for each of two gene loci coding for the proteins that give cell surfaces their molecular fingerprints (you'll read more about these cellular markers in Chapter 43). Of course, because most pathogens evolve rapidly in their ability to key on specific host receptors, resistance of a particular genotype to a given disease is not permanent. But sex provides a mechanism for "changing the locks" and varying them among offspring.

Such an example of coevolution, in which host and parasite must evolve quickly to keep up with each other, is sometimes described as a "Red Queen race," after the Red Queen in Lewis Carroll's *Through the Looking Glass,* who advised Alice to run as fast as she could just to stay in the same place.

Why Natural Selection Cannot Fashion Perfect Organisms

As we noted in Chapter 22, nature abounds with examples of organisms that seem to be less than ideally "engineered" for their lifestyles, for several reasons.

1. *Evolution is limited by historical constraints.* Each species has a legacy of descent with modification from a long line of ancestral forms. Evolution does not scrap ancestral anatomy and build each new complex structure from scratch; it co-opts existing structures and adapts them to new situations. For example, we could imagine how some bird species might benefit by having wings for flight as well as *four* legs for speedy, maneuverable running, instead of just two legs. But birds descended from reptiles that had only two pairs of limbs, and co-opting the forelimbs for flight left only the two hind limbs for moving around on the ground.

2. *Adaptations are often compromises.* Each organism must do many different things. A seal spends part of its time on rocks; it could probably walk better if it had legs instead of flippers, but it would not swim nearly as well. We humans owe much of our versatility and athleticism to our prehensile hands and flexible limbs, which also make us prone to sprains, torn ligaments, and dislocations. Structural reinforcement has been compromised for agility.

3. *Chance and natural selection interact.* Chance events affect the subsequent evolutionary history of populations. For instance, when a storm blows insects or birds hundreds of miles

over an ocean to an island, the wind does not necessarily transport the species, or the members of a species, that are best suited to the new environment. Thus, not all alleles present in the founding population's gene pool are better suited to the new environment than alleles "left behind."

4. *Selection can only edit existing variations.* Natural selection favors only the fittest phenotypes among those currently in the population, which may not be the ideal traits. New alleles do not arise on demand.

With these constraints, evolution cannot craft perfect organisms. Natural selection operates on a "better than" basis. We can see evidence for evolution in the many imperfections of the organisms it produces.

Concept Check 23.4

1. Does nucleotide variability in a population always correspond to phenotypic polymorphism? Why or why not?
2. What is the relative fitness of a sterile mule? Explain.
3. How does sexual selection lead to sexual dimorphism?
4. Explain what is meant by the "reproductive handicap" of sex.

For suggested answers, see Appendix A.

Chapter 23 Review

Go to the Campbell Biology website (**www.campbellbiology.com**) or CD-ROM to explore Activities, Investigations, and other interactive study aids.

SUMMARY OF KEY CONCEPTS

Concept 23.1

Population genetics provides a foundation for studying evolution

▶ **The Modern Synthesis (p. 455)** The modern synthesis integrates Mendelian genetics with the Darwinian theory of evolution by natural selection and focuses on populations as the basic unit of evolution.

▶ **Gene Pools and Allele Frequencies (pp. 455–456)** A population, a localized group of organisms that all belong to the same species, is united by its gene pool, the aggregate of all alleles in the population.

▶ **The Hardy-Weinberg Theorem (pp. 456–458)** The Hardy-Weinberg theorem states that the frequencies of alleles and genotypes in a population will remain constant if Mendelian segregation and random mating are the only processes that affect the gene pool. If p and q represent the relative frequencies of the only two possible alleles at a particular locus, then $p^2 + 2pq + q^2 = 1$, where p^2 and q^2 are the frequencies of the homozygous genotypes and $2pq$ is the frequency of the heterozygous genotype. Although many populations approximate Hardy-Weinberg equilibrium, the equilibrium in its strictest sense applies only if the population is large, mating is random, mutation is negligible, there is no gene flow from other populations, and all individuals have equal reproductive success.
Investigation *How Can Frequency of Alleles Be Calculated?*

Concept 23.2

Mutation and sexual recombination produce the variation that makes evolution possible

▶ **Mutation (pp. 459–460)** New genes and new alleles originate only by mutation. Most mutations have no effect or are harmful, but a few increase adaptation.

▶ **Sexual Recombination (p. 460)** Genetic recombination between sexually reproducing organisms produces most of the variation in traits that makes adaptation possible.
Activity *Genetic Variation from Sexual Recombination*

Concept 23.3

Natural selection, genetic drift, and gene flow can alter a population's genetic composition

▶ **Natural Selection (p. 460)** Differential success in reproduction results in certain alleles being passed to the next generation in greater proportions than others.

▶ **Genetic Drift (pp. 460–462)** Chance fluctuations in allele frequencies from generation to generation tend to reduce genetic variation in populations.

▶ **Gene Flow (p. 462)** Genetic exchange between populations tends to reduce differences between populations over time.
Biology Labs On-Line *PopulationGeneticsLab*
Activity *Causes of Evolutionary Change*

Concept 23.4

Natural selection is the primary mechanism of adaptive evolution

▶ **Genetic Variation (pp. 462–464)** Genetic variation includes variation among individuals within a population in discrete and quantitative characters, as well as geographic variation between populations.

▶ **A Closer Look at Natural Selection (pp. 464–466)** One organism has a greater relative fitness than another if it leaves more descendants. Selection favors certain genotypes in a population by acting on the phenotypes of individual organisms. Natural selection can favor relatively rare individuals at one end of the phenotypic range (directional selection), can favor individuals at both extremes of the range rather than intermediate phenotypes (disruptive selection), or can act against extreme phenotypes (stabilizing selection).

▶ **The Preservation of Genetic Variation (pp. 466–468)** Diploidy maintains a reservoir of concealed recessive variation in heterozygotes. Balanced polymorphism may maintain variation at some gene loci as a result of heterozygote advantage or frequency-dependent selection.

▶ **Sexual Selection (p. 468)** Sexual selection leads to the evolution of secondary sex characteristics, which can give individuals an advantage in mating.

▶ **The Evolutionary Enigma of Sexual Reproduction (p. 469)** Enhanced disease resistance based on genetic variation is one possible explanation for the persistence of sexual reproduction despite its lesser reproductive output compared to asexual reproduction.

► **Why Natural Selection Cannot Fashion Perfect Organisms** (pp. 469–470) Structures result from modified ancestral anatomy; adaptations are often compromises; the gene pool can be affected by genetic drift; and natural selection can act only on available variation.
Biology Labs On-Line *EvolutionLab*

TESTING YOUR KNOWLEDGE

Self-Quiz

1. In the gene pool of a population with 100 individuals, a fixed allele for a particular gene locus has a frequency of
   a. 0.   b. 0.5.   c. 1.   d. 100.
   e. cannot be calculated based on this information

2. Researchers examining a particular gene in a fruit fly population discovered that the gene can have either of two slightly different sequences, designated A1 and A2. Further tests showed that 70% of the gametes produced in the population contained the A1 sequence. If the population is at Hardy-Weinberg equilibrium, what proportion of the flies carries both A1 and A2?
   a. 0.7   b. 0.49   c. 0.21   d. 0.42   e. 0.09

3. At a locus with a dominant and a recessive allele in Hardy-Weinberg equilibrium, 16% of the individuals are homozygous for the recessive allele. What is the frequency of the dominant allele in the population?
   a. 0.84   b. 0.36   c. 0.6   d. 0.4   e. 0.48

4. The average length of jackrabbit ears decreases gradually with increasing latitude. This variation is an example of
   a. directional selection.   d. genetic drift.
   b. discrete variation.   e. disruptive selection.
   c. polymorphism.

5. Which of the following is a polymorphic trait in humans?
   a. variation in height
   b. variation in intelligence
   c. free versus attached earlobes (see Figure 14.14)
   d. variation in the number of fingers
   e. variation in fingerprints

6. Natural selection changes allele frequencies in populations because some _____ survive and reproduce more successfully than others.
   a. alleles   d. gene loci
   b. individual organisms   e. species
   c. gene pools

7. Longer tails of male barn swallows evolve because female barn swallows prefer to mate with the males that have the longest tails. This process is best described as
   a. genetic drift that changes the frequencies of the alleles for tail length.
   b. natural selection for sexual reproduction that maintains variation in the genes that influence tail length.
   c. intersexual selection for traits, such as long tails, that help males attract mates.
   d. intrasexual selection for traits, such as long tails, that help males win contests for access to females.
   e. directional selection for traits, such as long tails, that improve males' ability to fly strongly and forage for food over large areas.

8. No two human individuals are alike, except for identical twins. The chief cause of the variation among individuals is
   a. new mutations that occurred in the preceding generation.
   b. sexual recombination.
   c. genetic drift due to the small size of the population.
   d. geographic variation within the population.
   e. environmental effects.

9. Road construction has isolated a small portion of a beetle population from the main population. After a few generations, this new population exhibits dramatic genetic differences from the old one, most likely because
   a. mutations are more common in the new environment.
   b. allele frequencies among the stranded beetles differed by chance from those in the parent population's gene pool and subsequent genetic drift caused even more divergence from the original gene pool.
   c. the new environment is different from the old, favoring directional selection.
   d. gene flow increases in a new environment.
   e. members of a small population tend to migrate, removing alleles from the gene pool.

10. Sparrows with average-sized wings survive severe storms better than those with longer or shorter wings, illustrating
    a. the bottleneck effect.   d. neutral variation.
    b. stabilizing selection.   e. disruptive selection.
    c. frequency-dependent selection.

For Self-Quiz answers, see Appendix A.

Go to the website or CD-ROM for more quiz questions.

Evolution Connection

How is the process of evolution revealed by the imperfections of living organisms?

Scientific Inquiry

In the population of wildflowers we used to test the Hardy-Weinberg theorem, the frequency of C^R is 0.8 and the frequency of C^W is 0.2. In a different population of these flowers, the frequencies of genotypes do not conform to Hardy-Weinberg equilibrium: 60% of the plants are $C^R C^R$ and 40% are $C^W C^W$. Assuming that all Hardy-Weinberg conditions are met, show that genotypes will reach equilibrium in the next generation. Suppose instead that the plants mate only with themselves (self-fertilize). What will the allele and genotype frequencies be in the next generation?

Investigation *How Can Frequency of Alleles Be Calculated?*
Biology Labs On-Line *PopulationGeneticsLab*
Biology Labs On-Line *EvolutionLab*

Science, Technology, and Society

To what extent are humans living in a technological society exempt from natural selection? Justify your answer.

24

The Origin of Species

▲ Figure 24.1 **The flightless cormorant (*Nannopterum harrisi*), one of many new species that have originated on the isolated Galápagos Islands.**

Key Concepts

24.1 The biological species concept emphasizes reproductive isolation

24.2 Speciation can take place with or without geographic separation

24.3 Macroevolutionary changes can accumulate through many speciation events

Overview

That "Mystery of Mysteries"

Darwin came to the Galápagos Islands eager to explore landforms newly emerged from the sea. He noted that these volcanic islands, despite their geologic youth, were filled with plants and animals known nowhere else in the world, and later realized that these species, like the islands, were new **(Figure 24.1)**. He wrote in his diary: "Both in space and time, we seem to be brought somewhat near to that great fact—that mystery of mysteries—the first appearance of new beings on this Earth."

The origin of new species, or **speciation**, is at the focal point of evolutionary theory, because the appearance of new species is the source of biological diversity. It is not enough to explain how adaptations evolve in a population (the topic covered in Chapter 23; such changes, confined to a single gene pool, are described as **microevolution**). Evolutionary theory must also explain how new species originate and develop through the subdivision and subsequent divergence of gene pools. The fossil record reveals the cumulative effects of speciation over vast tracts of time. The term **macroevolution** refers to such evolutionary change above the species level—for example, the appearance of feathers during the evolution of birds from one group of dinosaurs, and other such "evolutionary novelties" that can be used to define higher taxa.

We can distinguish two basic patterns of evolutionary change: anagenesis and cladogenesis **(Figure 24.2)**. Anagenesis (from the Greek *ana*, new, and *genos*, race), also called phyletic evolution, is the accumulation of changes that gradually transform a given species into a species with different characteristics. Cladogenesis (from the Greek *klados*, branch), also called branching evolution, is the splitting of a gene pool into two or more separate pools, which each give rise to one or more new species. Only cladogenesis can promote biological diversity by increasing the number of species.

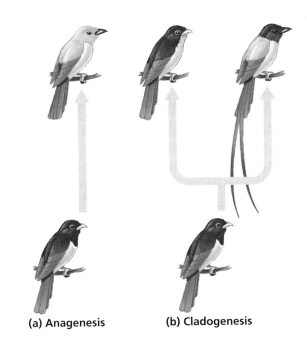

(a) Anagenesis   **(b) Cladogenesis**

▲ Figure 24.2 **Two patterns of evolutionary change.**
(a) Anagenesis is the accumulation of heritable changes, altering the characteristics of a species. **(b)** Cladogenesis is branching evolution, in which a new species arises from a population that buds from a parent species. (Note that the "parent" species may change as well.) Cladogenesis is the basis for biological diversity.

In this chapter, we will explore the mechanisms by which species arise. We will also examine the possible origins of some novel features that define higher taxonomic groups. But first, let's consider what we really mean when we refer to a "species."

Concept 24.1

The biological species concept emphasizes reproductive isolation

Species is a Latin word meaning "kind" or "appearance." We distinguish between various "kinds" of plants or animals—between dogs and cats, for instance—from differences in their appearance. But are organisms truly divided into the discrete units we call species, or is this classification an arbitrary attempt to impose order on the natural world? To answer this question, biologists have compared not only the morphology (body form) of different groups of organisms but also less obvious differences in physiology, biochemistry, and DNA sequences. The results generally confirm that morphologically distinct species are indeed discrete groups, with many differences in addition to morphological ones.

The Biological Species Concept

The primary definition of species used most frequently in this textbook was proposed in 1942 by biologist Ernst Mayr. This **biological species concept** defines a species as a population or group of populations whose members have the potential to interbreed in nature and produce viable, fertile offspring, but are unable to produce viable, fertile offspring with members of other populations **(Figure 24.3)**. In other words, the members of a biological species are united by being reproductively compatible, at least potentially. All humans, for example, belong to the same biological species. A businesswoman in Manhattan may be unlikely to meet a dairy farmer in Mongolia, but if the two should happen to get together, they could have viable babies that develop into fertile adults. In contrast, humans and chimpanzees remain distinct biological species even where they share territory, because many factors keep them from interbreeding and producing fertile offspring.

Reproductive Isolation

Because biological species are distinguished based on reproductive incompatibility, the concept hinges on **reproductive isolation**—the existence of biological factors (barriers) that impede members of two species from producing viable, fertile hybrids. Although a single barrier may not block all genetic exchange between species, a combination of several barriers can effectively isolate a species' gene pool.

Clearly, a fly cannot mate with a frog or a fern, but the reproductive barriers between more closely related species are

(a) Similarity between different species. The eastern meadowlark (*Sturnella magna*, left) and the western meadowlark (*Sturnella neglecta*, right) have similar body shapes and colorations. Nevertheless, they are distinct biological species because their songs and other behaviors are different enough to prevent interbreeding should they meet in the wild.

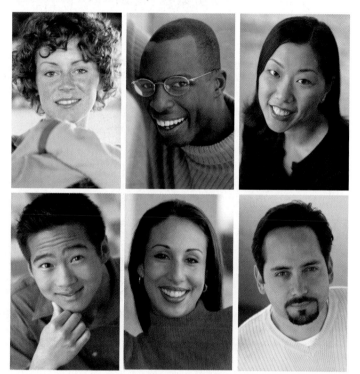

(b) Diversity within a species. As diverse as we may be in appearance, all humans belong to a single biological species (*Homo sapiens*), defined by our capacity to interbreed.

▲ Figure 24.3 **The biological species concept is based on the potential to interbreed rather than on physical similarity.**

not so obvious. These barriers can be classified according to whether they contribute to reproductive isolation before or after fertilization. **Prezygotic barriers** ("before the zygote") impede mating between species or hinder the fertilization of ova if members of different species attempt to mate. If a sperm cell from one species does overcome prezygotic barriers and fertilizes an ovum from another species, **postzygotic barriers** ("after the zygote") often prevent the hybrid zygote from developing into a viable, fertile adult. **Figure 24.4**, on the next two pages, describes various prezygotic and postzygotic barriers.

Figure 24.4

Exploring **Reproductive Barriers**

Prezygotic barriers impede mating or hinder fertilization if mating does occur

| Habitat isolation | Temporal isolation | Behavioral isolation | Mechanical isolation |

Individuals of different species

Mating attempt

HABITAT ISOLATION

Two species that occupy different habitats within the same area may encounter each other rarely, if at all, even though they are not isolated by obvious physical barriers such as mountain ranges.

Example: Two species of garter snakes in the genus *Thamnophis* occur in the same geographic areas, but one lives mainly in water (a) while the other is primarily terrestrial (b).

TEMPORAL ISOLATION

Species that breed during different times of the day, different seasons, or different years cannot mix their gametes.

Example: In North America, the geographic ranges of the eastern spotted skunk (*Spilogale putorius*) (c) and the western spotted skunk (*Spilogale gracilis*) (d) overlap, but *S. putorius* mates in late winter and *S. gracilis* mates in late summer.

BEHAVIORAL ISOLATION

Courtship rituals that attract mates and other behaviors unique to a species are effective reproductive barriers, even between closely related species.

Example: Blue-footed boobies, inhabitants of the Galápagos, mate only after a courtship display unique to their species. Part of the "script" calls for the male to high-step, a behavior that calls the female's attention to his bright blue feet (e).

MECHANICAL ISOLATION

Morphological differences can prevent successful mating.

Example: Even in closely related species of plants, the flowers often have distinct appearances that attract different pollinators. These two species of monkey flower (*Mimulus*) differ greatly in the shapes and colors of their blossoms (f, g). Thus, cross-pollination between the plants does not occur.

(b)

(a)

(e)

(g)

(d)

(c)

(f)

Postzygotic barriers prevent a hybrid zygote from developing into a viable, fertile adult

Gametic isolation

Reduced hybrid viability

Reduced hybrid fertility

Hybrid breakdown

Fertilization

Viable, fertile offspring

GAMETIC ISOLATION

REDUCED HYBRID VIABILITY

REDUCED HYBRID FERTILITY

HYBRID BREAKDOWN

Sperm of one species may not be able to fertilize the eggs of another species. Many mechanisms can produce this isolation. For instance, sperm may not be able to survive in the reproductive tract of females of the other species, or biochemical mechanisms may prevent the sperm from penetrating the membrane surrounding the other species' eggs.

Example: Gametic isolation separates certain closely related species of aquatic animals such as sea urchins (h). The sea urchins release their sperm and eggs into the surrounding water, where they fuse and form zygotes. Gametes of different species, like the red and purple urchins shown here, are unable to fuse.

The genes of different parent species may interact and impair the hybrid's development.

Example: Some salamander subspecies of the genus *Ensatina* live in the same regions and habitats, where they may occasionally hybridize. But most of the hybrids do not complete development, and those that do are frail (i).

Even if hybrids are vigorous, they may be sterile. If chromosomes of the two parent species differ in number or structure, meiosis in the hybrids may fail to produce normal gametes. Since the infertile hybrids cannot produce offspring when they mate with either parental species, genes cannot flow freely between the species.

Example: The hybrid offspring of a donkey (j) and a horse (k), a mule (l), is robust but sterile.

Some first-generation hybrids are viable and fertile, but when they mate with one another or with either parent species, offspring of the next generation are feeble or sterile.

Example: Strains of cultivated rice have accumulated different mutant recessive alleles at two loci in the course of their divergence from a common ancestor. Hybrids between them are vigorous and fertile (m, left and right), but plants in the next generation that carry too many of these recessive alleles are small and sterile (m, center). Although these rice strains are not yet considered different species, they have already begun to be separated by postzygotic barriers.

(i)

(h)

(j)

(k)

(l)

(m)

Limitations of the Biological Species Concept

While the biological species concept's emphasis on reproductive isolation has greatly influenced evolutionary theory, the number of species to which this concept can be usefully applied is limited. For example, there is no way to evaluate the reproductive isolation of fossils or asexual organisms such as prokaryotes. (Many prokaryotes do transfer genes by conjugation and other processes—see Chapter 18—but this transfer is different from sexual recombination. Furthermore, genes are often transferred between distantly related prokaryotes.) It is also difficult to apply the biological species concept to the many sexual organisms about which little is known regarding their ability to mate with different kinds of organisms. For such reasons, alternative species concepts are useful in certain situations.

Other Definitions of Species

While the biological species concept emphasizes the *separateness* of species from one another due to reproductive barriers, several other definitions emphasize the *unity* within a species. For example, the **morphological species concept** characterizes a species by its body shape, size, and other structural features. The morphological species concept has advantages: It can be applied to asexual and sexual organisms, and it can be useful even without information on the extent of gene flow. In practice, this is how scientists distinguish most species. One disadvantage, however, is that this definition relies on subjective criteria; researchers may disagree on which structural features distinguish a species.

The **paleontological species concept** focuses on morphologically discrete species known only from the fossil record. We are forced to distinguish many species in this way because there is little or no information about their mating capability.

The **ecological species concept** views a species in terms of its ecological niche, its role in a biological community (see Chapter 53). For example, two species of Galápagos finches may be similar in appearance but distinguishable based on what they eat. Unlike the biological species concept, this definition can accommodate asexual as well as sexual species.

The **phylogenetic species concept** defines a species as a set of organisms with a unique genetic history—that is, as one branch on the tree of life. Biologists trace the phylogenetic history of a species by comparing its physical characteristics or its molecular sequences with those of other organisms. Such analysis can distinguish groups of individuals that are sufficiently different to be considered separate species. (Of course, the difficulty is in determining the degree of difference required to indicate separate species.) Phylogenetic information sometimes reveals the existence of "sibling species": species that appear so similar that they cannot be distinguished on morphological grounds. Scientists can then apply the biological species concept to determine if the phylogenetic distinction is confirmed by reproductive incompatibility.

The usefulness of each of these definitions depends on the situation and the questions we are asking. The biological species concept, with its focus on reproductive barriers, is particularly valuable for studying how species originate.

Concept 24.2

Speciation can take place with or without geographic separation

Speciation can occur in two main ways, depending on how gene flow between the populations is interrupted **(Figure 24.5)**.

(a) Allopatric speciation. A population forms a new species while geographically isolated from its parent population.

(b) Sympatric speciation. A small population becomes a new species without geographic separation.

▲ Figure 24.5 **Two main modes of speciation.**

Allopatric ("Other Country") Speciation

In **allopatric speciation** (from the Greek *allos*, other, and *patra*, homeland), gene flow is interrupted when a population is divided into geographically isolated subpopulations. For example, the water level in a lake may subside, resulting in smaller lakes that are home to separated populations (see Figure 24.5). A river may change course and split a population of animals that cannot cross it. Allopatric speciation can also occur without geologic remodeling, such as when individuals colonize a remote area, and their descendants become geographically isolated from the parent population. An example is the speciation that occurred on the Galápagos Islands following colonization by mainland organisms.

How formidable must a geographic barrier be to keep allopatric populations apart? The answer depends on the ability of the organisms to move about. Birds, mountain lions, and coyotes can cross hills, rivers, and canyons. Nor do such barriers hinder the windblown pollen of pine trees or the seeds of many flowering plants. In contrast, small rodents may find a deep canyon or a wide river a formidable barrier **(Figure 24.6)**.

Once geographic separation has occurred, the separated gene pools diverge through any or all of the mechanisms described in Chapter 23: different mutations arise, sexual selection takes a different course in the respective populations, other selective pressures act differently on the separated organisms, and genetic drift alters allele frequencies. Because small, isolated populations are more likely than large populations to undergo a significant change in their gene pool in a relatively short time due to selection and drift, they are also more likely to experience allopatric speciation. In less than 2 million years, the few animals and plants from the South American mainland that colonized the Galápagos Islands gave rise to all the new species now found there. But for each small, isolated population that becomes a new species, many more perish in their new environment.

▲ **Figure 24.6 Allopatric speciation of antelope squirrels on opposite rims of the Grand Canyon.** Harris's antelope squirrel (*Ammospermophilus harrisi*) inhabits the canyon's south rim (left). Just a few miles away on the north rim (right) lives the closely related white-tailed antelope squirrel (*Ammospermophilus leucurus*). In contrast, birds and other organisms that can disperse easily across the canyon have not diverged into different species on opposite rims.

To confirm a case of allopatric speciation, it is necessary to determine whether the allopatric populations have changed enough that they no longer have the potential to interbreed and produce fertile offspring. In some cases, researchers evaluate whether speciation has occurred by bringing together members of separated populations in a laboratory setting **(Figure 24.7)**.

Figure 24.7

Inquiry Can divergence of allopatric fruit fly populations lead to reproductive isolation?

EXPERIMENT   Diane Dodd, of Yale University, divided a fruit-fly population, raising some populations on a starch medium and others on a maltose medium. After many generations, natural selection resulted in divergent evolution: Populations raised on starch digested starch more efficiently, while those raised on maltose digested maltose more efficiently. Dodd then put flies from the same or different populations in mating cages and measured mating frequencies.

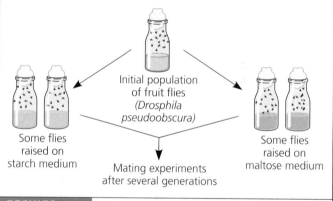

RESULTS   When flies from "starch populations" were mixed with flies from "maltose populations," the flies tended to mate with like partners. In the control group, flies taken from different populations that were adapted to the same medium were about as likely to mate with each other as with flies from their own populations.

Mating frequencies in experimental group:

Male		Female Starch	Female Maltose
	Starch	22	9
	Maltose	8	20

Mating frequencies in control group:

Male		Female Same population	Female Different populations
	Same population	18	15
	Different populations	12	15

CONCLUSION   The strong preference of "starch flies" and "maltose flies" to mate with like-adapted flies, even if they were from different populations, indicates that a reproductive barrier is forming between the divergent populations of flies. The barrier is not absolute (some mating between starch flies and maltose flies did occur) but appears to be under way after several generations of divergence resulting from the separation of these allopatric populations into different environments.

Biologists can also assess allopatric speciation in the wild. For example, females of the Galápagos ground finch *Geospiza difficilis* respond to the song of males from the same island, but ignore the songs of males of the same species from other islands (allopatric populations) that they encounter. This finding indicates that different behavioral (prezygotic) barriers have developed in these allopatric *G. difficilis* populations, which may eventually become separate species.

We need to emphasize that geographic isolation, though obviously preventing interbreeding between allopatric populations, is not in itself a biological isolating mechanism. Isolating mechanisms—which are intrinsic to the organisms themselves—prevent interbreeding even in the absence of geographic isolation.

Next, let's turn to mechanisms that can produce a new species *without* geographic isolation from the parent population.

Sympatric ("Same Country") Speciation

In **sympatric speciation** (from the Greek *syn*, together), speciation takes place in geographically overlapping populations. How can reproductive barriers between sympatric populations evolve when the members remain in contact with each other? Mechanisms of sympatric speciation include chromosomal changes and nonrandom mating that reduces gene flow.

Polyploidy

Some plant species have their origins in accidents during cell division that result in extra sets of chromosomes, a mutational change that results in the condition called **polyploidy**. An **autopolyploid** (from the Greek *autos*, self) is an individual that has more than two chromosome sets, all derived from a single species. For example, a failure of cell division can double a cell's chromosome number from the diploid number ($2n$) to a tetraploid number ($4n$) **(Figure 24.8)**. This mutation prevents a tetraploid from successfully interbreeding with diploid plants of the original population—the triploid ($3n$)

offspring of such unions are sterile because their unpaired chromosomes result in abnormal meiosis. However, the tetraploid plants can still produce fertile tetraploid offspring by self-pollinating or mating with other tetraploids. Thus, in just one generation, autopolyploidy can generate reproductive isolation without any geographic separation.

A much more common form of polyploidy can occur when two different species interbreed and produce a hybrid. Interspecific hybrids are often sterile because the set of chromosomes from one species cannot pair during meiosis with the set of chromosomes from the other species. However, though infertile, the hybrid may be able to propagate itself asexually (as many plants can do). In subsequent generations, various mechanisms can change a sterile hybrid into a fertile polyploid known as an **allopolyploid** (**Figure 24.9** illustrates one such mechanism). The allopolyploids are fertile with each other but cannot interbreed with either parental species—thus they represent a new biological species.

The origin of new polyploid plant species is common enough and rapid enough that scientists have documented several such speciations. For example, two new species of goatsbeard plants (genus *Tragopogon*) originated in the Pacific Northwest in the mid-1900s. Although the goatsbeard genus is native to Europe, humans had introduced three species to the Americas in the early 1900s. These species, *T. dubius*, *T. pratensis*, and *T. porrifolius*, are now common weeds in abandoned parking lots and other urban wastelands. In the 1950s, botanists identified two new *Tragopogon* species in regions of Idaho and Washington where all three European species are also found. One new species, *T. miscellus*, is a tetraploid hybrid of *T. dubius* and *T. pratensis;* the other new species, *T. mirus*, is also an allopolyploid, but its ancestors are *T. dubius* and *T. porrifolius*. While the *T. mirus* population grows mainly by reproduction of its own members, additional episodes of hybridization between the ancestral species are continuing to add to the *T. mirus* population—just one example of an ongoing speciation process that can be observed.

Many important agricultural crops—such as oats, cotton, potatoes, tobacco, and wheat—are polyploids. The wheat used for bread, *Triticum aestivum*, is an allohexaploid (six sets of chromosomes, two sets from each of three different species). The first of the polyploidy events that eventually led to modern wheat probably occurred about 8,000 years ago in the Middle East as a spontaneous hybrid of an early cultivated wheat and a wild grass. Today, plant geneticists create new polyploids in the laboratory by using chemicals that induce meiotic and mitotic errors. By harnessing the evolutionary process,

Failure of cell division in a cell of a growing diploid plant after chromosome duplication gives rise to a tetraploid branch or other tissue.

Gametes produced by flowers on this tetraploid branch are diploid.

Offspring with tetraploid karyotypes may be viable and fertile—a new biological species.

$2n = 6$ $4n = 12$ $2n$ $4n$

▲ **Figure 24.8 Sympatric speciation by autopolyploidy in plants.**

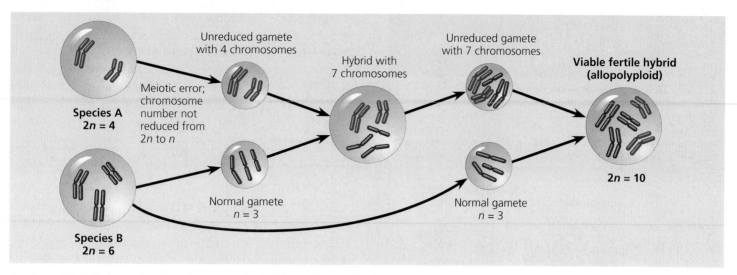

▲ Figure 24.9 One mechanism for allopolyploid speciation in plants. A hybrid of two different species is usually sterile because its chromosomes are not homologous and cannot pair during meiosis. However, such a hybrid may be able to reproduce asexually. This diagram traces one mechanism that can produce fertile hybrids (allopolyploids) as new species. The new species has a diploid chromosome number equal to the sum of the diploid chromosome numbers of the two parent species.

researchers can produce new hybrid species with desired qualities, such as a hybrid combining the high yield of wheat with the hardiness of rye.

Habitat Differentiation and Sexual Selection

Polyploid speciation also occurs in animals, although it is less common than in plants. Other mechanisms can also lead to sympatric speciation in both animals and plants. For example, reproductive isolation can occur when genetic factors enable a subpopulation to exploit a resource not used by the parent population. Such is the case with the North American apple maggot fly, *Rhagoletis pomonella*. The fly's original habitat was native hawthorn trees, but about 200 years ago, some populations colonized apple trees introduced by European settlers. Apples mature more quickly than hawthorn fruit, and so the apple-feeding flies have been selected for rapid development. These apple-feeding populations now show temporal isolation from the hawthorn-feeding *R. pomonella*. Although the two groups are still classified as subspecies rather than separate species, speciation appears to be well under way.

One of Earth's hot spots of animal speciation is Lake Victoria in eastern Africa. This vast, shallow lake has filled and dried up repeatedly in response to climate changes. The current lake, which is only 12,000 years old, is home to more than 500 species of cichlid fishes. The species are so genetically similar that it is very likely that many have arisen since the lake last filled. The subdivision of the original fish population into groups adapted to exploiting different food sources was one factor contributing to this rapid speciation. But researchers from the University of Leiden in the Netherlands

have shown that an additional factor may have been nonrandom mating (sexual selection), in which females select males based on their appearance.

These researchers studied two closely related sympatric species of cichlids that differ mainly in coloration: *Pundamilia pundamilia* has a blue-tinged back, and *Pundamilia nyererei* has a red-tinged back. It is a reasonable hypothesis that a preference for mates of like coloration functions as a behavioral barrier to interbreeding. In an aquarium with natural light, females of each species mated only with males of their own species. But in an aquarium illuminated with a monochromatic orange lamp, which made the two cichlid species appear identical, females of each species mated indiscriminately with males of both species (**Figure 24.10**, on the next page). The hybrids from the *P. pundamilia* × *P. nyererei* matings were viable and fertile.

From the results of these experiments, we can infer that mate choice based on coloration is the main reproductive barrier that normally keeps the gene pools of these two species separate. And we can also infer from their ability to interbreed in the laboratory that, like the apple maggot flies, these species have only begun to diverge. It seems likely that the ancestral population was polymorphic for color and that divergence began with the appearance of two ecological niches that divided the fish into subpopulations. Genetic drift resulted in chance differences in their genetic makeup, with the result that females in one subpopulation favored red in their mates, while females in the other subpopulation preferred blue. Sexual selection then reinforced the color difference as females mated preferentially with males having genes for the least mistakable coloration (see Chapter 23 to review sexual selection). Pollution is now clouding the waters of Lake Victoria, so perhaps the cichlids' divergence will be

Figure 24.10

Inquiry **Does sexual selection in cichlids result in reproductive isolation?**

EXPERIMENT Researchers from the University of Leiden placed males and females of *Pundamilia pundamilia* and *P. nyererei* together in two aquarium tanks, one with natural light and one with a monochromatic orange lamp. Under normal light, the two species are noticeably different in coloration; under monochromatic orange light, the two species appear identical in color. The researchers then observed the mating choices of the fish in each tank.

Normal light | Monochromatic orange light

P. pundamilia

P. nyererei

RESULTS Under normal light, females of each species mated only with males of their own species. But under orange light, females of each species mated indiscriminately with males of both species. The resulting hybrids were viable and fertile.

CONCLUSION The researchers concluded that mate choice by females based on coloration is the main reproductive barrier that normally keeps the gene pools of these two species separate. Since the species can still interbreed when this prezygotic behavioral barrier is breached in the laboratory, the genetic divergence between the species is likely to be small. This suggests that speciation in nature has occurred relatively recently.

reversed. As it becomes more difficult for female cichlids to visually distinguish between the males, the gene pools of *P. pundamilia* and *P. nyererei* may again blend together.

Allopatric and Sympatric Speciation: *A Summary*

Before continuing our discussion, let's recap the two main modes by which new species form. In allopatric speciation, a new species forms while geographically isolated from its parent population. As the isolated population evolves by natural selection and genetic drift, reproductive isolation from the ancestral species may arise as a by-product of the genetic change. Such reproductive barriers prevent interbreeding with the parent population, even if the populations come back into contact.

Sympatric speciation, in contrast, requires the emergence of a reproductive barrier that isolates a subset of a population without geographic separation from the parent population. A common mechanism, especially in plants, is

allopolyploidy: hybridization between closely related species coupled with errors during cell division that lead to fertile polyploid individuals. Sympatric speciation can also result when a subset of a population becomes reproductively isolated because of a switch to a habitat, food source, or other resource not used by the parent population. In animals, speciation can also result from sexual selection in a polymorphic population.

Adaptive Radiation

The evolution of many diversely adapted species from a common ancestor upon introduction to various new environmental opportunities and challenges is called **adaptive radiation.** Adaptive radiation typically occurs when a few organisms make their way to new, often distant areas **(Figure 24.11)** or when environmental changes cause numerous extinctions, opening up ecological niches for the survivors. For example, fossil evidence indicates that mammals underwent a dramatic adaptive radiation after the extinction of the dinosaurs 65 million years ago.

The Hawaiian archipelago is one of the world's great showcases of adaptive radiation, as Kenneth Kaneshiro explained in the interview on pages 436–437. Located about 3,500 km from the nearest continent, the volcanic islands are progressively younger as one follows the chain toward the southeast; the youngest island, Hawaii, is less than a million years old and still has active volcanoes. Each island was born "naked" and was gradually populated by stray organisms that rode the ocean currents and winds either from far-distant land areas or from older islands of the archipelago itself. The physical diversity of each island—including immense ranges of altitudes and rainfall—provides many opportunities for evolutionary divergence by natural selection **(Figure 24.12)**. Multiple

▲ **Figure 24.11 Long-distance dispersal.** Seeds of the plant *Pisonia* cling like Velcro to this migratory black noddy tern off the Australian coast. This mechanism enables the seeds to be transported over long distances. (In fact, studying how such seeds bind tightly but reversibly to feathers and fur inspired the inventors of Velcro.)

▲ **Figure 24.12 Adaptive radiation.** Molecular analysis indicates that these remarkably varied Hawaiian plants, known collectively as the "silversword alliance," are all descended from an ancestral tarweed that arrived on the islands about 5 million years ago from North America. Members of the silversword alliance have since spread into many different habitats on the islands, evolving into distinct forms through allopatric and sympatric speciation.

Dubautia laxa

Argyroxiphium sandwicense

Dubautia waialealae

Dubautia scabra

Dubautia linearis

invasions and allopatric and sympatric speciation events have ignited an explosion of adaptive radiation—most of the thousands of species that inhabit the islands are found nowhere else on Earth.

Studying the Genetics of Speciation

Rapid strides in genetics are enabling researchers to pinpoint genes that play a key role in particular cases of speciation. In one such study, Douglas Schemske and his colleagues at Michigan State University examined two species of monkey flower (*Mimulus*; see Figure 24.4f and g). *Mimulus lewisii* and *Mimulus cardinalis* are pollinated by bees and hummingbirds, respectively, keeping their gene pools separate through prezygotic isolation. But the species so far show no postzygotic isolation; they can be mated readily in the greenhouse. The resulting hybrids produce offspring with flowers

in a wide variety of colors and shapes. By observing which pollinators visit which flowers and then investigating the genetic differences among the plants, the researchers concluded that two gene loci are largely responsible for pollinator choice. One locus influences flower color and the other affects the amount of nectar that the flowers make. Thus, by determining the attractiveness of the flowers to different pollinators, allelic diversity at these loci has ultimately resulted in speciation.

The Tempo of Speciation

The fossil record includes many episodes in which new species appear suddenly in a geologic stratum, persist essentially unchanged through several strata, and then apparently disappear. Paleontologists Niles Eldredge of the American Museum of Natural History and Stephen Jay Gould of Harvard University

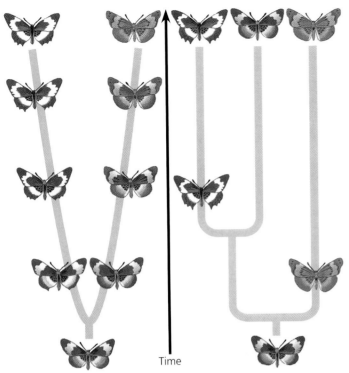

(a) Gradualism model. Species descended from a common ancestor gradually diverge more and more in their morphology as they acquire unique adaptations.

(b) Punctuated equilibrium model. A new species changes most as it buds from a parent species and then changes little for the rest of its existence.

▲ **Figure 24.13 Two models for the tempo of speciation.**

coined the term **punctuated equilibrium** to describe these periods of apparent stasis punctuated by sudden change.

Some scientists suggest that these patterns require an explanation outside the Darwinian model of gradual descent with modification. However, this is not necessarily the case. For one thing, such punctuations may have been less abrupt than they appear from the fossil record. Suppose that a species survived for 5 million years, but most of its morphological alterations occurred during the first 50,000 years of its existence—just 1% of its total lifetime. Because time periods this short often cannot be distinguished in fossil strata, the species would seem to have appeared suddenly and then lingered with little or no change before becoming extinct. Even though the emergence of this species actually took tens of thousands of years, this period of change left no fossil record **(Figure 24.13)**.

In fact, Darwin himself noted this pattern in the fossil record. He anticipated the concept of punctuated equilibrium when he wrote, "Although each species must have passed through numerous transitional stages, it is probable that the periods during which each underwent modification, though many and long as measured by years, have been short in comparison with the periods during which each remained in an unchanged condition."

Stasis, too, can be explained. All species continue to adapt after they come into existence, but often in ways that cannot be

detected from fossils, such as small modifications in their biochemistry. By necessity, paleontologists base hypotheses about descent almost entirely on external anatomy and skeletons. During periods of apparent equilibrium, changes in behavior, internal anatomy, and physiology may go undetected. If the environment changes, however, the stasis will be broken by punctuations that leave visible traces in the fossil record.

Concept 24.3

Macroevolutionary changes can accumulate through many speciation events

Speciation can result from differences as seemingly small as the color on a cichlid's back. However, as species diverge and speciate again and again, these differences can accumulate and become more pronounced. Thus, speciation constitutes the beginning of macroevolutionary change. Macroevolutionary transformations, like the microevolutionary changes that take place within a single gene pool, accumulate through the processes that we examined in Chapter 23—natural selection, mutation, genetic drift, and gene flow. It is the cumulative change during thousands of small speciation episodes that accounts for sweeping evolutionary changes. We will now look at some of the ways in which these major transformations have taken place.

Evolutionary Novelties

The Darwinian concept of descent with modification can be extended to account for even major morphological transformations. In most cases, complex structures have evolved in increments from much simpler versions that performed the same basic function.

For example, consider the human eye, an intricate organ constructed from numerous parts that work together in forming an image and transmitting it to the brain. How could the human eye have evolved in gradual increments? If the eye needs all its components to function, how could a partial eye have been of any use to our ancestors?

The flaw in this argument, as Darwin himself noted, lies in the assumption that only complicated eyes are useful. In fact, many animals depend on eyes that are far less complex than our own **(Figure 24.14)**. The simplest eyes that we know of are patches of light-sensitive photoreceptor cells. These simple eyes appear to have had a single evolutionary origin and are now found in a variety of animals, such as limpets, small molluscs (members of the phylum Mollusca). These eyes have no lenses or other equipment for focusing images, but they do enable the animal to distinguish light from dark. Limpets cling more tightly to their rock when a shadow falls on them—a behavioral adaptation that reduces the risk of being eaten. Since limpets have had a long evolutionary history, we can conclude that their "simple" eyes are quite adequate to support their survival and reproduction.

In the animal kingdom, complex eyes of various types evolved independently from such basic structures many times. Some molluscs, including the squids and octopuses, have eyes as complex as those of humans and other vertebrates (see Figure 24.14). Although complex mollusc eyes evolved independently of complex vertebrate eyes, both evolved from an ancestral simple cluster of photoreceptor cells. This divergence took place through a series of incremental modifications that benefited the eyes' owners at every stage. Evidence for this evolutionary divergence comes from phylogenetic analysis of the genes that act as "master regulators" of eye development and are shared by all animals with eyes.

Throughout their evolutionary history, eyes retained their basic function of vision. But evolutionary novelty can also arise when structures that originally played one role gradually acquire a different one. Structures that evolve in one context but become co-opted for another function are sometimes called *exaptations* to distinguish them from the adaptive origin of the original structure.

Note that the concept of exaptation does not imply that a structure somehow evolves in anticipation of future use. Natural selection cannot predict the future; it can only improve a structure in the context of its *current* utility. For example, the lightweight, honeycombed bones of birds are homologous to the bones of birds' earthbound ancestors. However, honeycombed bones could not have evolved in the ancestors as an adaptation for future flight—they must have had another benefit. Fossils of some close relatives of

(a) Patch of pigmented cells. The limpet *Patella* has a simple patch of photoreceptors.

(b) Eyecup. The slit shell mollusc *Pleurotomaria* has an eyecup.

(c) Pinhole camera-type eye. The *Nautilus* eye functions like a pinhole camera (an early type of camera lacking a lens).

(d) Eye with primitive lens. The marine snail *Murex* has a primitive lens consisting of a mass of crystal-like cells. The cornea is a transparent region of epithelium (outer skin) that protects the eye and helps focus light.

(e) Complex camera-type eye. The squid *Loligo* has a complex eye whose features (cornea, lens, and retina), though similar to those of vertebrate eyes, evolved independently.

▲ **Figure 24.14 A range of eye complexity among molluscs.**

birds have been found in China. These small animals were unable to fly but had feet that enabled them to climb and perch in trees. Lightweight bones would have aided this lifestyle. It is possible that winglike forelimbs and feathers, which would have increased the surface area of these small animals' forelimbs, were co-opted for flight after functioning in some other capacity, such as courtship, thermoregulation, or camouflage (functions that feathers still serve today). The first flights might have been only short glides. Indeed, the first feathers to leave traces in the fossil record were short and downy; feathers adapted for flight appeared later. Over time, natural selection screening additional mutations remodeled feathers and wings in ways that better fit their new function.

The concept of exaptation offers one explanation for how novel features can arise gradually through a series of intermediate stages, each of which has some function in the organism's current context. In the words of Harvard University zoologist Karel Liem, "Evolution is like modifying a machine while it's running."

Evolution of the Genes That Control Development

As you read in Chapter 21, "evo-devo"—the interface between evolutionary biology and developmental biology—is illuminating how slight genetic divergences can be magnified into major morphological differences between species. Genes that program development control the rate, timing, and spatial pattern of changes in an organism's form as it develops from a zygote into an adult.

(a) Differential growth rates in a human. The arms and legs lengthen more during growth than the head and trunk, as can be seen in this conceptualization of an individual at different ages all rescaled to the same height.

Newborn   2   5   15   Adult
Age (years)

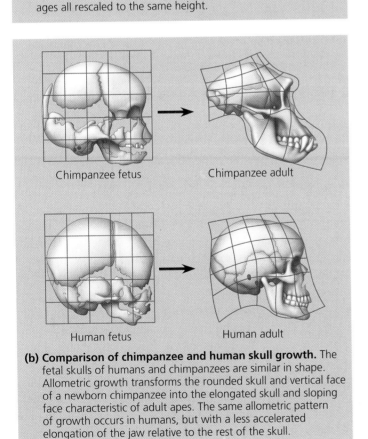

Chimpanzee fetus   Chimpanzee adult

Human fetus   Human adult

(b) Comparison of chimpanzee and human skull growth. The fetal skulls of humans and chimpanzees are similar in shape. Allometric growth transforms the rounded skull and vertical face of a newborn chimpanzee into the elongated skull and sloping face characteristic of adult apes. The same allometric pattern of growth occurs in humans, but with a less accelerated elongation of the jaw relative to the rest of the skull.

▲ **Figure 24.15 Allometric growth.** Different growth rates for different parts of the body determine body proportions.

Changes in Rate and Timing

Many striking evolutionary transformations are the result of **heterochrony** (from the Greek *hetero*, different, and *chronos*, time) an evolutionary change in the rate or timing of developmental events. For example, an organism's shape depends in part on the relative growth rates of different body parts during development. This proportioning that helps give a body its specific form is called **allometric growth** (from the Greek *allos*, other, and *metron*, measure). **Figure 24.15a** tracks how allometric growth alters human body proportions during development. Changing these relative rates of growth even slightly changes the adult form substantially. For example, different allometric patterns contribute to the contrasting shapes of human and chimpanzee skulls **(Figure 24.15b)**.

Heterochrony has also played a role in the evolution of salamander feet **(Figure 24.16)**. Most salamanders live on the ground, but some species live in trees. The feet of the tree-dwelling species are adapted for climbing vertically rather

(a) Ground-dwelling salamander. A longer time period for foot growth results in longer digits and less webbing.

(b) Tree-dwelling salamander. Foot growth ends sooner. This evolutionary timing change accounts for the shorter digits and more extensive webbing, which help the salamander climb vertically on tree branches.

▲ **Figure 24.16 Heterochrony and the evolution of salamander feet in closely related species.**

than walking on the ground; for example, their shorter digits and more extensive webbing provide better traction. The basis for this adaptation was probably selection for alleles of genes that control the timing of foot development. According to this hypothesis, the foot of the ancestral salamander grew until the products of certain regulatory genes switched off growth, resulting in a foot of a certain size. A mutation in one or more of these regulatory genes could have switched off foot growth sooner, resulting in the stunted feet of tree-dwelling salamanders. In this way, a relatively small amount of genetic change can be amplified into substantial morphological change.

Heterochrony can also alter the timing of reproductive development relative to the development of somatic (nonreproductive) organs. If the rate of reproductive development accelerates compared to somatic development, the sexually mature stage of a species may retain body features that were juvenile structures in an ancestral species—a condition called **paedomorphosis** (from the Greek *paedos*, of a child, and *morphosis*, formation). For example, most salamander species have a larval stage that undergoes metamorphosis in becoming an adult. But some species grow to adult size and become sexually mature while retaining gills and other larval features **(Figure 24.17)**. Such an evolutionary alteration of developmental timing can produce animals that appear very different from their ancestors, even though the overall genetic change may be small. Indeed, recent evidence indicates that a genetic change at a single locus was probably sufficient to bring about paedomorphosis in the axolotl salamander, although other genes may have contributed as well.

In summary, heterochrony affects the evolution of morphology by altering the rates at which various body parts

develop or by changing the timing of onset or completion of a particular part's development.

Changes in Spatial Pattern

Substantial evolutionary changes can also result from alterations in genes that control the placement and spatial organization of body parts. For example, as described in Chapter 21, **homeotic genes** determine such basic features as where a pair of wings and a pair of legs will develop on a bird or how a plant's flower parts are arranged.

The products of one class of homeotic genes called *Hox* genes provide positional information in an animal embryo. This information prompts cells to develop into structures appropriate for a particular location. Changes in *Hox* genes and in the genes that regulate them in turn can have a profound impact on morphology. Consider, for example, the evolution of tetrapods (the terrestrial vertebrates including amphibians, birds and other reptiles, and mammals) from fishes, which are aquatic vertebrates. During this process, four of the fish fins evolved into limbs. Among the adaptations of the tetrapod limb are digits (fingers and toes in humans) that extend skeletal support to the tip of the limb.

In fish embryos, a *Hox* gene is expressed in a band of cells running along one edge of the fin bud **(Figure 24.18)**. In

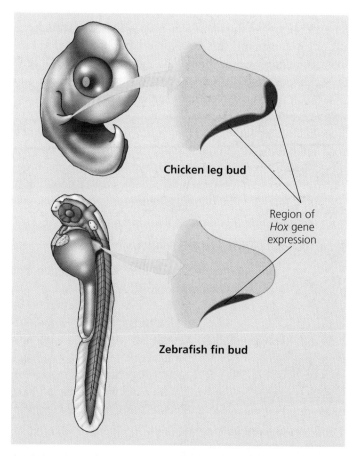

▲ **Figure 24.18** *Hox* **genes and the evolution of tetrapod limbs.** The red zones indicate regions where a *Hox* gene involved in skeleton development is expressed.

▲ **Figure 24.17 Paedomorphosis.** Some species retain as adults features that were juvenile in ancestors. This salamander is an axolotl, which grows to full size, becomes sexually mature, and reproduces while retaining certain larval (tadpole) characteristics, including gills.

① Most invertebrates have one cluster of homeotic genes (the *Hox* complex), shown here as colored bands on a chromosome. *Hox* genes direct development of major body parts.

Hypothetical vertebrate ancestor (invertebrate) with a single *Hox* cluster

First *Hox* duplication

② A mutation (duplication) of the single *Hox* complex occurred about 520 million years ago and may have provided genetic material associated with the origin of the first vertebrates.

③ In an early vertebrate, the duplicate set of genes took on entirely new roles, such as directing the development of a backbone.

Hypothetical early vertebrates (jawless) with two *Hox* clusters

Second *Hox* duplication

④ A second duplication of the *Hox* complex, yielding the four clusters found in most present-day vertebrates, occurred later, about 425 million years ago. This duplication, probably the result of a polyploidy event, allowed the development of even greater structural complexity, such as jaws and limbs.

⑤ The vertebrate *Hox* complex contains duplicates of many of the same genes as the single invertebrate cluster, in virtually the same linear order on chromosomes, and they direct the sequential development of the same body regions. Thus, scientists infer that the four clusters of the vertebrate *Hox* complex are homologous to the single cluster in invertebrates.

Vertebrates (with jaws) with four *Hox* clusters

▲ **Figure 24.19** *Hox* **mutations and the origin of vertebrates.**

tetrapod embryos, this same *Hox* gene is also expressed at the tip of the limb bud, the embryonic structure that develops into a forelimb or hind limb. The product of this *Hox* gene provides positional information about how far digits and other bones should extend from the limb.

The evolution of vertebrates from invertebrate animals was an even larger evolutionary change, and it, too, was associated with alterations in *Hox* genes and the genes that regulate them **(Figure 24.19)**. In producing such morphological novelties, changes in developmental dynamics have undoubtedly played important roles in macroevolution.

Evolution Is Not Goal Oriented

The fossil record often shows apparent trends in evolution. For instance, some evolutionary lineages exhibit a trend toward larger or smaller body size. An example is the evolution of the living horse (genus *Equus*), a descendant of the 40-million-year-old *Hyracotherium* **(Figure 24.20)**. About the size of a large dog, *Hyracotherium* had four toes on its front feet, three toes on its hind feet, and teeth adapted for browsing on bushes and trees. In comparison, living horses are larger, have only one toe on each foot, and possess teeth modified for grazing on grasses. Do these changes represent real trends, and if so, how do we account for them?

Extracting a single evolutionary progression from the fossil record can be misleading; it is like describing a bush as grow-

ing toward a single point by tracing only the branches that lead to that twig. For instance, by selecting certain species from the available fossils, it is possible to arrange a succession of animals intermediate between *Hyracotherium* and living horses that shows trends toward increased size, reduced number of toes, and modification of teeth for grazing (yellow line in Figure 24.20). However, if we include all fossil horses known today, this apparent trend vanishes. The genus *Equus* did not evolve in a straight line; it is the only surviving twig of an evolutionary tree that is so branched that it is more like a bush. *Equus* actually descended through a series of speciation episodes that included several adaptive radiations, not all of which led to large, one-toed, grazing horses. For instance, notice in Figure 24.20 that only those lineages derived from *Parahippus* include grazers; other lineages derived from *Miohippus*, all of which are now extinct, remained multi-toed browsers for 35 million years.

Branching evolution can result in an evolutionary trend even if some new species counter the trend. For example, one model of long-term trends proposed by Steven Stanley of Johns Hopkins University considers species to be analogous to individuals: Speciation is their birth, extinction is their death, and new species that diverge from them are their offspring. In this model, Stanley suggests that just as individual organisms undergo natural selection, species undergo **species selection**. The species that endure the longest and generate the most new offspring species determine the direction of major

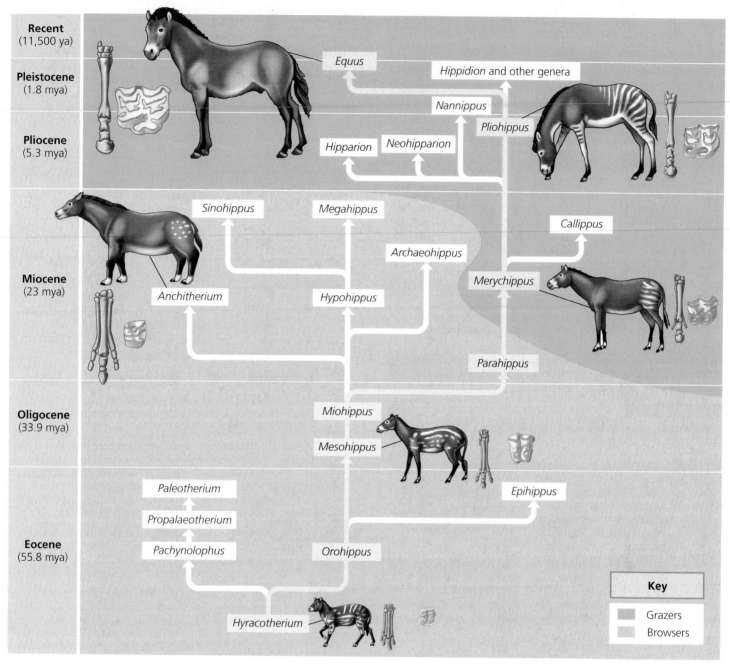

Recent
(11,500 ya)

Pleistocene
(1.8 mya)

Pliocene
(5.3 mya)

Miocene
(23 mya)

Oligocene
(33.9 mya)

Eocene
(55.8 mya)

Equus

Hippidion and other genera

Nannippus

Pliohippus

Hipparion | Neohipparion

Sinohippus

Megahippus

Callippus

Archaeohippus

Anchitherium

Hypohippus

Merychippus

Parahippus

Miohippus

Mesohippus

Epihippus

Paleotherium

Propalaeotherium

Pachynolophus

Orohippus

Hyracotherium

Key

Grazers

Browsers

▲ Figure 24.20 **The branched evolution of horses.** Using a yellow highlighter to trace the sequence of fossil horses that are intermediate in form between the living horse (*Equus*) and its Eocene ancestor *Hyracotherium* creates the illusion of a progressive trend toward larger size, reduced number of toes, and teeth modified for grazing. In fact, the living horse is the only surviving twig of an evolutionary bush with many divergent trends.

evolutionary trends. The species selection model suggests that "differential speciation success" plays a role in macroevolution similar to the role of differential reproductive success in microevolution.

To the extent that speciation rates and species longevity reflect success, the analogy to natural selection is even stronger. It is possible that qualities unrelated to the overall success of organisms in specific environments may become important when entire species are selected. For example, if a species is able to disperse easily to new locations, it may give rise to a large number of "daughter species."

Whether or not the species selection model is valid, there are other possible sources of trends observed in the fossil record. For example, sexual selection in the Irish elk of northern Europe drove an immense increase in the size of their antlers—though this did not prevent the elk from becoming extinct because of changing vegetation and hunting by humans. And when horse ancestors invaded the grasslands that spread during the Age of Mammals, there was strong selection for grazers that could escape predators by running faster. This trend would not have occurred without open grasslands.

Whatever its cause, the appearance of an evolutionary trend does not imply that there is some intrinsic drive toward a particular phenotype. Evolution is the result of the interactions between organisms and their current environments. If environmental conditions change, an apparent evolutionary trend may cease or even reverse itself.

In the next chapter, we will continue our study of speciation and the further divergence of organisms, with a more detailed look at the fossil record and the effects of significant environmental change.

Concept Check 24.3

1. How can the Darwinian concept of descent with modification explain the evolution of such complex structures as the vertebrate eye or heart?
2. Explain why the concept of exaptation does not mean that a structure evolves in anticipation of some future environmental change.
3. How can heterochrony cause the evolution of different body forms?

For suggested answers, see Appendix A.

Chapter 24 Review

Go to the Campbell Biology website (**www.campbellbiology.com**) or CD-ROM to explore Activities, Investigations, and other interactive study aids.

SUMMARY OF KEY CONCEPTS

Concept 24.1

The biological species concept emphasizes reproductive isolation

▶ **The Biological Species Concept (pp. 473–476)** A biological species is a group of populations whose individuals have the potential to interbreed and produce fertile offspring with each other but not with members of other species. The biological species concept emphasizes reproductive isolation through prezygotic and postzygotic barriers that can result in separating the gene pools of different populations.

▶ **Other Definitions of Species (p. 476)** Although particularly helpful in thinking about speciation processes, the biological species concept has some major limitations. For instance, it cannot be applied to organisms that are known only as fossils or to organisms that reproduce only asexually. Thus, scientists maintain alternative species concepts, such as the morphological species concept, that are useful in various contexts.
Activity *Overview of Macroevolution*

Concept 24.2

Speciation can take place with or without geographic separation

▶ **Allopatric ("Other Country") Speciation (pp. 477–478)** Allopatric speciation may occur when two populations of one species become geographically separated from each other. One or both populations may undergo evolutionary change during the period of separation. Should they come into contact once more, they may be separated by the prezygotic and postzygotic isolating mechanisms that have accumulated.

▶ **Sympatric ("Same Country") Speciation (pp. 478–480)** A new species can originate while remaining in a geographically overlapping area with the parent species. In particular, many plant species have evolved sympatrically through polyploidy (multiplications of the chromosome number). Autopolyploids are species derived this way from one ancestral species. Allopoly-

ploids are species with multiple sets of chromosomes derived from different species. Sympatric speciation can also result from the appearance of new ecological niches and from nonrandom mating in polymorphic populations.

▶ **Allopatric and Sympatric Speciation: A Summary (p. 480)** In allopatric speciation, a new species forms while geographically isolated from its parent population. In sympatric speciation, a reproductive barrier isolates a subset of a population without geographic separation.

▶ **Adaptive Radiation (pp. 480–481)** Adaptive radiation can occur when a population encounters a multiplicity of new or newly available ecological niches. This may happen during colonization of a new environment, such as newly formed volcanic islands, or after an environmental change that has resulted in mass extinctions of other species in an area.

▶ **Studying the Genetics of Speciation (p. 481)** The explosion of genomics is enabling researchers to identify specific genes involved in some cases of speciation.
Investigation *How Do New Species Arise by Genetic Isolation?*

▶ **The Tempo of Speciation (pp. 481–482)** Eldredge and Gould's punctuated equilibrium model draws on fossil evidence showing that species change most as they arise from an ancestral species, after which they undergo relatively little change for the rest of their existence. This model contrasts with a model of gradual change throughout a species' existence.

Concept 24.3

Macroevolutionary changes can accumulate through many speciation events

▶ **Evolutionary Novelties (pp. 482–483)** Most novel biological structures evolve in many stages from previously existing structures. Some complex structures, such as the eye, have had similar functions during all stages of their evolution. The most important functions of others, such as feathers, have changed.

▶ **Evolution of the Genes That Control Development (pp. 484–486)** Many large evolutionary changes may have been associated with mutations in genes that regulate development. Such changes can affect the timing of developmental events (heterochrony) or the spatial organization of body parts. Some of these changes result from mutational changes in homeotic genes and in the genes that regulate them.
Activity *Allometric Growth*

► **Evolution Is Not Goal Oriented** (pp. 486–488) Long-term evolutionary trends may arise because of adaptation to a changing environment. In addition, according to the species selection model, trends may result when species with certain characteristics endure longer and speciate more often than those with other characteristics.

TESTING YOUR KNOWLEDGE

Self-Quiz

1. The biological species concept is *not* useful for organisms known only from fossils because
   a. fossils are rarely preserved well enough to distinguish species based on morphology.
   b. it is not possible to test reproductive isolation of fossil forms.
   c. it is not possible to infer the types of habitats occupied by the fossil forms before their extinction.
   d. in examining fossil organisms, it is not possible to distinguish males from females.
   e. the fossil record can only be used for studying anagenesis, but not cladogenesis.

2. The *largest* unit within which gene flow can readily occur is a
   a. population.
   b. species.
   c. genus.
   d. hybrid.
   e. phylum.

3. Bird guides once listed the myrtle warbler and Audubon's warbler as distinct species. Recently, these birds have been classified as eastern and western forms of a single species, the yellow-rumped warbler. Which of the following pieces of evidence, if true, would be cause for this reclassification?
   a. The two forms are observed to interbreed successfully where their habitats overlap.
   b. The two forms live in similar habitats.
   c. The two forms have many genes in common.
   d. The two forms have similar food requirements.
   e. The two forms are very similar in coloration.

4. Males of different species of the fruit fly *Drosophila* that live in the same parts of the Hawaiian islands have different elaborate courtship rituals that involve fighting other males and stylized movements that attract females. What type of reproductive isolation does this represent?
   a. habitat isolation
   b. temporal isolation
   c. behavioral isolation
   d. gametic isolation
   e. postzygotic barriers

5. Which of the following factors would *not* contribute to allopatric speciation?
   a. A population becomes geographically isolated from the parent population.
   b. The separated population is small, and genetic drift occurs.

   c. The isolated population is exposed to different selection pressures than the ancestral population.
   d. Different mutations begin to distinguish the gene pools of the separated populations.
   e. Gene flow between the two populations is extensive.

6. Plant species A has a diploid number of 12. Plant species B has a diploid number of 16. A new species, C, arises as an allopolyploid from A and B. The likely diploid number for species C would probably be
   a. 12.
   b. 14.
   c. 16.
   d. 28.
   e. 56.

7. The speciation episode described in question 6 is most likely a case of
   a. allopatric speciation.
   b. sympatric speciation.
   c. speciation based on sexual selection.
   d. adaptive radiation.
   e. anagenesis.

8. *Mimulus lewisii* and *M. cardinalis* are plants that do not hybridize in nature but can be readily crossed in the laboratory to produce fertile offspring. Which of the following is *least* likely to keep the gene pools of these two plants separate in nature?
   a. gametic incompatibility
   b. different attractiveness to pollinators
   c. different ecological niches
   d. different geographic ranges
   e. seasonal differences in flowering

9. According to the punctuated equilibrium model,
   a. natural selection is unimportant as a mechanism of evolution.
   b. given enough time, most existing species will branch gradually into new species.
   c. most new species accumulate their unique features as they come into existence, then change little for the rest of their duration as a species.
   d. most evolution is goal oriented.
   e. speciation is usually due to a single mutation.

10. A genetic change that caused a certain *Hox* gene to be expressed along the tip of a vertebrate limb bud instead of farther back made possible the evolution of the tetrapod limb. This type of change is illustrative of
   a. the influence of environment on an individual's development.
   b. paedomorphosis, or retention of ancestral juvenile structures in an adult organism.
   c. a change in a developmental gene or in its regulation that altered the spatial organization of body parts.
   d. punctuated equilibrium.
   e. the origin of a new species due to allopolyploidy.

For Self-Quiz answers, see Appendix A.

Go to the website or CD-ROM for more quiz questions.

Evolution Connection

In the margin of one of his notebooks, Darwin scrawled a note to remind himself never to apply the terms *higher* or *lower* to species. It was, and still is, very common for people to think of some species or species groups as more or less evolved than others. This probably stems from a notion of evolutionary "progress." Is there such a thing as evolutionary progress? Why or why not? Defend your position as if you were debating someone holding the opposite view.

Scientific Inquiry

Cultivated American cotton plants have a total of 52 chromosomes ($2n = 52$). In each cell, 13 pairs of chromosomes (26 chromosomes) are smaller than the other 13 pairs. Old World cotton plants have a total of 26 chromosomes ($2n = 26$), all large. Wild American cotton plants have 26 chromosomes, all small. Propose a hypothesis to explain how cultivated American cotton may have originated. How could you test your hypothesis?

Investigation *How Do New Species Arise by Genetic Isolation?*

Science, Technology, and Society

What is the biological basis for assigning all human populations to a single species? Can you think of a scenario in which a second human species could arise in the future by cladogenesis?

25

Phylogeny and Systematics

Key Concepts

25.1 Phylogenies are based on common ancestries inferred from fossil, morphological, and molecular evidence

25.2 Phylogenetic systematics connects classification with evolutionary history

25.3 Phylogenetic systematics informs the construction of phylogenetic trees based on shared characters

25.4 Much of an organism's evolutionary history is documented in its genome

25.5 Molecular clocks help track evolutionary time

Overview

Investigating the Tree of Life

Evolutionary biology is about both process and history. In this unit, we have already examined the processes of evolution—natural selection and other mechanisms that change the genetic composition of populations (see Chapter 23) and that can lead to the origin of new species (see Chapter 24). But evolutionary biologists also seek to reconstruct the long-term results of these processes—the entire history of life on Earth.

This chapter describes how biologists trace **phylogeny** (from the Greek *phylon,* tribe, and *genesis,* origin), the evolutionary history of a species or group of species. In constructing phylogenies, biologists draw on the fossil record, which provides information about ancient organisms **(Figure 25.1)**. They also utilize **systematics,** an analytical approach to understanding the diversity and relationships of organisms, both present-day and extinct. Systematists have traditionally studied morphological and biochemical resemblances among organisms as a basis for inferring evolutionary relationships. In

recent decades, systematists have gained a powerful new tool: **molecular systematics,** which uses comparisons of DNA, RNA, and other molecules to infer evolutionary relationships between individual genes and even between entire genomes **(Figure 25.2)**. This information explosion is enabling evolutionary biologists to construct a universal tree of all life, which will continue to be refined as the database of DNA and RNA sequences grows.

▲ Figure 25.2 **An unexpected family tree.** What are the evolutionary relationships among a human, a mushroom, and a tulip? Molecular systematics has revealed that—despite appearances—animals, including humans, and fungi, such as mushrooms, are more closely related to each other than either are to plants.

Phylogenies are based on common ancestries inferred from fossil, morphological, and molecular evidence

In order to infer phylogenies, we must gather as much information as we can about the morphologies, development, and biochemistry of living organisms. But it is also essential to study fossils, the preserved remnants or impressions left by organisms that lived in the past. Fossils can help establish relationships between living organisms because they reveal ancestral characteristics that may have been lost over time in certain lineages.

The Fossil Record

Sedimentary rocks are the richest source of fossils. Sand and silt eroded from the land are carried by rivers to seas and swamps, where the minerals settle to the bottom along with the remains of organisms. Over millions of years, deposits pile up and compress the older sediments below into layers called strata **(Figure 25.3)**. The **fossil record** is based on the sequence in which fossils have accumulated in such strata.

Though sedimentary fossils are the most common, paleontologists also study other types of fossils **(Figure 25.4)**. But fossils inform phylogeny only if we can determine their ages, clarifying the order in which various characteristics appeared and disappeared. In Chapter 26, we will discuss methods for dating fossils and for assigning the divisions of the geologic record. For now, keep in mind that the fossil record is a sub-

stantial, but incomplete, chronicle of evolutionary change. A large number of Earth's species probably did not die in the right place at the right time to be captured in fossils; of those fossils that were formed, many were probably destroyed by later geologic processes; and only a fraction of existing fossils have been discovered. Rather than giving a true indication of the diversity of past life, the fossil record is biased in favor of species that existed for a long time, were abundant and widespread, and had hard shells, skeletons, or other hard parts that facilitated their fossilization. Even with its limitations, however, the fossil record is a remarkably detailed account of biological change over the vast scale of geologic time.

Morphological and Molecular Homologies

In addition to fossil organisms, phylogenetic history can be inferred from certain morphological and molecular similarities among living organisms. Recall that similarities due to shared ancestry are called homologies. For example, the similarity in the number and arrangement of bones in the forelimbs of mammals is due to their descent from a common ancestor with the same bone structure; this is an example of a morphological homology (see Figure 22.14). In the same way, genes or other DNA sequences are homologous if the nature of their similarity suggests that they are descended from the sequences carried by a common ancestor.

In general, organisms that share very similar morphologies or similar DNA sequences are likely to be more closely related than organisms with vastly different structures or sequences. In some cases, however, the morphological divergence between related species can be great and their genetic divergence small (or vice versa). For example, consider the Hawaiian silversword plants discussed in Chapter 24. These species vary dramatically in appearance throughout the islands: Some

❶ Rivers carry sediment to the ocean. Sedimentary rock layers containing fossils form on the ocean floor.

❷ Over time, new strata are deposited, containing fossils from each time period.

❸ As sea levels change and the seafloor is pushed upward, sedimentary rocks are exposed. Erosion reveals strata and fossils.

Younger stratum with more recent fossils

Older stratum with older fossils

▲ **Figure 25.3 Formation of sedimentary strata containing fossils.**

(a) Dinosaur bones being excavated from sandstone

(b) Petrified tree in Arizona, about 190 million years old

(c) Leaf fossil, about 40 million years old

(d) Casts of ammonites, about 375 million years old

(g) Tusks of a 23,000-year-old mammoth, frozen whole in Siberian ice

(f) Insects preserved whole in amber

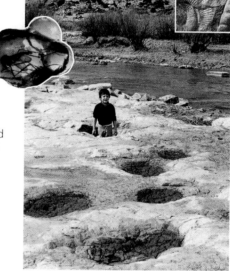

(e) Boy standing in a 150-million-year-old dinosaur track in Colorado

▲ **Figure 25.4 A gallery of fossil types.**
(a) An organism's mineral-containing hard parts, such as bones, shells, or teeth, are most likely to be preserved as fossils. **(b)** Some fossils form when minerals seep into and replace organic matter. **(c)** Some sedimentary fossils retain organic material from which scientists can extract molecules for analysis. **(d)** Buried organisms that decay may leave impressions that are filled by water containing dissolved minerals. The casts that form when the minerals harden are replicas of the organisms. **(e)** Trace fossils are footprints, burrows, and other remnants of an ancient organism's activities. **(f)** Entire organisms are sometimes found preserved in amber (hardened resin from a tree). **(g)** Rarely, ice or an acid bog preserves the body of a very large organism.

are tall, twiggy trees, and others are dense, ground-hugging shrubs (see Figure 24.12). But in spite of these striking phenotypic differences, the silverswords' genes are very similar. Based on these small molecular divergences, scientists estimate that the silversword group began to diverge 5 million years ago, which is also about the time when the oldest of the current islands formed. We can infer that the morphological diversity of the silverswords is controlled by relatively few genetic differences.

Sorting Homology from Analogy

A potential red herring in constructing a phylogeny is similarity due to convergent evolution—called **analogy**—rather than to shared ancestry (homology). As you read in Chapter 22, convergent evolution occurs when similar environmental pressures and natural selection produce similar (analogous) adaptations in organisms from different evolutionary lineages (see Figure 22.17). For example, Australian and North American burrowing moles are very similar in appearance **(Figure 25.5)**. However, their reproductive systems are very dissimilar: Australian moles are marsupials (their young complete their embryonic development in a pouch outside the mother's body), whereas North American moles are eutherians (their young complete their embryonic development in a uterus within the mother's body). Indeed, genetic comparisons and the fossil record provide evidence that the moles' common ancestor lived 120 million years ago, about the time the marsupial and eutherian mammals diverged. This ancestor and most of its descendants were not mole-like, but similar characteristics evolved independently in these two mole lineages as they adapted to similar lifestyles.

Distinguishing between homology and analogy is critical in reconstructing phylogenies. For example, both bats and birds have adaptations that enable them to fly. This superficial resemblance might imply that bats are more closely related to birds than they are to cats, which cannot fly. But a closer examination reveals that the complex structure of the bat's flight apparatus is far more similar to the forelimbs of cats and other mammals than to a bird's wing. Fossil evidence also documents that bat forelimbs and bird wings arose independently from walking forelimbs of different ancestors. Thus, we can state that the bat's forelimb is *homologous* to those of other mammals, but *analogous* in function to a bird's wing. Analogous structures that have evolved independently, such as bat forelimbs and bird wings, are also sometimes called **homoplasies** (from the Greek for "to mold in the same way").

Besides searching for corroborating similarities or fossil evidence, another clue to distinguishing between homology and analogy is to consider the complexity of the characters being compared. The more points of resemblance that two complex structures have, the less likely it is that they evolved independently. For instance, the skulls of a human and a chimpanzee do not consist of a single bone but rather of many bones fused together. The compositions of the two skulls match almost perfectly, bone for bone. It is highly improbable that such complex structures, matching in so many details, have separate origins. More likely, the genes involved in the development of both skulls were inherited from a common ancestor. The same argument applies to comparing genes themselves, which are sequences of thousands of nucleotides. Each nucleotide position along a stretch of DNA or RNA represents an inherited character in the form of one of the four DNA bases: A (adenine), G (guanine), C (cytosine), or T (thymine). Thus, comparable regions of DNA that are 1,000 nucleotides long provide 1,000 points of similarity or difference between two species. Systematists compare long stretches of DNA and even entire genomes to assess relationships between species. If genes in two organisms share many portions of their nucleotide sequences, it is highly likely that the genes are homologous.

Evaluating Molecular Homologies

Molecular comparisons of nucleic acids often pose technical challenges. The first step is to align comparable nucleic acid sequences from the two species being studied. If the species are very closely related, the sequences likely differ at only one or a few sites. In contrast, comparable nucleic acid sequences in distantly related species usually have different bases at many sites and may even have different lengths. This is because, over longer periods of time, insertions and deletions accumulate, altering the lengths of the gene sequences (see Chapter 23). Suppose, for example, that certain noncoding DNA sequences in a particular gene in two species are very similar, but a deletion mutation has eliminated the first base of the sequence in one of the species. The effect is that the remaining sequence shifts back one notch. A comparison of the two sequences that does not take this deletion into account would overlook what in fact is a very good match. To avoid this problem, systematists use computer programs to analyze comparable DNA segments of differing lengths and realign them appropriately **(Figure 25.6)**.

Such molecular comparisons reveal that a large number of base substitutions and other differences have accumulated between the comparable genes of the Australian and North American moles, indicating that their lineages have diverged greatly since their common ancestor; thus, we say that the living species are not closely related. In contrast, the high degree of gene-sequence similarity among the silverswords supports the hypothesis that they are all very closely related, in spite of their considerable morphological differences.

The fact that molecules have diverged between species does not in itself tell us how long ago their common ancestor lived.

▲ **Figure 25.5 Convergent evolution of analogous burrowing characteristics.** An elongated body, enlarged front paws, small eyes, and a pad of thickened skin that protects a tapered nose all evolved independently in the marsupial Australian mole (top) and eutherian North American mole (bottom).

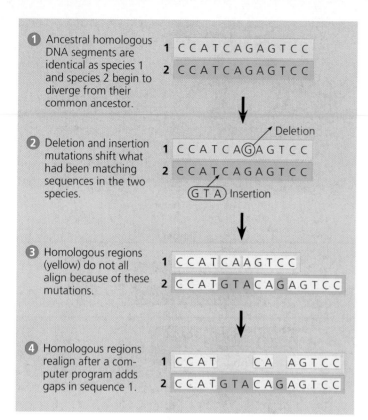

1 Ancestral homologous DNA segments are identical as species 1 and species 2 begin to diverge from their common ancestor.

1 C C A T C A G A G T C C
2 C C A T C A G A G T C C

2 Deletion and insertion mutations shift what had been matching sequences in the two species.

Deletion
1 C C A T C A (G) A G T C C
2 C C A T C A G A G T C C
(G T A) Insertion

3 Homologous regions (yellow) do not all align because of these mutations.

1 C C A T C A A G T C C
2 C C A T G T A C A G A G T C C

4 Homologous regions realign after a computer program adds gaps in sequence 1.

1 C C A T   C A   A G T C C
2 C C A T G T A C A G A G T C C

▲ **Figure 25.6 Aligning segments of DNA.** Systematists use computer software to find and realign similar sequences along DNA segments from two species. (In this example, no bases have changed and the comparable sequences are still identical once the length is adjusted.)

Sometimes, as in the case of the moles, the fossil record provides data about when their common ancestor probably lived. But in the case of the silverswords, few fossils have been found. For such species, researchers may be able to compare their molecular divergence with that found in other plant lineages that have more complete fossil records. These values can serve as a sort of molecular yardstick to measure the approximate time span of various degrees of divergence. (This is how researchers calculated that the silverswords' common ancestor lived approximately 5 million years ago, as we discussed earlier.) Just as with morphological characters, it is necessary to distinguish homology from analogy to determine the usefulness of molecular similarities for evolutionary studies. Two sequences that resemble each other at many points along their length are most likely homologous (see Figure 25.6). But in organisms that do not appear to be closely related, the bases that their otherwise very different sequences happen to share may simply be coincidental matches, or molecular homoplasies **(Figure 25.7)**. Scientists have developed mathematical tools that can distinguish "distant" homologies from such coincidental matches in extremely divergent sequences. For example, such molecular analysis has provided evidence that, despite our lack of morphological similarity, we humans do indeed share a distant common ancestor with bacteria.

A C G G A T A G T C C A C T A G G C A C T A
T C A C C G A C A G G T C T T T G A C T A G

▲ **Figure 25.7 A molecular homoplasy.** These two DNA sequences from organisms that are not closely related coincidentally share 25% of their bases. Many tools have been developed to determine whether DNA sequences that share higher proportions of bases do so because they are homologous.

Scientists have so far sequenced more than 20 billion bases' worth of nucleic acid data from thousands of species. This enormous collection of data has fed a boom in the study of phylogeny, clarifying many evolutionary relationships, such as those between the Australian and North American moles and those between the various silverswords. In the rest of this chapter and the next unit, you will see many examples of the tremendous impact of molecular systematics.

Concept Check 25.1

1. Suggest whether each of the following pairs of structures more likely represents analogy or homology, and explain your reasoning: (a) a porcupine's quills and a cactus's spines; (b) a cat's paw and a human's hand; (c) an owl's wing and a hornet's wing.
2. Which of the following are more likely to be closely related: two species with similar appearances but very divergent gene sequences, or two species with very different appearances but nearly identical genes? Explain.

For suggested answers, see Appendix A.

Concept 25.2

Phylogenetic systematics connects classification with evolutionary history

The discipline of systematics dates to the 18th century. In 1748, Swedish botanist and anatomist Carolus Linnaeus published *Systema naturae* ("System of Nature"), his taxonomic classification of all plants and animals known at the time. **Taxonomy** is an ordered division of organisms into categories based on a set of characteristics used to assess similarities and differences. Although Linneaus' classification was not based on evolutionary relationships but simply on resemblances, many features of his system remain useful in phylogenetic systematics. Two of these are binomial designations for species and hierarchical classification.

Binomial Nomenclature

Common names for organisms—such as monkey, finch, and lilac—convey meaning in casual usage, but they can also cause confusion. Each of these names, for example, refers to more than one species. Moreover, some common names do not accurately reflect the type of organism. Consider these three "fishes": jellyfish (a cnidarian), crayfish (a small lobster-like crustacean), and silverfish (an insect). And of course, different languages have different words for various organisms.

To avoid ambiguity when communicating about their research, biologists refer to organisms by Latin scientific names. The two-part format of the scientific name, called a **binomial**, was instituted by Linnaeus. The first part of a binomial is the **genus** (plural, *genera*) to which the species belongs. The second part, the **specific epithet**, refers to one species within the genus. An example of a binomial is *Panthera pardus*, the scientific name for the large cat commonly called the leopard. Notice that the first letter of the genus is capitalized and the entire binomial is italicized. (Scientific names are also "latinized"; you can name an insect you discover after a friend, but you must add an appropriate Latin ending.) Many of the more than 11,000 binomials assigned by Linnaeus are still used today, including the optimistic name he designated for our own species—*Homo sapiens,* meaning "wise man."

Hierarchical Classification

In addition to naming species, Linnaeus also grouped them into a hierarchy of increasingly broad categories. The first grouping is built into the binomial; species that appear to be closely related are grouped into the same genus. For example, the leopard (*Panthera pardus*) belongs to a genus that also includes the African lion (*Panthera leo*), the tiger (*Panthera tigris*), and the jaguar (*Panthera onca*). Beyond genera, systematists employ progressively comprehensive categories of classification **(Figure 25.8)**. They place related genera in the same **family**, group families into **orders**, orders into **classes**, classes into **phyla** (singular, *phylum*), phyla into **kingdoms**, and, more recently, kingdoms into **domains**. The named taxonomic unit at any level is called a **taxon** (plural, *taxa*). For example, *Panthera* is a taxon at the genus level, and Mammalia is a taxon at the class level that includes all the many orders of mammals. Note that taxa broader than the genus level are not italicized, though they are capitalized. The resulting biological classification of a particular organism is somewhat like a postal address identifying a person in a particular apartment, in a building with many apartments, on a street with many apartment buildings, in a city with many streets, in a state with many cities, and so on.

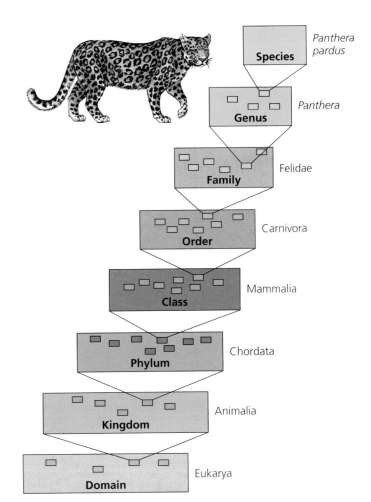

▲ **Figure 25.8 Hierarchical classification.** Species are placed into groups belonging to more comprehensive groups.

Classifying species seems to come naturally to humans—it is a way to structure our view of the world. We lump together several species of tree to which we give the common name of oaks and distinguish them from other species of trees we call chestnuts. Taxonomists have decided that oaks and chestnuts are different enough that they should belong to separate genera. Yet oaks and chestnuts are deemed similar enough to be grouped into the same family, the Fagaceae. This decision was ultimately arbitrary, because higher classification levels are generally defined by various morphological characters chosen by taxonomists rather than by some quantitative measurement applicable to all organisms. For this reason, the larger categories are often not comparable between lineages; that is, an order of snails does not necessarily exhibit the same degree of morphological or genetic diversity as an order of mammals.

Linking Classification and Phylogeny

We saw earlier how systematists explore phylogeny by examining various characteristics in living and fossil organisms. They use branching diagrams called **phylogenetic trees** to depict their hypotheses about evolutionary relationships. The

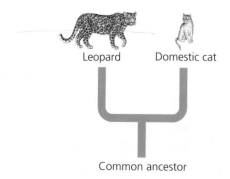

▲ **Figure 25.9 The connection between classification and phylogeny.** Hierarchical classification is reflected in the progressively finer branching of phylogenetic trees. This tree traces possible evolutionary relationships between some of the taxa within the order Carnivora, itself a branch of the class Mammalia.

branching of such trees reflects the hierarchical classification of groups nested within more inclusive groups **(Figure 25.9)**. A phylogenetic tree is often constructed from a series of dichotomies, or two-way branch points; each branch point represents the divergence of two species from a common ancestor. For example, we could represent a branch point within the cat family this way:

As in Figure 25.9, we can also diagram dichotomous branching of taxa that are more inclusive than species, such as families

and orders. Each of the "deeper" branch points represents progressively greater amounts of divergence:

Do not confuse the sequence of branching in a tree with the vintages (actual ages) of the particular species. The tree in Figure 25.9 does *not* indicate that the wolf evolved more recently than the European otter, but only that their common ancestor preceded the last common ancestor of the wolf and the domestic dog.

Methods for tracing phylogeny began with Darwin, who, unlike Linnaeus, realized the evolutionary implications of hierarchical classification. Darwin introduced phylogenetic systematics in *The Origin of Species,* writing: "Our classifications will come to be, as far as they can be so made, genealogies."

Concept 25.3

Phylogenetic systematics informs the construction of phylogenetic trees based on shared characters

Patterns of shared characteristics can be depicted in a diagram called a **cladogram** (see Figure 25.11b on p. 499). A cladogram by itself does not imply evolutionary history. But if the shared characteristics are due to common ancestry (that is, if they are homologous), then the cladogram forms the basis of a phylogenetic tree. Within the tree, a **clade** (from the Greek *klados,* branch) is defined as a group of species that includes an ancestral species and all its descendants. The analysis of how species may be grouped into clades is called **cladistics.**

(a) Monophyletic. In this tree, grouping 1, consisting of the seven species B–H, is a monophyletic group, or clade. A monophyletic group is made up of an ancestral species (species B in this case) and *all* of its descendant species. Only monophyletic groups qualify as legitimate taxa derived from cladistics.

(b) Paraphyletic. Grouping 2 does not meet the cladistic criterion: It is paraphyletic, which means that it consists of an ancestor (A in this case) and *some*, but not all, of that ancestor's descendants. (Grouping 2 includes the descendants I, J, and K, but excludes B–H, which also descended from A.)

(c) Polyphyletic. Grouping 3 also fails the cladistic test. It is polyphyletic, which means that it lacks the common ancestor (A) of the species in the group. Furthermore, a valid taxon that includes the extant species G, H, J, and K would necessarily also contain D and E, which are also descended from A.

▲ **Figure 25.10 Monophyletic, paraphyletic, and polyphyletic groupings.**

Cladistics

Clades, like taxonomic ranks, can be nested within larger clades. For example, the cat family represents a clade within a larger clade that also includes the dog family. But not all groupings of organisms qualify as clades. A valid clade is **monophyletic** (meaning "single tribe"), signifying that it consists of the ancestor species and all its descendants **(Figure 25.10a)**. When we lack information about some members of a clade, the result is a **paraphyletic** grouping that consists of an ancestral species and some, but not all, of the descendants **(Figure 25.10b)**. Or the result may be a **polyphyletic** grouping of several species that lack a common ancestor **(Figure 25.10c)**. Such situations call for further reconstruction to uncover species that tie together these groupings into monophyletic clades.

Shared Primitive and Shared Derived Characters

After systematists have separated homologous from analogous similarities, they must sort through the homologies to distinguish between shared primitive and shared derived characters. "Character" here refers to any feature that a particular taxon possesses. The characters that are relevant to phylogeny, of course, are the homologous ones. For example, all mammals share the homologous character of a backbone. However, the presence of a backbone does not distinguish mammals from other vertebrates because nonmammalian vertebrates such as fishes and reptiles also have backbones. The backbone is a homologous structure that predates the branching of the mammalian clade from the other vertebrates; it is a **shared primitive character,** a character that is shared beyond the taxon we are trying to define. In contrast, hair, a character shared by all mammals but not found in nonmammalian vertebrates, is a **shared derived character,** an evolutionary novelty unique to a particular clade—in this case, the mammalian clade.

Note that the backbone can also qualify as a shared derived character, but only at a deeper branch point that distinguishes *all* vertebrates from other animals. *Among* vertebrates, the backbone is considered a shared primitive character because it evolved in the ancestor common to all vertebrates.

Outgroups

Systematists use outgroup comparison to differentiate between shared derived characters and shared primitive characters. To demonstrate this method, let's arrange five vertebrates—a leopard, turtle, salamander, tuna, and lamprey (a jawless aquatic vertebrate)—into a cladogram. As a basis of comparison, we need to designate an **outgroup,** which is a species or group of species that is closely related to the **ingroup,** the various species we are studying; the outgroup is known to be less closely related than any of the ingroup members are to each other based on other evidence (such as paleontology, embryonic development, and gene sequences). A good choice of an outgroup for our example is a lancelet, a small animal that lives in mudflats and (like vertebrates) is a member of the phylum Chordata, but does not have a backbone. We can begin building our cladogram by comparing the ingroup with the outgroup.

Outgroup comparison is based on the assumption that homologies present in both the outgroup and ingroup must be primitive characters that predate the divergence of both groups from a common ancestor. In our study case, an example of such a character is a structure called a notochord, a flexible rod running the length of the animal. Lancelets have notochords throughout their lives, but in vertebrates the notochord is present only in embryos and is replaced later in development by the backbone. The species making up the ingroup display a mixture of shared primitive and shared derived characters. The outgroup comparison enables us to focus on just those characters that were derived at the various branch points of

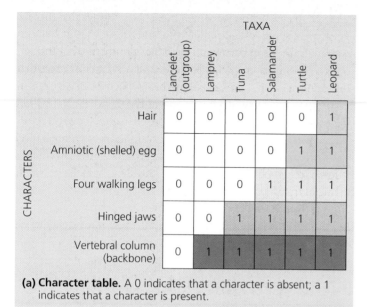

TAXA

CHARACTERS	Lancelet (outgroup)	Lamprey	Tuna	Salamander	Turtle	Leopard
Hair	0	0	0	0	0	1
Amniotic (shelled) egg	0	0	0	0	1	1
Four walking legs	0	0	0	1	1	1
Hinged jaws	0	0	1	1	1	1
Vertebral column (backbone)	0	1	1	1	1	1

(a) Character table. A 0 indicates that a character is absent; a 1 indicates that a character is present.

(b) Cladogram. Analyzing the distribution of these derived characters can provide insight into vertebrate phylogeny.

▲ **Figure 25.11 Constructing a cladogram.**

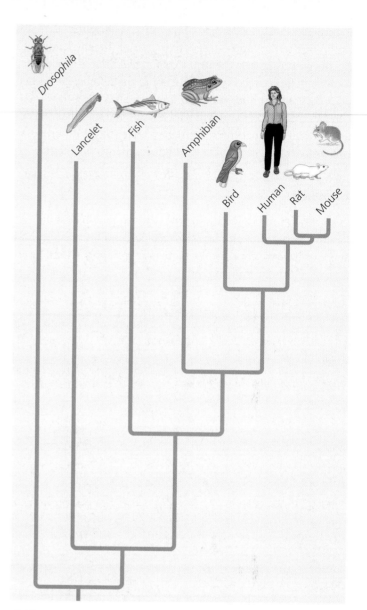

▲ **Figure 25.12 Phylogram.** This phylogram was constructed by comparing homologous *hedgehog* genes, employing the *Drosophila* gene as an outgroup. The *hedgehog* gene is important in development. The varying lengths of the branches indicate that the gene has evolved at slightly different rates in the different lineages.

vertebrate evolution. **Figure 25.11a** tabulates examples of these characters. Note that *all* the vertebrates in the ingroup have backbones; this is a shared primitive character that was present in the ancestral vertebrate, though not in the outgroup. Now note that hinged jaws are a character absent in lampreys but present in other members of the ingroup; this character helps us identify an early branch point in the vertebrate clade. **Figure 25.11b** illustrates how the data in our table of homologies can be translated into a cladogram.

Note that the cladogram in Figure 25.11b is *not* a phylogenetic tree. We may suspect that it tells an evolutionary story, but to convert it to a phylogenetic tree we would need more information—for example, from fossils, which can indicate when, and in which groups, the characters first appeared.

Phylogenetic Trees and Timing

Any chronology represented by the branching pattern of a phylogenetic tree is relative (earlier versus later) rather than absolute (so many millions of years ago). But some kinds of tree diagrams can be used to present more specific information about timing: Phylograms present information about the sequence of events relative to one another, and ultrametric trees present information about the actual time that given events occurred.

Phylograms

In a **phylogram**, the length of a branch reflects the number of changes that have taken place in a particular DNA sequence in that lineage **(Figure 25.12)**. Note that in the phylogram in

Figure 25.12, the *total length* of the vertical lines from the base of the tree to the mouse is less than that of the line leading to the outgroup species, the fruit fly *Drosophila*. This implies that more genetic changes have occurred in the *Drosophila* lineage than in the bird and mammal lineages since they diverged. Later in this chapter you will read about how scientists can estimate the time that likely must have elapsed for a particular number of changes in a DNA or RNA sequence to occur.

Ultrametric Trees

Even though the branches in a phylogram may have different lengths, all the different lineages that descend from a common ancestor have survived for the same number of years. To take an extreme example, humans and bacteria had a common ancestor that lived over 3 billion years ago. Evidence indicates that this ancestor was a single-celled prokaryote, and thus it must have been more like a modern bacterium than like a human. Even though bacteria have apparently changed little in their structure since that common ancestor, there have nonetheless been 3 billion years of evolution in the bacterial lineage, just as there have been 3 billion years of evolution in the eukaryote lineage that includes humans. These equal amounts of chronological time can be represented in an **ultrametric tree.** In an ultrametric tree, the branching pattern is the same as in a phylogram, but all the branches that can be traced from the common ancestor to the present are of equal length **(Figure 25.13)**. While ultrametric trees do not contain the information about different evolutionary rates that can be found in phylograms, they can draw on data from the fossil record to place certain branch points in the context of geologic time.

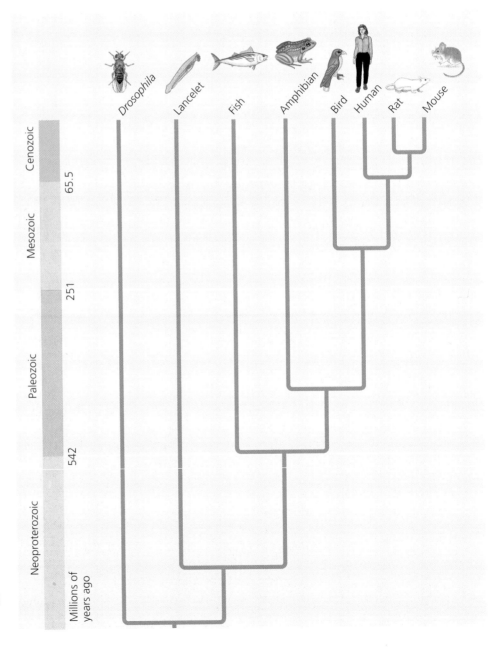

▶ **Figure 25.13 Ultrametric tree.** This ultrametric tree was constructed from the same molecular data as the phylogram in Figure 25.12. These data were then fit to known branching events in the fossil record. In this ultrametric tree, all the branches now have the same total length from the base of the tree through the various vertical segments leading to the labels at the top. This reflects the evidence that all of these lineages have diverged from the common ancestor at the base for equal amounts of time. Note also that as you move up the tree, each branch point sprouts two lineages of equal length, representing the equal times of divergence from that common ancestor. Because the root of the tree is located at a time before a substantial fossil record begins, its date is less certain.

Maximum Parsimony and Maximum Likelihood

As available data about DNA sequences increase and it becomes possible to link more and more species, the difficulty of building the phylogenetic tree that best describes evolutionary history also grows. What if you are analyzing data for 50 species? There are 3×10^{76} different ways to arrange 50 species into a tree! And which tree in this huge forest reflects the true phylogeny? Systematists can never be sure of finding the single best tree in such a large data set, but they can narrow the possibilities by applying the principles of maximum parsimony and maximum likelihood.

According to the principle of **maximum parsimony**, we should first investigate the simplest explanation that is consistent with the facts. (The parsimony principle is also called "Occam's Razor" after William of Occam, a 14th-century English philosopher who advocated this minimalist problem-solving approach of "shaving away" unnecessary complications.) In the case of trees based on morphological characters, the most parsimonious tree is the one that requires the fewest evolutionary events to have occurred in the form of shared derived characters. For phylograms based on DNA sequences, the most parsimonious tree requires the fewest base changes.

The principle of **maximum likelihood** states that, given certain rules about how DNA changes over time, a tree can be found that reflects the most likely sequence of evolutionary events. Maximum likelihood methods incorporate as much information as possible. As a simple example of more likely and less likely trees, let us return to the phylogenetic relationships between a human, a mushroom, and a tulip. **Figure 25.14** shows two possible, equally parsimonious trees for this trio. In tree 1, the human is more closely related to the mushroom, whereas in tree 2, the human is more closely related to the tulip. Tree 1 is more likely if we assume that DNA changes have occurred at equal rates along all the branches of the tree from the common ancestor. Tree 2 is also possible, but it requires assuming that the rates of evolution slowed greatly in the mushroom clade and sped up greatly in the tulip clade. Thus, assuming that equal rates are more common than unequal rates, tree 1 is more likely. We will soon see that many genes do evolve at approximately equal rates in different lineages. But note that if we find new evidence of unequal rates, tree 2 might be more likely! The likelihood of a tree depends on the assumptions on which it is based.

Many computer programs have been developed to search for trees that are parsimonious and likely. These include the following approaches:

1. "Distance" methods minimize the total of all the percentage differences among all the sequences.
2. More complex "character-state" methods minimize the total number of base changes or search for the most likely pattern of base changes among all the sequences.

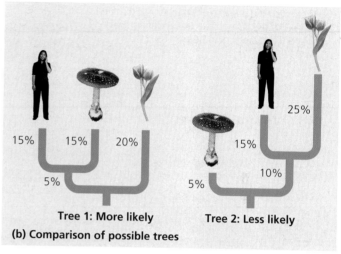

(a) **Percentage differences between sequences**

	Human	Mushroom	Tulip
Human	0	30%	40%
Mushroom		0	40%
Tulip			0

(b) **Comparison of possible trees**

Tree 1: More likely

Tree 2: Less likely

▲ **Figure 25.14 Trees with different likelihoods.** Based on percentage differences between genes carried by a human, a mushroom, and a tulip (a), we can construct two possible phylograms with the same total branch length (b). The sum of the percentages from a point of divergence in a tree equals the percentage differences as listed in (a). For example, in tree 1, the human–tulip divergence is 15% + 5% + 20% = 40%. In tree 2, this divergence also equals 40% (15% + 25%). Assuming that the genes have evolved at the same rate in the different branches, tree 1 is more likely than tree 2.

Although researchers can never be certain precisely which tree truly reflects phylogeny, if they have collected a large amount of accurate data, the various methods usually yield similar trees. As an example of one method, **Figure 25.15**, on the next two pages, walks you through the process of identifying the most parsimonious molecular tree for a four-species problem.

Phylogenetic Trees as Hypotheses

This is a good point at which to reiterate that any phylogenetic tree represents a hypothesis about how the various organisms in the tree are related to one another. The best hypothesis is the one that best fits all the available data. A phylogenetic hypothesis may be modified when new evidence compels systematists to revise their trees. Indeed, many older phylogenetic hypotheses have been changed or rejected since the introduction of molecular methods for comparing species and tracing phylogenies.

Figure 25.15

Applying Parsimony to a Problem in Molecular Systematics

APPLICATION   In considering possible phylogenies for a group of species, systematists compare molecular data for the species. The most efficient way to study the various phylogenetic hypotheses is to begin by first considering the most parsimonious—that is, which hypothesis requires the fewest total evolutionary events (molecular changes) to have occurred.

TECHNIQUE   Follow the numbered steps as we apply the principle of parsimony to a hypothetical phylogenetic problem involving four closely related bird species.

❶ First, draw the possible phylogenies for the species (only 3 of the 15 possible trees relating these four species are shown here).

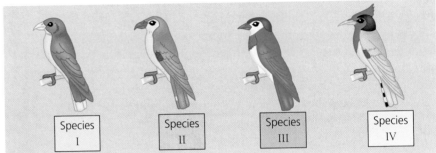

Three possible phylogenetic hypotheses

❷ Tabulate the molecular data for the species (in this simplified example, the data represent a DNA sequence consisting of just seven nucleotide bases).

Sites in DNA sequence

Species	1	2	3	4	5	6	7
I	A	G	G	G	G	G	T
II	G	G	G	A	G	G	G
III	G	A	G	G	A	A	T
IV	G	G	A	G	A	A	G

❸ Now focus on site 1 in the DNA sequence. A single base-change event, marked by the crossbar in the branch leading to species I, is sufficient to account for the site 1 data.

Bases at site 1 for each species

Base-change event

4 Continuing the comparison of bases at sites 2, 3, and 4 reveals that each of these possible trees requires a total of four base-change events (marked again by crossbars). Thus, the first four sites in this DNA sequence do not help us identify the most parsimonious tree.

5 After analyzing sites 5 and 6, we find that the first tree requires fewer evolutionary events than the other two trees (two base changes versus four). Note that in these diagrams, we assume that the common ancestor had GG at sites 5 and 6. But even if we started with an AA ancestor, the first tree still would require only two changes, while four changes would be required to make the other hypotheses work. Keep in mind that parsimony only considers the total number of events, not the particular nature of the events (how likely the particular base changes are to occur).

6 At site 7, the three trees also differ in the number of evolutionary events required to explain the DNA data.

RESULTS To identify the most parsimonious tree, we total all the base-change events noted in steps 3–6 (don't forget to include the changes for site 1, on the facing page). We conclude that the first tree is the most parsimonious of these three possible phylogenies. (But now we must complete our search by investigating the 12 other possible trees.)

Often, in the absence of conflicting information, the most parsimonious tree is also the most likely. But sometimes there is compelling evidence that the best hypothesis is *not* the most parsimonious (**Figure 25.16**). Nature does not always take the simplest course. Perhaps the particular morphological or molecular character we are using to sort taxa actually did evolve multiple times. For example, both birds and mammals have hearts with four chambers, whereas lizards, snakes, turtles, and crocodiles have hearts with three chambers (see Chapter 42). The parsimonious assumption would be that the four-chambered heart evolved once and was present in an ancestor common to birds and mammals but not to lizards, snakes, turtles, and crocodiles. However, abundant evidence indicates that birds are more closely related to lizards, snakes, turtles, and crocodiles than they are to mammals. Thus, the four-chambered heart appears to have evolved independently in

birds and mammals. Indeed, studies have shown that the four-chambered hearts of birds and mammals develop differently, which supports the hypothesis that they evolved independently. The apparently parsimonious tree in Figure 25.16a is not consistent with these facts, while the tree in Figure 25.16b is consistent with the additional facts.

In this example, the problem is not so much with the principle of parsimony as it is with the analogy-homology issue. The four-chambered hearts of birds and mammals turn out to be analogous, not homologous. Matching changes of bases in DNA sequences in two species can also occur independently, but the more bases that are involved, the less likely it is that the matching changes are coincidental. Applying parsimony in molecular systematics is more reliable for a data set of many long DNA sequences than for a smaller data set. Similarly, occasionally misjudging an analogous similarity in morphology as a shared derived (homologous) character is less likely to distort a phylogenetic tree if each clade in the tree is defined by several derived characters. The strongest phylogenetic hypotheses are those supported by multiple lines of molecular and morphological evidence as well as by fossil evidence.

(a) Mammal-bird clade

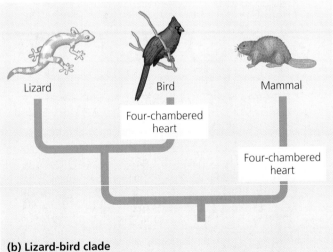

(b) Lizard-bird clade

▲ **Figure 25.16 Parsimony and the analogy-versus-homology pitfall.** If we interpret the four-chambered hearts of birds and mammals as homologous instead of analogous and use no other information, the tree in (a) appears to be the more parsimonious tree. In fact, abundant evidence supports the hypothesis that birds and lizards are more closely related than birds and mammals are and that four-chambered hearts evolved more than once, supporting the tree in (b).

Concept Check 25.3

1. To distinguish a particular clade of mammals within the larger clade that corresponds to class Mammalia, would hair be a useful character? Why or why not?
2. Why might the most parsimonious tree not necessarily be the most accurate in representing evolutionary relationships among a particular group of species?

For suggested answers, see Appendix A.

Concept 25.4

Much of an organism's evolutionary history is documented in its genome

You have seen throughout this chapter that molecular systematics—comparing nucleic acids or other molecules to infer relatedness—is a valuable tool for tracing organisms' evolutionary history. The molecular approach helps us to understand phylogenetic relationships that cannot be measured by nonmolecular methods such as comparative anatomy. For example, molecular systematics helps us uncover evolutionary relationships between groups that have little common ground for morphological comparison, such as mammals and bacteria. It is possible to reconstruct phylogenies among groups of present-day bacteria and other microorganisms for which we have no fossil record at all. And molecular systematics enables scientists to compare genetic divergence within a species. Molecular biology has helped to extend systematics to evolutionary relationships far above and below the species level, ranging from the major branches of the tree of life to its finest twigs. Still, its findings are often inconclusive, as in cases where taxa diverged at nearly the same time in the distant past. The differences may be apparent, but not the order of their appearance.

The ability of molecular trees to encompass both short and long periods of time is based on the fact that different genes evolve at different rates, even in the same evolutionary lineage. For example, the DNA that codes for ribosomal RNA (rRNA) changes relatively slowly, so comparisons of DNA sequences in these genes are useful for investigating relationships between taxa that diverged hundreds of millions of years ago. Studies of rRNA sequences, for example, indicate that fungi are more closely related to animals than to green plants (see Figure 25.2). In contrast, the DNA in mitochondria (mtDNA) evolves relatively rapidly and can be used to explore recent evolutionary events. One research team has traced the relationships among Native American groups through their mtDNA sequences. The molecular findings corroborate other evidence that the Pima of Arizona, the Maya of Mexico, and the Yanomami of Venezuela are closely related, probably descending from the first of three waves of immigrants that crossed the Bering Land Bridge from Asia to the Americas about 13,000 years ago.

Gene Duplications and Gene Families

Gene duplication is one of the most important types of mutation in evolution because it increases the number of genes in the genome, providing opportunities for further evolutionary changes. The molecular phylogenies of gene duplications and the influence of these duplications on genome evolution can now be followed in detail. These phylogenies must account for repeated duplications that have resulted in gene families, which are groups of related genes within an organism's genome (see Figure 19.17). Like homologous genes in different species, these duplicated genes have a common ancestor. We distinguish these types of homologous genes by different names: orthologous genes and paralogous genes.

The term **orthologous genes** (from the Greek *orthos*, straight) refers to homologous genes that are passed in a straight line from one generation to the next but have ended up in different gene pools because of speciation **(Figure 25.17a)**. The β hemoglobin genes in humans and in mice are orthologous.

Paralogous genes (from the Greek *para,* at the side of) result from gene duplication, so they are found in more than one copy in the same genome **(Figure 25.17b)**. In Chapter 23 you encountered an example: the olfactory receptor genes, which have undergone many gene duplications in vertebrate animals. Humans and mice each have huge families of more than 1,000 of these paralogous genes.

It is possible to describe most of the genes that make up genomes as representing one of these two types of homology.

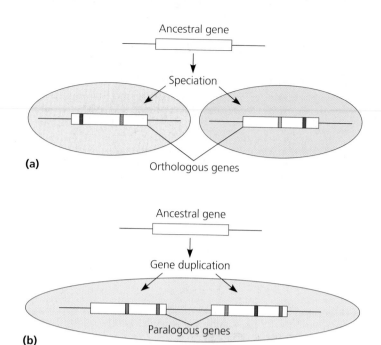

(a)

(b)

▲ **Figure 25.17 Two types of homologous genes.** The colored bands mark regions of the genes where differences in base sequences have accumulated. Orthologous genes can only diverge after speciation, whereas paralogous genes can diverge within the same evolutionary lineage.

Note that orthologous genes can only diverge after speciation has taken place, with the result that the genes are found in separate gene pools. For example, humans and mice each have one functioning β hemoglobin gene. These genes serve similar functions, but their sequences have diverged since the time that humans and mice had a common ancestor. Paralogous genes, on the other hand, can diverge even while they are in the same gene pool, because they are present in more than one copy in the genome. The paralogous genes comprising the olfactory receptor gene family in humans have diverged from each other during our long evolutionary history. They now specify proteins that confer sensitivity to a wide variety of odors, ranging from various foods to sex pheromones.

Genome Evolution

Now that we can compare the entire genomes of different organisms, including our own, two remarkable facts have emerged. First, orthologous genes are widespread and can extend over huge evolutionary distances. Ninety-nine percent of the genes of humans and mice are detectably orthologous, and 50% of our genes are orthologous with those of yeast. This remarkable commonality demonstrates that all living organisms share many biochemical and developmental pathways.

And second, the number of genes seems not to have increased through duplication at the same rate as phenotypic complexity. Humans have only about five times as many genes as yeast, a simple single-celled eukaryote, even though—unlike yeast cells—we have a large, complex brain and a body that contains more than 200 different types of tissues. Evidence is emerging that many human genes are more versatile than those of yeast and are able to carry out a wide variety of tasks in various body tissues. Before us lies a huge and exciting scientific challenge: unraveling the mechanisms that enable this genomic versatility.

Concept Check 25.4

1. Explain how comparisons between the proteins of two species can yield data about their evolutionary relationship.
2. Contrast orthologous genes with paralogous genes.

For suggested answers, see Appendix A.

Concept 25.5

Molecular clocks help track evolutionary time

As we stated at the beginning of this chapter, one of the goals of evolutionary biology is to understand the relationships between all living organisms, including those for which there are no fossils. When we extend molecular phylogenies beyond the fossil record, however, we must rely on an important assumption about how change occurs at the molecular level.

Molecular Clocks

Recall our statement earlier that researchers have estimated that the common ancestor of Hawaiian silverswords lived about 5 million years ago. How did they make this estimate? It relies on the concept of a **molecular clock,** a yardstick for measuring the absolute time of evolutionary change based on the observation that some genes and other regions of genomes appear to evolve at constant rates. The assumption underlying the molecular clock is that the number of nucleotide substitutions in orthologous genes is proportional to the time that has elapsed since the species branched from their common ancestor. In the case of paralogous genes, the number of substitutions is proportional to the time since the genes became duplicated.

We can calibrate the molecular clock of a gene that has a reliable average rate of evolution by graphing the number of nucleotide differences against the times of a series of evolutionary branch points that are known from the fossil record. The graph line representing the evolution rate of this molecular clock can then be used to estimate the date of evolutionary episodes that cannot be discerned from the fossil record, such as the origin of the silverswords.

Of course, no genes mark time with complete accuracy. In fact, some portions of the genome appear to have evolved in irregular fits and starts that are not at all clocklike. And even those genes that seem to have reliable molecular clocks are accurate only in the statistical sense of showing a fairly smooth *average* rate of change; over time, there may still be chance deviations above and below that average rate. Finally, even among genes that are clocklike, the rate of the clock may vary greatly from one gene to another; some genes evolve a million times faster than others.

Neutral Theory

The regularity of change that enables us to use some genes as molecular clocks raises the possibility that many of the changes in these sequences result from genetic drift, and the changes are mostly neutral—neither adaptive nor detrimental. In the 1960s, Jack King and Thomas Jukes, at the University of California, Berkeley, and Matoo Kimura, of the Japanese National Institute of Genetics, published papers supporting this **neutral theory**—that is, that much evolutionary change in genes and proteins has no effect on fitness and therefore is not influenced by Darwinian selection. Kimura pointed out that many new mutations are harmful and are removed quickly. But if most of the rest are neutral and have little or no effect on fitness, then the rate of molecular change should indeed be regular like a clock. Differences in the rate of the clock in different genes are a function of how important each gene is. If the exact sequence of amino acids a gene specifies is essential to survival, most of the mutational changes will be harmful and only a few will be neutral. As a result, such genes change only slowly. But if the exact sequence of amino acids is less critical, fewer of the new mutations will be harmful and more will be neutral. Such genes change more quickly.

Difficulties with Molecular Clocks

In fact, the molecular clock does not run as smoothly as neutral theory predicts. Many irregularities are likely to be the result of natural selection in which some DNA changes are favored over others. Consequently, some scientists question the utility of molecular clocks for timing evolution. Their skepticism is part of a broader debate about the extent to which neutral genetic variation can account for DNA diversity. Indeed, new evidence suggests that almost half of the amino acid differences in proteins of two *Drosophila* species, *D. simulans* and *D. yakuba,* are not neutral but have resulted from directional natural selection. Nonetheless, it is likely that over extremely long periods of time, fluctuations in evolutionary rate due to selective pressure will average out, so that even genes with irregular clocks can serve as approximate markers of elapsed time.

Another question arises when researchers attempt to extend molecular clocks beyond the time span documented by the fossil record. Although some fossils date back as far as 3 billion years, these are very rare. An abundant fossil record extends back only about 550 million years, but molecular clocks have been used to date evolutionary divergences that occurred a billion or more years ago. These estimates assume that the clocks have been constant for all that time. Thus, such estimates are likely to have a high degree of uncertainty.

Applying a Molecular Clock: The Origin of HIV

Recently, researchers at Los Alamos National Laboratory in New Mexico used a molecular clock to date the origin of HIV infection in humans. Phylogenetic analysis shows that HIV, the virus that causes AIDS, is descended from viruses that infect chimpanzees and other primates. (The viruses do not cause any AIDS-like diseases in nonhuman hosts.) When did HIV jump to humans? There is no simple answer, because the virus has spread to humans more than once. The multiple origins of HIV are reflected in the variety of strains (genetic types) of the virus. HIV's genetic material is made of RNA, and like other RNA viruses, it evolves quickly.

The most widespread strain in humans is HIV-1 M. To pinpoint the earliest HIV-1 M infection, the researchers compared samples of the virus from various times during the epidemic, including one partial viral sequence from 1959. The samples showed that the virus has evolved in a remarkably clocklike fashion since 1959. By extrapolating from their molecular clock, the researchers concluded that the first HIV-1 M invasion into humans took place during the 1930s.

The Universal Tree of Life

In the 1960s, researchers deciphering the genetic code found that it is universal in all forms of life. They inferred that all present-day organisms must therefore have a common ancestor. Today, researchers are applying systematics to link all organisms in a tree of life (**Figure 25.18**).

Investigators use two criteria to identify regions of DNA molecules that can demonstrate the branching pattern of this tree: The regions must be able to be sequenced, and they must have evolved so slowly that homologies between even distantly related organisms can still be detected. The rRNA genes, which code for the RNA parts of ribosomes, fit these requirements. Because rRNA genes are fundamental to the workings of the cell, their molecular clock runs so slowly that they can serve as the basis for a universal tree of life. We will examine this tree in greater detail in later chapters, but for the moment let us make two points:

1. **The tree of life consists of three great domains: Bacteria, Archaea, and Eukarya.** The domain Bacteria includes most of the currently known prokaryotes, including the bacteria closely related to chloroplasts and mitochondria (we'll examine the bacterial origins of these organelles in

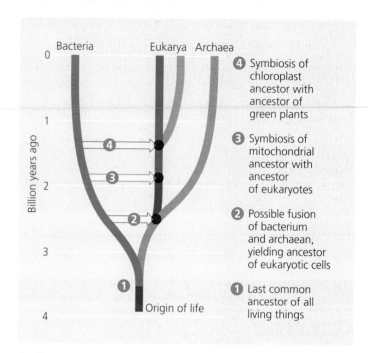

▲ **Figure 25.18 The universal tree of life.** All living organisms are divided into three domains: Bacteria, Archaea, and Eukarya. The details of this tree will change as further information emerges, but its general outlines appear firm.

Chapter 26). The second domain, Archaea, consists of a diverse group of prokaryotic organisms that inhabit a wide variety of environments. Some archaea can use hydrogen as an energy source, and some were the chief source of the deposits of natural gas that are found throughout Earth's crust. Chapter 27 will explore bacteria and archaea in more detail. The third domain, Eukarya, consists of all the organisms that have cells containing true nuclei. This domain includes many groups of single-celled organisms as well as multicellular plants, fungi, and animals, and is the topic of Chapters 28–34.

2. **The early history of these domains is not yet clear.** Comparisons of complete genomes from the three domains show that, especially during the early history of life, there have been substantial interchanges of genes between organisms in the different domains. These took place through **horizontal gene transfer**, in which genes are transferred from one genome to another through mechanisms such as transposable elements, and perhaps through fusions of different organisms. The first eukaryote may have arisen through such a fusion between an ancestral bacterium and an ancestral archaean. Because phylogenetic trees are based on the assumption that genes are passed vertically from one generation to the next, the occurrence of such horizontal events means that universal trees built from different genes often give inconsistent results, particularly near the root of the tree. As a result, details of the tree are continually being revised. However, the division into three great

domains has remained secure since systematists first glimpsed the overall shape of the universal tree.

In the next unit of chapters, we will explore the history of biological diversity and its current variety. Our study will be illuminated by the concepts of evolution and systematics you have learned in this unit.

Chapter 25 Review

Go to the Campbell Biology website (**www.campbellbiology.com**) or CD-ROM to explore Activities, Investigations, and other interactive study aids.

SUMMARY OF KEY CONCEPTS

Concept 25.1

Phylogenies are based on common ancestries inferred from fossil, morphological, and molecular evidence

▶ **The Fossil Record** (pp. 492–493) The fossil record is based on fossil organisms preserved in geologic strata of different ages and reveals ancestral characteristics that may have been lost.
Activity *A Scrolling Geologic Record*

▶ **Morphological and Molecular Homologies** (pp. 492–495) Organisms that share very similar morphologies or DNA sequences are likely to be more closely related than organisms with very different structures and genetic sequences. But homology (similarity due to shared ancestry) must be sorted from analogy (similarity due to convergent evolution).

Concept 25.2

Phylogenetic systematics connects classification with evolutionary history

▶ **Binomial Nomenclature** (p. 496) Linnaeus's system gives organisms two-part names: a genus plus a specific epithet.

▶ **Hierarchical Classification** (p. 496) Linnaeus introduced a system for grouping species in increasingly broad categories.

▶ **Linking Classification and Phylogeny** (pp. 496–497) Systematists depict evolutionary relationships as branching phylogenetic trees, which may be based on various kinds of evidence.
Activity *Classification Schemes*

Concept 25.3

Phylogenetic systematics informs the construction of phylogenetic trees based on shared characters

▶ **Cladistics** (pp. 498–499) A clade is a monophyletic grouping of species that includes an ancestral species and all its descendants. In cladistic analysis, clades are defined by their evolutionary novelties, or shared derived characters. These are identified by comparing ingroup species with an outgroup species that does not have the shared derived character.

▶ **Phylogenetic Trees and Timing** (pp. 499–500) In phylograms, the length of a branch reflects the number of evolutionary changes in that lineage. Ultrametric trees place evolutionary branch points in the context of geologic time.
Investigation *How Is Phylogeny Determined by Comparing Proteins?*

▶ **Maximum Parsimony and Maximum Likelihood** (pp. 501–503) Among phylogenetic hypotheses, the most parsimonious tree is the one that requires the fewest evolutionary changes, and the most likely tree is the one based on the most likely pattern of changes.

▶ **Phylogenetic Trees as Hypotheses** (pp. 501–504) The best phylogenetic hypotheses are those that are consistent with the most data: morphological, molecular, and fossil.

Concept 25.4

Much of an organism's evolutionary history is documented in its genome

▶ **Gene Duplications and Gene Families** (p. 505) Orthologous genes, found in a single copy in the genome, can diverge only after speciation has taken place. Paralogous genes arise through duplication within a genome and can diverge within a clade, often adding new functions.

▶ **Genome Evolution** (pp. 505–506) Orthologous genes are often shared by distantly related species. The relatively small variation in total gene number in organisms of varying complexity indicates that genes in complex organisms are extremely versatile and that each gene can perform many functions.

Concept 25.5

Molecular clocks help track evolutionary time

▶ **Molecular Clocks** (pp. 506–507) The base sequences of some regions of DNA change at a rate consistent enough to allow dating of episodes in past evolution. These molecular clocks may result from the fixation of neutral mutations, but even when selection plays a role, many genes have tended to change in a clocklike fashion over long periods of time. Researchers have measured some molecular clocks and shown that they are remarkably constant. Other genes, however, change in a less predictable fashion.

▶ **The Universal Tree of Life** (p. 507) The tree of life has three great clades (domains): Bacteria, Archaea, and Eukarya.

TESTING YOUR KNOWLEDGE

Self-Quiz

1. If humans and pandas belong to the same class, then they must also belong to the same
   a. order.   d. genus.
   b. phylum.   e. species.
   c. family.

2. Three living species X, Y, and Z share a common ancestor T, as do extinct species U and V. A grouping of species T, X, Y, and Z make up
   a. a valid taxon.
   b. a monophyletic clade.
   c. a paraphyletic grouping.
   d. a polyphyletic grouping.
   e. an ingroup for comparison with species U as the outgroup.

3. In a comparison of birds with mammals, having four appendages is
   a. a shared primitive character.
   b. a shared derived character.
   c. a character useful for distinguishing the birds from mammals.
   d. an example of analogy rather than homology.
   e. a character useful for sorting bird species.

4. How would one apply the principle of parsimony to the construction of a phylogenetic tree?
   a. Choose the tree that assumes all evolutionary changes are equally probable.
   b. Choose the tree in which the branch points are based on as many shared derived characters as possible.
   c. Base phylogenetic trees only on the fossil record, as this provides the simplest explanation for evolution.
   d. Choose the tree that represents the fewest evolutionary changes, either in DNA sequences or morphology.
   e. Choose the tree with the fewest branch points.

5. What would be the best source of data for determining phylogenetic relationships of lineages of protists that diverged hundreds of millions of years ago?
   a. fossils from the Proterozoic eon
   b. morphological characters that are shared and derived
   c. amino acid sequences of their various chlorophyll molecules
   d. mtDNA sequences
   e. rRNA gene sequences

6. If you were using cladistic analysis to build a phylogenetic tree of cats, which of the following would make the best outgroup?
   a. lion   d. leopard
   b. domestic cat e. tiger
   c. wolf

7. Which of the following would be most useful for constructing a phylogenetic tree for several fish species?
   a. several analogous characteristics shared by all the fishes
   b. a single homologous characteristic shared by all the fishes
   c. the total degree of morphological similarity among various fish species
   d. several characteristics thought to have evolved after different fishes diverged from one another
   e. a single characteristic that is different in all the fishes

8. The relative lengths of the amphibian and mouse branches in the phylogram in Figure 25.12 indicate that
   a. amphibians evolved before mice.
   b. mice evolved before amphibians.
   c. the genes of amphibians and mice have only coincidental homoplasies.

d. the homologous gene has evolved more rapidly in amphibians.
e. the homologous gene has evolved more rapidly in mice.

9. Choose the pair of orthologous genes from the following list:
   a. human α hemoglobin and chimpanzee α hemoglobin genes
   b. two alleles of the human α hemoglobin gene
   c. mouse insulin gene and yeast mating-type gene
   d. two different rat olfactory receptor genes
   e. the multiple copies of rRNA genes in a eukaryotic genome

10. The recent estimate that HIV-1 M first jumped from chimpanzees to humans in the 1930s is based on
   a. the first clinical evidence of AIDS recorded in local village records in Africa.
   b. a molecular clock that used changes in sequences of an HIV gene sampled from patients over the past 40 years to project backward to an estimated origin.
   c. a comparison of homologous genes in HIV found in chimpanzees and in humans.
   d. a parsimonious explanation of the evolutionary relationships between the various strains of the virus found in humans at the present time.
   e. the discovery of HIV in a blood sample from the 1930s.

For Self-Quiz answers, see Appendix A.

Go to the website or CD-ROM for more quiz questions.

Evolution Connection

Darwin suggested looking at a species' close relatives to learn what its ancestors may have been like. How does his suggestion anticipate the use of outgroups in cladistic analysis?

Biological Inquiry: A Workbook of Investigative Cases *Explore the use of outgroups and other methods of modern cladistic analysis in "Tree Thinking."*

Scientific Inquiry

Some nucleotide changes cause amino acid substitutions in the encoded protein (nonsynonymous changes), and others do not (synonymous changes). In a comparison of rodent and human genes, rodents were found to accumulate synonymous changes 2.0 times faster than humans, and nonsynonymous substitutions 1.3 times faster. What factors could explain this difference? How do such data complicate the use of molecular clocks to date evolutionary events?

Investigation *How Is Phylogeny Determined by Comparing Proteins?*

Science, Technology, and Society

The ability to compare genomes has opened up new avenues in medical research. Because humans and mice share so many orthologous genes, it is possible to infer gene function in humans by "knocking out" the corresponding orthologous genes in mice. What medical applications might such research lead to? What might be the consequences of these discoveries to society?

The Evolutionary History of Biological Diversity

AN INTERVIEW WITH
Linda Graham

Professor Linda Graham is a time traveler. By peering through microscopes at fossils of the earliest plants and their closest living relatives, Dr. Graham looks back a half-billion years to investigate a major breakthrough in the history of life: the origin of land plants from their aquatic algal ancestor. Those early plants were the first macroscopic creatures on land. In addition to her research on the origin and early diversification of land plants, Graham and her students study how plants, especially mosses, continue to have an enormous impact on the biosphere today. Dr. Graham, who is a professor of botany and environmental studies at the University of Wisconsin-Madison, is also a gifted teacher, and the interview that follows offers some sage advice for why the study of biological diversity is an important part of your education.

What is the ancestor of land plants?

Plants originated from a particular group of green algae known as charophyceans. The evidence is very strong that these ancestors had already acquired some degree of complexity in terms of being able to branch. They also had some reproductive complexities that were probably inherited by the earliest land plants as well.

How long ago did this origin of land plants from algae occur?

The origin of land plants is still somewhat controversial in terms of timeline. The consensus among the paleobotanical community is that there were plants on the terrestrial surface at about 475 million years ago. This conclusion is based on evidence from fossil spores and other types of fossilized plant material. However, some of my colleagues have found fossil spores that they believe to have originated from land

plants that lived as far back as 500 million years ago, in the mid-Cambrian period. I predict that in the future we will extend the origin of land plants back in time to at least the mid-Cambrian, perhaps even further back.

Which living plants do you think are most similar to the earliest land plants?

The molecular evidence indicates that the bryophytes—liverworts, hornworts, and mosses—are the oldest branches of the plant kingdom. And yet no one had found complete fossils of plants similar to bryophytes that were older than fossils of early vascular plants—plants with veins that transport water and nutrients—which the molecular data indicate diverged *after* bryophytes. That just didn't make sense. The standard explanation for the absence of early bryophyte fossils was that they just didn't preserve well. However, I knew that bryophytes produced spores and suspected that they produced other resistant materials as well. So, we wanted to test the idea that bryophytes have materials that could fossilize.

How did you do that?

We used two techniques to try to mimic the effects of degradation that would occur when a plant dies and falls into a water body and becomes partially degraded by microbial action. First, we treated living bryophyte material with an extreme technique known as acetolysis that combines high heat with strong acids. This is the same technique that the paleobotanists use to extract spores from rocks. We hypothesized that any plant material that would survive such an extreme treatment was fossilizable and should appear in a fossil record. Some of our colleagues argued that we might actually be generating resistant materials by such extreme treatment. So we added rotting techniques to our repertoire. We would

leave our living bryophyte material in moist soil for months, and then retrieve the material and see what was left. Amazingly, the same types of resistant bryophyte materials that stood up to acetolysis also survived the more gentle process of rotting. And amazingly, those bits and pieces that survived rotting and acetolysis looked like some scrappy fossils of very ancient origin that people simply didn't recognize as being plant material.

And some of those fossil fragments are older than vascular plants?

Yes. Those scrappy fossils consisting of spores, tubelike structures, and bits of cellular sheets were much older than the vascular plant fossils. So we think that our work helps cement the idea that bryophyte-like plants were indeed present prior to the origin of vascular plants, as is supported by the molecular data.

How did the spread of these early land plants change the biosphere?

First, they helped produce early soils. Even the earliest plants had some organic materials that weren't easily degraded by microbes. So these materials built up as an organic layer in the soil. Second, by this photosynthetic conversion of carbon dioxide to resistant organic materials, early plants began to lower the amount of CO_2 in the atmosphere. That started a trend that culminated in the lowest historic CO_2 level as a result of the early woody plants of the coal swamps during the Carboniferous period. In addition, by producing organic acids, early plants probably released phosphate from the soil, and the runoff of phosphate would have stimulated growth of photosynthetic microorganisms in marine and fresh water ecosystems. Finally, early land plants established terrestrial ecosystems that eventually had sufficient organic productivity to support early land animals through food chains.

CHAPTER 1

Concept Check 1.1

1. Examples: A molecule consists of *atoms* bonded together. Each organelle has an orderly arrangement of *molecules*. Photosynthetic plant cells contain the *organelles* called chloroplasts. An animal tissue consists of a group of similar *cells*. Organs such as the heart are constructed from several *tissues*. A complex organism, such as a plant, has several types of *organs*, including leaves and roots, in the case of the plant. A population is a set of *organisms* of the same species. A community consists of *populations* of the various species inhabiting a specific area. An ecosystem consists of a biological *community* along with the nonliving factors important to life, such as air, soil, and water. The biosphere is made up of all of Earth's *ecosystems*.
2. DNA is the chemical substance of genes. Genes are the hereditary units arranged along DNA molecules. The DNA molecules are built into the cellular structures called chromosomes.
3. Both plants and animals consist of eukaryotic cells, while the cells of bacteria are prokaryotic.

Concept Check 1.2

1. The meaning of a sentence is a property that emerges from the specific sequence of letters and spaces.
2. High-throughput data collection is the source of the enormous and expanding databases of biological information that make bioinformatics a necessary and productive field.
3. Negative feedback

Concept Check 1.3

1. An address pinpoints a location by tracking from broader to narrower categories—a state, city, zip, street, and house or apartment number. This is analogous to the groups-subordinate-to-groups structure of biological taxonomy.
2. Organisms of domain Eukarya are made of eukaryotic cells, in contrast to the prokaryotic cells of domains Bacteria and Archaea.

Concept Check 1.4

1. Natural selection does not "create" the variation that makes adaptation possible, but "edits" by selecting in favor of certain heritable traits in a naturally varying population.

2. Plants Fungi Animals

Ancestral
eukaryote

Concept Check 1.5

1. Inductive reasoning derives generalizations from specific cases; deductive reasoning predicts specific outcomes from general premises.
2. It's usually impossible to exclude all unwanted variables; instead, a controlled experiment cancels out those variables by comparing an experimental group with a control group that differs only in the variable of interest.
3. To test the prediction of the mimicry hypothesis that king snakes will only benefit from their coral snake coloration in environments where poisonous coral snakes also live
4. Compared to a hypothesis, a scientific theory is usually more general and more substantiated by an accumulation of evidence.

Concept Check 1.6

1. Example: Scientific inquiry and the technology it informs have an enormous impact on society.

Self-Quiz

| 1. b | 2. d | 3. a | 4. c | 5. c |
| 6. c | 7. c | 8. d | 9. b | 10. c |

CHAPTER 2

Concept Check 2.1

1. Table salt consists of two elements, whereas oxygen consists of only one.
2. Carbon, oxygen, hydrogen, and nitrogen

Concept Check 2.2

1. 7
2. Atomic number = 7; mass number = 15; $^{15}_{7}N$
3. Atomic number = 12; 12 protons, 12 electrons; three electron shells; 2 electrons in the valence shell
4. The electrons in the shell farthest from the nucleus have the most potential energy, and the electrons in the shell closest to the nucleus have the least.
5. 9 electrons; two electron shells; 1s, 2s, 2p (three of them); 1 unpaired electron

Concept Check 2.3

1. Each carbon atom has only three covalent bonds instead of the required four.

2. The attractions between oppositely charged ions form ionic bonds.

Concept Check 2.4

1.

$$2\ H_2 + O_2 \rightarrow 2\ H_2O$$

2. At equilibrium, the forward and reverse reactions occur at the same rate.

Self-Quiz

| 1. b | 2. a | 3. b | 4. b | 5. c |
| 6. b | 7. b | 8. a | 9. b | 10. b |

CHAPTER 3

Concept Check 3.1

1. Electronegativity is the attraction of an atom for the electrons of a covalent bond. Since oxygen is more electronegative than hydrogen, the oxygen atom in H_2O pulls electrons toward itself, resulting in a partial negative charge on the oxygen atom and partial positive charges on the hydrogen atoms. Oppositely charged ends of water molecules are attracted to each other, forming a hydrogen bond.
2. The hydrogen atoms of one molecule, with their partial positive charges, would repel the hydrogen atoms of the adjacent molecule.

Concept Check 3.2

1. Hydrogen bonds hold neighboring water molecules together; this cohesion helps the molecules resist the downward pull of gravity. Adhesion between water molecules and the walls of water-conducting cells also counters the downward pull of gravity. As water evaporates from the leaves, the chain of water molecules in water-conducting cells moves upward.
2. High humidity hampers cooling by suppressing the evaporation of sweat.
3. Water expands as it freezes, because the water molecules move farther apart in forming ice crystals. When there is water in a crevice of a boulder, expansion of the water due to freezing may crack the rock.
4. The molecular mass of NaCl is 58.5 daltons. A mole would have a mass of 58.5 g, so you would measure out 0.5 mole, or 29.3 g of NaCl, and gradually add water, stirring until it is dissolved. You would add water to bring the final volume to 1 L.

Concept Check 3.3
1. 10^5, or 100,000
2. $[H^+] = 0.01\ M = 10^{-2}\ M$, so pH = 2

Self-Quiz
1. d   2. d   3. b   4. c   5. b
6. c   7. c   8. d   9. c   10. c

CHAPTER 4

Concept Check 4.1
1. Urea is a molecule synthesized by living organisms and found in urine. Its synthesis from gases of the primitive atmosphere on Earth demonstrated that life's molecules could initially have been synthesized from nonliving molecules.

Concept Check 4.2
1.

$$H-\overset{\displaystyle H}{\underset{\displaystyle H}{C=C}}-H$$

2. The butanes in (b) are structural isomers, as are the butenes in (c).
3. Both consist largely of hydrocarbon chains.

Concept Check 4.3
1. It has both an amino group ($-NH_2$) and a carboxyl group ($-COOH$), which makes it a carboxylic acid.
2. The ATP molecule loses a phosphate, becoming ADP.

Self-Quiz
1. b   2. c   3. d   4. d   5. a
6. b   7. b   8. a   9. d
10. b, because there are not only the two electronegative oxygens of the carboxyl group, but also an oxygen on the next (carbonyl) carbon. All of these oxygens help make the bond between the O and H of the $-OH$ group more polar, thus making the dissociation of H^+ more likely.

CHAPTER 5

Concept Check 5.1
1. Proteins, carbohydrates, lipids, and nucleic acids
2. Nine, with one water required to hydrolyze each connected pair of monomers
3. The amino acids in the apple protein are released in hydrolysis reactions, and incorporated into your proteins in dehydration reactions.

Concept Check 5.2
1. $C_3H_6O_3$ or $C_3(H_2O)_3$
2. $C_{12}H_{22}O_{11}$
3. Both molecules are polymers of glucose made by plants, but the glucose monomers are arranged differently. Starch functions mainly for sugar storage. Cellulose is a structural polysaccharide that is the main material of plant cell walls.

Concept Check 5.3
1. Both have a glycerol molecule attached to fatty acids. The glycerol of a fat has three fatty acids attached, whereas the glycerol of a phospholipid is attached to two fatty acids and one phosphate group.
2. The fatty acids on a saturated fat have no double bonds in their hydrocarbon chains, whereas at least one fatty acid on an unsaturated fat has a double bond. Saturated fats tend to be solid at room temperature, while unsaturated fats are liquid.
3. Human sex hormones are steroids, a type of hydrophobic compound.

Concept Check 5.4
1. The function of each protein is a consequence of its specific shape, which is lost when a protein becomes denatured.
2. Secondary structure involves hydrogen bonds between atoms of the polypeptide backbone. Tertiary structure involves bonding between atoms of the R groups of the amino acid subunits.
3. Primary structure, the amino acid sequence, affects the secondary structure, which affects the tertiary structure, which affects the quaternary structure (if any). In short, the amino acid sequence affects the shape of the protein, and the function of a protein depends on its shape.

Concept Check 5.5
1.

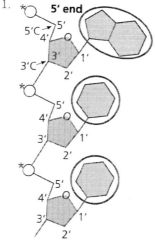

2. 3'-ATCCGGA-5'

Self-Quiz Answers
1. d   2. c   3. c, d, and e   4. c   5. b
6. d   7. d   8. b   9. b   10. b

CHAPTER 6

Concept Check 6.1
1. (a) Light microscope, (b) scanning electron microscope, (c) transmission electron microscope

Concept Check 6.2
1. See Figure 6.9.

Concept Check 6.3
1. Ribosomes in the cytoplasm translate the genetic message, carried from the DNA in the nucleus by mRNA, into a polypeptide chain.
2. Chromatin is composed of DNA and associated proteins; it carries the cell's genetic information. Nucleoli consist of RNA and proteins and are associated with particular regions of the DNA. In the nucleoli, rRNA is synthesized and ribosomal subunits are assembled.

Concept Check 6.4
1. The primary distinction between rough and smooth ER is the presence of bound ribosomes on the rough ER. While both types of ER synthesize phospholipids, membrane proteins are all produced on the ribosomes of the rough ER. The smooth ER also functions in detoxification, carbohydrate metabolism, and storage of calcium ions.
2. The mRNA is synthesized in the nucleus, then passes out through a nuclear pore to be translated on a bound ribosome, attached to the rough ER. The protein is synthesized into the lumen of the ER and perhaps modified there. A transport vesicle carries the protein to the Golgi apparatus. After further modification in the Golgi, another transport vesicle carries it back to the ER, where it will perform its cellular function.
3. Transport vesicles move membranes and substances they enclose between other components of the endomembrane system.

Concept Check 6.5
1. Both organelles are involved in energy transformation, mitochondria in cellular respiration and chloroplasts in photosynthesis. They are both composed of two or more separate membranes.
2. Mitochondria and chloroplasts contain DNA, which encodes some of their proteins. They are not connected physically or via transport vesicles to organelles of the endomembrane system.

Concept Check 6.6
1. Microtubules are hollow tubes that resist bending; microfilaments are more like strong cables that resist stretching. These opposing properties work together to define and maintain cell shape. Intermediate filaments also resist stretching, and they are more permanent tension-bearing elements that reinforce the shape of the cell.
2. Dynein arms, powered by ATP, move neighboring doublets of microtubules relative to one another. Because they are anchored within the organelle and with respect to each other, the doublets bend instead of sliding past one another.

Concept Check 6.7
1. The most obvious difference is the presence of direct cytoplasmic connections between cells of multicellular plants (plasmodesmata) and animals (gap junctions). These connections result in the cytoplasm being continuous between adjacent cells.

2. The cell wall or ECM must be permeable to the materials that enter and leave the cell, and to molecules that provide information about the cell's environment.

Self-Quiz
1. c   2. c   3. b   4. d   5. d
6. b   7. c   8. b   9. e   10. a

CHAPTER 7

Concept Check 7.1
1. Plants adapted to cold environments would be expected to have more unsaturated fatty acids in their membranes, since those remain fluid at lower temperatures. Plants adapted to hot environments would be expected to have more saturated fatty acids, which would allow the fatty acids to "stack" more closely, making the membranes less fluid and therefore helping them to stay intact at higher temperatures.
2. They are on the inner side of the transport vesicle membrane.

Concept Check 7.2
1. O_2 and CO_2 are both small, uncharged molecules that can easily pass through the hydrophobic core of a membrane.
2. Water is a very polar molecule, so it cannot pass very rapidly through the hydrophobic region in the middle of a phospholipid bilayer.

Concept Check 7.3
1. The activity of the *Paramecium*'s contractile vacuole would decrease. The vacuole pumps out excess water that flows into the cell; this flow occurs only in a hypotonic environment.

Concept Check 7.4
1. The pump would use ATP. To establish a voltage, ions would have to be pumped against their gradient, which requires energy.
2. Each ion is being transported against its electrochemical gradient. If either ion were flowing down its electrochemical gradient, this *would* be considered cotransport.

Concept Check 7.5
1. Exocytosis. When a transport vesicle fuses with the plasma membrane, the vesicle membrane becomes part of the plasma membrane.
2. Receptor-mediated endocytosis, because in this case one specific molecule needs to be taken up at a particular time; pinocytosis takes up substances in a nonspecific manner.

Self-Quiz Answers
1. b   2. c   3. a   4. d   5. b
6. Fructose
7. Glucose
8. Cell contents
9. Into the cell
10. b, c, and e. Regarding e: Even though sucrose can't reach the same concentration on each side, water flow (osmosis) will lead to isotonic conditions

CHAPTER 8

Concept Check 8.1
1. The second law is the trend toward randomness. Equal concentrations of a substance on both sides of a membrane is a more random distribution than unequal concentrations. Diffusion of a substance to a region where it is initially less concentrated increases entropy, as mandated by the second law.
2. Energy is the capacity to cause change, and some forms of energy can do work.
3. The apple has potential energy in its position hanging on the tree, and the sugars and other nutrients it contains have chemical energy. The apple has kinetic energy as it falls from the tree to the ground. Finally, thermal energy is lost as the apple is digested and its molecules broken down.

Concept Check 8.2
1. Cellular respiration is a spontaneous and exergonic process. The energy released from glucose is used to do work in the cell, or is lost as heat.
2. H^+ ions can perform work only if their concentrations on each side of a membrane differ. When the H^+ concentrations are the same, the system is at equilibrium and can do no work.

Concept Check 8.3
1. By phosphorylation, the addition of phosphate groups: ATP transfers energy to endergonic processes by phosphorylating other molecules. Exergonic processes phosphorylate ADP to regenerate ATP.
2. A set of coupled reactions can transform the first group into the second group. Since, overall, this is an exergonic process, ΔG is negative and the first group must have more free energy.

Concept Check 8.4
1. A spontaneous reaction is a reaction that is exergonic. However, if it has a high activation energy that is rarely attained, the rate of the reaction may be low.
2. Only the specific substrate(s) will fit into the active site of an enzyme, the part of the enzyme that carries out catalysis.
3. As a competitive inhibitor, malonate binds to the active site of succinate dehydrogenase and so prevents the normal substrate, succinate, from binding.

Concept Check 8.5
1. The activator binds in such a way that it stabilizes the active conformation of an enzyme, whereas the inhibitor stabilizes the inactive conformation.

Self-Quiz
1. b   2. c   3. b   4. b   5. e
6. a   7. e   8. c   9. a   10. c

CHAPTER 9

Concept Check 9.1
1. $C_4H_6O_5$ is oxidized and NAD^+ is reduced.

Concept Check 9.2
1. NAD^+ acts as the oxidizing agent in step 6, accepting electrons from glyceraldehyde-3-phosphate, which thus acts as the reducing agent.

Concept Check 9.3
1. NADH and $FADH_2$; they will donate electrons to the electron transport chain.
2. CO_2 is removed from pyruvate, which is produced by glycolysis, and CO_2 is produced by the citric acid cycle.

Concept Check 9.4
1. Oxidative phosphorylation would stop entirely, resulting in no ATP production. Without oxygen to "pull" electrons down the electron transport chain, H^+ would not be pumped into the mitochondrion's intermembrane space and chemiosmosis would not occur.
2. Because addition of H^+ (decreasing the pH) would establish a proton gradient even without the function of the electron transport chain, we would expect ATP synthase to function and synthesize ATP. (In fact, it was experiments like this one that provided support for chemiosmosis as an energy-coupling mechanism.)

Concept Check 9.5
1. A derivative of pyruvate—either acetaldehyde during alcohol fermentation or pyruvate itself during lactic acid fermentation; oxygen
2. The cell would need to consume glucose at a rate about 19 times the consumption rate in the aerobic environment (2 ATP are generated by fermentation versus up to 38 ATP by cellular respiration).

Concept Check 9.6
1. The fat is much more reduced; it has many —CH_2— units. The electrons present in a carbohydrate molecule are already somewhat oxidized, as some of them are bound to oxygen.
2. When we consume more food than necessary for metabolic processes, our bodies synthesize fat as a way of storing energy for later.
3. AMP will accumulate, stimulating phosphofructokinase, which increases the rate of glycolysis. Since oxygen is not present, the cell will convert pyruvate to lactate in lactic acid fermentation, providing a supply of ATP.

Self-Quiz
1. b   2. d   3. c   4. c   5. a
6. a   7. b   8. d   9. b   10. b

CHAPTER 10

Concept Check 10.1
1. CO_2 enters leaves via stomata, and water enters via roots and is carried to leaves through veins.
2. Using a heavy isotope of oxygen as a label, ^{18}O, van Niel was able to show that the oxygen produced during photosynthesis originates in water, not in carbon dioxide.

3. The Calvin cycle depends on the NADPH and ATP that the light reactions generate, and the light reactions depend on the $NADP^+$ and ADP and P_i that the Calvin cycle generates.

Concept Check 10.2
1. Green, because green light is mostly transmitted and reflected—not absorbed—by photosynthetic pigments
2. In chloroplasts, light-excited electrons are trapped by a primary electron acceptor, which prevents them from dropping back to the ground state. In isolated chlorophyll, there is no electron acceptor, so the photoexcited electrons immediately drop back down to the ground state, with the emission of light and heat.
3. Water (H_2O) is the electron donor; $NADP^+$ accepts electrons at the end of the electron transport chain, becoming reduced to NADPH.

Concept Check 10.3
1. 6, 18, 12
2. The more potential energy that a molecule stores, the more energy and reducing power required for the formation of that molecule. Glucose is a valuable energy source because it is highly reduced, storing lots of potential energy in its electrons. To reduce CO_2 to glucose, much energy and reducing power are required in the form of a high number of ATP and NADPH molecules, respectively.
3. The light reactions require ADP and $NADP^+$, which would not be formed from ATP and NADPH if the Calvin cycle stopped.

Concept Check 10.4
1. Photorespiration decreases photosynthetic output by adding oxygen, instead of carbon dioxide, to the Calvin cycle. As a result, no sugar is generated (no carbon is fixed), and O_2 is used rather than generated.
2. C_4 and CAM species would replace many of the C_3 species.

Self-Quiz
1. d	2. b	3. d	4. b	5. b
6. c	7. d	8. e	9. d	10. c

CHAPTER 11

Concept Check 11.1
1. The secretion of neurotransmitter molecules at a synapse is an example of local signaling. The electrical signal that travels along a very long nerve cell and is passed to the next nerve cell can be considered an example of long-distance signaling. (Note, however, that local signaling at the synapse between two cells is necessary for the signal to pass from one cell to the next.)
2. No glucose-1-phosphate is generated, because the activation of the enzyme requires an intact cell membrane with an intact receptor in the membrane. The enzyme cannot be activated directly by interaction with the signal molecule in the test tube.

Concept Check 11.2
1. The NGF receptor is in the plasma membrane. The water-soluble NGF molecule cannot pass through the lipid membrane to reach intracellular receptors, as steroid hormones can.

Concept Check 11.3
1. A protein kinase is an enzyme that transfers a phosphate group from ATP to a protein, usually activating that protein (often a second type of protein kinase). Many signal transduction pathways include a series of such interactions, in which each phosphorylated protein kinase, in turn phosphorylates the next protein kinase in the series. Such phosphorylation cascades carry a signal from outside the cell to the cellular protein(s) that will carry out the response.
2. Protein phosphatases reverse the effects of the kinases.
3. The IP_3-gated channel opens, allowing calcium ions to flow out of the ER, which raises the cytosolic Ca^{2+} concentration.

Concept Check 11.4
1. By a cascade of sequential activations, at each step of which one molecule may activate numerous molecules functioning in the next step
2. Scaffolding proteins hold molecular components of signaling pathways in a complex with each other. Different scaffolding proteins would assemble different collections of proteins, leading to different cellular responses in the two cells.

Self-Quiz
1. c	2. d	3. a	4. c	5. c
6. c	7. a	8. b	9. c	10. a

CHAPTER 12

Concept Check 12.1
1. 32 cells
2. 2
3. 39; 39; 78; 39

Concept Check 12.2
1. From the end of S phase of interphase through the end of metaphase of mitosis
2. 4; 8
3. Cytokinesis results in two genetically identical daughter cells in both plant cells and animal cells, but the mechanism of dividing the cytoplasm is different between animals and plants. In an animal cell, cytokinesis occurs by cleavage, which divides the parent cell in two with a contractile ring of actin filaments. In a plant cell, a cell plate forms in the middle of the cell and grows until its membrane fuses with the plasma membrane of the parent cell. A new cell wall is also produced from the cell plate, resulting in two daughter cells.
4. They elongate the cell during anaphase.
5. Sample answer: Each type of chromosome consists of a single molecule of DNA with attached proteins. If stretched out, the molecules of DNA would be many times longer

than the cells in which they reside. During cell division, the two copies of each type of chromosome actively move apart, and one copy ends up in each of the two daughter cells.

Concept Check 12.3
1. G_1
2. The nucleus on the right was originally in the G_1 phase; therefore, it had not yet duplicated its chromosome. The nucleus on the left was in the M phase, so it had already duplicated its chromosome.
3. A sufficient amount of MPF has to build up for a cell to pass the G_2 checkpoint.
4. The cells might divide even in the absence of PDGF, in which case they would not stop when the surface was covered; they would continue to divide, piling on top of one another.
5. Most body cells are not in the cell cycle, but rather are in a nondividing state called G_0.
6. Both types of tumors consist of abnormal cells. A benign tumor stays at the original site and can usually be surgically removed. Cancer cells from a malignant tumor spread from the original site by metastasis and may impair the functions of one or more organs.

Self-Quiz
1. b	2. b	3. a	4. a	5. c
6. c	7. c	8. e	9. a	10. b
11. See Figure 12.6.				

CHAPTER 13

Concept Check 13.1
1. Parents pass genes to their offspring that program cells to make specific enzymes and other proteins whose cumulative action produces an individual's inherited traits.
2. Such organisms reproduce by mitosis, which generates offspring whose genomes are virtually exact copies of the parent's genome.
3. Offspring resemble their parents but are not genetically identical to them or their siblings because sexual reproduction generates different combinations of genetic information.

Concept Check 13.2
1. A female has two X chromosomes; a male has an X and Y.
2. In meiosis, the chromosome count is reduced from diploid to haploid; the union of two haploid gametes in fertilization restores the diploid chromosome count.
3. Haploid number (n) is 39; diploid number ($2n$) is 78.
4. Meiosis is involved in the production of gametes in animals. Mitosis is involved in the production of gametes in plants and most fungi (see Figure 13.6).

Concept Check 13.3
1. In mitosis, a single replication of the chromosomes is followed by one division of the cell, so the number of chromosome sets in daughter cells is the same as in the parent cell. In meiosis, a single replication of the chromosomes is followed by two cell divisions that

reduce the number of chromosome sets from two (diploid) to one (haploid).

2. The chromosomes are similar in that each is composed of two sister chromatids, and the individual chromosomes are positioned similarly on the metaphase plate. The chromosomes differ in that in a mitotically dividing cell, sister chromatids of each chromosome are genetically identical, but in a meiotically dividing cell, sister chromatids are genetically distinct because of crossing over in meiosis I. Moreover, the chromosomes in metaphase of mitosis can be composed of a diploid set or a haploid set, but the chromosomes in metaphase of meiosis II always consist of a haploid set.

Concept Check 13.4

1. Even in the absence of crossing over, independent assortment of chromosomes during meiosis I theoretically can generate 2^n possible haploid gametes, and random fertilization can produce $2^n \times 2^n$ possible diploid zygotes. Since the haploid number (n) of honeybees is 16 and that of fruit flies is 4, two honeybees would be expected to produce a greater variety of zygotes than would two fruit flies.

2. If the segments of the maternal and paternal chromatids that undergo crossing over are genetically identical, then the recombinant chromosomes will be genetically equivalent to the parental chromosomes. Crossing over contributes to genetic variation only when it involves rearrangement of different versions of genes.

Self-Quiz

1. d	2. b	3. d	4. d	5. c
6. d	7. a	8. c	9. c	10. d

CHAPTER 14

Concept Check 14.1

1. First, all the F_1 plants had flowers with the same color (purple) as the flowers of one of the parental varieties, rather than an intermediate color as predicted by the "blending" hypothesis. Second, the reappearance of white flowers in the F_2 generation indicates that the allele controlling the white-flower trait was not lost in the F_1 generation; rather its phenotypic effect was masked by the effect of the dominant purple-flower allele.

2. According to the law of independent assortment, 25 plants ($^1/_{16}$ of the offspring) are predicted to be *aatt*, or recessive for both characters. The actual result is likely to differ slightly from this value.

Concept Check 14.2

1. $^1/_2$ dominant homozygous (*CC*), 0 recessive homozygous (*cc*), and $^1/_2$ heterozygous (*Cc*)
2. $^1/_4$ *BBDD*; $^1/_4$ *BbDD*; $^1/_4$ *BBDd*; $^1/_4$ *BbDd*
3. 0; since only one of the parents has a recessive allele for each character, there is no chance of producing homozygous recessive offspring that would display the recessive traits.

Concept Check 14.3

1. The black and white alleles are incompletely dominant, with heterozygotes being gray in color. A cross between a gray rooster and a black hen should yield approximately equal numbers of gray and black offspring.

2. Height is at least partially hereditary and appears to exhibit polygenic inheritance with a wide norm of reaction, indicating that environmental factors have a strong influence on phenotype.

Concept Check 14.4

1. $^1/_9$ (Since cystic fibrosis is caused by a recessive allele, Beth and Tom's siblings who have CF must be homozygous recessive. Therefore, each parent must be a carrier of the recessive allele. Since neither Beth nor Tom has CF, this means they each have a $^2/_3$ chance of being a carrier. If they are both carriers, there is a $^1/_4$ chance that they will have a child with CF. $^2/_3 \times ^2/_3 \times ^1/_4 = ^1/_9$); 0 (Both Beth and Tom would have to be carriers to produce a child with the disease.)

2. Joan's genotype is *Dd*. Because the allele for polydactyly (*D*) is dominant to the allele for five digits per appendage (*d*), the trait is expressed in people with either the *DD* or *Dd* genotype. If Joan's mother were homozygous dominant (*DD*), then all of her children would have polydactyly. But since some of Joan's siblings do not have this condition, her mother must be heterozygous (*Dd*). All the children born to her mother (*Dd*) and father (*dd*) have either the *dd* genotype (normal phenotype) or the *Dd* genotype (polydactyly phenotype).

Genetics Problems

1. Parental cross is *AARR* × *aarr*. Genotype of F_1 is *AaRr*; phenotype is all axial-pink. Genotypes of F_2 are 4 *AaRr* : 2 *AaRR* : 2 *AARr* : 2 *aaRr* : 2 *Aarr* : 1 *AARR* : 1 *aaRR* : 1 *AArr* : 1 *aarr*. Phenotypes of F_2 are 6 axial-pink : 3 axial-red : 3 axial-white : 2 terminal-pink : 1 terminal-white : 1 terminal-red.

2. a. $^1/_{64}$ b. $^1/_{64}$ c. $^1/_8$ d. $^1/_{32}$

3. Albino (*b*) is a recessive trait; black (*B*) is dominant. First cross: parents *BB* × *bb*; gametes *B* and *b*; offspring all *Bb* (black coat). Second cross: parents *Bb* × *bb*; gametes $^1/_2$ *B* and $^1/_2$ *b* (heterozygous parent) and *b*; offspring $^1/_2$ *Bb* and $^1/_2$ *bb*.

4. a. *PPLl* × *PPLl*, *PPLl* × *PpLl*, or *PPLl* × *ppLl*. b. *ppLl* × *ppLl*. c. *PPLL* × any of the 9 possible genotypes or *PPll* × *ppLL*. d. *PpLl* × *Ppll*. e. *PpLl* × *PpLl*.

5. Man $I^A i$; woman $I^B i$; child *ii*. Other genotypes for children are $^1/_4$ $I^A I^B$, $^1/_4$ $I^A i$, $^1/_4$ $I^B i$.

6. a. $^3/_4 \times ^3/_4 \times ^3/_4 = ^{27}/_{64}$
   b. $1 - ^{27}/_{64} = ^{37}/_{64}$
   c. $^1/_4 \times ^1/_4 \times ^1/_4 = ^1/_{64}$
   d. $1 - ^1/_{64} = ^{63}/_{64}$

7. a. $^1/_{256}$ b. $^1/_{16}$ c. $^1/_{256}$ d. $^1/_{64}$ e. $^1/_{128}$
8. a. 1 b. $^1/_{32}$ c. $^1/_8$ d. $^1/_2$
9. $^1/_9$
10. Matings of the original mutant cat with true-breeding noncurl cats will produce both curl and noncurl F_1 offspring if the curl allele is dominant, but only noncurl offspring if the curl allele is recessive. You would obtain some true-breeding offspring homozygous for the curl allele from matings between the F_1 cats resulting from the original curl × noncurl crosses whether the curl trait is dominant or recessive. You know that cats are true-breeding when curl × curl matings produce only curl offspring. As it turns out, the allele that causes curled ears is dominant.

11. $^1/_{16}$
12. 25% will be cross-eyed; all of the cross-eyed offspring will also be white.
13. The dominant allele *I* is epistatic to the *P/p* locus, and thus the genotypic ratio for the F_1 generation will be 9 *I_P_* (colorless) : 3 *I_pp* (colorless) : 3 *iiP_* (purple) : 1 *iipp* (red). Overall, the phenotypic ratio is 12 colorless : 3 purple : 1 red.
14. Recessive. All affected individuals (Arlene, Tom, Wilma, and Carla) are homozygous recessive *aa*. George is *Aa*, since some of his children with Arlene are affected. Sam, Ann, Daniel, and Alan are each *Aa*, since they are all unaffected children with one affected parent. Michael also is *Aa*, since he has an affected child (Carla) with his heterozygous wife Ann. Sandra, Tina, and Christopher can each have the *AA* or *Aa* genotype.
15. $^1/_2$
16. $^1/_6$
17. 9 *B_A_* (agouti) : 3 *B_aa* (black) : 3 *bbA_* (white) : 1 *bbaa* (white). Overall, 9 agouti : 3 black : 4 white.

CHAPTER 15

Concept Check 15.1

1. The law of segregation relates to the inheritance of alleles for a single character; the physical basis is the separation of homologues in anaphase I. The law of independent assortment of alleles relates to the inheritance of alleles for two characters; the physical basis is the alternative arrangements of homologous chromosome pairs in metaphase I.

2. About $^1/_4$ of the F_2 offspring would have red eyes, and about $^1/_4$ would have white eyes. About half of the white-eyed flies would be female and half would be male; about half of the red-eyed flies would be female and half would be male.

Concept Check 15.2

1. Crossing over during meiosis I in the heterozygous parent produces some gametes with recombinant genotypes for the two genes. Offspring with a recombinant phenotype arise from fertilization of the recombinant gametes by homozygous recessive gametes from the double-mutant parent.

2. In each case, the alleles contributed by the female parent determine the phenotype of the offspring because the male only contributes recessive alleles in this cross.

3. No, the order could be *A-C-B* or *C-A-B*. To determine which possibility is correct, you need to know the recombination frequency between *B* and *C*.

Concept Check 15.3

1. Because the gene for this eye-color character is located on the X chromosome, all female offspring will be red-eyed and heterozygous ($X^{w^+}X^w$); all male offspring will be white-eyed (X^wY).
2. $\frac{1}{4}$; $\frac{1}{2}$ chance that the child will inherit a Y chromosome from the father and be male × $\frac{1}{2}$ chance that he will inherit the X carrying the disease allele from his mother.

Concept Check 15.4

1. At some point during development, one of the embryo's cells may have failed to carry out mitosis after duplicating its chromosomes. Subsequent normal cell cycles would produce genetic copies of this tetraploid cell.
2. In meiosis, a combined 14-21 chromosome will behave as one chromosome. If a gamete receives the combined 14-21 chromosome and a normal copy of chromosome 21, trisomy 21 will result when this gamete combines with a normal gamete during fertilization.
3. An aneuploid male cat with more than one X chromosome could have a tortoiseshell phenotype if its X chromosomes have different alleles of the fur-color gene.

Concept Check 15.5

1. Inactivation of an X chromosome in females and genomic imprinting. Because of X inactivation, the effective dose of genes on the X chromosome is the same in males and females. As a result of genomic imprinting, only one allele of certain genes is phenotypically expressed.
2. The genes for leaf coloration are located in plastids within the cytoplasm. Normally, only the maternal parent transmits plastid genes to offspring. Since variegated offspring are produced only when the female parent is of the B variety, we can conclude that variety B contains both the wild-type and mutant alleles of pigment genes, producing variegated leaves.
3. Each cell contains numerous mitochondria, and in affected individuals, most cells contain a variable mixture of normal and abnormal mitochondria.

Genetics Problems

1. 0; $\frac{1}{2}$, $\frac{1}{16}$
2. Recessive; if the disorder were dominant, it would affect at least one parent of a child born with the disorder. The disorder's inheritance is sex-linked because it is seen only in boys. For a girl to have the disorder, she would have to inherit recessive alleles from *both* parents. This would be very rare, since males with the recessive allele on their X chromosome die in their early teens.
3. $\frac{1}{4}$ for each daughter ($\frac{1}{2}$ chance that child will be female × $\frac{1}{2}$ chance of a homozygous recessive genotype); $\frac{1}{2}$ for first son
4. 17%

5. 6%. Wild type (heterozygous for normal wings and red eyes) × recessive homozygote with vestigial wings and purple eyes
6. The disorder would always be inherited from the mother.
7. The inactivation of two X chromosomes in XXX women would leave them with one genetically active X, as in women with the normal number of chromosomes. Microscopy should reveal two Barr bodies in XXX women.
8. *D–A–B–C*
9. Fifty percent of the offspring would show phenotypes that resulted from crossovers. These results would be the same as those from a cross where *A* and *B* were not linked. Further crosses involving other genes on the same chromosome would reveal the linkage and map distances.
10. Between *T* and *A*, 12%; between *A* and *S*, 5%
11. Between *T* and *S*, 18%; sequence of genes is *T-A-S*
12. No. The child can be either $I^A I^A i$ or $I^A ii$. An ovum with the genotype *ii* could result from nondisjunction in the mother, while a sperm of genotype $I^A I^A$ could result from nondisjunction in the father.
13. 450 each of blue-oval and white-round (parentals) and 50 each of blue-round and white-oval (recombinants)
14. About one-third of the distance from the vestigial-wing locus to the brown-eye locus

CHAPTER 16

Concept Check 16.1

1. DNA from the dead pathogenic S cells was somehow taken up by the living, nonpathogenic R cells. The DNA from the S cells enabled the R cells to make a capsule, which protected them from the mouse's defenses. In this way, the R cells were transformed into pathogenic S cells.
2. When the proteins were radioactively labeled (batch 1), the radioactivity would have been found in the pellet of bacterial cells.
3. Chargaff's rules state that in DNA, the percentages of A and T and of G and C are essentially the same, and the fly data are consistent with those rules. (Slight variations are most likely due to limitations of analytical technique.)
4. Each A hydrogen-bonds to a T, so in a DNA double helix, their numbers are equal; the same is true for G and C.

Concept Check 16.2

1. Complementary base pairing ensures that the two daughter molecules are exact copies of the parent molecule. When the two strands of the parent molecule separate, each serves as a template on which nucleotides are arranged, by the base-pairing rules, into new complementary strands.
2. DNA pol III covalently adds nucleotides to new DNA strands and proofreads each added nucleotide for correct base pairing.

3. The leading strand is initiated by an RNA primer, which must be removed and replaced with DNA, a task performed by DNA pol I. In Figure 16.16 just to the left of the origin of replication, DNA pol I would replace the primer of the leading strand with DNA nucleotides.
4. The ends of eukaryotic chromosomes become shorter with each round of DNA replication, and telomeres at the ends of DNA molecules ensure that genes are not lost after numerous rounds of replication.

Self-Quiz

1. c	2. d	3. b	4. c	5. b
6. a	7. c	8. d	9. a	10. b

CHAPTER 17

Concept Check 17.1

1. The nontemplate strand would read 5'-TGGTTTGGCTCA-3'. The 5' → 3' direction is the same as that for the mRNA; the base sequence is the same except for the presence of U in the mRNA where there is T in the nontemplate strand of DNA.
2. A polypeptide made up of 10 Gly (glycine) amino acids

Concept Check 17.2

1. Both assemble nucleic acid chains from monomer nucleotides using complementary base pairing to a template strand. Both synthesize in the 5' → 3' direction, antiparallel to the template. DNA polymerase requires a primer, but RNA polymerase can start a nucleotide chain from scratch. DNA polymerase uses nucleotides with the sugar deoxyribose and the base T, whereas RNA polymerase uses nucleotides with the sugar ribose and the base U.
2. Upstream end
3. In a prokaryote, RNA polymerase recognizes the gene's promoter and binds to it. In a eukaryote, transcription factors mediate the binding of RNA polymerase to the promoter.
4. A prokaryotic primary transcript is immediately usable as mRNA, but a eukaryotic primary transcript must be modified before it can be used as mRNA.

Concept Check 17.3

1. The 5' cap and poly-A tail facilitate mRNA export from the nucleus, prevent the mRNA from being degraded by hydrolytic enzymes, and facilitate ribosome attachment.
2. snRNPs join with other proteins and form spliceosomes that cut introns out of a pre-mRNA molecule and join its exons together.
3. Alternative RNA splicing produces different mRNA molecules from a pre-mRNA molecule depending on which exons are included in the mRNA and which are not. By yielding more than one version of mRNA, a single gene can code for more than one polypeptide.

Concept Check 17.4

1. First, each aminoacyl-tRNA synthetase specifically recognizes a single amino acid and will only attach it to an appropriate tRNA. Second, a tRNA charged with its specific amino acid has an anticodon that will only bind to an mRNA codon for that amino acid.
2. Polyribosomes enable the cell to produce multiple copies of a polypeptide in a short amount of time.
3. A signal peptide on the leading end of the polypeptide being synthesized is recognized by a signal-recognition particle that brings the ribosome to the ER membrane. There the ribosome attaches and continues to synthesize the polypeptide, depositing it in the ER lumen.

Concept Check 17.5

1. RNA can form hydrogen bonds with either DNA or RNA, take on a specific three-dimensional shape, and catalyze chemical reactions. These abilities enable RNA to interact functionally with all the major types of molecules in a cell.

Concept Check 17.6

1. The RNA polymerase farthest to the right is first, since it has traveled the farthest along the DNA (and its mRNA is longest). The first ribosome is at the top of each mRNA, because it has traveled the farthest along the mRNA starting from the 5′ end; the second is immediately below it, and so on.
2. No, the processes of transcription and translation are separated in space and time in a eukaryotic cell, a result of the eukaryotic cell's compartmental organization.

Concept Check 17.7

1. In the mRNA, the reading frame downstream from the deletion is shifted, leading to a long string of incorrect amino acids in the polypeptide and, in most cases, premature termination. The polypeptide will most likely be nonfunctional.
2. The amino acid sequence of the wild-type protein is Met-Asn-Arg-Leu. The amino acid sequence of the mutant protein sequence would be the same, because the mRNA codons 5′-CUA-3′ and 5′-UUA-3′ both code for Leu.

Self-Quiz
| 1. c | 2. b | 3. d | 4. d | 5. a |
| 6. a | 7. c | 8. d | 9. e | 10. b |

CHAPTER 18

Concept Check 18.1

1. Lytic phages can only carry out lysis of the host cell, whereas lysogenic phages may either lyse the host cell or integrate into the host chromosome. In the latter case, the viral DNA (prophage) is simply replicated along with the host chromosome. Under certain conditions, a prophage may exit the host chromosome and initiate a lytic cycle.

2. The genetic material of these viruses is RNA, which is replicated inside the infected cell by special enzymes encoded by the virus. The viral genome (or a complementary copy of it) serves as mRNA for the synthesis of viral proteins.
3. Because it synthesizes DNA from its RNA genome. This is the reverse ("retro") of the usual DNA → RNA information flow.

Concept Check 18.2

1. Mutations can lead to a new strain of a virus that can no longer be recognized by the immune system, even if an animal has been exposed to the original strain; a virus can jump from one species to a new host; and a rare virus can spread if a population becomes less isolated.
2. In horizontal transmission, a plant is infected from an external source of virus, which could enter through a break in the plant's epidermis due to damage by insects or other animals. In vertical transmission, a plant inherits viruses from its parent either via infected seeds (sexual reproduction) or via an infected cutting (asexual reproduction).
3. A source of infection, such as prion-infected cattle, may show no symptoms for many years. Beef prepared from such animals before symptoms appear would not be recognized as hazardous and could transmit infection to people who eat the meat.

Concept Check 18.3

1. In transformation, naked, foreign DNA from the environment is taken up by a bacterial cell. In transduction, phages carry bacterial genes from one bacterial cell to another. In conjugation, a bacterial cell directly transfers plasmid or chromosomal DNA to another cell via a mating bridge that temporarily connects the two cells.
2. Both are episomes—that is, they can exist as part of the bacterial chromosome or independently. However, phage DNA can leave the cell in a protein coat (as a complete phage), whereas a plasmid cannot. Also, plasmids are generally beneficial to the cell, while phage DNA can direct the production of complete phages that may harm or kill the cell.
3. In an F⁺ × F⁻ mating, only plasmid genes are transferred, but in an Hfr × F⁻ mating, bacterial genes may be transferred, because the F factor is integrated into the donor cell's chromosome. In the latter case, the transferred genes may then recombine with the recipient F⁻ cell's chromosome.

Concept Check 18.4

1. The cell would continuously produce β-galactosidase and the two other enzymes for lactose utilization, even in the absence of lactose, thus wasting cell resources.
2. Binding by the *trp* corepressor (tryptophan) activates the *trp* repressor, shutting off transcription of the *trp* operon; binding by the *lac* inducer (allolactose) inactivates the *lac* repressor, leading to transcription of the *lac* operon.

Self-Quiz
| 1. d | 2. b | 3. b | 4. e | 5. d |
| 6. a | 7. d | 8. e | 9. c | 10. d |

CHAPTER 19

Concept Check 19.1

1. A nucleosome is made up of eight histone proteins, two each of four different types, around which DNA is wound. Linker DNA runs from one nucleosome to the next one.
2. Histones contain many basic (positively charged) amino acids, such as lysine and arginine, which can form weak bonds with the negatively charged phosphate groups on the sugar-phosphate backbone of the DNA molecule.
3. RNA polymerase and other proteins required for transcription do not have access to the DNA in tightly packed regions of a chromosome.

Concept Check 19.2

1. Histone acetylation is generally associated with gene expression, while DNA methylation is generally associated with lack of expression.
2. General transcription factors function in assembling the transcription initiation complex at the promoters for all genes. Specific transcription factors bind to control elements associated with a particular gene and once bound either increase (activators) or decrease (repressors) transcription of that gene.
3. The three genes should have some similar or identical sequences in the control elements of their enhancers. Because of this similarity, the same specific transcription factors could bind to the enhancers of all three genes and stimulate their expression coordinately.
4. Degradation of the mRNA, regulation of translation, activation of the protein (by chemical modification, for example), and protein degradation

Concept Check 19.3

1. The protein product of a proto-oncogene is usually involved in a pathway that stimulates cell division. The protein product of a tumor-suppressor gene is usually involved in a pathway that inhibits cell division.
2. A cancer-causing mutation in a proto-oncogene usually makes the gene product overactive, whereas a cancer-causing mutation in a tumor-suppressor gene usually makes the gene product nonfunctional.
3. When an individual has inherited an oncogene or a mutant allele of a tumor-suppressor gene

Concept Check 19.4

1. The number of genes is 5–15 times higher in mammals, and the amount of noncoding DNA is about 10,000 times greater. The presence of introns in mammalian genes makes them about 27 times longer, on average, than prokaryotic genes.

2. Introns are interspersed within the coding sequences of genes. Many copies of each transposable element are scattered throughout the genome. Simple sequence DNA is concentrated at the centromeres and telomeres.
3. In the rRNA gene family, identical transcription units encoding three different RNA products are present in long, tandemly repeated arrays. The large number of copies of the rRNA genes enable organisms to produce the rRNA for enough ribosomes to carry out active protein synthesis. Each globin gene family consists of a relatively small number of nonidentical genes clustered near each other. The differences in the globin proteins encoded by these genes result in production of hemoglobin molecules adapted to particular developmental stages of the organism.

Concept Check 19.5
1. If cytokinesis is faulty, two copies of the entire genome can end up in a single cell. Errors in crossing over during meiosis can lead to one segment being duplicated while another is deleted. During DNA replication, slippage backward along the template strand can result in a duplication.
2. Gene duplication and divergence by mutation. Movement of genes to different chromosomes also occurred.
3. For either gene, a mistake in crossing over during meiosis could have occurred between the two copies of that gene, such that one ended up with a duplicated exon. This could have happened several times, resulting in the multiple copies of a particular exon in each gene.
4. Homologous transposable elements scattered throughout the genome provide sites where recombination can occur between different chromosomes. Movement of these elements into coding or regulatory sequences may change expression of genes. Transposable elements also can carry genes with them, leading to dispersion of genes and in some cases different patterns of expression. Or transport of an exon during transposition and its insertion into a gene may add a new functional domain to the originally encoded protein, a type of exon shuffling.

Self-Quiz
1. c   2. a   3. a   4. a   5. e
6. a   7. c   8. c   9. b   10. b

CHAPTER 20

Concept Check 20.1
1. White (no functional *lacZ* gene is present)
2. A cDNA library, made using mRNA from developing red blood cells, which would be expected to contain many copies of β-globin mRNAs
3. Some human genes are too large to be incorporated into bacterial plasmids. Bacterial cells lack the means to process RNA transcripts, and even if the need for RNA processing is avoided by using cDNA, bacteria lack en-

zymes to catalyze the post-translational processing that many human proteins undergo.

Concept Check 20.2
1. Any restriction enzyme will cut genomic DNA in many places, generating such a large number of fragments that they would appear as a smear rather than distinct bands when the gel is stained after electrophoresis.
2. RFLPs are inherited in a Mendelian fashion, and variations in RFLPs among individuals can be detected by Southern blotting.

Concept Check 20.3
1. In a genetic linkage map, genes and other markers are ordered with respect to each other, but only the relative distances between them are known. In a physical map, the actual distances between markers, expressed in base pairs, are known.
2. The three-stage approach employed in the Human Genome Project involves genetic mapping, physical mapping, and then sequencing of short, overlapping fragments that previously have been ordered relative to each other (see Figure 20.11). The shotgun approach eliminates the genetic mapping and physical mapping stages; instead, short fragments generated by multiple restriction enzymes, are sequenced and then subsequently ordered by computer programs that identify overlapping regions (see Figure 20.13).

Concept Check 20.4
1. Alternative splicing of RNA transcripts from a gene and post-translational processing of polypeptides
2. It allows expression of thousands of genes to be examined simultaneously, thus providing a genome-wide view of which genes are expressed in different tissues, under particular conditions, or at different stages of development.
3. Because the human species arose more recently than many other species, there has been less time for genetic variations in coding and noncoding DNA to accumulate.

Concept Check 20.5
1. Stem cells continue to reproduce themselves.
2. Herbicide resistance, pest resistance, disease resistance, delayed ripening, and improved nutritional value

Self-Quiz
1. b   2. b   3. c   4. b   5. a
6. c   7. e   8. c   9. d   10. c

CHAPTER 21

Concept Check 21.1
1. Cells undergo differentiation during embryonic development, becoming different from each other; in the adult organism, there are many highly specialized cell types.
2. During animal development, movement of cells and tissues is a major mechanism, which is not the case in plants. In plants, growth

and morphogenesis continue throughout the life of the plant. This is true of only a few types of animal cells.

Concept Check 21.2
1. Information deposited by the mother in the egg (cytoplasmic determinants) is required for embryonic development.
2. No, primarily because of subtle (and perhaps not so subtle) differences in their environments
3. By binding to a receptor on the receiving cell's surface and triggering a signal transduction pathway that affects gene expression

Concept Check 21.3
1. Because their products, made by the mother, determine the head and tail ends, as well as the back and belly, of the egg (and eventually the adult fly)
2. The prospective vulval cells require an inductive signal from the anchor cell before they can differentiate into vulval cells.
3. A shoot is a differentiated structure, yet some of the cells that make it up are able to dedifferentiate and redifferentiate, forming all of the organs of an entire new plant.

Concept Check 21.4
1. Homeotic genes differ in their *non*homeobox sequences, which determine their interactions with other transcription factors and hence which genes are regulated by the homeotic genes. These differ in the two organisms, as do the expression patterns of the homeobox genes.

Self-Quiz
1. c   2. e   3. b   4. a   5. a
6. d   7. c   8. a   9. c   10. e

CHAPTER 22

Concept Check 22.1
1. Aristotle, Linnaeus, and Cuvier viewed species as fixed (though Cuvier noted that the species present in a particular location could change over time). Lamarck, Erasmus Darwin, and Charles Darwin thought species could change.
2. Lamarck observed evidence of changes in species over time and noted that evolution could result in organisms' adaptations to their environments, though his theory was based on an incorrect mechanism for evolution: that modifications an organism acquires during its lifetime can be passed to its offspring.

Concept Check 22.2
1. Species have the potential to produce more offspring than survive (overreproduction), leading to a struggle for resources, which are limited. Populations exhibit a range of heritable variations, some of which confer advantages to their bearers that make them more likely to leave more offspring than less well-suited individuals. Over time this natural selection can result in a greater proportion of favorable traits in a population (evolutionary adaptation).

2. Though an individual may become modified during its lifetime through interactions with its environment, this does not represent evolution. Evolution can only be measured as a change in proportions of heritable variations from generation to generation.

Concept Check 22.3

1. An environmental factor such as a drug does not create new traits such as drug resistance, but rather selects for traits among those that are already present in the population.
2. Despite their different functions, the forelimbs of different mammals are structurally similar because they all represent modifications of a structure found in the common ancestor. The similarities between the sugar glider and flying squirrel indicate that similar environments selected for similar adaptations despite different ancestry.
3. If molecular biology or biogeography indicates a particular branching pattern of descent from a single group of ancestral organisms, representatives of the ancestral group should appear earlier in the fossil record than representatives of the later organisms. Likewise, the many transitional forms that link ancient organisms to present-day species are evidence of descent with modification.

Self-Quiz

| 1. c | 2. b | 3. c | 4. d | 5. c |
| 6. b | 7. d | 8. c | 9. c | 10. d |

CHAPTER 23

Concept Check 23.1

1. Mendel showed that inheritance is particulate, and subsequently it was shown that this type of inheritance can preserve the variation on which natural selection acts.
2. 750. Half the loci (250) are fixed, meaning only one allele exists for each locus: $250 \times 1 = 250$. There are two alleles each for the other loci: $250 \times 2 = 500$. $250 + 500 = 750$.
3. $2pq + q^2$; $2pq$ represents heterozygotes with one PKU allele and q^2 represents homozygotes with two PKU alleles

Concept Check 23.2

1. Most mutations occur in somatic cells that do not produce gametes and so are lost when the organism dies. Of mutations that do occur in cell lines that produce gametes, many do not have a phenotypic effect on which natural selection can act. Others have a harmful effect and are thus unlikely to spread in a population from generation to generation because they decrease the reproductive success of their bearers.
2. A population contains a vast number of possible mating combinations, and fertilization brings together the gametes of individuals with different genetic backgrounds. Sexual reproduction reshuffles alleles into fresh combinations every generation.

Concept Check 23.3

1. Natural selection is more "predictable" in that it tends to increase or decrease the frequency of alleles that correspond to variations that increase or decrease an organism's fitness in its environment. Alleles subject to genetic drift all have the same likelihood of increasing or decreasing.
2. Genetic drift results from chance fluctuations of allele frequencies from generation to generation; it tends to decrease variation over time. Gene flow is the exchange of alleles between populations; it tends to increase variation within a population but decrease allele frequency differences between populations.

Concept Check 23.4

1. No; many nucleotides are in noncoding portions of DNA or in pseudogenes that have been inactivated by mutations. A change in a nucleotide may not even change the amino acid encoded because of the redundancy of the genetic code.
2. Zero, because fitness includes reproductive contribution to the next generation, and a sterile mule cannot produce offspring.
3. In sexual selection, organisms may compete for mates through behaviors or displays of secondary sexual characteristics; only the competing sex is selected for these characteristics.
4. Only *half* of the members (the females) of a sexual population actually produce offspring, while *all* the members of an asexual population can produce offspring.

Self-Quiz

| 1. c | 2. d | 3. c | 4. a | 5. c |
| 6. b | 7. c | 8. b | 9. b | 10. b |

CHAPTER 24

Concept Check 24.1

1. Since the birds are known to breed successfully in captivity, the reproductive barrier in nature must be prezygotic. Given the species differences in habitat preference, the reproductive barrier is most likely to be habitat isolation.
2. a. All species concepts except the biological species concept can be applied to both asexual and sexual species because they define species on the basis of characteristics other than ability to reproduce. b. The biological species concept can only be applied to extant sexual species. c. The easiest species concept to apply on a field trip would be the morphological species concept because it is based only on the appearance of the organism. Additional information about its ecological habits, evolutionary history, and reproduction are not required.

Concept Check 24.2

1. Continued gene flow between mainland populations and those on a nearby island reduces the chance that enough genetic divergence will take place for allopatric speciation to occur.
2. The diploid and tetraploid watermelons are separate species. Their hybrids are triploid

and as a result are sterile because of problems carrying out meiosis.
3. According to the model of punctuated equilibrium, in most cases the time during which speciation (that is, the distinguishing evolutionary changes) occurs is relatively short compared with the overall duration of the species' existence. Thus, on the vast geologic time scale of the fossil record, the transition of one species to another seems abrupt, and instances of gradual change in the fossil record are rare. Furthermore, some of the changes that transitional species underwent may not be apparent in fossils.

Concept Check 24.3

1. Such complex structures do not evolve all at once, but in increments, with natural selection selecting for adaptive variants of the earlier versions.
2. Although an exaptation is co-opted for new or additional functions in a new environment, it existed in the first place because it worked as an adaptation to the original environment.
3. The timing of different developmental pathways in organisms can change in different ways (heterochrony). This can result in differential growth patterns, such as those producing different patterns of webbing in salamander feet.

Self-Quiz

| 1. b | 2. b | 3. a | 4. c | 5. e |
| 6. d | 7. b | 8. a | 9. c | 10. c. |

CHAPTER 25

Concept Check 25.1

1. (a) Analogy, since porcupines and cacti are not closely related and also most other animals and plants do not have similar structures; (b) homology, since cats and humans are both mammals and have homologous forelimbs, of which the hand and paw are the lower part; (c) analogy, since owls and hornets are not closely related, and also the structure of their wings is very different.
2. The latter is more likely, since just small genetic changes can produce divergent physical appearances, but if genes have diverged greatly, that implies the lineages have been separate for some time.

Concept Check 25.2

1. We are classified the same down to the class level; both the leopard and human are mammals. Leopards belong to order Carnivora, whereas humans do not.
2. The branching pattern of the tree indicates that the skunk and the wolf share a common ancestor that is more recent than the ancestor these two animals share with the leopard.

Concept Check 25.3

1. No; hair is a shared primitive character common to all mammals and thus cannot be helpful in distinguishing different mammalian subgroups.

2. The principle of maximum parsimony states that the theory about nature we investigate first should be the simplest explanation found to be consistent with the facts. But nature does not always take the simplest course; thus, the most parsimonious tree (reflecting the fewest evolutionary changes) may not reflect reality.

Concept Check 25.4
1. Proteins are gene products. Their amino acid sequences are determined by the nucleotide sequences of the DNA that codes for them. Thus, differences between comparable proteins in two species reflect underlying genetic differences.
2. Orthologous genes are homologous genes that have ended up in different gene pools, whereas paralogous genes are found in multiple copies in a single genome because they are the result of gene duplication.

Concept Check 25.5
1. The molecular clock is a method of estimating the actual time of evolutionary events based on numbers of base changes in orthologous genes. It is based on the assumption that the regions of genomes being compared evolve at constant rates.
2. There are many portions of the genome that do not code for genes, in which many base changes could accumulate through drift without affecting an organism's fitness. Even in coding regions of the genome, some mutations may not have a critical effect on genes or proteins.

Self-Quiz
| 1. b | 2. c | 3. a | 4. d | 5. e |
| 6. c | 7. d | 8. d | 9. a | 10. b |

CHAPTER 26

Concept Check 26.1
1. The hypothesis that conditions on the early Earth could have permitted the synthesis of organic molecules from inorganic ingredients
2. In contrast to random mingling of molecules in an open solution, segregation of molecular systems by membranes could concentrate organic molecules, and electrical charge gradients across the membrane could assist biochemical reactions.
3. An RNA molecule that functions as a catalyst

Concept Check 26.2
1. 22,920 years (four half-life reductions)
2. About 2,000 million years, or 2 billion years

Concept Check 26.3
1. Prokaryotes must have existed at least 3.5 billion years ago, when the oldest fossilized stromatolites were formed.
2. Free oxygen attacks chemical bonds and can inhibit enzymes and damage cells. Some organisms were able to adapt, however.

Concept Check 26.4
1. All eukaryotes have mitochondria or genetic remnants of these organelles, but not all eukaryotes have plastids.
2. The chimera of Greek mythology contained parts from different animals. Similarly, a eukaryotic cell contains parts from various prokaryotes: mitochondria from one type of bacterium, plastids from another type, and a nuclear genome from parts of the genomes of these endosymbionts and at least one other prokaryote.

Concept Check 26.5
1. A single-celled organism must carry out all of the functions required to stay alive. Most multicellular organisms have many types of specialized cells, and life functions are divided among specific cell types.
2. Fossils of most major animal phyla appear suddenly in the first 20 million years of the Cambrian period. Molecular clocks suggest that many animal phyla originated much earlier.

Concept Check 26.6
1. Protista, Plantae, Fungi, and Animalia
2. Monera included both bacteria and archaea, but archaea are more closely related to eukaryotes than to bacteria.

Self-Quiz
| 1. b | 2. d | 3. b | 4. e | 5. d |
| 6. c | 7. d | 8. a | 9. e | 10. c |

CHAPTER 27

Concept Check 27.1
1. Adaptations include the capsule (shields prokaryotes from host's immune system), plasmids (confer "contingency" functions such as antibiotic resistance), and the formation of endospores (enable cells to survive harsh conditions and to revive when the environment becomes favorable).
2. Prokaryotic cells generally lack the internal compartmentalization of eukaryotic cells. Prokaryotic genomes have much less DNA than eukaryotic genomes, and most of this DNA is contained in a single ring-shaped chromosome located in a nucleoid region rather than within a true membrane-bounded nucleus. In addition, many prokaryotes also have plasmids, small ring-shaped DNA molecules containing a few genes.
3. Rapid reproduction enables a favorable mutation to spread quickly through a prokaryotic population by natural selection.

Concept Check 27.2
1. Chemoheterotrophy; the bacterium must rely on chemical sources of energy, since it is not exposed to light, and it must be a heterotroph if it requires an organic source of carbon rather than CO_2.

2. *Anabaena* is a photoautotroph that obtains its carbon from CO_2. As a nitrogen-fixing prokaryote, *Anabaena* obtains its nitrogen from N_2.

Concept Check 27.3
1. Before molecular systematics, taxonomists classified prokaryotes according to phenotypic characters that did not clarify evolutionary relationships. Molecular comparisons indicate key divergences in prokaryotic lineages.
2. Both diseases are caused by spirochetes.
3. The ability of various archaea to use hydrogen, sulfur, and other chemicals as energy sources and to survive or even thrive without oxygen enables them to live in environments where more commonly needed resources are not present.

Concept Check 27.4
1. Although prokaryotes are small, mostly unicellular organisms, they play key roles in ecosystems by decomposing wastes, recycling chemicals, and providing nutrients to other organisms.
2. *Bacteroides thetaiotaomicron,* which lives inside the human intestine, benefits by obtaining nutrients from the digestive system and by receiving protection from competing bacteria from host-produced antimicrobial compounds to which it is not sensitive. The human host benefits because the bacterium manufactures carbohydrates, vitamins, and other nutrients.

Concept Check 27.5
1. Exotoxins are proteins secreted by prokaryotes; endotoxins are lipopolysaccharides released from the outer membrane of gram-negative bacteria that have died.
2. Their quick reproduction can make it difficult to combat them with antibiotics, particularly as they may evolve resistance to the drugs. Some also have the ability to form endospores and withstand harsh environments, surviving until conditions become more favorable.
3. Sample answers: eating fermented foods such as yogurt, sourdough bread, or cheese; receiving clean water from sewage treatment; taking prokaryote-produced medicines

Self-Quiz
| 1. d | 2. a | 3. d | 4. d | 5. c |
| 6. d | 7. c | 8. d | 9. a | 10. a |

CHAPTER 28

Concept Check 28.1
1. Sample response: Protists include unicellular, colonial, and multicellular organisms; photoautotrophs, heterotrophs, and mixotrophs; and species that reproduce asexually, sexually, or both ways; and species that live in marine, freshwater, and moist terrestrial habitats.

2. Four: the inner and outer membranes of the bacterium, and the food vacuole membrane and plasma membrane of the eukaryotic cell

Concept Check 28.2

1. Their mitochondria do not have DNA, an electron transport chain, or citric-acid cycle enzymes.
2. Its flagella and undulating membrane enable it to move along the mucus-coated lining of these tracts inside its host.

Concept Check 28.3

1. The proteins have slightly different structures, but only one protein at a time is expressed. Frequent changes in expression prevent the host from developing immunity.
2. *Euglena* could be considered an alga because it is a photosynthetic autotroph; however, it could also be considered a fungus-like protist because it can absorb organic nutrients from its environment.

Concept Check 28.4

1. Membrane-bounded sacs under the plasma membrane
2. A red tide is a bloom of dinoflagellates, some of which produce deadly toxins that accumulate in molluscs and can affect people who eat the molluscs.
3. During conjugation, two ciliates exchange micronuclei, but no new individuals are produced.

Concept Check 28.5

1. A pair of flagella, one hairy and one smooth
2. Oomycetes acquire nutrition mainly as decomposers or parasites; golden algae are photosynthetic, but some also absorb dissolved organic compounds or ingest food particles and bacteria by phagocytosis.
3. The holdfast anchors the alga to the rocks, while the wide, flat blades provide photosynthetic surfaces. The cellulose and algin in the alga's cell walls cushion the thallus from waves and protect it from drying out.

Concept Check 28.6

1. Because foram tests are hardened with calcium carbonate, they form long-lasting fossils in marine sediments and sedimentary rocks.
2. Forams feed by extending their pseudopodia through pores in their tests. Radiolarians ingest smaller microorganisms by phagocytosis using their pseudopodia; cytoplasmic streaming carries the engulfed prey to the main part of the cell.

Concept Check 28.7

1. Amoebozoans have lobe-shaped pseudopodia, whereas forams have threadlike pseudopodia.
2. Slime molds are fungus-like in that they produce fruiting bodies that aid in the dispersal of spores, and they are animal-like in that they are motile and ingest food. However, slime molds are more closely related to gymnamoebas and entamoebas than to fungi or animals.

3. In the life cycle of a cellular slime mold, individual amoebas may congregate in response to a chemical signal, forming a sluglike aggregate form that can move. Then some of the cells form a stalk that supports an asexual fruiting body.

Concept Check 28.8

1. Many algae contain an accessory pigment called phycoerythrin, which gives them a reddish color and allows them to carry out photosynthesis in relatively deep coastal water. Also unlike brown algae, red algae have no flagellated stages in their life cycle and must depend on water currents to bring gametes together for fertilization.
2. *Ulva's* thallus contains many cells and is differentiated into leaflike blades and a rootlike holdfast. *Caulerpa's* thallus is composed of multinucleate filaments without cross-walls, so it is essentially one large cell.

Self-Quiz

1. d	2. b	3. b	4. c	5. e
6. d	7. c	8. a	9. d	10. b

CHAPTER 29

Concept Check 29.1

1. Land plants share some key traits only with charophyceans: rosette cellulose-producing complexes, presence of peroxisome enzymes, similarity in sperm structure, and similarity in cell division (the formation of a phragmoplast). Comparisons of nuclear and chloroplast genes also point to a common ancestry.

Concept Check 29.2

1. Spore walls toughened by sporopollenin; multicellular, dependent embryos; cuticle
2. a. diploid, b. haploid; c. haploid; d. diploid; e. haploid; f. haploid

Concept Check 29.3

1. Bryophytes are described as nonvascular plants because they do not have an extensive transport system. Another difference is that their life cycle is dominated by gametophytes rather than sporophytes.
2. Answers may include the following: large surface area of protonema enhances absorption of water and minerals; the vase-shaped archegonia protect eggs during fertilization and transport nutrients to the embryos via placental transfer cells; the stalklike seta conducts nutrients from the gametophyte to the capsule where sperm are produced; the peristome enables gradual spore discharge; stomata enable CO_2/O_2 exchange while minimizing water loss. Lightweight spores are wind-dispersed; mosses can lose water without drying and rehydrate when moisture is available.

Concept Check 29.4

1. Some characteristics that distinguish seedless vascular plants from bryophytes are a sporophyte-dominant life cycle, the presence of xylem and phloem, and the evolution of true

roots and leaves. A key similarity is flagellated sperm requiring moisture for fertilization.
2. Most lycophytes have microphylls, whereas ferns and most fern relatives have megaphylls.

Self-Quiz

1. b	2. c	3. d	4. a	5. a
6. b	7. c	8. c	9. a	10. a

CHAPTER 30

Concept Check 30.1

1. To have any chance of reaching the eggs, the flagellated sperm of seedless vascular plants must rely on swimming through a film of water, usually limited to a range of less than a few centimeters. In contrast, the sperm of seed plants are produced within durable pollen grains that can be carried long distances by wind or by animal pollinators. Although flagellated in some species, the sperm of most seed plants do not require water because pollen tubes convey them directly to the eggs.
2. The reduced gametophytes of seed plants are nurtured by sporophytes and protected from stress, such as drought conditions and UV radiation. Pollen grains have tough protective coats and can be carried long distances, facilitating widespread sperm transfer without reliance on water. Seeds are more resilient than spores, enabling better resistance to environmental stresses and wider distribution.

Concept Check 30.2

1. Although gymnosperms are similar in not having their seeds enclosed in ovaries and fruits, their seed-bearing structures vary greatly. For instance, cycads have large cones, whereas some gymnosperms, such as *Ginkgo* and *Gnetum,* have small cones that look somewhat like berries, even though they are not fruits. Leaf shape also varies greatly, from the needles of many conifers to the palmlike leaves of cycads to *Gnetum* leaves that look like those of flowering plants.
2. The life cycle illustrates heterospory, as ovulate cones produce megaspores and pollen cones produce microspores. The reduced gametophytes are evident in the form of the microscopic pollen grains and the microscopic female gametophyte within the megaspore. The egg is shown developing within an ovule, and the pollen tube is shown conveying the sperm. The figure also shows the protective and nutritive features of a seed.

Concept Check 30.3

1. In the oak's life cycle, the tree (the sporophyte) produces flowers, which contain gametophytes in pollen grains and ovules; the eggs in ovules are fertilized; the mature ovaries develop into dry fruits called acorns; and the acorn seeds germinate, resulting in embryos giving rise to seedlings and finally to mature trees, which produce flowers and then acorns.

2. Pine cones and flowers both have sporophylls, modified leaves that produce spores. Pine trees have separate pollen cones (with pollen grains) and ovulate cones (with ovules inside cone scales). In flowers, pollen grains are produced by the anthers of stamens, and ovules are within the ovaries of carpels. Unlike pine cones, many flowers produce both pollen and ovules.
3. Traditionally, angiosperms have been classified as either monocots or dicots, based on certain traits, such as the number of cotyledons. However, recent molecular evidence reveals that while monocots are a clade, dicots are not. Based on phylogenetic relationships, *most* dicots form a clade, now known as eudicots.

Concept Check 30.4
1. Because extinction is irreversible, it decreases the total diversity of plants, many of which may have brought important benefits to humans.

Self-Quiz
1. d	2. a	3. b	4. a	5. e
6. d	7. b	8. d	9. c	10. a

CHAPTER 31

Concept Check 31.1
1. Both a fungus and a human are heterotrophs. A fungus digests its food externally by secreting enzymes into the food and then absorbing the small molecules that result from digestion. In contrast, humans (and other animals) ingest relatively large pieces of food and digest the food within their bodies.
2. The extensive network of hyphae puts a large surface area in contact with the food source, and rapid growth of the mycelium extends hyphae into new territory.

Concept Check 31.2
1. The majority of the fungal life cycle consists of haploid stages, whereas the majority of the human life cycle consists of diploid stages.
2. The two mushrooms might be reproductive structures of the same mycelium (the same organism), Or they might be parts of two separate organisms that have arisen from a single parent organism through asexual reproduction and thus carry the same genetic information.

Concept Check 31.3
1. The fungal lineage thought to be the most primitive, the chytrids, have posterior flagella, as do most other opisthokonts. This suggests that other fungal lineages lost their flagella after diverging from the chytrid lineage.
2. This indicates that fungi had already established symbiotic relationships with plants by the date those fossils formed.

Concept Check 31.4
1. Flagellated spores
2. Most plants form arbuscular mycorrhizae with glomeromycetes; without the fungi, the plants would be poorly nourished.

3. Possible answers include the following: In zygomycetes, the sturdy, thick-walled zygosporangium can withstand harsh conditions and then undergo karyogamy and meiosis when the environment is favorable for reproduction. In ascomycetes, the asexual spores (conidia) are produced in chains or clusters at the tips of conidiophores, where they are easily dispersed by wind. The often cup-shaped ascocarps house the sexual spore-forming asci. In basidiomycetes, the basidiocarp supports and protects a large surface area of basidia, from which spores are dispersed.

Concept Check 31.5
1. A suitable environment for growth, retention of water and minerals, protection from sunlight, and protection from being eaten
2. A hardy spore stage enables dispersal to host organisms through a variety of mechanisms; their ability to grow rapidly in a favorable new environment enables them to capitalize on the host's resources.

Self-Quiz
1. b	2. c	3. c	4. d	5. e
6. d	7. b	8. e	9. b	10. a

CHAPTER 32

Concept Check 32.1
1. Plants are autotrophs; animals are heterotrophs. Plants have cell walls that provide structural support; animals lack strong cell walls (their bodies are held together by structural proteins, including collagen). Animals have unique cell types and tissues (muscle and nerve) and unique patterns of development, including the multicellular blastula stage.
2. These basic patterns of early development arose early in animal evolution and have been conserved across the diverse phyla within this clade today.

Concept Check 32.2
1. c, b, a, d
2. This diversification may have resulted from such external factors as changing ecological relationships (for instance, predator-prey interactions) and environmental conditions (for instance, increased oxygen levels) and from such internal factors as the evolution of the *Hox* complex.

Concept Check 32.3
1. Grade-level characteristics are those that multiple lineages share regardless of evolutionary history. Some grade-level characteristics may have evolved multiple times independently. Features that unite clades are those that were possessed by a common ancestor and were passed on to the various descendants.
2. Snail has spiral and determinate cleavage pattern; human has radial, indeterminate cleavage. Snail has schizocoelous development

(characterized by a coelomic cavity formed by splitting of mesoderm masses); human has enterocoelous development (coelom forms from folds of archenteron). In a snail, the mouth forms from the blastopore; in a human, the anus develops from the blastopore.

Concept Check 32.4
1. Cnidarians possess true tissues, while sponges do not. Also unlike sponges, cnidarians exhibit body symmetry, though it is radial and not bilateral as in other animal phyla.
2. The morphology-based tree divides Bilateria into two clades: Deuterostomia and Protostomia. The molecule-based tree recognizes three clades: Deuterostomia, Ecdysozoa, and Lophotrochozoa, as well as the phylum Rotifera.
3. Each type of data contributes to scientists' ability to test hypotheses about relationships; the more lines of data that support a particular hypothesis, the more likely it is to be valid.

Self-Quiz
1. a	2. c	3. c	4. e	5. b
6. c	7. b	8. e	9. e	10. d

CHAPTER 33

Concept Check 33.1
1. The flagella of choanocytes draw water through their collars, which trap food particles. The particles are engulfed by phagocytosis and digested, either by choanocytes or by amoebocytes.
2. Sponges release their sperm into the surrounding water; changes in current direction will affect the odds that the sperm will be drawn into neighboring individuals.

Concept Check 33.2
1. Both the polyp and the medusa are composed of an outer epidermis and an inner gastrodermis separated by a gelatinous layer, the mesoglea. The polyp is a cylindrical form that adheres to the substrate by its aboral end; the medusa is a flattened, mouth-down form that moves freely in the water.
2. Cnidarian stinging cells (cnidocytes) function in defense and prey capture. They contain capsule-like organelles (cnidae), which in turn contain inverted threads. The threads either inject poison or stick to and entangle small prey.

Concept Check 33.3
1. Tapeworms can absorb food from their environment and release ammonia into their environment through their body surface because their body is very flat.
2. No. Rotifers are microscopic but have an alimentary canal, whereas tapeworms can be very large but lack any digestive system.
3. Ectoprocts and corals are both sessile animals that collect suspended food with their tentacles and build reefs with their exoskeletons.

Concept Check 33.4

1. The function of the foot reflects the locomotion required in each class. Gastropods use their foot as a holdfast or to move slowly on the substrate. In cephalopods, the foot functions as a siphon and tentacles.
2. The shell has become divided in two halves connected by a hinge, and the mantle cavity has enlarged gills that function in feeding as well as gas exchange. The radula has been lost, as bivalves have become adapted to suspension feeding.

Concept Check 33.5

1. The inner tube is the alimentary canal, which runs the length of the body. The outer tube is the body wall. The two tubes are separated by the coelom.
2. Each segment is surrounded by longitudinal and circular muscles. These muscles work against the fluid-filled coelom, which acts as a hydrostatic skeleton. Coordinated contraction of the muscles produces movement.

Concept Check 33.6

1. Incomplete cooking doesn't kill nematodes and other parasites that might be present in the meat.
2. Nematodes lack body segments and a true coelom; annelids have both.

Concept Check 33.7

1. Arthropod mouthparts are modified appendages, which are bilaterally paired.
2. Two-thirds of all known animal species are arthropods, which are found in nearly all habitats of the biosphere.
3. The arthropod exoskeleton, which had already evolved in the ocean, allowed terrestrial species to retain water and support their bodies on land. Wings allowed them to disperse quickly to new habitats and to find food and mates.

Concept Check 33.8

1. Both echinoderms and cnidarians have radial symmetry. However, the ancestors of echinoderms had bilateral symmetry, and adult echinoderms develop from bilaterally symmetrical larvae. Therefore, the radial symmetry of echinoderms and cnidarians is analogous (resulting from convergent evolution), not homologous.
2. Each tube foot consists of an ampulla and a podium. When the ampulla squeezes, it forces water into the podium and makes the podium expand. When the muscles in the wall of the podium contract, they force water back into the ampulla, making the podium shorten and bend.

Self-Quiz

1. c	2. a	3. a	4. a	5. d
6. d	7. a	8. e	9. b	10. e

CHAPTER 34

Concept Check 34.1

1. In humans, these characters are present only in the embryo. The notochord becomes disks between the vertebrae, the tail is almost completely lost, and the pharyngeal clefts develop into various adult structures.
2. As water passes through the slits, food particles are filtered from the water and transported to the digestive system.

Concept Check 34.2

1. *Haikouichthys;* it had a skull and thus was a craniate, as are humans. *Haikouella* did not have a skull.
2. Hagfishes have a head and skull made of cartilage, plus a small brain, sensory organs, and tooth-like structures. They have a neural crest, gill slits, and more extensive organ systems. In addition, hagfishes have slime glands that ward off predators and may repel competing scavengers.

Concept Check 34.3

1. Lampreys have a round, rasping mouth, which they use to attach to fish. Conodonts had two sets of mineralized dental elements, which may have been used to impale prey and cut it into smaller pieces.
2. Mineralized dental elements allowed vertebrates to become scavengers and predators. In armored jawless vertebrates, bone served as external defensive armor.

Concept Check 34.4

1. Both are gnathostomes and have jaws, four clusters of *Hox* genes, enlarged forebrains, and lateral line systems. Sharks secondarily lost much mineralization in their skeletons, which consist mainly of cartilage, whereas tuna have bony skeletons. Sharks also have a spiral valve. Tuna have an operculum and a swim bladder, as well as flexible rays supporting their fins.
2. Coelacanths live in deep marine waters, lungfishes live in ponds and swamps, and terrestrial vertebrates live on land.

Concept Check 34.5

1. No. Though it had four limb-like fins with fully formed legs, ankles, and digits, its pectoral and pelvic girdles could not carry its body on land. It had gills and a tail fin that propelled it in water.
2. Some fully aquatic species are paedomorphic, retaining larval features as adults. Species that live in dry environments may avoid dehydration by burrowing or living under moist leaves, and they protect their eggs with foam nests, viviparity, and other adaptations.

Concept Check 34.6

1. The amniotic egg is not an entirely closed system. Nutrients used by the embryo are stored within the egg (in the yolk sac and albumen) as are some metabolic wastes produced by the embryo (in the allantois). However, the embryo exchanges oxygen and carbon dioxide with the outside environment via the chorion, allantois, and egg shell.
2. Birds have weight-saving modifications, including having no teeth or urinary bladder and only one ovary in females. The wings and feathers are adaptations that facilitate flight, as well as an efficient respiratory and circulatory system that support a high metabolic rate.

Concept Check 34.7

1. Monotremes lay eggs. Marsupials give birth to very small live young that remain attached to the mother in a pouch. Eutherians give birth to more developed live young.
2. Hands and feet adapted for grasping, flat nails, large brain, forward-looking eyes on a flat face, parental care, mobile big toe and thumb

Concept Check 34.8

1. Hominoids are a clade including gibbons, orangutans, gorillas, chimpanzees, bonobos, and humans, along with extinct species that descended from the same ancestor. Hominids are a clade including humans and all species more closely related to humans than other living hominoids.
2. *Homo ergaster* was fully upright, bipedal, and as tall as modern humans, but its brain was significantly smaller than that of modern humans. This difference in the evolutionary change of different body parts is known as mosaic evolution.

Self-Quiz

1. e	2. c	3. d	4. a	5. d
6. b	7. c	8. c	9. c	10. b

CHAPTER 35

Concept Check 35.1

1. The vascular tissue system connects leaves and roots, allowing sugars to move from leaves to roots in the phloem, and allowing water and minerals to move to the leaves in the xylem.
2. Here are a few examples: The tubular, hollow structures of the tracheids and vessel elements of the xylem and the sieve plates in the sieve-tube members of the phloem facilitate transport. Root hairs aid in absorption of water and nutrients. The cuticle in leaves and stems protects from desiccation and pathogens. Leaf trichomes protect from herbivores and pathogens. Collenchyma and sclerenchyma cells have thick walls that provide support for plants.
3. The dermal tissue system is the leaf's protective covering. The vascular tissue system consists of the transport tissues xylem and phloem. The ground tissue system performs metabolic functions such as photosynthesis.

Concept Check 35.2

1. Your dividing cells are normally limited in the types of cells they can form. In contrast, the products of cell division in a plant meristem differentiate into all the diverse types of plant cells.

2. Primary growth arises from apical meristems and involves the production and elongation of organs. Secondary growth arises from lateral meristems and adds to the girth of roots and stems.

Concept Check 35.3

1. Lateral roots emerge from the root's interior (from the pericycle), pushing through cortical and epidermal cells. In contrast, shoot branches arise on the exterior of a shoot (from axillary buds).
2. In roots, primary growth occurs in three successive stages, moving away from the root tip: the zones of cell division, elongation, and maturation. In shoots, it occurs at the tip of terminal buds, with leaf primordia arising along the sides of apical meristems. Most growth in length occurs in older internodes below the shoot apex.
3. Veins are a network of vascular tissue that provide water and minerals to leaf cells and carry organic products of photosynthesis to other parts of the plant.

Concept Check 35.4

1. The sign is still 2 m above the ground because only secondary growth occurs in this part of the tree.
2. A hollow tree can survive because water, minerals, and organic nutrients are conducted by the younger secondary vascular tissues, some of which remain intact: the outer secondary xylem (sapwood) and youngest secondary phloem. However, girdling removes an entire ring of secondary phloem (part of the bark), completely preventing transport of organic nutrients from the shoots to the roots.

Concept Check 35.5

1. Differential gene expression.
2. In *fass* mutants, the arrangement of microtubules is disrupted so that the preprophase band does not form. This results in random planes of cell division, rather than the ordered planes of division that normally occur. Disruption of microtubule organization also prevents the alignment of cellulose microfibrils that sets the plane of cell elongation. Because of this randomness, directional growth is disrupted, and the plant becomes stubby instead of elongated.

Self-Quiz
1. d   2. c   3. c   4. d   5. a
6. e   7. d   8. c   9. b   10. c

CHAPTER 36

Concept Check 36.1

1. The relatively high concentration of salts might cause the soil's water potential to be more negative, thereby reducing water uptake by lowering the water potential gradient from the soil to the roots.

2. The cell's ψ is 0.7 MPa. In a solution with a ψ of -0.4 MPa, the cell's ψ_p at equilibrium would be 0.3 MPa.

Concept Check 36.2

1. The fungicide may kill the mycorrhizal fungi that function in phosphate uptake.
2. The endodermis regulates the passage of water-soluble solutes by requiring all such molecules to cross a selectively permeable membrane.

Concept Check 36.3

1. By lowering the solute potential (and water potential) of the soil, the fertilizer would make it harder for the plant to absorb water.
2. The humid air has higher water potential than the leaves.
3. After the flowers are cut, transpiration from any leaves and from the petals (which are modified leaves) will continue to draw water up the xylem. If cut flowers are transferred directly to a vase, air pockets in xylem vessels prevent delivery of water from the vase to the flowers. Cutting stems again underwater, a few centimeters from the original cut, will sever the xylem above the air pocket. The water droplets prevent another air pocket from forming while placing flowers in a vase.

Concept Check 36.4

1. Accumulation of potassium by guard cells results in osmotic water uptake, and the turgid condition of the cells keeps the stomata open. This enables the mold to grow into the leaf interior via the stomata.
2. A sunny, warm, but not hot, day; high humidity; low wind speed

Concept Check 36.5

1. In both cases, the long-distance transport is a bulk flow driven by a pressure difference at opposite ends of tubes. Pressure is generated at the source end of a sieve tube by the loading of sugar and resulting osmotic flow of water into the phloem, and this pressure *pushes* sap from the source end to the sink end of the tube. In contrast, transpiration generates a negative pressure (tension) as a force that *pulls* the ascent of xylem sap.
2. Under low temperature, the higher sugar content of a growing potato tuber would lower the solute potential (and water potential) of the tuber and reduce the bulk flow of sugar into it.

Self-Quiz
1. e   2. c   3. d   4. c   5. b
6. c   7. a   8. b   9. c   10. c

CHAPTER 37

Concept Check 37.1

1. Table 37.1 shows that CO_2 is the source of 90% of a plant's dry weight, supporting Hales' view that plants are nourished mostly by air. However, van Helmont's hypothesis is correct with respect to a plant's overall increase in size, which is based mainly on accumulation of water in cell vacuoles.

2. No, because even though macronutrients are required in greater amounts, all essential elements are necessary for the plant to complete its life cycle.
3. No, because deficiencies of nutrients that are more mobile show up first in older leaves, whereas deficiencies in nutrients that are less mobile show up first in younger leaves.

Concept Check 37.2

1. The topsoil has a mixture of larger particles (which provide aeration) and smaller particles (which facilitate water and mineral retention), as well as an adequate amount of humus (which supplies mineral nutrients) and suitable pH.
2. Overwatering deprives roots of oxygen and can lead to mold, and overfertilizing can result in waste and pollution of groundwater.

Concept Check 37.3

1. Nitrogen-fixing bacteria provide the long-term supply of nitrogenous minerals essential for the survival of plants, which are directly or indirectly the source of food for humans.

Concept Check 37.4

1. Both involve mutualistic symbiotic relationships in which other organisms interact with plant roots. Root nodules involve nitrogen-fixing bacteria, whereas mycorrhizae involve fungi that facilitate absorption of both water and minerals. In both relationships, the plant provides organic compounds. Unlike root nodules, mycorrhizae occur in most plant species, but both relationships are important agriculturally.
2. Epiphytes use another plant as a substratum without stealing nutrients from the other plant. In contrast, parasitic plants extract nutrients from their host plants.

Self-Quiz
1. b   2. b   3. c   4. b   5. b
6. c   7. d   8. a   9. d   10. b

CHAPTER 38

Concept Check 38.1

1. Sepals usually protect the unopened floral bud, and petals often help attract animal pollinators to a flower. Stamens, the pollen-producing parts, are long structures that facilitate distribution of pollen. Carpels, parts that produce female gametophytes, have stigmas, platforms that facilitate receipt of pollen. The ovary of a carpel provides protection for developing eggs in ovules. Variations in arrangement of floral organs reflect adaptations to animal pollinators and may also reduce self-fertilization, as in the case of "pin" and "thrum" flower types.
2. In angiosperms, pollination is the transfer of pollen from an anther to a stigma. It is the subsequent development of the pollen tube that eventually enables fertilization, the fusion of egg and sperm to form the zygote.

3. In the short term, selfing may be advantageous in a population that is so dispersed and sparse that pollen delivery is unreliable. In the long term, however, selfing is an evolutionary dead end because it leads to a loss of genetic diversity that may preclude adaptive evolution, including reversion from selfing to outcrossing.

Concept Check 38.2
1. Fifty percent of the ovules would have XXX endosperm and XX embryos, and 50% would have XXY endosperm and XY embryos.
2. Seeds contain endosperm that nourishes a developing embryo and have a seed coat that protects the embryo until conditions are suited for germination. Fruits, regardless of whether they are dry or fleshy, enhance seed dispersal by being eaten by animals or carried by wind.
3. Seed dormancy prevents the premature germination of seeds. A seed will germinate only when the environmental conditions are optimal for the survival of its embryo as a young seedling.

Concept Check 38.3
1. Sexual reproduction produces genetic variety, which may be advantageous in an unstable environment. The likelihood is better that at least one offspring of sexual reproduction will survive in a changed environment. Asexual reproduction can be advantageous in a stable environment because individual plants that are well-suited to that environment pass on all their genes to offspring without mates. Asexual reproduction also generally results in offspring that are less fragile than the seedlings produced by sexual reproduction. However, sexual reproduction offers the advantage of dispersal of tough seeds.
2. Asexually propagated crops lack genetic diversity. Genetically diverse populations are less likely to become extinct in the face of an epidemic because there is a greater likelihood that a few individuals in the population may be resistant.

Concept Check 38.4
1. Traditional breeding and genetic engineering both involve artificial selection for desired traits. However, genetic engineering techniques facilitate faster gene transfer and are not limited to transferring genes between closely related varieties or species.
2. GM crops may be more nutritious and less susceptible to insect damage or pathogens that invade insect-damaged plants. They also do not require as much chemical spraying. However, continued field testing of GM crops remains important to avoid adverse effects on human health and nontarget organisms and the possibility of transgene escape.

Self-Quiz
1. d   2. a   3. c   4. a   5. b
6. c   7. e   8. a   9. c   10. e

CHAPTER 39

Concept Check 39.1
1. No. Viagra, like injection of cyclic GMP, should cause only a partial de-etiolation response.
2. Cycloheximide should inhibit de-etiolation by preventing the synthesis of new proteins necessary for de-etiolation.

Concept Check 39.2
1. The plant will exhibit a constitutive triple response. Because the kinase that normally prevents the triple response is dysfunctional, the plant will undergo the triple response regardless of whether ethylene is present or the ethylene receptor is functional.
2. The pathogen might induce an increase in cytokinin concentration or a decrease in auxin concentration in the infected host plant.
3. Fusicoccin, like auxin, causes an increase in plasma H^+ pump activity and, like auxin, leads to a promotion of stem cell elongation.

Concept Check 39.3
1. It is impossible to say. To establish that this species is a short-day plant, it would be necessary to establish the critical night length for flowering and that this species only flowers when the night is longer than the critical night length.
2. The use of far-red light would maintain phytochrome in its Pr form, allowing flowering to occur.
3. An experiment could involve use of an action spectrum to determine which wavelengths of light are most effective. If the action spectrum indicates phytochrome, further testing could involve red/far-red experiments to check for photosensitivity.

Concept Check 39.4
1. A plant that overproduces ABA would undergo less evaporative cooling because its stomata would be less open.
2. Plants growing close to the aisles may be more subject to mechanical stresses caused by passing workers and air currents within the greenhouse. The plants nearer to the center of the bench may also be taller as a result of shading.

Concept Check 39.5
1. Mechanical damage breaches a plant's first line of defense against infection, its protective dermal tissue.
2. Perhaps the breeze dilutes the local concentration of a volatile defense compound that the plants have produced.

Self-Quiz
1. b   2. a   3. b   4. d   5. b
6. e   7. b   8. b   9. c   10. c

CHAPTER 40

Concept Check 40.1
1. The small intestine, the lungs, and the kidneys contain internal exchange surfaces through which nutrients, gases, and chemicals, respectively, flow. A large surface area facilitates this exchange and enables the body to carry out the exchange more efficiently than if there were less surface area available.

Concept Check 40.2
1. The glandular epithelium lining the inner surface of the stomach secretes mucus, which lubricates and protects the surface, and the tight packing of the epithelial tissue ensures that digestive juices don't leak from the stomach and damage underlying tissues.
2. Connective tissue is an important part of most organs, and sheets of connective tissue support many of the body's organs.
3. Both nervous tissue and muscle tissue are required to carry out a response to a stimulus. Muscle tissue contracts in response to nerve impulses transmitted by nerve cells.

Concept Check 40.3
1. The mouse, because it is an endotherm and therefore has a higher basal metabolic rate than the ectothermic lizard's standard metabolic rate
2. Intense activity quickly depletes existing ATP. Because alligators are ectotherms, they are relatively slow to generate more ATP by aerobic respiration.
3. The house cat; the smaller the animal, the higher its metabolic rate per gram and thus the demand for more food per unit of body mass.

Concept Check 40.4
1. No; even though an animal regulates some aspects of its internal environment, often by negative feedback mechanisms, the internal environment fluctuates slightly around a set point. Homeostasis is a dynamic state. And some changes, such as radical increases in hormones at particular times in development, are programmed to occur.
2. In negative feedback, a change triggers control mechanisms that counteract further change in that direction. But in positive feedback, a change triggers mechanisms that amplify the change.

Concept Check 40.5
1. Yes, ectotherms in the deep sea and in constant-temperature freshwater springs have constant body temperatures. And terrestrial ectotherms can maintain relatively constant body temperatures by behavioral means.
2. Heat loss through convection
3. Food and water supplies may be short during the dry season, and torpor enables animals to survive at a much lower metabolic rate.

Self-Quiz
1. a   2. b   3. e   4. d   5. c
6. b   7. c   8. c   9. d   10. c

CHAPTER 41

Concept Check 41.1
1. Body weight is stable when caloric intake (food) is balanced by caloric expenditure (metabolic rate).

2. Over the long term, the body converts excess calories to fat whether those calories are consumed as fat, carbohydrate, or protein.
3. Both hormones have appetite-suppressing effects on the brain's satiety center. During the course of a day, PYY, secreted by the small intestine, suppresses appetite after meals. Over the longer term, leptin, produced by adipose tissue, normally reduces appetite as fat storage increases.

Concept Check 41.2
1. Undernutrition is a deficiency of calories in the diet. In contrast, malnutrition results from a deficiency of one or more essential nutrients, even though total caloric intake may be adequate.
2. A balanced vegetarian meal combines vegetables and fruits that complement one another, each providing certain essential amino acids that may be deficient in the other food items.
3. Vitamins and minerals are essential nutrients required in relatively small daily amounts. Vitamins are organic nutrients, whereas minerals are inorganic nutrients.

Concept Check 41.3
1. A gastrovascular cavity is a digestive sac with a single opening that functions in both ingestion and elimination; an alimentary canal is a digestive tube with a separate mouth and anus on opposite ends.
2. As long as nutrients are within the cavity of the alimentary canal, they are in a compartment that is continuous with the outside environment via the mouth and anus and have not yet crossed a membrane to enter the body.

Concept Check 41.4
1. Peristalsis can squeeze food through the esophagus even without the help of gravity.
2. The acid breaks down the tissues in plant and animal materials by its harsh, nonenzymatic, chemical attack. The acid also activates the protein-digesting enzyme pepsin and destroys any bacteria that may have been ingested with food.
3. The partially digested meal entering from the stomach as acid chyme + pancreatic juice containing hydrolytic enzymes + intestinal juice with enzymes + bile, which includes bile salts that aid in digestion by emulsifying fats
4. The villi and microvilli of the intestinal epithelium provide an enormous surface area for absorption, the transport of nutrients from the lumen of the small intestine into blood capillaries and lacteals.
5. Long-term use of antibiotics can kill colon bacteria that augment nutrition by producing vitamin K.
6. As it receives acid chyme from the stomach, the duodenum secretes the hormone cholecystokinin (CCK), which reaches the pancreas via the bloodstream and stimulates release of pancreatic juice.

Concept Check 41.5
1. The sharp incisors are adapted for cutting pieces of meat and plants. The broad, ridged surfaces of molars are adapted for grinding tough foods, especially fibrous fruits and vegetables and large pieces of meat.
2. The tadpole is herbivorous (eats mostly algae), while the adult frog is carnivorous (eats insects, for example).
3. The cud is a regurgitated brew of material from the rumen—once-chewed vegetation with fatty acids and other metabolic byproducts of the rumen bacteria. After a second chewing, which increases surface area of the plant material, the cow swallows the cud, where microbial action in the stomach chambers continues to convert cellulose to a diversity of nutrients.

Self-Quiz
1. a 2. b 3. e 4. c 5. c
6. c 7. c 8. d 9. c 10. e

CHAPTER 42

Concept Check 42.1
1. The inefficiency of diffusion to deliver nutrients and remove wastes at high enough rates to sustain a large organism
2. Advantage: high rate of delivery of nutrients and removal of wastes. Disadvantage: requires more energy to build, operate, and maintain.
3. Two main advantages of separate respiratory and systemic circuits are higher blood pressure in the systemic circuit and a higher rate of blood circulation.

Concept Check 42.2
1. This condition would reduce the oxygen content by mixing O_2-depleted blood returned to the right ventricle from the systemic circuit with the O_2-rich blood of the left ventricle.
2. The delay ensures that the atria empty completely before the ventricles contract.

Concept Check 42.3
1. The large total cross-sectional area of the capillaries
2. These changes increase the capacity for action by increasing the rate of blood circulation and delivery of oxygen and nutrients to the skeletal muscles.
3. Plasma proteins remaining in the blood in a capillary maintain fairly constant osmotic pressure, whereas blood pressure drops from the arteriole end to the venule end. This difference allows fluid to reenter the capillary at the venule end; if plasma proteins are deficient, fluid will remain in the tissues and cause swelling.

Concept Check 42.4
1. About 200 billion, or 2.08×10^{11}, calculated by dividing the total number of cells, 2.5×10^{13}, by 120 days
2. An increase in leukocytes may indicate that the person is combating an infection.
3. Bone marrow stem cells divide repeatedly and are pluripotent.

Concept Check 42.5
1. If the respiratory surfaces of lungs extended out into the terrestrial environment, they would quickly dry out, and diffusion of O_2 and CO_2 across the membrane would stop.
2. The countercurrent results in a diffusion gradient for O_2 over the entire length of capillaries in the gill lamellae. As water flows over the gill lamellae, the opposite direction of blood flow in the capillaries enables the blood to continue loading O_2 because the O_2-rich blood "downstream" encounters the even more O_2-rich water just beginning to flow over the lamellae.

Concept Check 42.6
1. An increase in CO_2 in the blood increases the rate of CO_2 diffusion into the cerebrospinal fluid, where the CO_2 combines with water, forming carbonic acid. Dissociation of carbonic acid releases hydrogen ions, decreasing the pH of cerebrospinal fluid.
2. Increased heart rate increases the rate at which CO_2-rich blood is delivered to the lungs, where it is removed.
3. Air flow in the lungs of birds passes through the lungs in one direction only.

Concept Check 42.7
1. Differences in partial pressure; gases diffuse from areas of higher partial pressure to areas of lower partial pressure.
2. The Bohr shift causes hemoglobin to release oxygen at a lower pH, which occurs in the vicinity of tissues with high rates of respiration and carbon dioxide release.
3. The decrease in concentration of CO_2 in the plasma as it diffuses into the alveolar spaces causes the carbonic acid within the red blood cells to break down, yielding CO_2, which diffuses into the plasma.
4. Examples: more blood volume relative to body mass; much larger spleen; more oxygen-storing myoglobin in muscles; heart rate and metabolic rate decrease during dive

Self-Quiz
1. c 2. b 3. d 4. c 5. e
6. b 7. c 8. b 9. a 10. a

CHAPTER 43

Concept Check 43.1
1. Macrophages have receptors that bind to polysaccharides present on the surface of bacterial cells but not on body cells.
2. Vessel dilation, which allows enhanced blood flow, and increased vessel permeability result in the common signs of inflammation. These vascular changes aid in delivering clotting factors, antimicrobial proteins, and phagocytic cells to the tissue of the affected region; all of these help in repairing tissue damage and stopping the spread of infection.
3. The exoskeleton of insects provides an external barrier similar to the skin and mucous membranes of vertebrates. Phagocytic cells and antimicrobial proteins also contribute to innate defenses in both insects and vertebrates.

Concept Check 43.2

1. See Figure 43.8a: a secreted antibody lacks a transmembrane region and cytoplasmic tails.
2. B cell receptors bind intact extracellular antigens present on the surface of microbes or free in body fluids. T cell receptors bind small fragments of intracellular antigens that are complexed with class I or class II MHC molecules.
3. Specificity: Only B cells with receptors that bind to the antigen are selected to proliferate and differentiate into plasma cells secreting antibodies specific for the antigen and memory B cells bearing receptors specific for the same antigen. Memory: The large number of memory B cells generated respond more rapidly to that same antigen the next time it enters the body.
4. 40 V × 5 J = 200 possible light chains; 51 V × 6 J × 27 D = 8,262 possible heavy chains. Each antigen-binding site is formed from a region on a light chain and heavy chain. The number of possible random combinations is 200 light chains × 8,262 heavy chains = $1.65 × 10^6$ possible antigen-binding specificities.

Concept Check 43.3

1. An activated helper T cell secretes cytokines that promote activation of both cytotoxic T cells and B cells. An activated cytotoxic T cell kills infected cells and tumor cells by apoptosis. An activated B cell differentiates into plasma cells that secrete antibodies.
2. A child lacking a thymus would have no functional T cells. Without helper T cells to help activate B cells, the child would be unable to produce antibodies against extracellular bacteria. Without cytotoxic T cells or helper T cells to help activate them, the child's immune system would be unable to kill virus-infected cells.
3. Antibodies bound to viruses can block their attachment to potential host cells (viral neutralization). Coating of bacteria or other particles by antibodies bound to surface antigens increases their phagocytosis by macrophages (opsonization). Antibodies bound to antigens on bacterial cells also can activate a cascade of complement proteins leading to lysis of the bacteria (complement activation). Cross-linking of antigens on many bacterial cells or viruses by binding of multiple antibody molecules can lead to formation of large clumps (agglutination), which are then phagocytosed.
4. Passive immunization, the transfer of antibodies from one individual to another, is protective only as long as the antibody molecules last. Active immunization, the introduction of antigen, induces an immune response in the recipient that can lead to the generation of long-lived memory cells. Someone who is actively immunized may be immune to that antigen for life.

Concept Check 43.4

1. Because individuals with type AB blood do not produce antibodies against either the A or the B antigens, they can safely receive type A blood, type B blood, type AB blood, or type O blood—that is, they are universal recipients. In the case of donated type O blood, packed cells should be used, since the donor serum (fluid part of blood) would contain antibodies to A and to B, which could react with the recipient's red blood cells.
2. The danger of the graft rejecting the host arises because transplanted bone marrow contains lymphocytes that could react against components of the recipient's body.
3. An autograft will not trigger a rejection reaction.

Concept Check 43.5

1. A person with a macrophage deficiency would have frequent infections. This would be due to poor innate responses, particularly diminished phagocytosis and inflammation, and poor acquired responses because of the role of macrophages in presenting antigens to helper T cells.
2. Binding of antigens by IgE molecules attached to mast cells induces degranulation of these cells, releasing histamine and other inflammatory agents, which cause typical allergy symptoms. Drugs that block the degranulation response prevent the release of inflammatory agents and hence the symptoms they cause.
3. Myasthenia gravis is considered an autoimmune disease because the immune system produces antibodies against self molecules (acetylcholine receptors).
4. To enter a host cell, HIV requires CD4 and a co-receptor. The co-receptor for HIV normally functions as a chemokine receptor. If a person's chemokine receptors are faulty, HIV cannot use them for entry into cells.

Self-Quiz

1. e   2. d   3. b   4. c   5. b
6. d   7. c   8. d   9. e   10. b

CHAPTER 44

Concept Check 44.1

1. Because the salt is moved against the concentration gradient, from a hypoosmotic to a hyperosmotic environment
2. A freshwater osmoconformer would have body fluids too dilute to carry out life's processes.
3. By maintaining high concentrations of urea and TMAO in their blood, sharks reduce the osmotic gradient between their blood and seawater.

Concept Check 44.2

1. The aquatic larvae can dispose of the very toxic ammonia continuously by secreting it across epithelium into the surrounding water. The adults conserve water by excreting the nontoxic uric acid.
2. The liver is the site of urea synthesis.
3. Because uric acid is insoluble in water, it can be excreted as a semisolid paste, thereby reducing an animal's water loss.

Concept Check 44.3

1. Filtration (of blood, hemolymph, or coelomic fluid) and selective reabsorption or secretion of solutes
2. A large surface area for exchange of water and solutes

Concept Check 44.4

1. A decline in blood pressure in the afferent arteriole would reduce the rate of filtration.
2. The kidney medulla would absorb less water and thus the drug would increase water loss in the urine.
3. Bowman's capsule, proximal tubule, loop of Henle, distal tubule

Concept Check 44.5

1. Alcohol inhibits the release of ADH, causing an increase in urinary water loss and increasing the chance of dehydration.
2. Consuming salty food increases the osmolarity of the blood, which triggers the thirst center in the hypothalamus to stimulate drinking and the pituitary to release ADH, which increases the rate of water reabsorption by the distal tubules and collecting ducts.
3. The capacity to conserve water by producing hyperosmotic urine

Concept Check 44.6

1. Numerous nephrons and well-developed glomeruli are characteristic of the kidneys of freshwater fishes, while reduced numbers of nephrons and smaller glomeruli indicate marine environments. The numerous nephrons and well-developed glomeruli of freshwater fishes produce urine at a high rate, while small numbers of nephrons and smaller glomeruli produce urine at a low rate.

Self-Quiz

1. d   2. d   3. e   4. e   5. c
6. d   7. c   8. b   9. d   10. b

CHAPTER 45

Concept Check 45.1

1. Hormones are produced by endocrine cells, whereas neurohormones are produced by specialized nerve cells called neurosecretory cells. Both hormones and neurohormones are secreted into the blood and act on target tissues.
2. See Figure 45.2a and b.
3. In negative feedback, the effector response reduces the initial stimulus, so eventually the response ceases as the variable being controlled reaches the set point. In positive feedback, the effector response causes an increase in the stimulus, leading to an even greater response.

Concept Check 45.2

1. Water-soluble hormones, which cannot penetrate the plasma membrane, bind to cell-surface receptors. This interaction triggers an intracellular multicomponent signal transduction pathway that ultimately alters the activity of a preexisting cytoplasmic protein and/or changes transcription of specific genes

in the nucleus. Steroid hormones are lipid-soluble and can cross the plasma membrane into the cell interior, where they bind to receptors located in the cytoplasm or nucleus. In both cases, the hormone-receptor complex functions directly as a transcription factor that binds to the cell's DNA and activates or inhibits transcription of specific genes.

2. A particular hormone may cause diverse responses in target cells having different receptors for the hormone, different signal transduction pathways, and/or different proteins for carrying out the response.

3. Once secreted, local regulators can diffuse rapidly to their nearby target cells. Hormones circulate in the bloodstream from their sites of synthesis to their target tissues, a slower process.

Concept Check 45.3

1. The posterior pituitary, an extension of the hypothalamus that contains the axons of neurosecretory cells, is the storage and release site for two neurohormones, oxytocin and antidiuretic hormone (ADH). The anterior pituitary, derived from tissue of the embryonic mouth, contains endocrine cells that make at least six different hormones. Secretion of anterior pituitary hormones is controlled by hypothalamic hormones that travel via portal vessels to the anterior pituitary.

2. Tropic hormones control the synthesis and/or secretion of hormones from other endocrine tissues. Releasing and inhibiting hormones produced in the hypothalamus control hormone secretion by the anterior pituitary. The anterior pituitary produces several tropic hormones that control the hormonal function of the thyroid gland, adrenal cortex, and gonads.

3. (a) Prolactin functions in a simple neuroendocrine pathway. (b) ACTH functions in a complex neuroendocrine pathway. (c) Oxytocin functions in a neurohormone pathway.

Concept Check 45.4

1. By negative feedback on the hypothalamus and anterior pituitary (see Figure 45.9)

2. The hormone-secreting cells themselves monitor the blood Ca^{2+} levels. An increase in blood Ca^{2+} above the set point stimulates the thyroid gland to release calcitonin. By promoting deposition of Ca^{2+} in the bones and excretion of Ca^{2+} by the kidneys, calcitonin decreases the blood Ca^{2+} level. PTH, secreted by the parathyroid glands in response to low blood Ca^{2+}, has the opposite effects on bones and kidneys, thereby increasing blood Ca^{2+}. The response to one hormone triggers release of the antagonistic hormone, a feedback mechanism that minimizes extreme deviations of blood Ca^{2+} from the set point.

3. In a diabetic, the initial increase in blood glucose is greater than in a nondiabetic, and it remains high for a prolonged period. In a nondiabetic, insulin released in response to the initial rise in blood glucose stimulates uptake of glucose by body cells. In a diabetic, however, inadequate production of insulin or

nonresponsiveness of target cells decreases the body's ability to clear excess glucose from the blood.

4. The levels of these hormones in the blood would become very high owing to the absence of negative feedback on the secretion of ACTH from the hypothalamus.

Concept Check 45.5

1. During larval stages, neurosecretory cells produce a tropic hormone (brain hormone) that stimulates production of ecdysone, the molting hormone, by endocrine cells in the prothoracic glands.

2. Juvenile hormone promotes the retention of larval characteristics. In insecticides, it prevents larvae from maturing into adults that can reproduce.

Self-Quiz

1. c	2. d	3. d	4. c	5. b
6. e	7. c	8. b	9. c	10. a

CHAPTER 46

Concept Check 46.1

1. The offspring of sexual reproduction are genetically diverse.

2. The term could be considered misleading in the sense that a sequentially hermaphroditic organism is never of two sexes (hermaphroditic) at the same time; first it is of one sex and later of the other sex.

Concept Check 46.2

1. Fertilization allows the sperm to reach the egg without either gamete drying out.

2. (a) Animals with external fertilization tend to release many gametes at once, resulting in the production of enormous numbers of zygotes. This increases the chances that some will survive to adulthood. (b) Animals with internal fertilization produce fewer offspring but generally exhibit greater care of the embryos and the young.

Concept Check 46.3

1. Seminiferous tubule, epididymis, vas deferens, urethra

2. The fluid from the seminal vesicles provides most of the fluid in which the sperm swim; furthermore, it includes a sugar that is a source of energy for the sperm and prostaglandins that cause changes in the uterus that help move the sperm toward the egg after coitus; also, its alkalinity helps neutralize the acidic vaginal environment, which could harm the sperm. The fluid from the prostate contains another sperm nutrient and anticoagulants that help the sperm swim by keeping the semen liquid. The fluid from the bulbourethral glands, secreted just before ejaculation, neutralizes any acidic urine remaining in the urethra.

3. Primarily the penis and clitoris, but also the testes, labia, breasts, and outer third of the vagina

Concept Check 46.4

1. In the testis, FSH stimulates the Sertoli cells, which nourish developing sperm. LH stimulates the production of androgens (mainly testosterone), which in turn stimulate sperm production. In both females and males, FSH encourages the growth of cells that support and nourish developing gametes (follicle cells in females and Sertoli cells in males), and LH stimulates the production of sex hormones that promote gametogenesis (estrogen in females and androgens, especially testosterone, in males).

2. In estrous cycles, which occur in most female mammals, the endometrium is reabsorbed (rather than shed) if fertilization does not occur. Estrous cycles often occur just one or a few times a year, and the female is usually receptive to copulation only during the period around ovulation. Menstrual cycles are found only in humans and some other primates.

3. Hormones produced in the ovarian cycle control the uterine cycle (see Figure 46.13). Also, the occurrence of pregnancy (implantation in the uterus) turns off the ovarian cycle.

4. Ovulation is triggered by a surge in LH. The secretion of LH has been stimulated by the influence of a rising estrogen level on GnRH.

Concept Check 46.5

1. The embryo is a blastocyst, a ball of cells containing a cavity.

2. HCG secreted by the early embryo stimulates the corpus luteum to make progesterone, which helps maintain the pregnancy. During the second trimester, however, HCG production drops, the corpus luteum disintegrates, and the placenta completely takes over progesterone production.

3. Vasectomy, females

4. Because, in all cases where IVF is used, the embryo grows and develops in a woman's uterus

Self-Quiz

1. d	2. b	3. a	4. b	5. c
6. a	7. a	8. a	9. d	10. b

CHAPTER 47

Concept Check 47.1

1. The increased Ca^{2+} would cause the cortical granules to fuse with the plasma membrane, releasing their contents and causing a fertilization envelope to form, even though no sperm had entered. This would prevent fertilization.

2. During the cleavage stage in frogs and many other animals, the cell cycle is modified so that it lacks G_1 and G_2, the growth phases. As a result, the early cleavage divisions divide the zygote's cytoplasm into many smaller cells; the embryo's size thus remains the same.

3. Gastrulation organizes the embryo's cells into three tissue layers: ectoderm on the outside, endoderm on the inside, and mesoderm between them.

4. Gastrulation involves global rearrangement of cells in the embryo, generating three tissue layers. Organogenesis involves local changes in cell position and cell shape.

Concept Check 47.2
1. Microtubules elongate, lengthening the cell along one axis, while microfilaments oriented crosswise at one end of the cell contract, making that end smaller and the whole cell wedge-shaped.
2. The cells of the notochord migrate toward the midline of the embryo, rearranging themselves so there are fewer cells across the notochord, which thus becomes longer overall (see Figure 47.20).

Concept Check 47.3
1. Once the first two axes are specified, the third one is automatically determined. (Think of your own body: If you know where your head and tail are and where your left and right sides are, you automatically know which are your front and back.)
2. A second embryo would probably not form, since the cells of a late gastrula, including the ventral cells, are already determined and cannot change their fate, even if an organizer is present.
3. A second embryo could develop because inhibiting BMP-4 activity would have the same effect as transplanting an organizer.

Self-Quiz
| 1. a | 2. b | 3. e | 4. c | 5. a |
| 6. c | 7. b | 8. c | 9. e | 10. d |

CHAPTER 48

Concept Check 48.1
1. (a) Sensory neuron → interneuron → motor neuron (b) Interneuron
2. Transmitting information, as the axon transmits away from the cell body
3. The axons in the CNS would not have myelin sheaths.

Concept Check 48.2
1. $E_X = 62$ mV log $(10/100) = -62$ mV
2. A decrease in permeability to K^+, an increase in permeability to Na^+, or both
3. Ligand-gated ion channels open when a specific chemical binds to the channel, whereas voltage-gated ion channels open when the membrane potential changes.

Concept Check 48.3
1. A graded potential has a magnitude that varies with stimulus strength, whereas an action potential has an all-or-none magnitude that is independent of stimulus strength.
2. The maximum frequency would decrease.
3. c, a, b

Concept Check 48.4
1. Chemical synapses would be most affected because they require the influx of Ca^{2+} into the synaptic terminal for neurotransmitter release.

2. These poisons would prolong the EPSPs that acetylcholine produces.
3. It can bind to different types of receptors, each triggering a specific response in postsynaptic cells.

Concept Check 48.5
1. The sympathetic division, which mediates the "fight-or-flight" response in stressful situations
2. Functions include controlling breathing, heart and blood vessel activity, swallowing, vomiting, and digestion and coordinating large-scale body movements such as walking.
3. A part of the reticular formation, the reticular activating system, acts as a sensory filter, selecting which information reaches the cerebral cortex. The thalamus sorts information from all the senses and sends it to the appropriate cerebral centers for further processing.

Concept Check 48.6
1. More sensory neurons innervate the hand than the neck. This conclusion is supported by the fact that the cortical surface area devoted to the hand is larger than that devoted to the neck.
2. Each cerebral hemisphere is specialized for different parts of this task—the right for face recognition and the left for language. Without an intact corpus callosum, neither hemisphere can take advantage of the other's processing abilities.
3. Broca's area, which is active during the generation of speech, is located near the part of the primary motor cortex that controls muscles in the face. Wernicke's area, which is active when speech is heard, is located near the part of the temporal lobe that is involved in hearing.
4. Direct: The receptor is part of an ion channel; when glutamate binds, Ca^{2+} diffuses through the channel. Indirect: Ca^{2+} influx through the channel activates signal transduction pathways that produce long-lasting changes.

Concept Check 48.7
1. Without Netrin-1 receptors, the axons of interneurons would not be attracted toward the floor plate and might grow randomly through the spinal cord. Without Slit receptors, the axons would not be repelled by the floor plate and might grow back across the midline.
2. In all three diseases, identical twins have about a 50% chance of sharing the disease, which implies that genetic and environmental components are of nearly equal importance. Also, there is evidence that stress may be an environmental factor in bipolar disorder and major depression.
3. Both are progressive brain diseases whose risk increases with advancing age. Both result from the death of brain neurons and are associated with the accumulation of peptide or protein aggregates.

Self-Quiz
| 1. c | 2. b | 3. c | 4. a | 5. c |
| 6. a | 7. d | 8. d | 9. b | 10. e |

CHAPTER 49

Concept Check 49.1
1. Such drugs block sensations transmitted by sensory neurons that synapse with receptors. Sensory neurons that *are* receptors (such as stretch receptors) transmit sensations without a synapse, so they are unaffected by such drugs.
2. Pain and light touch should be affected first because they involve receptors in the epidermis. Senses related to hair movement, strong pressure, and vibrations are affected last or not at all because they involve receptors deep in the dermis.

Concept Check 49.2
1. Statocysts detect the animal's orientation with respect to gravity, providing information that is essential in environments such as these, where light cues are absent.
2. The stapes and the other middle ear bones transmit vibrations from the tympanic membrane to the oval window. Fusion of these bones blocks this transmission, resulting in hearing loss.
3. As a sound that changes gradually from a very low to a very high pitch

Concept Check 49.3
1. As a fly walks on an object, gustatory sensilla on the feet determine whether the object contains food-related molecules, such as sugars. Sensilla on the mouthparts also detect these molecules when the fly begins to feed.
2. Both chemoreceptors have receptor proteins in their plasma membrane that bind certain substances, leading to membrane depolarization through a signal transduction pathway involving cAMP. In gustatory chemoreceptors for sweetness, depolarization triggers neurotransmitter release; in olfactory chemoreceptors, it triggers action potential production.

Concept Check 49.4
1. Planarians have ocelli that cannot form images but can sense the intensity and direction of light, providing enough information to enable the animals to find protection in shaded places. Flies have compound eyes that form images and excel at detecting movement; both are adaptations for more active behaviors, including flight.
2. The person would be able to focus on distant but not close objects (without glasses) because close focusing requires the lens to become almost spherical.
3. When illuminated, the photoreceptor hyperpolarizes, stopping its release of glutamate. If bipolar cells that it synapses with are hyperpolarized by glutamate, they will depolarize in the light and release more neurotransmitter. If that neurotransmitter is excitatory, the ganglion cells they synapse with will produce action potentials at a higher frequency.

Concept Check 49.5
1. The earthworm would elongate each body segment by contracting all of its circular muscles and relaxing all of its longitudinal muscles.

Answers

Appendix A

2. The exoskeleton on its gripping surfaces is hardened with calcium salts and with organic compounds that cross-link proteins. The exoskeleton on its joints lacks these compounds and salts and therefore is flexible.
3. The hinge joint between the humerus and ulna allows the ulna and radius to move toward or away from the humerus in a single plane. The pivot joint between the ulna and radius allows the radius to rotate.

Concept Check 49.6

1. During contraction, the Z lines, which mark the ends of a sarcomere, move closer together; the A band, which marks the length of the thick filaments, stays the same length; and both the I band, which contains only thin filaments, and the H zone, which contains only thick filaments, shrink.
2. By causing all of the motor neurons that innervate the muscle to generate action potentials at a rate high enough to produce tetanus in all of the muscle fibers
3. In a skeletal muscle fiber, calcium ions bind to the troponin complex, which moves tropomyosin away from the myosin-binding sites on actin and allows cross-bridges to form. In a smooth muscle cell, calcium ions bind to calmodulin, which activates an enzyme that phosphorylates the myosin head.

Concept Check 49.7

1. The main problem in swimming is drag; a fusiform body minimizes drag. The main problem in flying is overcoming gravity; wings shaped like airfoils provide lift, and adaptations such as air-filled bones reduce body mass.
2. A 1-g flyer

Self-Quiz

| 1. c | 2. d | 3. b | 4. a | 5. c |
| 6. e | 7. b | 8. d | 9. c | 10. b |

CHAPTER 50

Concept Check 50.1

1. *Ecology* is the scientific study of the interactions between organisms and their environment; *environmentalism* is advocacy for the environment. Ecology provides scientific understanding that can inform decision making about environmental issues.
2. Interactions in ecological time that affect the survival or reproduction of organisms could result in changes to the population's gene pool, and ultimately result in change in the population on an evolutionary time scale.
3. a. Population ecology; b. Community ecology

Concept Check 50.2

1. a. Humans could transplant a species to a new area that it could not previously reach because of a geographic barrier (dispersal change). b. Humans could change a species' biotic interactions by eliminating a predator species, such as sea urchins, from an area.

2. The sun's unequal heating of Earth's surface produces temperature variations between the warmer tropics and colder polar regions, and influences the movement of air masses and thus the distribution of moisture at different latitudes.

Concept Check 50.3

1. Oligotrophic lakes, because they tend to be nutrient-poor and oxygen-rich
2. The benthic zone lies below the photic zone, so the water is too deep for enough light to support photosynthetic organisms on the bottom.

Concept Check 50.4

1. Higher average temperature in deserts
2. Answers will vary by location, but should be based on the information and maps in Figure 50.19. How much your local area has been altered from its natural state will influence how much it reflects the expected characteristics of your biome, particularly the expected plants and animals.

Self-Quiz

| 1. c | 2. c | 3. d | 4. a | 5. d |
| 6. b | 7. d | 8. d | 9. e | 10. a |

CHAPTER 51

Concept Check 51.1

1. Sample response: How does the squirrel produce the sound (proximate)? Does the behavior change over the course of the squirrel's development (proximate)? Do other closely related squirrel species utter similar calls (ultimate)? How does the call affect the squirrel's reproductive fitness (ultimate)?
2. It is an example of a fixed action pattern. The proximate explanation might be that nudging and rolling are released by the sign stimulus of an object located outside the nest, and the behavior is carried to completion once initiated. The ultimate explanation might be that ensuring that eggs remain in the nest increases the chance of producing healthy offspring.

Concept Check 51.2

1. All behaviors are influenced by both "nature" (genes) and "nurture" (environment), though certain behaviors have especially strong genetic components or environmental components.
2. Sample response: In the green lacewing example, researchers isolated hybrid offspring of two lacewings with distinct songs to eliminate the environmental (learning) component and demonstrate the genetic basis of the hybrids' song.

Concept Check 51.3

1. Using general rules to learn spatial relationships reduces the details that must be memorized to relocate objects of interest.
2. Diet (as in the *D. mojavensis* example, in which mate choice by females is influenced by the medium on which the larvae feed);

social environment (as in the study of aggressive behavior in which cross-fostering mice caused them to adopt some behaviors of their foster parents' species); and learning (in which animals modify their behavior based on specific experiences).
3. Natural selection would tend to favor convergence in color pattern, since a predator learning to associate a particular pattern with a sting or bad taste would avoid all other individuals with that same color pattern, regardless of species.

Concept Check 51.4

1. Because this geographic variation corresponds to differences in prey availability between two garter snake habitats, it seems likely that snakes with characteristics enabling them to feed on the abundant prey in their particular locale would have had increased survival and reproductive success, and thus natural selection would have resulted in the divergent foraging behaviors.
2. To show that their differences in aggressiveness are due to genetic differences between the populations
3. Berthold and his colleagues concluded that migratory orientation in blackcaps has a genetic basis, since laboratory-raised offspring of both British blackcaps and German blackcaps showed different migratory orientations. Furthermore, the westward-migrating blackcaps appear to have evolved over about the last 50 years.

Concept Check 51.5

1. Certainty of paternity is higher with external fertilization.
2. Optimal foraging theory predicts that mule deer will forage in a way that incorporates the risk of predation as well as the benefit of food availability. This explains why, despite the fact that food is slightly less abundant in open areas than in forest edges or interiors, mule deer feed most frequently in open areas, where risk of predation by mountain lions is significantly lower than in forest edges.
3. If the female chooses a mate that is in fact healthy, there is an increased chance that their offspring will inherit some of these healthy genes, making them both inherently more likely to survive and reproduce as well as to be favored themselves by choosy females in the next generation.

Concept Check 51.6

1. Enhanced reproductive success of closely related individuals that have many genes in common with the altruist, including genes for altruism
2. Reciprocal altruism, the exchange of helpful behaviors for future similar behaviors, can explain cooperative behaviors between unrelated animals, though often the behavior has some potential benefit to the benefactor as well.
3. Yes, since parental behavior in these mice changes the future parental behavior of offspring, the changes in behavior produced by

cross-fostering could be passed on through cultural inheritance.

Self-Quiz
1. d   2. d   3. d   4. a   5. c
6. a   7. d   8. c   9. b   10. c

CHAPTER 52

Concept Check 52.1

1. The territorial species likely has a uniform pattern of dispersion, since the interactions between individuals will maintain constant space between them. The flocking species is probably clumped, since most individuals probably live in one of the clumps (flocks).
2. A Type III survivorship curve, since very few of the young probably survive
3. 0.5; divide the mean number of females in a litter by the mean size of litters for each age when reproduction occurs and take the average.

Concept Check 52.2

1. The constant, spring-fed stream. In more constant physical conditions, where populations are more stable and competition for resources more likely, larger well-provisioned young have a better chance of surviving.

Concept Check 52.3

1. Though r_{max} is constant, N, the population size, is increasing. As r_{max} is applied to an increasingly large N, population growth $(r_{max}N)$ steepens to produce the J-shaped curve.
2. On the new island. The first plants that found suitable habitat on the island would encounter an abundance of space, nutrients, and light. In the rain forest, competition among plants for these resources is intense.

Concept Check 52.4

1. When N (population size) is small, there are relatively few individuals producing offspring. When N is large, near the carrying capacity, per capita growth is relatively small because it is limited by available resources. The steepest part of the logistic growth curve corresponds to a population with a number of reproducing individuals that is substantial but not yet near carrying capacity.

Concept Check 52.5

1. Competition for resources and space can negatively impact population growth by limiting reproductive output. Diseases that are transmitted more easily in crowded populations can exert negative feedback on increasing population size. Some predators feed preferentially on species at higher population densities, since they are easier to find than are the members of less dense prey populations. In crowded populations, toxic metabolic wastes can build up and poison the organisms.

Concept Check 52.6

1. A bottom-heavy age structure, with a disproportionate number of young people, portends continuing growth of the population as these young people begin reproducing. In contrast, a more evenly distributed age structure predicts a more stable population size.
2. Carrying capacity is the sustainable number of people that can be supported by available resources in a country. Ecological capacity is the actual resource base of the country, as measured by hectares per person. Ecological footprint is a country's actual resource consumption, again converted to hectares per person. A country exceeds its carrying capacity if its footprint is greater than its ecological capacity.

Self-Quiz
1. c   2. c   3. c   4. d   5. b
6. e   7. c   8. d   9. c   10. d

CHAPTER 53

Concept Check 53.1

1. Interspecific competition has negative effects on both species $(-/-)$. In predation, the predator population benefits at the expense of the prey population $(+/-)$. Mutualism is a symbiosis in which both species benefit $(+/+)$.
2. One of the competing species will become locally extinct because of the greater reproductive success of the more efficient competitor.
3. No. Coevolution involves adaptive responses of two species to each other. In the case of Batesian mimicry, the model species is not generally adapting to changes in the mimic.

Concept Check 53.2

1. Species richness is the number of species in the community. Relative abundance is the proportions of the community represented by the various species. Compared to a community with a very high proportion of one species, one with more even proportions of species is considered to be more diverse. Higher species richness and a more even distribution of abundance among species both contribute to higher species diversity.
2. The energetic hypothesis suggests that the length of a food chain is limited by the inefficiency of energy transfer along the chain, while the dynamic stability hypothesis proposes that long food chains are less stable than short chains. The energetic hypothesis predicts that food chains will be longer in habitats with higher primary productivity. The dynamic stability hypothesis predicts that food chains will be longer in more predictable environments.
3. Dominant species have major effects on communities owing to their high abundance or high biomass. Keystone species exert strong control on community structure by virtue of their ecological roles.
4. In top-down control, consumer organisms control community structure, particularly the abundance of primary producers. In bottom-up control, environmental factors, such as nutrients and moisture, control primary producers.

Concept Check 53.3

1. High levels of disturbance are generally so disruptive that they eliminate many species from communities, leaving the community dominated by a few tolerant species. Meanwhile, low levels of disturbance permit competitively dominant species to exclude other species from the community. In contrast, moderate levels of disturbance can facilitate coexistence of more species in a community by preventing competitively dominant species from becoming abundant enough to eliminate other species from the community.
2. The initial absence of soil in primary succession and its presence at the beginning of secondary succession
3. Early successional species can facilitate the arrival of other species in many ways, including increasing the fertility or water-holding capacity of soils or providing shelter to seedlings from wind and intense sunlight.

Concept Check 53.4

1. Larger areas are thought to support more species mainly because larger areas include a greater diversity of habitats.
2. Ecologists propose that the greater species richness of tropical regions is the result of their longer evolutionary history and the greater solar energy input and water availability in tropical regions.
3. Immigration of species to islands declines with distance from the mainland and increases with island area. Extinction of species is lower on larger islands and on less isolated islands. Since the number of species on islands is largely determined by the difference between rates of immigration and extinction, the number of species will be highest on large islands near the mainland and lowest on small islands far from the mainland.

Concept Check 53.5

1. The individualistic hypothesis of communities proposes that communities are assemblages of species distributed independently of other species along environmental gradients. This hypothesis is closely related to the more recent redundancy model, which proposes that most species in a community are not tightly associated with one another. The integrated hypothesis proposes that communities are highly integrated assemblages of interdependent species. This idea has been reincarnated as the rivet model.

Self-Quiz
1. c   2. d   3. b   4. c   5. d
6. c   7. b   8. d   9. b   10. c

CHAPTER 54

Concept Check 54.1

1. Energy passes (flows) through an ecosystem, entering as sunlight, moving as transfers of chemical energy in the food web, and leaving the ecosystem as heat. It is not recycled within the ecosystem.

2. The second law states that in any energy transfer or transformation, some of the energy is dissipated to the surroundings as heat. This "escape" of energy from an ecosystem is offset by the continuous influx of solar radiation; otherwise, the ecosystem would eventually run out of energy.

3. By decomposing organic material and returning vital chemical elements to the environment in inorganic form, detritivores are central to nutrient recycling. They also provide key linkages between primary producers and consumers.

Concept Check 54.2

1. Only a small fraction of solar radiation strikes photosynthetic organisms, only a portion of that fraction is of wavelengths suitable for photosynthesis, and only a portion of that radiation is converted to chemical energy by the photosynthetic organisms.

2. By manipulating the factors of interest, such as light availability, nutrient availability or soil moisture, and recording the primary producers' responses

3. Because the open ocean covers such a large proportion of Earth's surface

4. Net primary production reflects the loss of organic material due to the cellular respiration of the primary producers.

Concept Check 54.3

1. 20 J; 40%

2. Decomposer organisms (detritivores) consume most of what herbivores leave.

3. The biggest producers in most ecosystems comprise the most biomass, like plants in terrestrial ecosystems. However, in some ecosystems, such as aquatic systems supported by phytoplankton that reproduce rapidly, a relatively small standing crop of primary producers can sustain a much larger biomass of primary consumers. In these cases, the biomass pyramid is top-heavy, whereas the production pyramid is bottom-heavy.

Concept Check 54.4

1. For example, for the carbon cycle:

Cycling of a carbon atom

2. Removal of the trees disrupts nitrogen cycling in the forest, and the nitrate that accumulates in the soil runs off into the stream.

Concept Check 54.5

1. Adding nutrients causes population explosions of algae and the organisms that feed on them. Increased respiration by algae and consumers, including detritivores, depletes the lake's oxygen, which the fish need to survive.

2. Without the growing trees to assimilate minerals from the soil, more of the minerals run off and end up polluting nearby water resources.

3. At a lower trophic level, because biological magnification increases the concentration of toxins up the food chain

4. Thawing of these frozen soils could lead to decomposition of the organic matter, further increasing the carbon dioxide in the atmosphere.

Self-Quiz
1. c 2. e 3. d 4. e 5. d
6. a 7. b 8. c 9. d 10. c

CHAPTER 55

Concept Check 55.1

1. In addition to species loss, the biodiversity crisis includes the loss of genetic diversity within populations and species, and the degradation of entire ecosystems.

2. Habitat destruction, such as deforestation, channelizing of rivers, or conversion of natural ecosystems to agriculture or cities, deprives species of places to live. Introduced species, which are transported by humans to regions outside of their native range where they are not controlled by their natural pathogens or predators, often reduce the population sizes of native species through competition or predation. Overexploitation has reduced populations of plants and animals or driven them to extinction. Disruption of interaction networks, such as food webs or networks of mutualism, threatens species that depend on interactions, such as pollination, for their survival.

3. The benefits of biodiversity to humans include the potential use of genetic diversity to improve crop qualities; the capacity of threatened species to provide food, fibers, or medicines for human use; and ecosystem services.

Concept Check 55.2

1. Reduced genetic variation decreases the capacity of a population to evolve in the face of change.

2. The small-population approach focuses on management that increases the genetic diversity within small populations and on increasing effective population size. The declining-population approach emphasizes improvement of environmental conditions, such as habitat destruction, pollution, or overexploitation, that may be the source of a population's decline.

3. The effective population size is almost always smaller than the total population size, because effective population size is based on only the numbers of males and females that actually breed.

Concept Check 55.3

1. A small area supporting an exceptionally large number of endemic species, as well as a disproportionate number of endangered and threatened species.

2. Zoned reserves may provide sustained supplies of forest products, water, hydroelectric power, educational opportunities, and income from ecotourism.

3. Habitat corridors could increase the rate of movement between habitat patches and thus the rate of gene flow between subpopulations. However, corridors may also speed the transmission of disease in some endangered species.

Concept Check 55.4

1. In many situations, ecological damage is reversible, and the concepts of ecology can be used to accelerate ecosystem recovery. However, each case is unique, and restoration ecologists must continue to experiment with remedies as they apply what they have learned from past successes and failures.

2. Bioremediation uses living organisms, generally bacteria, fungi, or plants, to detoxify or remove pollutants from ecosystems. Biological augmentation uses organisms, such as nitrogen-fixing plants, to add essential materials to degraded ecosystems.

Concept Check 55.5

1. Sustainable development is an approach to development that works toward the long-term prosperity of human societies and the ecosystems that support them, which requires linking the biological sciences with the social sciences, economics, and humanities.

2. Biophilia, our sense of connection to nature and other forms of life, may act as a significant motivation for the development of an environmental ethic that resolves not to allow species to become extinct or ecosystems to be destroyed. Such an ethic is necessary if we are to become more attentive and effective custodians of the environment.

Self-Quiz
1. c 2. b 3. d 4. d 5. d
6. e 7. b 8. c 9. a 10. b

Measurement	Unit and Abbreviation	Metric Equivalent	Metric-to-English Conversion Factor	English-to-Metric Conversion Factor
Length	1 kilometer (km)	= 1000 (10^3) meters	1 km = 0.62 mile	1 mile = 1.61 km
	1 meter (m)	= 100 (10^2) centimeters	1 m = 1.09 yards	1 yard = 0.914 m
		= 1000 millimeters	1 m = 3.28 feet	1 foot = 0.305 m
			1 m = 39.37 inches	
	1 centimeter (cm)	= 0.01 (10^{-2}) meter	1 cm = 0.394 inch	1 foot = 30.5 cm
				1 inch = 2.54 cm
	1 millimeter (mm)	= 0.001 (10^{-3}) meter	1 mm = 0.039 inch	
	1 micrometer (μm)	= 10^{-6} meter (10^{-3}mm)		
	(formerly micron, μ)			
	1 nanometer (nm)	= 10^{-9} meter (10^{-3}μm)		
	(formerly millimicron, μm)			
	1 angstrom (Å)	= 10^{-10} meter (10^{-4}μm)		
Area	1 hectare (ha)	= 10,000 square meters	1 ha = 2.47 acres	1 acre = 0.405 ha
	1 square meter (m^2)	= 10,000 square centimeters	1 m^2 = 1.196 square yards	1 square yard = 0.8361 m^2
			1 m^2 = 10.764 square feet	1 square foot = 0.0929 m^2
	1 square centimeter (cm^2)	= 100 square millimeters	1 cm^2 = 0.155 square inch	1 square inch = 6.4516 cm^2
Mass	1 metric ton (t)	= 1000 kilograms	1 t = 1.103 tons	1 ton = 0.907 t
	1 kilogram (kg)	= 1000 grams	1 kg = 2.205 pounds	1 pound = 0.4536 kg
	1 gram (g)	= 1000 milligrams	1 g = 0.0353 ounce	1 ounce = 28.35 g
			1 g = 15.432 grains	
	1 milligram (mg)	= 10^{-3} gram	1 mg = approx. 0.015 grain	
	1 microgram (μg)	= 10^{-6} gram		
Volume (solids)	1 cubic meter (m^3)	= 1,000,000 cubic centimeters	1 m^3 = 1.308 cubic yards	1 cubic yard = 0.7646 m^3
			1 m^3 = 35.315 cubic feet	1 cubic foot = 0.0283 m^3
	1 cubic centimeter (cm³ or cc)	= 10^{-6} cubic meter	1 cm^3 = 0.061 cubic inch	1 cubic inch = 16.387 cm^3
	1 cubic millimeter (mm^3)	= 10^{-9} cubic meter (10^{-3} cubic centimeter)		
Volume (liquids and gases)	1 kiloliter (kl or kL)	= 1000 liters	1 kL = 264.17 gallons	1 gallon = 3.785 L
	1 liter (L)	= 1000 milliliters	1 L = 0.264 gallons	1 quart = 0.946 L
			1 L = 1.057 quarts	
	1 milliliter (mL)	= 10^{-3} liter	1 mL = 0.034 fluid ounce	1 quart = 946 mL
		= 1 cubic centimeter	1 mL = approx. 1/4 teaspoon	1 pint = 473 mL
				1 fluid ounce = 29.57 mL
			1 mL = approx. 15 – 16 drops (gtt.)	1 teaspoon = approx. 5 mL
	1 microliter (μl or μL)	= 10^{-6} liter (10^{-3} milliliters)		
Time	1 second (s)	= 1/60 minute		
	1 millisecond (ms)	= 10^{-3} second		
Temperature	Degrees Celsius (°C) (Absolute zero, when all molecular motion ceases, is −273°C. The Kelvin [K] scale, which has the same size degrees as Celsius, has its zero point at absolute zero. Thus, 0°K = −273°C.)		°F = 9/5°C + 32	°C = 5/9(°F − 32)

Appendix B

Light Microscope

In light microscopy, light is focused on a specimen by a glass condenser lens; the image is then magnified by an objective lens and an ocular lens, for projection on the eye or on photographic film.

Electron Microscope

In electron microscopy, a beam of electrons (top of the microscope) is used instead of light, and electromagnets are used instead of glass lenses. The electron beam is focused on the specimen by a condenser lens; the image is magnified by an objective lens and a projector lens for projection on a screen or on photographic film.

This appendix presents a taxonomic classification for the major extant groups of organisms discussed in this text; not all phyla are included. The classification presented here is based on the three-domain system, which assigns the two major groups of prokaryotes, archaea and bacteria, to separate domains (with eukaryotes making up the third domain). This classification contrasts with the traditional five-kingdom system, which groups all prokaryotes in a single kingdom, Monera (see Chapter 26).

Various alternative classification schemes are discussed in Unit Five of the text. The taxonomic turmoil includes debates about the number and boundaries of kingdoms. In this review, asterisks (*) indicate "candidate kingdoms," major clades of prokaryotes and protists that many systematists have elevated to the kingdom level. Other debates concern the alignment of the Linnaean classification hierarchy with the findings of modern cladistic analysis. Daggers (†) indicate currently recognized phyla thought by some systematists to be paraphyletic.

DOMAIN ARCHAEA

*Kingdom Euryarchaeota

*Kingdom Crenarchaeota

*Kingdom Korarchaeota

*Kingdom Nanoarchaeota

DOMAIN BACTERIA

*Kingdom Proteobacteria

*Kingdom Gram-Positive Bacteria

*Kingdom Cyanobacteria

*Kingdom Spirochetes

*Kingdom Chlamydia

DOMAIN EUKARYA
The five-kingdom classification scheme unites all the eukaryotes generally called protists in a single kingdom, Protista. This book adopts the cladistic argument for dividing the protists into several "candidate kingdoms" (*). This review also includes some protistan groups of less certain phylogeny (see Chapter 28).

*Kingdom Parabasala (parabasalids)

*Kingdom Diplomonadida (diplomonads)

*Kingdom Euglenozoa
  Phylum Euglenophyta (euglenids)
  Phylum Kinetoplastida (kinetoplastids)

*Kingdom Alveolata
  Phylum Dinoflagellata (dinoflagellates)
  Phylum Apicomplexa (apicomplexans)
  Phylum Ciliophora (ciliates)

*Kingdom Stramenopila
  Phylum Phaeophyta (brown algae)
  Phylum Oomycota (water molds)
  Phylum Chrysophyta (golden algae)
  Phylum Bacillariophyta (diatoms)

*Kingdom Rhodophyta (red algae)

*Kingdom Chlorophyta (green algae: chlorophytes and charophyceans, which some biologists now place with plants in the kingdom Viridiplantae)

*Kingdom Amoebozoa
  Phylum Myxogastrida (plasmodial slime molds)
  Phylum Dictyostelida (cellular slime molds)
  Phylum Gymnamoeba (gymnamoebas)
  Phylum Entamoeba (entamoebas)

Protists of less certain phylogenetic affinities:
  Phylum Radiolaria (radiolarians)
  Phylum Foraminifera (forams)

Kingdom Plantae

Phylum Hepatophyta (liverworts) ⎫
Phylum Anthocerophyta (hornworts) ⎬ Bryophytes (nonvascular plants)
Phylum Bryophyta (mosses) ⎭

Phylum Lycophyta (lycophytes) ⎫
Phylum Pterophyta (ferns, horsetails, whisk ferns) ⎬ Seedless vascular plants

Phylum Ginkgophyta (ginkgo) ⎫
Phylum Cycadophyta (cycads) ⎬ Gymnosperms ⎫
Phylum Gnetophyta (gnetophytes) ⎪   ⎬ Seed plants
Phylum Coniferophyta (conifers) ⎭   ⎪
Phylum Anthophyta (flowering plants) ⎬ Angiosperms ⎭

Kingdom Fungi

†Phylum Chytridiomycota (chytrids)
†Phylum Zygomycota (zygomycetes)
Phylum Glomeromycota (glomeromycetes)
Phylum Ascomycota (sac fungi)
Phylum Basidiomycota (club fungi)

Kingdom Animalia

†Phylum Porifera (sponges)
Phylum Cnidaria (cnidarians)
    Class Hydrozoa (hydrozoans)
    Class Scyphozoa (jellies)
    Class Cubozoa (box jellies and sea wasps)
    Class Anthozoa (sea anemones and most corals)
Phylum Placozoa (placozoans)
Phylum Kinorhyncha (kinorhynchs)
Phylum Platyhelminthes (flatworms)
    Class Turbellaria (free-living flatworms)
    Class Trematoda (flukes)
    Class Monogenea (monogeneans)
    Class Cestoda (tapeworms)

Phylum Nemertea (proboscis worms)
Phylum Ectoprocta (ectoprocts) ⎫
Phylum Phoronida (phoronids) ⎬ Lophophorates
Phylum Brachiopoda (brachiopods) ⎭
Phylum Rotifera (rotifers)
Phylum Mollusca (molluscs)
    Class Polyplacophora (chitons)
    Class Gastropoda (gastropods)
    Class Bivalvia (bivalves)
    Class Cephalopoda (cephalopods)
Phylum Acanthocephala (spiny-headed worms)
Phylum Ctenophora (comb jellies)
Phylum Loricifera (loriciferans)
Phylum Priapula (priapulans)
Phylum Annelida (segmented worms)
    Class Oligochaeta (oligochaetes)
    Class Polychaeta (polychaetes)
    Class Hirudinea (leeches)
Phylum Nematoda (roundworms)
Phylum Arthropoda (This survey groups arthropods into a single phylum, but some zoologists now split the arthropods into multiple phyla.)
    Subphylum Cheliceriformes (horseshoe crabs, arachnids)
    Subphylum Myriapoda (millipedes, centipedes)
    Subphylum Hexapoda (insects, springtails)
    Subphylum Crustacea (crustaceans)
Phylum Cycliophora (cycliophorans)
Phylum Tardigrada (tardigrades)
Phylum Onychophora (velvet worms)
Phylum Hemichordata (hemichordates)
Phylum Echinodermata (echinoderms)
    Class Asteroidea (sea stars)
    Class Ophiuroidea (brittle stars)
    Class Echinoidea (sea urchins and sand dollars)
    Class Crinoidea (sea lilies)
    Class Concentricycloidea (sea daisies)
    Class Holothuroidea (sea cucumbers)
Phylum Chordata (chordates)
    Subphylum Urochordata (urochordates: tunicates)
    Subphylum Cephalochordata (cephalochordates: lancelets)
    Subphylum Craniata (craniates)
        Class Myxini (hagfishes)
        Class Cephalaspidomorphi (lampreys) ⎫
        Class Chondrichthyes (sharks, rays, chimaeras) ⎪
        Class Actinopterygii (ray-finned fishes) ⎪
        Class Actinistia (coelacanths) ⎪
        Class Dipnoi (lungfishes) ⎬ Vertebrates
        Class Amphibia (amphibians) ⎪
        Class Reptilia (tuatara, lizards, snakes, turtles, crocodilians, birds) ⎪
        Class Mammalia (mammals) ⎭

Credits

This section constitutes a continuation of the copyright page.

PHOTO CREDITS
Cover Image Linda Broadfoot

Unit Opening Interviews
Unit I Paul Ossa, Benjamin Cummings Publishing; **Unit II** Sam Kittner; **Unit III** Justin Allardyce Knight; **Unit IV** Angela Elbern, Benjamin Cummings Publishing; **Unit V** Lee W. Wilcox, Benjamin Cummings Publishing; **Unit VI** Steve Walag, Benjamin Cummings Publishing; **Unit VII** Les Todd, Duke University Photography; **Unit VIII** John Sherman, Benjamin Cummings Publishing

Detailed Contents
p. xxv Wolfgang Kaehler/Liaison; **p. xxvi** Boehringer Ingelheim International GmbH, photo Lennart Nilsson/Albert Bonniers Forlag AB, The Body Victorious, Delacorte Press, Dell Publishing Co., Inc; **p. xxviii** Andrew Syred/Photo Researchers; **p. xxxi** Steve P. Hopkin/Taxi; **p. xxxii** Garry McCarthy; **p. xxxv** Robert Holmes/CORBIS; **p. xxxvi** Dave Watts/NHPA/Photo Researchers; **p. xxxix** Gerry Ellis/Minden Pictures

Chapter 1
1.1 Linda Broadfoot; 1.2a Image State; 1.2b Fred Bavendam/Minden Pictures; 1.2c Dorling Kindersley; 1.2d Joe McDonald/CORBIS; 1.2e Michael & Patricia Fogden/CORBIS; 1.2f Frans Lanting/Minden Pictures; 1.2g Frans Lanting/Minden Pictures; 1.3.1 WorldSat International/Photo Researchers; 1.3.2 Yann Arthus-Bertrand/CORBIS; 1.3.3 Gary Carter/Visuals Unlimited; 1.3.4 Michael Orton/Photographer's Choice; 1.3.5 Carol Fuegi/CORBIS; 1.3.6 Photodisc; 1.3.7 Jeremy Burgess/SPL/Photo Researchers; 1.3.8 Manfred Kage/Peter Arnold; 1.3.9 E. H. Newcomb & W.P.Wergin/ Biological Photo Service; 1.3.10 Benjamin Cummings; 1.4 Photodisc; 1.5 both Conly Rieder; 1.6 Camille Tokerud/Stone; 1.7 Photodisc; 1.8a S. C. Holt, University of Texas Health Center/Biological Photo Service; 1.8b Dr. D. W. Fawcett/Visuals Unlimited; 1.9 David Parker/SPL/Photo Researchers; 1.13 Charles H. Phillips; 1.15.1 Oliver Meckes/Nicole Ottawa/Photo Researchers; 1.15.2 Ralph Robinson/Visuals Unlimited; 1.15.3 D. P. Wilson/Photo Researchers; 1.15.4 Konrad Wothe/Minden Pictures; 1.15.5 Peter Lilja/Taxi; 1.15.6 Anup Shah/Nature Picture Library; 1.16a VVG/SPL/Photo Researchers; 1.16b OMIKRON/Photo Researchers; 1.16c W. L. Dentler, University of Kansas/Biological Photo Sevices; 1.17 Mike Hettwer; 1.18 American Museum of Natural History; 1.19a Hal Horwitz, CORBIS; 1.19b-c Dorling Kindersley; 1.22 Dorling Kindersley; 1.24a Karl Ammann/CORBIS; 1.24b Dorling Kindersley; 1.26a Hans Pfletschinger/Peter Arnold; 1.26b John Alcock/Visuals Unlimited; 1.27a Breck P. Kent; 1.27b E. R. Degginger/Photo Resarchers; 1.28 both David Pfennig; 1.31 Don Hammerman/NYU; 1.32 Stone; Table 1.1 left Dr. D. W. Fawcett/Visuals Unlimited; Table 1.1 right S. C. Holt, University of Texas Health Center/Biological Photo Service; Table 1.2 Photodisc; Table 1.5 Photodisc; Table 1.6 Michael & Patricia Fogden/CORBIS; Table 1.7 left Hal Horwitz, CORBIS; Table 1.7 right Dorling Kindersley; Table 1.9 Dorling Kindersley; Table 1.10 Karl Ammann/CORBIS; Table 1.11 Stone

Chapter 2
2.1 Thomas Eisner; 2.2 left Chip Clark; 2.2 middle & right Benjamin Cummings; 2.3a Grant Heilman Photography; 2.3b Ivan Polunin/Bruce Coleman; 2.5 Terraphotographics/Biological Photo Service; 2.6 CTI; 2.14 Benjamin Cummings; gecko p40 Dorling Kindersley; 2.18 Runk/Schoenberger/Grant Heilman Photography; moth p44 E. R. Degginger/Color-Pic

Chapter 3
3.1 NASA; 3.3 left PhotoDisc; 3.3 right Richard Kessel & Gene Shih/Visuals Unlimited; 3.4 George Bernard/Animals Animals; 3.5 Flip Nicklin/Minden Pictures; 3.9 Oliver Strewe/Stone

Chapter 4
4.1 Gerry Ellis/Minden Pictures; 4.2 Roger Ressmeyer/CORBIS; 4.6 Manfred Kage/Peter Arnold; 4.9 both Digital Vision

Chapter 5
5.1 Lester Lefkowitz/CORBIS; 5.6a John N. A. Lott, McMaster University/Biolog-ical Photo Service; 5.6b H. Shio and P.B. Lazarow; 5.8 J. Litray/Visuals Unlimited; 5.9 left Jeremy Woodhouse/PhotoDisc; 5.9 right T.J. Beveridge/Visuals Unlimited; 5.10b F. Collet/Photo Researchers; 5.10c CORBIS; 5.12a Dorling Kindersley; 5.12b Photodisc Green; 5.20 Wolfgang Kaehler/Liaison; 5.21 both Eye of Science/Photo Researchers; 5.23 P. B. Sigler from Z. Xu, A. L. Horwich, and P. B. Sigler, Nature (1997) 388:741-750. ©1997 Macmillan Magazines, Ltd.; 5.24a Marie Green, University of California, Riverside

Chapter 6
6.1 Molecular Probes; 6.3a Biophoto Associates/Photo Researchers; 6.3b Ed Reschke; 6.3c-d David M. Phillips/Visuals Unlimited; 6.3e Molecular Probes; 6.3f both Karl Garsha; 6.4a-b William L. Dentler, University of Kansas/Biological Photo Service; 6.6 S. C. Holt, University of Texas Health Center/Biological Photo Service; 6.8 Daniel Friend; 6.10 top left From L. Orci and A. Perelet, Freeze-Etch Histology. (Heidelberg: Springer-Verlag, 1975) © 1975 Springer-Verlag; 6.10 bottom left From A. C. Faberge, Cell Tiss. Res. 151 (1974):403. © 1974 Springer-Verlag; 6.10 right U. Aebi et al. Nature 323 (1996):560-564, figure 1a. Used with permission; 6.11 D. W. Fawcett/Photo Researchers; 6.12 R. Bolender, D. Fawcett/Photo Researchers; 6.13 Don Fawcett/Visuals Unlimited; 6.14a R. Rodewald, University of Virginia/Biological Photo Service; 6.14b Daniel S. Friend, Harvard Medical School; 6.15 E. H. Newcomb; 6.17 Daniel S. Friend, Harvard Medical School; 6.18 W. P. Wergin and E. H. Newcomb, University of Wisconsin, Madison/Biological Photo Service; 6.19 From S. E. Fredrick and E. H. Newcomb, The Journal of Cell Biology 43 (1969):343. Provided by E. H. Newcomb; 6.20 John E. Heuser, Washington University School of Medicine, St. Louis, MO; 6.21 B. J. Schapp et al., 1985, Cell 40:455; Table 6.1 left Mary Osborn, Max Planck Institute; middle Frank Solomon and J. Dinsmore, Massachusetts Institute of Technology; right Mark S. Ladinsky and J. Richard McIntosh, University of Colorado; 6.22 Kent McDonald; 6.23a Biophoto Associates/Photo Researchers; 6.23b Oliver Meckes & Nicole Ottawa/Photo Researchers; 6.24a OMIKRON/Science Source/Photo Researchers; 6.24b-c W. L. Dentler, University of Kansas/Biological Photo Service; 6.26 From Hirokawa Nobutaka, The Journal of Cell Biology 94 (1982):425 by copyright permission of The Rockefeller University Press; 6.28 G. F. Leedale/Photo Researchers; 6.30 W. P. Wergin, provided by E. H. Newcomb; 6.31 top From Douglas J. Kelly, The Journal of Cell Biology 28 (1966):51 by copyright permission of The Rockefeller University Press; 6.31 middle From L. Orci and A. Perelet, Freeze-Etch Histology. (Heidelberg: Springer-Verlag, 1975) copyright 1975 Springer-Verlag; 6.31 bottom From C. Peracchia and A. F. Dulhunty, The Journal of Cell Biology 70 (1976):419 by copyright permission of The Rockefeller University Press; 6.32 Boehringer Ingelheim International GmbH, photo Lennart Nilsson/Albert Bonniers Forlag AB, The Body Victorious, Delacorte Press, Dell Publishing Co., Inc.

Chapter 7
7.4 both D. W. Fawcett/Photo Researchers; 7.14a-b Cabisco/Visuals Unlimited; 7.20 top R. N. Band and H. S. Pankratz, Michigan State University/Biological Photo Service; 7.20 middle D. W. Fawcett/Photo Researchers; 7.20 bottom, both M. M. Perry and A. B. Gilbert, J. Cell Science 39 (1979) 257. Copyright 1979 by The Company of Biologists Ltd.

Chapter 8
8.1 Jean-Marie Bassot/Photo Researchers; 8.2 David W. Hamilton/Image Bank; 8.3a Joe McDonald/CORBIS; 8.3b Manoj Shah/Stone; 8.4 Brian Capon; 8.16a-b Thomas Steitz, Yale University; 8.22 R. Rodewald, University of Virginia/Biological Photo Service

Chapter 9
9.1 Frans Lanting/Minden Pictures

Chapter 10
10.1 Bob Rowan, Progressive Image/CORBIS; 10.2a Jim Brandenburg/Minden Pictures; 10.2b Bob Evans/Peter Arnold; 10.2c Michael Abbey/Visuals Unlimited; 10.2d Susan Barns; 10.3 middle M. Eichelberger/Visuals Unlimited; 10.3 bottom W. P. Wergin and E. H. Newcomb, University of Wisconsin/Biological Photo Service; 10.11b Christine L. Case, Skyline College; 10.20a David Muench/CORBIS; 10.20b Dave Bartruff/CORBIS

Researchers; **34.18** Richard Ellis/Photo Researchers; **34.21a** Alberto Fernandez/AGE Fotostock; **34.21b-c** Michael Fogden/Bruce Coleman; **34.22 all** Hans Pfletschinger/Peter Arnold; **34.25** Jessie Cohen, National Zoological Park, © Smithsonian Institution; **34.26 left** Department of Library Services, American Museum of Natural History; **34.26 right** John Sibbick/National Geographic Magazine; **34.27a** Doug Wechsler; **34.27b** Matt Lee; **34.27c** Michael & Patricia Fogden/Minden Pictures; **34.27d** Medford Taylor/National Geographic Image Collection; **34.27e** Carl & Ann Purcell/CORBIS; **34.28 right** Janice Sheldon; **34.28 left** Stephen J. Kraseman/DRK Photo; **34.30a** Russell Mountford/Alamy Images; **34.30b** CORBIS; **34.30c** Frans Lanting/Minden Pictures; **34.30d** franzfoto.com/Alamy Images; **34.33** Mervyn Griffiths/CSIRO; **34.33 inset** D. Parer and E. Parer Cook/Auscape; **34.34a** Dan Hadden/Ardea Ltd; **34.34b** Fritz Prenzel/Animals Animals; **34.37** Frans Lanting/Minden Pictures; **34.39a** Kevin Schafer/AGE Fotostock; **34.39b** Frans Lanting/Minden Pictures; **34.40a** Morales/AGE Fotostock; **34.40b** Anup Shah/ImageState/Alamy Images; **34.40c** T. J. Rich/Nature Photo Library; **34.40d** E. A. Janes/AGE Fotostock; **34.40e** Frans Lanting/Minden Pictures; **34.42a** Cleveland Museum of Natural History; **34.42b** John Reader/SPL/Photo Researchers; **34.42c** John Gurche; **34.43 left** Alan Walker, National Museum of Kenya; **34.43 right** Jay Matternes; **34.44** David L. Brill; **34.45** C. Henshilwood & F. d'Errico

Chapter 35
35.3 Robert & Linda Mitchell/Robert & Linda Mitchell Photography; **35.4a** James Strawser/Grant Heilman Photography; **35.4b** Dorling Kindersley; **35.4c** Drew Weiner; **35.4d** Robert Holmes/CORBIS; **35.4e** Geoff Tompkinson/Science Photo Library/Photo Researchers; **35.5a** Dorling Kindersley; **35.5b** Gusto Productions/Science Photo Library/Photo Researchers; **35.5c** Barry Runk/Stan/Grant Heilman Photography; **35.5d** Dorling Kindersley; **35.7a** Scott Camazine/Photo Researchers; **35.7b** Fritz Polking/Visuals Unlimited; **35.7c** Mike Zens/CORBIS; **35.7d** James Strawser/Grant Heilman Photography; **35.7e** Jerome Wexler/Photo Researchers; **35.9.1** Brian Capon; **35.9.2** Graham Kent/Benjamin Cummings; **35.9.3 both** Graham Kent/Benjamin Cummings; **35.9.4** Richard Kessel and Gene Shih/Visuals Unlimited; **35.9.5 both** Graham Kent/Benjamin Cummings; **35.12** Carolina Biological Supply/Phototake; **35.13a-b** Ed Reschke; **35.13c** Carolina Biological Supply/Phototake; **35.14** Michael Clayton; **35.15** Ed Reschke; **35.16 both** Ed Reschke; **35.17b-c** Ed Reschke; **35.18 left** Michael Clayton; **35.18 right** Alison W. Roberts **35.21** Janet Braam, from Cell 60 (9 February 1990) copyright 1990 by Cell Press; **35.23 all** Susan Wick, University of Minnesota; **35.24** B. Wells and Kay Roberts; **35.25a-b** From figure 1 in B. Scheres et al, Development 121:53-62. © 1995 The Company of Biologists Ltd.; **35.25c** From figure 6c in R. Torres Ruiz and G. Jurgens, Development 120:2967-2978. © 1994 The Company of Biologists Ltd.; **35.26** From figure 1a in U. Mayer et al, Development 117 (1): 149-162. © 1993 The Company of Biologists Ltd.; **35.27 both** From figure 1 in D. Hareven et al, Cell 84 (5): 735-744. 1996 reprinted with permission of Elsevier Science; **35.28** From figure 2g in Hung et al, Plant Physiology 117:73-84. © 1998 Plant Physiology. Photo courtesy John Schiefelbein/University of Michigan; **35.29** Gerald D. Carr; **35.30 both** Elliot M Meyerowitz and John Bowman, Development 112 1991:1-2 31.2

Chapter 36
36.1 Gary Randall/Taxi; **36.7** Nigel Cattlin/Holt Studios International/Photo Researchers; **36.10** Dana Richter/Visuals Unlimited; **36.11** Scott Camazine/Photo Researchers; **36.14** Jeremy Burgess/Science Photo Library/Photo Researchers; **36.16** John D. Cunningham/Visuals Unlimited; **36.16 inset** Dorling Kindersley; **36.19 all** M. H. Zimmerman, courtesy of Professor P. B. Tomlinson, Harvard University

Chapter 37
37.1 Adam Hart-Davis/SPL/Photo Researchers; **37.4** Maurice Reece. From the Country Gentleman, courtesy of the Curtis Publishing Co.; **37.5** U. S. Department of Agriculture; **37.7** White et al, Plant Physiology, June 2003; **37.8** Kevin Horan/Stone; **37.10a** Breck P. Kent/Earth Scenes; **37.10b** E. H. Newcomb/Biological Photo Service; **37.12a both** Gerald Van Dyke/Visuals Unlimited; **37.12b** Carolina Biological Supply/Phototake NYC; **37.13.1** Wolfgang Kaehler/CORBIS; **37.13.2 left to right** James Strawser/Grant Heilman Photography; Kevin Schafer/CORBIS; Andrew Syred/Science Photo Library/Photo Researchers; Gary W. Carter/CORBIS; **37.13.3 left to right** Dorling Kindersley; Biophoto Associates/Photo Researchers; Dorling Kindersley; Paul A. Zahl/Photo Researchers; Fritz Polking/Frank Lane Picture Agency/CORBIS

Chapter 38
38.1 COMPOST/VISAGE/Peter Arnold; **38.3.1 left to right** Karen Tweedy-Holmes/CORBIS; Dorling Kindersley; Craig Lovell/CORBIS; John Cancalosi/Nature Photo Library; **38.3.2 left to right** D. Cavagnaro/Visuals Unlimited; David Sieren/Visuals Unlimited; Marcel E. Dorken (2 photos); **38.4a left** Ed Reschke; **38.4a right** David Scharf/Peter Arnold; **38.4b** Ed Reschke; **38.11** David Cav-

agnaro/DRK; **38.12a, b** Bruce Iverson; **38.13** Sinclair Stammers/Photo Researchers; **38.14 both** Dorling Kindersley; **38.15** Steve Ferreira, University of Hawaii and Dennis Gonsalves, Cornell University; courtesy American Phytopathological Society; **38.16** Peter Berger, Institut für Biologie, Freiburg

Chapter 39
39.1 Malcolm Wilkins, University of Glasgow; **39.2 both** Natalie Bronstein; **39.7 both** Regulation of Polar Auxin Transport ATPIN1 in Arabidopsis Vascular Tissue," by Leo Galweiler, et al) Science 18 Dec 1998 , vol. 282, pp. 2226-2229; **39.9 both** Malcolm Wilkins, University of Glasgow; **39.10** Fred Jensen/Kearney Agricultural Center; **39.12** Karen E. Koch; **39.14a** Kurt Stepnitz, DOE Plant Research Laboratory, Michigan State University; **39.14b** Joe Kieber, University of North Carolina; **39.16** Ed Reschke; **39.17 all** Malcolm Wilkins, University of Glasgow; **39.18 all** Malcolm Wilkins, University of Glasgow; **39.21 both** Malcolm Wilkins, University of Glasgow; **39.25 all** Michael Evans, Ohio State University; **39.26** Janet Braam, from Cell 60 (9 February 1990); cover. © 1990 by Cell Press; **39.27a-b** David Sieren/Visuals Unlimited, **39.27c** From K. Esau, anatomy of Seed Plants, 2nd ed. (New York: John Wiley and sons, 1977), fig. 19.4, p. 358; **39.28** J. L. Basq and M. C. Drew

Chapter 40
40.1 Mitsuhiko Imamori/Minden Pictures; **40.2a** Flip Nicklin/Minden Pictures; **40.2b** Andrew Sallmon/Mondragon Photography; **40.2c** Tui De Roy/Minden Pictures; **40.2d** Bill Varie/CORBIS; **40.2e** Norbert Wu/Minden Pictures; **40.4 top right** D. M. Phillips/Visuals Unlimited; **40.4 left** G. Shih-R. Kessel/Visuals Unlimited; **40.4 bottom right** Dr. Richard Kessel & Dr. Randy Kardon/Tissues & Organs/Visuals Unlimited; **40.5.1** CNRI/SPL/Photo Researchers; **40.5.2 top left** Nina Zanetti; **40.5.2 top right** Chuck Brown/Photo Researchers; **40.5.2 middle left** Science VU/Visuals Unlimited; **40.5.2 middle right** Nina Zanetti; **40.5.2 bottom left** Nina Zanetti; **40.5.2 bottom right** Dr. Gopal Murti/SPL/Photo Researchers; **40.5.3 top to bottom** Nina Zanetti; Gladden Willis, M. D./Visuals Unlimited; Manfred Kage/Peter Arnold; Ed Reschke; **40.6** Dr. Richard Kessel & Dr. Randy Kardon/Tissues & Organs/Visuals Unlimited; **40.8a** Robert Full, University of California; **40.8b** Yoav Levy/Phototake NY; **40.18** Daniel Lyons/Bruce Coleman; **40.19** Robert Ganz; **40.22** John Gerlach/Visuals Unlimited

Chapter 41
41.1 AP World Wide Photos; **41.2 top left** Flip Nicklin/Minden Pictures; **41.2 top right** Tom Eisner, Cornell University; **41.2 middle right** Lennart Nilsson; **41.2 bottom** Gunter Ziesler/Peter Arnold, Inc.; **41.4** Susumu Nishinaga/SPL/Photo Researchers; **41.6** The Jackson Laboratory; **41.7** Wolfgang Kaehler/CORBIS; **41.8** Thomas Mangelsen/Minden Pictures; **41.9** Dagmar Fabricius/Stock Boston; **41.10 both** Digital Vision/CORBIS; **41.11** Roland Seitre/Peter Arnold; **41.17** Fred E. Hossler/Visuals Unlimited; **41.18** Eye of Science/Photo Researchers; **41.25** Kelley Wise/Vital Imaging; **41.27 both** PhotoDisc

Chapter 42
42.1 George Bernard/Animals Animals; **42.2** Norbert Wu/Mo Young Productions; **42.9** Dr. Richard Kessel & Dr. Randy Kardon/Tissues & Organs/Visuals Unlimited; **42.13** CNRI/Phototake; **42.14** Lennart Nilsson, The Body Victorious, Dell Publishing Company; **42.17** Science Source/Photo Researchers; **42.18a** Ed Reschke; **42.18b** W. Ober/Visuals Unlimited; **42.20a** Frans Lanting/Minden Pictures; **42.20b** Peter Batson/Image Quest Marine; **42.20c** H. W. Pratt/Biological Photo Service; **42.20d** Dave Haas; **42.22b** Thomas Eisner; **42.23 left** Dr. Richard Kessel & Dr. Randy Kardon/Tissues & Organs/Visuals Unlimited; **42.23 right** CNRI/ Photo Researchers; **42.25** Hans Rainer Dunker, Justus Leibig University, Giessen; **42.31** Stan Lindstedt

Chapter 43
43.1 Biology Media/Photo Researchers; **43.3** Science Photo Library/Photo Researchers; **43.15** David Scharf/Peter Arnold; **43.16** Lennart Nilsson/Boehringer Ingelheim International GmbH; **43.17** Gopal Murti/Phototake; **43.20** Lennart Nilsson/Boehringer Ingelheim International GmbH; **43.21** CNRI/SPL/Photo Researchers; **43.22** Lennart Nilsson/Boehringer Ingelheim International GmbH

Chapter 44
44.1 Peter Reese/Nature Photo Library; **44.2** Nigel J. Dennis/NHPA/Photo Researchers; **44.4 both** John Crowe; **44.13b** Lise Bankir. From Urinary concentrating ability: insights from comparative anatomy, Bankir and de Rouffignac, Am J. Physiol Regul Integr Comp Physiol, 1985; 249: 643-666; **44.13d** Dr. Richard Kessel & Dr. Randy Kardon/Tissues & Organs/Visuals Unlimited; **44.17** Michael & Patricia Fogden/Minden Pictures; **44.18 kangaroo rat** Mary McDonald/Nature Photo Library; **44.18 beaver** Michael Quinton/Minden Pictures; **44.18 road runner** Gerry Ellis/Minden Pictures; **44.18 iguana** Daniel Heuclin/NHPA/Photo Researchers; **44.18 trout** Tim Martin/Nature Photo Library; **44.18 frog** Laurie Campbell/NHPA/Photo Researchers; **44.18 tuna** Juan Carlos Calvin/AGE fotostock

Chapter 45
45.1 Ralph A. Clevenger/CORBIS; 45.5 VVG/SPL/Photo Researchers; 45.10 Custom Medical Stock Photo; 45.14 Photodisc

Chapter 46
46.1 Robin Chittenden/CORBIS; 46.2 David Wrobel, Monterey Bay Aquarium; 46.3 David Crews, photo by P. de Vries; 46.4 Stephan Myers; 46.5 Dwight Kuhn; 46.6 William Ferguson; 46.17 all Lennart Nilsson/Albert Bonniers Vorlag AB; 46.21 UHB Trust/Stone

Chapter 47
47.1 Lennart Nilsson/Albert Bonniers Vorlag AB; 47.2 Historical Collections, College of Physicians, Philadelphia; 47.4 all Jerry Schatten et al; 47.7a-d George von Dassow; 47.9 both Dr. Richard Kessel & Dr. Gene Shih/Visuals Unlimited; 47.11 Charles A Ettensohn, Carnegie Mellon University; 47.14.1 CABISCO/Visuals Unlimited; 47.14.3 Thomas Poole, SUNY Health Science Center; 47.15 Carolina Biological Supply/Phototake; 47.21 Reproduced form Dr. Jean Paul Thiery Journal of Cell Biology 96 (1983): 462-473; 47.22 both Janet Heasman, University of Minnesota; 47.23 both Hiroki Nishida, Developmental Biology 121 (1987): 526. Reprinted by permission of Academic Press; 47.26a Kathryn Tosney, University of Michigan; 47.27 Courtesy of Dennis Summerbell

Chapter 48
48.1 G. Fesl MD, Dept. of Neuroradiology, LMU Munich, Germany; 48.7 N. Kedersha/Photo Researchers; 48.8 Alan Peters, from Bear, Connors, and Paradiso, Neuroscience: Exploring the Brain © 1996, p. 43; 48.16 E. R Lewis, University of California; 48.29 Marcus Raichle, MD, Washington University School of Medicine; 48.34 Fred H. Gage, The Salk Institute, Laboratory of Genetics; 48.35 Martin M. Rotker/Photo Researchers

Chapter 49
49.1 Stephen Dalton/NHPA; 49.4 top OSF/Animals Animals; 49.4 bottom R. A. Steinbrecht, Max Planck Institute; 49.5a Joe McDonald/Animals Animals; 49.5b Flip Nicklin/Minden Pictures; 49.7 John L. Pontier/Animals Animals; 49.16 From Richard Elzinga, Fundamentals of Entomology 3 ed. ©1987, p. 185. Reprinted by permission of Prentice-Hall, Upper Saddle River, NJ; 49.29 all Dr. H. E Huxley; 49.36 Dave Watts/NHPA/Photo Researchers; 49.37 Vance A. Tucker

Chapter 50
50.1 Mark Moffett/Minden Pictures; 50.2 PhotoDisc; 50.3a Amos Nachoum/The Image Bank; 50.3b Joe McDonald/CORBIS; 50.3c Tom Bean/CORBIS; 50.3d B. Tharp/Photo Researchers; 50.3e Yann Arthus-Bertrand/CORBIS; 50.4 Erich Hartmann/Magnum Photos; 50.7 Richard Ditch; 50.9 Hubert Stadler/CORBIS; 50.17.1 left Allen Russell/Index Stock; 50.17.1 right Gerry Ellis/Minden Pictures; 50.17.2 David Muench/CORBIS; 50.17.3 left Ron Watts/CORBIS; 50.17.3 right Charles McDowell/Grant Heilman Photography; 50.17.4 James Randklev/The Image Bank; 50.17.5 Stuart Westmorland/CORBIS; 50.17.6 Stuart Westmorland/CORBIS; 50.17.7 Digital Vision; 50.17.8 William Lange/Woods Hole Oceanographic Institution; 50.20.1 Frans Lanting/Minden Pictures; 50.20.2 Joe McDonald/CORBIS; 50.20.3 Wolfgang Kaehler/CORBIS; 50.20.4 John D. Cunningham/Visuals Unlimited; 50.20.5 Tom Bean/The Image Bank; 50.20.6 Bill Ross/CORBIS; 50.20.7 Kennan Ward/CORBIS; 50.20.8 Darrell Gulin/CORBIS

Chapter 51
51.1 Tim Davis/Stone; 51.2 Anthony Calfo; 51.3 Kim Taylor/Bruce Coleman; 51.6 Operation Migration; 51.8 Michael Quinton/Minden Pictures; 51.10 Robert Pickett/CORBIS; 51.11 Lowell L. Getz and Lisa Davis; 51.13 Therese Markow and Tom Watts; 51.16 Harry Engels/Animals Animals; 51.17 Clive Bromhall/OSF/Animals Animals; 51.18a Gary A. Nafis; 51.18b Breck P. Kent/Animals Animals/Earth Scenes; 51.25a Thomas Mangelsen/Minden Pictures; 51.25b James H. Robinson/Animals Animals/Earth Scenes; 51.25c Bill Schomoker; 51.26 Fred Bavendam/Minden Pictures; 51.27 Dorling Kindersley; 51.29 G. S. Wilkinson; 51.30 Michio Hoshino/Minden Pictures; 51.32 Erik Svensson; 51.33 Jennifer Jarvis, University of Cape Town; 51.35 Stephen Kraseman/Peter Arnold; 51.37 main Richard Wrangham, Harvard University; 51.37 inset Alissa Crandall/CORBIS; 51.38 Bob Winsett/Index Stock Imagery

Chapter 52
52.1 Yva Momatiuk, John Eastcott/Minden Pictures; 52.3a Stone; 52.3b Frans Lanting/Minden Pictures; 52.3c Niall Benvie/CORBIS; 52.6 Tom Bean/CORBIS; 52.7 H. Wilcox/Wildlife Pictures/Peter Arnold; 52.8a Jean Louis Batt/Taxi; 52.8b Christine Osborne/CORBIS; 52.16 Adrian Bailey/Aurora Photos; 52.17 Wolfgang Kaehler/CORBIS; 52.21 Joe McDonald/CORBIS

Chapter 53
53.1 Martin Harvey/Peter Arnold; 53.3 left Joseph T. Collins/Photo Researchers; 53.3 right Kevin de Queiroz, National Museum of Natural History; 53.5 C. Allan Morgan/Peter Arnold; 53.6 Michael & Patricia Fogden/CORBIS; 53.7a Stephen J. Krasemann/Photo Researchers; 53.7b Michael & Patricia Fogden/Minden Pictures; 53.8a Edward S. Ross; 53.8b Runk/Schoenberger/Grant Heilman Photography; 53.9 Michael & Patricia Fogden/CORBIS; 53.10 Peter Johnson/CORBIS; 53.16a Bill Curtsinger/National Geographic Image Collection; 53.18 Darrell Gulin/CORBIS; 53.19 Sally D. Hacker, Oregon State University; 53.21 all Frank Gilliam, Marshall University; 53.22a Michael Quinton/Minden Pictures; 53.22b Scott T. Smith/CORBIS; 53.23 Tom Bean/CORBIS; 53.24a Charles Mauzy/CORBIS; 53.24b Tom Bean/DRK; 53.24c Glacier Bay National Park and Preserve

Chapter 54
54.1 Alex Wetmore; 54.3 Fritz Poelking/AGE fotostock; 54.5 C. B. Field, M. J. Behrenfeld, J. T. Randerson, and P. Falkowski. 1998. "Primary production of the bio-sphere: Integrating terrestrial and oceanic components." Science 281:237-240; 54.7 Reprinted with permission from D.W. Schindler, Science 184 (1974): 897, Figure 1.49. ©1974 American Association for the Advancement of Science; 54.15 Thomas Del Brase/Photographer's Choice; 54.19a-b Hubbard Brook Research Foundation; 54.20 Javier Larrea/AGE Fotostock; 54.25 Will Owens Photography; 54.28a-b NASA/Goddard Space Flight Center Scientific Visualization Studio

Chapter 55
55.1 Wayne Lawler/CORBIS; 55.3a Neil Lucas/Nature Picture Library; 55.3b Mark Carwardine/Still Pictures/Peter Arnold; 55.3c Foead, Yahya & Sumiadi/WWF & BTNUK; 55.4 Scott Camazine/Photo Researchers; 55.5 Gary Braasch/Woodfin Camp & Associates; 55.6a Michael Fogden/Animals Animals; 55.6b Mark E. Gibson/Visuals Unlimited; 55.7 Richard Vogel/Gamma Liaison/Getty Images; 55.8 Merlin D. Tuttle, Bat Conservation International; 55.10 William Ervin/SPL/Photo Researchers; 55.11 Craighead Environmental Research Institute; 55.13a Tim Thompson/CORBIS; 55.13b David Sieren/Visuals Unlimited; 55.13c Blanche Haning/The Lamplighter; 55.14a Yann Arthus-Bertrand/CORBIS; 55.14b James P. Blair/National Geographic Image Collection; 55.15 Richard O. Bierregaard, Jr.; 55.16 Alan Sirulnikoff/SPL/Photo Researchers; 55.19 Frans Lanting/Minden Pictures; 55.20 Photo by John Parks/WWF with approval from Verata District, Fiji; 55.22.1 left Stewart Rood, University of Lethbridge; 55.22.1 right South Florida Water Management District (WPB); 55.22.2 top left Daniel H. Janzen; 55.22.2 bottom left Bert Boekhoven; 55.22.2 top right Jean Hall/Holt Studios/Photo Researchers; 55.22.2 bottom right Kenji Morita/Environment Division, Tokyo Kyuei Co., Ltd.; 55.24a Serge de Sazo/Photo Researchers; 55.24b Frans Lanting/Minden Pictures

ILLUSTRATION CREDITS

The following figures are adapted from Christopher K. Matthews and K. E. van Holde, Biochemistry, 2nd ed., Menlo Park, CA: Benjamin Cummings. © 1996 The Benjamin Cummings Publishing Company, Inc.: 4.6, 9.9, and 17.16b and c.

The following figures are adapted from Wayne M. Becker, Jane B. Reece, and Martin F. Poenie, The World of the Cell, 3rd ed., Menlo Park, CA: Benjamin Cummings. © 1996 The Benjamin Cummings Publishing Company, Inc.: 4.7, 6.7, 7.8, 11.7a, 11.10, 17.10, 19.13, 19.16, and 20.7.

Figures 6.9 and 6.23 and cell organelle drawings in Figures 6.12, 6.13, 6.14, and 6.20 are adapted from illustrations by Tomo Narashima in Elaine N. Marieb, Human Anatomy and Physiology, 5th ed., San Francisco, CA: Benjamin Cummings. © 2001 Benjamin Cummings, an imprint of Addison Wesley Longman, Inc. Figures 6.12, 49.10, and 49.11 are also from Human Anatomy and Physiology, 5th ed.

Figures 46.16, 48.22, 48.24, 49.26, 49.29, and 49.33 are adapted from Elaine N. Marieb, Human Anatomy and Physiology, 4th ed., Menlo Park, CA: Benjamin Cummings. © 1998 Benjamin Cummings, an imprint of Addison Wesley Longman, Inc.

The following figures are adapted from Murray W. Nabors, Introduction to Botany, San Francisco, CA: Benjamin Cummings. © 2004 Pearson Education, Inc., Upper Saddle River, New Jersey: 30.12j, 38.3c, 39.13, and 41.10.

Some illustrations used in BIOLOGY, Seventh Edition, are adapted from Neil Campbell, Brad Williamson, and Robin Heyden, Biology: Exploring Life. Needham, MA, Prentice Hall School Division. © 2004 by Pearson Education, Inc., Upper Saddle River, NJ. Artists: Jennifer Fairman; Mark Foerster; Carlyn Iverson; Phillip Guzy; Steve McEntee; Stephen McMath; Karen Minot; Quade and Emi Paul, Fivth Media; and Nadine Sokol.

1.10 and **graphic in Table 1.1** Adapted from Figure 4 from L. Giot et al., "A Protein Interaction Map of *Drosophila melanogaster*," *Science*, Dec. 5, 2003, p. 1733 Copyright © 2003 AAAS. Reprinted with permission from the American Association for the Advancement of Science; **1.27** Map provided courtesy of David W. Pfennig, University of North Carolina at Chapel Hill; **1.29** Map provided courtesy of David W. Pfennig, University of North Carolina at Chapel Hill. Data in pie charts based on D. W. Pfennig et al. 2001. Frequency-dependent Batesian mimicry. *Nature* 410: 323.

3.7a Adapted from *Scientific American*, Nov. 1998, p. 102.

4.8 Adapted from an illustration by Clark Still, Columbia University.

5.13 From *Biology: The Science of Life*, 3/e by Robert Wallace et al. Copyright © 1991. Reprinted by permission of Pearson Education, Inc.; **5.20a and b** Adapted from D. W. Heinz, W. A. Baase, F. W. Dahlquist, B. W. Matthews. 1993. How amino-acid insertions are allowed in an alpha-helix of T4 lysozyme. *Nature* 361:561; **5.20e and f** © Illustration, Irving Geis. Rights owned by Howard Hughes Medical Institute. Not to be reproduced without permission; **Table 6.1** Adapted from W. M. Becker, L. J. Kleinsmith, and J. Hardin, *The World of the Cell*, 4th ed. (San Francisco, CA: Benjamin Cummings, 2000), p. 753.

9.5a and b Copyright © 2002 from *Molecular Biology of the Cell*, 4th ed. by Bruce Alberts et al., fig. 2.69, p. 92. Garland Science/Taylor & Francis Books, Inc.

10.14 Adapted from Richard and David Walker. *Energy, Plants and Man*, fig. 4.1, p. 69. Sheffield: University of Sheffield. © Richard Walker. Used courtesy of Oxygraphics.

12.12 Copyright © 2002 from *Molecular Biology of the Cell*, 4th ed., by Bruce Alberts et al., fig. 18.41, p. 1059. Garland Science/Taylor & Francis Books, Inc.

17.12 Adapted from L. J. Kleinsmith and V. M. Kish. 1995. *Principles of Cell and Molecular Biology*, 2nd ed. New York, NY: HarperCollins. Reprinted by permission of Addison Wesley Educational Publishers.

19.17b © Illustration, Irving Geis. Rights owned by Howard Hughes Medical Institute. Not to be reproduced without permission; **Table 19.1** From A. Griffiths et al. 2000. *An Introduction to Genetic Analysis*, 7/e, Table 26-4, p. 787. New York: W. H. Freeman and Company. Copyright © 2000 W. H. Freeman and Company.

20.9 Adapted from Peter Russell, *Genetics*, 5th ed., fig. 15.24, p. 481, San Francisco, CA: Benjamin Cummings. © 1998 Pearson Education, Inc., Upper Saddle River, New Jersey; **20.11** Adapted from a figure by Chris A. Kaiser and Erica Beade.

21.15 Copyright © 2002 from *Molecular Biology of the Cell*, 4th ed., by Bruce Alberts et al., fig. 21.17, p. 1172. Garland Science/Taylor & Francis Books, Inc.; **21.23** Adapted from an illustration by William McGinnis; **21.24** Brine shrimp adapted from M. Akam. 1995. *Hox* genes and the evolution of diverse body plans. *Philosophical Transactions B.* 349:313-319. © 1995 Royal Society of London. In Wolpert et al. 1998. Principles of Development, fig. 15.10, p. 452. Oxford: Oxford University Press.

22.13 Adapted from R. Shurman et al. 1995. *Journal of Infectious Diseases* 171:1411.

23.13 Adapted from A. C. Allison. 1961. Abnormal hemoglobin and erythrocyte enzyme-deficiency traits. In *Genetic Variation in Human Populations*, ed. G. A. Harrison. Oxford: Elsevier Science.

24.7 Adapted from D. M. B. Dodd, *Evolution* 11: 1308-1311; **24.14** Adapted from M. Strickberger. 1990. *Evolution*. Boston: Jones & Bartlett; **24.16** Adapted from L. Wolpert. 1998. *Principles of Development*. Oxford University Press; **24.18** Adapted from M. I. Coates. 1995. *Current Biology* 5:844-848.

25.18 Adapted from S. Blair Hedges. The origin and evolution of model organisms. fig. 1, p. 840. *Nature Reviews Genetics* 3: 838-849.

26.7 Adapted from D. Futuyma. 1998. *Evolutionary Biology*, 3rd ed., p. 128. Sunderland, MA: Sinauer Associates; **26.18a** Map adapted from http://geology.er.usgs.gov/eastern/plates.html; **26.8** Data from M. J. Benton. 1995. Diversification and extinction in the history of life. *Science* 268:55; **26.15** Figure 4c from "The Antiquity of RNA-based Evolution" by G.F. Joyce et al., *Nature*, Vol. 418, p. 217. Copyright © 2002 Nature Publishing Co.; **26.10** Adapted from David J. Des Marais. September 8, 2000. When did photosynthesis emerge on Earth? *Science* 289:1703-1705; **26.17** Data from A. H. Knoll and S. B. Carroll, June 25, 199. *Science* 284:2129-2137.

27.6 Adapted from Gerard J. Tortora, Berdell R. Funke, and Christine L. Case. 1998. *Microbiology: An Introduction*, 6th ed. Menlo Park, CA: Benjamin Cummings. © 1998 Benjamin Cummings, an imprint of Addison Wesley Longman, Inc.

28.3 Figure 3 from Archibald and Keeling. "Recycle Plastics," *Trends in Genetics*, Vol. 18. No. 1, 2, 2002, p. 352. Copyright © 2002, with permission from Elsevier; **28.12** Adapted from R. W. Bauman. 2004. *Microbiology*, fig. 12.7, p. 350. San Francisco, CA: Benjamin Cummings. © 2004 Pearson Education, Inc., Upper Saddle River, New Jersey.

29.13 Adapted from Raven et al. *Biology of Plants*, 6th ed., fig. 19.7.

Table 30.1 Adapted from Randy Moore et al., *Botany*, 2nd ed. Dubuque, IA: Brown, 1998, Table 2.2, p. 37.

34.8a Adapted From J. Mallatt and J. Chen, "Fossil sister group of craniates: predicted and found," *Journal of Morphology*, Vol. 251 no. 1, fig 1, 5/15/03,© 2003 Wiley-Liss, Inc. a Wiley Co.; **34.8b** Adapted from D.-G. Shu et al. 2003 Head and backbone of the early Cambrian vertebrate *Haikouichthys*. *Nature* 421:528, fig. 1, part 1. © 2003 Nature Publishing Group; **34.12** Adapted from K. Kardong, *Vertebrates: Comparative Anatomy, Function and Evolution*, 3/e. © 2001 McGraw-Hill Science/Engineering/Mathematics; **34.19** Adapted from C. Zimmer. 1999. *At the Water's Edge*. Free Press, Simon & Schuster p. 90, **34.20** Adapted from C. Zimmer. 1999. *At the Water's Edge* Free Press, Simon & Schuster p. 99; **34.32-+** Adapted from Stephen J. Gould et al. 1993. *The Book of Life*. London: Ebury Press, p. 96. Reprinted by permission of Random House UK Ltd; **34.41** Drawn from photos of fossils: *O. tugenensis* photo in Michael Balter, Early hominid sows division. *ScienceNow*, Feb. 22, 2001. © 2001 American Association for the Advancement of Science. *A. ramidus kadabba* photo by Timothy White, 1999/Brill Atlanta. *A. anamensis, A. garhi,* and *H. neanderthalensis* adapted from *The Human Evolution Coloring Book*. *K platyops* drawn from photo in Meave Leakey et al., New hominid genus from eastern Africa shows diverse middle Pliocene lineages. *Nature*, March 22, 2001, 410:433. *P. boisei* drawn from a photo by David Bill. *H. ergaster* drawn from a photo at www.inhandmuseum.com. *S. tchadensis* drawn from a photo in Michel Brunet et al., A new hominid from the Upper Miocene of Chad, Central Africa, *Nature*, July 11, 2002, 418:147, fig. 1b.

35.21 Pie chart adapted from *Nature*, Dec. 14, 2000, 408:799

39.17(graph), **38.18** Adapted from M. Wilkins. 1988. *Plant Watching*. Facts of File Publ.; **39.29** Reprinted with permission from Edward Framer. 1997. *Science* 276:912. Copyright © 1997 American Association for the Advancement of Science.

40.17 Adapted from an illustration by Enid Kotschnig in B. Heinrich. 1987. Thermoregulation in a winter moth. *Scientific American* 105; **40.20** Adapted with permission from B. Heinrich. 1974. *Science* 185:747-756. © 1974 American Association for the Advancement of Science.

41.5 Adapted from J. Marx. "Cellular Warriors at the Battle of the Bulge." *Science*, Vol. 299, p. 846. Copyright © 2003 American Association for the Advancement of Science. Illustration: Katharine Sutliff; **41.13** Adapted from Lawrence G. Mitchell, John A. Mutchmor, and Warren D. Dolphin. 1988. *Zoology*. Menlo Park, CA: Benjamin Cummings. © 1988 The Benjamin Cummings Publishing Company; **41.15** Adapted from R. A. Rhoades and R. G. Pflanzer 1996. *Human Physiology*, 3/e., fig. 22-1, p. 666. Copyright © 1996 Saunders

43.7 Adapted from Gerard J. Tortora, Berdell R. Funke, and Christine L. Case. 1998. *Microbiology: An Introduction*, 6th ed. Menlo Park, CA: Benjamin/Cummings. © 1998 Benjamin Cummings, an imprint of Addison Wesley Longman, Inc.

44.5 Kangaroo rat data adapted from Schmidt-Nielsen. 1990. *Animal Physiology: Adaptation and Environment*, 4th ed., p. 330. Cambridge: Cambridge University Press; **44.6** Adapted from K.B. Schmidt-Nielsen et al., "Body temperature of the camel and its relation to water economy," *American Journal of Physiology*, Vol. 10, No. 188, (Dec.), 1956, figure 7. Copyright © 1956 American Physiological Society. Used with permission; **44.8** Adapted from Lawrence G. Mitchell, John A. Mutchmor, and Warren D. Dolphin. 1988. *Zoology*. Menlo Park, CA: Benjamin Cummings. © 1988 The Benjamin Cummings Publishing Company.

47.20 From Wolpert et al. 1998. *Principles of Development*. fig. 8.25, p. 251 (right). Oxford: Oxford University Press. By permission of Oxford University Press; **47.23b** From Hiroki Nishida, *Developmental Biology* Vol. 121, p 526, 1987. Copyright © 1987, with permission from Elsevier. **47.25 Experiment and left side of "Results"**: From Wolpert et al. 1998. *Principles of Development*. fig. 1.10, Oxford: Oxford University Press. By permission of Oxford University Press. **Right**

Glossary

5′ cap The 5′ end of a pre-mRNA molecule modified by the addition of a cap of guanine nucleotide.

A band The broad region that corresponds to the length of the thick filaments of myofibrils.

A site One of a ribosome's three binding sites for tRNA during translation. The A site holds the tRNA carrying the next amino acid to be added to the polypeptide chain. (A stands for aminoacyl tRNA.)

ABC model A model of flower formation identifying three classes of organ identity genes that direct formation of the four types of floral organs.

abdominal cavity The body cavity in mammals that primarily houses parts of the digestive, excretory, and reproductive systems. It is separated from the thoracic cavity by the diaphragm.

abiotic (ā-bī-ot′-ik) Nonliving.

ABO blood groups Genetically determined classes of human blood that are based on the presence or absence of carbohydrates A and B on the surface of red blood cells. The ABO blood group phenotypes, also called blood types, are A, B, AB, and O.

abortion The termination of a pregnancy in progress.

abscisic acid (ABA) (ab-sis′-ik) A plant hormone that slows down growth, often antagonizing actions of growth hormones. Two of its many effects are to promote seed dormancy and facilitate drought tolerance.

absorption The uptake of small nutrient molecules by an organism's own body; the third main stage of food processing, following digestion.

absorption spectrum The range of a pigment's ability to absorb various wavelengths of light.

abyssal Referring to the very deep benthic zone of the ocean.

acanthodian (ak′-an-thō′-dē-un) Any of a group of ancient jawed fishes from the Devonian period.

acclimatization (uh-klī′-muh-tī-zā′-shun) Physiological adjustment to a change in an environmental factor.

accommodation The automatic adjustment of an eye to focus on near objects.

acetyl CoA Acetyl coenzyme A; the entry compound for the citric acid cycle in cellular respiration, formed from a fragment of pyruvate attached to a coenzyme.

acetylcholine (as′-uh-til-kō′-lēn) One of the most common neurotransmitters; functions by binding to receptors and altering the permeability of the postsynaptic membrane to specific ions, either depolarizing or hyperpolarizing the membrane.

acid A substance that increases the hydrogen ion concentration of a solution.

acid chyme (kīm) A mixture of recently swallowed food and gastric juice.

acid precipitation Rain, snow, or fog that is more acidic than pH 5.6.

acoelomate (uh-sē′-lō-māt) A solid-bodied animal lacking a cavity between the gut and outer body wall.

acquired immunity The kind of defense that is mediated by B lymphocytes (B cells) and T lymphocytes (T cells). It exhibits specificity, memory, and self-nonself recognition. Also called adaptive immunity.

acrosomal reaction The discharge of a sperm's acrosome when the sperm approaches an egg.

acrosome (ak′-ruh-sōm) A vesicle at the tip of a sperm cell that helps the sperm penetrate the egg.

actin (ak′-tin) A globular protein that links into chains, two of which twist helically about each other, forming microfilaments in muscle and other contractile elements in cells.

action potential A rapid change in the membrane potential of an excitable cell, caused by stimulus-triggered, selective opening and closing of voltage-sensitive gates in sodium and potassium ion channels.

action spectrum A graph that depicts the relative effectiveness of different wavelengths of radiation in driving a particular process.

activation energy See free energy of activation.

activator A protein that binds to DNA and stimulates transcription of a specific gene.

active immunity Long-lasting immunity conferred by the action of a person's B cells and T cells and the resulting B and T memory cells specific for a pathogen. Active immunity can develop as a result of natural infection or immunization.

active site The specific portion of an enzyme that attaches to the substrate by means of weak chemical bonds.

active transport The movement of a substance across a biological membrane against its concentration or electrochemical gradient with the help of energy input and specific transport proteins.

actual evapotranspiration The amount of water annually transpired by plants and evaporated from a landscape, usually measured in millimeters.

adaptive radiation The emergence of numerous species from a common ancestor introduced into an environment that presents a diversity of new opportunities and problems.

adenohypophysis (ad′-uh-nō-hī-pof′-uh-sis) See anterior pituitary.

adenylyl cyclase (ad′-en-uh-lil) An enzyme that converts ATP to cyclic AMP in response to a chemical signal.

adhesion The attraction between different kinds of molecules.

adipose tissue A connective tissue that insulates the body and serves as a fuel reserve; contains fat-storing cells called adipose cells.

adrenal gland (uh-drē′-nul) One of two endocrine glands located adjacent to the kidneys in mammals. Endocrine cells in the outer portion (cortex) respond to ACTH by secreting steroid hormones that help maintain homeostasis during long-term stress. Neurosecretory cells in the central portion (medulla) secrete epinephrine and norepinephrine in response to nervous inputs triggered by short-term stress.

adrenocorticotropic hormone (ACTH) A tropic hormone produced and secreted by the anterior pituitary that stimulates the production and secretion of steroid hormones by the adrenal cortex.

adventitious A term describing any plant organ that grows in an atypical location, such as roots growing from stems.

aerobic (âr-ō′-bik) Containing oxygen; referring to an organism, environment, or cellular process that requires oxygen.

afferent arteriole (af′-er-ent) The blood vessel supplying a nephron.

age structure The relative number of individuals of each age in a population.

aggregate fruit A fruit derived from a single flower that has more than one carpel.

agonistic behavior (a′-gō-nis′-tik) A type of behavior involving a contest of some kind that determines which competitor gains access to some resource, such as food or mates.

AIDS (acquired immunodeficiency syndrome) The name of the late stages of HIV infection, defined by a specified reduction of T cells and the appearance of characteristic secondary infections.

alcohol fermentation The conversion of pyruvate to carbon dioxide and ethyl alcohol.

aldosterone (al-dos′-tuh-rōn) An adrenal hormone that acts on the distal tubules of the kidney to stimulate the reabsorption of sodium (Na$^+$) and the passive flow of water from the filtrate.

alga (plural, **algae**) (al -guh, al -je) A photosynthetic, plant-like protist.

alimentary canal (al -uh-men -tuh-re) A digestive tract consisting of a tube running between a mouth and an anus.

allantois (al -an-to-is) One of four extraembryonic membranes; serves as a repository for the embryo's nitrogenous waste.

alleles (uh-le -ulz) Alternative versions of a gene that produce distinguishable phenotypic effects.

allometric growth (al -o-met -rik) The variation in the relative rates of growth of various parts of the body, which helps shape the organism.

allopatric speciation (al -o-pat -rik) A mode of speciation induced when an ancestral population becomes segregated by a geographic barrier or is itself divided into two or more geographically isolated subpopulations.

allopolyploid (al -o-pol -e-ployd) A common type of polyploid species resulting from two different species interbreeding and combining their chromosomes.

allosteric regulation The binding of a molecule to a protein that affects the function of the protein at a different site.

alpha (α) helix (al -tuh he -liks) A spiral shape constituting one form of the secondary structure of proteins, arising from a specific hydrogen-bonding structure.

alternation of generations A life cycle in which there is both a multicellular diploid form, the sporophyte, and a multicellular haploid form, the gametophyte, characteristic of plants and some algae.

alternative RNA splicing A type of regulation at the RNA-processing level in which different mRNA molecules are produced from the same primary transcript, depending on which RNA segments are treated as exons and which as introns.

altruism (al -true-iz-um) Behavior that reduces an individual's fitness while increasing the fitness of another individual.

alveolus (al-ve -uh-lus) (plural **alveoli**) One of the dead-end, multilobed air sacs that constitute the gas exchange surface of the lungs.

Alzheimer's disease An age-related dementia (mental deterioration) characterized by confusion, memory loss, and other symptoms.

amacrine cell (am -uh-krin) A neuron of the retina that helps integrate information before it is sent to the brain.

amino acid (uh-men -o) An organic molecule possessing both carboxyl and amino groups. Amino acids serve as the monomers of proteins.

amino group A functional group that consists of a nitrogen atom bonded to two hydrogen atoms; can act as a base in solution, accepting a hydrogen ion and acquiring a charge of 1+.

aminoacyl-tRNA synthetase An enzyme that joins each amino acid to the correct tRNA.

ammonia A small, very toxic molecule made up of three hydrogen atoms and one nitrogen atom; produced by nitrogen fixation and as a metabolic waste product of protein and nucleic acid metabolism.

ammonite A shelled cephalopod that was the dominant invertebrate predator for millions of years until the end of the Cretaceous period.

amniocentesis (am -ne-o-sen te -sis) A technique of prenatal diagnosis in which amniotic fluid, obtained by aspiration from a needle inserted into the uterus, is analyzed to detect certain genetic and congenital defects in the fetus.

amnion (am -ne-on) The innermost of four extraembryonic membranes; encloses a fluid-filled sac in which the embryo is suspended.

amniote Member of a clade of tetrapods that have an amniotic egg containing specialized membranes that protect the embryo, including mammals and birds and other reptiles.

amoeba (uh-me -buh) A protist grade characterized by the presence of pseudopodia.

amoebocyte (uh-me -buh-sit) An amoeba-like cell that moves by pseudopodia; found in most animals; depending on the species, may digest and distribute food, dispose of wastes, form skeletal fibers, fight infections, and change into other cell types.

amphibian Member of the tetrapod class Amphibia, including salamanders, frogs, and caecilians.

amphipathic molecule (am -fe-path -ik) A molecule that has both a hydrophilic region and a hydrophobic region.

amplification The strengthening of stimulus energy that is otherwise too weak to be carried into the nervous system.

anabolic pathway (an -uh-bol -ik) A metabolic pathway that synthesizes a complex molecule from simpler compounds.

anaerobic (an -ar-o -bik) Lacking oxygen; referring to an organism, environment, or cellular process that lacks oxygen and may be poisoned by it.

anaerobic respiration The use of inorganic molecules other than oxygen to accept electrons at the "downhill" end of electron transport chains.

analogy Similarity between two species that is due to convergent evolution rather than to descent from a common ancestor with the same trait.

anaphase The fourth stage of mitosis, in which the chromatids of each chromosome have separated and the daughter chromosomes are moving to the poles of the cell.

anaphylactic shock (an -uh-fi-lak-tic) An acute, whole-body, life-threatening, allergic response.

anatomy The study of the structure of an organism.

anchorage dependence The requirement that to divide, a cell must be attached to the substratum.

androgen (an -dro-jen) Any steroid hormone, such as testosterone, that stimulates the development and maintenance of the male reproductive system and secondary sex characteristics.

aneuploidy (an -yu-ploy-de) A chromosomal aberration in which one or more chromosomes are present in extra copies or are deficient in number.

angiosperm (an -je-o-sperm) A flowering plant, which forms seeds inside a protective chamber called an ovary.

angiotensin II A hormone that stimulates constriction of precapillary arterioles and increases reabsorption of NaCl and water by the proximal tubules of the kidney, increasing blood pressure and volume.

anhydrobiosis (an -hi -dro-bi-o -sis) The ability to survive in a dormant state when an organism's habitat dries up.

animal pole The portion of the egg where the least yolk is concentrated, opposite of vegetal pole.

Animalia The kingdom that consists of multicellular eukaryotes that ingest their food.

anion (an -i-on) A negatively charged ion.

annual A flowering plant that completes its entire life cycle in a single year or growing season.

anterior Referring to the head end of a bilaterally symmetrical animal.

anterior pituitary Also called the adenohypophysis; portion of the pituitary that develops from nonneural tissue; consists of endocrine cells that synthesize and secrete several tropic and nontropic hormones.

anther (an -ther) In an angiosperm, the terminal pollen sac of a stamen, where pollen grains with male gametes form.

antheridium (an -thuh-rid -e-um) (plural, **antheridia**) In plants, the male gametangium, a moist chamber in which gametes develop.

anthropoid (an -thruh-poyd) A member of a primate group made up of the apes (gibbon, orangutan, gorilla, chimpanzee, and bonobo), monkeys, and humans.

antibody A protein secreted by plasma cells (differentiated B cells) that binds to a particular antigen and marks it for elimination; also called immunoglobulin. All antibody molecules have the same Y-shaped structure and in their monomer form consist of two identical heavy chains and two identical light chains joined by disulfide bridges.

anticodon (an -ti-ko -don) A specialized base triplet at one end of a tRNA molecule that recognizes a particular complementary codon on an mRNA molecule.

antidiuretic hormone (ADH) A hormone produced in the hypothalamus and released from the posterior pituitary. It promotes water retention by the kidneys as part of an elaborate feedback scheme that helps regulate the osmolarity of the blood.

antigen (an´-tuh-jen) A macromolecule that elicits an immune response by lymphocytes.

antigen presentation The process by which an MHC molecule binds to a fragment of an intracellular protein antigen and carries it to the cell surface, where it is displayed and can be recognized by a T cell.

antigen receptor The general term for a surface protein, located on B cells and T cells, that binds to antigens, initiating acquired immune responses. The antigen receptors on B cells are called B cell receptors (or membrane immunoglobulins), and the antigen receptors on T cells are called T cell receptors.

antigen-presenting cell A cell that ingests bacteria and viruses and destroys them, generating peptide fragments that are bound by class II MHC molecules and subsequently displayed on the cell surface to helper T cells. Macrophages, dendritic cells, and B cells are the primary antigen-presenting cells.

antiparallel The opposite arrangement of the sugar-phosphate backbones in a DNA double helix.

aphotic zone (a´-fo´-tik) The part of the ocean beneath the photic zone, where light does not penetrate sufficiently for photosynthesis to occur.

apical dominance (a´-pik-ul) Concentration of growth at the tip of a plant shoot, where a terminal bud partially inhibits axillary bud growth.

apical ectodermal ridge A limb-bud organizer region consisting of a thickened area of ectoderm at the tip of a limb bud.

apical meristem (a´-pik-ul mar´-uh-stem) Embryonic plant tissue in the tips of roots and in the buds of shoots that supplies cells for the plant to grow in length.

apicomplexan (ap´-e-kom-pleks´-un) A parasitic protozoan. Some apicomplexans cause human diseases.

apomixis (ap´-uh-mik´-sis) The asexual production of seeds.

apoplast (ap´-o-plast) In plants, the continuum of cell walls plus the extracellular spaces.

apoptosis The changes that occur within a cell as it undergoes programmed cell death, which is brought about by signals that trigger the activation of a cascade of suicide proteins in the cell destined to die.

aposematic coloration (ap´-o-so-mat´-ik) The bright coloration of animals with effective physical or chemical defenses that acts as a warning to predators.

appendix A small, fingerlike extension of the vertebrate cecum; contains a mass of white blood cells that contribute to immunity.

aquaporin A transport protein in the plasma membrane of a plant or animal cell that

specifically facilitates the diffusion of water across the membrane (osmosis).

aqueous humor (a´-kwe-us hyu´-mer) Plasma-like liquid in the space between the lens and the cornea in the vertebrate eye; helps maintain the shape of the eye, supplies nutrients and oxygen to its tissues, and disposes of its wastes.

aqueous solution (a´-kwe-us) A solution in which water is the solvent.

arbuscular mycorrhiza A distinct type of endomycorrhiza formed by glomeromycete fungi, in which the tips of the fungal hyphae that invade the plant roots branch into tiny treelike structures called arbuscules.

Archaea (ar´-ke-uh) One of two prokaryotic domains, the other being Bacteria.

archegonium (ar-ki-go´-ne-um) (plural, **archegonia**) In plants, the female gametangium, a moist chamber in which gametes develop.

archenteron (ar-ken´-tuh-ron) The endoderm-lined cavity, formed during the gastrulation process, that develops into the digestive tract of an animal.

archosaur Member of the reptilian group that includes crocodiles, alligators, dinosaurs, and birds.

arteriole (ar-ter´-e-ol) A vessel that conveys blood between an artery and a capillary bed.

artery A vessel that carries blood away from the heart to organs throughout the body.

arthropod A segmented coelomate with a chitinous exoskeleton, jointed appendages, and a body formed of distinct groups of segments.

artificial selection The selective breeding of domesticated plants and animals to encourage the occurrence of desirable traits.

ascocarp The fruiting body of a sac fungus (ascomycete).

ascomycete See sac fungus.

ascus (plural, **asci**) A saclike spore capsule located at the tip of a dikaryotic hypha of a sac fungus.

asexual reproduction A type of reproduction involving only one parent that produces genetically identical offspring by budding or by the division of a single cell or the entire organism into two or more parts.

aspartate An amino acid that functions as a CNS neurotransmitter.

assisted reproductive technology (ART) Fertilization procedures that generally involve the surgical removal of eggs (secondary oocytes) from a woman's ovaries after hormonal stimulation, fertilizing the eggs, and returning them to the woman's body.

associative learning The acquired ability to associate one stimulus with another; also called classical conditioning.

aster A radial array of short microtubules that extends from each centrosome toward the plasma membrane in a cell undergoing mitosis.

astrocyte A glial cell that provides structural and metabolic support for neurons.

atherosclerosis A cardiovascular disease in which growths called plaques develop in the inner walls of the arteries, narrowing their inner diameters.

atom The smallest unit of matter that retains the properties of an element.

atomic mass The total mass of an atom, which is the mass in grams of one mole of the atom.

atomic nucleus An atom's central core, containing protons and neutrons.

atomic number The number of protons in the nucleus of an atom, unique for each element and designated by a subscript to the left of the elemental symbol.

ATP (adenosine triphosphate) (a-den´-o-sen tri-fos´-fat) An adenine-containing nucleoside triphosphate that releases free energy when its phosphate bonds are hydrolyzed. This energy is used to drive endergonic reactions in cells.

ATP synthase A cluster of several membrane proteins found in the mitochondrial crista (and bacterial plasma membrane) that function in chemiosmosis with adjacent electron transport chains, using the energy of a hydrogen ion concentration gradient to make ATP. ATP synthases provide a port through which hydrogen ions diffuse into the matrix of a mitochondrion.

atrial natriuretic factor (ANF) (a´-tre-al na´-tre-u-ret´-ik) A peptide hormone that opposes the renin-angiotensin-aldosterone system (RAAS).

atrioventricular (AV) node A region of specialized muscle tissue between the right atrium and right ventricle where electrical impulses are delayed for about 0.1 second before spreading to the ventricles and causing them to contract.

atrioventricular (AV) valve A valve in the heart between each atrium and ventricle that prevents a backflow of blood when the ventricles contract.

atrium (a´-tre-um) (plural, **atria**) A chamber that receives blood returning to the vertebrate heart.

autoimmune disease An immunological disorder in which the immune system turns against self.

autonomic nervous system (ot´-o-nom´-ik) A subdivision of the motor nervous system of vertebrates that regulates the internal environment; consists of the sympathetic, parasympathetic, and enteric divisions.

autopolyploid (ot´-o-pol´-e-ploid) An individual that has more than two chromosome sets, all derived from a single species.

autosome (ot´-o-som) A chromosome that is not directly involved in determining sex, as opposed to a sex chromosome.

autotroph (ot´-o-trof) An organism that obtains organic food molecules without eating other organisms or substances derived from other organisms. Autotrophs use energy from the sun or from the oxidation of inorganic substances to make organic molecules from inorganic ones.

auxin (ok -sin) A term that primarily refers to indoleacetic acid (IAA), a natural plant hormone that has a variety of effects, including cell elongation, root formation, secondary growth, and fruit growth.

average heterozygosity The percent, on average, of a population's loci that are heterozygous in members of the population.

avirulent A term describing a pathogen that can only mildly harm, but not kill, the host plant.

axillary bud (ak -sil ar ē) A structure that has the potential to form a lateral shoot, or branch. The bud appears in the angle formed between a leaf and a stem.

axon (ak -son) A typically long extension, or process, from a neuron that carries nerve impulses away from the cell body toward target cells.

axon hillock The conical region of a neuron's axon where it joins the cell body; typically the region where nerve signals are generated.

B cell receptor The antigen receptor on B cells, a Y-shaped, membrane-bound molecule consisting of two identical heavy chains and two identical light chains linked by disulfide bridges and containing two antigen-binding sites; also called a membrane immunoglobulin or membrane antibody.

B lymphocyte (B cell) A type of lymphocyte that develops to maturity in the bone marrow. After encountering antigen, B cells differentiate into antibody-secreting plasma cells, the effector cells of humoral immunity.

Bacteria One of two prokaryotic domains, the other being Archaea.

bacterial artificial chromosome (BAC) An artificial version of a bacterial chromosome that can carry inserts of 100,000 to 300,000 base pairs.

bacteriophage (bak-ter -ē-o-fāj) A virus that infects bacteria; also called a phage.

bacteroids A form of *Rhizobium* contained within the vesicles formed by the root cells of a root nodule.

baculum (bak -ū-lum) A bone that is contained in, and helps stiffen, the penis of rodents, raccoons, walruses, whales, and several other mammals.

balanced polymorphism The ability of natural selection to maintain diversity in a population.

balancing selection Natural selection that maintains stable frequencies of two or more phenotypic forms in a population (balanced polymorphism).

bark All tissues external to the vascular cambium, consisting mainly of the secondary phloem and layers of periderm.

Barr body A dense object lying along the inside of the nuclear envelope in female mammalian cells, representing an inactivated X chromosome.

barrier method Contraception that relies on a physical barrier to block the passage of sperm. Examples include condoms and diaphragms.

Bartholin's glands (bar -to-linz) Glands near the vaginal opening in a human female that secrete lubricating fluid during sexual arousal.

basal angiosperms The most primitive lineages of flowering plants, including *Amborella*, water lilies, and star anise and relatives.

basal body (bā -sul) A eukaryotic cell organelle consisting of a 9 + 0 arrangement of microtubule triplets; may organize the microtubule assembly of a cilium or flagellum; structurally identical to a centriole.

basal metabolic rate (BMR) The metabolic rate of a resting, fasting, and nonstressed endotherm.

basal nuclei A cluster of nuclei deep within the white matter of the cerebrum.

base A substance that reduces the hydrogen ion concentration of a solution.

basement membrane The floor of an epithelial membrane on which the basal cells rest.

base-pair substitution A type of point mutation; the replacement of one nucleotide and its partner in the complementary DNA strand by another pair of nucleotides.

basidiocarp Elaborate fruiting body of a dikaryotic mycelium of a club fungus.

basidiomycete See club fungus.

basidium (plural, **basidia**) A reproductive appendage that produces sexual spores on the gills of mushrooms (club fungi).

Batesian mimicry (bāt -ze-un mim -uh-krē) A type of mimicry in which a harmless species looks like a species that is poisonous or otherwise harmful to predators.

behavior Everything an animal does and how it does it, including muscular activities such as chasing prey, certain nonmuscular processes such as secreting a hormone that attracts a mate, and learning.

behavioral ecology The scientific study of animal behavior, including how it is controlled and how it develops, evolves, and contributes to survival and reproductive success.

benign tumor A mass of abnormal cells that remains at the site of origin.

benthic zone The bottom surface of an aquatic environment.

benthos (ben -thoz) The communities of organisms living in the benthic zone of an aquatic biome.

beta oxidation A metabolic sequence that breaks fatty acids down to two-carbon fragments that enter the citric acid cycle as acetyl CoA.

beta (β) pleated sheet One form of the secondary structure of proteins in which the polypeptide chain folds back and forth. Two

regions of the chain lie parallel to each other and are held together by hydrogen bonds.

biennial (bī-en -ē-ul) A flowering plant that requires two years to complete its life cycle.

big-bang reproduction A life history in which adults have but a single reproductive opportunity to produce large numbers of offspring, such as the life history of the Pacific salmon; also known as semelparity.

bilateral symmetry Characterizing a body form with a central longitudinal plane that divides the body into two equal but opposite halves.

bilaterian (bī -luh-ter -ē-uhn) Member of the clade Bilateria, animals with bilateral symmetry.

bile A mixture of substances that is produced in the liver, stored in the gallbladder, and acts as a detergent to aid in the digestion and absorption of fats.

binary fission The type of cell division by which prokaryotes reproduce. Each dividing daughter cell receives a copy of the single parental chromosome.

binomial The two-part latinized name of a species, consisting of genus and specific epithet.

biodiversity hot spot A relatively small area with an exceptional concentration of endemic species and a large number of endangered and threatened species.

bioenergetics The flow of energy through an animal, taking into account the energy stored in the food it consumes, the energy used for basic functions, activity, growth, reproduction, and regulation, and the energy lost to the environment as heat or in waste.

biofilm A surface-coating colony of prokaryotes that engage in metabolic cooperation.

biogenic amine A neurotransmitter derived from an amino acid.

biogeochemical cycle Any of the various nutrient circuits, which involve both biotic and abiotic components of ecosystems.

biogeography The study of the past and present distribution of species.

bioinformatics Using computing power, software, and mathematical models to process and integrate biological information from large data sets.

biological augmentation An approach to restoration ecology that uses organisms to add essential materials to a degraded ecosystem.

biological clock An internal timekeeper that controls an organism's biological rhythms. The biological clock marks time with or without environmental cues but often requires signals from the environment to remain tuned to an appropriate period. See also circadian rhythm.

biological magnification A trophic process in which retained substances become more concentrated with each link in the food chain.

biological species concept Definition of a species as a population or group of populations whose members have the potential to interbreed in nature and produce viable, fertile offspring, but are not able to produce viable, fertile offspring with members of other populations.

biology The scientific study of life.

biomanipulation A technique for restoring eutrophic lakes that reduces populations of algae by manipulating the higher-level consumers in the community rather than by changing nutrient levels or adding chemical treatments.

biomass The dry weight of organic matter comprising a group of organisms in a particular habitat.

biome (bī´-om) Any of the world's major ecosystems, classified according to the predominant vegetation and characterized by adaptations of organisms to that particular environment.

bioremediation The use of living organisms to detoxify and restore polluted and degraded ecosystems.

biosphere (bī´-o-sfēr) The entire portion of Earth inhabited by life; the sum of all the planet's ecosystems.

biota All the organisms that are part of an ecosystem.

biotechnology The manipulation of living organisms or their components to produce useful products.

biotic (bī-ot´-tik) Pertaining to the living organisms in the environment.

bipolar cell A neuron that synapses with the axon of a rod or cone in the retina of the eye.

bipolar disorder Depressive mental illness characterized by swings of mood from high to low; also called manic-depressive disorder.

birth control pills Chemical contraceptives that inhibit ovulation, retard follicular development, or alter a woman's cervical mucus to prevent sperm from entering the uterus.

blade (1) A leaflike structure of a seaweed that provides most of the surface area for photosynthesis. (2) The flattened portion of a typical leaf.

blastocoel (blas´-tuh-sēl) The fluid-filled cavity that forms in the center of the blastula embryo.

blastocyst An embryonic stage in mammals; a hollow ball of cells produced one week after fertilization in humans.

blastoderm An embryonic cap of dividing cells resting on a large undivided yolk.

blastomere A small cell of an early embryo.

blastopore (blas´-to-pōr) The opening of the archenteron in the gastrula that develops into the mouth in protostomes and the anus in deuterostomes.

blastula (blas´-tyū-luh) The hollow ball of cells marking the end stage of cleavage during early embryonic development.

blood A type of connective tissue with a fluid matrix called plasma in which blood cells are suspended.

blood pressure The hydrostatic force that blood exerts against the wall of a vessel.

blood vessels A set of tubes through which the blood moves through the body.

blood-brain barrier A specialized capillary arrangement in the brain that restricts the passage of most substances into the brain, thereby preventing dramatic fluctuations in the brain's environment.

blue-light photoreceptors A class of light receptors in plants. Blue light initiates a variety of responses, such as phototropism and slowing of hypocotyl elongation.

body cavity A fluid-containing space between the digestive tract and the body wall.

body plan In animals, the set of morphological and developmental traits that define a grade (level of organizational complexity).

Bohr shift A lowering of the affinity of hemoglobin for oxygen, caused by a drop in pH, facilitates the release of oxygen from hemoglobin in the vicinity of active tissues.

bolus A lubricated ball of chewed food.

bone A type of connective tissue, consisting of living cells held in a rigid matrix of collagen fibers embedded in calcium salts.

book lung An organ of gas exchange in spiders, consisting of stacked plates contained in an internal chamber.

bottleneck effect Genetic drift resulting from the reduction of a population, typically by a natural disaster, such that the surviving population is no longer genetically representative of the original population.

bottom-up model A model of community organization in which mineral nutrients control community organization because nutrients control plant numbers, which in turn control herbivore numbers, which in turn control predator numbers.

Bowman's capsule (bō´-munz) A cup-shaped receptacle in the vertebrate kidney that is the initial, expanded segment of the nephron where filtrate enters from the blood.

brachiopod A marine lophophorate with a shell divided into dorsal and ventral halves. Brachiopods are also called lamp shells.

brain hormone A hormone, produced by neurosecretory cells in the insect brain, that promotes development by stimulating the prothoracic glands to secrete ecdysone.

brainstem Collection of structures in the adult brain, including the midbrain, the pons, and the medulla oblongata; functions in homeostasis, coordination of movement, and conduction of information to higher brain centers.

brassinosteroids Steroid hormones in plants that have a variety of effects, including cell elongation, retarding leaf abscission, and promoting xylem differentiation.

breathing The process involving alternate inhalation and exhalation of air that ventilates the lungs.

breathing control center A brain center that directs the activity of organs involved in breathing.

bronchiole One of the fine branches of the bronchus that transport air to alveoli.

bronchus (bron´-kus) (plural, **bronchi**) One of a pair of breathing tubes that branch from the trachea into the lungs.

brown alga A phaeophyte; a marine, multicellular, autotrophic protist that is the most common type of seaweed. Brown algae include the kelps.

brown fat A tissue in some mammals, located in the neck and between the shoulders, that is specialized for rapid heat production.

bryophyte (brī´-uh-fīt) A moss, liverwort, or hornwort; a nonvascular plant that inhabits the land but lacks many of the terrestrial adaptations of vascular plants.

budding An asexual means of propagation in which outgrowths from the parent form and pinch off to live independently or else remain attached to eventually form extensive colonies.

buffer A substance that consists of acid and base forms in a solution and that minimizes changes in pH when extraneous acids or bases are added to the solution.

bulbourethral gland (bul´-bō-yū-rē´-thrul) One of a pair of glands near the base of the penis in the human male that secretes fluid that lubricates and neutralizes acids in the urethra during sexual arousal.

bulk feeder An animal that eats relatively large pieces of food.

bulk flow The movement of water due to a difference in pressure between two locations.

bundle sheath A protective covering around a leaf vein, consisting of one or more cell layers, usually parenchyma.

bundle-sheath cell A type of photosynthetic cell arranged into tightly packed sheaths around the veins of a leaf.

C₃ plant A plant that uses the Calvin cycle for the initial steps that incorporate CO_2 into organic material, forming a three-carbon compound as the first stable intermediate.

C₄ plant A plant that prefaces the Calvin cycle with reactions that incorporate CO_2 into a four-carbon compound, the end product of which supplies CO_2 for the Calvin cycle.

cadherins An important class of cell-to-cell adhesion molecules.

calcitonin (kal´-si-tō´-nin) A hormone secreted by the thyroid gland that lowers blood calcium levels by promoting calcium deposition in bone and calcium excretion from the kidneys.

callus A mass of dividing, undifferentiated cells at the cut end of a shoot.

calorie (cal) The amount of heat energy required to raise the temperature of 1 g of water by 1°C; also the amount of heat energy that 1 g of water releases when it cools by 1°C. The Calorie (with a capital C), usually used to indicate the energy content of food, is a kilocalorie.

Calvin cycle The second of two major stages in photosynthesis (following the light reactions), involving atmospheric CO_2 fixation and reduction of the fixed carbon into carbohydrate.

calyptra A protective cap of gametophyte tissue that wholly or partially covers an immature capsule in many mosses.

CAM plant A plant that uses crassulacean acid metabolism, an adaptation for photosynthesis in arid conditions, first discovered in the family Crassulaceae. Carbon dioxide entering open stomata during the night is converted into organic acids, which release CO_2 for the Calvin cycle during the day, when stomata are closed.

Cambrian explosion A burst of evolutionary origins when most of the major body plans of animals appeared in a relatively brief time in geologic history, recorded in the fossil record about 542–525 million years ago.

canopy The uppermost layer of vegetation in a terrestrial biome.

capillary (kap-il-ar-ē) A microscopic blood vessel that penetrates the tissues and consists of a single layer of endothelial cells that allows exchange between the blood and interstitial fluid.

capillary bed A network of capillaries that infiltrate every organ and tissue in the body.

capsid The protein shell that encloses a viral genome. It may be rod-shaped, polyhedral, or more complex in shape.

capsule (1) A sticky layer that surrounds the cell walls of some prokaryotes, protecting the cell surface and sometimes helping to glue the cell to surfaces. (2) The sporangium of a bryophyte (moss, liverwort, or hornwort).

carbohydrate (kar-bo-hī-drāt) A sugar (monosaccharide) or one of its dimers (disaccharides) or polymers (polysaccharides).

carbon fixation The incorporation of carbon from CO_2 into an organic compound by an autotrophic organism (a plant, another photosynthetic organism, or a chemoautotrophic prokaryote).

carbonyl group (kar-buh-nel) A functional group present in aldehydes and ketones and consisting of a carbon atom double-bonded to an oxygen atom.

carboxyl group (kar-bok-sil) A functional group present in organic acids and consisting of a single carbon atom double-bonded to an oxygen atom and also bonded to a hydroxyl group.

cardiac cycle (kar-dē-ak) The alternating contractions and relaxations of the heart.

cardiac muscle A type of muscle that forms the contractile wall of the heart. Its cells are joined by intercalated disks that relay each heartbeat.

cardiac output The volume of blood pumped per minute by the left ventricle of the heart.

cardiovascular disease (kar-dē-ō-vas-kyū-ler) Diseases of the heart and blood vessels.

cardiovascular system A closed circulatory system with a heart and branching network of arteries, capillaries, and veins. The system is characteristic of vertebrates.

carnivore An animal, such as a shark, hawk, or spider, that eats other animals.

carotenoid (kuh-rot-uh-noyd) An accessory pigment, either yellow or orange, in the chloroplasts of plants. By absorbing wavelengths of light that chlorophyll cannot, carotenoids broaden the spectrum of colors that can drive photosynthesis.

carpel (kar-pul) The ovule-producing reproductive organ of a flower, consisting of the stigma, style, and ovary.

carrier In genetics, an individual who is heterozygous at a given genetic locus, with one normal allele and one potentially harmful recessive allele. The heterozygote is phenotypically normal for the character determined by the gene but can pass on the harmful allele to offspring.

carrying capacity The maximum population size that can be supported by the available resources, symbolized as K.

cartilage (kar-til-ij) A type of flexible connective tissue with an abundance of collagenous fibers embedded in chondroitin sulfate.

Casparian strip (kas-par-ē-un) A water impermeable ring of wax in the endodermal cells of plants that blocks the passive flow of water and solutes into the stele by way of cell walls.

catabolic pathway (kat-uh-bol-ik) A metabolic pathway that releases energy by breaking down complex molecules to simpler compounds.

catalyst A chemical agent that changes the rate of a reaction without being consumed by the reaction.

catastrophism The hypothesis by Georges Cuvier that each boundary between strata corresponded in time to a catastrophe, such as a flood or drought, that had destroyed many of the species living there at that time.

catecholamine Any of a class of compounds, including the hormones epinephrine and norepinephrine, that are synthesized from the amino acid tyrosine.

cation (kat-i-on) An ion with a positive charge, produced by the loss of one or more electrons.

cation exchange A process in which positively charged minerals are made available to a plant when hydrogen ions in the soil displace mineral ions from the clay particles.

CD4 A surface protein, present on most helper T cells, that binds to class II MHC molecules on antigen-presenting cells, enhancing the interaction between the T cell and the antigen-presenting cell.

CD8 A surface protein, present on most cytotoxic cells, that binds to class I MHC molecules on target cells, enhancing the interaction between the T cell and the target cell.

cDNA library A limited gene library using complementary DNA. The library includes only the genes that were transcribed in the cells examined.

cecum (sē-kum) (plural, ceca) A blind outpocket of a hollow organ such as an intestine.

cell Life's fundamental unit of structure and function.

cell adhesion molecules (CAMs) Glycoproteins that contribute to cell migration and stable tissue structure.

cell body The part of a neuron that houses the nucleus and other organelles.

cell cycle An ordered sequence of events in the life of a eukaryotic cell, from its origin in the division of a parent cell until its own division into two; composed of the M, G_1, S, and G_2 phases.

cell cycle control system A cyclically operating set of molecules in the cell that triggers and coordinates key events in the cell cycle.

cell differentiation The structural and functional divergence of cells as they become specialized during a multicellular organism's development; dependent on the control of gene expression.

cell division The reproduction of cells.

cell fractionation The disruption of a cell and separation of its organelles by centrifugation.

cell lineage The ancestry of a cell.

cell-mediated immune response The branch of acquired immunity that involves the activation of cytotoxic T cells, which defend against infected cells, cancer cells, and transplanted cells.

cell plate A double membrane across the midline of a dividing plant cell, between which the new cell wall forms during cytokinesis.

cellular respiration The most prevalent and efficient catabolic pathway for the production of ATP, in which oxygen is consumed as a reactant along with the organic fuel.

cellular slime mold A type of protist that has unicellular amoeboid cells and aggregated reproductive bodies in its life cycle.

cellulose (sel-yū-lōs) A structural polysaccharide of cell walls, consisting of glucose monomers joined by β-1,4-glycosidic linkages.

cell wall A protective layer external to the plasma membrane in plant cells, prokaryotes, fungi, and some protists. In plant cells, the wall is formed of cellulose fibers embedded in a polysaccharide-protein matrix. The primary cell wall is thin and flexible, whereas the secondary cell wall is stronger and more rigid and is the primary constituent of wood.

Celsius scale (sel'-sē-us) A temperature scale (°C) equal to 5/9 (°F − 32) that measures the freezing point of water at 0°C and the boiling point of water at 100°C.

central canal The narrow cavity in the center of the spinal cord that is continuous with the fluid-filled ventricles of the brain.

central nervous system (CNS) In vertebrate animals, the brain and spinal cord.

central vacuole A membranous sac in a mature plant cell with diverse roles in reproduction, growth, and development.

centriole (sen'-trē-ōl) A structure in an animal cell composed of cylinders of microtubule triplets arranged in a 9 + 0 pattern. An animal cell usually has a pair of centrioles involved in cell division.

centromere (sen'-trō-mēr) The centralized region joining two sister chromatids.

centrosome (sen'-trō-sōm) Material present in the cytoplasm of all eukaryotic cells, important during cell division; the microtubule-organizing center.

cephalization (sef-uh-luh-zā'-shun) An evolutionary trend toward the concentration of sensory equipment on the anterior end of the body.

cerebellum (sār'-ruh-bel'-um) Part of the vertebrate hindbrain located dorsally; functions in unconscious coordination of movement and balance.

cerebral cortex (suh-rē'-brul) The surface of the cerebrum; the largest and most complex part of the mammalian brain, containing sensory and motor nerve cell bodies of the cerebrum; the part of the vertebrate brain most changed through evolution.

cerebral hemisphere The right or left side of the vertebrate brain.

cerebrospinal fluid (suh-rē'-brō-spī'-nul) Blood-derived fluid that surrounds, protects against infection, nourishes, and cushions the brain and spinal cord.

cerebrum (suh-rē'-brum) The dorsal portion of the vertebrate forebrain, composed of right and left hemispheres; the integrating center for memory, learning, emotions, and other highly complex functions of the central nervous system.

cervix (ser'-viks) The neck of the uterus, which opens into the vagina.

chaparral (shap-uh-ral') A scrubland biome of dense, spiny evergreen shrubs found at mid-latitudes along coasts where cold ocean currents circulate offshore; characterized by mild, rainy winters and long, hot, dry summers.

chaperonin A protein molecule that assists the proper folding of other proteins.

character An observable heritable feature.

character displacement The tendency for characteristics to be more divergent in sympatric populations of two species than in allopatric populations of the same two species.

checkpoint A critical control point in the cell cycle where stop and go-ahead signals can regulate the cycle.

chelicera One of a pair of clawlike feeding appendages characteristic of cheliceriforms.

cheliceriform An arthropod that has chelicerae and a body divided into a cephalothorax and an abdomen. Living cheliceriforms include sea spiders, horseshoe crabs, scorpions, ticks, and spiders.

chemical bond An attraction between two atoms, resulting from a sharing of outer-shell electrons or the presence of opposite charges on the atoms. The bonded atoms gain complete outer electron shells.

chemical energy Energy stored in the chemical bonds of molecules; a form of potential energy.

chemical equilibrium In a reversible chemical reaction, the point at which the rate of the forward reaction equals the rate of the reverse reaction.

chemical reaction A process leading to chemical changes in matter; involves the making and/or breaking of chemical bonds.

chemiosmosis (kem-ē-oz-mō'-sis) An energy-coupling mechanism that uses energy stored in the form of a hydrogen ion gradient across a membrane to drive cellular work, such as the synthesis of ATP. Most ATP synthesis in cells occurs by chemiosmosis.

chemoautotroph (ke'-mō-ot'-ō-trōf) An organism that needs only carbon dioxide as a carbon source but that obtains energy by oxidizing inorganic substances.

chemoheterotroph (kē-mō-het'-er-ō-trōf) An organism that must obtain both energy and carbon by consuming organic molecules.

chemokine Any of about 50 different proteins, secreted by many cell types near a site of injury or infection, that help direct migration of white blood cells to an injury site and induces other changes central to inflammation.

chemoreceptor A receptor that transmits information about the total solute concentration in a solution or about individual kinds of molecules.

chiasma (plural, **chiasmata**) (ki-az'-muh, ki-az'-muh-tuh) The X-shaped, microscopically visible region representing homologous chromatids that have exchanged genetic material through crossing over during meiosis.

chimera An organism with a mixture of genetically different cells.

chitin (kī-tin) A structural polysaccharide of an amino sugar found in many fungi and in the exoskeletons of all arthropods.

chlorophyll (klōr'-ō-fil) A green pigment located within the chloroplasts of plants. Chlorophyll *a* can participate directly in the light reactions, which convert solar energy to chemical energy.

chlorophyll *a* A type of blue-green photosynthetic pigment that participates directly in the light reactions.

chlorophyll *b* A type of yellow-green accessory photosynthetic pigment that transfers energy to chlorophyll *a*.

chloroplast (klōr'-ō-plast) An organelle found only in plants and photosynthetic protists that absorbs sunlight and uses it to drive the synthesis of organic compounds from carbon dioxide and water.

choanocyte (kō-an'-uh-sit) A flagellated feeding cell found in sponges. Also called a collar cell, it has a collar-like ring that traps food particles around the base of its flagellum.

cholesterol (kō-les'-tuh-rol) A steroid that forms an essential component of animal cell membranes and acts as a precursor molecule for the synthesis of other biologically important steroids.

chondrichthyan Member of the class Chondrichthyes, vertebrates with skeletons made mostly of cartilage, such as sharks and rays.

chondrocyte Cartilage cell that secretes collagen and chondroitin sulfate.

chordate (kōr'-dāt) Member of the phylum Chordata, animals that at some point during their development have a notochord; a dorsal, hollow nerve cord; pharyngeal slits or clefts; and a muscular, post-anal tail.

chorion (kōr'-ē-on) The outermost of four extraembryonic membranes; contributes to the formation of the mammalian placenta.

chorionic villus sampling (CVS) (kōr-ē-on'-ik vil'-us) A technique of prenatal diagnosis in which a small sample of the fetal portion of the placenta is removed and analyzed to detect certain genetic and congenital defects in the fetus.

choroid A thin, pigmented inner layer of the vertebrate eye.

chromatin (krō'-muh-tin) The complex of DNA and proteins that makes up a eukaryotic chromosome. When the cell is not dividing, chromatin exists as a mass of very long, thin fibers that are not visible with a light microscope.

chromosome (krō'-muh-sōm) A threadlike, gene-carrying structure found in the nucleus. Each chromosome consists of one very long DNA molecule and associated proteins. *See* chromatin.

chromosome theory of inheritance A basic principle in biology stating that genes are located on chromosomes and that the behavior of chromosomes during meiosis accounts for inheritance patterns.

chylomicron (kī-lō-mī'-kron) One of the small intracellular globules composed of fats that are mixed with cholesterol and coated with special proteins.

chytrid (kī'-trid) Member of the fungal phylum Chytridiomycota, mostly aquatic fungi with flagellated zoospores that probably represent the most primitive fungal lineage.

ciliary body A portion of the vertebrate eye associated with the lens. It produces the clear, watery aqueous humor that fills the anterior cavity of the eye.

ciliate (sil-ē-it) A type of protozoan that moves by means of cilia.

cilium (sil-ē-um) (plural, **cilia**) A short cellular appendage specialized for locomotion, formed from a core of nine outer doublet microtubules and two inner single microtubules ensheathed in an extension of plasma membrane.

circadian rhythm (ser-kā-dē-un) A physiological cycle of about 24 hours that is present in all eukaryotic organisms and that persists even in the absence of external cues.

cis Arrangement of two noncarbon atoms, each bound to one of the carbons in a carbon-carbon double bond, where the two noncarbon atoms are on the same side relative to the double bond.

citric acid cycle A chemical cycle involving eight steps that completes the metabolic breakdown of glucose molecules to carbon dioxide; occurs within the mitochondrion; the second major stage in cellular respiration.

clade A group of species that includes an ancestral species and all its descendants.

cladistics (kluh-dis-tiks) The analysis of how species may be grouped into clades.

cladogram A diagram depicting patterns of shared characteristics among species.

class In classification, the taxonomic category above order.

class I MHC molecules A collection of cell surface proteins encoded by a family of genes called the major histocompatibility complex. Class I MHC molecules are found on nearly all nucleated cells.

class II MHC molecules A collection of cell surface proteins encoded by a family of genes called the major histocompatibility complex. Class II MHC molecules are restricted to a few specialized cell types, commonly called antigen presenting cells (dendritic cells, macrophages, and B cells).

classical conditioning A type of associative learning; the association of a normally irrelevant stimulus with a fixed behavioral response.

cleavage The process of cytokinesis in animal cells, characterized by pinching of the plasma membrane. Also, the succession of rapid cell divisions without growth during early embryonic development that converts the zygote into a ball of cells.

cleavage furrow The first sign of cleavage in an animal cell; a shallow groove in the cell surface near the old metaphase plate.

climate The prevailing weather conditions at a locality.

climograph A plot of the temperature and precipitation in a particular region.

cline A graded variation in a trait that parallels a gradient in the environment.

clitoris (klit-uh-ris) An organ in the female that engorges with blood and becomes erect during sexual arousal.

cloaca (klō-ā-kuh) A common opening for the digestive, urinary, and reproductive tracts found in many nonmammalian vertebrates but in few mammals.

clonal selection The process by which an antigen selectively binds to and activates only those lymphocytes bearing receptors specific for the antigen. The selected lymphocytes proliferate and differentiate into a clone of effector cells and a clone of memory cells specific for the stimulating antigen. Clonal selection accounts for the specificity and memory of acquired immune responses.

clone (1) A lineage of genetically identical individuals or cells. (2) In popular usage, a single individual organism that is genetically identical to another individual. (3) As a verb, to make one or more genetic replicas of an individual or cell. See also gene cloning.

cloning Using a somatic cell from a multicellular organism to make one or more genetically identical individuals.

cloning vector An agent used to transfer DNA in genetic engineering. A plasmid that moves recombinant DNA from a test tube back into a cell is an example of a cloning vector, as is a virus that transfers recombinant DNA by infection.

closed circulatory system A circulatory system in which blood is confined to vessels and is kept separate from the interstitial fluid.

club fungus The common name for members of the phylum Basidiomycota. The name comes from the club-like shape of the basidium.

cnidocyte (ni-duh-sit) A specialized cell for which the phylum Cnidaria is named; contains a capsule containing a fine coiled thread, which, when discharged, functions in defense and prey capture.

cochlea (kok-lē-uh) The complex, coiled organ of hearing that contains the organ of Corti.

codominance The situation in which the phenotypes of both alleles are exhibited in the heterozygote.

codon (kō-don) A three-nucleotide sequence of DNA or mRNA that specifies a particular amino acid or termination signal; the basic unit of the genetic code.

coefficient of relatedness The probability that a particular gene present in one individual will also be inherited from a common parent or ancestor in a second individual.

coelom (sē-lōm) A body cavity completely lined with mesoderm.

coelomate (sē-lō-māt) Animal that possesses a true coelom (fluid-filled body cavity lined by tissue completely derived from mesoderm).

coenocytic (sē-nō-sit-ik) Referring to a multinucleated condition resulting from the repeated division of nuclei without cytoplasmic division.

coenzyme (kō-en-zīm) An organic molecule serving as a cofactor. Most vitamins function as coenzymes in important metabolic reactions.

coevolution The mutual evolutionary influence between two different species interacting with each other and reciprocally influencing each other's adaptations.

cofactor Any nonprotein molecule or ion that is required for the proper functioning of an enzyme. Cofactors can be permanently bound to the active site or may bind loosely with the substrate during catalysis.

cognition The ability of an animal's nervous system to perceive, store, process, and use information obtained by its sensory receptors.

cognitive ethology The scientific study of cognition; the study of the connection between data processing by nervous systems and animal behavior.

cognitive map A representation within the nervous system of spatial relations between objects in an animal's environment.

cohesion The binding together of like molecules, often by hydrogen bonds.

cohort A group of individuals of the same age, from birth until all are dead.

coitus (kō-uh-tus) The insertion of a penis into a vagina; also called sexual intercourse.

coleoptile (kō-lē-op-tul) The covering of the young shoot of the embryo of a grass seed.

coleorhiza (kō-lē-uh-ri-zuh) The covering of the young root of the embryo of a grass seed.

collagen A glycoprotein in the extracellular matrix of animal cells that forms strong fibers; found extensively in connective tissue and bone; the most abundant protein in the animal kingdom.

collagenous fiber A tough fiber of the extracellular matrix. Collagenous fibers are made of collagen, are nonelastic, and do not tear easily when pulled lengthwise.

collecting duct The location in the kidney where filtrate from renal tubules is collected; the filtrate is now called urine.

collenchyma cell (kō-len-kim-uh) A flexible plant cell type that occurs in strands or cylinders that support young parts of the plant without restraining growth.

colloid A mixture made up of a liquid and particles that (because of their large size) remain suspended in that liquid.

colon See large intestine.

colony A collection of autonomously replicating cells of the same species.

columnar The column shape of a type of epithelial cell.

commensalism (kuh-men-suh-lizm) A symbiotic relationship in which one organism benefits but the other is neither helped nor harmed.

communication Animal behavior involving transmission of, reception of, and response to signals.

community All the organisms that inhabit a particular area; an assemblage of populations of different species living close enough together for potential interaction.

community ecology The study of how interactions between species affect community structure and organization.

companion cell A type of plant cell that is connected to a sieve-tube member by many plasmodesmata and whose nucleus and ribosomes may serve one or more adjacent sieve-tube members.

competitive exclusion The concept that when populations of two similar species compete for the same limited resources, one population will use the resources more efficiently and have a reproductive advantage that will eventually lead to the elimination of the other population.

competitive inhibitor A substance that reduces the activity of an enzyme by entering the active site in place of the substrate whose structure it mimics.

complement system A group of about 30 blood proteins that may amplify the inflammatory response, enhance phagocytosis, or directly lyse pathogens. The complement system is activated in a cascade initiated by surface antigens on microorganisms or by antigen-antibody complexes.

complementary DNA (cDNA) A DNA molecule made in vitro using mRNA as a template and the enzyme reverse transcriptase. A cDNA molecule therefore corresponds to a gene, but lacks the introns present in the DNA of the genome.

complete digestive tract A digestive tube that runs between a mouth and an anus; also called an alimentary canal. An incomplete digestive tract has only one opening.

complete dominance The situation in which the phenotypes of the heterozygote and dominant homozygote are indistinguishable.

complete flower A flower that has all four basic floral organs: sepals, petals, stamens, and carpels.

complete metamorphosis The transformation of a larva into an adult that looks very different, and often functions very differently, than the larva.

compound A substance consisting of two or more elements in a fixed ratio.

compound eye A type of multifaceted eye in insects and crustaceans consisting of up to several thousand light-detecting, focusing ommatidia; especially good at detecting movement.

concentration gradient An increase or decrease in the density of a chemical substance in an area. Cells often maintain concentration gradients of ions across their membranes.

When a gradient exists, the ions or other chemical substances involved tend to move from where they are more concentrated to where they are less concentrated.

conception The fertilization of the egg by a sperm cell in humans.

condensation reaction A reaction in which two molecules become covalently bonded to each other through the loss of a small molecule, usually water; also called a dehydration reaction.

condom A thin, latex rubber or natural membrane sheath that fits over the penis to collect semen.

condont Ancient lineage of jawless vertebrates that arose during the Cambrian period.

conduction The direct transfer of thermal motion (heat) between molecules of objects in direct contact with each other.

cone cell One of two types of photoreceptors in the vertebrate eye; detects color during the day.

conformer A characterization of an animal in regard to environmental variables. A conformer allows some conditions within its body to vary with certain external changes.

conidia Naked, asexual spores produced at the ends of specialized hyphae in ascomycetes.

conifer A gymnosperm whose reproductive structure is the cone. Conifers include pines, firs, and redwoods.

coniferous forest A terrestrial biome characterized by long, cold winters and dominated by cone-bearing trees.

conjugation (kon-jū-gā-shun) In prokaryotes, the direct transfer of DNA between two cells that are temporarily joined. In ciliates, a sexual process in which two cells exchange haploid micronuclei.

conjunctiva (kon-junk-tī-vuh) A mucous membrane that helps keep the eye moist; lines the inner surface of the eyelid and covers the front of the eyeball, except the cornea.

connective tissue Animal tissue that functions mainly to bind and support other tissues, having a sparse population of cells scattered through an extracellular matrix.

conodont An early, soft-bodied vertebrate with prominent eyes and dental elements.

conservation biology The integrated study of ecology, evolutionary biology, physiology, molecular biology, genetics, and behavioral biology in an effort to sustain biological diversity at all levels.

contraception The prevention of pregnancy.

contractile vacuole A membranous sac that helps move excess water out of certain cells.

control element A segment of noncoding DNA that helps regulate transcription of a gene by binding proteins called transcription factors.

controlled experiment An experiment in which an experimental group is compared to a control group that varies only in the factor being tested.

convection The mass movement of warmed air or liquid to or from the surface of a body or object.

convergent extension A mechanism of cell crawling in which the cells of a tissue layer rearrange themselves in such a way that the sheet of cells becomes narrower while it becomes longer.

cooperativity An interaction of the constituent subunits of a protein whereby a conformational change in one subunit is transmitted to all the others.

copepod (kō-puh-pod) Any of a group of small crustaceans that are important members of marine and freshwater plankton communities.

coral reef A warm-water, tropical ecosystem dominated by the hard skeletal structures secreted primarily by the resident cnidarians.

corepressor A small molecule that cooperates with a repressor protein to switch an operon off.

cork cambium (kam-bē-um) A cylinder of meristematic tissue in woody plants that replaces the epidermis with thicker, tougher cork cells.

cornea (kor-nē-uh) The transparent frontal portion of the sclera, which admits light into the vertebrate eye.

corpus callosum (kor-pus kuh-lō-sum) The thick band of nerve fibers that connect the right and left cerebral hemispheres in placental mammals, enabling the hemispheres to process information together.

corpus luteum (kor-pus lū-tē-um) A secreting tissue in the ovary that forms from the collapsed follicle after ovulation and produces progesterone.

cortex Ground tissue that is between the vascular tissue and dermal tissue in a root or dicot stem.

cortical granules Vesicles located just under the plasma membrane of an egg cell that undergo exocytosis during the cortical reaction.

cortical nephrons Nephrons located almost entirely in the renal cortex. These nephrons have a reduced loop of Henle.

cortical reaction Exocytosis of enzymes from cortical granules in the egg cytoplasm during fertilization.

corticosteroid Any steroid hormone produced and secreted by the adrenal cortex.

cotransport The coupling of the "downhill" diffusion of one substance to the "uphill" transport of another against its own concentration gradient.

cotyledon (kot-uh-lē-don) A seed leaf of an angiosperm embryo. Some species have one cotyledon, others two.

countercurrent exchange The opposite flow of adjacent fluids that maximizes transfer rates; for example, blood in the gills flows in the opposite direction in which water passes over the gills, maximizing oxygen uptake and carbon dioxide loss.

Glossary

countercurrent heat exchanger An arrangement of blood vessels that helps trap heat in the body core and is important in reducing heat loss in many endotherms.

countercurrent multiplier system A countercurrent system in which energy is expended in active transport to facilitate exchange of materials and create concentration gradients. For example, the loop of Henle actively transports NaCl from the filtrate in the upper part of the ascending limb of the loop, making the urine-concentrating function of the kidney more effective.

covalent bond (kō-vā-lent) A type of strong chemical bond in which two atoms share one or more pairs of valence electrons.

cranial nerve A nerve that leaves the brain and innervates an organ of the head or upper body.

craniate A chordate with a head.

crassulacean acid metabolism (CAM) A type of metabolism in which carbon dioxide is taken in at night and incorporated into a variety of organic acids.

crista (plural, **cristae**) (kris-tuh, kris-tē) An infolding of the inner membrane of a mitochondrion that houses the electron transport chain and the enzyme catalyzing the synthesis of ATP.

critical load The amount of added nutrient, usually nitrogen or phosphorus, that can be absorbed by plants without damaging ecosystem integrity.

crop rotation The alternation of planting a nonlegume one year and a legume the next year to restore concentration of fixed nitrogen in the soil.

crossing over The reciprocal exchange of genetic material between nonsister chromatids during prophase I of meiosis.

cross-pollination In angiosperms, the transfer of pollen from an anther of a flower on one plant to the stigma of a flower on another plant of the same species.

crustacean A member of a subphylum of arthropods that includes lobsters, crayfish, crabs, shrimps, and barnacles.

cryptic coloration Camouflage, making potential prey difficult to spot against its background.

cuboidal The cubic shape of a type of epithelial cell.

culture The ideas, customs, skills, rituals, and similar activities of a people or group that are passed along to succeeding generations.

cuticle (kyū-tuh-kul) (1) A waxy covering on the surface of stems and leaves that acts as an adaptation to prevent desiccation in terrestrial plants. (2) The exoskeleton of an arthropod, consisting of layers of protein and chitin that are variously modified for different functions. (3) A tough coat that covers the body of a nematode.

cyclic AMP (cAMP) Cyclic adenosine monophosphate, a ring-shaped molecule made from ATP that is a common intracellular signaling molecule (second messenger) in eukaryotic cells (for example, in vertebrate endocrine cells). It is also a regulator of some bacterial operons.

cyclic electron flow A route of electron flow during the light reactions of photosynthesis that involves only photosystem I and that produces ATP but not NADPH or oxygen.

cyclin (sī-klin) A regulatory protein whose concentration fluctuates cyclically.

cyclin-dependent kinase (Cdk) A protein kinase that is active only when attached to a particular cyclin.

cystic fibrosis A human genetic disorder caused by a recessive allele for a chloride channel protein, characterized by an excessive secretion of mucus and consequent vulnerability to infection; fatal if untreated.

cytochrome (sī-tō-krom) An iron-containing protein, a component of electron transport chains in mitochondria and chloroplasts.

cytogenetic map Chart of a chromosome that locates genes with respect to chromosomal features.

cytokine Any of a group of proteins secreted by a number of cell types, including macrophages and helper T cells, that regulate the function of lymphocytes and other cells of the immune system.

cytokinesis (sī-tō-kuh-nē-sis) The division of the cytoplasm to form two separate daughter cells immediately after mitosis.

cytokinins (sī-tō-kī-nins) A class of related plant hormones that retard aging and act in concert with auxin to stimulate cell division, influence the pathway of differentiation, and control apical dominance.

cytoplasm (sī-tō-plaz-um) The entire contents of the cell, exclusive of the nucleus, and bounded by the plasma membrane.

cytoplasmic determinants The maternal substances in the egg that influence the course of early development by regulating the expression of genes that affect the developmental fate of cells.

cytoplasmic streaming A circular flow of cytoplasm, involving myosin and actin filaments, that speeds the distribution of materials within cells.

cytoskeleton A network of microtubules, microfilaments, and intermediate filaments that branch throughout the cytoplasm and serve a variety of mechanical and transport functions.

cytosol (sī-tō-sol) The semifluid portion of the cytoplasm.

cytotoxic T cell A type of lymphocyte that, when activated, kills infected cells, cancer cells, and transplanted cells.

daily torpor A daily decrease in metabolic activity and body temperature during times of inactivity for some small mammals and birds.

dalton A measure of mass for atoms and subatomic particles.

data Recorded observations.

day-neutral plant A plant whose flowering is not affected by photoperiod.

decapod A member of the group of crustaceans that includes lobsters, crayfish, crabs, and shrimps.

decomposer Any of the saprobic fungi and prokaryotes that absorb nutrients from nonliving organic material such as corpses, fallen plant material, and the wastes of living organisms, and convert them into inorganic forms.

deductive reasoning A type of logic in which specific results are predicted from a general premise.

deep-sea hydrothermal vent A dark, hot, oxygen-deficient environment associated with volcanic activity. The food producers are chemoautotrophic prokaryotes.

de-etiolation The changes a plant shoot undergoes in response to sunlight; also known informally as greening.

dehydration reaction A chemical reaction in which two molecules covalently bond to each other with the removal of a water molecule.

deletion (1) A deficiency in a chromosome resulting from the loss of a fragment through breakage. (2) A mutational loss of one or more nucleotide pairs from a gene.

demographic transition A shift from zero population growth in which birth rates and death rates are high to zero population growth characterized instead by low birth and death rates.

demography The study of statistics relating to births and deaths in populations.

denaturation (dē-nā-chur-a-shun) In proteins, a process in which a protein unravels and loses its native conformation, thereby becoming biologically inactive. In DNA, the separation of the two strands of the double helix. Denaturation occurs under extreme conditions of pH, salt concentration, and temperature.

dendrite (den-drīt) One of usually numerous, short, highly branched processes of a neuron that convey nerve impulses toward the cell body.

dendritic cell An antigen-presenting cell, located mainly in lymphatic tissues and skin, that is particularly efficient in presenting antigens to naive helper T cells, thereby initiating a primary immune response.

density The number of individuals per unit area or volume.

density dependent Referring to any characteristic that varies according to an increase in population density.

density-dependent inhibition The phenomenon observed in normal animal cells that causes them to stop dividing when they come into contact with one another.

density independent Referring to any characteristic that is not affected by population density.

deoxyribonucleic acid (DNA) (dē-ok´-sē-rī-bō-nu-klā´-ik) A double-stranded, helical nucleic acid molecule capable of replicating and determining the inherited structure of a cell's proteins.

deoxyribose The sugar component of DNA, having one less hydroxyl group than ribose, the sugar component of RNA.

depolarization An electrical state in an excitable cell whereby the inside of the cell is made less negative relative to the outside than at the resting membrane potential. A neuron membrane is depolarized if a stimulus decreases its voltage from the resting potential of −70 mV in the direction of zero voltage.

derivatives New cells that are displaced from an apical meristem and continue to divide until the cells they produce become specialized.

dermal tissue system The outer protective covering of plants.

descent with modification Darwin's initial phrase for the general process of evolution.

desert A terrestrial biome characterized by very low precipitation.

desmosome (dez´-muh-sōm) A type of intercellular junction in animal cells that functions as an anchor.

determinate cleavage A type of embryonic development in protostomes that rigidly casts the developmental fate of each embryonic cell very early.

determinate growth A type of growth characteristic of most animals and some plant organs, in which growth stops after a certain size is reached.

determination The progressive restriction of developmental potential, causing the possible fate of each cell to become more limited as the embryo develops.

detritivore A consumer that derives its energy from nonliving organic material; a decomposer.

detritus (di-trī´-tus) Dead organic matter.

deuteromycete Traditional classification for a fungus with no known sexual stage. When a sexual stage for a so-called deuteromycete is discovered, the species is assigned to a phylum. Also called an imperfect fungus.

deuterostome development In animals, a developmental mode distinguished by the development of the anus from the blastopore; often also characterized by enterocoelous development of the body cavity and by radial cleavage.

diabetes mellitus An endocrine disorder marked by inability to maintain glucose homeostasis. The type I form results from autoimmune destruction of insulin-secreting cells; treatment usually requires insulin injections several times a day. The type II form most commonly results from reduced responsiveness of target cells to insulin; obesity and lack of exercise are risk factors.

diacylglycerol (DAG) A second messenger produced by the cleavage of a certain kind of phospholipid in the plasma membrane.

diaphragm (1) A sheet of muscle that forms the bottom wall of the thoracic cavity in mammals; active in ventilating the lungs. (2) A dome-shaped rubber cup fitted into the upper portion of the vagina before sexual intercourse. It serves as a physical barrier to block the passage of sperm.

diapsid Member of an amniote clade distinguished by a pair of holes on each side of the skull, including the lepidosaurs and archosaurs.

diastole (di-as´-tō-lē) The stage of the heart cycle in which the heart muscle is relaxed, allowing the chambers to fill with blood.

diastolic pressure Blood pressure that remains between heart contractions.

diatom (dī´-uh-tom) A unicellular photosynthetic alga with a unique, glassy cell wall containing silica.

dicots A term traditionally used to refer to flowering plants that have two embryonic seed leaves, or cotyledons. Recent molecular evidence indicates that dicots do not form a clade (see eudicots).

differential gene expression The expression of different sets of genes by cells with the same genome.

diffusion The spontaneous tendency of a substance to move down its concentration gradient from a more concentrated to a less concentrated area.

digestion The process of breaking down food into molecules small enough for the body to absorb.

dihybrid (dī´-hī´-brid) An organism that is heterozygous with respect to two genes of interest. All the offspring from a cross between parents doubly homozygous for different alleles are dihybrids. For example, parents of genotypes *AABB* and *aabb* produce a dihybrid of genotype *AaBb*.

dikaryotic Referring to a fungal mycelium with two haploid nuclei per cell, one from each parent.

dinoflagellate (dī-nō-flaj´-uh-let) Member of a group of mostly unicellular photosynthetic algae with two flagella situated in perpendicular grooves in cellulose plates covering the cell.

dinosaur Member of an extremely diverse group of ancient reptiles varying in body shape, size, and habitat.

dioecious (dī-ē´-shus) A term typically used to describe an angiosperm species in which carpellate and staminate flowers are on separate plants.

diploblastic Having two germ layers.

diploid cell (dip´-loid) A cell containing two sets of chromosomes (2n), one set inherited from each parent.

diplomonad A protist that has modified mitochondria, two equal-sized nuclei, and multiple flagella.

directional selection Natural selection that favors individuals at one end of the phenotypic range.

disaccharide (dī-sak´-uh-rīd) A double sugar, consisting of two monosaccharides joined by dehydration synthesis.

discovery science The process of scientific inquiry that focuses on describing nature.

dispersal The distribution of individuals within geographic population boundaries.

dispersion The pattern of spacing among individuals within geographic population boundaries.

disruptive selection Natural selection that favors individuals on both extremes of a phenotypic range over intermediate phenotypes.

dissociation curve A chart showing the relative amounts of oxygen bound to hemoglobin when the pigment is exposed to solutions varying in their partial pressure of dissolved oxygen, pH, or other characteristics.

distal tubule In the vertebrate kidney, the portion of a nephron that helps refine filtrate and empties it into a collecting duct.

disturbance A force that changes a biological community and usually removes organisms from it. Disturbances, such as fire and storms, play pivotal roles in structuring many biological communities.

disulfide bridge A strong covalent bond formed when the sulfur of one cysteine monomer bonds to the sulfur of another cysteine monomer.

DNA fingerprint An individual's unique collection of DNA restriction fragments, detected by electrophoresis and nucleic acid probes.

DNA ligase (lī´-gās) A linking enzyme essential for DNA replication; catalyzes the covalent bonding of the 3′ end of a new DNA fragment to the 5′ end of a growing chain.

DNA microarray assay A method to detect and measure the expression of thousands of genes at one time. Tiny amounts of a large number of single-stranded DNA fragments representing different genes are fixed to a glass slide. These fragments, ideally representing all the genes of an organism, are tested for hybridization with various samples of cDNA molecules.

DNA polymerase (puh-lim´-er-ās) An enzyme that catalyzes the elongation of new DNA at a replication fork by the addition of nucleotides to the existing chain.

domain (1) A taxonomic category above the kingdom level. The three domains are Archaea, Bacteria, and Eukarya. (2) An independently folding part of a protein.

dominant allele An allele that is fully expressed in the phenotype of a heterozygote.

dominant species Those species in a community that have the highest abundance or highest biomass. These species exert a powerful control over the occurrence and distribution of other species.

dopamine A biogenic amine closely related to epinephrine and norepinephrine.

dormancy A condition typified by extremely low metabolic rate and a suspension of growth and development.

dorsal Pertaining to the back (top) of a bilaterally symmetrical animal.

dorsal lip The dorsal side of the blastopore.

double circulation A circulation scheme with separate pulmonary and systemic circuits, which ensures vigorous blood flow to all organs.

double fertilization A mechanism of fertilization in angiosperms, in which two sperm cells unite with two cells in the embryo sac to form the zygote and endosperm.

double helix The form of native DNA, referring to its two adjacent polynucleotide strands wound into a spiral shape.

Down syndrome A human genetic disease caused by presence of an extra chromosome 21; characterized by mental retardation and heart and respiratory defects.

Duchenne muscular dystrophy (duh-shen) A human genetic disease caused by a sex-linked recessive allele; characterized by progressive weakening and a loss of muscle tissue.

duodenum (du-ö-dē -num) The first section of the small intestine, where acid chyme from the stomach mixes with digestive juices from the pancreas, liver, gallbladder, and gland cells of the intestinal wall.

duplication An aberration in chromosome structure due to fusion with a fragment from a homologous chromosome, such that a portion of a chromosome is duplicated.

dynamic stability hypothesis The idea that long food chains are less stable than short chains.

dynein (di -nin) A large contractile protein forming the side-arms of microtubule doublets in cilia and flagella.

E site One of a ribosome's three binding sites for tRNA during translation. The E site is the place where discharged tRNAs leave the ribosome. (E stands for exit.)

ecdysone (ek -duh-sön) A steroid hormone, secreted by the prothoracic glands, that triggers molting in arthropods.

ecdysozoan Member of a group of animal phyla with protostome development that some systematists hypothesize form a clade, including many molting animals.

echinoderm (uh-kī -nō-derm) A slow-moving or sessile marine deuterostome with a water vascular system and, in adults, radial anatomy. Echinoderms include sea stars, brittle stars, sea urchins, feather stars, and sea cucumbers.

ecological capacity The actual resource base of a country.

ecological footprint A method of using multiple constraints to estimate the human carrying capacity of Earth by calculating the aggregate land and water area in various ecosystem categories appropriated by a nation to produce all the resources it consumes and to absorb all the waste it generates.

ecological niche (nich) The sum total of a species' use of the biotic and abiotic resources in its environment.

ecological species concept Defining species in terms of ecological roles (niches).

ecological succession Transition in the species composition of a biological community, often following ecological disturbance of the community; the establishment of a biological community in an area virtually barren of life.

ecology The study of how organisms interact with their environment.

ecosystem All the organisms in a given area as well as the abiotic factors with which they interact; a community and its physical environment.

ecosystem ecology The study of energy flow and the cycling of chemicals among the various biotic and abiotic factors in an ecosystem.

ecosystem services Functions performed by natural ecosystems that directly or indirectly benefit humans.

ecotone The transition from one type of habitat or ecosystem to another, such as the transition from a forest to a grassland.

ectoderm (ek -tō-derm) The outermost of the three primary germ layers in animal embryos; gives rise to the outer covering and, in some phyla, the nervous system, inner ear, and lens of the eye.

ectomycorrhiza (ek -tō-mī -kō-rī -zuh) A type of mycorrhiza in which the mycelium forms a dense sheath, or mantle, over the surface of the root. Hyphae extend from the mantle into the soil, greatly increasing the surface area for water and mineral absorption.

ectomycorrhizal fungus A fungus that forms ectomycorrhizae with plant roots.

ectoparasite A parasite that feeds on the external surface of a host.

ectoproct A sessile, colonial lophophorate commonly called a bryozoan.

ectotherm (ek -tō-therm) An animal, such as a reptile (other than birds), fish, or amphibian, that must use environmental energy and behavioral adaptations to regulate its body temperature.

ectothermic Referring to organisms that do not produce enough metabolic heat to have much effect on body temperature.

Ediacaran fauna Earliest generally accepted animal fossils, dating from about 575 million years ago.

effective population size An estimate of the size of a population based on the numbers of females and males that successfully breed; generally smaller than the total population.

effector cell A muscle cell or gland cell that performs the body's responses to stimuli; responds to signals from the brain or other processing center of the nervous system.

efferent arteriole The blood vessel draining a nephron.

egg-polarity gene Another name for a maternal effect gene, a gene that helps control the orientation (polarity) of the egg.

ejaculation The propulsion of sperm from the epididymis through the muscular vas deferens, ejaculatory duct, and urethra.

ejaculatory duct The short section of the ejaculatory route in mammals formed by the convergence of the vas deferens and a duct from the seminal vesicle. The ejaculatory duct transports sperm from the vas deferens to the urethra.

elastic fiber A long thread made of the protein elastin. Elastic fibers provide a rubbery quality to the extracellular matrix that complements the nonelastic strength of collagenous fibers.

electrocardiogram (ECG or EKG) A record of the electrical impulses that travel through cardiac muscle during the heart cycle.

electrochemical gradient The diffusion gradient of an ion, representing a type of potential energy that accounts for both the concentration difference of the ion across a membrane and its tendency to move relative to the membrane potential.

electrogenic pump An ion transport protein that generates voltage across a membrane.

electromagnetic receptor A receptor of electromagnetic energy, such as visible light, electricity, and magnetism.

electromagnetic spectrum The entire spectrum of radiation ranging in wavelength from less than a nanometer to more than a kilometer.

electron A subatomic particle with a single negative charge. One or more electrons move around the nucleus of an atom.

electron microscope (EM) A microscope that focuses an electron beam through a specimen, resulting in resolving power a thousandfold greater than that of a light microscope. A transmission electron microscope (TEM) is used to study the internal structure of thin sections of cells. A scanning electron microscope (SEM) is used to study the fine details of cell surfaces.

electron shell An energy level represented as the distance of an electron from the nucleus of an atom.

electron transport chain A sequence of electron carrier molecules (membrane proteins) that shuttle electrons during the redox reactions that release energy used to make ATP.

electronegativity The attraction of an atom for the electrons of a covalent bond.

electroporation A technique to introduce recombinant DNA into cells by applying a brief electrical pulse to a solution containing cells. The electricity creates temporary holes in the cells' plasma membranes, through which DNA can enter.

element Any substance that cannot be broken down to any other substance.

elicitor A molecule that induces a broad type of host defense response.

elimination The passing of undigested material out of the digestive compartment.

embryo New developing individual.

embryo sac (em´-brē-ō) The female gametophyte of angiosperms, formed from the growth and division of the megaspore into a multicellular structure with eight haploid nuclei.

embryonic lethal A mutation with a phenotype leading to death at the embryo or larval stage.

embryophyte Another name for land plants, recognizing that land plants share the common derived trait of multicellular, dependent embryos.

emergent properties New properties that emerge with each step upward in the hierarchy of life, owing to the arrangement and interactions of parts as complexity increases.

emigration The movement of individuals out of a population.

enantiomer (en-an´-tē-ō-mer) One of two molecules that are mirror images of each other.

endangered species A species that is in danger of extinction throughout all or a significant portion of its range.

endemic species (en-dem´-ik) Species that are confined to a specific, relatively small geographic area.

endergonic reaction (en´-der-gon´-ik) A non-spontaneous chemical reaction, in which free energy is absorbed from the surroundings.

endocrine gland (en´-dō-krin) A ductless gland that secretes hormones directly into the interstitial fluid, from which they diffuse into the bloodstream.

endocrine system The internal system of chemical communication involving hormones, the ductless glands that secrete hormones, and the molecular receptors on or in target cells that respond to hormones; functions in concert with the nervous system to effect internal regulation and maintain homeostasis.

endocytosis (en´-dō-sī-tō´-sis) The cellular uptake of macromolecules and particulate substances by localized regions of the plasma membrane that surround the substance and pinch off to form an intracellular vesicle.

endoderm (en´-dō-derm) The innermost of the three primary germ layers in animal embryos; lines the archenteron and gives rise to the liver, pancreas, lungs, and the lining of the digestive tract.

endodermis The innermost layer of the cortex in plant roots; a cylinder one cell thick that forms the boundary between the cortex and the vascular cylinder.

endomembrane system The collection of membranes inside and around a eukaryotic cell, related either through direct physical contact or by the transfer of membranous vesicles.

endometrium (en-dō-mē´-trē-um) The inner lining of the uterus, which is richly supplied with blood vessels.

endomycorrhiza (en-dō-mī´-kō-rī´-zuh) A type of mycorrhiza that, unlike ectomycorrhizae, does not have a dense mantle ensheathing the root. Instead, microscopic fungal hyphae extend from the root into the soil.

endomycorrhizal fungus A fungus that forms endomycorrhizae with plant roots.

endoparasite A parasite that lives within a host.

endoplasmic reticulum (ER) (en´-dō-plaz´-mik ruh-tik´-yū-lum) An extensive membranous network in eukaryotic cells, continuous with the outer nuclear membrane and composed of ribosome-studded (rough) and ribosome-free (smooth) regions.

endorphin (en-dôr´-fin) Any of several hormones produced in the brain and anterior pituitary that inhibits pain perception.

endoskeleton A hard skeleton buried within the soft tissues of an animal, such as the spicules of sponges, the plates of echinoderms, and the bony skeletons of vertebrates.

endosperm A nutrient-rich tissue formed by the union of a sperm cell with two polar nuclei during double fertilization, which provides nourishment to the developing embryo in angiosperm seeds.

endospore A thick-coated, resistant cell produced within a bacterial cell exposed to harsh conditions.

endothelium (en-dō-thē´-lē-um) The innermost, simple squamous layer of cells lining the blood vessels; the only constituent structure of capillaries.

endotherm An animal, such as a bird or mammal, that uses metabolic heat to regulate body temperature.

endothermic Referring to organisms with bodies that are warmed by heat generated by metabolism. This heat is usually used to maintain a relatively stable body temperature higher than that of the external environment.

endotoxin A toxic component of the outer membrane of certain gram-negative bacteria that is released only when the bacteria die.

energetic hypothesis The concept that the length of a food chain is limited by the inefficiency of energy transfer along the chain.

energy The capacity to do work (to move matter against an opposing force).

energy coupling In cellular metabolism, the use of energy released from an exergonic reaction to drive an endergonic reaction.

energy level Any of several different states of potential energy for electrons in an atom.

enhancer A DNA segment containing multiple control elements that may be located far away from the gene it regulates.

enteric division Complex networks of neurons in the digestive tract, pancreas, and gallbladder; normally regulated by the sympathetic and parasympathetic divisions of the autonomic nervous system.

enterocoelous (en-ter-ō-sē´-lus) Pattern of formation of the body cavity common in deuterostome development, in which the mesoderm buds from the wall of the archenteron and hollows, forming the body cavity.

entropy (en´-truh-pē) A quantitative measure of disorder or randomness, symbolized by S.

enzymatic hydrolysis The process in digestion that splits macromolecules from food by the enzymatic addition of water.

enzyme (en´-zīm) A protein serving as a catalyst, a chemical agent that changes the rate of a reaction without being consumed by the reaction.

enzyme-substrate complex A temporary complex formed when an enzyme binds to its substrate molecule(s).

eosinophil A type of white blood cell with low phagocytic activity that is thought to play a role in defense against parasitic worms by releasing enzymes toxic to these invaders.

epicotyl (ep´-uh-cot´-ul) In an angiosperm embryo, the embryonic axis above the point of attachment of the cotyledon(s).

epidermis (1) The dermal tissue system of nonwoody plants, usually consisting of a single layer of tightly packed cells. (2) The outer covering of animals.

epididymis (ep´-uh-did´-uh-mus) A coiled tubule located adjacent to the testes where sperm are stored.

epigenetic inheritance Inheritance of traits transmitted by mechanisms not directly involving the nucleotide sequence.

epiglottis A cartilaginous flap that blocks the top of the windpipe, the glottis, during swallowing, which prevents the entry of food or fluid into the respiratory system.

epinephrine A catecholamine hormone secreted from the adrenal medulla that mediates "fight-or-flight" responses to short-term stress; also functions as a neurotransmitter.

epiphyte (ep´-uh-fīt) A plant that nourishes itself but grows on the surface of another plant for support, usually on the branches or trunks of tropical trees.

episome (ep´-uh-sōm) A genetic element that can exist either as a plasmid or as part of the bacterial chromosome.

epistasis A type of gene interaction in which one gene alters the phenotypic effects of another gene that is independently inherited.

epithalamus A brain region, derived from the diencephalon, that contains several clusters of capillaries that produce cerebrospinal fluid.

epithelial tissue (ep´-uh-thē´-lē-ul) Sheets of tightly packed cells that line organs and body cavities.

epitope A small, accessible region of an antigen to which an antigen receptor or antibody binds; also called an antigenic determinant.

equilibrium potential (E_{ion}) The magnitude of a cell's membrane voltage at equilibrium; calculated using the Nernst equation.

erythrocyte (eh-rith´-rō-sit) A red blood cell; contains hemoglobin, which functions in transporting oxygen in the circulatory system.

erythropoietin (EPO) (eh-rith´-rō-poy´-uh-tin) A hormone produced in the kidney when tissues of the body do not receive enough oxygen. This hormone stimulates the production of erythrocytes.

esophagus (eh-sof´-uh-gus) A channel that conducts food, by peristalsis, from the pharynx to the stomach.

essential amino acid An amino acid that an animal cannot synthesize itself and must be obtained from food. Eight amino acids are essential in the human adult.

essential element In plants, a chemical element that is required for the plant to grow from a seed and complete the life cycle, producing another generation of seeds.

essential fatty acids Certain unsaturated fatty acids that animals cannot make.

essential nutrient A substance that an organism must absorb in preassembled form because it cannot be synthesized from any other material. In humans, there are essential vitamins, minerals, amino acids, and fatty acids.

estivation (es-tuh-vā-shun) Summer torpor; a physiological state that is characterized by slow metabolism and inactivity and that permits survival during long periods of elevated temperature and diminished water supplies.

estrogen (es-trō-jen) Any steroid hormone, such as estradiol, that stimulates the development and maintenance of the female reproductive system and secondary sex characteristics.

estrous cycle (es-trus) A type of reproductive cycle in all female mammals except higher primates, in which the nonpregnant endometrium is reabsorbed rather than shed, and sexual response occurs only during mid-cycle at estrus.

estrus A period of sexual activity associated with ovulation.

estuary The area where a freshwater stream or river merges with the ocean.

ethology The study of animal behavior in natural conditions.

ethylene (eth´-uh-len) The only gaseous plant hormone. Among its many effects are response to mechanical stress, programmed cell death, leaf abscission, and fruit ripening.

etiolation Plant morphological adaptations for growing in darkness.

euchromatin (ū-krō´-muh-tin) The more open, unraveled form of eukaryotic chromatin that is available for transcription.

eudicots (ū-dī-kots) A clade consisting of the vast majority of flowering plants that have two embryonic seed leaves, or cotyledons.

euglenid A protist, such as *Euglena* or its relatives, characterized by an anterior pocket, or chamber, from which one or two flagella emerge.

Eukarya The domain that includes all eukaryotic organisms.

eukaryotic cell (ū-kar-ē-ot-ik) A type of cell with a membrane-enclosed nucleus and membrane-enclosed organelles; present in protists, plants, fungi, and animals; also called eukaryote.

eumetazoan (ū-met-uh-zō-uhn) Member of the clade Eumetazoa, animals with true tissues (all animals except sponges).

euryhaline Referring to organisms that can tolerate substantial changes in external osmolarity.

eurypterid An extinct carnivorous cheliceriform also called a water scorpion.

Eustachian tube The tube that connects the middle ear to the pharynx.

eutherian (ū-thēr´-ē-un) Placental mammal; mammal whose young complete their embryonic development within the uterus, joined to the mother by the placenta.

eutrophic lake A nutrient-rich and oxygen-poor lake, having a high rate of biological productivity.

eutrophication A process by which nutrients, particularly phosphorus and nitrogen, become highly concentrated in a body of water, leading to increased growth of organisms such as algae. Cultural eutrophication refers to situations where the nutrients added to the water body originate mainly from human sources, such as agricultural drainage or sewage.

evaporation The removal of heat energy from the surface of a liquid that is losing some of its molecules.

evaporative cooling The property of a liquid whereby the surface becomes cooler during evaporation, owing to a loss of highly kinetic molecules to the gaseous state.

evapotranspiration The evaporation of water from soil plus the transpiration of water from plants.

evolution All the changes that have transformed life on Earth from its earliest beginnings to the diversity that characterizes it today.

evolutionary adaptation An accumulation of inherited characteristics that enhance organisms' ability to survive and reproduce in specific environments.

excitatory postsynaptic potential (EPSP) An electrical change (depolarization) in the membrane of a postsynaptic neuron caused by the binding of an excitatory neurotransmitter from a presynaptic cell to a postsynaptic receptor; makes it more likely for a postsynaptic neuron to generate an action potential.

excretion The disposal of nitrogen-containing waste products of metabolism.

exergonic reaction (ek-ser-gon-ik) A spontaneous chemical reaction, in which there is a net release of free energy.

exocytosis (ek-sō-si-tō-sis) The cellular secretion of macromolecules by the fusion of vesicles with the plasma membrane.

exoenzyme A powerful hydrolytic enzyme secreted by a fungus outside its body to digest food.

exon A coding region of a eukaryotic gene. Exons, which are expressed, are separated from each other by introns.

exoskeleton A hard encasement on the surface of an animal, such as the shell of a mollusc or the cuticle of an arthropod, that provides protection and points of attachment for muscles.

exotoxin (ek-sō-tok-sin) A toxic protein that is secreted by a prokaryote and that produces specific symptoms even in the absence of the prokaryote.

expansins Plant enzymes that break the cross-links (hydrogen bonds) between cellulose microfibrils and other cell wall constituents, loosening the wall's fabric.

exponential population growth The geometric increase of a population as it grows in an ideal, unlimited environment.

expression vector A cloning vector that contains the requisite prokaryotic promoter just upstream of a restriction site where a eukaryotic gene can be inserted.

external fertilization The fusion of gametes that parents have discharged into the environment.

exteroreceptor A sensory receptor that detects stimuli outside the body, such as heat, light, pressure, and chemicals.

extinction vortex A downward population spiral in which positive-feedback loops of inbreeding and genetic drift cause a small population to shrink and, unless reversed, become extinct.

extracellular digestion The breakdown of food outside cells.

extracellular matrix (ECM) The substance in which animal tissue cells are embedded, consisting of protein and polysaccharides.

extraembryonic membranes Four membranes (yolk sac, amnion, chorion, allantois) that support the developing embryo in mammals and birds and other reptiles.

extreme halophile A prokaryote that lives in a highly saline environment, such as the Great Salt Lake or the Dead Sea.

extreme thermophile A prokaryote that thrives in hot environments (often 60–80°C or hotter).

extremophile A prokaryote that lives in an extreme environment. Extremophiles include methanogens, extreme halophiles, and extreme thermophiles.

F factor A fertility factor in bacteria; a DNA segment that confers the ability to form pili for conjugation and associated functions.

required for the transfer of DNA from donor to recipient. It may exist as a plasmid or be integrated into the bacterial chromosome.

F plasmid The plasmid form of the F factor.

F₁ generation The first filial, or hybrid, offspring in a series of genetic crosses.

F₂ generation Offspring resulting from interbreeding of the hybrid F₁ generation.

facilitator A species that has a positive effect on the survival and reproduction of other species in a community and that contributes to community structure.

facilitated diffusion The spontaneous passage of molecules and ions, bound to specific carrier proteins, across a biological membrane down their concentration gradients.

facultative anaerobe (fak-ul-ta-tiv an'-uh-rob) An organism that makes ATP by aerobic respiration if oxygen is present but that switches to fermentation under anaerobic conditions.

family In classification, the taxonomic category above genus.

fast block to polyspermy The depolarization of the egg membrane within 1–3 seconds after sperm binding to the vitelline layer. The reaction prevents additional sperm from fusing with the egg's plasma membrane.

fast muscle fibers Muscle cells used for rapid, powerful contractions.

fat (triacylglycerol) (tri-as'-ul-glis'-uh-rol) A biological compound consisting of three fatty acids linked to one glycerol molecule.

fate map Territorial diagram of embryonic development that reveals the future development of individual cells and tissues.

fatty acid A long carbon chain carboxylic acid. Fatty acids vary in length and in the number and location of double bonds; three fatty acids linked to a glycerol molecule form fat.

feces The wastes of the digestive tract.

feedback inhibition A method of metabolic control in which the end product of a metabolic pathway acts as an inhibitor of an enzyme within that pathway.

fermentation A catabolic process that makes a limited amount of ATP from glucose without an electron transport chain and that produces a characteristic end product, such as ethyl alcohol or lactic acid.

fertilization The union of haploid gametes to produce a diploid zygote.

fertilization envelope The swelling of the vitelline layer away from the plasma membrane.

fetus (fe'-tus) A developing human from the ninth week of gestation until birth; has all the major structures of an adult.

fiber A lignified cell type that reinforces the xylem of angiosperms and functions in mechanical support; a slender, tapered sclerenchyma cell that usually occurs in bundles.

fibrin (fi'-brin) The activated form of the blood-clotting protein fibrinogen, which aggregates into threads that form the fabric of the clot.

fibrinogen The inactive form of the plasma protein that is converted to the active form fibrin, which aggregates into threads that form the framework of a blood clot.

fibroblast (fi'-bro-blast) A type of cell in loose connective tissue that secretes the protein ingredients of the extracellular fibers.

fibronectin A glycoprotein that helps cells attach to the extracellular matrix.

fibrous connective tissue A dense tissue with large numbers of collagenous fibers organized into parallel bundles. This is the dominant tissue in tendons and ligaments.

fibrous root system A root system common to monocots consisting of a mat of thin roots spreading out below the soil surface.

filament The stalk of a stamen.

filtrate Fluid extracted by the excretory system from the body fluid. The excretory system produces urine from the filtrate after extracting valuable solutes from it and concentrating it.

filtration The extraction of water and small solutes, including metabolic wastes, from the body fluid into the excretory system.

fimbria (plural, **fimbriae**) A short, hairlike prokaryotic appendage that functions in adherence to the substrate or to other cells.

first law of thermodynamics The principle of conservation of energy. Energy can be transferred and transformed, but it cannot be created or destroyed.

fission The separation of a parent into two or more individuals of approximately equal size.

fitness The contribution an individual makes to the gene pool of the next generation, relative to the contributions of other individuals.

fixed action pattern (FAP) A sequence of behavioral acts that is essentially unchangeable and usually carried to completion once initiated.

flaccid (flas'-id) Limp. A walled cell is flaccid in surroundings where there is no tendency for water to enter.

flagellum (fluh-jel'-um) (plural, **flagella**) A long cellular appendage specialized for locomotion. The flagella of prokaryotes and eukaryotes differ in both structure and function.

florigen A flowering signal, not yet chemically identified, that may be a hormone or may be a change in relative concentrations of multiple hormones.

flower In an angiosperm, a short stem with up to four sets of modified leaves, bearing structures that function in sexual reproduction.

fluid feeder An animal that lives by sucking nutrient-rich fluids from another living organism.

fluid mosaic model The currently accepted model of cell membrane structure, which envisions the membrane as a mosaic of individual protein molecules drifting laterally in a fluid bilayer of phospholipids.

follicle (fol'-uh-kul) A microscopic structure in the ovary that contains the developing ovum and secretes estrogens.

follicle-stimulating hormone (FSH) A tropic hormone produced and secreted by the anterior pituitary that stimulates the production of eggs by the ovaries and sperm by the testes.

follicular phase That part of the ovarian cycle during which follicles are growing and oocytes maturing.

food chain The pathway along which food is transferred from trophic level to trophic level, beginning with producers.

food vacuole A membranous sac formed by phagocytosis.

food web The elaborate, interconnected feeding relationships in an ecosystem.

foot (1) The portion of a bryophyte sporophyte that gathers sugars, amino acids, water, and minerals from the parent gametophyte via transfer cells. (2) One of the three main parts of a mollusc; a muscular structure usually used for movement.

foraging Behavior necessary to recognize, search for, capture, and consume food.

foraminiferan (foram) An aquatic protist that secretes a hardened shell containing calcium carbonate and extends pseudopodia through pores in the shell.

forebrain One of three ancestral and embryonic regions of the vertebrate brain; develops into the thalamus, hypothalamus, and cerebrum.

fossil A preserved remnant or impression of an organism that lived in the past.

fossil record The chronicle of evolution over millions of years of geologic time engraved in the order in which fossils appear in rock strata.

founder effect Genetic drift that occurs when a few individuals become isolated from a larger population, with the result that the new population's gene pool is not reflective of the original population.

fovea (fo-ve'-uh) An eye's center of focus and the place on the retina where photoreceptors are highly concentrated.

fragmentation A means of asexual reproduction whereby a single parent breaks into parts that regenerate into whole new individuals.

frameshift mutation A mutation occurring when the number of nucleotides inserted or deleted is not a multiple of three, resulting in the improper grouping of the following nucleotides into codons.

free energy The portion of a system's energy that can perform work when temperature and pressure are uniform throughout the system. The change in free energy of a system is calculated by the equation $\Delta G = \Delta H - T\Delta S$, where T is absolute temperature.

free energy of activation The amount of energy that reactants must absorb before a chemical reaction will start; also called activation energy.

frequency-dependent selection A decline in the reproductive success of a morph resulting from the morph's phenotype becoming too common in a population; a cause of balanced polymorphism in populations.

fruit A mature ovary of a flower that protects dormant seeds and aids in their dispersal.

functional group A specific configuration of atoms commonly attached to the carbon skeletons of organic molecules and usually involved in chemical reactions.

Fungi (fun -jē) The eukaryotic kingdom that includes organisms that absorb nutrients after decomposing organic material.

fusiform initials Cells within the vascular cambrium that produce elongated cells such as tracheids, vessel elements, fibers, and sieve-tube members.

G protein A GTP-binding protein that relays signals from a plasma membrane signal receptor, known as a G-protein-linked receptor, to other signal transduction proteins inside the cell. When such a receptor is activated, it in turn activates the G protein, causing it to bind a molecule of GTP in place of GDP. Hydrolysis of the bound GTP to GDP inactivates the G protein.

G_0 phase A nondividing state in which a cell has left the cell cycle.

G_1 phase The first growth phase of the cell cycle, consisting of the portion of interphase before DNA synthesis begins.

G_2 phase The second growth phase of the cell cycle, consisting of the portion of interphase after DNA synthesis occurs.

gallbladder An organ that stores bile and releases it as needed into the small intestine.

gametangium (gam -uh-tan -jē-um) (plural, **gametangia**) Multicellular plant structures in which gametes are formed. Female gametangia are called archegonia, and male gametangia are called antheridia.

gamete (gam -ēt) A haploid cell, such as an egg or sperm. Gametes unite during sexual reproduction to produce a diploid zygote.

game theory An approach to evaluating alternative strategies in situations where the outcome depends not only on each individual's strategy but also on the strategies of other individuals; a way of thinking about behavioral evolution in situations where the fitness of a particular behavioral phenotype is influenced by other behavioral phenotypes in the population.

gametogenesis The process by which gametes are produced in the mammalian body.

gametophore The mature gamete-producing structure of a gametophyte body of a moss.

gametophyte (guh-mē -to-fīt) In organisms undergoing alternation of generations, the multicellular haploid form that mitotically produces haploid gametes that unite and grow into the sporophyte generation.

gamma aminobutyric acid (GABA) An amino acid that functions as a CNS neurotransmitter.

ganglion (gang -glē un) (plural, **ganglia**) A cluster (functional group) of nerve cell bodies in a centralized nervous system.

ganglion cell A type of neuron in the retina that synapses with bipolar cells and transmits action potentials to the brain via axons in the optic nerve.

gap junction A type of intercellular junction in animal cells that allows the passage of material or current between cells.

gas exchange The uptake of molecular oxygen from the environment and the discharge of carbon dioxide to the environment.

gastric juice A digestive fluid secreted by the stomach.

gastrovascular cavity An extensive pouch that serves as the site of extracellular digestion and a passageway to disperse materials throughout most of an animal's body.

gastrula (gas -tru-luh) The three-layered, cup-shaped embryonic stage.

gastrulation (gas -tru là -shun) The formation of a gastrula from a blastula.

gated channel A protein channel in a cell membrane that opens or closes in response to a particular stimulus.

gated ion channel A gated channel for a specific ion. When ion channels are opened or closed, the membrane potential of the cell is altered.

gel electrophoresis (ē-lek -trō-fōr-ē -sis) The separation of nucleic acids or proteins, on the basis of their size and electrical charge, by measuring their rate of movement through an electrical field in a gel.

gene A discrete unit of hereditary information consisting of a specific nucleotide sequence in DNA (or RNA, in some viruses).

gene cloning The production of multiple copies of a gene.

gene flow Genetic additions to or subtractions from a population resulting from the movement of fertile individuals or gametes.

gene-for-gene recognition A widespread form of plant disease resistance involving recognition of pathogen-derived molecules by the protein products of specific plant disease resistance genes.

gene pool The total aggregate of genes in a population at any one time.

gene therapy The alteration of the genes of a person afflicted with a genetic disease.

genetic annealing The production of a new genome through the transfer of part of the genome of one organism to another organism.

genetic drift Unpredictable fluctuations in allele frequencies from one generation to the next because of a population's finite size.

genetic engineering The direct manipulation of genes for practical purposes.

genetic map An ordered list of genetic loci (genes or other genetic markers) along a chromosome.

genetic polymorphism The existence of two or more distinct alleles at a given locus in a population's gene pool.

genetic recombination General term for the production of offspring that combine traits of the two parents.

genetically modified (GM) organism An organism that has acquired one or more genes by artificial means; also known as a transgenic organism.

genetics The scientific study of heredity and hereditary variation.

genome (jē -nōm) The complete complement of an organism's genes; an organism's genetic material.

genomic imprinting Phenomenon in which expression of an allele in offspring depends on whether the allele is inherited from the male or female parent.

genomic library A set of thousands of DNA segments from a genome, each carried by a plasmid, phage, or other cloning vector.

genomics (guh-nō -miks) The study of whole sets of genes and their interactions.

genotype (jē -nō-tīp) The genetic makeup, or set of alleles, of an organism.

genus (jē -nus) (plural, **genera**) A taxonomic category above the species level, designated by the first word of a species' two-part scientific name.

geographic variation Differences between the gene pools of separate populations or population subgroups.

geologic record The division of Earth's history into time periods, grouped into three eras—Archaean, Proterozoic, and Phanerozoic, and further subdivided into eras and epochs.

geometric isomer One of several organic compounds that have the same molecular formula but differ in the spatial arrangements of their atoms.

germ layers Three main layers that form the various tissues and organs of an animal body.

gestation (jes-tā -shun) Pregnancy; the state of carrying developing young within the female reproductive tract.

gibberellins (jib-uh-rel -inz) A class of related plant hormones that stimulate growth in the stem and leaves, trigger the germination of seeds and breaking of bud dormancy, and stimulate fruit development with auxin.

gill A localized extension of the body surface of many aquatic animals, specialized for gas exchange.

gill circulation The flow of blood through gills.

glandular epithelium An epithelium that absorbs or secretes chemical solutions.

glans penis The head end of the penis.

glia Supporting cells that are essential for the structural integrity of the nervous system and for the normal functioning of neurons.

glomeromycete Member of the fungal phylum Glomeromycota, characterized by forming a distinct branching form of endomycorrhizae (symbiotic relationships with plant roots) called arbuscular mycorrhizae.

glomerulus (glō-mār'-ū-lus) A ball of capillaries surrounded by Bowman's capsule in the nephron and serving as the site of filtration in the vertebrate kidney.

glucagon (glū'-kuh-gon) A hormone secreted by pancreatic alpha cells that raises blood glucose levels. It promotes glycogen breakdown and release of glucose by the liver.

glucocorticoid A steroid hormone secreted by the adrenal cortex that influences glucose metabolism and immune function.

glutamate An amino acid that functions as a CNS neurotransmitter.

glyceraldehyde-3-phosphate (G3P) (glis-er-al-de-hīd') The carbohydrate produced directly from the Calvin cycle.

glycine (glī'-sēn) An amino acid that functions as a CNS neurotransmitter.

glycogen (glī'-kō-jen) An extensively branched glucose storage polysaccharide found in the liver and muscle of animals; the animal equivalent of starch.

glycolipid A lipid covalently attached to a carbohydrate.

glycolysis (glī-kol'-uh-sis) The splitting of glucose into pyruvate. Glycolysis is the one metabolic pathway that occurs in all living cells, serving as the starting point for fermentation or aerobic respiration.

glycoprotein A protein covalently attached to a carbohydrate.

glycosidic linkage A covalent bond formed between two monosaccharides by a dehydration reaction.

gnathostome (nā'-thuh-stōm) Member of the vertebrate subgroup possessing jaws.

golden alga A chrysophyte; a typically unicellular, biflagellated alga with yellow and brown carotenoid pigments.

Golgi apparatus (gol'-jē) An organelle in eukaryotic cells consisting of stacks of flat membranous sacs that modify, store, and route products of the endoplasmic reticulum.

gonadotropin (gō-nah'-dō-trō'-pin) A hormone that stimulates the activities of the testes and ovaries. Follicle-stimulating hormone and luteinizing hormone are gonadotropins.

gonads (gō'-nadz) The male and female sex organs; the gamete-producing organs in most animals.

G-protein-linked receptor A signal receptor protein in the plasma membrane that responds to the binding signal molecule by activating a G protein.

grade Group of animal species that share the same level of organizational complexity.

graded potential A local voltage change in a neuron membrane induced by stimulation of a neuron, with strength proportional to the strength of the stimulus and lasting about a millisecond.

gradualism A view of Earth's history that attributes profound change to the cumulative product of slow but continuous processes.

graft versus host reaction An attack against a patient's body cells by lymphocytes received in a bone marrow transplant.

gram-negative Describing the group of bacteria with a cell wall that is structurally more complex and contains less peptidoglycan than that of gram-positive bacteria. Gram-negative bacteria are often more toxic than gram-positive bacteria.

gram-positive Describing the group of bacteria with a cell wall that is structurally less complex and contains more peptidoglycan than that of gram-negative bacteria. Gram-positive bacteria are usually less toxic than gram-negative bacteria.

Gram stain A staining method that distinguishes between two different kinds of bacterial cell walls.

granum (gran'-um) (plural, **grana**) A stacked portion of the thylakoid membrane in the chloroplast. Grana function in the light reactions of photosynthesis.

gravitropism (grav'-uh-trō'-pizm) A response of a plant or animal to gravity.

gray crescent A light-gray region of cytoplasm located near the equator of the egg on the side opposite the sperm entry.

gray matter Regions of dendrites and clusters of neuron cell bodies within the CNS.

green alga A unicellular, colonial, or multicellular photosynthetic protist that has grass-green chloroplasts. Green algae are closely related to true plants.

greenhouse effect The warming of planet Earth due to the atmospheric accumulation of carbon dioxide, which absorbs reflected infrared radiation and re-reflects some of it back toward Earth.

green world hypothesis The conjecture that terrestrial herbivores consume relatively little plant biomass because they are held in check by a variety of factors, including predators, parasites, and disease.

gross primary production (GPP) The total primary production of an ecosystem.

ground tissue system Plant tissues that are neither vascular nor dermal, fulfilling a variety of functions, such as storage, photosynthesis, and support.

growth cone Responsive region at the leading edge of a growing axon.

growth factor A protein that must be present in the extracellular environment (culture medium or animal body) for the growth and normal development of certain types of cells; a local regulator that acts on nearby cells to stimulate cell proliferation and differentiation.

growth hormone (GH) A hormone produced and secreted by the anterior pituitary that has both direct (nontropic) effects and tropic effects on a wide variety of tissues.

guard cells The two cells that flank the stomatal pore and regulate the opening and closing of the pore.

gustatory receptor Taste receptor.

guttation The exudation of water droplets, caused by root pressure in certain plants.

gymnosperm (jim'-nō-sperm) A vascular plant that bears naked seeds—seeds not enclosed in specialized chambers.

habituation A very simple type of learning that involves a loss of responsiveness to stimuli that convey little or no information.

hair cell A type of mechanoreceptor that detects sound waves and other forms of movement in air or water.

half-life The number of years it takes for 50% of a sample of an isotope to decay.

Hamilton's rule The principle that for natural selection to favor an altruistic act, the benefit to the recipient, devalued by the coefficient of relatedness, must exceed the cost to the altruist.

haploid cell (hap'-loyd) A cell containing only one set of chromosomes (n).

Hardy-Weinberg equilibrium The condition describing a non-evolving population (one that is in genetic equilibrium).

Hardy-Weinberg theorem The principle that frequencies of alleles and genotypes in a population remain constant from generation to generation, provided that only Mendelian segregation and recombination of alleles are at work.

haustorium (plural, **haustoria**) In certain symbiotic fungi, specialized hyphae that can penetrate the tissues of host organisms.

heart A muscular pump that uses metabolic energy to elevate hydrostatic pressure of the blood. Blood then flows down a pressure gradient through blood vessels that eventually return blood to the heart.

heart attack The death of cardiac muscle tissue resulting from prolonged blockage of one or more coronary arteries.

heart murmur A hissing sound that occurs when blood squirts backward through a leaky valve in the heart.

heart rate The rate of heart contraction.

heartwood Older layers of secondary xylem, closer to the center of a stem or root, that no longer transport xylem sap.

heat The total amount of kinetic energy due to molecular motion in a body of matter. Heat is energy in its most random form.

heat of vaporization The quantity of heat a liquid must absorb for 1 g of it to be converted from the liquid to the gaseous state.

heat-shock protein A protein that helps protect other proteins during heat stress. Heat-shock proteins are found in plants, animals, and microorganisms.

heavy chain One of the two types of polypeptide chains that make up an antibody molecule and B cell receptor; consists of a variable region, which contributes to the antigen-binding site, and a constant region.

helicase An enzyme that untwists the double helix of DNA at the replication forks.

helper T cell A type of T cell that, when activated, secretes cytokines that promote the response of B cells (humoral response) and cytotoxic T cells (cell-mediated response) to antigens.

hemocyanin (hē´-muh-si´-uh-nin) A type of respiratory pigment that uses copper as its oxygen-binding component. Hemocyanin is found in the hemolymph of arthropods and many molluscs.

hemoglobin (hē´-mo-glō-bin) An iron-containing protein in red blood cells that reversibly binds oxygen.

hemolymph In invertebrates with an open circulatory system, the body fluid that bathes tissues.

hemophilia A human genetic disease caused by a sex-linked recessive allele; characterized by excessive bleeding following injury.

hepatic portal vein A large circulatory channel that conveys nutrient-laden blood from the small intestine to the liver, which regulates the blood's nutrient content.

herbaceous Referring to nonwoody plants.

herbivore A heterotrophic animal that eats plants.

herbivory An interaction in which an herbivore eats parts of a plant or alga.

heredity The transmission of traits from one generation to the next.

hermaphrodite (her-maf´-rō-dit) An individual that functions as both male and female in sexual reproduction by producing both sperm and eggs.

hermaphroditism (her-maf´-rō-dī-tizm) A condition in which an individual has both female and male gonads and functions as both a male and female in sexual reproduction by producing both sperm and eggs.

heterochromatin (het´-er-ō-krō´-muh-tin) Nontranscribed eukaryotic chromatin that is so highly compacted that it is visible with a light microscope during interphase.

heterochrony (het´-uh-rok´-ruh-nē) Evolutionary change in the timing or rate of an organism's development.

heterocyst (het´-er-ō-sist) A specialized cell that engages in nitrogen fixation in some filamentous cyanobacteria.

heterokaryon A fungal mycelium formed by the fusion of two hyphae that have genetically different nuclei.

heteromorphic (het´-er-ō-mōr´-fik) Referring to a condition in the life cycle of all living plants and certain algae in which the sporophyte and gametophyte generations differ in morphology.

heterosporous (het´-er-os´-por-us) A term referring to a plant species that has two kinds of spores: microspores that develop into male gametophytes and megaspores that develop into female gametophytes.

heterotroph (het´-er-ō-trōf) An organism that obtains organic food molecules by eating other organisms or their by-products.

heterozygote advantage Greater reproductive success of heterozygous individuals compared to homozygotes; tends to preserve variation in gene pools.

heterozygous (het´-er-ō-zī-gus) Having two different alleles for a given gene.

hexapod An insect or closely related wingless, six-legged arthropod.

hibernation A physiological state that allows survival during long periods of cold temperatures and reduced food supplies, in which metabolism decreases, the heart and respiratory system slow down, and body temperature is maintained at a lower level than normal.

high-density lipoprotein (HDL) A cholesterol-carrying particle in the blood, made up of cholesterol and other lipids surrounded by a single layer of phospholipids in which proteins are embedded. An HDL particle carries less cholesterol than a related lipoprotein, LDL, and may be correlated with a decreased risk of blood vessel blockage.

hindbrain One of three ancestral and embryonic regions of the vertebrate brain; develops into the medulla oblongata, pons, and cerebellum.

histamine (his´-tuh-mēn) A substance released by mast cells that causes blood vessels to dilate and become more permeable during an inflammatory response.

histone (his´-tōn) A small protein with a high proportion of positively charged amino acids that binds to the negatively charged DNA and plays a key role in its chromatin structure.

histone acetylation The attachment of acetyl groups to certain amino acids of histone proteins.

HIV (human immunodeficiency virus) The infectious agent that causes AIDS. HIV is a retrovirus.

holdfast A rootlike structure that anchors a seaweed.

holoblastic cleavage (hō´-lō-blas´-tik) A type of cleavage in which there is complete division of the egg, as in eggs having little yolk (sea urchin) or a moderate amount of yolk (frog).

homeobox (hō´-mē-ō-boks´) A 180-nucleotide sequence within homeotic genes and some other developmental genes that is widely conserved in animals. Related sequences occur in plants and prokaryotes.

homeostasis (hō´-mē-ō-stā´-sis) The steady-state physiological condition of the body.

homeotic gene (hō´-mē-ot´-ik) Any of the genes that control the overall body plan of animals and plants by controlling the developmental fate of groups of cells.

hominid (hah´-mi-nid) A species on the human branch of the evolutionary tree; a member of the family Hominidae, including *Homo sapiens* and our ancestors.

hominoid A term that refers to great apes and humans.

homologous chromosomes (hō-mol´-uh-gus) Chromosome pairs of the same length, centromere position, and staining pattern that possess genes for the same characters at corresponding loci. One homologous chromosome is inherited from the organism's father, the other from the mother.

homologous structures Structures in different species that are similar because of common ancestry.

homology (hō-mol´-uh-jē) Similarity in characteristics resulting from a shared ancestry.

homoplasy Similar (analogous) structure or molecular sequence that has evolved independently in two species.

homosporous (hō-mos´-por-us) A term referring to a plant species that has a single kind of spore, which typically develops into a bisexual gametophyte.

homozygous (hō-mō-zī-gus) Having two identical alleles for a given gene.

horizon A distinct layer of soil, such as topsoil.

horizontal cell A neuron of the retina that helps integrate information before it is sent to the brain.

hormone In multicellular organisms, one of many types of circulating chemical signals that are formed in specialized cells, travel in body fluids, and act on specific target cells to change their functioning.

hornwort A small, herbaceous nonvascular plant that is a member of the phylum Anthocerophyta.

host The larger participant in a symbiotic relationship, serving as home and feeding ground to the symbiont.

host range The limited range of host cells that each type of virus can infect and parasitize.

human chorionic gonadotropin (HCG) (kōr´-ē-on´-ik gō-nah´-dō-trō´-pin) A hormone secreted by the chorion that maintains the corpus luteum of the ovary during the first three months of pregnancy.

Human Genome Project An international collaborative effort to map and sequence the DNA of the entire human genome.

humoral immune response (hyu´-mor-al) The branch of acquired immunity that involves the activation of B cells and that leads to the production of antibodies, which defend against bacteria and viruses in body fluids.

humus (hyū´-mus) Decomposing organic material found in topsoil.

Huntington's disease A human genetic disease caused by a dominant allele; characterized by uncontrollable body movements and degeneration of the nervous system; usually fatal 10 to 20 years after the onset of symptoms.

hybridization In genetics, the mating, or crossing, of two true-breeding varieties.

hydration shell The sphere of water molecules around each dissolved ion.

hydrocarbon An organic molecule consisting only of carbon and hydrogen.

hydrogen bond A type of weak chemical bond formed when the slightly positive hydrogen atom of a polar covalent bond in one molecule is attracted to the slightly negative atom of a polar covalent bond in another molecule.

hydrogen ion A single proton with a charge of 1+. The dissociation of a water molecule (H_2O) leads to the generation of a hydroxide ion (OH^-) and a hydrogen ion (H^+).

hydrolysis (hī-drol'-uh-sis) A chemical process that lyses, or splits, molecules by the addition of water.

hydrophilic (hī-drō-fil'-ik) Having an affinity for water.

hydrophobic (hī-drō-fō-bik) Having an aversion to water; tending to coalesce and form droplets in water.

hydrophobic interaction A type of weak chemical bond formed when molecules that do not mix with water coalesce to exclude the water.

hydroponic culture A method in which plants are grown without soil by using mineral solutions.

hydrostatic skeleton (hī-drō-stat'-ik) A skeletal system composed of fluid held under pressure in a closed body compartment; the main skeleton of most cnidarians, flatworms, nematodes, and annelids.

hydroxide ion A water molecule that has lost a proton; OH^-.

hydroxyl group (hī-drok'-sil) A functional group consisting of a hydrogen atom joined to an oxygen atom by a polar covalent bond. Molecules possessing this group are soluble in water and are called alcohols.

hymen A thin membrane that partly covers the vaginal opening in the human female. The hymen is ruptured by sexual intercourse or other vigorous activity.

hyperpolarization An electrical state in which the inside of the cell is more negative relative to the outside than at the resting membrane potential. A neuron membrane is hyperpolarized if a stimulus increases its voltage from the resting potential of -70 mV, reducing the chance that the neuron will transmit a nerve impulse.

hypersensitive response (HR) A plant's localized defense response to a pathogen.

hypertension Chronically high blood pressure within the arteries.

hypertonic In comparing two solutions, referring to the one with a greater solute concentration.

hypha (plural, **hyphae**) (hī'-fuh, hī'-fē) A filament that collectively makes up the body of a fungus.

hypocotyl (hī'-puh-cot'-ul) In an angiosperm embryo, the embryonic axis below the point of attachment of the cotyledon(s) and above the radicle.

hypothalamus (hī-pō-thal'-uh-mus) The ventral part of the vertebrate forebrain; functions in maintaining homeostasis, especially in coordinating the endocrine and nervous systems; secretes hormones of the posterior pituitary and releasing factors that regulate the anterior pituitary.

hypothesis A tentative answer to a well-framed question.

hypotonic In comparing two solutions, referring to the one with a lower solute concentration.

I band The area near the edge of the sarcomere where there are only thin filaments.

immigration The influx of new individuals from other areas.

immunization The process of generating a state of immunity by artifical means. In active immunization, a nonpathogenic version of a normally pathogenic microbe is administered, inducing B and T cell responses and immunological memory. In passive immunization, antibodies specific for a particular microbe are administered, conferring immediate but temporary protection. Also called vaccination.

immunoglobulin (Ig) (im'-ū-nō-glob'-ū-lin) Any of the class of proteins that function as antibodies. Immunoglobulins are divided into five major classes that differ in their distribution in the body and antigen disposal activities.

imperfect fungus See deuteromycete.

imprinting A type of learned behavior with a significant innate component, acquired during a limited critical period.

in vitro fertilization (vē'-trō) Fertilization of ova in laboratory containers followed by artificial implantation of the early embryo in the mother's uterus.

in vitro mutagenesis A technique to discover the function of a gene by introducing specific changes into the sequence of a cloned gene, reinserting the mutated gene into a cell, and studying the phenotype of the mutant.

inclusive fitness The total effect an individual has on proliferating its genes by producing its own offspring and by providing aid that enables other close relatives to increase the production of their offspring.

incomplete dominance The situation in which the phenotype of heterozygotes is intermediate between the phenotypes of individuals homozygous for either allele.

incomplete flower A flower in which one or more of the four basic floral organs (sepals, petals, stamens, or carpels) are either absent or nonfunctional.

incomplete metamorphosis A type of development in certain insects, such as grasshoppers, in which the young (called nymphs) resemble adults but are smaller and have different body proportions. The nymph goes through a series of molts, each time looking more like an adult, until it reaches full size.

incus The second of the three middle ear bones.

indeterminate cleavage A type of embryonic development in deuterostomes, in which each cell produced by early cleavage divisions retains the capacity to develop into a complete embryo.

indeterminate growth A type of growth characteristic of plants, in which the organism continues to grow as long as it lives.

individualistic hypothesis The concept, put forth by H. A. Gleason, that a plant community is a chance assemblage of species found in the same area simply because they happen to have similar biotic requirements.

induced fit The change in shape of the active site of an enzyme so that it binds more snugly to the substrate, induced by entry of the substrate.

inducer A specific small molecule that inactivates the repressor in an operon.

induction The ability of one group of embryonic cells to influence the development of another.

inductive reasoning A type of logic in which generalizations are based on a large number of specific observations.

infant mortality The number of infant deaths per 1,000 live births.

inflammatory response A localized innate immune defense triggered by physical injury or infection of tissue in which changes to nearby small blood vessels enhance the infiltration of white blood cells, antimicrobial proteins, and clotting elements that aid in tissue repair and destruction of invading pathogens; may also involve systemic effects such as fever and increased production of white blood cells.

inflorescence A group of flowers tightly clustered together.

ingestion A heterotrophic mode of nutrition in which other organisms or detritus are eaten whole or in pieces.

ingroup In a cladistic study of evolutionary relationships among taxa of organisms, the group of taxa that is actually being analyzed.

inhibitory postsynaptic potential (IPSP) (pōst'-sin-ap'-tik) An electrical charge (hyperpolarization) in the membrane of a postsynaptic neuron caused by the binding of an inhibitory neurotransmitter from a presynaptic cell to a postsynaptic receptor; makes it more difficult for a postsynaptic neuron to generate an action potential.

initials Cells that remain within an apical meristem as sources of new cells.

innate behavior Behavior that is developmentally fixed and under strong genetic control. Innate behavior is exhibited in virtually the same form by all individuals in a population despite internal and external environmental differences during development and throughout their lifetimes.

innate immunity The kind of defense that is mediated by phagocytic cells, antimicrobial proteins, the inflammatory response, and natural killer (NK) cells. It is present before exposure to pathogens and is effective from the time of birth.

inner cell mass A cluster of cells in a mammalian blastocyst that protrudes into one end of the cavity and subsequently develops into the embryo proper and some of the extraembryonic membranes.

inner ear One of three main regions of the vertebrate ear; includes the cochlea, organ of Corti, and semicircular canals.

inositol trisphosphate (IP$_3$) (in-ō-suh-tol) A second messenger that functions as an intermediate between certain nonsteroid hormones and a third messenger, a rise in cytoplasmic Ca^{2+} concentration.

inquiry The search for information and explanation, often focused by specific questions.

insertion A mutation involving the addition of one or more nucleotide pairs to a gene.

insertion sequence The simplest kind of transposable element, consisting of inverted repeats of DNA flanking a gene for transposase, the enzyme that catalyzes transposition.

insulin (in-sū-lin) A hormone secreted by pancreatic beta cells that lowers blood glucose levels. It promotes the uptake of glucose by most body cells and the synthesis and storage of glycogen in the liver and also stimulates protein and fat synthesis.

insulin-like growth factor A hormone produced by the liver whose secretion is stimulated by growth hormone. It directly stimulates bone and cartilage growth.

integral protein Typically a transmembrane protein with hydrophobic regions that completely spans the hydrophobic interior of the membrane.

integrated hypothesis The concept, put forth by F. E. Clements, that a community is an assemblage of closely linked species, locked into association by mandatory biotic interactions that cause the community to function as an integrated unit, a sort of superorganism.

integration The interpretation of sensory signals within neural processing centers of the central nervous system.

integrin A receptor protein built into the plasma membrane that interconnects the extracellular matrix and the cytoskeleton.

integument (in-teg-ū-ment) Layer of sporophyte tissue that contributes to the structure of an ovule of a seed plant.

integumentary system The outer covering of a mammal's body, including skin, hair, and nails.

intercalated disk A specialized junction between cardiac muscle cells that provides direct electrical coupling between cells.

interferon (in-ter-fēr-on) A protein that has antiviral or immune regulatory functions. Interferon-α and interferon-β, secreted by virus-infected cells, help nearby cells resist viral infection; interferon-γ, secreted by T cells, helps activate macrophages.

intermediate disturbance hypothesis The concept that moderate levels of disturbance can foster greater species diversity than low or high levels of disturbance.

intermediate filament A component of the cytoskeleton that includes all filaments intermediate in size between microtubules and microfilaments.

internal fertilization Reproduction in which sperm are typically deposited in or near the female reproductive tract and fertilization occurs within the tract.

interneuron (in-ter-nūr-on) An association neuron; a nerve cell within the central nervous system that forms synapses with sensory and motor neurons and integrates sensory input and motor output.

internode A segment of a plant stem between the points where leaves are attached.

interoparity A life history in which adults produce large numbers of offspring over many years; also known as repeated reproduction.

interoreceptor A sensory receptor that detects stimuli within the body, such as blood pressure and body position.

interphase The period in the cell cycle when the cell is not dividing. During interphase, cellular metabolic activity is high, chromosomes and organelles are duplicated, and cell size may increase. Interphase accounts for 90% of the cell cycle.

intersexual selection Selection whereby individuals of one sex (usually females) are choosy in selecting their mates from individuals of the other sex; also called mate choice.

interspecific competition Competition for resources between plants, between animals, or between decomposers when resources are in short supply.

interspecific interaction Relationships between species of a community.

interstitial fluid The internal environment of vertebrates, consisting of the fluid filling the spaces between cells.

intertidal zone The shallow zone of the ocean where land meets water.

intracellular digestion The joining of food vacuoles and lysosomes to allow chemical digestion to occur within the cytoplasm of a cell.

intrasexual selection A direct competition among individuals of one sex (usually the males in vertebrates) for mates of the opposite sex.

introduced species A species moved by humans, either intentionally or accidentally, from its native location to a new geographic region; also called an exotic species.

intron (in-tron) A noncoding, intervening sequence within a eukaryotic gene.

invagination The infolding of cells.

invasive species A species that takes hold outside of its native range, usually introduced by humans.

inversion An aberration in chromosome structure resulting from reattachment in a reverse orientation of a chromosomal fragment to the chromosome from which the fragment originated.

invertebrate An animal without a backbone. Invertebrates make up 95% of animal species.

involution Cells rolling over the edge of the lip of the blastopore into the interior of the embryo during gastrulation.

ion (ī-on) An atom that has gained or lost electrons, thus acquiring a charge.

ion channel Protein channel in a cell membrane that allows passage of a specific ion down its concentration gradient.

ionic bond (ī-on-ik) A chemical bond resulting from the attraction between oppositely charged ions.

ionic compound A compound resulting from the formation of an ionic bond; also called a salt.

islets of Langerhans Clusters of endocrine cells within the pancreas that produce and secrete the hormones glucagon (alpha cells) and insulin (beta cells).

isomer (ī-sō-mer) One of several organic compounds with the same molecular formula but different structures and therefore different properties. The three types of isomers are structural isomers, geometric isomers, and enantiomers.

isomorphic Referring to alternating generations in plants and certain algae in which the sporophytes and gametophytes look alike, although they differ in chromosome number.

isopod A member of one of the largest groups of crustaceans, which includes terrestrial, freshwater, and marine species. Among the terrestrial isopods are the pill bugs, or wood lice.

isotonic (ī-sō-ton-ik) Having the same solute concentration as another solution.

isotope (ī-sō-tōp) One of several atomic forms of an element, each containing a different number of neutrons and thus differing in atomic mass.

jasmonic acid An important molecule in plant defense against herbivores.

joule (J) A unit of energy: 1 J = 0.239 cal; 1 cal = 4.184 J.

juvenile hormone A hormone in arthropods, secreted by the corpora allata glands, that promotes the retention of larval characteristics.

juxtaglomerular apparatus (JGA) (juks -tuh-gluh-mâr -û-ler) A specialized tissue that releases the enzyme renin when blood pressure or blood volume drops in the afferent arteriole that supplies blood to the glomerulus.

juxtamedullary nephrons Nephrons with well-developed loops of Henle that extend deeply into the renal medulla.

karyogamy (kâr -ê-og -uh-mê) The fusion of nuclei of two cells, as part of syngamy.

karyotype (kâr -ê-ô-tîp) A display of the chromosome pairs of a cell arranged by size and shape.

keystone species A species that is not necessarily abundant in a community yet exerts strong control on community structure by the nature of its ecological role or niche.

kilocalorie (kcal) A thousand calories, the amount of heat energy required to raise the temperature of 1 kg of water by 1°C.

kin selection A phenomenon of inclusive fitness, used to explain altruistic behavior between related individuals.

kinesis (kuh-nê -sis) A change in activity or turning rate in response to a stimulus.

kinetic energy (kuh-net -ik) The energy of motion, which is directly related to the speed of that motion. Moving matter does work by imparting motion to other matter.

kinetochore (kuh-net -uh-kôr) A specialized region on the centromere that links each sister chromatid to the mitotic spindle.

kinetoplastid A protist, such as *Trypanosoma*, which has a single large mitochondrion that houses extranuclear DNA.

kingdom A taxonomic category, the second broadest after domain.

K-selection The concept that in certain (K-selected) populations, life history is centered around producing relatively few offspring that have a good chance of survival.

labia majora A pair of thick, fatty ridges that enclose and protect the labia minora and vestibule.

labia minora A pair of slender skin folds that enclose and protect the vestibule.

labor A series of strong, rhythmic contractions of the uterus that expel a baby out of the uterus and vagina during childbirth.

lactation The continued production of milk.

lacteal (lak -tê-al) A tiny lymph vessel extending into the core of an intestinal villus and serving as the destination for absorbed chylomicrons.

lactic acid fermentation The conversion of pyruvate to lactate with no release of carbon dioxide.

lagging strand A discontinuously synthesized DNA strand that elongates in a direction away from the replication fork.

lancelet Member of the subphylum Cephalochordata, small blade-shaped marine chordates that lack a backbone.

landmark A point of reference for orientation during navigation.

landscape Several different, primarily terrestrial ecosystems linked by exchanges of energy, materials, and organisms.

landscape ecology The study of past, present, and future patterns of landscape use, as well as ecosystem management and the biodiversity of interacting ecosystems.

large intestine (colon) (kô -len) The tubular portion of the vertebrate alimentary tract between the small intestine and the anus; functions mainly in water absorption and the formation of feces.

larva (lar -vuh) (plural, **larvae**) A free-living, sexually immature form in some animal life cycles that may differ from the adult in morphology, nutrition, and habitat.

larynx (lâr -inks) The voice box, containing the vocal cords.

lateral geniculate nuclei The destination in the thalamus for most of the ganglion cell axons that form the optic nerves.

lateral inhibition A process that sharpens the edges and enhances the contrast of a perceived image by inhibiting receptors lateral to those that have responded to light.

lateralization Segregation of functions in the cortex of the left and right hemispheres of the brain.

lateral line system A mechanoreceptor system consisting of a series of pores and receptor units (neuromasts) along the sides of the body in fishes and aquatic amphibians; detects water movements made by the animal itself and by other moving objects.

lateral meristem (mâr -uh-stem) A meristem that thickens the roots and shoots of woody plants. The vascular cambium and cork cambium are lateral meristems.

lateral root A root that arises from the outermost layer of the pericycle of an established root.

law of independent assortment Mendel's second law, stating that each pair of alleles segregates independently during gamete formation; applies when genes for two characters are located on different pairs of homologous chromosomes.

law of segregation Mendel's first law, stating that each allele in a pair separates into a different gamete during gamete formation.

leading strand The new continuous complementary DNA strand synthesized along the template strand in the mandatory 5' → 3' direction.

leaf The main photosynthetic organ of vascular plants.

leaf primordia Fingerlike projections along the flanks of a shoot apical meristem, from which leaves arise.

leaf trace A small vascular bundle that extends from the vascular tissue of the stem through the petiole and into a leaf.

learning A behavioral change resulting from experience.

lens The structure in an eye that focuses light rays onto the retina.

lenticels Small raised areas in the bark of stems and roots that enable gas exchange between living cells and the outside air.

lepidosaur Member of the reptilian group that includes lizards, snakes, and two species of New Zealand animals called tuataras.

leukocyte (lû -kô-sît) A white blood cell; typically functions in immunity, such as phagocytosis or antibody production.

Leydig cell A cell that produces testosterone and other androgens and is located between the seminiferous tubules of the testes.

lichen (lî -ken) The symbiotic collective formed by the mutualistic association between a fungus and a photosynthetic alga or cyanobacterium.

life cycle The generation-to-generation sequence of stages in the reproductive history of an organism.

life expectancy at birth The predicted average length of life at birth.

life history The series of events from birth through reproduction and death.

life table A table of data summarizing mortality in a population.

ligament A type of fibrous connective tissue that joins bones together at joints.

ligand (lig -und) A molecule that binds specifically to a receptor site of another molecule.

ligand-gated ion channel A protein pore in the plasma membrane that opens or closes in response to a chemical signal, allowing or blocking the flow of specific ions.

light chain One of the two types of polypeptide chains that make up an antibody molecule and B cell receptor; consists of a variable region, which contributes to the antigen-binding site, and a constant region.

light-harvesting complex Complex of proteins associated with pigment molecules (including chlorophyll a, chlorophyll b, and carotenoids) that captures light energy and transfers it to reaction-center pigments in a photosystem.

light microscope (LM) An optical instrument with lenses that refract (bend) visible light to magnify images of specimens.

light reactions The steps in photosynthesis that occur on the thylakoid membranes of the chloroplast and that convert solar energy to the chemical energy of ATP and NADPH, evolving oxygen in the process.

lignin (lig -nin) A hard material embedded in the cellulose matrix of vascular plant cell walls that functions as an important adaptation for support in terrestrial species.

limbic system (lim -bik) A group of nuclei (clusters of nerve cell bodies) in the lower part of the mammalian forebrain that interact with the cerebral cortex in determining

Glossary

emotions; includes the hippocampus and the amygdala.

limiting nutrient An element that must be added for production to increase in a particular area.

limnetic zone In a lake, the well-lit, open surface waters farther from shore.

linkage map A genetic map based on the frequencies of recombination between markers during crossing over of homologous chromosomes.

linked genes Genes located close enough together on a chromosome to be usually inherited together.

lipid (lip´-id) One of a family of compounds, including fats, phospholipids, and steroids, that are insoluble in water.

littoral zone In a lake, the shallow, well-lit waters close to shore.

liver The largest organ in the vertebrate body. The liver performs diverse functions, such as producing bile, preparing nitrogenous wastes for disposal, and detoxifying poisonous chemicals in the blood.

liverwort A small, herbaceous nonvascular plant that is a member of the phylum Hepatophyta.

loam The most fertile of all soils, made up of roughly equal amounts of sand, silt, and clay.

lobe-fin Member of the vertebrate subgroup Sarcopterygii, osteichthyans with rod-shaped muscular fins, including coelacanths and lungfishes, as well as the lineage that gave rise to tetrapods.

local regulator A chemical messenger that influences cells in the vicinity.

locomotion Active movement from place to place.

locus (lō´-kus) (plural, **loci**) A specific place along the length of a chromosome where a given gene is located.

logistic population growth A model describing population growth that levels off as population size approaches carrying capacity.

long-day plant A plant that flowers (usually in late spring or early summer) only when the light period is longer than a critical length.

long-term memory The ability to hold, associate, and recall information over one's life.

long-term potentiation (LTP) An enhanced responsiveness to an action potential (nerve signal) by a receiving neuron.

loop of Henle The long hairpin turn, with a descending and ascending limb, of the renal tubule in the vertebrate kidney; functions in water and salt reabsorption.

loose connective tissue The most widespread connective tissue in the vertebrate body. It binds epithelia to underlying tissues and functions as packing material, holding organs in place.

lophophore (lof´-uh-fōr) A horseshoe-shaped or circular fold of the body wall bearing ciliated tentacles that surround the mouth.

lophotrochozoan Member of a group of animal phyla with protostome development that some systematists hypothesize form a clade, characterized by lophophores or trochophore larvae.

low-density lipoprotein (LDL) A cholesterol carrying particle in the blood, made up of cholesterol and other lipids surrounded by a single layer of phospholipids in which proteins are embedded. An LDL particle carries more cholesterol than a related lipoprotein, HDL, and high LDL levels in the blood correlate with a tendency to develop blocked blood vessels and heart disease.

lung An invaginated respiratory surface of terrestrial vertebrates, land snails, and spiders that connects to the atmosphere by narrow tubes.

luteal phase That portion of the ovarian cycle during which endocrine cells of the corpus luteum secrete female hormones.

luteinizing hormone (LH) (lü´-te-uh-nī´-zing) A tropic hormone produced and secreted by the anterior pituitary that stimulates ovulation in females and androgen production in males.

lycophyte An informal name for any member of the phylum Lycophyta, which includes club mosses, spike mosses, and quillworts.

lymph The colorless fluid, derived from interstitial fluid, in the lymphatic system of vertebrate animals.

lymph node Organ located along a lymph vessel. Lymph nodes filter lymph and help attack viruses and bacteria.

lymphatic system A system of vessels and lymph nodes, separate from the circulatory system, that returns fluid, proteins, and cells to the blood.

lymphocyte A type of white blood cell that mediates acquired immunity. Lymphocytes that complete their development in the bone marrow are called B cells, and those that mature in the thymus are called T cells.

lysogenic cycle (lī-sō-jen´-ik) A phage replication cycle in which the viral genome becomes incorporated into the bacterial host chromosome as a prophage and does not kill the host.

lysosome (lī´-so-sōm) A membrane-enclosed sac of hydrolytic enzymes found in the cytoplasm of eukaryotic cells.

lysozyme (lī´-so-zīm) An enzyme in sweat, tears, and saliva that attacks bacterial cell walls.

lytic cycle (lit´-ik) A type of viral (phage) replication cycle resulting in the release of new phages by lysis (and death) of the host cell.

M phase See mitotic (M) phase.

macroclimate Large-scale variations in climate; the climate of an entire region.

macroevolution Evolutionary change above the species level, including the appearance of major evolutionary developments, such as flight, that we use to define higher taxa.

macromolecule A giant molecule formed by the joining of smaller molecules, usually by a condensation reaction. Polysaccharides,

proteins, and nucleic acids are macromolecules.

macronutrient A chemical substance that an organism must obtain in relatively large amounts. See also micronutrient.

macrophage (mak´-rō-fāj) A phagocytic cell present in many tissues that functions in innate immunity by destroying microbes and in acquired immunity as an antigen-presenting cell.

magnetic reversal A reversal of the polarity of Earth's magnetic field.

magnoliids A flowering plant clade that evolved later than basal angiosperms but before monocots and eudicots. Extant examples are magnolias, laurels, and black pepper plants.

major depression Depressive mental illness characterized by experiencing a low mood most of the time.

major histocompatibility complex (MHC) A family of genes that encode a large set of cell surface proteins called MHC molecules. Class I and class II MHC molecules function in antigen presentation to T cells. Foreign MHC molecules on transplanted tissue can trigger T cell responses that may lead to rejection of the transplant.

malignant tumor A cancerous tumor that is invasive enough to impair the functions of one or more organs.

malleus The first of the three middle ear bones.

malnourished Referring to an animal whose diet is missing one or more essential nutrients.

Malpighian tubule (mal-pig´-ē-un) A unique excretory organ of insects that empties into the digestive tract, removes nitrogenous wastes from the hemolymph, and functions in osmoregulation.

mammal Member of the class Mammalia, amniotes with mammary glands that produce milk.

mammary glands Exocrine glands that secrete milk to nourish the young. These glands are characteristic of mammals.

mandible One of a pair of jaw-like feeding appendages found in myriapods, hexapods, and crustaceans.

mantle A fold of tissue in molluscs that drapes over the visceral mass and may secrete a shell.

mantle cavity A water-filled chamber that houses the gills, anus, and excretory pores of a mollusc.

map unit A unit of measurement of the distance between genes. One map unit is equivalent to a 1% recombination frequency.

marine benthic zone The ocean floor.

mark-recapture method A sampling technique used to estimate wildlife populations.

marsupial (mar-sü´-pē-ul) A mammal, such as a koala, kangaroo, or opossum, whose young complete their embryonic development inside a maternal pouch called the marsupium.

mass number The sum of the number of protons and neutrons in an atom's nucleus.

mast cell A vertebrate body cell that produces histamine and other molecules that trigger the inflammatory response.

mate choice copying Behavior in which individuals in a population copy the mate choice of others, apparently as a result of social learning.

maternal effect gene A gene that, when mutant in the mother, results in a mutant phenotype in the offspring, regardless of the genotype.

matter Anything that takes up space and has mass.

maximum likelihood A principle that states that when considering multiple phylogenetic hypotheses, one should take into account the one that reflects the most likely sequence of evolutionary events, given certain rules about how DNA changes over time.

maximum parsimony A principle that states that when considering multiple explanations for an observation, one should first investigate the simplest explanation that is consistent with the facts.

mechanoreceptor A sensory receptor that detects physical deformations in the body's environment associated with pressure, touch, stretch, motion, and sound.

medulla oblongata The lowest part of the vertebrate brain, commonly called the medulla, a swelling of the hindbrain dorsal to the anterior spinal cord that controls autonomic, homeostatic functions, including breathing, heart and blood vessel activity, swallowing, digestion, and vomiting.

medusa (muh-dū´-suh) The floating, flattened, mouth-down version of the cnidarian body plan. The alternate form is the polyp.

megapascal (MPa) (meg-uh-pas-kal´) A unit of pressure equivalent to 10 atmospheres of pressure.

megaphyll A leaf with a highly branched vascular system, characteristic of the vast majority of vascular plants.

megaspore A spore from a heterosporous plant species that develops into a female gametophyte.

meiosis (mī-ō´-sis) A two-stage type of cell division in sexually reproducing organisms that results in cells with half the chromosome number of the original cell.

meiosis I The first division of a two-stage process of cell division in sexually reproducing organisms that results in cells with half the chromosome number of the original cell.

meiosis II The second division of a two-stage process of cell division in sexually reproducing organisms that results in cells with half the chromosome number of the original cell.

melanocyte-stimulating hormone (MSH) A hormone produced and secreted by the anterior pituitary that regulates the activity of pigment-containing cells in the skin of some vertebrates.

melatonin A hormone secreted by the pineal gland that regulates body functions related to seasonal day length.

membrane attack complex (MAC) A molecular complex consisting of a set of complement proteins that forms a pore in the membrane of bacterial and transplanted cells, causing the cells to die by lysis.

membrane potential The charge difference between a cell's cytoplasm and the extracellular fluid, due to the differential distribution of ions. Membrane potential affects the activity of excitable cells and the transmembrane movement of all charged substances.

memory cell One of a clone of long-lived lymphocytes, formed during the primary immune response, that remains in a lymphoid organ until activated by exposure to the same antigen that triggered its formation. Activated memory cells mount the secondary immune response.

menopause The cessation of ovulation and menstruation.

menstrual cycle (men´-stru-ul) A type of reproductive cycle in higher female primates, in which the nonpregnant endometrium is shed as a bloody discharge through the cervix into the vagina.

menstrual flow phase That portion of the uterine (menstrual) cycle when menstrual bleeding occurs.

menstruation The shedding of portions of the endometrium during a uterine (menstrual) cycle.

meristem (mār´-uh-stem) Plant tissue that remains embryonic as long as the plant lives, allowing for indeterminate growth.

meristem identity gene A plant gene that promotes the switch from vegetative growth to flowering.

meroblastic cleavage (mār-ō-blas´-tik) A type of cleavage in which there is incomplete division of yolk-rich egg, characteristic of avian development.

mesentery (mez´-en-tār-ē) A membrane that suspends many of the organs of vertebrates inside fluid-filled body cavities.

mesoderm (mez´-ō-derm) The middle primary germ layer of an early embryo that develops into the notochord, the lining of the coelom, muscles, skeleton, gonads, kidneys, and most of the circulatory system.

mesohyl (mes´-uh-hil) A gelatinous region between the two layers of cells of a sponge.

mesophyll (mez´-ō-fil) The ground tissue of a leaf, sandwiched between the upper and lower epidermis and specialized for photosynthesis.

mesophyll cell A loosely arranged photosynthetic cell located between the bundle sheath and the leaf surface.

messenger RNA (mRNA) A type of RNA, synthesized from DNA, that attaches to ribosomes in the cytoplasm and specifies the primary structure of a protein.

metabolic pathway A series of chemical reactions that either builds a complex molecule (anabolic pathway) or breaks down a complex molecule into simpler compounds (catabolic pathway).

metabolic rate The total amount of energy an animal uses in a unit of time.

metabolism (muh-tab´-uh-lizm) The totality of an organism's chemical reactions, consisting of catabolic and anabolic pathways.

metamorphosis (met´-uh-mor´-fuh-sis) The resurgence of development in an animal larva that transforms it into a sexually mature adult.

metanephridium (met´-uh-nuh-frid´-ē-um) (plural, **metanephridia**) In annelid worms, a type of excretory tubule with internal openings called nephrostomes that collect body fluids and external openings called nephridiopores.

metaphase The third stage of mitosis, in which the spindle is complete and the chromosomes, attached to microtubules at their kinetochores, are all aligned at the metaphase plate.

metaphase plate An imaginary plane during metaphase in which the centromeres of all the duplicated chromosomes are located midway between the two poles.

metapopulation A subdivided population of a single species.

metastasis (muh-tas´-tuh-sis) The spread of cancer cells to locations distant from their original site.

methanogen A microorganism that obtains energy by using carbon dioxide to oxidize hydrogen, producing methane as a waste product.

microclimate Very fine scale variations of climate, such as the specific climatic conditions underneath a log.

microevolution Evolutionary change below the species level; change in the genetic makeup of a population from generation to generation.

microfilament A solid rod of actin protein in the cytoplasm of almost all eukaryotic cells, making up part of the cytoskeleton and acting alone or with myosin to cause cell contraction.

micronutrient An element that an organism needs in very small amounts and that functions as a component or cofactor of enzymes. *See also* macronutrient.

microphyll In lycophytes, a small leaf with a single unbranched vein.

micropyle A pore in the integument(s) of an ovule.

micro-RNA (miRNA) A small, single-stranded RNA molecule that binds to a complementary sequence in mRNA molecules and directs associated proteins to degrade or prevent translation of the target mRNA.

microspore A spore from a heterosporous plant species that develops into a male gametophyte.

microsporidia Unicellular parasites of animals and protists that molecular comparisons suggest may be most closely related to zygomycete fungi.

microtubule A hollow rod of tubulin protein in the cytoplasm of all eukaryotic cells and in cilia, flagella, and the cytoskeleton.

microvillus (plural, **microvilli**) One of many fine, fingerlike projections of the epithelial cells in the lumen of the small intestine that increase its surface area.

midbrain One of three ancestral and embryonic regions of the vertebrate brain; develops into sensory integrating and relay centers that send sensory information to the cerebrum.

middle ear One of three main regions of the vertebrate ear; a chamber containing three small bones (the hammer, anvil, and stirrup) that convey vibrations from the eardrum to the oval window.

middle lamella (luh-mel-uh) A thin layer of adhesive extracellular material, primarily pectins, found between the primary walls of adjacent young plant cells.

mineral In nutrition, a chemical element other than hydrogen, oxygen, or nitrogen that an organism requires for proper body functioning.

mineral nutrient An essential chemical element absorbed from the soil in the form of inorganic ions.

mineralocorticoid A steroid hormone secreted by the adrenal cortex that regulates salt and water homeostasis.

minimum viable population (MVP) The smallest population size at which a species is able to sustain its numbers and survive.

mismatch repair The cellular process that uses special enzymes to fix incorrectly paired nucleotides.

missense mutation The most common type of mutation, a base-pair substitution in which the new codon makes sense in that it still codes for an amino acid.

mitochondrial matrix The compartment of the mitochondrion enclosed by the inner membrane and containing enzymes and substrates for the Krebs cycle.

mitochondrion (mi-tō-kon-drē-on) (plural, **mitochondria**) An organelle in eukaryotic cells that serves as the site of cellular respiration.

mitosis (mi-tō-sis) A process of nuclear division in eukaryotic cells conventionally divided into five stages: prophase, prometaphase, metaphase, anaphase, and telophase. Mitosis conserves chromosome number by equally allocating replicated chromosomes to each of the daughter nuclei.

mitotic (M) phase The phase of the cell cycle that includes mitosis and cytokinesis.

mitotic spindle An assemblage of microtubules and associated proteins that is involved in the movements of chromosomes during mitosis.

mixotroph An organism that is capable of both photosynthesis and heterotrophy.

model A representation of a theory or process.

model organism An organism chosen to study broad biological principles.

modern synthesis A comprehensive theory of evolution emphasizing populations as units of evolution and integrating ideas from many fields, including genetics, statistics, paleontology, taxonomy, and biogeography.

molarity A common measure of solute concentration, referring to the number of moles of solute per liter of solution.

mold A rapidly growing fungus that reproduces asexually by producing spores.

mole (mol) The number of grams of a substance that equals its molecular weight in daltons and contains Avogadro's number of molecules.

molecular clock An evolutionary timing method based on the observation that at least some regions of genomes evolve at constant rates.

molecular formula A type of molecular notation indicating only the quantity of the constituent atoms.

molecular mass The sum of the masses of all the atoms in a molecule; sometimes called molecular weight.

molecular systematics The comparison of nucleic acids or other molecules in different species to infer relatedness.

molecule Two or more atoms held together by covalent bonds.

molting A process in arthropods in which the exoskeleton is shed at intervals, allowing growth by the production of a larger exoskeleton.

monoclonal antibody (mon-ō-klon-ul) Any of a preparation of antibodies that have been produced by a single clone of cultured cells and thus are all specific for the same epitope.

monocots A clade consisting of flowering plants that have one embryonic seed leaf, or cotyledon.

monocyte A type of white blood cell that migrates into tissues and develops into a macrophage.

monoecious (muh-nē-shus) A term typically used to describe an angiosperm species in which carpellate and staminate flowers are on the same plant.

monogamous A type of relationship in which one male mates with just one female.

monohybrid An organism that is heterozygous with respect to a single gene of interest. All the offspring from a cross between parents homozygous for different alleles are monohybrids. For example, parents of genotypes AA and aa produce a monohybrid of genotype Aa.

monomer (mon-uh-mer) The subunit that serves as the building block of a polymer.

monophyletic (mon-ō-fī-let-ik) Pertaining to a grouping of species consisting of an ancestral species and all its descendants; a clade.

monosaccharide (mon-ō-sak-uh-rīd) The simplest carbohydrate, active alone or serving as a monomer for disaccharides and polysaccharides. Also known as simple sugars, the molecular formulas of monosaccharides are generally some multiple of CH_2O.

monosomic Referring to a cell that has only one copy of a particular chromosome, instead of the normal two.

monotreme (mon-uh-trēm) An egg-laying mammal, represented by the platypus and echidna.

morphogen A substance, such as Bicoid protein, that provides positional information in the form of a concentration gradient along an embryonic axis.

morphogenesis (mōr-fō-jen-uh-sis) The development of body shape and organization.

morphological species concept Defining species by measurable anatomical criteria.

morula (mōr-yuh-luh) A solid ball of blastomeres formed by early cleavage.

mosaic evolution The evolution of different features of organisms at different rates.

moss A small, herbaceous nonvascular plant that is a member of the phylum Bryophyta.

motor neuron A nerve cell that transmits signals from the brain or spinal cord to muscles or glands.

motor unit A single motor neuron and all the muscle fibers it controls.

movement corridor A series of small clumps or a narrow strip of quality habitat (usable by organisms) that connects otherwise isolated patches of quality habitat.

MPF Maturation-promoting factor (M-phase-promoting factor), a protein complex required for a cell to progress from late interphase to mitosis. The active form consists of cyclin and a protein kinase.

mucous membrane (myu-kus) Smooth moist epithelium that lines the digestive tract and air tubes leading to the lungs.

Müllerian mimicry (myu-lār-ē-un) A mutual mimicry by two unpalatable species.

multifactorial Referring to a phenotypic character that is influenced by multiple genes and environmental factors.

multigene family A collection of genes with similar or identical sequences, presumably of common origin.

multiple fruit A fruit derived from an inflorescence, a group of flowers tightly clustered together.

muscle spindle A mechanoreceptor stimulated by mechanical distortion.

muscle tissue Tissue consisting of long muscle cells that are capable of contracting when stimulated by nerve impulses.

mutagen (myu-tuh-jen) A chemical or physical agent that interacts with DNA and causes a mutation.

mutation (myu-tā-shun) A change in the DNA of a gene, ultimately creating genetic diversity.

or take in water if it inhabits a hyperosmotic environment.

osmosis (oz-mō´-sis) The diffusion of water across a selectively permeable membrane.

osmotic potential A component of water potential that is proportional to the number of dissolved solute molecules in a solution and measures the effect of solutes on the direction of water movement; also called solute potential; it can be either zero or negative.

osteichthyan Member of a vertebrate subgroup with jaws and mostly bony skeletons.

osteoblast A bone-forming cell that deposits collagen.

osteon The repeating organizational unit forming the microscopic structure of hard mammalian bone.

outer ear One of three main regions of the ear in reptiles, birds, and mammals; made up of the auditory canal and, in many birds and mammals, the pinna.

outgroup A species or group of species that is closely related to the group of species being studied, but clearly not as closely related as any study-group members are to each other.

oval window In the vertebrate ear, a membrane-covered gap in the skull bone, through which sound waves pass from the middle ear to the inner ear.

ovarian cycle (ō-vâr´-ē-un) The cyclic recurrence of the follicular phase, ovulation, and the luteal phase in the mammalian ovary, regulated by hormones.

ovary (ō´-vuh-rē) (1) In flowers, the portion of a carpel in which the egg-containing ovules develop. (2) In animals, the structure that produces female gametes and reproductive hormones.

overexploitation Harvesting by humans of wild plants or animals at rates exceeding the ability of populations of those species to rebound.

overnourishment A diet that is chronically excessive in calories.

oviduct (ō´-vuh-duct) A tube passing from the ovary to the vagina in invertebrates or to the uterus in vertebrates.

oviparous (ō-vip´-uh-rus) Referring to a type of development in which young hatch from eggs laid outside the mother's body.

ovoviviparous (ō-vō-vī-vip´-uh-rus) Referring to a type of development in which young hatch from eggs that are retained in the mother's uterus.

ovulation The release of an egg from ovaries. In humans, an ovarian follicle releases an egg during each uterine (menstrual) cycle.

ovule (ō´-vyūl) A structure that develops within the ovary of a seed plant and contains the female gametophyte.

ovum (ō´-vum) The female gamete; the haploid, unfertilized egg, which is usually a relatively large, nonmotile cell.

oxidation The loss of electrons from a substance involved in a redox reaction.

oxidative phosphorylation (fos´-for-uh-lā-shun) The production of ATP using energy derived from the redox reactions of an electron transport chain.

oxidizing agent The electron acceptor in a redox reaction.

oxytocin A hormone produced by the hypothalamus and released from the posterior pituitary. It induces contractions of the uterine muscles and causes the mammary glands to eject milk during nursing.

P generation The parent individuals from which offspring are derived in studies of inheritance; P stands for "parental."

P site One of a ribosome's three binding sites for tRNA during translation. The P site holds the tRNA carrying the growing polypeptide chain. (P stands for peptidyl tRNA.)

p53 gene The "guardian angel of the genome," a gene that is expressed when a cell's DNA is damaged. Its product, p53 protein, functions as a transcription factor for several genes.

pacemaker A specialized region of the right atrium of the mammalian heart that sets the rate of contraction; also called the sinoatrial (SA) node.

paedomorphosis (pē´-duh-môr´-fuh-sis) The retention in an adult organism of the juvenile features of its evolutionary ancestors.

pain receptor A kind of interoreceptor that detects pain; also called a nociceptor.

paleoanthropology The study of human origins and evolution.

paleontological species concept Definition of species based on morphological differences known only from the fossil record.

paleontology (pā´-lē-un-tol´-ō-jē) The scientific study of fossils.

palisade mesophyll One or more layers of elongated photosynthetic cells on the upper part of a leaf; also called palisade parenchyma.

pancreas (pan´-krē-us) A gland with dual functions: The nonendocrine portion secretes digestive enzymes and an alkaline solution into the small intestine via a duct; the endocrine portion secretes the hormones insulin and glucagon into the blood.

Pangaea (pan-jē´-uh) The supercontinent formed near the end of the Paleozoic era when plate movements brought all the landmasses of Earth together.

parabasalid A protist such as a trichomonad, with modified mitochondria.

parabronchus (plural, **parabronchi**) A site of gas exchange in bird lungs. Parabronchi allow air to flow past the respiratory surface in just one direction.

paralogous genes Homologous genes that are found in the same genome due to gene duplication.

paraphyletic (pâr´-uh-fī-let´-ik) Pertaining to a grouping of species that consists of an ancestral species and some, but not all, of its descendants.

parareptile First major group of reptiles to emerge, mostly large, stocky quadrupedal herbivores; died out in the late Triassic period.

parasite (pâr´-uh-sīt) An organism that benefits by living in or on another organism at the expense of the host.

parasitism (pâr´-uh-sīt-izm) A symbiotic relationship in which the symbiont (parasite) benefits at the expense of the host by living either within the host (as an endoparasite) or outside the host (as an ectoparasite).

parasitoidism A type of parasitism in which an insect lays eggs on or in a living host; the larvae then feed on the body of the host, eventually killing it.

parasympathetic division One of three divisions of the autonomic nervous system; generally enhances body activities that gain and conserve energy, such as digestion and reduced heart rate.

parathyroid gland Any of four small endocrine glands, embedded in the surface of the thyroid gland, that secrete parathyroid hormone.

parathyroid hormone (PTH) A hormone secreted by the parathyroid glands that raises blood calcium level by promoting calcium release from bone and calcium retention by the kidneys.

parazoan Animal belonging to a grade of organization lacking true tissues (collections of specialized cells isolated from other tissues by membranes); a sponge (phylum Porifera).

parenchyma cell (puh-ren´-kim-uh) A relatively unspecialized plant cell type that carries out most of the metabolism, synthesizes and stores organic products, and develops into a more differentiated cell type.

parental type An offspring with a phenotype that matches one of the parental phenotypes.

Parkinson's disease A motor disorder caused by a progressive brain disease and characterized by difficulty in initiating movements, slowness of movement, and rigidity.

parthenogenesis (par´-thuh-no´-jen´-uh-sis) A type of reproduction in which females produce offspring from unfertilized eggs.

partial pressure A measure of the concentration of one gas in a mixture of gases; the pressure exerted by a particular gas in a mixture of gases (for instance, the pressure exerted by oxygen in air).

parturition The expulsion of a baby from the mother; also called birth.

passive immunity Short-term immunity conferred by the administration of ready-made antibodies or the transfer of maternal antibodies to a fetus or nursing infant; lasts only a few weeks or months because the immune system has not been stimulated by antigens.

passive transport The diffusion of a substance across a biological membrane.

patchiness Localized variation in environmental conditions within an ecosystem, arranged spatially into a complex of discrete areas that may be characterized by distinctive groups of species or ecosystem processes.

pathogen A disease-causing agent.

pattern formation The ordering of cells into specific three-dimensional structures, an essential part of shaping an organism and its individual parts during development.

peat Extensive deposits of undecayed organic material formed primarily from the wetland moss *Sphagnum*.

pedigree A diagram of a family tree showing the occurrence of heritable characters in parents and offspring over multiple generations.

pelagic zone (puh-laj -ik) The area of the ocean past the continental shelf, with areas of open water often reaching to very great depths.

penis The copulatory structure of male mammals.

PEP carboxylase An enzyme that adds carbon dioxide to phosphoenolpyruvate (PEP) to form oxaloacetate.

pepsin An enzyme present in gastric juice that begins the hydrolysis of proteins.

pepsinogen The inactive form of pepsin that is first secreted by specialized (chief) cells located in gastric pits of the stomach.

peptide bond The covalent bond between two amino acid units, formed by a dehydration reaction.

peptidoglycan (pep -tid-ō-glī -kun) A type of polymer in bacterial cell walls consisting of modified sugars cross-linked by short polypeptides.

perception The interpretation of sensations by the brain.

perennial (puh-ren -ē-ul) A flowering plant that lives for many years.

pericarp The thickened wall of a fruit.

pericycle (pār -uh-sī-kul) The outermost layer of the vascular cylinder of a root, where lateral roots originate.

periderm (pār-uh-derm) The protective coat that replaces the epidermis in plants during secondary growth, formed of the cork and cork cambium.

periodic table of the elements A chart of the chemical elements, arranged in three rows, corresponding to the number of electron shells in their atoms.

peripheral nervous system (PNS) The sensory and motor neurons that connect to the central nervous system.

peripheral protein A protein appendage loosely bound to the surface of a membrane and not embedded in the lipid bilayer.

peripheral resistance The impedance of blood flow by the arterioles.

peristalsis (pār -uh-stal -sis) (1) Rhythmic waves of contraction of smooth muscle that push food along the digestive tract. (2) A type of movement on land produced by rhythmic waves of muscle contractions passing from front to back, as in many annelids.

peristome The upper part of the moss capsule (sporangium) often specialized for gradual spore discharge.

peritubular capillaries The network of tiny blood vessels that surrounds the proximal and distal tubules in the kidney.

permafrost A permanently frozen stratum below the arctic tundra.

peroxisome (puh-rok -suh-som) A microbody containing enzymes that transfer hydrogen from various substrates to oxygen, producing and then degrading hydrogen peroxide.

petal A modified leaf of a flowering plant. Petals are the often colorful parts of a flower that advertise it to insects and other pollinators.

petiole (pet -ē-ōl) The stalk of a leaf, which joins the leaf to a node of the stem.

pH A measure of hydrogen ion concentration equal to $-\log [H^+]$ and ranging in value from 0 to 14.

phage (fāj) A virus that infects bacteria, also called a bacteriophage.

phagocytosis (fag -ō-sī-tō -sis) A type of endocytosis involving large, particulate substances, accomplished mainly by macrophages, neutrophils, and dendritic cells.

pharyngeal clefts In chordate embryos, grooves that separate a series of pouches along the sides of the pharynx and may develop into pharyngeal slits.

pharyngeal slits In chordate embryos, slits that form from the pharyngeal clefts and communicate to the outside, later developing into gill slits in many vertebrates.

pharynx (fār -inks) An area in the vertebrate throat where air and food passages cross; in flatworms, the muscular tube that protrudes from the ventral side of the worm and ends in the mouth.

phase change A shift from one developmental phase to another.

phenotype (fē -nō-tīp) The physical and physiological traits of an organism, which are determined by its genetic makeup.

phenotypic polymorphism The existence of two or more distinct morphs (discrete forms), each represented in a population in high enough frequencies to be readily noticeable.

pheromone (fār -uh-mōn) In animals and fungi, a small, volatile chemical that functions in communication and that in animals acts much like a hormone in influencing physiology and behavior.

phloem (flō -um) Vascular plant tissue consisting of living cells arranged into elongated tubes that transport sugar and other organic nutrients throughout the plant.

phoronids A tube-dwelling marine lophophorate.

phosphate group (fos -fāt) A functional group important in energy transfer.

phospholipid (fos -fō-lip -id) A molecule that is a constituent of the inner bilayer of biological membranes, having a polar, hydrophilic head and a nonpolar, hydrophobic tail.

phosphorylated Referring to a molecule that has been the recipient of a phosphate group.

photic zone (fō -tic) The narrow top slice of the ocean, where light permeates sufficiently for photosynthesis to occur.

photoautotroph (fō -tō-ot -ō-trōf) An organism that harnesses light energy to drive the synthesis of organic compounds from carbon dioxide.

photoheterotroph (fō -tō-het -uh-rō-trōf) An organism that uses light to generate ATP but that must obtain carbon in organic form.

photomorphogenesis Effects of light on plant morphology.

photon (fō -ton) A quantum, or discrete amount, of light energy.

photoperiodism (fō -tō-pēr -ē-ō-dizm) A physiological response to photoperiod, the relative lengths of night and day. An example of photoperiodism is flowering.

photophosphorylation (fō -tō-fos -for-uh-lā -shun) The process of generating ATP from ADP and phosphate by means of a proton-motive force generated by the thylakoid membrane of the chloroplast during the light reactions of photosynthesis.

photopsin (fō-top -sin) One of a family of visual pigments in the cones of the vertebrate eye that absorb bright, colored light.

photoreceptor An electromagnetic receptor that detects the radiation known as visible light.

photorespiration A metabolic pathway that consumes oxygen, releases carbon dioxide, generates no ATP, and decreases photosynthetic output, generally occurs on hot, dry, bright days, when stomata close and the oxygen concentration in the leaf exceeds that of carbon dioxide.

photosynthesis The conversion of light energy to chemical energy that is stored in glucose or other organic compounds, occurs in plants, algae, and certain prokaryotes.

photosystem Light-capturing unit located in the thylakoid membrane of the chloroplast, consisting of a reaction center surrounded by numerous light-harvesting complexes. There are two types of photosystems, I and II, they absorb light best at different wavelengths.

photosystem I One of two light-capturing units in a chloroplast's thylakoid membrane; it has two molecules of P700 chlorophyll *a* at its reaction center.

photosystem II One of two light-capturing units in a chloroplast's thylakoid membrane; it has two molecules of P680 chlorophyll *a* at its reaction center.

phototropism (fō -tō-trō -pizm) Growth of a plant shoot toward or away from light.

phragmoplast An alignment of cytoskeletal elements and Golgi-derived vesicles across the midline of a dividing plant cell.

phylogenetic tree A branching diagram that represents a hypothesis about evolutionary relationships.

phylogeny (fī-loj´-uh-nē) The evolutionary history of a species or group of related species.

phylogram A phylogenetic tree in which the lengths of the branches reflect the number of genetic changes that have taken place in a particular DNA or RNA sequence in the various lineages.

phylum (fī´-lum) In classification, the taxonomic category above class.

physical map A genetic map in which the actual physical distances between genes or other genetic markers are expressed, usually as the number of base pairs along the DNA.

physiology The study of the functions of an organism.

phytoalexin (fī-tō-uh-lek´-sin) An antibiotic, produced by plants, that destroys microorganisms or inhibits their growth.

phytochromes (fī-tuh-krōmz) A class of light receptors in plants. Mostly absorbing red light, these photoreceptors regulate many plant responses, including seed germination and shade avoidance.

phytoplankton (fī-tō-plank´-ton) Algae and photosynthetic bacteria that drift passively in the pelagic zone of an aquatic environment.

phytoremediation An emerging nondestructive technology that seeks to cheaply reclaim contaminated areas by taking advantage of the remarkable ability of some plant species to extract heavy metals and other pollutants from the soil and to concentrate them in easily harvested portions of the plant.

pilus (plural, **pili**) (pī´-lus, pī´-lī) A long, hairlike prokaryotic appendage that functions in adherence or in the transfer of DNA during conjugation.

pineal gland (pin´-ē-ul) A small gland on the dorsal surface of the vertebrate forebrain that secretes the hormone melatonin.

pinocytosis (pī-nō-sī-tō´-sis) A type of endocytosis in which the cell ingests extracellular fluid and its dissolved solutes.

pistil A single carpel or a group of fused carpels.

pitch A function of a sound wave's frequency, or number of vibrations per second, expressed in hertz.

pith Ground tissue that is internal to the vascular tissue in a stem; in many monocot roots, parenchyma cells that form the central core of the vascular cylinder.

pit A thinner region in the walls of tracheids and vessels where only primary wall is present.

pituitary gland (puh-tū´-uh-tār-ē) An endocrine gland at the base of the hypothalamus; consists of a posterior lobe (neurohypophysis), which stores and releases two hormones produced by the hypothalamus, and an anterior lobe (adenohypophysis), which produces and secretes many hormones that regulate diverse body functions.

placenta (pluh-sen´-tuh) A structure in the pregnant uterus for nourishing a viviparous fetus with the mother's blood supply; formed from the uterine lining and embryonic membranes.

placental transfer cell A plant cell that enhances the transfer of nutrients from parent to embryo.

placoderm (plak´-ō-derm) A member of an extinct class of fishlike vertebrates that had jaws and were enclosed in a tough, outer armor.

planarian A free-living flatworm found in unpolluted ponds and streams.

plankton Mostly microscopic organisms that drift passively or swim weakly near the surface of oceans, ponds, and lakes.

Plantae (plan´-tā) The kingdom that consists of multicellular eukaryotes that carry out photosynthesis.

plasma (plaz´-muh) The liquid matrix of blood in which the cells are suspended.

plasma cell The antibody-secreting effector cell of humoral immunity; arises from antigen-stimulated B cells.

plasma membrane The membrane at the boundary of every cell that acts as a selective barrier, thereby regulating the cell's chemical composition.

plasmid (plaz´-mid) A small ring of DNA that carries accessory genes separate from those of a bacterial chromosome; also found in some eukaryotes, such as yeast.

plasmodesma (plaz´-mō-dez´-muh) (plural, **plasmodesmata**) An open channel in the cell wall of a plant through which strands of cytosol connect from an adjacent cell.

plasmodial slime mold (plaz-mō-dē-ul) A type of protist that has amoeboid cells, flagellated cells, and a plasmodial feeding stage in its life cycle.

plasmodium A single mass of cytoplasm containing many diploid nuclei that forms during the life cycle of some slime molds.

plasmogamy The fusion of the cytoplasm of cells from two individuals; occurs as one stage of syngamy.

plasmolysis (plaz-mol´-uh-sis) A phenomenon in walled cells in which the cytoplasm shrivels and the plasma membrane pulls away from the cell wall when the cell loses water to a hypertonic environment.

plasmolyze To shrink and pull away from a cell wall, or when a plant cell protoplast pulls away from the cell wall as a result of water loss.

plasticity An organism's ability to alter or "mold" itself in response to local environmental conditions.

plastid One of a family of closely related plant organelles that includes chloroplasts, chromoplasts, and amyloplasts (leucoplasts).

platelet A small enucleated blood cell important in blood clotting, derived from large cells in the bone marrow.

pleiotropy (plī-uh-trō-pē) The ability of a single gene to have multiple effects.

pluripotent Describing a stem cell, from an embryo or adult organism, that can give rise to multiple but not all differentiated cell types.

point mutation A change in a gene at a single nucleotide pair.

polar covalent bond A covalent bond between atoms that differ in electronegativity. The shared electrons are pulled closer to the more electronegative atom, making it slightly negative and the other atom slightly positive.

polar molecule A molecule (such as water) with opposite charges on opposite sides.

polarity A lack of symmetry. Structural differences in opposite ends of an organism or structure, such as the root end and shoot end of a plant.

pollen grains The structures that contain the male gametophyte of seed plants.

pollination (pol-uh-nā´-shun) The transfer of pollen to the part of a seed plant containing the ovules, a process that is a prerequisite for fertilization.

poly-A tail The modified end of the 3′ end of an mRNA molecule consisting of the addition of some 50 to 250 adenine nucleotides.

polyandry (pol-ē-an´-drē) A polygamous mating system involving one female and many males.

polygamous A type of relationship in which an individual of one sex mates with several of the other.

polygenic inheritance (pol-ē-jen´-ik) An additive effect of two or more gene loci on a single phenotypic character.

polygyny (puh-lij´-en-ē) A polygamous mating system involving one male and many females.

polymer (pol´-uh-mer) A long molecule consisting of many similar or identical monomers linked together.

polymerase chain reaction (PCR) (puh-lim´-uh-rās) A technique for amplifying DNA in vitro by incubating with special primers, DNA polymerase molecules, and nucleotides.

polymorphism (pol-ē-mōr´-fizm) The coexistence of two or more distinct forms in the same population.

polynucleotide (pol´-ē-nū´-klē-ō-tīd) A polymer consisting of many nucleotide monomers; serves as a blueprint for proteins and, through the actions of proteins, for all cellular activities. The two types are DNA and RNA.

polyp (pol´-ip) The sessile variant of the cnidarian body plan. The alternate form is the medusa.

polypeptide (pol-ē-pep´-tīd) A polymer (chain) of many amino acids linked together by peptide bonds.

polyphyletic Pertaining to a grouping of species derived from two or more different ancestral forms.

Glossary

Glossary

polyploidy (pol'-e-ploy-dē) A chromosomal alteration in which the organism possesses more than two complete chromosome sets.

polyribosome (polysome) (pol-e-rī'-bō-sōm) An aggregation of several ribosomes attached to one messenger RNA molecule.

polysaccharide (pol-e-sak'-uh-rīd) A polymer of up to over a thousand monosaccharides, formed by dehydration reactions.

pons Portion of the brain that participates in certain automatic, homeostatic functions such as regulating the breathing centers in the medulla.

population A localized group of individuals that belong to the same biological species that are capable of interbreeding and producing fertile offspring.

population dynamics The study of how complex interactions between biotic and abiotic factors influence variations in population size.

population ecology The study of populations in relation to the environment, including environmental influences on population density and distribution, age structure, and variations in population size.

population genetics The study of how populations change genetically over time.

population viability analysis (PVA) A method of predicting whether or not a population will persist.

positional information Signals to which genes regulating development respond, indicating a cell's location relative to other cells in an embryonic structure.

positive feedback A physiological control mechanism in which a change in some variable triggers mechanisms that amplify the change.

positive pressure breathing A breathing system in which air is forced into the lungs.

posterior Pertaining to the rear, or tail end, of a bilaterally symmetrical animal.

posterior pituitary Also called the neurohypophysis, an extension of the hypothalamus composed of nervous tissue that secretes oxytocin and antidiuretic hormone made in the hypothalamus; a temporary storage site for these hormones.

postsynaptic cell The target cell at a synapse.

postzygotic barrier (pōst'-zī-got'-ik) Any of several species-isolating mechanisms that prevent hybrids produced by two different species from developing into viable, fertile adults.

potential energy The energy stored by matter as a result of its location or spatial arrangement.

precautionary principle A guiding principle in making decisions about the environment, cautioning to consider carefully the potential consequences of actions.

predation An interaction between species in which one species, the predator, eats the other, the prey.

pregnancy The condition of carrying one or more embryos in the uterus.

preprophase band Microtubules in the cortex (outer cytoplasm) of a cell that are concentrated into a ring.

prepuce (prē'-pyūs) A fold of skin covering the head of the clitoris and penis.

pressure potential (Ψ_p) A component of water potential that consists of the physical pressure on a solution, which can be positive, zero, or negative.

presynaptic cell The transmitting cell at a synapse.

prezygotic barrier (prē'-zī-got'-ik) A reproductive barrier that impedes mating between species or hinders fertilization of ova if interspecific mating is attempted.

primary cell wall A relatively thin and flexible layer first secreted by a young plant cell.

primary consumer An herbivore; an organism in the trophic level of an ecosystem that eats plants or algae.

primary electron acceptor A specialized molecule sharing the reaction center with the pair of reaction-center chlorophyll *a* molecules; it accepts an electron from one of these two chlorophylls.

primary growth Growth produced by apical meristems, lengthening stems and roots.

primary immune response The initial acquired immune response to an antigen, which appears after a lag of about 10 to 17 days.

primary oocyte (ō'-uh-sīt) A diploid cell, in prophase I of meiosis, that can be hormonally triggered to develop into an ovum.

primary plant body The tissues produced by apical meristems, which lengthen stems and roots.

primary producer An autotroph, usually a photosynthetic organism. Collectively, autotrophs make up the trophic level of an ecosystem that ultimately supports all other levels.

primary production The amount of light energy converted to chemical energy (organic compounds) by autotrophs in an ecosystem during a given time period.

primary structure The level of protein structure referring to the specific sequence of amino acids.

primary succession A type of ecological succession that occurs in a virtually lifeless area, where there were originally no organisms and where soil has not yet formed.

primary transcript An initial RNA transcript; also called pre-mRNA when transcribed from a protein-coding gene.

primary visual cortex The destination in the occipital lobe of the cerebrum for most of the axons from the lateral geniculate nuclei.

primase An enzyme that joins RNA nucleotides to make the primer.

primer A polynucleotide with a free 3' end, bound by complementary base pairing to the template strand, that is elongated during DNA replication.

primitive streak A groove on the surface of an early avian embryo along the future long axis of the body.

prion An infectious form of protein that may increase in number by converting related proteins to more prions.

product An ending material in a chemical reaction.

production efficiency The fraction of energy stored in food that is not used for respiration.

progestin (prō-jes'-tin) One of a family of steroid hormones, including progesterone that prepare the uterus for pregnancy.

progymnosperms Extinct seedless vascular plants that may be ancestral to seed plants.

prokaryotic cell (prō-kār'-ē-ot-ik) A type of cell lacking a membrane-enclosed nucleus and membrane-enclosed organelles; found only in the domains Bacteria and Archaea.

prolactin (PRL) A hormone produced and secreted by the anterior pituitary with a great diversity of effects in different vertebrate species. In mammals, it stimulates growth of and milk production by the mammary glands.

proliferative phase That portion of the uterine (menstrual) cycle when the endometrium regenerates and thickens.

prometaphase The second stage of mitosis, in which discrete chromosomes consisting of identical sister chromatids appear, the nuclear envelope fragments, and the spindle microtubules attach to the kinetochores of the chromosomes.

promiscuous A type of relationship in which mating occurs with no strong pair-bonds or lasting relationships.

promoter A specific nucleotide sequence in DNA that binds RNA polymerase and indicates where to start transcribing RNA.

prophage (prō'-fāj) A phage genome that has been inserted into a specific site on the bacterial chromosome.

prophase The first stage of mitosis, in which the chromatin is condensing and the mitotic spindle begins to form, but the nucleolus and nucleus are still intact.

prostaglandin (PG) (pros'-nuh-glan'-din) One of a group of modified fatty acids secreted by virtually all tissues and performing a wide variety of functions as local regulators.

prostate gland (pros'-tāt) A gland in human males that secretes an acid-neutralizing component of semen.

proteasome A giant protein complex that recognizes and destroys proteins tagged for elimination by the small protein ubiquitin.

protein (prō'-tēn) A three-dimensional biological polymer constructed from a set of 20 different monomers called amino acids.

protein kinase An enzyme that transfers phosphate groups from ATP to a protein.

protein phosphatase An enzyme that removes phosphate groups from proteins, often functioning to reverse the effect of a protein kinase.

proteoglycan (prō-tē-ō-glī-kun) A glycoprotein in the extracellular matrix of animal cells, rich in carbohydrate.

proteomics The systematic study of the full protein sets (proteomes) encoded by genomes.

protist An informal term applied to any eukaryote that is not a plant, animal, or fungus. Most protists are unicellular, though some are colonial or multicellular.

protobiont An aggregate of abiotically produced molecules surrounded by a membrane or membrane-like structure.

proton (prō-ton) A subatomic particle with a single positive electrical charge, found in the nucleus of an atom.

proton pump An active transport mechanism in cell membranes that uses ATP to force hydrogen ions out of a cell, generating a membrane potential in the process.

protonema A mass of green, branched, one-cell-thick filaments produced by germinating moss spores.

protonephridium (prō-tō-nuh-frid-ē-um) An excretory system, such as the flame-bulb system of flatworms, consisting of a network of closed tubules having external openings called nephridiopores and lacking internal openings.

proton-motive force The potential energy stored in the form of an electrochemical gradient, generated by the pumping of hydrogen ions across biological membranes during chemiosmosis.

proto-oncogene (prō-tō-on´-kō-jēn) A normal cellular gene corresponding to an oncogene; a gene with a potential to cause cancer but that requires some alteration to become an oncogene.

protoplast The contents of a plant cell exclusive of the cell wall.

protoplast fusion The fusing of two protoplasts from different plant species that would otherwise be reproductively incompatible.

protostome development In animals, a developmental mode distinguished by the development of the mouth from the blastopore, often also characterized by schizocoelous development of the body cavity and by spiral cleavage.

protozoan (prō-tō-zō-un) A protist that lives primarily by ingesting food, an animal-like mode of nutrition.

provirus Viral DNA that inserts into a host genome.

proximal tubule In the vertebrate kidney, the portion of a nephron immediately downstream from Bowman's capsule that conveys and helps refine filtrate.

proximate question In animal behavior, an inquiry that focuses on the environmental stimuli, if any, that trigger a particular behavioral act, as well as the genetic, physiological, and anatomical mechanisms underlying it.

PR protein A protein involved in plant responses to pathogens (PR = pathogenesis-related).

pseudocoelomate (sū-dō-sē-lō-māt) An animal whose body cavity is not completely lined by mesoderm.

pseudogene A DNA segment very similar to a real gene but which does not yield a functional product; a gene that has become inactivated in a particular species because of mutation.

pseudopodium (sū-dō-pō-dē-um) (plural **pseudopodia**) A cellular extension of amoeboid cells used in moving and feeding.

pterophyte An informal name for any member of the phylum Pterophyta, which includes ferns, horsetails, whisk ferns, and the genus *Tmesipteris*.

pterosaur Winged reptile that lived during the time of dinosaurs.

pulmocutaneous circuit The route of circulation that directs blood to the skin and lungs.

pulmonary circuit The branch of the circulatory system that supplies the lungs.

pulse The rhythmic stretching of the arteries caused by the pressure of blood forced through the arteries by contractions of the ventricles during systole.

punctuated equilibrium In evolutionary theory, long periods of apparent stasis (no change) interrupted by relatively brief periods of sudden change.

Punnett square A diagram used in the study of inheritance to show the results of random fertilization in genetic crosses.

pupil The opening in the iris, which admits light into the interior of the vertebrate eye. Muscles in the iris regulate its size.

purine (pyū-rēn) One of two types of nitrogenous bases found in nucleotides. Adenine (A) and guanine (G) are purines.

pyloric sphincter (pī-lor-ik sfink-ter) In the vertebrate digestive tract, a muscular ring that regulates the passage of food out of the stomach and into the small intestine.

pyrimidine (puh-rim´-uh-dēn) One of two types of nitrogenous bases found in nucleotides. Cytosine (C), thymine (T), and uracil (U) are pyrimidines.

quantitative character A heritable feature that varies continuously over a range rather than in an either-or fashion.

quaternary structure (kwot-er-nār-ē) The particular shape of a complex, aggregate protein, defined by the characteristic three-dimensional arrangement of its constituent subunits, each a polypeptide.

R plasmid A bacterial plasmid carrying genes that confer resistance to certain antibiotics.

radial cleavage A type of embryonic development in deuterostomes in which the planes of cell division that transform the zygote into a ball of cells are either parallel or perpendicular to the polar axis, thereby aligning tiers of cells one above the other.

radial glia In an embryo, supporting cells that form tracks along which newly formed neurons migrate from the neural tube; can also act as stem cells that give rise to neurons and other glia.

radial symmetry Characterizing a body shaped like a pie or barrel, with many equal parts radiating outward like the spokes of a wheel; present in cnidarians and echinoderms; also can refer to flower structure.

radiation The emission of electromagnetic waves by all objects warmer than absolute zero.

radicle An embryonic root of a plant.

radioactive isotope An isotope (an atomic form of a chemical element) that is unstable; the nucleus decays spontaneously, giving off detectable particles and energy.

radiolarian A protist, usually marine, with a shell generally made of silica and pseudopodia that radiate from the central body.

radiometric dating A method paleontologists use for determining the ages of rocks and fossils on a scale of absolute time, based on the half-life of radioactive isotopes.

radula A straplike rasping organ used by many molluscs during feeding.

ras gene A gene that codes for Ras protein, a G protein that relays a growth signal from a growth factor receptor on the plasma membrane to a cascade of protein kinases that ultimately results in the stimulation of the cell cycle. Many *ras* oncogenes have a point mutation that leads to a hyperactive version of the Ras protein that can lead to excessive cell division.

ratite (rat-īt) Member of the group of flightless birds.

ray initials Cells within the vascular cambium that produce xylem and phloem rays, radial files that consist mostly of parenchyma cells.

ray-finned fish Member of the class Actinopterygii, aquatic osteichthyans with fins supported by long, flexible rays, including tuna, bass, and herring.

reactant A starting material in a chemical reaction.

reaction center Complex of proteins associated with two special chlorophyll *a* molecules and a primary electron acceptor. Located centrally in a photosystem, this complex triggers the light reactions of photosynthesis. Excited by light energy, one of the chlorophylls donates an electron to the primary electron acceptor, which passes an electron to an electron transport chain.

reading frame The way a cell's mRNA-translating machinery groups the mRNA nucleotides into codons.

receptacle The base of a flower, the part of the stem that is the site of attachment of the floral organs.

reception In cellular communication, the target cell's detection (by binding to a receptor protein) of a signal molecule from outside the cell.

receptor-mediated endocytosis (en-dō-si-tō-sis) The movement of specific molecules into a cell by the inward budding of membranous vesicles containing proteins with receptor sites specific to the molecules being taken in; enables a cell to acquire bulk quantities of specific substances.

receptor potential An initial response of a receptor cell to a stimulus, consisting of a change in voltage across the receptor membrane proportional to the stimulus strength. The intensity of the receptor potential determines the frequency of action potentials traveling to the nervous system.

receptor tyrosine kinase A receptor protein in the plasma membrane that responds to the binding of a signal molecule by catalyzing the transfer of phosphate groups from ATP to tyrosines on the cytoplasmic side of the receptor. The phosphorylated tyrosines activate other signal transduction proteins within the cell.

recessive allele An allele whose phenotypic effect is not observed in a heterozygote.

reciprocal altruism Altruistic behavior between unrelated individuals, whereby the current altruistic individual benefits in the future when the current beneficiary reciprocates.

recombinant An offspring whose phenotype differs from that of the parents; also called recombinant type.

recombinant chromosome A chromosome created when crossing over combines the DNA from two parents into a single chromosome.

recombinant DNA A DNA molecule made in vitro with segments from different sources.

recruitment The process of progressively increasing the tension of a muscle by activating more and more of the motor neurons controlling the muscle.

rectum The terminal portion of the large intestine where the feces are stored until they are eliminated.

red alga A photosynthetic marine protist that contains the accessory pigment phycoerythrin. Most are multicellular.

red blood cell A blood cell containing hemoglobin, which transports O_2; also called an erythrocyte.

redox reaction (rē-doks) A chemical reaction involving the transfer of one or more electrons from one reactant to another; also called oxidation-reduction reaction.

reducing agent The electron donor in a redox reaction.

reduction The addition of electrons to a substance involved in a redox reaction.

reductionism Reducing complex systems to simpler components that are more manageable to study.

redundancy model The concept, put forth by Henry Gleason and Brian Walker, that most of the species in a community are not tightly coupled with one another (that is, the web of life is very loose). According to this model, an increase or decrease in one species in a community has little effect on other species, which operate independently.

reflex An automatic reaction to a stimulus, mediated by the spinal cord or lower brain.

refractory period (rē-frak-tōr-ē) The short time immediately after an action potential in which the neuron cannot respond to another stimulus, owing to an increase in potassium permeability.

regeneration The regrowth of body parts from pieces of an organism.

regulator A characterization of an animal in regard to environmental variables. A regulator uses mechanisms of homeostasis to moderate internal changes in the face of external fluctuations.

regulatory gene A gene that codes for a protein, such as a repressor, that controls the transcription of another gene or group of genes.

relative abundance Differences in the abundance of different species within a community.

relative fitness The contribution of one genotype to the next generation compared to that of alternative genotypes for the same locus.

renal artery The blood vessel bringing blood to the kidney.

renal cortex The outer portion of the vertebrate kidney.

renal medulla The inner portion of the vertebrate kidney, beneath the renal cortex.

renal pelvis Funnel-shaped chamber that receives processed filtrate from the vertebrate kidney's collecting ducts and is drained by the ureter.

renal vein The blood vessel draining the kidney.

renin-angiotensin-aldosterone system (RAAS) A part of a complex feedback circuit that helps regulate blood pressure and blood volume.

repeated reproduction A life history in which adults produce large numbers of offspring over many years; also known as iteroparity.

repetitive DNA Nucleotide sequences, usually noncoding, that are present in many copies in a eukaryotic genome. The repeated units may be short and arranged tandemly (in series) or long and dispersed in the genome.

replication fork A Y-shaped region on a replicating DNA molecule where new strands are growing.

repressor A protein that suppresses the transcription of a gene.

reproductive isolation The existence of biological factors (barriers) that impede members of two species from producing viable, fertile hybrids.

reproductive table An age-specific summary of the reproductive rates in a population.

reptile Member of the clade of amniotes that includes tuatara, lizards, snakes, turtles, crocodilians, and birds.

residual volume The amount of air that remains in the lungs after forcefully exhaling.

resource partitioning The division of environmental resources by coexisting species such that the niche of each species differs by one or more significant factors from the niches of all coexisting species.

respiratory medium The source of oxygen. It is typically air for terrestrial animals and water for aquatic organisms.

respiratory pigment A protein that transports most of the oxygen in blood.

respiratory surface The part of an animal where gases are exchanged with the environment.

response In cellular communication, the change in a specific cellular activity brought about by a transduced signal from outside the cell.

resting potential The membrane potential characteristic of a nonconducting, excitable cell, with the inside of the cell more negative than the outside.

restoration ecology A goal-directed science that applies ecological principles in an effort to return degraded ecosystems to conditions as similar as possible to their natural, predegraded state.

restriction enzyme A degradative enzyme that recognizes and cuts up DNA (including that of certain phages) that is foreign to a bacterium.

restriction fragment DNA segment resulting from cutting of DNA by a restriction enzyme.

restriction fragment length polymorphisms (RFLPs) Differences in DNA sequence on homologous chromosomes that can result in different patterns of restriction fragment lengths (DNA segments resulting from treatment with restriction enzymes); useful as genetic markers for making linkage maps.

restriction site A specific sequence on a DNA strand that is recognized as a "cut site" by a restriction enzyme.

reticular fiber A very thin and branched fiber made of collagen. Reticular fibers form a tightly woven fabric that is continuous with the collagenous fibers of the extracellular matrix.

reticular formation A system of neurons, containing over 90 separate nuclei, that passes through the core of the brainstem.

retina (ret-uh-nuh) The innermost layer of the vertebrate eye, containing photoreceptor cells (rods and cones) and neurons; transmits images formed by the lens to the brain via the optic nerve.

retinal The light-absorbing pigment in rods and cones of the vertebrate eye.

retrotransposon A transposable element that moves within a genome by means of an RNA intermediate, a transcript of the retrotransposon DNA.

sickle-cell disease A human genetic disease caused by a recessive allele that results in the substitution of a single amino acid in the hemoglobin protein; characterized by deformed red blood cells that can lead to numerous symptoms.

sieve plate An end wall in a sieve-tube member, which facilitates the flow of phloem sap in angiosperm sieve tubes.

sieve-tube member A living cell that conducts sugars and other organic nutrients in the phloem of angiosperms. They form chains called sieve tubes.

sign stimulus An external sensory stimulus that triggers a fixed action pattern.

signal A behavior that causes a change in behavior in another animal.

signal peptide A stretch of amino acids on a polypeptide that targets the protein to a specific destination in a eukaryotic cell.

signal-recognition particle (SRP) A protein-RNA complex that recognizes a signal peptide as it emerges from the ribosome.

signal transduction pathway A mechanism linking a mechanical or chemical stimulus to a specific cellular response.

simple fruit A fruit derived from a single carpel or several fused carpels.

simple epithelium An epithelium consisting of a single layer of cells that all touch the basal lamina.

single nucleotide polymorphisms (SNPs) One base-pair variation in the genome sequence.

single-lens eye The camera-like eye found in some jellies, polychaetes, spiders, and many molluscs.

single-strand binding protein During DNA replication, molecules that line up along the unpaired DNA strands, holding them apart while the DNA strands serve as templates for the synthesis of complementary strands of DNA.

sinoatrial (SA) node A region of the heart composed of specialized muscle tissue that sets the rate and timing at which all cardiac muscle cells contract; the pacemaker.

sinus Any of the spaces surrounding the organs of the body in animals with open circulatory systems.

sister chromatids Replicated forms of a chromosome joined together by the centromere and eventually separated during mitosis or meiosis II.

skeletal muscle (striated muscle) Muscle generally responsible for the voluntary movements of the body.

sliding-filament model The theory explaining how muscle contracts, based on change within a sarcomere, the basic unit of muscle organization, stating that thin (actin) filaments slide across thick (myosin) filaments, shortening the sarcomere. The shortening of all sarcomeres in a myofibril shortens the entire myofibril.

slow block to polyspermy The formation of the fertilization envelope and other changes in the egg's surface that prevent fusion of the egg with more than one sperm.

slow muscle fibers Muscle cells that can sustain long contractions.

small intestine The longest section of the alimentary canal; the principal site of the enzymatic hydrolysis of food macromolecules and the absorption of nutrients.

smooth ER That portion of the endoplasmic reticulum that is free of ribosomes.

smooth muscle A type of muscle lacking the striations of skeletal and cardiac muscle because of the uniform distribution of myosin filaments in the cell; responsible for involuntary body activities.

snowball Earth hypothesis The hypothesis that glaciers covered the planet's landmasses from pole to pole 750–570 million years ago, confining life to very limited areas.

social learning Modification of behavior through the observation of other individuals.

sociobiology The study of social behavior based on evolutionary theory.

sodium-potassium pump A special transport protein in the plasma membrane of animal cells that transports sodium out of the cell and potassium into the cell against their concentration gradients.

solute (sol -üt) A substance that is dissolved in a solution.

solute potential (Ψ_s) A component of water potential that is proportional to the number of dissolved solute molecules in a solution and measures the effect of solutes on the direction of water movement; also called osmotic potential; it can be either zero or negative.

solution A liquid that is a homogeneous mixture of two or more substances.

solvent The dissolving agent of a solution. Water is the most versatile solvent known.

somatic cell (sō-mat´-ik) Any cell in a multicellular organism except a sperm or egg cell.

somatic nervous system The branch of the motor division of the vertebrate peripheral nervous system composed of motor neurons that carry signals to skeletal muscles in response to external stimuli.

somites Paired blocks of mesoderm just lateral to the notochord of a vertebrate embryo.

soredia In lichens, small clusters of fungal hyphae with embedded algae.

sorus (plural, **sori**) A cluster of sporangia on a fern sporophyll. Sori may be arranged in various patterns, such as parallel lines or dots, that are useful in fern identification.

Southern blotting A hybridization technique that enables researchers to determine the presence of certain nucleotide sequences in a sample of DNA.

spatial learning Modification of behavior based on experience of the spatial structure of the environment.

spatial summation A phenomenon of neural integration in which the membrane potential of the postsynaptic cell is determined by the combined effect of EPSPs or IPSPs produced nearly simultaneously by different synapses.

speciation (spē -sē-a -shun) The origin of new species in evolution.

species A group whose members possess similar anatomical characteristics and have the ability to interbreed.

species-area curve The biodiversity pattern, first noted by Alexander von Humboldt, that illustrates that the larger the geographic area of a community, the greater the number of species.

species diversity The number and relative abundance of species in a biological community.

species richness The number of species in a biological community.

species selection A theory maintaining that species living the longest and generating the greatest number of species determine the direction of major evolutionary trends.

specific epithet The second part of a binomial, referring to one species within a genus.

specific heat The amount of heat that must be absorbed or lost for 1 g of a substance to change its temperature by 1°C.

spectrophotometer An instrument that measures the proportions of light of different wavelengths absorbed and transmitted by a pigment solution.

sperm The male gamete.

spermatheca (sper -muh-thē -kuh) A sac in the female reproductive system where sperm are stored.

spermatogenesis The continuous and prolific production of mature sperm cells in the testis.

spermatogonia Stem cells that give rise to sperm.

sphincter (sfink -ter) A ringlike valve consisting of modified muscles in a muscular tube, such as a digestive tract; closes off the tube like a drawstring.

spinal nerve In the vertebrate peripheral nervous system, a nerve that carries signals to or from the spinal cord.

spiral cleavage A type of embryonic development in protostomes, in which the planes of cell division that transform the zygote into a ball of cells occur obliquely to the polar axis, resulting in cells of each tier sitting in the grooves between cells of adjacent tiers.

spiral valve A corkscrew-shaped ridge that increases surface area and prolongs the passage of food along the short digestive tract.

spliceosome (splī -sē-ō-sōm) A complex assembly that interacts with the ends of an RNA intron in splicing RNA, releasing the intron and joining the two adjacent exons.

spongocoel (spon -jō-sēl) The central cavity of a sponge.

spongy mesophyll Loosely arranged photosynthetic cells located below the palisade mesophyll cells in a leaf.

sporangium (plural, **sporangia**) A capsule in fungi and plants in which meiosis occurs and haploid spores develop.

spore In the life cycle of a plant or alga undergoing alternation of generations, a meiotically produced haploid cell that divides mitotically, generating a multicellular individual, the gametophyte, without fusing with another cell.

sporocyte A diploid cell, also known as a spore mother cell, that undergoes meiosis and generates haploid spores.

sporophyll A leaf specialized for reproduction.

sporophyte (spôr -ō-fīt) In organisms undergoing alternation of generations, the multicellular diploid form that results from a union of gametes and that meiotically produces haploid spores that grow into the gametophyte generation.

sporopollenin (spor -uh-pol -uh-nin) A durable polymer that covers exposed zygotes of charophycean algae and forms walls of plant spores, preventing them from drying out.

sporozoite (spôr -uh-zō -īt) A tiny infectious cell that represents a stage in the apicomplexan life cycle.

squamous The flat, tile-like shape of a type of epithelial cell.

stabilizing selection Natural selection that favors intermediate variants by acting against extreme phenotypes.

stamen (stā -men) The pollen-producing reproductive organ of a flower, consisting of an anther and filament.

standard metabolic rate (SMR) The metabolic rate of a resting, fasting, and nonstressed ectotherm.

stapes The third of the three middle ear bones.

starch A storage polysaccharide in plants consisting entirely of glucose.

statocyst (stat -uh-sist) A type of mechanoreceptor that functions in equilibrium in invertebrates through the use of statoliths, which stimulate hair cells in relation to gravity.

statolith (1) In plants, a specialized plastid that contains dense starch grains and may play a role in detecting gravity. (2) In invertebrates, a grain or other dense granule that settles in response to gravity and is found in sensory organs that function in equilibrium.

stele The vascular tissue of a stem or root.

stem A vascular plant organ consisting of an alternating system of nodes and internodes that support the leaves and reproductive structures.

stem cell Any relatively unspecialized cell that can divide during a single division into one identical daughter cell and one more specialized daughter cell, which can undergo further differentiation.

stenohaline Referring to organisms that cannot tolerate substantial changes in external osmolarity.

steroid A type of lipid characterized by a carbon skeleton consisting of four rings with various functional groups attached.

sticky end A single-stranded end of a double-stranded DNA restriction fragment.

stigma (plural, **stigmata**) The sticky part of a flower's carpel, which traps pollen grains.

stipe A stemlike structure of a seaweed.

stock The plant that provides the root system when making a graft.

stoma (stō -muh) (plural, **stomata**) A microscopic pore surrounded by guard cells in the epidermis of leaves and stems that allows gas exchange between the environment and the interior of the plant.

stomach An organ of the digestive system that stores food and performs preliminary steps of digestion.

stratified epithelium An epithelium consisting of more than one layer of cells in which some but not all cells touch the basal lamina.

stream A flowing body of water that is generally small, cold, and clear.

stress-induced proteins Molecules, including heat-shock proteins, that are produced within cells in response to exposure to marked increases in temperature and to other forms of severe stress, such as toxins, rapid pH changes, and viral infections.

stretch-gated ion channel Protein pore in a cell's plasma membrane that opens when the membrane is mechanically deformed, allowing the passage of certain ions.

striated muscle See skeletal muscle.

strobili The technical term for clusters of sporophylls known commonly as cones, found in most gymnosperms and some seedless vascular plants.

stroke The death of nervous tissue in the brain, usually resulting from rupture or blockage of arteries in the head.

stroke volume The amount of blood pumped by the left ventricle in each contraction.

stroma (strō -muh) The fluid of the chloroplast surrounding the thylakoid membrane; involved in the synthesis of organic molecules from carbon dioxide and water.

stromatolite Rocklike structure composed of layers of prokaryotes and sediment.

structural formula A type of molecular notation in which the constituent atoms are joined by lines representing covalent bonds.

structural isomer One of several organic compounds that have the same molecular formula but differ in the covalent arrangements of their atoms.

style The stalk of a flower's carpel, with the ovary at the base and the stigma at the top.

substance P A neuropeptide that is a key excitatory signal that mediates our perception of pain.

substrate The reactant on which an enzyme works.

substrate feeder An organism that lives in or on its food source, eating its way through the food.

substrate-level phosphorylation The formation of ATP by directly transferring a phosphate group to ADP from an intermediate substrate in catabolism.

sugar sink A plant organ that is a net consumer or storer of sugar. Growing roots, shoot tips, stems, and fruits are sugar sinks supplied by phloem.

sugar source A plant organ in which sugar is being produced by either photosynthesis or the breakdown of starch. Mature leaves are the primary sugar sources of plants.

sulfhydryl group A functional group consisting of a sulfur atom bonded to a hydrogen atom (—SH).

suprachiasmatic nuclei (SCN) A pair of structures in the hypothalamus of mammals that functions as a biological clock.

surface tension A measure of how difficult it is to stretch or break the surface of a liquid. Water has a high surface tension because of the hydrogen bonding of surface molecules.

survivorship curve A plot of the number of members of a cohort that are still alive at each age; one way to represent age-specific mortality.

suspension feeder An aquatic animal, such as a clam or a baleen whale, that sifts small food particles from the water.

sustainable agriculture Long-term productive farming methods that are environmentally safe.

sustainable development The long-term prosperity of human societies and the ecosystems that support them.

swim bladder In aquatic osteichthyans, an air sac that enables the animal to control its buoyancy in the water.

symbiont (sim -bē-unt) The smaller participant in a symbiotic relationship, living in or on the host.

symbiosis An ecological relationship between organisms of two different species that live together in direct contact.

sympathetic division One of three divisions of the autonomic nervous system of vertebrates; generally increases energy expenditure and prepares the body for action.

sympatric speciation (sim-pat -rik) A mode of speciation occurring as a result of a radical change in the genome of a subpopulation, reproductively isolating the subpopulation from the parent population.

symplast In plants, the continuum of cytoplasm connected by plasmodesmata between cells.

synapse (sin -aps) The locus where one neuron communicates with another neuron in a neural pathway; a narrow gap between a synaptic terminal of an axon and a signal-receiving portion (dendrite or cell body) of

mutualism (myü -chü-ul-ızm) A symbiotic relationship in which both participants benefit.

mycelium (mī-sē´-lē-um) The densely branched network of hyphae in a fungus.

mycorrhizae (mī-kō-rī´-zē) Mutualistic associations of plant roots and fungi.

mycosis The general term for a fungal infection.

myelin sheath (mī -uh-lin) In a neuron, an insulating coat of cell membrane from Schwann cells that is interrupted by nodes of Ranvier, where saltatory conduction occurs.

myofibril (mī´-ō-fī´-bril) A fibril collectively arranged in longitudinal bundles in muscle cells (fibers), composed of thin filaments of actin and a regulatory protein and thick filaments of myosin.

myofilaments The thick and thin filaments that form the myofibrils.

myogenic heart A type of heart, such as in vertebrate animals, in which the pacemaker is made up of specialized muscle tissues and located within the heart itself.

myoglobin (mī -uh-glō´-bin) An oxygen-storing, pigmented protein in muscle cells.

myosin (mī´-uh-sin) A type of protein filament that interacts with actin filaments to cause cell contraction.

myotonia Increased muscle tension.

myriapod A terrestrial arthropod with many body segments and one or two pairs of legs per segment. Millipedes and centipedes comprise the two classes of living myriapods.

NAD⁺ Nicotinamide adenine dinucleotide, a coenzyme present in all cells that helps enzymes transfer electrons during the redox reactions of metabolism.

NADP⁺ Nicotinamide adenine dinucleotide phosphate, an acceptor that temporarily stores energized electrons produced during the light reactions.

natural family planning A form of contraception that relies on refraining from sexual intercourse when conception is most likely to occur; also called the rhythm method.

natural killer (NK) cell A type of white blood cell that can kill tumor cells and virus-infected cells; an important component of innate immunity.

natural selection Differential success in the reproduction of different phenotypes resulting from the interaction of organisms with their environment. Evolution occurs when natural selection causes changes in relative frequencies of alleles in the gene pool.

negative feedback A primary mechanism of homeostasis, whereby a change in a physiological variable that is being monitored triggers a response that counteracts the initial fluctuation.

negative pressure breathing A breathing system in which air is pulled into the lungs.

nematocyst (nem´-uh-tuh-sist) A stinging, capsule-like organelle in a cnidocyte.

neocortex In the mammalian brain, the outermost region of the cerebral cortex.

nephron (nef´-ron) The tubular excretory unit of the vertebrate kidney.

neritic zone (nuh-rit´-ik) The shallow region of the ocean overlying the continental shelf.

nerve A ropelike bundle of neuron fibers (axons and dendrites) tightly wrapped in connective tissue.

nerve cord A ropelike arrangement of neurons characteristic of animals with bilateral symmetry and cephalization.

nerve net A weblike system of neurons, characteristic of radially symmetrical animals, such as hydra.

nervous tissue Tissue made up of neurons and supportive cells.

net primary production (NPP) The gross primary production of an ecosystem minus the energy used by the producers for respiration.

neural crest A band of cells along the border where the neural tube pinches off from the ectoderm. The cells migrate to various parts of the embryo and form the pigment cells in the skin, bones of the skull, the teeth, the adrenal glands, and parts of the peripheral nervous system.

neural tube A tube of cells running along the dorsal axis of the body, just dorsal to the notochord. It will give rise to the central nervous system.

neurogenic heart A type of heart, such as in insects, in which the pacemakers originate in motor nerves arising from outside the heart.

neurohypophysis (ner -ō-hi-pof´-uh-sis) See posterior pituitary.

neuron (ner´-on) A nerve cell; the fundamental unit of the nervous system, having structure and properties that allow it to conduct signals by taking advantage of the electrical charge across its cell membrane.

neuropeptide A relatively short chain of amino acids that serves as a neurotransmitter.

neurosecretory cell A specialized nerve cell that releases a hormone into the bloodstream in response to signals from other nerve cells; located in the hypothalamus and adrenal medulla.

neurotransmitter A chemical messenger released from the synaptic terminal of a neuron at a chemical synapse that diffuses across the synaptic cleft and binds to and stimulates the postsynaptic cell.

neutral theory The hypothesis that much evolutionary change in genes and proteins has no effect on fitness and therefore is not influenced by Darwinian natural selection.

neutral variation Genetic diversity that confers no apparent selective advantage.

neutron An electrically neutral particle (a particle having no electrical charge), found in the nucleus of an atom.

neutrophil The most abundant type of white blood cell. Neutrophils are phagocytic and tend to self-destruct as they destroy foreign invaders, limiting their life span to a few days.

niche See ecological niche.

nitric oxide (NO) A gas produced by many types of cells that functions as a local regulator, a neurotransmitter, and an antibacterial agent.

nitrogen fixation The assimilation of atmospheric nitrogen by certain prokaryotes into nitrogenous compounds that can be directly used by plants.

nitrogenase (nī-troj´-uh-nāz) An enzyme complex, unique to certain prokaryotes, that reduces N_2 to NH_3.

nitrogen-fixing bacteria Microorganisms that restock nitrogenous minerals in the soil by converting nitrogen to ammonia.

nociceptor A class of naked dendrites in the epidermis of the skin.

node A point along the stem of a plant at which leaves are attached.

nodule A swelling on the root of a legume. Nodules are composed of plant cells that contain nitrogen-fixing bacteria of the genus *Rhizobium*.

noncompetitive inhibitor A substance that reduces the activity of an enzyme by binding to a location remote from the active site, changing its conformation so that it no longer binds to the substrate.

noncyclic electron flow A route of electron flow during the light reactions of photosynthesis that involves both photosystems and produces ATP, NADPH, and oxygen. The net electron flow is from water to NADP⁺.

nondisjunction An error in meiosis or mitosis, in which both members of a pair of homologous chromosomes or both sister chromatids fail to move apart properly.

nonequilibrium model The model of communities that emphasizes that they are not stable in time but constantly changing after being buffeted by disturbances.

nonpolar covalent bond A type of covalent bond in which electrons are shared equally between two atoms of similar electronegativity.

nonsense mutation A mutation that changes an amino acid codon to one of the three stop codons, resulting in a shorter and usually nonfunctional protein.

nonshivering thermogenesis (NST) The increased production of heat in some mammals by the action of certain hormones that cause mitochondria to increase their metabolic activity and produce heat instead of ATP.

norepinephrine A hormone that is chemically and functionally similar to epinephrine.

norm of reaction The range of phenotypes produced by a single genotype, due to environmental influences.

notochord A longitudinal, flexible rod that runs along the dorsal axis of an animal's body in the future position of the vertebral column.

nuclear envelope The membrane in eukaryotes that encloses the nucleus, separating it from the cytoplasm.

nuclear lamina A netlike array of protein filaments that maintains the shape of the nucleus.

nuclease An enzyme that hydrolyzes DNA and RNA into their component nucleotides.

nucleic acid A polymer (polynucleotide) consisting of many nucleotide monomers; serves as a blueprint for proteins and, through the actions of proteins, for all cellular activities. The two types are DNA and RNA.

nucleic acid hybridization Base pairing between a gene and a complementary sequence on another nucleic acid molecule.

nucleic acid probe (nū-klā-ik) In DNA technology, a labeled single-stranded nucleic acid molecule used to tag a specific nucleotide sequence in a nucleic acid sample. Molecules of the probe hydrogen-bond to the complementary sequence wherever it occurs; radioactive or other labeling of the probe allows its location to be detected.

nucleoid (nū-klē-oid) A dense region of DNA in a prokaryotic cell.

nucleoid region The region in a prokaryotic cell consisting of a concentrated mass of DNA.

nucleolus (nū-klē-ō-lus) (plural, **nucleoli**) A specialized structure in the nucleus, formed from various chromosomes and active in the synthesis of ribosomes.

nucleosome (nū-klē-ō-sōm) The basic, bead-like unit of DNA packaging in eukaryotes, consisting of a segment of DNA wound around a protein core composed of two copies of each of four types of histone.

nucleotide (nū-klē-ō-tīd) The building block of a nucleic acid, consisting of a five-carbon sugar covalently bonded to a nitrogenous base and a phosphate group.

nucleotide excision repair The process of removing and then correctly replacing a damaged segment of DNA using the undamaged strand as a guide.

nucleus (1) An atom's central core, containing protons and neutrons. (2) The chromosome-containing organelle of a eukaryotic cell. (3) A cluster of neurons.

obligate aerobe (ob-lig-et är-ōb) An organism that requires oxygen for cellular respiration and cannot live without it.

obligate anaerobe (ob-lig-et an-uh-rob) An organism that cannot use oxygen and is poisoned by it.

oceanic pelagic biome Most of the ocean's waters far from shore, constantly mixed by ocean currents.

oceanic zone The region of water lying over deep areas beyond the continental shelf.

Okazaki fragment A short segment of DNA synthesized on a template strand during DNA replication. Many Okazaki fragments make up the lagging strand of newly synthesized DNA.

olfactory receptor Smell receptor.

oligodendrocyte (ol-ig-ō-den-druh-sīt) A type of glial cell that forms insulating myelin sheaths around the axons of neurons in the central nervous system.

oligosaccharin A type of elicitor (molecule that induces a broad defense response in plants) that is derived from cellulose fragments released by cell wall damage.

oligotrophic lake A nutrient-poor, oxygen-rich, clear, deep lake with few phytoplankton.

ommatidium (plural, **ommatidia**) (ōm-uh-tid-ē-um) One of the facets of the compound eye of arthropods and some polychaete worms.

omnivore A heterotrophic animal that consumes both meat and plant material.

oncogene (on-kō-jēn) A gene found in viruses or as part of the normal genome that is involved in triggering cancerous characteristics.

one gene–one polypeptide hypothesis The premise that a gene is a segment of DNA that codes for one polypeptide.

oogenesis (o-uh-jen-uh-sis) The process in the ovary that results in the production of female gametes.

oogonia Ovary-specific stem cells.

oomycete A protist with flagellated cells, such as a water mold, white rust, or downy mildew, that acquires nutrition mainly as a decomposer or plant parasite.

open circulatory system A circulatory system in which fluid called hemolymph bathes the tissues and organs directly and there is no distinction between the circulating fluid and the interstitial fluid.

operant conditioning (op-er-ent) A type of associative learning in which an animal learns to associate one of its own behaviors with a reward or punishment and then tends to repeat or avoid that behavior; also called trial-and-error learning.

operator In prokaryotic DNA, a sequence of nucleotides near the start of an operon to which an active repressor can attach. The binding of the repressor prevents RNA polymerase from attaching to the promoter and transcribing the genes of the operon.

operculum In aquatic osteichthyans, a protective bony flap that covers and protects the gills.

operon (op-er-on) A unit of genetic function common in bacteria and phages, consisting of coordinately regulated clusters of genes with related functions.

opisthokont Member of the clade Opisthokonta, organisms that descended from an ancestor with a posterior flagellum, including fungi, animals, and certain protists.

opposable thumb An arrangement of the fingers such that the thumb can touch the ventral surface of the fingertips of all four fingers.

opsin A membrane protein bonded to a light-absorbing pigment molecule.

optic chiasm The arrangement of the nerve tracts of the eye such that the visual sensations from the left visual field of both eyes are transmitted to the right side of the brain and the sensations from the right visual field of both eyes are transmitted to the left side of the brain.

optimal foraging theory The basis for analyzing behavior as a compromise of feeding costs versus feeding benefits.

oral cavity The mouth of an animal.

orbital The three-dimensional space where an electron is found 90% of the time.

order In classification, the taxonomic category above family.

organ A specialized center of body function composed of several different types of tissues.

organ identity genes Plant homeotic genes that use positional information to determine which emerging leaves develop into which types of floral organs.

organ of Corti The actual hearing organ of the vertebrate ear, located in the floor of the cochlear canal in the inner ear; contains the receptor cells (hair cells) of the ear.

organ system A group of organs that work together in performing vital body functions.

organelle (ōr-guh-nel) One of several formed bodies with specialized functions, suspended in the cytoplasm of eukaryotic cells.

organic chemistry The study of carbon compounds (organic compounds).

organism An individual living thing.

organismal ecology The branch of ecology concerned with the morphological, physiological, and behavioral ways in which individual organisms meet the challenges posed by their biotic and abiotic environments.

organogenesis (ōr-gan-ō-jen-uh-sis) The development of organ rudiments from the three germ layers.

orgasm Rhythmic, involuntary contractions of certain reproductive structures in both sexes during the human sexual response cycle.

origin of replication Site where the replication of a DNA molecule begins.

orthologous genes Homologous genes that are passed in a straight line from one generation to the next, but have ended up in different gene pools because of speciation.

osculum A large opening in a sponge that connects the spongocoel to the environment.

osmoconformer An animal that does not actively adjust its internal osmolarity because it is isoosmotic with its environment.

osmolarity (oz-mō-lār-uh-tē) Solute concentration expressed as molarity.

osmoregulation How organisms regulate solute concentrations and balance the gain and loss of water.

osmoregulator An animal whose body fluids have a different osmolarity than the environment and that must either discharge excess water if it lives in a hypoosmotic environment

retrovirus (ret -trō-vī -rus) An RNA virus that reproduces by transcribing its RNA into DNA and then inserting the DNA into a cellular chromosome; an important class of cancer-causing viruses.

reverse transcriptase (tran-skrip -tās) An enzyme encoded by some certain viruses (retroviruses) that uses RNA as a template for DNA synthesis.

Rh factor A protein antigen on the surface of red blood cells designated Rh-positive. If an Rh-negative mother is exposed to blood from an Rh-positive fetus, she produces anti-Rh antibodies of the IgG class.

rhizoid Long tubular single cell or filament of cells that anchors bryophytes to the ground. Rhizoids are not composed of tissues, lack specialized conducting cells, and do not play a primary role in water and mineral absorption.

rhodopsin A visual pigment consisting of retinal and opsin. When rhodopsin absorbs light, the retinal changes shape and dissociates from the opsin, after which it is converted back to its original form.

rhythm method A form of contraception that relies on refraining from sexual intercourse when conception is most likely to occur; also called natural family planning.

ribonucleic acid (RNA) (rī -bō-nū-klā -ik) A type of nucleic acid consisting of nucleotide monomers with a ribose sugar and the nitrogenous bases adenine (A), cytosine (C), guanine (G), and uracil (U); usually single-stranded; functions in protein synthesis and as the genome of some viruses.

ribose The sugar component of RNA.

ribosomal RNA (rRNA) (rī -buh-sō -mul) The most abundant type of RNA, which together with proteins forms the structure of ribosomes. Ribosomes coordinate the sequential coupling of tRNA molecules to mRNA codons.

ribosome A cell organelle constructed in the nucleolus and functioning as the site of protein synthesis in the cytoplasm; consists of rRNA and protein molecules, which make up two subunits.

ribozyme (rī -bō-zīm) An enzyme-like RNA molecule that catalyzes reactions during RNA splicing.

river A flowing body of water.

rivet model The concept, put forth by Paul and Anne Ehrlich, that many or most of the species in a community are associated tightly with other species in a web of life. According to this model, an increase or decrease in one species in a community affects many other species.

RNA interference (RNAi) A technique to silence the expression of selected genes in nonmammalian organisms. The method uses synthetic double-stranded RNA molecules matching the sequence of a particular gene to trigger the breakdown of the gene's messenger RNA.

RNA polymerase An enzyme that links together the growing chain of ribonucleotides during transcription.

RNA processing Modification of RNA before it leaves the nucleus, a process unique to eukaryotes.

RNA splicing The removal of noncoding portions (introns) of the RNA molecule after initial synthesis.

rod cell One of two kinds of photoreceptors in the vertebrate retina; sensitive to black and white and enables night vision.

root An organ in vascular plants that anchors the plant and enables it to absorb water and nutrients from the soil.

root cap A cone of cells at the tip of a plant root that protects the apical meristem.

root hair A tiny extension of a root epidermal cell, growing just behind the root tip and increasing surface area for absorption of water and minerals.

root pressure The upward push of xylem sap in the vascular tissue of roots.

root system All of a plant's roots that anchor it in the soil, absorb and transport minerals and water, and store food.

rosette cellulose-synthesizing complex Rose-shaped array of proteins that synthesize the cellulose microfibrils of the cell walls of charophyceans and land plants.

rough ER That portion of the endoplasmic reticulum studded with ribosomes.

round window The point of contact between the stapes and the cochlea. It is where the vibrations of the stapes create a traveling series of pressure waves in the fluid of the cochlea.

r-selection The concept that in certain (r-selected) populations, a high reproductive rate is the chief determinant of life history.

rubisco Ribulose carboxylase, the enzyme that catalyzes the first step of the Calvin cycle (the addition of CO_2 to RuBP or ribulose bisphosphate).

ruminant An animal, such as a cow or a sheep, with an elaborate, multicompartmentalized stomach specialized for an herbivorous diet.

S phase The synthesis phase of the cell cycle; the portion of interphase during which DNA is replicated.

sac fungus Member of the phylum Ascomycota. Sac fungi range in size and complexity from unicellular yeasts to minute leafspot fungi to elaborate cup fungi and morels. About half of the sac fungi live with algae or cyanobacteria in the mutualistic associations called lichens.

saccule A chamber in the vestibule behind the oval window that participates in the sense of balance.

salicylic acid A plant hormone that may be partially responsible for activating systemic acquired resistance to pathogens.

salivary amylase A salivary gland enzyme that hydrolyzes starch and glycogen.

salivary glands Exocrine glands associated with the oral cavity. The secretions of salivary glands contain substances to lubricate food, adhere together chewed pieces into a bolus, and begin the process of chemical digestion.

salt A compound resulting from the formation of an ionic bond; also called an ionic compound.

saltatory conduction (sol -tuh-tōr -ē) Rapid transmission of a nerve impulse along an axon, resulting from the action potential jumping from one node of Ranvier to another, skipping the myelin-sheathed regions of membrane.

sapwood Outer layers of secondary xylem that still transport xylem sap.

sarcomere (sar -kō-mēr) The fundamental, repeating unit of striated muscle, delimited by the Z lines.

sarcoplasmic reticulum (SR) A specialized endoplasmic reticulum that regulates the calcium concentration in the cytosol.

saturated fatty acid A fatty acid in which all carbons in the hydrocarbon tail are connected by single bonds, thus maximizing the number of hydrogen atoms that can attach to the carbon skeleton.

savanna (suh-van -uh) A tropical grassland biome with scattered individual trees, large herbivores, and three distinct seasons based primarily on rainfall, maintained by occasional fires and drought.

scaffolding protein A type of large relay protein to which several other relay proteins are simultaneously attached to increase the efficiency of signal transduction.

scanning electron microscope (SEM) A microscope that uses an electron beam to scan the surface of a sample to study details of its topography.

schizocoelous Pattern of formation of the body cavity common in protostome development, in which initially solid masses of mesoderm split, forming the body cavity.

schizophrenia Severe mental disturbance characterized by psychotic episodes in which patients lose the ability to distinguish reality from hallucination.

Schwann cell A type of glial cell that forms insulating myelin sheaths around the axons of neurons in the peripheral nervous system.

scion (sī -un) The twig grafted onto the stock when making a graft.

sclera (sklār -uh) A tough, white outer layer of connective tissue that forms the globe of the vertebrate eye.

sclereid (sklār -ē-id) A short, irregular sclerenchyma cell in nutshells and seed coats and scattered through the parenchyma of some plants.

sclerenchyma cell (skluh-ren -kē-muh) A rigid, supportive plant cell type usually lacking protoplasts and possessing thick secondary walls strengthened by lignin at maturity.

scrotum A pouch of skin outside the abdomen that houses a testis; functions in cooling sperm, thereby keeping them viable.

scutellum (sku-tel'-um) A specialized type of cotyledon found in the grass family.

seascape Several different, primarily aquatic ecosystems linked by exchanges of energy, materials, and organisms.

second law of thermodynamics The principle whereby every energy transfer or transformation increases the entropy of the universe. Ordered forms of energy are at least partly converted to heat, and in spontaneous reactions, the free energy of the system also decreases.

second messenger A small, nonprotein, water-soluble molecule or ion, such as calcium ion or cyclic AMP, that relays a signal to a cell's interior in response to a signal received by a signal receptor protein.

secondary cell wall A strong and durable matrix often deposited in several laminated layers for plant cell protection and support.

secondary consumer A member of the trophic level of an ecosystem consisting of carnivores that eat herbivores.

secondary endosymbiosis A process in eukaryotic evolution in which a heterotrophic eukaryotic cell engulfed a photosynthetic eukaryotic cell, which survived in a symbiotic relationship inside the heterotrophic cell.

secondary growth Growth produced by lateral meristems, thickening the roots and shoots of woody plants.

secondary immune response The acquired immune response elicited on second or subsequent exposures to a particular antigen. The secondary immune response is more rapid, of greater magnitude, and of longer duration than the primary immune response.

secondary oocyte A haploid cell resulting from meiosis I in oogenesis, which will become an ovum after meiosis II.

secondary plant body The tissues produced by the vascular cambium and cork cambium, which thicken the stems and roots of woody plants.

secondary production The amount of chemical energy in consumers' food that is converted to their own new biomass during a given time period.

secondary structure The localized, repetitive coiling or folding of the polypeptide backbone of a protein due to hydrogen bond formation between peptide linkages.

secondary succession A type of succession that occurs where an existing community has been cleared by some disturbance that leaves the soil intact.

secretion (1) The discharge of molecules synthesized by a cell. (2) The discharge of wastes from the body fluid into the filtrate.

secretory phase That portion of the uterine (menstrual) cycle when the endometrium continues to thicken, becomes more vascularized, and develops glands that secrete a fluid rich in glycogen.

sedimentary rock (sed'-uh-men'-tuh-re) Rock formed from sand and mud that once settled in layers on the bottom of seas, lakes, and marshes. Sedimentary rocks are often rich in fossils.

seed An adaptation for terrestrial plants consisting of an embryo packaged along with a store of food within a resistant coat.

seed coat A tough outer covering of a seed, formed from the outer coat of an ovule. In a flowering plant, the seed coat encloses and protects the embryo and endosperm.

seedless vascular plants The informal collective name for the phyla Lycophyta (club mosses and their relatives) and Pteridophyta (ferns and their relatives).

segmentation gene A gene of the embryo that directs the actual formation of segments after the embryo's axes are defined.

selective permeability A property of biological membranes that allows some substances to cross more easily than others.

selective reabsorption The selective uptake of solutes from a filtrate of blood, coelomic fluid, or hemolymph in the excretory organs of animals.

self-incompatibility The ability of a seed plant to reject its own pollen and sometimes the pollen of closely related individuals.

semelparity A life history in which adults have but a single reproductive opportunity to produce large numbers of offspring, such as the life history of the Pacific salmon; also known as big-bang reproduction.

semen (se'-mun) The fluid that is ejaculated by the male during orgasm; contains sperm and secretions from several glands of the male reproductive tract.

semicircular canals A three-part chamber of the inner ear that functions in maintaining equilibrium.

semiconservative model Type of DNA replication in which the replicated double helix consists of one old strand, derived from the old molecule, and one newly made strand.

semilunar valve A valve located at the two exits of the heart, where the aorta leaves the left ventricle and the pulmonary artery leaves the right ventricle.

seminal vesicle (sem'-uh-nul ves'-uh-kul) A gland in males that secretes a fluid component of semen that lubricates and nourishes sperm.

seminiferous tubule (sem'-uh-nif'-uh-rus) A highly coiled tube in the testis in which sperm are produced.

sensation An impulse sent to the brain from activated receptors and sensory neurons.

sensitive period A limited phase in an individual animal's development when learning of particular behaviors can take place.

sensory adaptation The tendency of sensory neurons to become less sensitive when they are stimulated repeatedly.

sensory neuron A nerve cell that receives information from the internal and external environments and transmits the signals to the central nervous system.

sensory reception The detection of the energy of a stimulus by sensory cells.

sensory receptor A cellular system that collects information about the physical world outside the body and inside the organism.

sensory transduction The conversion of stimulus energy to a change in the membrane potential of a sensory receptor.

sepal (se'-pul) A modified leaf in angiosperms that helps enclose and protect a flower bud before it opens.

septum (plural, **septa**) One of the cross-walls that divide a fungal hypha into cells. Septa generally have pores large enough to allow ribosomes, mitochondria, and even nuclei to flow from cell to cell.

sequential hermaphroditism A reproductive pattern in which an individual reverses its sex during its lifetime.

serial endosymbiosis A model of the origin of eukaryotes consisting of a sequence of endosymbiotic events in which mitochondria, chloroplasts, and perhaps other cellular structures were derived from small prokaryotes that had been engulfed by larger cells.

serotonin A biogenic amine synthesized from the amino acid tryptophan.

seta (se'-tuh) The elongated stalk of a bryophyte sporophyte, such as in a moss.

sex chromosome One of the pair of chromosomes responsible for determining the sex of an individual.

sex-linked gene A gene located on a sex chromosome.

sexual dimorphism (di-mor'-fizm) A special case of polymorphism based on the distinction between the secondary sex characteristics of males and females.

sexual reproduction A type of reproduction in which two parents give rise to offspring that have unique combinations of genes inherited from the gametes of the two parents.

sexual selection Natural selection for mating success.

shared derived character An evolutionary novelty that evolved within a particular clade.

shared primitive character A character displayed in species outside a particular taxon.

shoot system The aerial portion of a plant body, consisting of stems, leaves, and (in angiosperms) flowers.

short-day plant A plant that flowers (usually in late summer, fall, or winter) only when the light period is shorter than a critical length.

short-term memory The ability to hold information, anticipations, or goals for a time and then release them if they become irrelevant.

Glossary

another neuron or effector cell. Neurotransmitter molecules released by synaptic terminals diffuse across the synapse, relaying messages to the dendrite or effector.

synapsid Member of an amniote clade distinguished by a single hole on each side of the skull, including the mammals.

synapsis The pairing of replicated homologous chromosomes during prophase I of meiosis.

synaptic cleft (sin-ap -tik) A narrow gap separating the synaptic knob of a transmitting neuron from a receiving neuron or an effector cell.

synaptic terminal A bulb at the end of an axon in which neurotransmitter molecules are stored and released.

synaptic vesicle Membranous sac containing neurotransmitter molecules at the tip of the presynaptic axon.

system A more complex organization formed from a combination of components.

systematics The analytical study of the diversity and relationships of organisms, both present-day and extinct.

systemic acquired resistance (SAR) A defensive response in infected plants that helps protect healthy tissue from pathogenic invasion.

systemic circuit The branch of the circulatory system that supplies all body organs and then returns oxygen-poor blood to the right atrium via the veins.

systemic circulation Movement of blood through the systemic circuit.

systems biology An approach to studying biology that aims to model the dynamic behavior of whole biological systems.

systole (sis -tō-lē) The stage of the heart cycle in which the heart muscle contracts and the chambers pump blood.

systolic pressure Blood pressure in the arteries during contraction of the ventricles.

T cell receptor The antigen receptor on T cells; a membrane-bound molecule consisting of one α chain and one β chain linked by a disulfide bridge and containing one antigen-binding site.

T lymphocyte (T cell) A type of lymphocyte, including the helper T cells and cytotoxic T cells, that develops to maturity in the thymus. After encountering antigen, T cells are responsible for cell-mediated immunity.

taproot system A root system common to eudicots, consisting of one large, vertical root (the taproot) that produces many smaller lateral, or branch, roots.

taste buds Collections of modified epithelial cells that are scattered in several areas of the tongue and mouth and are receptors for taste in humans.

TATA box A promoter DNA sequence crucial in forming the transcription initiation complex.

taxis (tak -sis) Movement toward or away from a stimulus.

taxon (plural, **taxa**) The named taxonomic unit at any given level of classification.

taxonomy (tak-son -uh-mē) Ordered division of organisms into categories based on a set of characteristics used to assess similarities and differences, leading to a classification scheme; the branch of biology concerned with naming and classifying the diverse forms of life.

Tay-Sachs disease A human genetic disease caused by a recessive allele for a dysfunctional enzyme, leading to accumulation of certain lipids in the brain. Seizures, blindness, and degeneration of motor and mental performance usually become manifest a few months after birth.

technology The application of scientific knowledge for a specific purpose.

telomerase An enzyme that catalyzes the lengthening of telomeres. The enzyme includes a molecule of RNA that serves as a template for new telomere segments.

telomere (tel -uh-mêr) The protective structure at each end of a eukaryotic chromosome. Specifically, the tandemly repetitive DNA at the end of the chromosome's DNA molecule. *See also* repetitive DNA.

telophase The fifth and final stage of mitosis, in which daughter nuclei are forming and cytokinesis has typically begun.

temperate broadleaf forest A biome located throughout midlatitude regions where there is sufficient moisture to support the growth of large, broadleaf deciduous trees.

temperate grassland A terrestrial biome dominated by grasses and forbs.

temperate phage A phage that is capable of reproducing by either the lytic or lysogenic cycle.

temperature A measure of the intensity of heat in degrees, reflecting the average kinetic energy of the molecules.

template strand The DNA strand that provides the template for ordering the sequence of nucleotides in an RNA transcript.

temporal summation A phenomenon of neural integration in which the membrane potential of the postsynaptic cell in a chemical synapse is determined by the combined effect of EPSPs or IPSPs produced in rapid succession.

tendon A type of fibrous connective tissue that attaches muscle to bone.

terminal bud Embryonic tissue at the tip of a shoot, made up of developing leaves and a compact series of nodes and internodes.

terminator In prokaryotes, a special sequence of nucleotides in DNA that marks the end of a gene. It signals RNA polymerase to release the newly made RNA molecule, which then departs from the gene.

territoriality A behavior in which an animal defends a bounded physical space against encroachment by other individuals, usually of its own species. Territory defense may involve direct aggression or indirect mechanisms such as scent marking or singing.

tertiary consumer A member of the trophic level of an ecosystem consisting of carnivores that eat mainly other carnivores.

tertiary structure (ter -shē-âr-ē) Irregular contortions of a protein molecule due to interactions of side chains involved in hydrophobic interactions, ionic bonds, hydrogen bonds, and disulfide bridges.

test The hardened shell of some protists, including forams and radiolarians, or the rigid endoskeleton of a sea urchin or sand dollar.

testcross Breeding of an organism of unknown genotype with a homozygous recessive individual to determine the unknown genotype. The ratio of phenotypes in the offspring determines the unknown genotype.

testis (plural, **testes**) The male reproductive organ, or gonad, in which sperm and reproductive hormones are produced.

testosterone The most abundant androgen hormone in the male body.

tetanus (tet -uh-nus) The maximal, sustained contraction of a skeletal muscle, caused by a very fast frequency of action potentials elicited by continual stimulation.

tetrad A paired set of homologous chromosomes, each composed of two sister chromatids. Tetrads form during prophase I of meiosis.

tetrapod A vertebrate with two pairs of limbs, including mammals, amphibians, and birds and other reptiles.

thalamus (thal -uh-mus) One of two integrating centers of the vertebrate forebrain. Neurons with cell bodies in the thalamus relay neural input to specific areas in the cerebral cortex and regulate what information goes to the cerebral cortex.

thallus (plural, **thalli**) A seaweed body that is plantlike but lacks true roots, stems, and leaves.

theory An explanation that is broad in scope, generates new hypotheses, and is supported by a large body of evidence.

thermal energy *See* heat.

thermocline A narrow stratum of rapid temperature change in the ocean and in many temperate-zone lakes.

thermodynamics (ther -mō-dī-nam'-iks) (1) The study of energy transformations that occur in a collection of matter. *See* first law of thermodynamics and second law of thermodynamics. (2) A phenomenon in which external DNA is taken up by a cell and functions there.

thermoreceptor An interoreceptor stimulated by either heat or cold.

thermoregulation The maintenance of internal body temperature within a tolerable range.

theropod A member of an ancient group of dinosaurs that were bipedal carnivores.

thick filament A filament composed of staggered arrays of myosin molecules; a component of myofibrils in muscle fibers.

thigmomorphogenesis A response in plants to chronic mechanical stimulation, resulting from increased ethylene production. An example is thickening stems in response to strong winds.

thigmotropism (thig-mō-trō-pizm) A directional growth of a plant in response to touch.

thin filament The smaller of the two myofilaments, consisting of two strands of actin and two strands of regulatory protein coiled around one another.

thoracic cavity The body cavity in mammals that houses the lungs and heart. It is surrounded in part by ribs and separated from the lower abdominal cavity by the diaphragm.

threatened species A species that is considered likely to become endangered in the foreseeable future.

three-domain system A system of taxonomic classification based on three "superkingdoms": Bacteria, Archaea, and Eukarya.

threshold The potential an excitable cell membrane must reach for an action potential to be initiated.

thrombus A clump of platelets and fibrin that blocks the flow of blood through a blood vessel.

thylakoid (thī-luh-koyd) A flattened membrane sac inside the chloroplast, used to convert light energy to chemical energy.

thymus (thī-mus) A small organ in the thoracic cavity of vertebrates where maturation of T cells is completed.

thyroid gland An endocrine gland, located on the ventral surface of the trachea, that secretes two iodine-containing hormones, triiodothyronine (T_3) and thyroxine (T_4), and calcitonin.

thyroid-stimulating hormone (TSH) A tropic hormone produced and secreted by the anterior pituitary that regulates the release of thyroid hormones.

thyroxine (T_4) One of two iodine-containing hormones that are secreted by the thyroid gland and help regulate metabolism, development, and maturation in vertebrates.

Ti plasmid A plasmid of a tumor-inducing bacterium that integrates a segment of its DNA into the host chromosome of a plant; frequently used as a carrier for genetic engineering in plants.

tidal volume The volume of air an animal inhales and exhales with each breath.

tight junction A type of intercellular junction in animal cells that prevents the leakage of material between cells.

tissue An integrated group of cells with a common function, structure, or both.

tissue system One or more tissues organized into a functional unit connecting the organs of a plant.

tonicity The ability of a solution to cause a cell within it to gain or lose water.

tonoplast A membrane that encloses the central vacuole in a plant cell, separating the cytosol from the vacuolar contents, called cell sap; also known as the vacuolar membrane.

top-down model A model of community organization in which predation controls community organization because predators control herbivores, which in turn control plants, which in turn control nutrient levels; also called the trophic cascade model.

topoisomerase A protein that functions in DNA replication, helping to relieve strain in the double helix ahead of the replication fork.

topsoil A mixture of particles derived from rock, living organisms, and humus.

torpor In animals, a physiological state that conserves energy by slowing down metabolism.

torsion A characteristic of gastropods in which the visceral mass rotates during development.

totipotent Describing a cell that can give rise to all parts of an organism.

trace element An element indispensable for life but required in extremely minute amounts.

trachea (trā-kē-uh) The windpipe; that portion of the respiratory tube that has C-shaped cartilaginous rings and passes from the larynx to two bronchi.

tracheal system A gas exchange system of branched, chitin-lined tubes that infiltrate the body and carry oxygen directly to cells in insects.

tracheid (trā-kē-id) A long, tapered water-conducting cell that is dead at maturity and is found in the xylem of all vascular plants.

trait Any detectable variation in a genetic character.

trans Arrangement of two noncarbon atoms, each bound to one of the carbons in a carbon-carbon double bond, where the two noncarbon atoms are on opposite sides relative to the double bond.

transcription The synthesis of RNA on a DNA template.

transcription factor A regulatory protein that binds to DNA and stimulates transcription of specific genes.

transcription initiation complex The completed assembly of transcription factors and RNA polymerase bound to the promoter.

transcription unit A region of a DNA molecule that is transcribed into an RNA molecule.

transduction (1) A DNA transfer process in which phages carry bacterial genes from one host cell to another. (2) In cellular communication, the conversion of a signal from outside the cell to a form that can bring about a specific cellular response.

transfer cell A companion cell with numerous ingrowths of its wall, increasing the cell's surface area and enhancing the transfer of solutes between apoplast and symplast.

transfer RNA (tRNA) An RNA molecule that functions as an interpreter between nucleic acid and protein language by picking up specific amino acids and recognizing the appropriate codons in the mRNA.

transformation (1) The conversion of a normal animal cell to a cancerous cell. (2) A change in genotype and phenotype due to the assimilation of external DNA by a cell.

transgenic Pertaining to an individual plant or animal whose genome contains a gene introduced from another organism, either from the same or a different species.

translation The synthesis of a polypeptide using the genetic information encoded in an mRNA molecule. There is a change of "language" from nucleotides to amino acids.

translocation (1) An aberration in chromosome structure resulting from attachment of a chromosomal fragment to a nonhomologous chromosome. (2) During protein synthesis, the third stage in the elongation cycle when the RNA carrying the growing polypeptide moves from the A site to the P site on the ribosome. (3) The transport of organic nutrients in the phloem of vascular plants.

transmission The conduction of impulses to the central nervous system.

transmission electron microscope (TEM) A microscope that passes an electron beam through very thin sections, primarily used to study the internal ultrastructure of cells.

transpiration The evaporative loss of water from a plant.

transport epithelium One or more layers of specialized epithelial cells that regulate solute movements.

transport protein A transmembrane protein that helps a certain substance or class of closely related substances to cross the membrane.

transport vesicle A tiny membranous sac in a cell's cytoplasm carrying molecules produced by the cell.

transposable element A segment of DNA that can move within the genome of a cell by means of a DNA or RNA intermediate; also called a transposable element.

transposon A transposable element that moves within a genome by means of a DNA intermediate.

transverse (T) tubules Infoldings of the plasma membrane of skeletal muscle cells.

triacylglycerol Three fatty acids linked to one glycerol molecule.

triiodothyronine (T_3) (trī-ī-ō-dō-thī-rō-nēn) One of two iodine-containing hormones that are secreted by the thyroid gland and help regulate metabolism, development, and maturation in vertebrates.

trilobite An extinct arthropod with pronounced segmentation and appendages that varied little from segment to segment.

trimester In human development, one of three 3-month-long periods of pregnancy.

triple response A plant growth maneuver in response to mechanical stress, involving slowing of stem elongation, a thickening of the stem, and a curvature that causes the stem to start growing horizontally.

triplet code A set of three-nucleotide-long words that specify the amino acids for polypeptide chains.

triploblastic Possessing three germ layers: the endoderm, mesoderm, and ectoderm. Most eumetazoans are triploblastic.

trisomic Referring to a cell that has three copies of a particular chromosome, instead of the normal two.

trochophore larva Distinctive larval stage observed in certain invertebrates, including some annelids and molluscs.

trophic efficiency The percentage of production transferred from one trophic level to the next.

trophic structure The different feeding relationships in an ecosystem, which determine the route of energy flow and the pattern of chemical cycling.

trophoblast The outer epithelium of the blastocyst, which forms the fetal part of the placenta.

tropical rainforest A terrestrial biome characterized by high levels of precipitation and warm temperatures year-round.

tropic hormone A hormone that has another endocrine gland as a target.

tropics Latitudes between 23.5° north and south.

tropism A growth response that results in the curvature of whole plant organs toward or away from stimuli owing to differential rates of cell elongation.

tropomyosin The regulatory protein that blocks the myosin-binding sites on the actin molecules.

troponin complex The regulatory proteins that control the position of tropomyosin on the thin filament.

true-breeding Referring to plants that produce offspring of the same variety when they self-pollinate.

tubal ligation A means of sterilization in which a woman's two oviducts (Fallopian tubes) are tied closed to prevent eggs from reaching the uterus. A segment of each oviduct is removed.

tube foot One of numerous extensions of an echinoderm's water vascular system. Tube feet function in locomotion, feeding, and gas exchange.

tumor-suppressor gene A gene whose protein products inhibit cell division, thereby preventing uncontrolled cell growth (cancer).

tundra A biome at the extreme limits of plant growth. At the northernmost limits, it is called arctic tundra, and at high altitudes, where plant forms are limited to low shrubby or matlike vegetation, it is called alpine tundra.

tunicate Member of the subphylum Urochordata, sessile marine chordates that lack a backbone.

turgid (ter'-jid) Very firm. A walled cell becomes turgid if it has a greater solute concentration than its surroundings, resulting in entry of water.

turgor pressure The force directed against a cell wall after the influx of water and the swelling of a walled cell due to osmosis.

turnover The mixing of waters as a result of changing water-temperature profiles in a lake.

turnover time The time required to replace the standing crop of a population or group of populations (for example, of phytoplankton), calculated as the ratio of standing crop biomass to production.

tympanic membrane Another name for the eardrum.

tyrosine kinase An enzyme that catalyzes the transfer of phosphate groups from ATP to the amino acid tyrosine on a substrate protein.

ultimate question In animal behavior, an inquiry that focuses on the evolutionary significance of a behavioral act.

ultrametric tree A phylogenetic tree in which the lengths of the branches reflect measurements of geologic time.

undernourishment A diet that is chronically deficient in calories.

uniformitarianism Charles Lyell's idea that geologic processes have not changed throughout Earth's history.

unsaturated fatty acid A fatty acid possessing one or more double bonds between the carbons in the hydrocarbon tail. Such bonding reduces the number of hydrogen atoms attached to the carbon skeleton.

urea A soluble nitrogenous waste excreted by mammals, most adult amphibians, sharks, and some marine bony fishes and turtles; produced in the liver by a metabolic cycle that combines ammonia with carbon dioxide.

ureter A duct leading from the kidney to the urinary bladder.

urethra A tube that releases urine from the body near the vagina in females and through the penis in males; also serves in males as the exit tube for the reproductive system.

uric acid An insoluble precipitate of nitrogenous waste excreted by land snails, insects, and many reptiles, including birds.

urinary bladder The pouch where urine is stored prior to elimination.

uterine cycle The changes that occur in the uterus during the reproductive cycle of the human female; also called the menstrual cycle.

uterus A female organ where eggs are fertilized and/or development of the young occurs.

utricle A chamber behind the oval window that opens into the three semicircular canals.

vaccination See immunization.

vaccine A harmless variant or derivative of a pathogen that stimulates a host's immune system to mount defenses against the pathogen.

vacuolar membrane A membrane that encloses the central vacuole in a plant cell, separating the cytosol from the vacuolar contents, called cell sap; also known as the tonoplast.

vagina Part of the female reproductive system between the uterus and the outside opening;

the birth canal in mammals; also accommodates the male's penis and receives sperm during copulation.

valence The bonding capacity of an atom, generally equal to the number of unpaired electrons in the atom's outermost shell.

valence electron An electron in the outermost electron shell.

valence shell The outermost energy shell of an atom, containing the valence electrons involved in the chemical reactions of that atom.

van der Waals interactions Weak attractions between molecules or parts of molecules that are brought about by localized charge fluctuations.

variation Differences between members of the same species.

vas deferens The tube in the male reproductive system in which sperm travel from the epididymis to the urethra.

vasa recta The capillary system that serves the loop of Henle.

vascular bundle (vas'-kyū-ler) A strand of vascular tissues (both xylem and phloem) in a stem or leaf.

vascular cambium A cylinder of meristematic tissue in woody plants that adds layers of secondary vascular tissue called secondary xylem (wood) and secondary phloem.

vascular cylinder The central cylinder of vascular tissue in a root.

vascular plant A plant with vascular tissue. Vascular plants include all living species except mosses, liverworts, and hornworts.

vascular tissue Plant tissue consisting of cells joined into tubes that transport water and nutrients throughout the plant body.

vascular tissue system A system formed by xylem and phloem throughout a vascular plant, serving as a transport system for water and nutrients, respectively.

vasectomy The cutting of each vas deferens to prevent sperm from entering the urethra.

vasocongestion The filling of a tissue with blood caused by increased blood flow through the arteries of that tissue.

vasoconstriction A decrease in the diameter of superficial blood vessels triggered by nerve signals that contract the muscles of the vessel walls.

vasodilation An increase in the diameter of superficial blood vessels triggered by nerve signals that relax the muscles of the vessel walls.

vegetal pole The portion of the egg where most yolk is concentrated; opposite of animal pole.

vegetative reproduction Cloning of plants by asexual means.

vein (1) In animals, a vessel that returns blood to the heart. (2) In plants, a vascular bundle in a leaf.

ventilation Any method of increasing contact between the respiratory medium and the respiratory surface.

ventral Pertaining to the underside, or bottom, of a bilaterally symmetrical animal.

ventricle (ven-truh-kul) (1) A heart chamber that pumps blood out of a heart. (2) A space in the vertebrate brain, filled with cerebrospinal fluid.

venule (ven-ūl) A vessel that conveys blood between a capillary bed and a vein.

vernalization The use of cold treatment to induce a plant to flower.

vertebrate A chordate animal with a backbone: the mammals, reptiles (including birds), amphibians, sharks and rays, ray-finned fishes, and lobe-fins.

vesicle A sac made of membrane inside of cells.

vessel element A short, wide, water-conducting cell found in the xylem of most angiosperms and a few nonflowering vascular plants. Dead at maturity, vessel elements are aligned end to end to form micropipes called vessels.

vessels Continuous water-conducting micropipes found in most angiosperms and a few nonflowering vascular plants.

vestibule The cavity enclosed by the labia minora; the space into which the vagina and urethral opening empty.

vestigial organ A structure of marginal, if any, importance to an organism. Vestigial organs are historical remnants of structures that had important functions in ancestors.

villus (plural, **villi**) (1) A fingerlike projection of the inner surface of the small intestine. (2) A fingerlike projection of the chorion of the mammalian placenta. Large numbers of villi increase the surface areas of these organs.

viral envelope A membrane that cloaks the capsid that in turn encloses a viral genome.

viroid (vi-royd) A plant pathogen composed of molecules of naked circular RNA only several hundred nucleotides long.

virulent A term describing a pathogen against which a plant has little specific defense.

virulent phage A phage that reproduces only by a lytic cycle.

visceral mass One of the three main parts of a mollusc, containing most of the internal organs.

visible light That portion of the electromagnetic spectrum detected as various colors by the human eye, ranging in wavelength from about 380 nm to about 750 nm.

vital capacity The maximum volume of air that a respiratory system can inhale and exhale.

vitamin An organic molecule required in the diet in very small amounts. Vitamins serve primarily as coenzymes or parts of coenzymes.

vitamin D One of the fat-soluble vitamins. The active form functions as a hormone, acting in concert with parathyroid hormone in bone and promoting the uptake of calcium from food within the intestines.

vitreous humor The jellylike material that fills the posterior cavity of the vertebrate eye.

viviparous (vi-vip-uh-rus) Referring to a type of development in which the young are born alive after having been nourished in the uterus by blood from the placenta.

vocal cord One of a pair of stringlike tissues in the larynx. Air rushing past the tensed vocal cords makes them vibrate, producing sounds.

voltage-gated ion channel A specialized ion channel that opens or closes in response to changes in membrane potential.

vulva Collective term for the female external genitalia.

water potential The physical property predicting the direction in which water will flow, governed by solute concentration and applied pressure.

water vascular system A network of hydraulic canals unique to echinoderms that branches into extensions called tube feet, which function in locomotion, feeding, and gas exchange.

wavelength The distance between crests of waves, such as those of the electromagnetic spectrum.

wetland An ecosystem intermediate between an aquatic one and a terrestrial one. Wetland soil is saturated with water permanently or periodically.

white blood cell A blood cell that functions in defending the body against infections and cancer cells; also called a leukocyte.

white matter Tracts of axons within the CNS.

wild type An individual with the normal (most common) phenotype.

wilting The drooping of leaves and stems as a result of plant cells becoming flaccid.

wobble A violation of the base-pairing rules in that the third nucleotide (5' end) of a tRNA anticodon can form hydrogen bonds with more than one kind of base in the third position (3' end) of a codon.

xerophyte A plant adapted to an arid climate.

X-ray crystallography A technique that depends on the diffraction of an X-ray beam by the individual atoms of a molecule to study the three-dimensional structure of the molecule.

xylem (zī-lum) Vascular plant tissue consisting mainly of tubular dead cells that conduct most of the water and minerals upward from roots to the rest of the plant.

yeast Single-celled fungi that inhabit liquid or moist habitats and reproduce asexually by simple cell division or by the pinching of small buds off a parent cell.

yeast artificial chromosome (YAC) A vector that combines the essentials of a eukaryotic chromosome—an origin for DNA replication, a centromere, and two telomeres—with foreign DNA.

yolk Nutrients stored in an egg.

yolk plug Large food-laden endodermal cells surrounded by the blastopore of an amphibian gastrula.

yolk sac One of four extraembryonic membranes that support embryonic development; the first site of blood cells and circulatory system function.

Z lines The borders of a sarcomere.

zero population growth (ZPG) A period of stability in population size, when the per capita birth rate and death rate are equal.

zona pellucida The extracellular matrix of a mammalian egg.

zone of cell division The zone of primary growth in roots consisting of the root apical meristem and its derivatives. New root cells are produced in this region.

zone of elongation The zone of primary growth in roots where new cells elongate, sometimes up to ten times their original length.

zone of maturation The zone of primary growth in roots where cells complete their differentiation and become functionally mature.

zone of polarizing activity (ZPA) A limb-bud organizer region consisting of a block of mesoderm located where the posterior side of the bud is attached to the body.

zoned reserve An extensive region of land that includes one or more areas undisturbed by humans surrounded by lands that have been changed by human activity and are used for economic gain.

zoospore Flagellated spore occurring in chytrid fungi.

zygomycete Member of the fungal phylum Zygomycota, characterized by forming a sturdy structure called a zygosporangium during sexual reproduction.

zygosporangium In zygomycete fungi, a sturdy multinucleate structure in which karyogamy and meiosis occur.

zygote The diploid product of the union of haploid gametes in conception; a fertilized egg.

Index

3' end, DNA, 88, 89, 302*f*, 323
5' cap, DNA, **317**
5' end, DNA, 88, 89, 302*f*, 317, 323
30-nm fiber, 360, 361*f*
300-nm fiber, 360, 361*f*

A band, muscle, **1066**, 1067*f*
ABC model of flower formation, 734, 735*f*
Abdominal cavity, **827**
Abiotic components of environment, **1081**, 1086–87
   climate as, 1081
   distribution of organisms affected by, 1081*f*
   disturbances in communities as, 1171–75
   influence of, on aquatic biomes, 1092–93
   influence of, on populations, 1148–52
Abiotic stresses affecting plants, **811**
Abiotic synthesis
   of organic compounds, 59*f*, 513–14
   of polymers, 514–15
ABO blood groups, 462
   carbohydrates on red blood cell surface and, 129
   immune response to transfusions from, 915*t*
   multiple alleles as determiners of, 262*t*
Abortion, **983**
Abscisic acid (ABA), 798–99
   drought tolerance in plants and, 799
   seed dormancy and, 798, 799*f*
Absorption, **853**
   in animal food processing, 853, 859–61
   as fungal nutritional mode, 608–10
   in small intestine, 859–61
   of water and minerals by plant roots, 744, 745*f*, 746
Absorption spectrum, **187**
   determining, with spectrophotometers, 187*f*
   photosynthetically important, 187*f*
Abyssal zone, 1093*f*, **1097**
Acacia koa, phase change in shoot system of, 733*f*
Acanthocephalans (thorny-headed worms), 640*f*
Acanthodians, **680**
Acanthostega, 684*f*
Acclimatization, **839**
Accomodation in vision, **1059***f*
Acetic acid, 64*f*
Acetone, 64*f*
Acetylcholine as neurotransmitter, **1024***t*
Acetyl CoA, conversion of pyruvate to, in cellular respiration, **168***f*
Achillea (yarrow), 464*f*
Achondroplasia (dwarfism), 267
Acid, **53**–54
Acid chyme, **858**
Acid growth hypothesis in plants, 794, 795*f*
Acid precipitation, **55**–56
   deforestation and, 1199
   distribution of, in North America and Europe, 1201*f*
   effects on wildlife, 686
   human activities as cause of, 1201–2
   G. Likens on, 1078
   in United States, 1202*f*
Acid rain. *See* Acid precipitation
Acoelomates, **631***f*
Acquired characteristics, Lamarck's theory of, 441
Acquired immunity, **898**, 903–8
   active and passive immunization and, 914

antigen recognition by lymphocytes in, 903–5
cell-mediated immune response and humoral immune response as branches of, 908–14
innate immunity versus, 899*t*
lymphocyte development in, 905–8
overview of, 909*f*
Acquired immunodeficiency syndrome, **918**. *See also* AIDS (acquired immunodeficiency syndrome)
Acrosomal process, 988
Acrosomal reaction, **988**, 989*f*, 991*f*
Acrosome, **975**, **988**, 989*f*
Actin, **116**
   cell cleavage and, 226
   cytokinesis and, 226
   microfilaments, motility, and, 116, 117*f*, 118
   muscle contraction and, 117*f*, 1068*f*
Actin filaments. *See* Microfilaments
Actinopterygii (ray-finned fishes), 683
Action potential, **1018**
   changes in membrane potential and triggering of, 1017–18
   conduction of, 1020*f*, 1021
   graded potentials and, 1018*f*
   in plants, **810**
   production of, 1018–20
   refractory period following, 1020
   role of voltage-gated ion channels in, 1018, 1019*f*
   saltatory conduction and, 1021*f*
   sensory perception and transmission of, 1046–47
Action spectrum, **188**, **802**
   for photosynthesis, 187*f*, 188
Activation energy (E_A), 150, **151**, 152
   for exergonic reaction, 151*f*
   lowering barrier of, by enzymes, 152*f*
Activator, **356**, **365**
   eukaryotic gene expression and role of, 365, 366*f*
   prokaryotic gene expression and role of, 356
Active immunity, **914**
Active site, enzyme, **152**, 153*f*
   catalytic cycle and, 153*f*
   induced fit between substrate and, 152, 153*f*
Active transport, **134**–36, **738**
   cotransport, 136
   energy required for, 134
   maintenance of membrane potential by ion pumps and, 134–36
   passive transport compared with, 135*f*
Actual evapotranspiration, 1176, **1190**
   terrestrial net primary production and, 1190*f*
Adaptation. *See* Evolutionary adaptation
Adaptive immunity. *See* Acquired immunity
Adaptive radiation, **480**, 481*f*
   of Galápagos finches, 18*f*
   on Hawaiian Islands, 436, 480, 481*f*
Addition rule and Mendelian genetics, 258–59
Adenine (A), 88
   DNA structure and, 296*f*, 297*f*, 298*f*
Adenohypophysis (anterior pituitary), 949*t*, **950**, 951*f*, 952
Adenomatous polyposis coli (APC) tumor-suppressor gene, 373*f*, 374
Adenosine triphosphate. *See* ATP (adenosine triphosphate)
Adenoviruses, structure, 336*f*
Adenylyl cyclase, **210**, 1056
ADH. *See* Antidiuretic hormone (ADH)
Adhesion, **49**
   in ascent of xylem sap, 748*f*
   water transport in plants and, 48*f*

Adipose tissue, 61*f*, 76, **825***f*
   obesity and, 847*f*
   thermoregulation and, 835
Adrenal cortex, 958
Adrenal glands, **956**
   catecholamine hormones produced by, 956–58
   hormones secreted by, 949*t*, 956–58
   nervous system regulation of, 957
   steroid hormones produced by, 958
   stress and response of, 957*f*
Adrenaline. *See* Epinephrine
Adrenal medulla, 956–58
Adrenocorticotropic hormone (ACTH), **952**
Adult stem cells, 418*f*
Adventitious roots, **713**
Aerobic conditions, **174**
Afferent arteriole, **933**
Afghanistan, population age structure in, 1154*f*
Aflatoxins, 622
Africa
   cichlid fish speciation in Lake Victoria, 479, 480*f*
   human origins in, 705
   malaria and sickle-cell allele in, 466*f*
African-Americans, sickle-cell trait in, 267
African cichlid (*Neolamprologus tetracephalus*), 1107*f*
Agave, reproductive life history traits in, 1141*f*
Age structure of populations, **1154**–55
   in Afghanistan, Italy, and United States, 1154*f*
Agglutination of pathogens, 913
Aggregate fruit, **779**
Aging, cytokinins and retardation of plant, 797
Aglaophyton major, 584*f*
Agonistic behavior, **1126**, 1127*f*
Agre, Peter, 130
   on aquaporins and cell biology, 92–93
Agriculture. *See also* Crop plants
   angiosperms and, 605, 771
   Arabidopsis studies applied to, 711
   DNA technology applied in, 406–7
   hydroponic, 757*f*
   impact of, on freshwater ecosystems, 1200–1201
   impact of, on soil and nutrient cycling, 1200
   mycorrhizae and, 20, 767
   soil conservation and sustainable, 761–63
   symbiotic nitrogen fixation and, 766
Agrobacterium, 390, 542*f*
Agrobacterium tumefaciens, Ti plasmid from, 406, 407*f*
Agrostis tenuis (bent grass), 454*f*
Ahrens, Mitchell, 1113
AIDS (acquired immunodeficiency syndrome), 341, **918**, 1155
   drug therapy for, 918–19
   HIV infection and, 447–48, 918–19
Air circulation, global patterns of, 1089*f*
Alarm calls
   Belding's ground squirrel and, 1128
   social learning of, in vervet monkeys, 1131–32
Alarm signals, minnow response to, 1111*f*, 1116
Alaska, glacial retreat and ecological succession in, 1174*f*, 1175*f*
Albatross, 926*f*
   Laysan, 693*f*
   Salvin's (*Diomeda canta salvini*), 922*f*
Albizzia procera, biological augmentation project using, 1226
Albumin, 419
   regulation of gene expression for synthesis of, 367*f*
Alcohol(s), **64***f*
Alcohol fermentation, **175**

Aldehydes, 64f
Aldoses, 70f
Aldosterone, **937**
Aleuria aurantia, 616f
Algae
    alternation of generations in, 242
    blue-green (*see* Cyanobacteria)
    brown (phaeophytes), 560–62
    diatoms (bacillariophytes), 559–60
    fungi and (lichens), 621–22
    golden (chrysophytes), 560
    green (chlorophytes), 567–69
    life cycles, 242f, 562f, 569f
    photosynthesis in, 560
    red algae (rhodophytes), 567
    secondary endosymbiosis and diversity of, 551
Alimentary canal, **648**, 854f, **855**
    evolutionary adaptations in, 863f
    peristalsis in, 855
Alkaptonuria, 310
Allantois, 688, **1001**
Allee, W. C., 1146
Allee effect, 1146
Alleles, **254**. *See also* Gene(s)
    as alternate form of gene, 253–54, 255f
    for blood groups, 260
    codominant, 260
    complete dominance of, 260
    correlating behavior of chromosome pair with,
        276, 277f
    dominant, 254, 260, 261–62, 267–68
    elimination of, by bottleneck effect, 461
    fertilization and segregation of, as chance events,
        259f
    frequencies of, in populations, 455–62
    frequency of dominant, 261–62
    genetic disorders and (*see* Genetic disorders)
    incomplete dominance of, 260, 261f
    law of independent assortment of, 256–58, 274,
        275f
    law of segregation of, 253–55, 275f
    microevolution and change in frequencies of, 454,
        455–56, 459–70
    multiple, 262
    mutations in (*see* Mutations)
    natural selection and changes in frequencies of,
        460, 462–70
    recessive, 254, 283–84
    relationship between phenotype and dominance
        of, 261
    spectrum of dominance of, 260–62
Allergens, 916
Allergies
    anaphylactic shock and, 917
    histamine release and, 901, 916–17
    mast cells, IgE, and, 916, 917f
Alligators, 691f
    metabolic rate, 834
Allolactose, 355, 356
Allometric growth, **484f**
Allopatric speciation, 476f, 477, 480
Allopolyploidy, **478**, 479f, 480
Allosteric regulation of enzymes, **156f**–57
Almonds, 605
Alpha (α) helix of protein, **82f**, 85
Alpine pennycress (*Thlaspi caerulescens*), 763
Alternation of generations, **242**, **461**, **561**, **576**
    heteromorphic and isomorphic, 562
    in plants, 242f, 576f
    in protists (algae), 242f, 561–62
Alternative RNA splicing, **319**, **368**, 399
Altman, Sidney, 515
Altruism, **1128**–33
    Hamilton's rule and kin selection, 1130
    inclusive fitness and, 1129–31
    reciprocal, 1130–31
Alu elements, 376, 381
Alvarez, Walter and Luis, 520

Alveolates (Alveolata), 555–58
    apicomplexans, 555–56
    ciliates, 556–58
    dinoflagellates, 555
Alveoli, 555f, **887**
Alvin research submarine, 514f
Alzheimer's disease, 290, **1040–41**
Amacrine cells, 1061f, **1062**
Amborella trichopoda, 602f
Amebic dysentery, 564
American alligator (*Alligator mississipiensis*), 691f
American beech tree (*Fagus grandifolia*), climate
        change and range of, 1092f
American chestnut tree, diseases of, 1168
Amines, 65f
Amino acid(s), **78**. *See also* Protein(s)
    binding of tRNA to specific, 321f
    as essential nutrients, 849–50
    monomers, 78–80
    as neurotransmitters, 1024t, 1025
    polymers, 80
    of proteins, 79f
    sequence of, in polypeptides, 80–81
    triplet code for, 312–14
    twenty, of proteins, 79f
Aminoacyl-tRNA synthetase, **321f**
Amino functional group, **65f**
Ammonia, **927**
    hydrogen ions and, 54
    as nitrogenous waste, 927
    soil bacteria and production of nitrates from,
        763f, 764
Ammonites, **652**
Ammospermophilus harrisi (Harris's antelope squirrel),
        477f
Ammospermophilus leucurus (white-tailed antelope
        squirrel), 477f
Amniocentesis, **269**, 270f
Amnion, **1000**
Amniotes, **687–94**, **999**
    birds as, 691–94
    derived characters of, 688
    developmental adaptations of, 998–99
    early, 688
    mammals as, 694–701
    phylogeny of, 687f
    reptiles as, 688–94
Amniotic egg, 688f
Amoebas, **563**
    exchange with environment and body structure
        of, 821f
    movement of, 117f, 118
    phagocytosis feeding, 107, 564f
Amoeba sp., 564f
Amoebocytes, **642**
Amoebozoans, 564–66
    entamoebas, 564
    gymnamoebas, 564
    slime molds, 564–66
AMPA receptors, 1036, 1037f
Amphibians (Amphibia), **685–86**
    body axes in, 992, 993f, 1004
    breathing in, 888
    cadherins and formation of blastula in, 1003f
    circulatory system, 870f, 871
    cleavage in embryo of, 992, 993f
    decline in populations of, 686
    fate map of embryo of, 1004f
    frog skin color, 946
    gastrulation in, 995, 996f
    hearing and equilibrium in, 1053–54
    kidney adaptations in, 939f
    lateral line system in, 680, 1054
    metamorphosis in, 686f
    nitrogenous wastes of, 927f, 928
    orders of, 685f
    organogenesis in, 997f
    reproduction in, 967f
    thermoregulation in, 833, 837, 838

Amphipathic molecule, **124**
Amplification
    DNA, 391–92
    of cell signals, 214
    of genes, 371
    of sensory stimuli energy, **1046**
amp^R gene, 387f
Amygdala, 1034, 1035f
β-Amyloid, 1040, 1041
Amylopectin, 71, 72f
Amyloplasts, 110
Amylose, 71, 72f
Amylotrophic lateral sclerosis (ALS), 1069
Anabaena, 539
Anabolic steroids, 959f
Anabolism and anabolic pathways, **142**, 177
    products of glycolysis and citric acid cycle
        diverted to, 177
    protein synthesis as, 309–33
Anaerobic conditions, **174**
Anaerobic respiration, **539**
Anagenesis as evolutionary pattern, 472f
Analogy, homology versus, **493–94**
    parsimony principle and, 504f
Anaphase
    of meiosis, 244f, 245f
    of mitosis, **221**, 223f, 225f, 226f
Anaphylactic shock, **917**
Anatomy. *See* Animal anatomy and physiology; Plant
        structure
Anchorage dependence, **231**, 232f
Anchor cells, 426
Androgens, **958**
Anemia, 881. *See also* Sickle-cell disease
Aneuploidy, **285**
    of sex chromosomes, 287
Angina pectoris, 883
Angiosperms, **579**, 598–604
    agriculture and, 605, 771
    basal, 602
    body structure of, 713f (*see also* Plant structure)
    characteristics of, 598–601
    dicots and monocots, 602, 780f
    diversity of, 602–3f
    evolutionary links between animals and, 604
    evolution of, 601–2
    flower of, 598f (*see also* Flower)
    fossil, 601
    fruit of, 598, 599f, 778, 779f
    leaves, and classification of, 716f
    life cycle of, 599, 600f, 601
    phylogeny, 602f
    pressure flow as translocation mechanism in, 753f
    seed of, 593 (*see also* Seed)
    sexual reproduction in, 600f, 772f
    translocation in, 753f
    vascular tissue of (*see* Vascular tissue system)
Angiotensin II, kidney function, osmoregulation, and,
        937
Anhydrobiosis, **925**
Animal(s), 626–36
    anatomy and physiology of (*see* Animal anatomy
        and physiology)
    aquatic (*see* Aquatic animals)
    behavior of (*see* Behavior)
    bioenergetics of, 828–31
    body of, 630–33
    Cambrian explosion and diversity of, 526, 527f,
        629
    chemical signals in (*see* Chemical signals in animals)
    circulation (*see* Circulatory system)
    cloning of, 416–17
    cognition in, 1117–18
    defenses of (*see* Animal defense systems)
    definitions and characteristics of, 626–28
    development (*see* Animal development;
        Development)
    diseases in (*see* Diseases and disorders; Genetic
        disorders; Pathogens)

evolutionary links between angiosperms and, 604
evolution of, 628–30
excretion in, 927–39
gas exchange (see Gas exchange in animals)
homeostasis in (see Homeostasis)
human (see Human(s))
invertebrate (see Invertebrates)
land colonization by, 527, 573, 574, 575–79
movement in (see Motor mechanisms)
nervous system (see Nervous system)
nutrition (see Animal nutrition)
phylogeny and diversity of, 633–36
polyploid speciation in, 479f
polyploidy in, 286f
regulatory systems (see Animal regulatory systems)
reproduction in (see Animal reproduction)
sensory mechanisms (see Sensory mechanisms)
sexual life cycle in, 242f
stenohaline versus euryhaline, 923
territoriality in (see Territoriality)
transgenic, 406
vertebrate (see Vertebrates)
viruses of (see Animal viruses)
Animal anatomy and physiology, 820–43
bioenergetics and, 828–31
body plans and, 630–33
development and (see Animal development)
evidence for evolution in homologies of, 448–51
form and function of, 17f, 820
as intrinsic factor limiting population density, 1150
physical and environmental constraints on, 820–22
regulation of internal environment and, 831–33
tissue organization, 630–31
tissue structure and function, 823–27
Animal cell, 626–27
calcium ion maintenance in, 211f
cholesterol within membranes of, 126f
cytokinesis and cleavage in, 225f
dehydration in, 136
expansion of, 730
extracellular matrix in, 119f–20
fate of, during development process, 1003–8
glycogen storage in, 72f
intercellular junctions and, 120, 121f
meiotic division of, 244–45f
microvilli, 116, 117f
plasma membrane of, 127f
size of, compared with virus and bacterium, 335f
structure of generalized, 100f
water balance in, 132, 133f
Animal control systems. See Animal regulatory systems
Animal defense systems
acquired immune system as, 898, 903–14
chemical, 32f
innate immune system as, 898–903
lymphatic system and, 878–79
against predators, 32f
Animal development, 412–14, 627f, 987–1010. See
also Development
apoptosis in, 427–29
brain, 1028f, 1029
cell differentiation and, 420, 421f, 987
cell fate and fate mapping in, 1003–8
cell lineage in, 426f
cleavage of zygote in, 627f, 978, 979f, 992–94
conservation of developmental genes, 431f, 432
cytoplasmic determinants of, 420, 421f, 423–25,
987
of embryo, 412–13, 414f, 485–86, 627f, 988–1001
epigenesis and animal form, 987
evolutionary novelty, 482–83
evolution of genes controlling, 484–86
fertilization, 978, 979f, 988
genomic imprinting and, 289, 364
hormonal regulation of insect, 960f
Hox genes and, 432f, 485–86, 627
induction and cell signaling in, 420, 421f, 1006–8
model organisms for study of, 412–13f
morphogenesis and, 987, 1001–3

nuclear transplantation and, 415–17
organogenesis in, 997f, 998f
overview, 987–88
pattern formation in, 421–29, 1006–8
plant development compared with, 414f, 433
transcriptional gene regulation during, 418–20
Animal growth. See Growth
Animalia (kingdom), 626. See also Animal(s)
Animal nutrition, 626, 855–66
carbon skeletons and essential nutrients provided
by diet, 849–52
evolutionary adaptations of vertebrate digestive
systems, 862–64
feeding categories, overview, 844
feeding mechanisms of animals, four types, 845f
food processing stages and, 853–55
homeostatic mechanisms for management of animal energy budget, 844–48
mammalian digestive system and organs and,
855–62
nutritional requirements, 33f, 34, 849–52
Animal pole, 992
Animal regulatory systems, 831–33
endocrine and nervous system overlap in, 943–44
(see also Endocrine system; Nervous system)
energy budget, nutrition, and, 844–48
excretory systems as, 927–39
homeostatic mechanisms, overview of, 832–33
hormonal controls, 860f, 943–63
interstitial fluid and, 831–32, 879f
in invertebrates, 959–61
osmoregulation, 132, 922–27
regulation of body temperature
(thermoregulation), 833–41
regulation versus conforming and, 832
thermoregulation, 833–41
water balance (osmoregulation) and waste
disposal, 132
Animal reproduction, 627, 964–86
asexual, 648–49, 964–65
cartilaginous fishes, 681
embryonic and fetal development in, 978–82
hormonal regulation of, 973–78
mammalian (human), 969–84
in placental mammals, 978–84
sexual, mechanisms of, 967–69
sexual, overview of, 964
sexual reproductive organs, 969–73
variations in cycles and patterns of, 965–66
Animal viruses
classes of, 340t
diseases caused by, 340t
reproductive cycles of, 339–42
RNA as genetic material of, 340–42
viral envelopes of, 340, 341f
Anion, 41
cotransport of, 740f
Annelids (Annelida), 640f, 653–55
classes of phylum, 653t
coelomate of, 631f
Hirudinea (leeches), 655f
hydrostatic skeleton in, 1063, 1064f
Oligochaeta (earthworms), 654f
Polychaeta (polychaetes), 655
Annuals, plant, 720
Anopheles mosquito, 555, 556f
Antelope squirrels (Ammospermophilus sp.), allopatric
speciation of, 477f
Anterior pituitary gland, 950
hormones secreted by, 949t, 951f, 952, 976f
Anterior side of body, 630
Anther, flower, 598, 772, 774
Antheridium (antheridia), 577f
Anthocerophyta (hornworts), 580, 582f
Anthozoans (sea anemones, corals), 644f, 645
Anthrax (Bacillus anthracis), 538f, 543f, 546
Anthroceros hornwort, 582f
Anthropoids (Anthropoidea), 697. See also Human
evolution

Antibiotics, 343, 898
action of, on prokaryotic cell walls, 535–36
action of, on prokaryotic ribosomes, 322, 537
bacterial resistance to, and R plasmids, 351
as enzyme inhibitors, 155
fungal production of, 623f
sponge production of, 643
Antibodies
immunoglobulins as classes of, 880, 912f
monoclonal, 913
polyclonal, 912
Anticodon, 320
protein synthesis, binding of RNA codons and, 320f
Antidiuretic hormone (ADH), 936, 951
kidney function and water balance regulated by,
936, 937f
secretion of, by posterior pituitary, 950f, 951
Antigen, 903
antibody-mediated disposal of, 913f, 914
B cell receptors for, 903–4f
B cell response to, 910–14
binding site for, 903f
clonal selection of lymphocytes in response to,
907–8
cytotoxic T cell response to, 910, 911f
epitope of, 903
helper T cell response to, 909–10
lymphocyte development and, 905–8
lymphocyte recognition of, 903–5
T cell receptors for, and role of MHC, 904f, 905
T-dependent, and T-independent, 912
Antigen presentation, 904, 905f
Antigen-presenting cells (APCs), 905
Antigen receptors, 903
B cell, 903, 904f
T cell, 904, 905f
Antimicrobial proteins, 900–901
Antioxidants, 188
Antiparallel, 89
Antiviral drugs, 343–44
Ants
as invasive species, 437
mutualism between acacia trees and, 1164f
symbiosis between fungus and leaf-cutting, 620f
Anurans (frogs, toads), 685. See also Frogs (Anura)
APC (adenomatous polyposis coli) tumor-suppressor
gene, 373f, 374
Aphotic zone, 1093
Apical dominance, 715
cytokinins and control of, 796f, 797
Apical ectodermal ridge (AER), 1007f
Apical meristems, 414, 576, 720
primary growth and, 576f, 720f–21, 722–25
Apicomplexans, 555, 556f
Apodans (caecilians), 685f, 686
Apomixis, 781
Apoplast, 743
Apoptosis (programmed cell death), 108, 427–29,
800, 902
cancer and failed, 373
cytotoxic T cells and, 911f
in human white blood cells, 428f
molecular basis of, in C. elegans, 428f
mouse paw development and effects of, 429f
natural killer cells and, 902
in plants, 800
Aposematic coloration, 1162f
Appendix, 862
Apple maggot fly, North American (Rhagoletis
pomonella), 479
Aquaporins, 130, 131, 133, 742
P. Agre on discovery and function of, 92–93
water transport and, 742
Aquarium as ecosystem, 1184f
Aquatic animals. See also Fish(es); Marine animals
body plan of, and swimming, 821f
gas exchange and gills in, 884, 885f, 886f
lateral line system in select, 680, 1054f
nitrogenous waste of, 927f

osmoregulation in, 923f, 924–25
thermoregulation in, 833, 834f, 835, 836f, 837f
Aquatic biomes, 1092–97
coral reefs, 1097f
distribution of, 1092f
estuaries, 1095f
freshwater, 1093f, 1094f, 1095f
human impact on, 1200–1201
intertidal zone, 1096f
lakes, 1094f
marine, 1093f, 1096f, 1097f
marine benthic zone, 1097f
ocean pelagic, 1096f
streams and rivers as, 1095f
wetlands, 1094f
zonation in, 1093f
Aquatic ecosystems
freshwater, 1187f, 1188–91
marine, 1166f, 1187f, 1188–90
nutrient enrichment of, 1200–1201
Aqueous humor, 1059
Aqueous solution, 51
concentration of solute in, 52–53
pH of select, 54f
Arabidopsis thaliana, 728
auxin transport in, 795f
brassinosteroid deficiency in, 798
clock mutants, 805
ethylene triple response in, 800f
fass mutants, and growth of, 730, 731f
genome of, 400, 729f, 802
gnom mutant, and axial polarity of, 732f
homeobox genes in, 432
as model organism, 413f
normal and abnormal flowering in, 734f
N. Raikhel on systems biology and study of, 710–11
responses to light and photoreceptors, 791, 802, 804
root gravitropism in, 809
thigmomorphogenesis in, 809f
Arachnids (scorpions, spider, mites), 641f, 658, 659f
Araschnia levana (map butterflies), 462f
Arbuscular mycorrhizae, 615f
Archaea (domain), 13, 14f, 98, 507, 521, 534. See also Prokaryotes
compared with Bacteria and Eukarya, 541t
Archaefructus liaoningensis, 601f
Archaefructus sinensis, 601f
Archaeopteris, 596f
Archaeopteryx fossil, 693f
Archegonium (archegonia), 577
Archenteron, 631, 632, 995
Archosaurs, 689
Ardipithecus ramidus, 703
Arginine
biosynthesis, 310, 311f
genetic recombination of bacteria synthesizing, 347f
Arginine-vasopressin (AVP), 1113
Argyroxiphium sandwicense, 481f
Aristotle, 439, 756
Arnold, Stevan, 1118–19
Arousal, human brain and state of, 1029–30
Art
as human characteristic, 706f
Paleolithic, in Lascaux, France, 1230f
Arteries, 869
blood flow velocity through, 875f
countercurrent heat exchanger in, 836f
diseases and blockages in, 883f
structure and function of, 874, 875f
Arterioles, 869, 875f
Arthrobotrys fungus, 610f
Arthropods (Arthropoda), 640f, 656–65
characteristics of, 656–58
cheliceriforms (spiders, mites), 658, 659f
circulatory system of, 657
crustaceans (lobsters, crabs), 657f, 658t, 664–65
exoskeleton of, 74f, 657f, 1064
hexapoda (insects), 658t, 660–64

myriapods (millipedes, centipedes), 658t, 659–60
nervous sytem, 1012f
subphyla of, 658t
Artificial chromosomes, bacterial, 396
Artificial selection, 445
plant breeding and, 764, 783–84
of vegetables from wild mustard, 445f
Asci (ascus), 616
Ascocarps, 616
Ascomycetes (Ascomycota), 616–17
examples of, 616f
life cycle of, 617f
as pathogen, 622
Asexual reproduction, 239, 781, 964. See also Clone; Cloning
in animals, 649
in bacteria, 226, 227f, 346, 537
in fungi, 611–12
in hydra, 239f
mechanisms of, 964–65
in seed plants, 781–83
sexual reproduction compared with, 239
A site, tRNA binding, 322f
Aspen trees, asexual reproduction in, 781f
Aspergillus mold, 622, 623
Assisted reproductive technology (ART), 984
Association areas, 1032
Associative learning, 1116–17
Aster (microtubule), 221, 222f
Asteroid, mass extinctions and indications of, 520f
Asteroidea (sea stars), 666t, 667f
Astrocytes, 1015f
Asymmetrical cell division, 730
Atherosclerosis, 76, 883
Athyrium filix-femina lady fern, 587f
Atmosphere
carbon dioxide concentrations in, 1203–5
depletion of ozone in upper, 1205–6
effect of human activities on (see Human environmental impact)
global air circulation and winds in, 1089f
greenhouse effect in, and global warming, 1204–5
organic compounds and Earth's earliest, 59f, 513–14
origins of oxygen in, 522–23
Atom(s), 34–39
chemical bonding of, 39–42
electron configuration and chemical properties, 37–38
electron orbitals of, 37f, 38–39
electron transfer between, and ion formation, 41f
energy levels of electrons in, 36–37
isotopes, 35–36
number and mass of, 34–35
subatomic particles, 34
tracking, through photosynthesis, 183, 184f
valence, 40
Atomic mass, 35
Atomic mass unit (amu), 34
Atomic nucleus, 34
Atomic number, 34–35
ATP (adenosine triphosphate), 66
active transport and, 134
allosteric regulation of enzymes and role of, 156
animal nutrition and, 844, 846
bioenergetics and, 828, 844, 846
Calvin cycle and conversion of carbon dioxide to glucose using, 193–95
catabolic pathways and, 161
cellular respiration and synthesis of, 170–72, 173f, 174
cellular work powered by, 149f–150
citric acid cycle and synthesis of, 168–70
dynein "walking" powered by, 116f
energy coupling by using hydrolysis of, 149f
fermentation and production of, 174–76
glycolysis and synthesis of, 165–67
hydrolysis of, 148f, 149
metabolic rate and, 830

oxidative phosphorylation and synthesis of 164–65, 170–74
photosynthetic light reactions and synthesis of, 184, 185f, 190–91, 193f
regeneration of, 150
structure of, 148f, 149
ATP cycle, 150f
ATP synthase, 171
ATP synthesis in cellular respiration and, 171–73, 192
Atria (atrium), heart, 869
Atrial natriuretic factor (ANF), 938
Atrioventricular (AV) node, 874
Atrioventricular (AV) valve, 873
Auditory communication, 1111–12
Aurelia sp., internal transport in, 868f
Australia
distribution and abundance of red kangaroos in, 1081f
marsupials and monotremes of, 695, 696f
Australian thorny devil lizard (Moloch horridus), 691f
Australopithecus afarensis, 703, 704f
Australopithecus africanus, 703
Australopithecus anamensis, 702–3
Autoimmune diseases, 917
Type I diabetes mellitus as, 956
Autonomic nervous system, 1027
neurotransmitters in, 1025
sympathetic division of, 957
Autophagy, 107–8
lysosomes and, 107f
Autopolyploidy, 478f
Autosomes, 240
Autotrophs, 181, 538, 539t
Auxin, 794–97
cell elongation, plant growth, and, 791, 792, 793f, 794, 795f
fruit growth and, 797
as herbicides, 795–96
lateral and adventitious root formation and, 795
polar transport of, 794, 795f
secondary growth in plants and, 796
Average heterozygosity, 463
Avery, Oswald, DNA studies by, 294
Avirulence (avr) gene, 813, 814f
Avirulent pathgens, 813
plant response to, 814f, 815f
Avogadro's number, 52
Axelrod, Robert, 1130
Axillary bud, 715
Axis establishment in early development, 423–25
Axolotl, 485f
Axon(s), 1014
action potentials conducted along, 1020f, 1021
migration of vesicles to tips of neuron, 112f
molecular signals directing growth of developing, 1038f
myelinated, 1015f
Axon hillock, 1014

Bacillariophytes (diatoms), 559–60
Bacillus coagulans, 98f
Bacillus thuringiensis, 784
Backbone, as homologous structure, 498
Bacteria. See also Prokaryotes; Prokaryotic cell
alcohol fermentation by, 175
antibiotic action on, 535–36
antibiotic resistance in, 535
binary fission in, 226, 227f, 346, 537
cell walls of, 534–36
compared with Archaea and Eukarya, 541t
as decomposers, 544, 1186
disease-causing (see Pathogens)
DNA replication in, 300–305
DNA transformation of, in F. Griffith experiments, 294
expression systems, 390
gene expression in, regulation, 352–56
genetic recombination in, 346–51

Index

genome, 346–56, 374, 537
major groups of, 542–43f
metabolism and nutrition in, 538–40
motility of, 536f, 537
nitrogen fixation by, 763f, 764–66
photosynthesis in, 184
plasmids of (see Plasmids)
regulation of metabolic pathways in, 352–56
reproduction and adaptation in, 537–38
size of, 98, 335f
structure, 98f
translation and transcription coupled in, 328f
transposable genetic elements in, 351–52
ulcer-causing, 858f
viral infection of (see Bacteriophage (phage))
Bacteria (domain), 13, 14f. 98, 507f, 521, 534, 541t
Bacterial artificial chromosome (BAC), 396
Bacterial chromosome, replication of, 346, 347f
Bacterial mats, 522f
Bacterial plasmid. See Plasmids
Bacteriophage (phage), 294–96, 336
bacteria infected by virus, 295f
as cloning vector, 388
genetic recombination by bacterial transduction
due to, 348–49
genomic libraries of, 389f
Hershey and Chase experiment on bacterial infec-
tion by, 294, 295f, 296
phage λ, 338, 339f
prophage, 339, 349
reproductive (lytic and lysogenic cycles) of, 337,
338f, 339f
T2, infection of E. coli by, 294, 295f
T4, 334f, 336f, 338f
temperate, 338, 349
Bacteriorhodopsin, transmembrane protein structure
in, 128f
Bacteroid, 764
in soybean roots, 765f
Bacteroides thetaiotaomicron, 545
Baculum, 972
Balanced polymorphism, 466
Balancing selection, 466–68
Baleen, 845f
Ball-and-socket joint, 1065f
Banana slug (Ariolimus californicus), 1119f
Bandicoot, 696
Bannertail kangaroo rat (Dipodomys spectabilis), 939f
Bark, 727f, 728
Barnacles, 664f–65
competition between species of, 1160f
Barn swallows, 693f
Barr body, 284
Barrier methods of contraception, 983
Bartholin's glands, 970
Basal angiosperms, 602
Basal body, 114, 115f
Basal metabolic rate (BMR), 829
Basal nuclei, 1031
Base(s), 54
Base(s), nitrogenous. See Nitrogenous bases
Basement membrane, 824
Basidiocarps, 618
Basidiomycetes (Basidiomycota), 618f–19
life cycle, 619f
Basidium, 618
Basilar membrane, 1052f, 1053f
Basophils, 880f, 881
Bat(s)
disruption of interaction networks involving,
1214, 1215f
excretory system of vampire, 938f
form and function in anatomy of, 17f
as pollinators, 604f
predation using sonar by, 1045f
Bates, Henry, 22
Batesian mimicry, 1162f
B cell receptors, 903
for antigens, 903, 904f

B cells. See B lymphocytes (B cells)
Bdellovibrio bacteria, 542f
Beadle, George, one gene-one enzyme hypothesis of,
310, 311f
Beagle, H.M.S., Charles Darwin's voyage on, 441, 442f
Bean (Phaseolus vulgaris)
germination of, 780f
seed of, 778f
sleep movements in, 805f
Bears, 465
classification of American black, 13f
extinction vortex and case study of grizzly, 1217–18
Beaver (Castor canadensis)
as foundation species, 1169f, 1214
kidney, 939f
Bees, 22f, 661
chemical signals among, 111
cognitive maps of, 1116
cuckoo, 1162f
learning in, 1117
as pollinator, 604f
reproductive anatomy of, 969f
thermoregulation in, 836–37
Beetle
bombardier, 32f
Hercules scarab, 1080f
Behavior, 1107
agonistic, 1126, 1127f
altruistic, 1128–33
bird songs and, 1111, 1118
cognition in animals and, 1117–18
communication methods and, 1111–12
competitive, 160–61
courtship and mating, 1106
defined, 1107
ethology as study of, 1107–9
foraging, 1119, 1120, 1122–23
genetic component of, 1109–13
genetic and environmental interaction resulting
in, 1113–18
imprinting, 1108, 1109f
mating behaviors in, 1123–27
natural selection and, 1118–28
parental (see Parental behavior)
proximate and ultimate causes of, 1106, 1107,
1108f, 1109f
as reproductive barrier, 474f
sensory input and, 1063–64
social, 1128–33
species distribution, habitat, and, 1085
thermoregulation and responses of, 837–38
Behavioral ecology, 1106–35
altruistic behavior and, 1128–33
genetics and, 1109–13
genetics and environment interactions resulting in
behaviors, 1113–18
natural selection and, 1118–28
overview, 1106
proximate and ultimate causes of behavior and,
1106–9
Behavioral isolation as prezygotic reproductive
barrier, 474f
Behavioral variation in natural populations, 1118–20
in aggressive behavior, 1119–20
in prey selection, 1118–19
Beijerinck, Martinus, 335
Belding's ground squirrel (Spermophilus beldingi)
altruistic behavior in, 1128, 1130f
hibernation and thermoregulation, 840f
immigration of, 1138, 1151
life table for, 1139t
reproductive table for, 1141t
survivorship curves for, 1140f
Benign tumor, 232
Bent grass (Agrostis tenuis), 454f
Benthic zone, 1093f
in lakes, 1094f
in oceans, 1097f
Benthos, 1093

Benzer, Seymour, 1116
Bernard, Claude, 831
Berthold, Peter, 1110–11, 1121
Bertness, Mark, 1170
Berzelius, Jöns Jakob, 59
Bester-Meredith, Janet, 1114
β-Amyloid, 1040, 1041
β-Galactosidase, 335f, 387
β globin gene
evolution of, 379f
gene families for, 377f, 378
RNA processing in transcription, 318f
restriction fragment analysis of, 392, 393f, 394
beta oxidation, 177
β pleated sheet, protein, 82f, 85
Bicarbonate
ion (HCO_3^-), 55
produced by pancreas, 858
Bicoid gene and protein, effects of, 424f
Biennials, 720
Big-bang reproduction, 1141
Bilateral symmetry, 630
in animal body plan, 630f, 646
in flower structure, 773f
Bilaterians (Bilateria), 633, 646–50
Bile, 858
Binary fission, 226, 227f, 346, 347f, 537, 558
Binomial name, 496
Biochemistry, 97
Biodiversity, 12–15. See also Tree of life
as biological theme, 27f
in communities, 1165–66, 1175–78
conservation of (see Conservation biology)
hot spots for, 437, 1222
human activities and threats to, 1211–14
human welfare dependent upon, 1211–12
mass extinctions of, 518f, 520–21
nature reserves and parks for protection of, 1222–24
threats to, 606, 1211–14
three levels of, 1210f–11
unity in, 14, 15f
Biodiversity hotspot, 437, 1222
Earth's terrestrial, 1222f
Bioenergetics, 142, 828
in animal body, 828–31, 844–48
ATP and cellular work, 148–50, 828 (see also ATP
(adenosine triphosphate))
energy budgets and, 830–31
energy forms and, 142–43
enzyme activity and, 150–57
free energy, 145–48
gas exchange and, 884f
glucose and, 958
homeostasis and (see Homeostasis)
laws of energy transformation (thermodynamics),
143–44
metabolic pathways and, 141–42 (see also
Metabolism)
metabolic rate and, 828, 829–30
thyroid hormones and, 953
Biofilms, 539f–40
Biogenic amines as neurotransmitters, 1024t, 1025
Biogeochemical cycles, 1195–98
carbon, 1196f
generalized scheme for, 1198f
human disruption of, 1200–1206
nitrogen, 1197f
phosphorus, 1197f
water, 1196f
Biogeographic realms, 1083, 1084f
Biogeography, 450f, 1083
distribution of organisms and, 1083–92
as evidence for natural selection in, 450
of islands, 1177–78
Bioinformatics, 11, 819
Biological augmentation, 1226
Biological clocks, 1030
circadian rhythms and (see Circadian rhythms)
light and, in animals, 1030, 1031f

light and, in plants, 805, 806
pineal gland, melatonin, and, 959
Biological diversity. See Biodiversity; Tree of life
Biological Dynamics of Forest Fragments Project,
    Brazil, 1221
Biological magnification, **1202**
Biological order and disorder, 144
Biological organization, 3–6
    cell as basic unit of, 5f, 6–8
    ecosystems as level of, 4f, 6
    emergent properties in levels of, 9
    levels of, 4–5f
Biological species concept, **473–76**
    alternatives to, 476
    limitations of, 476
    reproductive isolation of gene pools and, 473,
        474–75f
Biology, 2
    conservation, 1209–32
    evolution as core theme of, 15–19
    forms of inquiry in, 19–26
    grouping of diverse species and life domains by,
        12–15
    organizational hierarchy of, 3, 4–5f, 6–8
    themes unifying, 26, 27f
    systems concept applied to, 9–12
Bioluminescence
    in bacteria, 545f
    in fungi, 141f
    in protists, 555
Biomass, **1168**
    standing crop of, 1187, 1194f
Biomass pyramid, 1192
Biomanipulation, **1171**
Biomes, **1092**. See also Ecosystem(s)
    abiotic factors affecting, 1086–87
    aquatic, 1092–97
    climate, 1098
    terrestrial, 1098–1104
Biophilia, 1230
Bioremediation, **546–47, 1226**
Biorhythms, 959. See also Biological clocks
Biosafety Protocol, 408
Biosphere, 4f, **1083**
    abiotic factors in, 1081, 1086–87
    autotrophs and heterotrophs in, 181
    biomes of, 1092–1104
    biophilia and future of, 1230
    human impact on, 1200–1206
    organisms in (see Organism(s); Species)
Biosynthesis, 177. See also Anabolism and anabolic
    pathways
Biotechnology, **384**, 783–86. See also DNA technology
Bioterrorism, 546
Biota, **1081**
Biotic boundary versus legal boundary of reserves,
    1222, 1223f
Biotic components of environment, **1081**. See also Organism(s); Species
    distribution of species affected by, 1085–86
    influence of, on aquatic biomes, 1092–93
    influence of, on populations, 1148–52
Biotic stresses affecting plants, **811**
Bipedal posture, human evolution and, 703–4
Bipolar cells in retina, **1061**f
Bipolar disorder, **1040**
Birds, 691–94
    bones of, 483
    circulatory system, 870f, 871
    cleavage in embryo of, 992, 993f
    countercurrent heat exchanger in, 836f
    courtship behaviors in, 1106f
    derived characters of, 691–92
    digestion in, 854f, 863
    edge-adapted species, 1221
    feathers and wings of, 692f
    feet, 694f
    finches (see Finches)
    flight in, 483, 692

    fossil, 693f
    gastrulation in embryo of, 995–96, 997f
    imprinting of graylag geese, 1108, 1109f
    kidney adaptations in, 939f
    learning and problem solving, 1117
    limb development in, 1007f
    living, 693–94
    migration of, 1106, 1109f, 1110–11
    nitrogenous wastes of, 927f, 928
    organogenesis in, 998f
    origin of, 692–93
    parental caregiving in, 1142f
    as pollinators, 604f
    respiratory system and breathing by, 889f
    salt excretion in marine, 926f
    songs of (see Bird songs)
    species-area curves for North American breeding,
        1177f
    thermoregulation in, 833, 836f, 838
    vision in, 1060
Bird songs, 1111
    E. Jarvis on genetics of, 818–19
    sensitive period for learning, 1118
Birth control pills, **983**
Birth rate in populations, per capita, 1143–44
Bivalves (Bivalvia), 652f
Black bread mold (Rhizopus stolonifer), life cycle of,
    614f
Blackcap (Sylvia atricapilla), 1110–11
    migratory patterns in, 1120, 1121f
Black mold (Stachybotrys chartarum), 623
Black rush (Juncos gerardi) as facilitator species, 1170f
Blacktip reef shark (Carcharhinus melanopterus), 681f
Blade, algae, **560**, 561f
Blade, leaf, **715**
Blastocoel, **992**, 993f
Blastocyst, **978**, 979f, **1000**
Blastoderm, **994**
Blastomeres, **992**
Blastopore, **632, 995**
    developmental modes and fate of, 632–33
    dorsal lip of, as induction organizer, 1006f
Blastula, **627, 992**
    cadherins and formation of frog, 1003f
    cleavage and creation of, 992f, 993f
    gastrulation and rearrangement of, 994
Blending hypothesis of heredity, 251
Blood, **825, 868**, 879–83
    capillary exchange between interstitial fluid and,
        875, 879f
    cellular elements in, 880f, 881
    clotting of, 880f, 882f
    composition of, 879, 880t, 879–82
    as connective tissue, 825f
    filtration of, by kidneys, 931, 932f, 933f, 934
    groups of (see ABO blood groups; Blood groups,
        human)
    osmolarity of, 936, 937f, 938
    pH of, 55
    plasma of, 879–80
    Rh factor in, 92, 915–16
    stem cells and, 881–82
    transfusions of, immune system and, 262, 915–16
    volume of, and cardiac output, 872–73
Blood-brain barrier, **1015**
Blood doping, 881
Blood electrolytes, 880t
Blood flow velocity, 875
    blood pressure and, 876f
    in veins, 875f
Blood fluke (Schistosoma manson), 30, 1163
    life cycle, 647f
Blood groups, human
    ABO, 129, 262t, 915t (see also ABO blood groups)
    M,N,and MN, 269
    multiple alleles and, 262f
    Rh factor and, 92, 915–16
    self-nonself recognition of, and blood
        transfusions, 915–16

Blood pressure, **868**, 876–77
    blood flow velocity and, 876f
    high (hypertension), 883
    measurement of, 877f
    norepinephrine and, 957
Blood transfusions, 262, 915–16
Blood vascular system in animals. See Circulatory system
Blood vessels, **868**, 869–70
    associated with nephrons, 933
    blood flow velocity in, 875f
    blood pressure in, 876, 877f
    structure and function of, 874, 875f
Blowfly (Phormia regina), taste in, 1055f
Bluegill sunfish, energy costs and benefits of feeding
    behavior in, 1122, 1123f
Bluehead wrasse fish, hermaphroditism in, 966f
Blue jays, studying effects of selection in populations
    of North American, 467f
Blue-light photoreceptors, 750, **802**
B lymphocytes (B cells), 881, **903**, 910–14
    antibody classes and, 912–13
    antibody-mediated disposal of antigens and, 913f,
        914
    clonal selection of, 907f, 908
    development of, 905f
    gene rearrangement in, 906f, 907
    humoral immune response and, 911f
    polyclonal and monoclonal antibodies and, 912, 913
    as receptors for antigens, 903, 904f
    response of, to extracellular pathogens, 910–14
Body cavity, **631**f
Body plan, 421, 630–33. See also Pattern formation
    acoelomate, coelomate, and pseudocoelomate, 631f
    animal development and, 987–88, 992, 993f
    axial polarity in plant, 731, 732f
    bilateral symmetry, 630f, 646
    body axes, 993f, 1004–5
    body cavities, 631f
    cnidarian, 643
    cytoplasmic determinants affecting animal, 420,
        421f, 423–25, 987
    exchanges with environment and, 821s, 822f
    homeotic genes and, 485–86
    molluscs, 650f
    physical laws constraining, 820, 821
    protostome versus deuterostome, 631–33
    segmentation, 425
    symmetry in, 630
    tissues and, 630–31
Body size
    metabolic rate and, 829
    skeleton and, 1064–65
Body temperature
    heart rate and, 874
    regulation of, 833–41
Bohr shift, **893**
Bolus, **856**
Bombardier beetle, 32f
Bond, Alan, 467f
Bone(s), **825**f
    of birds, 483, 692f
    as connective tissue, 825f
    mammalian jaw and ear, 695f
    origins of, 679, 680
Bone morphogenic protein (BMP-4), 1006
Bonnemaisonia hamifera, 567f
Bony fishes (Osteichthyes), 682–84
Boobies, blue-footed, 474f
Book lungs, **658**
Bormann, Herbert, 1078
Borneo, deforestation in, 1209f
Botswana, savanna community in, 1159f
Bottleneck effect, **461**f
    founder effect and isolation, 462
Bottom-up model of community organization, **1170**
Botulism (Clostridium botulinum), 206f, 339, 543f, 1069
Bound ribosomes, 102, 103f, 325
Boveri, Theodor, 274
Bowman's capsule, **931**, 932f

Boysen-Jensen, Peter, 792
Brachiopods (lamp shells), 640f, **649**
Bracts, 716f
Brain
  brainstem, 1028f, 1029–30
  cerebellum, 1030
  cerebral cortex, 1028f, 1029, 1031, 1032–37
  cerebrum, 1028f, 1031–32
  control of breathing by, 890
  development of embryonic, 1028f–29
  diencephalon, 1028, 1030–31
  evolution of chordate, 675
  human (see Human brain)
  injuries to, 1035, 1037–41
  mammalian, 694
  neural processing of vision in, 1062f, 1063
  primary motor and somatosensory cortices of, 1033f
  thalamus and epithalamus of, 1030
  ventricles of, 1026f
Brain hormone, **960**
Brainstem, 1028f, **1029**–30
Braithwaite, Victoria, 1113–14
Branchiostoma, 675f
Brassinosteroids, 791, **798**
Brazil, Biological Dynamics of Forest Fragments
      Project, 1221
BRCA1 and BRCA2 genes and breast cancer, 374
Bread mold (*Neurospora crassa*), 310, 311f, 616f
  life cycle, 617f
Breast cancer, 400
  genetic basis of some, 374
  growth and metastasis of malignant, 233f
Breathing, **888**–90
  in amphibians, 888
  in birds, 889f
  centers in human brain for automatic control of, 890
  in mammals, 888, 889f
  negative pressure, 888, 889f
  positive pressure, 888
Breathing control centers, **890**
Brenner, Sidney, 429
Briggs, Robert, 416
Brightfield microscopes, 96f
Bristlecone pine (*Pinus longaeva*), 595f
Brittle stars (Ophiuroidea), 666, 667f
Broad Institute, Eric Lander at, 236–37
Broca, Pierre, 1034
Broca's area, brain, 1034, 1035
Bronchi, **887**
Bronchioles, **887**
Brown algae (phaeophytes), 560–62
  alternation of generations in, 561–62f
  human uses of, 561
  structure, 560, 561f
Brown fat, **838**
Brush border, 858, 860
Bryophyta (division), 580
Bryophytes, 578t, 580–83
  diversity of, 582f
  ecological and economic importance of, 583
  gametophyte and sporophyte of, 580–81, 583
  L. Graham on evolution of, 510
  life cycle, 581f
Bryozoans (ectoprocts), 640f
Bt toxin, 784
Budding, asexual reproduction by, **965**
  in yeast, 611f
Buffers, **55**
Bulbourethral glands, **972**
Bulbs, 715f
Bulk feeders, 845f
Bulk flow, **743**
  in circulatory systems, 868, 878
  long distance transport in plants and, 743–44
  transport of xylem sap as, 748f, 749
Bulk transport across plasma membrane, 137, 138f
Bundle-sheath cells, **196**f, **724**
Burgess Shale, 629f
Burkitt's lymphoma, 370

Butterflies
  metamorphosis in, 661f, 943f
  nonheritable variation with populations of map,
      462f
Buttress roots, 714f

C_3 plants, **195**
C_4 plants, **196**
  anatomy and pathway of, 196f
  CAM plants compared to, 197f
Cacti, 749
Cactus ground finch (*Geospiza scandens*), 443f
Cadherins, **1002**
  role in development of blastula, 1003f
Caecilians (Apoda), 685f, 686
Caenorhabditis elegans (nematode)
  cell lineage of, 426f
  cell signaling and induction in, 425–26, 427f
  genome, 394, 399t, 400
  hydrostatic skeleton in, 1063
  as model organism, 412f
  programmed cell death in, 427–29
  as pseudocoelomate, 631f
Calcitonin, 954, **955**
  calcium homeostasis and, 954f, 955
Calcium
  cortical reaction in egg fertilization and role of,
      989, 990f
  deforestation and loss of soil, 1199
  hormonal control of homeostasis in, 954f, 955
  maintenance of calcium ions in animal cells, 211f
  muscle contraction and role of, 1068, 1069f
  neural chemical synapses and role of, 1022f
  regulation of blood concentrations of, in kidney, 934
  as second messenger, 211, 212f, 790
  storage of, in smooth ER tissue, 104–5
Callus, **782**
Calmodulin, 1072
Caloric imbalance, 846–48
Calorie, **49**, 828
Calvin, Melvin, 185
Calvin cycle, photosynthesis, **184**–85, 198f
  conversion of carbon dioxide to glucose in, 193,
      194f, 195
  cooperation between light reactions and, 185f
  role of G3P in, 194
Calyptra, 581f
Cambrian explosion, 526–27, **629**
Camel, role of fur in water conservation by, 926f
Camouflage, 446f
CAM (crassulacean acid metabolism) plants, 196, **197**
  C_4 plants compared to, 197f
cAMP. *See* Cyclic AMP
Campylobacter, 542f
Canavanine, 813
Cancer, 370–74
  abnormal cell cycle and, 370, 371–73
  breast, 232f
  cell-signaling pathways, interference with, 371,
      372f, 373
  colon/colorectal, 305, 373f, 374
  cytotoxic T cell response to, 910, 911f
  environmental factors and, 370
  faulty gene expression as cause of, 362
  inherited predisposition to, 374
  leukemia, 288f, 404, 882
  loss of cell cycle controls and, 232–33, 371–73
  multistep model of development of, 373f, 374
  mutations as cause of, 370, 330
  obesity and, 847
  oncogenes, proto-oncogenes, and, 371
  skin, 305f, 306
  tumor-suppressor genes, faulty, 371
  types of genes associated with, 370–71
  viruses as cause of, 370, 374
Candida albicans, 623
Cannibalism, population fluctuations and, 1151
Canopy, forest, **1098**
Canyon tree frog, cryptic coloration in, 1162f

CAP (catabolite activator protein), 356
Capases, 428
Capillaries, **869**
  as base of hypothalamus, 951
  blood flow through, 877, 878f
  blood flow velocity through, 875
  exchange between interstitial fluid and blood at,
      875, 879f
  structure of, 874, 875f
Capillary bed, **869**
  blood flow through, 877, 878f
Capsid, viral, **335**, 336f
Capsomeres, 335, 336f
Capsule
  bryophyte sporangium, **580**, 581f
  prokaryotic, **536**f
Carbohydrates, 69–74
  catabolism of, 161, 176, 177f
  cell-cell recognition and membrane, 129
  digestion of, 859f
  disaccharides, 70, 71f
  monosaccharides (sugars), 70
  polysaccharides (sugar polymers), 71–74
  role of membrane, in cell-cell recognition, 129
α Carbon, 78
Carbon, 58–67
  as backbone of biological molecules, 58
  formation of chemical bonds with, 59–61
  functional groups attached to compounds
        containing, 63–66
  organic chemistry and study of, 58–59
  valences of, 60f
  variations in skeletons of, 61f, 62, 63
  versatility of, in molecular formation, 59–63
Carbon cycle in ecosystems, 1196f
Carbon dioxide (CO_2)
  atmospheric, and climate change, 1196f, 1203–5
  atmospheric, in Carboniferous period, 588
  Calvin cycle and conversion of, to sugar, 193–95
  covalent bonding of, 60
  gas exchange in animals and disposal of, 750
  peat bogs and absorption of, 511
  plant guard-cell opening/closing and levels of, 751
  respiratory pigments and transport of respiratory,
      893f, 894
Carbon fixation, **185**
  alternative mechanisms of, 195–98
  Calvin cycle and, 185, 193–95
Carbonic acid, 54, 55
Carboniferous period, 596
  swamp forests of, 588f
Carbon monoxide (CO) as neurotransmitter, 1025
Carbon skeletons, 61–63
  animal diet and provision of, 844, 849–52
Carbonyl functional group, 64f
Carboxyl end, protein, 82f, 323
Carboxyl functional group, **64**f
Carboxylic acids, **64**f
Cardiac cycle, **872**, 873f
Cardiac muscle, **826**f, **1072**
  acetylcholine, G proteins and synaptic transmis-
      sions in, 1024
Cardiac output, **873**
Cardiovascular disease, 76, 847, **882**–83
Cardiovascular system, 869–71
  blood composition and function, 879–82
  blood flow velocity in, 875f
  blood pressure in, 876–77
  blood vessels of, 874, 875f
  diseases of, in humans, 76
  heart of, 868, 871–74
  lymphatic system and, 878, 879f
  metabolic rate and, 870
Caribou, 849f
  populations of, 455f
Carnivores, **844**
  digestive tract and dentition in, 862, 863f
  plants as, 767, **768**f
Carotenoids, **188**, 189

Carpels, flower, 429f, 430, **598**, **772**
Carrier proteins, 130
    facilitated diffusion and, 133, 134f
Carriers of genetic disorders, **266**
    testing to identify, 269
Carrots, test-tube cloning of, 782f
Carrying capacity, **1145**
    estimates of, 1155
    human ecological footprint and, 1155–56
Carson, Rachel, 1083f
Cartilage, **825**f
    vertebrate skeletons of, 678
Casparian strip, **745**
Castor bean (*Rincinus communis*), 778f
Cat
    cloning of, 417f
    four stages of food processing in, 853f
    X chromosome inactivation and, fur color in, 284f
Catabolism and catabolic pathways, **142**
    cellular respiration as, 142, 161–74
    connection of, to other metabolic pathways, 176–78
    fermentation as, 174–76
Catalyst, **77**, **150**. *See also* Enzyme(s); Ribozymes
Catalytic cycle, 78f
Catastrophism, **440**
Catecholamines, **957**
Cation, **41**
    membrane potential and uptake of, 740f
Cation exchange in soil, **760**, 761f
Catolite activator protein (CAP), 356f
Cattle egret
    distribution of, 1084
    mutualism between water buffalo and, 1164f
Caulerpa sp., 568f, 569
CD4 cell surface protein, **909**
CD8 cell surface protein, **910**
Cdks (cyclin-dependent kinases), **229–30**
cDNA (complementary DNA), **390**, 400
cDNA library, **390**
Cech, Thomas, 515
Cecum, **862**
ced-3 gene, 427–28
ced-4 gene, 427–28
ced-9 gene, 428
Celera Genomics, 398
Cell(s), 5f, 6–8, 94–123
    animal (*see* Animal cell)
    ATP and work performed by, 148–50, 828
    as biological theme, 27f
    cell fractionation and study of, 97
    cell-to-cell communication (*see* Cell signaling)
    differentiation of (*see* Cell differentiation)
    division of (*see* Cell division)
    eukaryotic, 8, 9f (*see also* Eukaryotic cells)
    heritable information in, 7f
    importance of, 94
    information flow in (DNA → RNA → protein),
        86f, 87
    membranes of (*see* Plasma membrane)
    microscopes and study of, 95–97
    morphogenesis and changes in shape of, 1001f
    motility of (*see* Cell motility)
    organization of genetic material in, 219
    plant (*see* Plant cell)
    programmed death of (*see* Apoptosis)
    prokaryotic, 8, 9f (*see also* Prokaryotic cell)
    protobionts as precursors to, 513, 515
    size of, compared with virus and bacterium, 335f
    size range of, 95f, 98
    surface-to-volume ratio of, 99f
    three types of work performed by, 148
    ultrastructure, 95
    water channel proteins of, 93
Cell adhesion molecules (CAMs), **1002**
Cell body (neuron), **1014**
Cell-cell communication. *See* Cell signaling
Cell-cell recognition
    membrane carbohydrates, and, 129
    membrane proteins and, 128f

Cell crawling during morphogenesis, 1001–2
Cell cycle, 218–35
    alternation of mitotic phase and interphase in,
        221–28
    cancer and abnormal, 232–33, 370, 371–73
    cell division, roles of, in, 218–20
    cell division and formation of daughter cells in,
        219–20
    cell division by binary fission and, 226–27
    cytokinesis in, 224–26
    defined, **219**
    phases of, 221f
    regulation of, by cytoplasmic signals, 228–33
Cell-cycle control system, **229–31**
    cancer as failure of, 232–33
    clock for, 229–30
    G_1 checkpoint in, 229f
    G_2 checkpoint in, 230f
    mechanical analogy for, 229f
    stop and go (internal and external signals) in,
        230–31
Cell death, programmed. *See* Apoptosis
Cell differentiation, **362**, **413**, **987**
    cell-cell signals and, 420, 421f, 429–30
    cell determination and, 418–20, 1003–8
    cytoplasmic determinants affecting, 420, 421f, 987
    determination of muscle cells and, 419f, 420
    embryonic development and (*See* Embryonic
        development)
    in plants, 732, 733f
Cell division, 218–28
    asymmetrical, 730
    binary fission as bacterial, 226, 227f
    cancer as uncontrolled, 232–33
    cellular organization of genetic material and, 219
    chromosome distribution during, 219–20
    cytokinesis and, 224–26
    daughter cells produced by, 219–20
    density-dependent inhibition of, 231, 232f
    embryonic development and role of, 218f
    functions of, 218f
    key roles of, 218–19
    mitosis and, 221, 222–23f, 224, 225f, 226f, 227–28
    plane and symmetry of, and plant morphogenesis,
        729f
    platelet-derived growth factor (PDGF) and, 231f
    preprophase band and plane of, 730f
    reproduction and role of, 218f
    tissue renewal and role of, 218f
Cell expansion, 730
    in plants, 731f
Cell fate in animal development, 1003–8
    blastopore dorsal lip, effect on, 1006f
    determination of, and pattern formation by induc-
        tive signals, 1006–8
    determination of, and transcriptional regulation of
        gene expression, 418–20f
    establishing cellular asymmetries, 1004–5
    fate mapping, 1004f
Cell fate in plant development, 732–33
Cell fractionation, **97**f
Cell lineage, **426**
    of nematodes, 426f
Cell-mediated immune response, 899f, 908, **909**
    cytotoxic T cell function against pathogens in,
        910, 911f
    helper T lymphocyte function in, 909, 910f
    overview of, 909f
Cell migration in animal morphogenesis, 1001–2
    role of fibronectin in, 1002f
Cell motility, 112, 114, 115f, 116f, 117f, 118f
    in animal morphogenesis, 1001f, 1002–3
Cell plate, 225f, **226**
Cell signaling, 201–17
    in animal development, 425–29, 1006–8
    cell differentiation and, 420, 421f, 429–30
    control of coordinate gene expression by, 367
    conversion of external signals into cell responses,
        201–4

efficiency of, 215
    in embryonic development, 420, 421f
    endocrine system and, 945–48
    evolution of, 201–2
    interference with normal, and development of
        cancer, 371, 372f, 373
    local and distant, 202f, 203f
    nerve cell development and, 1037, 1038f
    nervous system, neurotransmitters, and, 1021–25
    overview of, 201, 204f
    pattern formation in animal development, and
        inductive, 1006–8
    in plant development, 429–30
    responses to, through regulation or transcription,
        204, 212–15
    root nodule formation in legumes and role of, 766
    reception of signals, 204–8, 945–46
    signal amplification, 214
    signal transduction pathways in, 202, 208, 945–48
    specificity of, 214f
    termination of, 215
    three stages of, 203–4
    transduction and relay of signals to target cells,
        204, 208–12
Cell size, 335f
Cell-surface receptors for water-soluble hormones,
        946–47
Cellular energetics. *See* Bioenergetics
Cellular respiration, 142, 160, **161–80**
    anabolic pathways and, 177
    ATP synthesis in, 170–74
    catabolic pathways of, 161–65
    citric acid cycle of, 168, 169f, 170
    disequilibrium in, 147f
    electron transport chain in, 163f, 164
    as exergonic reaction, 146, 163f
    feedback mechanisms for regulation of, 177, 178f
    fermentation compared to, 175–76
    formula, 146
    glycolysis in, 165, 166f, 167
    mitochondria as site of, 109, 110f, 164–65, 168–74
    redox reactions in, 161–64
    stages of, overview, 164f, 65
    versatility of catabolism and, 176, 177f
Cellular slime molds, **565**
    life cycle of *Dictyostelium*, 566f
Cellulose, 52, **72**, 106, 558
    arrangement of, in plant cell walls, 73f
    bacterial digestion of, 74f
    cell expansion and orientation of microfibrils of,
        72, 73f
    structure of, compared with starch, 73f
Cell wall (plant), **118**, 119f
    transport in plants and, 743
    water balance and, 132, 133f
Cell wall (prokaryote), 534–36
    water balance and, 132
Celsius scale, 49
Cenozoic era, 519t, 521f, 629
Center for Conservation Research and Training,
        Hawaii, 436–37
Centipedes (Chilopoda), 659, 660f
Central canal of central nervous system, **1026**
Central nervous system (CNS), **1012**, 1026f
    brain, 1028–37
    central canal of, 1026
    injuries and diseases of, 1035, 1037–41
    oligodendrocytes of, 1015
    organization of vertebrate, 1012–13
Central vacuole, **108**f
Centrioles, **114**f
Centromere, **220**, 222f, 991
Centrosome, **114**f, **221**, 222f, 223f
Cephalization, **630**
Cephalochordates (Cephalochordata), 674, 675f
Cephalopods (Cephalopoda), 652, 653f
Ceratium tripos, 550f
Cercozoans (Cercozoa), 563
Cerebellum, **1030**

Cerebral cortex, 1028f, **1029**, 1031, 1032–37
  consciousness and, 1036–37
  emotions and, 1034–35
  information processing in, 1032–33
  language, speech, and, 706, 1034f
  lateralization of function in, 1033–34
  lobes of, 1032f, 1035
  memory, learning, and, 1035–36
  primary motor and somatosensory cortices of, 1033f
Cerebral hemispheres, **1031**
  lateralization of cortical function and, 1033–34
Cerebrospinal fluid, **1026**
Cerebrum, 1028f, 1031–32. *See also* Cerebral cortex
  hemispheres of, 1031f
Certainty of paternity, 1124–25
Certhidea olivacea(green warbler finch), 443f
Cervix, **970**
Cestoda (tapeworms), 646t, 648f
cGMP (cyclic GMP), 211, 790
Chagas' disease, 554
Chambered nautilus, 653f
Channel proteins, 130
  facilitated diffusion and, 133, 134f
Chaparral, 1101f
Chaperonin, 85f, 325
Chaperon protein, 85, 325
Character, genetic, **252**. *See also* Trait, genetic
  discrete, 463
  law of independent assortment and, 256–58
  law of segregation and, 253–56
  multifactorial, 264
  quantitative, 263, 463
Character displacement, **1161**
Characters
  shared derived, and shared primitive, 498
  table of, 499f
Chara sp., 574f
Chargaff, Erwin, experiments on DNA nucleotides by, 296
Chargaff's rules, 296, 298, 313f
  wobble and relaxation of, 322
Charophyceans, 567, 569
  evolution of land plants from, 510–11, 573–74
  examples of, 574f
Chase, Martha, experiments on genetic material by, 294, 295f, 296
Cheating and noncheating cells on cellular slime mold, 566
Checkpoints in cell-cycle control system, 229f, 230f
Cheetah
  energy transformations and metabolism in, 143f
  territoriality in, 1149f
Chelicerae, **658**
Cheliceriforms, **658**f, 659f
Chemical(s)
  as mutagens, 330
  protein denaturation caused by, 85
Chemical bonds, **39–43**
  of carbon, 59–63
  chemical reactions and, 44–45
  covalent, 39f, 40, 60
  hydrogen, 42
  ionic, 41f, 42
  van der Waals interactions and, 42
  weak, 42
Chemical cycling in ecosystems, 160f, 1184–86, 1195–98
  carbon cycle, 1196f
  decomposition and, 1185–86
  disruption of, by human population, 1200–1206
  general model of, 1195
  nitrogen cycle, 1197f
  overview, 1185f
  phosphorus cycle, 1197f
  regulation of, by vegetation, 1198–99
  role of prokaryotes in, 544
  trophic relationships as determinants of, 1185
  water cycle, 1196f
Chemical elements. *See* Element(s)

Chemical energy, 142. *See also* Chemical reactions
  conversion of light energy into, in photosynthesis, 182–85
Chemical equilibrium, **44**
Chemical markers of territory, 1149f
Chemical messengers, cell signaling using, 205. *See also* Signal transduction pathways
Chemical properties, electron configuration and, 37–38
Chemical reactions
  effects of enzymes on (*see* Enzyme(s))
  energy levels of electrons and, 36
  exergonic and endergonic, 146, 147f, 148, 149f
  free energy and, 146
  making and breaking chemical bonds in, 44–45
  reactants and products of, 44
Chemical signals in animals. *See also* Cell signaling
  animal communication behavior and, 1149f
  cell-surface receptors for, 946, 947f
  endocrine system and, 205, 943–44, 945f (*see also* Endocrine system)
  hormones as, 945–48, 949t, 951–59
  intracellular receptors for, 205f, 947
  local, 202–3
  nervous system and, 943–44, 945f, 1021–25 (*see also* Nervous system)
  neurosecretory cells as, 944
  neurotransmitters as, 947–48, 1024f, 1025
  paracrine signaling, 947–48
  pheromones as, 437, 610, 945
  signal transduction pathways initiated by, 1024
Chemical signals in plants. *See* Cell signaling; Plant hormones
Chemical synapses, 1021–25
  diagram of, 1022f
  direct synaptic transmission and, 1022–23
  indirect synaptic transmission and, 1023–24
  neurotransmitters in, 1024–25
  synaptic vesicles and, 1021
Chemical work, cellular, 148
  driven by ATP, 149f, 828
Chemiosmosis, **171**, **740**
  in chloroplasts, during photosynthesis, 110, 111f, 173
  in chloroplasts versus in mitochondria, 109–11, 173, 192–93
  in mitochondria, during cellular respiration, 109, 110f, 164–65, 171–73
  in prokaryotes, 521–22
  transport in plants and, 740
Chemistry, 32–46
  atomic structure and properties of elements, 34–39
  chemical bonding of atoms and molecule formation and function, 39–43
  chemical reactions, 44–45
  foundations of biology in, 32
  L. Makhubu on medicine and, 30–31
  matter, elements, and compounds, 32–34
  of metabolism (*see* Metabolism)
  molecular shape and biological function, 42–43
Chemoautotrophs, 538, 539t
Chemoheterotrophs, **539**t
Chemokines, **901**
Chemoreceptors, **1048**
  in insects, 1048, 1049f, 1055f
  for taste and olfaction, 1054–56
Chemotaxis, 537
Chemotrophs, 538–39
Cheny, Dorothy, 1131–32
Chesapeake Bay, partial food web for, 1167f
Chiasma, **247**
Chick embryo, homologous structures in human and, 449f
Chicxulub asteroid and crater, Caribbean Sea, 520f
Chief cells, 857f
Childbirth, 981f
  positive feedback mechanisms in, 833f
Chile, relationship between rainfall and herbaceous plant cover in desert community in, 1171f
Chilopoda (centipedes), 659, 660f

Chimeras, **430**
Chimpanzees, 701f
  cognition and problem solving in, 1117, 1118f
  skull of, 484f, 494
China
  birth rate and population growth in, 1154
  fossils found in, 676, 677f
Chinese river dolphin, 1211f
Chitin, **74**, **609**, **1064**
  in exoskeletons, 74f, 1064
  in fungal walls, 609
  medical uses of, 74f
  structure of, 74f
Chitons (Polyplacophora), 651f
  nervous system, 1012f
Chlamydia trachomatis, 543f
Chlamydomonas sp., 567, 568f, 569f
Chlorofluorocarbons (CFCs), atmospheric ozone depletion and, 1205–6
Chlorophyll(s), **182**
  chlorophyll a, **187**, 188, 189, 190
  chlorophyll b, **188**, 189, 190
  light reception by, 187f, 189
  photoexcitation of, 188, 189f
  structure of, 188f
Chlorophytes (green algae), 567–69, 575f
  colonial and multicellular, 568f
  life cycle of *Chlamydomonas*, 569f
Chloroplasts, **109**, 110, 111f
  capture of light energy by, 110, 111f
  chemiosmosis in mitochondria versus in, 109–11, 173, 192–93
  chlorophylls in, 182 (*see also* Chlorophyll(s))
  in green algae, 567
  green leaves as interaction of light with, 186f
  as site of photosynthesis, 109, 110, 111f, 182, 183f
  starch storage in, 71, 72f
  structure of chlorophyll in, 188f
Choanocytes, **642**
Choanoflagellates, 628f
Cholecystokinin (CCK), 860f
Cholera (*Vibrio cholerae*), 206f, 211, 542f, 546
Cholesterol, **77**
  diseases associated with, 882–83
  low-density and high-density lipoproteins of, 137, 883
  membrane fluidity and role of, 126f
  structure of, 77f
  transport of, 137, 882–83
Chondrichthyans, **680–82**
Chondrocytes, **825**f
Chordates (Chordata), 641f, **671**
  craniates as, 675–77
  derived characters of, 673
  early evolution of, 674–75
  fate mapping for two, 1004f
  invertebrate, 667
  lancelets as, 674, 675f
  nervous system, 1012f (*see also* Nervous system)
  phylogeny, 671, 672f, 673
  skeleton of, 1064, 1065f
  tunicates as, 673–74
Chorion, **1000**
Chorionic villus sampling (CVS), **269**, 270f
Choroid, 1058, 1059f
Chory, Joanne, 798
Christmas tree worm, 638f
Chromatids
  chiasmata of nonsister, 247
  crossing over of nonsister, 247
  sister, 219, 220f
  tetrad of, 247
Chromatin, **102**, **219**, 359
  DNA packing and structure of eukaryotic, 350–60, 361f
  euchromatin and heterochromatin in, 360
  nuclear transplantation and changes in, 416
  nucleosomes of, 360, 361f

structural modifications of, as regulation of
　　eukaryotic gene expression, 363–64
Chromatium, 542f
Chromoplasts, 110
Chromosomal basis of inheritance, 274–92
　　alterations of chromosomes, genetic disorders,
　　　and, 285–88
　　behavior of chromosomes, and Mendelian
　　　inheritance, 274–77
　　linked genes and, 277–82
　　locating genes on chromosomes and, 274
　　select inheritance patterns as exceptions to theory
　　　of, 288–90
　　sex-linked genes and, 282–84
Chromosome(s), 98, 102, **102**, 219. *See also* DNA
　　(deoxyribonucleic acid); Gene(s)
　　alterations in structure of, 286f, 287, 288
　　bacterial, 226, 227f, 346, 347f
　　bacterial artificial, 396
　　during cell division, 218f, 219, 220f
　　chromatin in (*see* Chromatin)
　　description and terms related to, 241f
　　distribution of, to daughter cells during mitosis,
　　　219, 220f, 222–23f, 225f
　　eukaryotic, 219f, 359f
　　extra set of (polyploidy), 285, 378
　　gene locus on, 239
　　genetic disorders due to structural alterations of, 288
　　genetic maps of, 279–81
　　genetic recombination and, 278–79, 280f
　　independent assortment of, 247, 248f, 274, 275f,
　　　278
　　homologous, 240 (*see also* Homologous
　　　chromosomes)
　　karyotype of, 240f
　　locating genes on, 274
　　Mendelian inheritance based in behavior of, 274–77
　　mutations in, leading to genetic variation, 463–64
　　nondisjunction of, 285f–86
　　number of human (*see* Chromosome number in
　　　humans)
　　Philadelphia, 288
　　prokaryotic, 537f
　　reduction of, from diploid to haploid during
　　　meiosis, 242, 243–47
　　sex, 282–83 (*see also* X chromosome; Y
　　　chromosome)
　　translocations of, 286f, 287, 288f, 459
　　"walking" of, during mitosis, 224, 225f
Chromosome number in humans, 102, 240–41
　　abnormal, 285f–86
　　aneuploidy and polyploidy, 285, 378
　　genetic disorders caused by alteration of, 285–88
　　reduction of, by meiosis, 243–47
　　in somatic cells, 219, 240
Chromosome theory of inheritance, **274–77**
　　exceptions to, 288–90
　　Mendelian inheritance related to, 274, 275f,
　　　276–77 (*see also* Mendelian inheritance)
　　T.H. Morgan's experimental evidence supporting,
　　　276–77
　　sex chromosomes and, 285–88
Chronic myelogenous leukemia (CML), 288f
Chrysophytes (golden algae), 560
Chylomicrons, 861f
Chytridium, 613f
Chytrids (Chytridiomycota), **613**
Cichlid fishes
　　speciation in, 479, 480f
　　territoriality in, 1107f
Cilia, 15f, **114–16**
　　dynein "walking" and movement of, 116f
　　motion of, 115f
　　ultrastructure of, 115f
Ciliary body, **1059**
Ciliates, 550f, **556**, 557f, 558
Circadian rhythms, **751**, **805**
　　in animals, 1030–31
　　in plants, 751, 805

Circular DNA, 289
Circulatory system, 867–83
　　adaptations of, for thermoregulation, 835–37
　　amphibian, 870f, 871
　　animal phylogeny reflected in, 867–71
　　arthropod, 657
　　blood composition and function, 879–82
　　blood flow velocity, 875f
　　blood pressure, 876–77
　　blood vessels, 874, 875f
　　capillary function, 877–78
　　closed, 868, 869f
　　diseases of, in humans, 882–83
　　double, in mammals, 871–74
　　in fish, 870f, 871
　　heart, 871–74
　　human, 871–83
　　invertebrate, 868–69
　　gas exchange and, 885, 891–95
　　lymphatic system and, 878–79
　　mammalian, 870f, 871–83
　　open, 657, 868, 869f
　　physical principles governing, 874–79
　　placenta, and fetal, 980f
　　reptile, 870f, 871
　　vertebrate, 869–71
Cisternae of golgi apparatus, 105, 106f
Cisternal maturation model, 106
Citric acid cycle, **164**, 168–70
　　connection of, to other metabolic pathways, 176–78
　　junction between glycolysis and, 168f
　　overview, 168f
　　steps of, 169f
Clade(s), **497**
　　grades versus, 630
　　lizard-bird, 504f
　　mammal-bird, 504f
　　plant kingdom, 575f
Cladistics, **497**, 498
Cladogenesis as evolutionary pattern, 472f
Cladogram, **497**
　　construction of, 499f
Clams, 639f, 652
　　anatomy of, 652f
Clark's nutcrackers (*Nucifraga columbiana*), 1116
Class (taxonomy), **496**
Classical conditioning, **1116–17**
Classification of life, 12, 13f, 14–15. *See also* Taxonomy
Claviceps purpurea, 622
Clayton, David, 818
Cleavage, 224–26, **627**, **978**, **992**
　　in amphibian, 992, 993f
　　in animal cells, 225f, 627f, 978, 979f, 992–94
　　in bird embryo, 994f
　　cleavage of zygote, 627f, 978, 979f, 992–94
　　cytokinesis and, 224, 225f, 226
　　in frog embryo, 992, 993f
　　gray crescent, distribution at first, 1005f
　　in human zygote, 978, 979f, 999, 1000f
　　in mammals, 999, 1000f, 1001
　　meroblastic, and holoblastic, 994
　　in plant cells, 225f
　　in protostomes versus deuterostomes, 631–32
　　in sand dollar embryo, 992f
Cleavage furrow, **224**
Clements, F. E., 1178
Climate, **1087–92**
　　as abiotic factor, 1087–92
　　air circulation, wind and, 1089f
　　alternative carbon fixation in plants living in arid,
　　　195–98
　　changes in (global warming), 1204–5
　　Cretaceous mass extinctions and, 518–20
　　Earth's latitude and, 1088f
　　effect of bodies of water on, 1987, 1090f
　　effect of mountains on, 1090f
　　effect of seasonality on, 1088f, 1090, 1091f
　　global patterns of, 1087, 1088–89f
　　latitudinal gradient in biodiversity and, 1176

long-term change/warming in, 1091, 1092f
　　microclimate, 1087, 1091
　　terrestrial biome distribution and structure deter-
　　　mined by, 1098–1104
Climate change, 1091–92
　　effect of, on forests and trees, 1092f
　　global warming, greenhouse effect, and, 1204–5
Climatius acanthodian, 680f
Climograph, **1098**f
Cline, **464**
Clitoris, **970**
Cloaca, **682**, **968**
Clock mutants, 805
Clonal selection, **907**
Clone, **239**, **385**, **415**. *See also* Gene clones
　　animal, 415–17
　　asexual reproduction and production of, 239
　　plant, 415, 781–83
Cloning, **415**
　　of animals, 415–17
　　of DNA and genes, 385–92
　　of plants, 415, 782–83
Cloning vectors, **386**
　　expression vector as, 390
　　phages as, 388, 389f
　　plasmids as, 386–88
Closed circulatory system, **650**, **868**
　　open circulatory system versus, 869f
　　in vertebrates (*see* Circulatory system)
Closed system, 143
　　equilibrium and work in, 147f
Clostridium botulinum (botulism), 206f, 339, 543f, 1069
Clownfish (*Amphiprion ocellaris*), 683f
Club fungus (Basidiomycota), **618–19**
Club moss, 586, 587f
Clumped pattern of population dispersion, 1138f
Cnidarians (Cnidaria), 633, 639f, **643–46**
　　anthozoans, 645
　　cubozoans, 645
　　classes of, 644t
　　digestion in, 854f
　　hydra (*see* Hydra)
　　hydrozoans, 644, 645f
　　hydrostatic skeleton in, 1063
　　internal transport in *Aurelia*, 868
　　life cycle of *Obelia*, 645f
　　nervous system, 1012f
　　origins of, 526
　　polyp and medusa forms of, 643f
　　scyphozoans, 644
Cnidocytes (cnidarians), **643**
Coal formation, 588
Cocci (spherical-shaped) prokaryotes, 534, 535f
Coccidioidomycosis, 623
Coccosteus placoderm, 680f
Cochlea, hearing and, **1051**f
　　pitch and, 1052, 1053f
　　transduction in, 1052f
Coconut, seed crop size in, 1142f
Codominance of allele, **260**
Codons, 312, **313**
　　start and stop, 313, 314f, 324
Coefficient of relatedness, **1129–30**
Coelacanth (*Latimeria*), 683f, 684
Coelom, **631**
Coelomates, **631**f
　　deuterostomes (*see* Deuterostomes (Deuterostomia))
　　protostomes, 369, 370
Coenocytic fungi, **609**f
Coenzyme, **155**
Coevolution, **1164–65**
　　relationship between angiosperms and animals as,
　　　604
Cofactors, enzyme, **155**
Cognition, **1117–18**
Cognitive ethology, **1117**
Cognitive maps, **1116**
Cohesion, **48**
　　in ascent of xylem sap, 748f

Cohort, population, 1139
Coitus, 972
Cold, plant response to, 812
Cold virus, 337, 343
Coleochaete sp., 574*f*
Coleoptile, 778
    response of, to light, 792*f*
Coleorhiza, 778
Collagen, 119, 380
    animal cells, 626–27
    in extracellular matrix of animal cell, 119
    quaternary structure of protein in, 83*f*
Collagenous fibers, 823
Collecting duct, 931, 932*f*, 933*f*, 934
Collenchyma cells, 718
Colloid, 52
Colon, 861–62
    cancer of, 305
Colonies, 526
    of eukaryotes, 526
    of prokaryotes, 539*f*
    of protists, 568*f*
Coloration
    aposematic, 1162*f*
    cryptic, 1162
    in plant leaves, 789*f*, 790*f*, 791
    in skin, 685, 946
    warning, in snakes, 21–24
Color blindness, 283, 1061
Colorectal cancer, model for development of, 373*f*, 374
Color vision, 1059–60, 1061
Colpidium, cilia motion in, 115*f*
Columnar epithelia, 823, 824*f*
Comb jellies (Ctenophora), 633, 640*f*
Commensalism, 545, 1164
Commercial applications/uses
    of angiosperms, 605
    of fungi, 623
    pharmaceuticals (*see* Pharmaceutical products)
Common juniper (*Juniperus communis*), 595*f*
Communication, animal, 1111–12
Community(communities), 4*f*, 1082, 1159
    adaptation and interspecific interactions in, 1164–65
    biogeographical factors affecting biodiversity in, 1175–78
    bottom-up versus top-down models of structure in, 1170–71
    commensalism in, 545, 1164
    competition in, 1160–61
    conservation of (*see* Conservation biology)
    contrasting views on structure of, 1178–80
    controls in, 1170–71
    disease in, 1163
    disturbances in, 1171–75
    dominant species in, 1168
    ecological succession in, 1173–75
    foundation species in, 1169–70
    herbivory in, 1163
    humans as agents of disturbance in, 1173
    individualistic versus interactive hypotheses on structure of, 1178, 1179*f*
    interspecific interactions in, overview, 1159–60
    keystone species in, 1168*f*, 1169*f*, 1214
    mutualism in, 1164
    parasitism in, 1163
    predation in, 1161–62
    recovery time for disasters in, 1226*f*
    rivet and redundancy models on structure of, 1180
    species diversity and richness in, 1165–66
    stability and change in, 1171–72
    trophic structure of, 1166–68
Community ecology, 1082, 1159–82
    biogeographic factors affecting biodiversity, 1175–78
    debate on structure of communities, 1178–80
    defining "community," 1159
    disturbances affecting species diversity and composition, 1171–75
    dominant and keystone species and, 1165–71
    interspecific interactions, 1159–65

Companion cells, 719
Competition, 16, 1160–61
    character displacement and, 1161*f*
    competitive exclusion principle and, 1160
    ecological niches and, 1160–61
    resource partitioning and, 1161*f*
Competitive enzyme inhibitors, 155*f*
Competitive exclusion, 1160
Complementary DNA (cDNA), 390, 400
Complement system, 900, 914
Complete digestive tract, 855. *See also* Alimentary canal
Complete dominance of allele, 260
Complete flowers, 773
Complete metamorphosis, 661
Compound(s), 33
    elements and 33–34
    emergent properties of, 33*f*
    organic, 59–66, 513–14
Compound eyes, 1058*f*
Compound leaf, 716*f*
Concentration gradient, 131, 135
    cotransport as active transport driven by, 136
Concentricycloidea (sea daisies), 666*t*, 667*f*
Conception, 978, 979*f*
Condensation reactions, 68, 69*f*
Condom, contraceptive, 983
Conduction, 835
Cone cells, eye, 1059, 1061
Confocal microscopy, 96*f*
Conformers versus regulators, 832
Conidia, 616
Coniferous forest, 1102*f*
Conifers (Coniferophyta), 593
    diversity of, 595*f*
    forest biome of, 1102
    life cycle of pine, 596, 597*f*
Conjugation, 349, 558
    in bacteria, 349*f*, 536, 538
    in ciliate *Paramecium*, 557*f*
    plasmids and bacterial, 349–51
Conjunctiva, 1058, 1059*f*
Connective tissue, 823, 825
    types of, 825*f*
Connell, Joseph, studies of competition and niches of barnacles, 1160*f*
Conodonts, 678, 679*f*
Consciousness, human, 1036–37
Conservation biology, 1209–32
    biodiversity and human welfare in, 1211–12
    human threats to biodiversity and, 1212–14
    K. Kaneshiro on, 437
    at landscape and regional level, 1220–24
    levels of biodiversity addressed by, 1210–11
    at population and species levels, 1215–20
    restoration ecology and, 1224–28
    species area curves used in, 1176
    sustainable development and, 1229–30
    threat of human activities and need for, 1209–14
Conservation of energy, 143
Conservative model of DNA replication, 300*f*
Constant (C) regions, lymphocytes, 904*f*
Consumers, 6
Continental drift, 527, 528*f*
    history of, during Phanerozoic, 529*f*
    plate movements and, 528*f*
    species distribution and, 528
Contour tillage, 762*f*
Contraception, 982–83
    mechanisms of, 982*f*
    reproductive technology and, 983–84
Contractile vacuoles, 108
    in *Paramecium*, 132, 133*f*
Control center, animal's internal environment and, 832, 944
Control elements, eukaryotic gene, 364–66, 367*f*
    proximal, and distal, 364–65
Controlled experiment, 23–24
Convection, 835
Convergent evolution

    of aquatic animals, 821*f*
    of marsupials and eutherian mammals, 450, 494*f*, 495, 696*f*
    of oomycetes and fungi, 558
    in terrestrial biomes, 1099
Convergent extension, 1002
    animal morphogenesis and cell sheet, 1002*f*
Cooperativity, enzyme activity and, 156*f*, 157
Copepods, 664
Coppola, Francis Ford, and family, 238*f*
Coquerel's sifakas (*Propithecus verreauxi coquereli*), 697*f*
Coral reef, 1097*f*
    algae and, 567*f*
Corals, 639*f*, 645
Coral snake, eastern, case study on mimicry of warning coloration in, 21–24
Corepressor, 354
Cork cambium, 720
    production of periderm and, 728
Corn. *See* Maize (*Zea mays*)
Corn borer, European, 1085
Cornea, 1058, 1059*f*
Coronavirus, 344
Corpus callosum, 1031*f*, 1032
Corpus luteum, 969
Correns, Karl, 289
Corridors between ecosystems, 1221–22
Cortex, plant tissue, 717
    in roots, 722–23
Cortical granules, 989
Cortical nephrons, 931, 932*f*
Cortical reaction, 989*f*, 990*f*
Corticosteroids, 958
Coruzzi, Gloria, 25*f*
Costa Rica
    infant mortality and life expectancy in, 1229*f*
    parks and zoned reserves in, 1223*f*, 1224
    restoration project in tropical dry forest of, 1228*f*
    sustainable development in, 1229–30
Cotransport, 136, 740
    solute transport in plants and, 740*f*
Cotyledons, 600, 780*f*
Countercurrent exchange, 885
    in blood vessels of fish gills, 885, 886*f*
    thermoregulation and, 836*f*
Countercurrent heat exchanger, 836
Countercurrent multiplier systems, 936
Courtship behaviors, 1106. *See also* Mating
    in *Drosophila*, 436–37
Covalent bonds, 39–40
    carbon and, 60
    double, 40
    formation of, 39*f*
    in four molecules, 40*f*
    nonpolar and polar, 40, 41*f*
Cowbird, brown-headed (*Molothrus ater*), 1221
Cowpox, 914
Cows
    cellulose-digesting bacteria in, 74*f*
    ruminant digestion in, 864*f*
Coyote, digestive tract of, 863*f*
Crabs, 664
    ghost crabs (*Ocypode*), 664*f*, 829*f*
    population fluctuations in Dungeness, 1151*f*
Cranial nerves, 1026
Craniates, 675, 676
    derived characters of, 676
    hagfishes as, 676, 677*f*
    neural crest of, 676*f*
    origin of craniates, 676, 677*f*
Crassulacean acid metabolism (CAM), 197
Crawling, 1073–74
Crayfish, 664
    gills, 885*f*
    stretch receptors in, 1047*f*
Crenarchaeota, 544
Cretaceous period mass extinctions, 518–21
Cretinism, 953, 954
Creutzfeldt-Jacob disease, 345

Cribrostatin, 643
Crick, Francis, 9
    on DNA replication, 299
    modeling of DNA structure by J. Watson and, 88–89, 293f
Cri du chat syndrome, 288
Crinoidea (sea lilies, feather star), 666t, 667f
Cristae, 110f
Critical load of nutrients in ecosystems, 1200
Crocodiles, 691f
Crop plants. See also Agriculture
    angiosperms, 605
    genetic engineered, 407
    improving protein yield in, 764
    polyploidy in, 478
Crop rotation, 766
Cross-fostering, influence of, on male mice, 1114t
Crossing over, 247, 278, 348
    genetic recombination of linked genes by, 278, 279f, 280f
    introns and, 319
    production of recombinant chromosomes by, 248, 249f
    unequal, and gene duplication, 378f, 379
Cross-pollination, 599
Crows (Corvus caurinus), energy costs/benefits of feeding behavior in, 1122
Crustaceans (lobsters, shrimp, crabs), 641f, 658t, 664f–65
    exoskeleton in, 657f
    Hox gene expression in, 432f
Cryoprotectants, 840
Cryphonectria parasitica, 622
Cryptic coloration, 1162
Cryptochromes, 802
Crystallin, 419
    regulation of gene expression for synthesis of, 367f
Ctenophora (comb jellies), 633, 640f
ctr (constitutive triple-response) mutant, 800f
Cuban tree snails, 454f
Cuboidal epithelia, 823, 824f
Cubozoans (box jellies, sea wasps), 644f, 645
Cultural eutrophication of lakes, 1201
Culture, 1131
Cuticle, 575, 655
    plant, 575, 717
Cuttings, plant, 781–82
Cuvier, Georges, 440
Cyanobacteria, 537f, 539f, 543f
    blooms of, 1171, 1190f
    lichens and, 621–22
    oxygen production by, 522
    plastids and, 551f
Cycads (Cycadophyta), 593, 594f
Cycas revoluta, 594f
Cyclic AMP (cAMP), 210, 356
    as second messenger, 210f, 211f, 1024, 1056
Cyclic electron flow, photosynthesis, 191f, 192
Cyclin, 229–30
Cyclin-dependent kinases (Cdks), 229–30
Cycliophoran Symbion Pandora, 641f
Cystic fibrosis, 266, 403
    as recessively inherited disorder, 266
Cystinuria, 134
Cytochromes (cyt), 170, 851
    cytochrome c, 428
Cytogenetic maps, 281, 396f
Cytokines, 903, 948
Cytokinesis, 220, 223f, 245f
    in animal and plant cells, 225f
    cleavage and, 224, 225f, 226
Cytokinins, 796–97
    anti-aging effects of, 797
    control of apical dominance in plants by, 796f, 797
    control of plant cell division and differentiation by, 796
Cytology, microscopes as tool in, 97
Cytoplasm, 98
    cell cycle regulated by signals in, 228–33

cytokinesis and division of, 220, 224–26
    response of, to cell signaling, 212, 213f
Cytoplasmic determinants, 420, 987
    cell differentiation and, 420, 421f
    pattern formation and, 423–25
Cytoplasmic streaming, 117f, 118
Cytosine (C), 88
    DNA structure and, 296f, 297f, 298f, 364
Cytoskeleton, 112–18
    animal morphogenesis and changes in, 1001f
    components of, 113–18
    intermediate filaments of, 113t, 118
    membrane proteins and, 128f
    microfilaments of, 113t, 116–18
    microtubules of, 113t, 114–16
    motor molecules in, 112f
    role of, in cell support, motility and regulation, 112f–13
    structure and function of, 113t
Cytosol, 98
    ionic gradients across neuron membrane and, 1016f
    transport in plant cells and, 743
Cytotoxic T cells, 904, 905f
    function of, against intracellular pathogens, 910, 911f
    interaction of, with MHC molecules, 905f

Daffodil, radial symmetry in, 773f
DAG (diacylglycerol), 212
Daily torpor, 841
Dalton, 34, 52
Dalton, John, 34
Dandelion, seed crop size, 1142f
Danielli, James, 125
Darwin, Charles, 15f–19, 438–51, 482, 497, 601, 682, 1081, 1143, 1175
    adaptation in research and theory of, 442, 443f, 444–46
    Beagle voyage and field research of, 441–43
    descent with modification and theory of, 443–44
    evidence supporting theory of, 446–51
    genetic variation and theory of, 248–49
    historical context of life and ideas of, 439f
    modern synthesis of Mendelian inheritance and evolutionary theory of, 455
    natural selection and evolutionary adaptation as theory of, 16, 17f, 438, 441–46
    On the Origin of Species by, 15, 438, 439, 443–46, 455
    on resistance to idea of evolution and, 439–40
    studies on phototropism by, 792
Darwin, Francis, 792
Data, scientific, 19–20
Davson, Hugh, 125
Davson-Danielli membrane model, 125
Day-neutral plants, 806
DCC (deleted in colorectal cancer) tumor-suppressor gene, 373f
Ddel restriction site, 393f
D-dopa, 62, 63f
DDT pesticide, 155
    biological magnification of, in food webs, 1202–3
Death rate in populations, per capita, 1143–44
Decapods, 664
Declining-population approach to species conservation, 1218–19
    case study of red-cockaded woodpecker, 1218, 1219f
    steps for analysis and intervention, 1218
Decomposers, 544, 1185
    fungi as, 620, 1186f
    prokaryotes as, 544, 1186
Decomposition in ecosystems, 1185–86
    rates of, and nutrient cycling, 1198
Deductive reasoning, 20–21
Deep-diving mammals, respiratory adaptations of, 894–95
Deep-sea hydrothermal vents, 514f, 541, 1097f

De-etiolation in plants, 789f
    as response to cell signaling, 789–91
Defensins, 901
Deforestation, 606
    in Hubbard Brook Experimental Forest, 1078–79, 1198, 1199f
    of tropical forests, 1209f, 1212, 1221f
Dehydration in animal cells, 136
Dehydration reactions, 68, 69f
    synthesis of fats, 75f
    synthesis of maltose and sucrose, 71f
Delesseria sanguinea, 550f
Deletions
    chromosomal, 286f
    of nucleotides, as point mutation, 329, 330f
Demographic transition, 1153–54, 1230
Demography, 1139
    age structure and sex ratio as factors in, 1154–55
    life tables and survivorship curves in, 1139–40
    reproductive rates and, 1140–41
Denaturation
    of DNA, 388
    of proteins, 84, 85f
Dendrites, 1014
    stretch receptors and, 1047f
    thermoreceptors and, 1048f, 1049
Dendritic cells, 900, 909f, 910f
Dense bodies, 1072
Density-dependent birth/death rates, 1148–50
Density-dependent inhibition of cell division, 231, 232f
Density-independent birth/death rates, 1148
Density of populations, 1137–38
    density dependent birth/death rates, 1148–50
    density independent birth/death rates, 1148
    determining equilibrium for, 1148f
    dispersion patterns and, 1137–39
    population change and, 1148
Dental plaque, 539f
Dentition, evolutionary adaptions of, 862, 863f
Deoxyribonucleic acid. See DNA (deoxyribonucleic acid)
Deoxyribose, 88
Depolarization, membrane potential and, 1018f
Depression, mental, 1025, 1040
Derivatives, 721
Derived traits of plants, 575, 576–77f
Dermal tissue system, 717
Dermis, animal, 835f
Descent with modification, 16, 18f, 443, 444f. See also Natural selection
Desert biomes, 1100f
Desmosomes, 120, 121f, 627
Determinant growth, 720
Determinate cleavage, 632
Determination, 419. See also Cell differentiation
Detritus, 1093, 1185
Detrivores, 1185, 1186. See also Decomposers
Deuteromycetes (imperfect fungi), 612
Deuterostome, 633–34
    Chordata, 641f (see also Chordates)
    cleavage and, 631–32
    coelom formation in, 632
    Echinodermata, 641f
    fate of blastopore, 632–33
    protostome development versus, 632f
Deuterostome development mode, 631–33
Development, 411–33. See also Animal development; Embryonic development; Plant development
    cell division, cell differentiation, and morphogenesis during, 412–14
    cell fate during, 1003–8
    differential gene expression in, 415–20
    evolutionary novelty and, 482–83
    evolution of, and morphological diversity, 431–33
    evolution of genes controlling, 484–86
    hormonal regulation of insect, 960f
    model organisms for study of, 412–13f
    pattern formation mechanisms in process of, 421–31
    as property of life, 3

Developmental potential of cells, 418, 1004
Devonian period, 629
Diabetes mellitus, **956**
   two forms of, 956
Diacylglycerol (DAG), **212**
Diaphragm, contraceptive, **983**
Diaphragm, respiratory, **888**
Diapsids, 689
Diastole, cardiac cycle, **872**
Diastolic pressure, **876**
Diatoms (bacillariophyta), **559**, 560f
Dicots (Dicotyledon), **602**
   germination and cotyledons of, 780f
Dictyostelium discoideum, life cycle, 566f
Dideoxy chain-termination method, sequencing DNA
   using, 397f, 398
Diencephalon, 1028
Diet. See also Food; Nutrition
   dentition and, 862, 863f
   disease and, 847, 849f, 851t, 852t
   evolutionary adaptations of vertebrate digestive
      systems and, 862–64
   mate selection and, in *Drosophila*, 1113f
   nutritional requirements in animal, 844, 849–52
   vegetarian, 850f
Differential gene expression, **362–63**
Differential-interference-contrast (Nomarski)
   microscopy, 96f
Diffusion, **130**
   facilitated, 133–34
   free energy and, 146f
   of solutes, 131f
Digestion, **853–55**
   in alimentary canals, 854f, 855
   enzyme function in, 857, 858, 859f
   extracellular, 853–55
   in gastrovascular cavities, 854
   hormonal control of, 860f
   intracellular, 853
   in small intestine, 858–61
   in stomach, 857–58
Digestive system, 855–62
   bacteria in, 862
   evolutionary adaptations of, 862–64
   hormones and, 860f
   human, 855f–62
   large intestine, 861–62
   oral cavity, pharynx, and esophagus, 856
   small intestine, 858–61
   stomach, 857–58
Digestive tract
   bird, 854f, 863
   diet and evolutionary adaptions in, 862–64
   earthworm, 854f
   insect, 660f, 854f
   mammalian, 855–62
   ruminant, 864f
Digger wasp nest-locating behavior, 1115f
Dihybrid(s), **257**
Dihybrid cross, 257
Dikaryon, **611**
Dimetrodon, jaw and ear bones of, 695f
Dinobryon, 560f
Dinoflagellates (Dinoflagellata), **555**f
   mitosis in, 228
Dinosaurs, 629, **689**
   blood pressure and feeding in, 877
   parental care among, 690f
   P. Sereno on searching for fossils of, 15f
Dioecious plants, **773**
Diphasiastrum tristachyum club moss, 587f
Diphtheria, 339
Diploblastic animals, **631**
Diploid cells, **241**
   genetic variation preserved in, 466
   reduction of chromosomes from, to haploid cells,
      242, 243–47
Diplomonads, **552**, 553f
Diplopodes (millipedes), 659f

Directional selection, **465**f
Direct synaptic transmission, 1022–23
Disaccharides, **70**, 71f. See also Sucrose
Discovery science, **19–20**
Discrete characters, 463
Diseases and disorders, 1163. See also Genetic disor-
      ders; names of specific diseases
   allergies, 916–17
   autoimmune, 917, 956
   of brain and nervous system, 1039–41
   cancer (see Cancer)
   cardiovascular, 76, 882–83
   DNA technology applied to diagnosis of, 403
   erectile dysfunction, 211, 948
   fungal, 622–23
   gene therapy for, 403–4
   G-proteins and, 206f, 211
   growth disorders, 952, 953
   hormonal, 952, 953f, 954, 956
   hypercholesterolemia, 137
   immunodeficiency, 917–19
   of muscle fiber excitation by motor neurons, 1069
   obesity, 847–48
   parasites as cause of (see Parasite(s))
   pathogens as cause of (see Pathogens)
   in plants (see Plant disease)
   sexual reproduction and resistance to, 469
   vaccination against, 914
   viral, in animals, 343–44
   viroids and prions as cause of, 345, 346f
Disease vectors, insects as, 554f, 555, 556f, 664. See
      also Pathogens
Dispersal of organisms, **1084–85**
Dispersion patterns, population, **1137**, 1138–39
Dispersive model of DNA replication, 299, 300f
Disruptive selection, 465f, **466**
Dissociation curve of oxygen for hemoglobin, 892f
Distal control elements, 365
Distal tubule, **931**, 932f
   regulation of calcium and potassium concentra-
      tion by, 934
Distribution of species, 1083–92
   abiotic factors affecting, 1086–87
   behavior, habitat selection, and, 1085
   biotic factors affecting, 1085–86
   climate and, 1087–92
   dispersal and, 1084–85
   species transplants and, 1084–85
Disturbances in communities, **1172–73**
   community recovery from, 1226f
   ecological succession following, 1173–75
   fire as, 1172f, 1173f
   humans as agents of, 1173
   immediate, 1172
Disulfide bridges, **83**
Diuresis, 936
DNA (deoxyribonucleic acid), 7f, **86**
   amplification of, by polymerase chain reaction, 391f
   chromatin structure and packing of, 359–60, 361f
   chromosomes formed from (see Chromosome(s))
   circular, 289 (see also Plasmids)
   complementary (cDNA), 390, 400
   denaturation of, 388
   discovery of, as key genetic material, 293–98
   DNA-protein complex (see Chromatin)
   double helix structure of, 7f, 88f, 89, 293f, 296–98
   duplication and divergence in segments of, 378–80
   genes as segments of (see Gene(s))
   intron and exon segments of, 318 (see also Exons;
      Introns)
   methylation of, 284, 289, 364, 417
   nitrogenous bases of, 87f, 88, (see also
      Nitrogenous bases)
   physical mapping of fragments of, 396f
   plasmids, 537
   proteins specified by, 86f (see also Protein synthesis)
   radioactive isotopes and research on, 35f
   recombinant, 385f, 386f
   repetitive, 375, 376–77

   replication of (see DNA replication)
   restriction fragment analysis of differences in,
      392–94
   satellite, 377
   sequences of (see DNA sequences)
   sticky ends, 386
   strands of (see DNA strand(s))
   telomeres ending molecules of, 306f, 307
   transcription of RNA under direction of (see
      Transcription)
DNA cloning, 385–92
   of eukaryotic gene in bacterial plasmid, 386, 387f,
      388, 389f
   gene cloning and applications, 385f, 386
   storing cloned genes in DNA libraries, 388, 389f,
      390
   using restriction enzymes to make recombinant
      DNA, 386f
DNA fingerprinting, forensic investigations and, 405f
DNA ligase, **303**f, **304**t, **386**
   creating recombinant DNA with, 386f
DNA methylation, 284, 417
   control of eukaryotic gene expression and effects
      of, 364
   genomic imprinting and, 289
DNA microarray, 384f, 400
DNA microarray assays, **400**, 401f
DNA nucleotide sequence. See DNA sequences
DNA polymerases, **301**, 302, 303, 304t, 305, 306
DNA replication, 88f, 89
   antiparallel arrangement of DNA strands and, 89,
      297f
   in bacteria, 346, 347f, 350f
   base pairing to template strands in, 89, 299f, 300f
   models of, 299f, 300f
   origins of, in eukaryotes, 302f
   proofreading and repair of, 305–6
   priming, 303
   in prokaryotes and eukaryotes, 300–305, 537
   proteins facilitating in, 301–3, 304t
   radioactive tracers used to study, 35f
   rolling, 350f
   summary of bacterial, 304f
DNA sequences, 88
   analysis of, 392–94
   homeobox, 431–32, 627
   identifying protein-coding genes in, 399
   insertion, 351, 352f
   introns and exons, 318 (see also Exons; Introns)
   mapping, 396, 397f, 398
   molecular homologies in, 494, 495f
   mutations in (see Mutations)
   noncoding, 374–78
   phylogeny inferred from, 492, 494–95
   principle of maximum likelihood applied to, 501f
   promoter, 315f, 316f
   repetitive, 375
   TATA box , 315, 316f, 364
   terminator, 315f, 317
   types of, in human genome, 375f
DNA strand(s), 7f
   antiparallel arrangement and elongation of, 89,
      297f, 302–3
   complementary, 89
   directionality (5' end and 3' end), 88, 89, 302f
   elongation of, in replication process, 301–2
   incorporation of nucleotide into, 302f
   nontemplate, 313
   structure of, 88f, 296f
   synthesis of leading and lagging strands of, 302f,
      303f
   telomeres at end of, 306f, 307
   template, 313
DNA technology, 26f, 384–409
   DNA cloning and, 385–92
   genomics and, 398–402
   Human Genome Project (see Human Genome
      Project)
   manipulation of genomes as, 384

Index

mapping genomes at DNA level, 394–98
   practical applications of, 402–7
   restriction fragment analysis, 392–94
   safety and ethical questions related to, 26, 404, 407–8
Dobzhansky, Theodosius, 455
Dodd, Diane, on reproductive isolation in divergent *Drosophila* populations, 477f
Dodder (*Cuscuta*), 768f
Dolphin, 821f
   Chinese river, 1211f
   countercurrent heat exchanger in, 836f
Domains, protein, 319
   correspondence between exons and, 319f
Domains of life, 13–14, 496. *See also* Archaea (domain); Bacteria (domain); Eukarya (domain)
   phylogeny of (*see* Phylogeny)
   three-domain system, 14f, 530–31f, 532
Dominant allele, 254
   complete dominance of, 260
   frequency of, 261–62
   genetic disorders due to, 267–68
   incomplete dominance, 260, 261f
   relationship between phenotype and, 261
Dominant species, 1168
Dominant trait, 253
Donoghue, Philip, 679
Doolittle, Ford, 525
Dopamine, 1025, 1039, 1041
Doppler, Christian, 252
Dormancy, seed, 779–80
   abscisic acid and, 798, 799f
Dorsal lip, blastopore, 995
   as induction organizer, 1006f
Dorsal side, body, 630
Double bond, 40
Double circulation, 871
   in mammals, 871–74
Double fertilization, 599, 600f, 776, 777
Double helix, 7f, 88f, 89, 296, 297f, 298. *See also* DNA (deoxyribonucleic acid)
   antiparallel structure of, 89, 297f
   base pairing in, 89, 298f
   complementary strands of, 89
   key features of, 297f
Douglas fir (*Pseudotsuga menziesii*), 595f
Down syndrome, 287f
Downy mildews (Oomycota), 558
Dragonfly, 661
   fossil, 491f
Drosophila. See Fruit fly (*Drosophila* sp.)
Drought
   abscisic acid and plant tolerance of, 799
   plant response to, 811
Drug(s). *See also* Pharmaceutical products
   antibiotics (*see* Antibiotics)
   antiviral, 343–44
   DNA technology and development of new, 404
   enantiomers as, 62, 63f
   for HIV and AIDS, 918–19
   opiates, as mimics of endorphins, 43, 81, 1025
   penicillin, 623
   Prozac, 1025, 1040
   psychoactive, 1025
   smooth endoplasmic reticulum and detoxification of, 104
   Viagra, 201, 211
Drug resistance
   in bacteria, 535
   in HIV, 447, 448f
Dubautia laxa, 481f
Dubautia linearis, 481f
Dubautia scabra, 481f
Dubautia waialealae, 481f
Duchenne muscular dystrophy, 283–84, 403
Dugatkin, Lee, 1131
Dulse (*Palmaria palmate*), 567f
Dungeness crab, population fluctuations in, 1151f

Duodenum, 858f–59f
Duplication
   chromosomal, 286f
   gene, 459
Dust mites, 659f
Dutch elm disease (*Ophiostoma ulmi*), 622
Dwarfism, 952
Dynamic stability hypothesis on food chain length, 1167
Dynein, 114–16
   "walking" of, and cilia and flagella movement, 116f
Dyson, Freeman, 516

Ear
   balance, equilibrium, and, 1052–53
   evolution of mammalian jaw and bones of, 695f
   hearing in mammalian (human), 1050, 1051f, 1052
Earlobes, attached, as recessive trait, 265f
Earth. *See also* Environment
   atmosphere of (*see* Atmosphere)
   biodiversity hotspots on, 1222f
   carrying capacity of, 1145, 1155
   chemical conditions of early, and origins of life, 513–16
   classifying life on (*see* Systematics; Taxonomy)
   clock analogy for key events in history of, 521f
   continental drift and plate tectonics of, 527–29
   continuum of life on, 512
   global climate patterns, 1088–89f
   global energy budget, 1186–87
   moderation of temperatures on, by water, 50
   prokaryote evolution and changes to, 521–23
   regional annual net primary production for, 1188f
Earthworm (Oligochaeta), 640f, 653–54
   anatomy, 654f
   closed circulatory system, 869f
   defense systems, 903
   digestion in, 854f
   excretory system (metanephridia) of, 930f
   gas exchange in, 884
   peristalsis and locomotion in, 1064f
   reproduction in, 964f
Eastern box turtle (*Terrapene carolina carolina*), 691f
Ebola virus, 344
Ecdysis, 634, 635f, 657
Ecdysone, 960
Ecdysozoans (Ecdysozoa), 634
Echinoidea (sea urchins), 666t, 667f, 988–990
Echinoderms (Echinodermata), 641f, 665–67
   anatomy, 665f
   brittle stars, 666, 667f
   classes of, 666t
   nervous system, 1012f
   sea daisies, 666, 667f
   sea lilies, feather stars, 666, 667f
   sea stars, 665f, 666, 667f
   sea urchins, sand dollars, 666, 667f (*see also* Sea urchin)
   sea cucumbers, 666, 667f
E. coli. See Escherichia coli (*E. coli*)
Ecological capacity, 1156
Ecological footprint, 1156. *See also* Carrying capacity
   in relation to available ecological capacity, 1156f
Ecological niche, 1160
Ecological pyramids, 1192–93
Ecological species concept, 476
Ecological succession, 1173
Ecology, 1080–1105
   abiotic and biotic factors and, 1081
   of aquatic biomes, 1092–93
   of behavior (*see* Behavioral ecology)
   biosphere and, 1083 (*see also* Biosphere)
   of communities (*see* Community ecology)
   conservation and (*see* Conservation biology)
   distribution of species in, 1083–92
   ecosystem approach to, 1082 (*see also* Ecosystem(s))
   environmental issues and, 1083
   evolutionary biology related to, 1081
   landscape, 1082, 1220–24

of organisms, 1082
   organisms and environment in study of, 1081
   of populations (*see* Population ecology)
   prokaryotes and, 544–45
   restoration of degraded, 1224–28
   scope of, 1080
   subfields of, 1082–83
   of terrestrial biomes, 1098–1104
Ecosystem(s), 4f, 1082, 1184–1208. *See also* Biomes
   aquatic, 1188–90
   as biodiversity level, 1211
   chemical cycling in, 160f, 1184–86, 1195–99
   communities of species in (*see* Community(ies))
   disruption of chemical cycles by humans, 1200–1206
   edges between, 1220f, 1221
   effects of acid precipitation on, 55–56, 1201–2
   energy and matter in, 1184
   energy budgets of, 1186–88
   energy conversion in, 6
   energy flow in, 160f, 1184–86
   energy transfer between trophic levels in, 1191–94
   "engineers" (foundation species) in, 1169–70
   fragmentation of, 1220–21
   human impact on, 1200–1206
   limitations on primary production in marine and freshwater, 1188–91
   producers and consumers in, 6
   role of fungi in, 620
   role of prokaryotes in, 544–45
   services of, promoting human welfare, 1212
   terrestrial and wetland, 1190–91
   trophic structure of, 1166–68
Ecosystem ecology, 1082. *See also* Ecosystem(s)
Ecosystem services, 1212
Ecotone, 1099
Ectoderm, 631, 994
   gastrulation and formation of, 994
   organs and tissues formed from, 999t
Ectomycorrhizae, 610, 766, 767f
Ectoparasites, 1163
Ectoprocts (bryozoans), 640f, 649f
Ectotherms (ectothermic animals), 689, 829, 833
   energy budgets in, 830, 831f
   thermoregulation in, 833–34
   reptiles as, 689
Edges (boundaries) between ecosystems, 1220f, 1221
Ediacaran fauna, 628
Effective population size, 1216–17
Effector cells, 907, 944, 1013
Efferent arteriole, 933
Efferent signal, 944
Egg, 964. *See also* Ovum
   activation of, 990
   amniotic, 688f
   cytoplasmic determinants in, 987
   development of human, 973, 974f
   fertilization of human, 978, 979f, 991
   fertilization of mammalian, 990–91f
   fertilization of sea urchin, 988, 989f, 990f
Egg-polarity genes, 424
Ehrlich, Anne, 1180
Ehrlich, Paul, 1180
ein (ethylene-insensitive) mutants, 800f
Ejaculation, 971
Ejaculatory duct, 972
Elastic fibers, 823
Eldredge, Niles, 481
Electrical membrane potential. *See* Membrane potentials
Electrical synapses, 1021
Electrocardiogram (EKG/ECG), 874
Electrochemical gradient, 135
Electrogenic pump, 136f
Electromagnetic receptors, 1048, 1049f
Electromagnetic spectrum, 186f
Electron(s), 34
   configuration of, and chemical properties, 37–38
   cyclic and noncyclic flow of, in photosynthetic light reactions, 190f, 191f, 192

energy levels of, 36–37f
ionic bonding and transfer of, 41f
orbitals of, 38f, 39
transport of, in cellular respiration, 170–3
valence, 38
Electronegativity, 40
Electron microscope (EM), 95–97
freeze-fracture preparation of cells for, 125, 126f
scanning (SEM), and transmission (TEM), 96f
Electron shells, 36
of eighteen elements, 37f
valences for elements of major organic molecules, 60f
Electron transport chain, 163–64
in cellular respiration, versus in uncontrolled reaction, 163f
energy coupling to chemiosmosis, and ATP synthesis, 171, 172f, 173
evolution of, 521–22
free energy change during, 171f
pathway of, during oxidative phosphorylation, 170–71
in photosynthetic light-harvesting, 190f
Electroporation, 390–91
Element(s), 33
atomic structure and properties of, 34
cycling of, in ecosystems, 160f, 1184–86, 1195–98
electron shells of eighteen, 37f
essential, required by life, 33–34
in human body, 33t
periodic table of, 37
plant nutritional requirements for, 756–59
trace, 34
Elephants
evolutionary tree of, 443, 444f
exponential growth in population of African, 1144f
overexploitation of African, 1214
thermoregulation in, 837f
Elephant seals, bottleneck effect in populations of northern, 461f
Elicitors, 814
Elimination as stage in food processing, 853
Elk, mating behaviors in, 1124f
El Nino Southern Oscillation, 1170, 1171f
Elongation factors, polypeptide synthesis, 323, 324f
Elton, Charles, 1166, 1167
Embolus, 883
Embryo
cleavage of zygote and formation of human, 978, 979f
development (Embryonic development)
ensuring survival of animal, 967–68
epigenesis and, 987
fertilization and formation of animal, 967, 978, 979f, 988–91
gastrulation and tissue formation in, 994–97
homologous structures in, 448, 449f
maternal effect (egg-polarity) genes, effects of, 424f
organogenesis in, 997f, 998f
pattern formation in (see Pattern formation)
plant, 577f, 777f, 778
restriction of cellular potency in, 1005
stem cells of, 418
Embryology, 411. See also Development; Embryonic development
Embryonic development, 412–14
of animal, 412–13, 414f, 485–86, 627f, 988–1001
cell division, cell differentiation and, 413
cell fate during, 1003–8
development of brain in, 1028f, 1029
differential gene expression and, 415–20
effects of DNA methylation on, 364
Hox genes and, 485–86, 627
human, 978, 979f, 980f, 987f, 1028–29
morphogenesis and, 413, 431–33, 987
pattern formation and, 421–31
plant, 414f, 777f–78
restriction of cellular potency in, 1005
Embryonic lethals, 423

Embryonic stem cells, 418f, 1039
Embryophytes, plant, 575f, 577f
Embryo sac, plant, 599
Encephalitis virus, 337
Emergent properties, 9
of biological systems, 9
as biological theme, 27f
cellular functions, 120, 121f
chemistry of life, 89
of compound, 33f
of water, 48–53
Emigration, population density and influence of, 1137
Emotions, human brain and, 1034–35
Emu, 693f
Enantiomers, 62, 63f
amino acids in proteins, 79f
pharmaceuticals and, 62, 63f
Endangered species, 1210–11
Endangered Species Act, U.S., 1210
Endemic species, 450
Endergonic reactions, 146
coupling of, to exergonic reactions by ATP, 148, 149f
free energy changes in, 146, 147f
Endler, John, research on guppy evolution by, 446, 447f
Endocrine glands, 944
adrenal, 956–58
gonads, 958–59
hypothalamus, 948, 950–51
major glands and hormones, 949t, 950t
pancreas, 955–56
parathyroid, 954–55
pineal, 959
pituitary, 948–52
thyroid, 953–54
Endocrine pathway, 945f
Endocrine signaling, 203
Endocrine system, 943–63
control pathways and feedback loops in, 944, 945f
defined, 944
hormones as chemical signals of, 945–48
invertebrate, 959–61
major glands and hormones of, 949t, 950f
nervous system overlap with, 943, 944
nonpituitary glands of, 953–59
pituitary gland and hypothalamus of, 948–52
Endocytosis, transport by, 137, 138f
Endoderm, 631, 994
gastrulation and formation of, 994
organs and tissues formed from, 999t
Endodermis, plant root, 723, 744
water/mineral absorption and, 744, 745f, 746
Endolymph in inner ear, 1053f
Endomembrane system, 104–9
endoplasmic reticulum, 104, 105f
Golgi apparatus, 105, 106f, 107
lysosomes, 107f, 108
relationships of organelles within, 108, 109f
review of, 108
vacuoles, 108f
Endometrium, 970
Endomycorrhizae, 610, 766, 767f
Endoparasites, 1163
Endoplasmic reticulum (ER), 104, 105f
origins of, 525
rough, functions of, 105
smooth, 104, 105f
transitional, 105
Endorphin(s), 952, 1025
opiate drugs as mimics of, 43, 81, 1025
pain reduced by, 43, 81, 952
structure, 43f
Endorphin receptors, 43
Endoskeleton, 1064
human, 1065f
vertebrate, 682
Endosperm, 600, 777
development of, 777

Endospores, 537, 538f
Endosymbiont, 523
Endosymbiosis, 550–51
origins of mitochondria and plastids in, 523–25
secondary, 551f
serial, 524
Endothelium, 874
in blood vessels, 874
Endotherms (endothermic animals), 689, 829, 833
birds as, 689
energy budgets in, 830, 831f, 871
thermoregulation in, 833–34
Endotoxins, 546
Energetic hypothesis on food chain length, 1167
Energy, 36, 142. See also Bioenergetics
animal communication and cost of, 1111
chemical, 142, 828
free, 145–48
kinetic, 49, 142
forms of, 142–43
laws of thermodynamics applied to, 143–44
life and, as biological theme, 27f
locomotion and requirements for, 1074f
potential, 36, 142
species richness, water, and, 1176f
storage of, in fats, 76
thermal (heat), 142 (see also Heat)
transfer of, between ecosystem trophic levels, 1191–94
transformations of, in metabolic processes, 141–44
Energy budget
of animals, 830, 831f, 844–48, 928
of ecosystems, 1186–88
Energy costs
of animal locomotion, 1074
of animal signals, 1111
of foraging behavior, 1122
Energy coupling, 148
Energy flow in ecosystems, 6f, 160f, 1184–86
decomposition and, 1185–86
overview of, 1185f
physical laws and, 1185
primary productivity and energy budget, 1186–91
secondary productivity and 1191
trophic efficiency, ecological pyramids, and, 1192–93
trophic relationships as determinants of, 1185
Energy levels of electrons, 36, 37f
Energy processing as property of life, 3f
Energy transformation, laws of, 143–44
Engelmann, Theodor, 187f, 188
Engelmann's experiment, 187f, 188
Enhancers, 364, 365f
function of, in control of eukaryotic gene expression, 365, 366f
Entamoebas, 564
Enteric division of autonomic nervous system, 1028
Enterocoelous development, 632
Enthalpy, change in (ΔH), 145
Entropy, 144
change in (ΔS), 145
Environment. See also Biosphere; Earth
cancer caused by factors in, 370 (see also Cancer)
carrying capacity of, 1145, 1155
emerging viruses linked to changes in, 344
genetics combined with influences of, resulting in animal behaviors, 1113–18
impact of, on phenotype, 264
influence of, on animal nitrogenous waste, 928
interactions between organisms and, 27f, 1080–83 (see also Ecology)
regulation of animal's internal, 831–33
signal transduction pathways in plant responses to, 788–91
water and fitness of, 47–57
Environmental education, 437, 1079
Environmentalism, 1083
Environmental problems
acid precipitation, 55–56, 1201–2

atmospheric carbon dioxide and climate change, 1203–5
decline in amphibian species due to, 686
disrupted chemical cycling, 1200–1206
DNA technology applied to solving, 405–6
ecology and evaluation of, 1083
human population growth as, 1155–56
humans as cause of (*see* Human environmental impact)
ozone depletion, 1205–6
soil depletion, 1200
toxins in ecosystems, 1202–3
Environmental stress, plant responses to, 810–12
Enzymatic hydrolysis, **853**
Enzyme(s), **77, 150–55**
activation energy barrier and, 150–51
active site of, 152, 153*f*
allosteric regulation of, 156–57
catalysis in active site of, 152, 153*f*, 154
as catalysts, 77, 150
catalytic cycle of, 78*f*, 153*f*
cofactors of, 155
conformation of lysozyme, 81*f*
digestive, 857, 858, 859*f*
DNA proofreading and damage repair by, 305–6
DNA replication and role of, 301–3, 304*t*
effects of temperature and pH on, 154
induced fit between substrate and, 152, 153*f*
inhibitors of, 155*f*
localization of, within cells, 157
lowering of activation energy barrier by, 152
membrane protein as, 128*f*
normal binding of, 155*f*
one gene–one enzyme hypothesis, 310, 311*f*
repressible, and inducible, 354–56
substrates of, 152
substrate specificity of, 81, 152
Enzyme-substrate complex, **152**
Eosinophils, 880*f*, 881, **900**
Ephedra, 594*f*
Ephrussi, Boris, 310
Epiblast, 994, 1000
Epicotyl, **778**
Epidermis
animal, 835*f*
plant, **717**, 724, 813
Epididymis, **971**
Epigenesis, 987
Epigenetic inheritance, **364**
Epiglottis, **856**
Epilepsy, 1032
Epinephrine, 944, **956, 1025**
cell signaling and glycogen breakdown by, 203–4, 213*f*, 946
different responses to, 947*f*
effects of, on cardiovascular and respiratory systems, 874, 957
stress and secretion of, 874, 946, 947*f*
Epiphytes, 767, 768
Episome, **349**
Epistasis, **262**, 263*f*
Epithalamus, **1030**
Epithelial tissue, **823**
transport, 926–27
Epitope, **903**
Epstein-Barr virus, 370, 910
Equatorial-polar gradients in biodiversity, 1176
Equilibrium
free energy and, 145, 146*f*
metabolism and, 147–48
organs of, in vertebrates, 1052, 1053*f*
work and, in closed and open systems, 147*f*
Equilibrium potential (E$_{ion}$), **1016**
Equisetum arvense field horsetail, 587*f*
Erectile dysfunction, 211, 948, 1025
Eriksson, Peter, 1038–39
Ergotism, 622
Erythrocytes, 825*f*, **880–81**. *See also* Red blood cells (erythrocytes)

Erythromycin, 537
Erythropoietin (EPO), **881**
Escherichia coli (*E. coli*)
chaperone protein in, 85
chemotaxis in, 537
chromosome and DNA of, 537*f*
chromosome length of, 226
DNA replication in, 300–305, 347*f*
genetic recombination in, 460, 346–51
genome and replication of, 346, 347*f*
genome map, 394
Hershey and Chase experiment on viral DNA infection of, 294, 295*f*, 296
in human colon, 542*f*, 862
as pathogen, 460, 546
restriction site, 386*f*
reproduction rates of, 346, 538
T2 bacteriophage infection of, 294, 295*f*
T4 bacteriophage infection of, 334*f*
transcription and translation in, 328*f*
transposition of genetic elements in, 351–52
E site, tRNA binding, **322***f*
Esophagus, **856**
peristalsis in, 856*f*
Essential amino acids, **849–50**
in vegetarian diet, 850*f*
Essential element, **757**
Essential fatty acids, 850
Essential nutrients, **849**
in animals, 849–52
in plants, 757, 758*t*
Estivation, **841**
Estradiol, 63*f*
Estrogen, **958**
human pregnancy and childbirth and role of, 981
intracellular receptors for, 947
Estrous cycles, **973**
Estrus, **973**
Estuary(ies), **1095***f*
partial food web for Chesapeake Bay, 1167*f*
Etges, William, 1113
Ethane, molecular shape of, 60*f*
Ethanethiol, **65***f*
Ethanol, **64***f*
Ethene, molecular shape of, 60*f*
Ethics
DNA technology and, 26, 404, 407–8
human cloning and, 417
Ethology, **1107–9**
Ethylene, **799–801**
fruit ripening and, 203, 801
leaf abscission and, 800, 801*f*
programmed cell death and, 800
root apoptosis and, 811
triple response induced by, 799–80
Etiolation in plants, **789**
eto (ethylene-overproducing) mutants, 800
Euchromatin, **360**
Eudicots, **602**, 603*f*
embryo development, 777*f*
monocots compared with, 603*f*
stem tissue in, 724*f*
Euglena sp., 529, 554*f*
Euglenids, **554***f*
Euglenozoans, 553–54
Eukarya (domain), 14*f*, 507*f*, 521
compared with Archaea and Bacteria, 541*t*
Eukaryotes
animals as (*see* Animal(s))
cells of (*see* Eukaryotic cell)
cilia of, 15*f* (*see also* Cilia)
cloning and expression genes of, 390–91
cloning genes of, in bacterial plasmid, 386, 387*f*, 388, 389*f*
endosymbiosis in evolution of, 523–25, 550–51
gene expression in (*see* Gene expression)
genome (*see* Eukaryotic genome)
fungi as (*see* Fungi)
multicellularity and evolution of, 525–28

origins of, and relationship to prokaryotes, 523, 524*f*, 525
phylogeny of, 552*f*
plants as (*see* Plant(s))
protists as, 549–51 (*see also* Protists)
Eukaryotic cell, **8, 98–109**
animal, 100*f* (*see also* Animal cell)
chromosomes of, 219*f*
cytoskeleton of, 112–18
DNA replication in, 301*f*, 306–7
endomembrane system of, 104–9
extracellular components of, 118–20, 121*f*
gene expression in, differential, 362–63
gene expression in prokaryotic cell compared with, 327, 328*f*
as genetic chimera, 525
infection of, by microsporidia, 615*f*
as living unit greater than sum of parts, 120
mitochondria and chloroplasts of, 109–11
modification of RNA after transcription in, 317–19
nucleus of, 102, 103*f*
panoramic view of, 99, 100*f*, 101*f*
plant, 101*f* (*see also* Plant cell)
prokaryotic cell compared with, 8*f*, 98–99, 312*f*
protein synthesis in, versus in prokaryotes, 327–28
ribosomes of, 102, 103*f*, 104, 322
RNA polymerases of, 316
RNA processing in, 312*f*
RNA types in, 327*t*
size of, 98
transcription in, 311, 312*f*, 315, 316*f*, 317, 328*f*, 331*f*
translation in, 311, 312*f*, 328*f*, 331*f*
Eukaryotic genome, 359–81. *See also* Genome
cancer resulting from genetic changes affecting cell cycle controls in, 370–74
complexity of, 374–75
chromatin structure based on DNA packing in, 359–61
control of gene expression in (*see* Gene expression)
DNA duplications, rearrangement, and mutations contributing to evolution of, 378–81
gene and multigene families in, 377–78
gene expression, regulation of, 362–70
human (*see* Human genome)
noncoding DNA sequences in, 374–78
overview, 359
as product of genetic annealing, 525
relationship between organismal complexity and complexity of, 374–75
transposable elements in, 375–76
Eumetazoans, **633**, 643
Europa, 514
Europe
acid precipitation in, 55*f*, 1201*f*
blackcap migration in, 1120, 1121*f*
European kestrel, parental caregiving by, 1142*f*
Euryarchaeota, 544
Euryhaline animals, **923**
Eurypterids, **658**
Eustachian tube, **1051**
Eutherian (placental) mammals, **697–701**
biogeography and evolution of, 528
convergent evolution of marsupials and, 450, 494*f*
reproduction in, 967–84
Eutrophication in freshwater ecosystems, **1190**
Eutrophic lakes, **1094**
experimental creation of, 1190
human impact and creation of, 1201
Evaporation, 50, **835**
Evaporative cooling, **50**
in animals, 837
transpiration in plants and, 749
Evapotranspiration, **1176**
actual, 1190
species richness and, 1176*f*
"Evo-devo" (evolutionary developmental biology) 431
origin of flowers and, 601–2

Evolution, 15–19, **438**
  adaptation and (see Evolutionary adaptation)
  anagenesis and cladogenesis as patterns of, 472*f*
  of angiosperms, 601–2
  of animals, 628–30
  of behavioral traits, 1118–21
  of birds, 692–93
  chordate, 674–75
  coevolution, 1164–65
  convergent (see Convergent evolution)
  C. Darwin's field research and his ideas about, 441–43
  C. Darwin's theory of, 438, 443–53
  of development, leading to morphological diversity, 431–33
  DNA and proteins as measure of, 89
  effects of differential predation on guppy, 446, 447*f*
  of eukaryotes, 523–28
  evolutionary novelty, 482–83
  fossil, homologies, and biogeography as evidence of, 448–51
  of genes controlling development, 484–86
  of genetic code, 314
  gradualism theory, 440
  of gymnosperms, 596
  human culture and, 1132–33
  influence of, on animal nitrogenous waste, 928
  of jaw and ear bones in mammals, 695*f*
  J. B. Lamarck's theory of, 440–41
  E. Lander on genomics and, 237
  of leaves, 585, 586*f*
  macroevolution, 472, 482–88
  of mammals, 694–95
  microevolution (see Microevolution)
  of mitosis, 227*f*, 228
  modern synthesis of Mendelian and Darwinian ideas, 455
  mosaic, 703
  of multicellularity, 525–28
  natural selection and, 16*f*, 17*f* (see also Natural selection)
  obesity and, 848
  of organic compounds, 59
  origin of species (see Speciation; Species)
  of plants, from charophyceans (green algae), 573–74
  of plants, highlights of, 579*f*
  of plants, seed plants, 591–93
  of plants, vascular, 584–86
  of populations, 454–70
  of prokaryotes, 521–23
  of reptiles, 689–90
  resistance to idea of, 439–40
  of roots in plants, 585–85
  of tetrapods, 684, 685*f*
  vertebrate digestive systems, 862–64
  of viruses, 342–43
Evolutionary adaptation, **16**, **438**. See also Natural selection
  camouflage as example of, 446*f*
  C. Darwin's theory of natural selection and, 16, 442–43, 444–46
  in prokaryotes, 537–40
  as property of life, 3*f*
Evolutionary biology. See also Evolution
  ecology and, 1081
  K. Kaneshiro on, 436–37
  modern synthesis of Darwinism and Mendelism in, 455
Evolutionary fitness, 464–65
Exaptation, 483
Excitatory postsynaptic potential (EPSP), **1022**
Excretion, **922**
Excretory systems, 928–39
  excretory processes and, 929
  homeostasis and, 937*f*
  key functions of, 929*f*
  kidneys, 931–39
  Malpighian tubules as, 930*f*–31
  mammalian (human), 931–38

  metanephridia as, 930*f*
  nitrogenous waste and, 927–28
  protonephridia (flame-bulb) as, 929*f*–30
  water conservation and, 862
Exercise
  blood pressure during, 876
  health benefits of, 883
Exergonic reaction, **146**
  cellular respiration as, 146, 163*f*
  coupling of, to endergonic reactions by ATP, 148, 149*f*
  energy profile of, 151*f*
  DNA replication, 302*f*
  free energy changes in, 146, 147*f*
Exit tunnel, ribosome, 323
Exocytosis, transport of large molecules by, **137**
Exoenzymes, **609**
Exons, **318**
  correspondence between protein domains and, 319*f*
  duplication of, 380
Exon shuffling, 319, 380–81
  evolution of new gene by, 380*f*
Exoskeleton, **657**, **1064**
  arthropod, 74*f*, 657*f*
  molluscs, 1064
Exotic (introduced) species, 1213–14
Exotoxins, **546**
Expansins, **795**
Exponential population growth, **1144–45**
  global human, 1152, 1153*f*
  intrinsic rate of increase (r_{max}) and, 1144*f*
Expression vector, **390**
Express sequence tags (ESTs), 399
External fertilization, **967**
Exteroreceptors, **1046**
Extinction of species, 1209–10
  mass, 518–21
  overexploitation and, 1214
Extinction vortex, **1215**
  greater prairie chicken case study, 1216
  grizzly bear case study, 1217–18
  process culminating in, 1215*f*
Extracellular components, 118–20
Extracellular digestion, **853–55**
Extracellular fluid, ionic gradients across neuron plasma membrane and, 1016*f*
Extracellular matrix (ECM), **119–20**
  animal morphogenesis and role of, 1002–3
  membrane proteins and, 128*f*
  structure, 119*f*
Extraembryonic membranes, **688**, **999**
  in birds/reptiles, 688, 999*f*
  as derived character of amniotes, 688*f*
  in human embryo, 1000*f*
Extranuclear genes, 289–90
Extraterrestial sources of life, 514
Extreme halophiles, **541**, 544*f*
Extreme thermophiles, 534*f*, **541**
Extremophiles, **541**
Eye
  compound, 1058
  of *Drosophila* fruit fly, 276*f*, 277*f*, 280, 281*f*, 411*f*
  evolution of, 483
  invertebrate, 1057*f*, 1058*f*
  lens cells of, gene expression in, 367*f*
  molluscs, 483*f*
  resolving power of, 95
  single-lens, 1058
  vertebrate, 1058, 1059*f*, 1060*f*
Eye cup, 1058 *See also* Ocellus
Eyespot, 1058 *See also* Ocellus

F_1 generation, **253**
  incomplete dominance and, 261*f*
  law of segregation and, 253*f*, 254*t*, 255*f*, 257*f*
F_2 generation, **253**
  incomplete dominance and, 261*f*
  law of segregation and, 253*f*, 254*t*, 255*f*, 257*f*

Facilitated diffusion, **133**, 134*f*
Facilitators in communities, **1170**
Facultative anaerobes, **176**, **539**
FADH$_2$, as source of electrons for electron transport chain, 170, 171*f*
Fairy ring, 618*f*
Family (taxonomy), **496**
Famine, 558, 1156
Fasciated (f) allele, 430
Fass mutants, plant growth and, 730, 731*f*
Fast block to polyspermy, **989**
Fast muscle fibers, 1071, 1072*t*
Fat(s), **75–76**
  catabolism of, 177*f*
  digestion and absorption of, 859*f*, 861*f*
  hydrocarbons and, 61*f*
  saturated and unsaturated, 75*f*, 76
  synthesis and structure of, 75*f*
Fat, body
  adipose tissue, 61*f*, 76
  obesity and, 847–48
Fate maps, **1004**
  of frog and tunicate embryos, 1004*f*
Fatty acids, **75**
  digestion of, 861*f*
  essential dietary, 850
  saturated and unsaturated, 75*f*, 76
Feathers, bird, 472*f*, 692*f*
Feather star (Crinoidea), 666, 667*f*
Feces, **862**
Feedback inhibition of enzyme activity, **157***f*
  in cellular respiration, 177, 178*f*
Feedback mechanisms
  in biological systems, 11–12
  in cellular respiration, 177, 178*f*
  in endocrine and nervous system pathways, 944
  negative, 11*f*
  positive, 12*f*
  regulation of homeostasis by, 832–33
  regulation of kidney function by, 937*f*
  in thermoregulation, 838–39
Feeding
  bulk, 845*f*
  energy costs and benefits of foraging, 1122, 1123*f*
  fluid, 845*f*
  mineralization of bone and mechanisms for, 679
  pseudopodia for, 563, 564*f*
  substrate, 845*f*
  suspension, 845*f*
Females, human
  conception, embryonic development and childbirth in, 978–82
  contraception and abortion in, 982–83
  hormonal regulation of reproductive system of, 958–59, 973, 976–77
  menopause in, 977
  menstruation in, 973
  oogenesis in, 973, 974*f*
  pregnancy in, 915–16, 978–81
  reproductive anatomy, 969, 970*f*, 971
  reproductive cycle of, 973, 976–77
  semen in reproductive tract of, 972
  sex hormones of, 63*f*, 958–59
  sexual dimorphism and, 468
  sexual response in, 972–73
  X chromosome inactivation in, 284*f*
Females, mate choice by, 1125–26
Fermentation, **161**, **174–76**
  alcohol, 175
  cellular respiration compared with, 175–76
  glycolysis and, 174
  lactic acid, 175
  types of, 175
Ferns (Pterophyta), 2*f*, 588
  life cycle of, 585*f*
  sporophylls of 586
Fertilization, 238, **241–42**, **967**, **988–91**
  acrosomal reaction in, 988, 989*f*
  in animals, 967–69

contraception against human, 982–83
cortical reaction in, 989, 990*f*
double, in angiosperm plants, 599, 600*f*
egg activation in process of, 990
internal versus external, 967
in vitro, 984
in mammals, 990, 991*f*
human, 978, 979*f*, 991
in plants, and seed development, 592, 593*f*, 777*f*–78
prezygotic barriers to, 473, 474*f*
random, as source of genetic variation, 248
in sea urchins, 988–90
segregation of alleles and, as chance events, 259*f*, 275*f*
Fertilization envelope, **989**
Fertilizers, agricultural, 761–62
Fetoscopy, 269
Fetus, **979**
birth of, 981
circulation in placenta and, 980*f*
development of human, 980*f*
maternal antibodies, Rh factor and, 92, 915–16
passive immunity in, 914
testing of, for genetic disorders, 268–70, 983–84
Fever, 85, 874, 948
F factor, **349**
Fibers, sclerenchyma, **718***f*
Fibrin, **882**
Fibrinogen, 880, **882**
Fibroblast, **823**
platelet-derived growth factor and stimulation of human, 231*f*
Fibroblast growth factor (FGF), 1007
Fibronectins, **119**
cell migration in animal morphogenesis and role of, 1002*f*
in extracellular matrix of animal cell, 119*f*, 1002–3
Fibrous connective tissue, **825***f*
Fibrous root system, **713**
Fiji, intertidal reserve in, 1224*f*
Filaments, flower, **598**
Filter feeders. *See* Suspension feeders
Filtrate, production of urine from, **929**, 931–34
Filtration, **929**
Fimbriae, **536***f*
Finches
adaptive radiation of, on Galápagos Islands, 17, 18*f*
beak variations in, 443*f*
character displacement in communities of, 1161*f*
C. Darwin's studies of Galápagos Islands, 442, 443*f*, 450
disruptive selection in case of, black-bellied seed-cracker, 466
speciation in, 478
zebrafinches, mate selection in, 1125–26
Finland, biomanipulation of Lake Vesijärvi in, 1171
Fire
as community disturbance, 1172, 1173*f*
wildfire as component of terrestrial biomes, 1099
Firefly, 314*f*
First law of thermodynamics, **143**
Fish(es)
bony, 682–84
circulatory system of, 870*f*, 871
countercurrent exchange in, 885, 886*f*
effect of differential predation on evolution of guppies, 446, 447*f*
gills of, 885, 886*f*
hearing and equilibrium in, 1053–54
hermaphroditic, 966*f*
jawed, 679, 680*f*, 682–84
jawless, 678–79
kidney adaptations in, 939*f*
lateral line system of, 680, 1054*f*
lobe-finned and lungfishes, 683–84
mutualism between bacteria and, 545*f*
nitrogenous wastes of, 927*f*
osmoregulation in, 923*f*, 924–25

ray-finned, 682–83
rheotaxis in, 1110*f*
sequential hermaphroditism in species of, 966
speciation of cichlid, 479, 480*f*
territoriality of, 1107*f*, 1108*f*
thermoregulation in, 834*f*, 836, 837*f*
Fisher, R. A., 455
Fission
binary, in bacteria, 226, 227*f*, 346, 347*f*, 537, 558
invertebrate, **964**, 965*f*
Fitness, 464–65
relative, 464
Fitzroy, Robert, 441
Five-kingdom taxonomic system, 529*f*, 530
Fixed action pattern (FAP), **1108**
Flaccid plant cell, **133**, **741**, 750*f*
Flagella, **114**–16
beating of, versus beating of cilia, 115*f*
dynein "walking" and movement of, 116*f*
fungi and evolutionary loss of, 613*f*
motion of, 115*f*
prokaryotic, 536*f*
of protist Euglenozoa, 553*f*
of stramenopile, 558*f*
ultrastructure of, 115*f*
Flagellates, protistan, 628*f*
Flagellin, 536*f*
Flame-bulb system, 929*f*, 930
Flashlight fish (*Photoblepharon palpebratus*), 545*f*
Flatworms (Platyhelminthes), 639*f*, 646–48
as acoelomate, 631*f*
blood fluke, 647*f*, 1163
classes of, 646*t*
hydrostatic skeleton in, 1063
monogeneans and trematodes, 647
nervous system, 1012*f*
planarian anatomy, 647*f*
reproductive anatomy of, 968*f*
tapeworm anatomy, 648*f*
turbellarians, 646–47
Flavonoids, 575, 766
Flavoprotein, 170
Fletcher, W. J., 1085, 1086*f*
Flight
in birds, 483, 692*f*
energy cost of, 1074*f*
in insects, 660–61
theropods and, 692–93
Flooding, plant response to, 811
Florigen, **808**
Flower, **598**
cell signaling in development of, 429–31
complete versus incomplete, 773*f*
development of, 429*f*
diversity in types and structures, 773*f*
environmental effect of phenotype on, 264*f*
evo-devo hypothesis on origins of, 601–2
monoecious versus dioecious, 773*f*
pattern formation in development of, 429*f*, 430*f*, 431*f*
"pin" and "thrum" types of, 775*f*
pollinators of, 604*f*
self-pollinating, versus self-incompatible, 775–76
structure of, 598*f*, 772*f*
Flower fly, 22*f*
Flowering
evidence for hormonal control of, 808*f*
genetic control of, 734–35
photoperiodic control of, 806–8
vernalization and, 807
Flowering plants. *See* Angiosperms
Fluid feeders, 845*f*
Fluid mosaic model of plasma membrane, **124**, 125*f*
Flukes, 639*f*
Fluorescence, 189*f*
Fluorescence microscopy, 94*f*, 96*f*
Fly agaric (*Amanita muscaria*), 618*f*
Flying squirrel, 450*f*
Flying squirrel, northern (*Glaucomys sabrinus*), 1031*f*

Follicle, **969**
Follicle-stimulating hormone (FSH), **952**, 959
female reproductive cycle and, 976, 977
Follicular phase, ovarian cycle, **976**
Food
angiosperms as, 605
caloric imbalance in, 846–48
catabolism of, in cellular respiration, 161–65
energy of, available at different tropic levels, 1193*f*
feeding (*see* Feeding)
as fuel and nutrition for animals, 828–31, 844–46
functions of, 177
fungi as, 623
fungi as spoilers of, 622
fungi in production of, 623
genetically modified organisms as, 407–8
photosynthesis, and conversion of light energy into chemical energy of, 182–85
plant biotechnology and increased supply of, 784
seaweed as, 561*f*
Food chain, **1166**
energy partitioning, 1192*f*
examples of terrestrial and marine, 1166*f*
limits on length of, 1167–68
Food plants. *See* Crop plants
Food poisoning, 460, 542*f*
Food processing in animals, 853–55
Food vacuoles, 107, **108**
as digestive compartment, 853
in *Paramecium*, 557*f*
Food web, **1166**–67
biological magnification of PCBs (polychlorinated biphenyls) in, 1202*f*
in marine ecosystems, 1166*f*
partial, in Chesapeake Bay estuary, 1167*f*
Foot, **650**
bird, 694*f*
moss sporophyte, **580**
mollusc, 650
Foraging behavior, **1119**, 1122–23
energy costs and benefits of, 1122
Foraminiferans (forams), **563**
Forebrain, 680
human, **1028**
Forelimb, homologous structures in mammalian, 449*f*
Forensic science, DNA technology and, 26*f*, 404–5
Forest
canopy of, 1098
coniferous, 1102*f*
deforestation of, 606, 1078–79, 1198, 1199*f*, 1209*f*, 1212, 1221*f*
determining species diversity in, 1165*f*
effects of acid precipitation on, 55*f*
effects of climate change on, 1092*f*, 1204
management of, based on Hubbard Brook Experimental Forest findings, 1078–79
temperate broadleaf, 1103*f*
tropical, 1100*f*
Forest Atmosphere Carbon Transfer and Storage (FACTS-1) experiment, effects of elevated CO_2 on, 1204
Form and function
bat anatomy and, 17*f*
fluid mosaic model of plasma membrane and, 130
Fossil(s), 15*f*, **439**. *See also* Fossil record
amniotes, 688
angiosperm, 601*f*
birds, 693*f*
from Burgess Shale, Canada, 629*f*
from China, 676, 677*f*
dating of, 517–18
of dragonfly, 491*f*
of early chordates, 676, 677*f*
of early vertebrates, 678, 679*f*
Ediacaran, 628*f*
examples of, 493*f*
fungi, 612*f*
gnathostome, 680
human, 706*f*

index, 491f, 517f
insect, 660
mass extinctions and, 518–21
primate, 697
Proterozoic, 526f
in sedimentary rocks, 439, 440f, 492f
stromatolites, 521
transitional, 451f
trilobite, 657f
Fossil fuel, 61
acid precipitation caused by burning, 55–56
increased atmospheric carbon dioxide due to
combustion of, 1196f
Fossil record, 492. *See also* Fossil(s)
mass extinctions revealed in, 518–21
evidence for natural selection in, 451
phylogenies inferred from, 492
in sedimentary rock, 439, 440f, 492f
Foundation species, 1169–70
Founder cells, 1004
Founder effect, 462
Fovea, 1060
FOXP2 gene, language ability in humans linked to, 706
F plasmid, 349
bacterial conjugation and, 349, 350f
Fragmentation, 781
asexual reproduction beginning with, 965
of ecosystems, 1220–21
Frameshift mutation, 329
Franklin, Rosalind, discovery of DNA structure and
contribution of, 296, 297f, 298
Free energy, 145–48
change in (ΔG), 145
electron transport and changes in, 171f
in exergonic and endergonic reactions, 146, 147f
metabolism and, 146–48
relationship of, to stability, work capacity, and
spontaneous change, 146f
stability (equilibrium) and, 145
Free energy of activation, 151
lowering barrier of, by enzymes, 152f
Free ribosomes, 102, 103f, 105, 325
Freeze-fracture method of cell preparation, 126, 126f
Frequency-dependent selection, 467–68
Freshwater animals, osmoregulation in, 924–25
Freshwater biomes
estuaries as, 1095f
lakes as, 1093f, 1094f
streams and rivers as, 1095f
wetlands as, 1094f
Freshwater ecosystems, primary productivity of,
1187f, 1188–91
Fringe wetlands, 1094
Fritillaria assyriaca, 399
Frogs (Anura), 685
aposematic coloration in poison arrow, 1162
body axes in, 1004
cadherins and formation of blastula in, 1003f
cleavage in embryo of, 992, 993f
cryptic coloration in canyon, 1162f
fate map of embryo of, 1004f
gastrulation in, 995, 996f
metamorphosis in, 686f
organogenesis in, 997f
poisonous, 685
reproduction in, 967f
skin color, 685, 946
Frohlich, Michael, 601
Fructose, hydrolysis of sucrose to glucose and, 150, 151f
Fruit, 598–99, 774, 778
development of, 778, 779f
ethylene and ripening of, 801
gibberellins and growth of, 797f
seed dispersal and adaptations of, 599f
variations in structures of, 599f
Fruit fly (*Drosophila* sp.)
associative learning in, 1116
axis establishment in development of, 423–25
average heterozygosity of, 463

biological clocks in, 1030
body color and wing size, 277–78, 279f, 280, 281f
chromosome number in, 102
courtship and mating in, 436–37
defense system of, 902
diet and mate choice in, 1113f, 1114
effect of bicoid gene in, 424f
evolution of, on Hawaiian Islands, 436–37
eye color, 276f, 277f, 280, 281f
eye development, 411f
foraging behavior in, 1120
genetic analysis of early development in, 423
genome, 394, 398, 399t, 401
hierarchy of gene activity in development of, 425
homeotic genes in, 425, 431f
identity of body parts and homeotic genes in development of, 425
interactions among proteins in cell of, 10f
life cycle of, 421, 422f, 423
logistic model of population growth and life history of, 1147
as model organism, 412f
T. Morgan's studies of, 276, 277f, 277–78, 279f
natural selection and evolution of, 506
radiation and mutations in, 329–30
reproductive isolation of populations of, 477f
segmentation pattern in development of, 425
sex differences in, due to RNA splicing, 319
sex-linked inheritance in, 276, 277f
songs of, 1111–12
zygote, 994
Functional groups, 63–66
ATP and, 66
in female and male sex hormones, 63f
important, in organic compounds, 64–65f
RNA and, 327
significance of, to life, 63
Fungi, 608–25
ascomycetes (Ascomycota), 616–17, 622
basidiomycetes (Basidiomycota), 618–19
bioluminescent, 141f
chytrids (Chytridiomycota), 613
club, 618–19
as decomposers, 620, 1186f
ecological impact of, 620–22
evolution of, 612
as food and in food production, 623
fossils, 612f
generalized life cycle, 611f
glomeromycetes (Glomeromycota), 615
land colonization by, 527, 612
lichens, 621–22
nutrition in, 608–10
as pathogens, 622–23
phyla of, 612–19
phylogeny of, 612, 613f
reproduction of, 610, 611f, 614f, 617f, 619f
sac fungi (Ascomycota),
sexual life cycle in, 242f
structure of, 609f
zygomycetes (Zygomycota), 613–15
Funnel web spider, feeding and aggressive behavior
in, 1119f, 1120
Fusiform initials, 727

G₀ phase, molecular control of cell cycle and, 229
G₁ phase of cell cycle, 221f
G₂ phase of cell cycle, 221f, 222f, 228
molecular control of cell cycle at, 230f
G3P (glyceraldehyde-3-phosphate), 194
Gage, Fred, 1038
Gage, Phineas, 1035
β-Galactosidase, 355f, 387
Galápagos ground finch (*Geospiza dificilis*), 478
Galápagos Islands
adaptive radiation and evolution of finches on, 17,
18f, 443f, 450
C. Darwin's studies of species on, 442–43
Gallbladder, 855

Gametangia (gametangium), 577f
Gametes, 219, 239, 241, 964. *See also* Egg; Sperm
animal, 968–69
chromosome number in, 219
crossing over and recombinant chromosomes in,
248, 249f
fertilization and formation of, 241–42 (*see also*
Fertilization)
genetic variation in populations of, 459–60
independent assortment of chromosomes and genetic variation in, 247, 248f
isolation of, as reproductive barrier, 475f
law of segregation and alleles for genetic character
in separate, 254, 255f
meiosis as cell division of, 220
plant, 771–76 (*see also* Gametophyte)
random fertilization and genetic variation in, 248
Game theory, 1127
applied to reciprocal altruism, 1130–31
applied to survival and mating strategies,
1127–28
Gametogenesis, 973
Gametophore, 580, 581f
Gametophyte, 242, 576
of bryophytes, 580, 581f
as haploid stage, 242
reduced, in seed plants, 591–93, 772, 774–75
relationship of sporophyte to, 592f
Gamma aminobutyric acid (GABA), 1025
Ganglia (ganglion) cells, 1012, 1061f, 1062
Gannets, territoriality in, 1149f
Gap genes, 425
Gap junctions, 120, 121f, 627
electrical synapses containing, 1021
Garrod, Archibald, 309–10
Garstang, William, 675
Garter snake (*Thamnophis elegans*), 474f
behavioral variation in selection of prey by, 1118,
1119f
Gas exchange in animals, 884–95
in arthropods, 657, 658
bioenergetics and, 884f
body size and shape and, 821–22
breathing and, 888–90
in elite athletes and deep-diving mammals,
894–95
gills and, 884, 885f, 886f
lungs and, 886–87, 888f
oxygen uptake and carbon dioxide disposal, 867,
892–94
partial pressure gradients and, 891
in protists, 884
respiratory pigments and gas transport in blood,
892–94
respiratory surfaces for, 884–87
tracheal systems in insects and, 886, 887f
Gastric gland, 857f
Gastric juice, 857
Gastric ulcers, 858f
Gastropods (Gastropoda), 651–52
torsion in, 651f
Gastrovascular cavity, 643, 854
cnidarian, 643, 868f
internal transport and circulation through
invertebrate, 868
Gastrula, 627, 994
Gastrula organizer, 1006
Gastrulation, 627, 994–97
in bird embryo, 995–96, 997f
embryonic tissue layers formed by, 994
in frog embryo, 995, 996f
in human embryo, 1000f
of sea urchin embryo, 995f
Gated channels, 133
Gated ion channels, action potentials in nervous system and, 1017–21, 1046
Gause, G. F., competitive exclusion principle and, 1160
Gecko lizard, van der Waals interactions and climbing
ability of, 42

Geese, imprinting of graylag, 1108, 1109f
Gel electrophoresis, **392**
  of restriction fragments, 392, 393f
Gene(s), 7, **86, 239**. *See also* Chromosome(s); DNA
      (deoxyribonucleic acid)
  activation of, by growth-factor, 213f
  allele as alternate form of, 253–54, 255f (*see also*
      Alleles)
  avirulence (*avr*) gene, 813, 814f
  BRCA1 and BRCA2, and breast cancer, 374
  cloning of (*see* Gene cloning)
  coordinately controlled, 367
  definition of, 330
  determining function of, 400
  duplications of, 378f, 380, 459
  egg-polarity, 424
  evidence for association of specific chromsosome
      with specific, 276–77
  evolution of, controlling development, 484–86
  exon duplication and exon shuffling in, 380
  expression of (*see* Gene expression)
  extending Mendelian genetics for single, 260–62
  extending Mendelian genetics for two or more,
      262–63
  extranuclear, 289–90
  FOXP2, 706
  gap, 425
  genetic recombination of unlinked and linked,
      278–79, 280f
  hedgehog, 499f
  homeotic, 485
  homologous, 505f
  horizontal transfer of, in prokaryotes, 538, 541, 546
  Hox (*see Hox* genes)
  in human genome (*see* Human genome)
  immunoglobulin, gene rearrangement in, 906f
  jumping, 351–52, 371, 375–76
  E. Lander on identifying, 236–37
  linked, 277–82
  location of, on chromosomes (*see* Gene locus)
  maternal effect, 424
  molecular homologies in, 494, 495f
  multigene families, 377–78
  mutations in (*see* Mutations)
  nod, 766
  with novel functions, 380
  number of, in select genomes, 399t
  organelle, inheritance of, 289–90
  organ-identity, 430
  organization of typical eukaryotic, 364, 365f
  orthologous, 505f
  pair-rule, 425
  paralogous, 505f
  point mutations in, 328–30, 459
  R, 813, 814f
  rearrangement of, in lymphocytes, 906–7
  relationship of proteins to (*see also* Protein synthesis)
  RNA splicing and split, 318f, 319
  S-, and self-incompatibility in plants, 776
  segmentation, 425
  segment polarity, 425
  sex-linked, 282–84
  transcription factors and controls on, 205, 364–66
  transfer of, in bacteria, 348–51
Gene clones, **385**
  identification of, 388, 389f
  libraries of, 388, 389f
Gene cloning, **385**
  bacterial plasmids and production of, 385, 386,
     387f, 388, 389f
  overview of, 385f–86
  recombinant DNA and, 385f, 386f
Gene expression, 309–33
  cellular differentiation in plants and, 732, 733f
  cloning and, in eukaryotic genes, 390–91
  different cell types resulting from differential,
     415–20
  expression systems, in bacteria, 390
  genetic code and, 312–14

genomics and study of interacting groups of
     genes, 400, 401f
  flow of genetic information and, 309
  identifying protein-coding genes in DNA
     sequences, 399
  point mutations and, 328–30
  in prokaryotes (bacteria), and metabolic
     adjustments, 352–56
  in prokaryotes compared with eukaryotes, 327,
     328f
  regulation of, during development, 418–20
  relationship between genes and proteins and,
     309–10
  roles of RNA in, 327
  summary, 331f
  translation, 311–12, 320–26
  transcription, 311–12, 315–17
  transcription in eukaryotic cells, 317–19
  transcription in eukaryotic cells, regulation of,
     362–70
  viruses and, 339
Gene flow, **462**
  lack of, 458
Gene-for-gene recognition, **813–14**
Gene locus, **239**
  mapping of, using recombination data, 279–81
Gene pool, **455**
  allele frequencies in, 455–56
  of nonevolving population, 457–58
  mutations and sexual recombination as cause of
     change in, 459–60
  natural selection, genetic drift, and gene flow as
     cause of change in, 460–62
  reproductive barriers and isolation of, 473,
     474–75f
Generalized transduction, 348f, 349
Generative cell, 599
Gene regulation
  in eukaryotic cells, 362–70
  negative, 354–56
  positive, 356
  in prokaryotic cells, 352–56
Gene segments (J), 906, 907
Gene therapy, **403–4**
Genetic annealing, **525**
Genetically modified (GM) organisms, **407–8**
  plants as, 784–86
Genetic code, 8, 312–14, 459
  deciphering, 313–14
  dictionary of, 314f
  evolution of, 314
  reading frame for, 314
  redundancy in, 314
  triplet code of, 312, 313f
Genetic disorders. *See also names of specific disorders*
  cancer as, 305 (*see also* Cancer)
  carriers of, 266
  chromosomal alterations as cause of, 285–88
  color blindness, 283, 1061
  cystinuria, 134
  diagnosis of, 269, 270f, 983–84
  dominantly inherited, 267–68
  exchange of (*see* Genetic recombination)
  extranuclear genes and, 289–90
  gene therapy for, 403–4
  genetic drift, founder effect and, 462
  genomic imprinting and, 289
  genomics and, 401–2
  growth disorders, 952
  karyotyping for determining, 287f
  Mendelian patterns of inheritance and, 266–68
  metabolic, 309–10
  multifactorial, 268
  phenotype, recessive traits, and, 261
  population genetics and, 458
  relay proteins in cell signaling, and, 215
  sex-linked, 283–84
  testing and counseling for, 268–70
Genetic diversity. *See* Genetic variation

Genetic drift, **460–62**
  bottleneck effect and, 461f
  example of, in wildflower population, 461f
  founder effect and, 462f
  lack of, 458
Genetic engineering, **384**. *See also* DNA technology
  in animals, 406, 416
  in plants, 783–86
Genetic map, **279**
  cytogenetic map as, 281, 396f
  partial, of *Drosophila* chromosome, 281f
Genetic markers, RFLPs as, 394, 396f, 403f
Genetic polymorphisms, **463**
Genetic prospecting, 541
Genetic recombination, **278**. *See also* Recombinant
     DNA
  in bacteria, gene transfer and, 348–51
  in bacteria, mutations and, 346–48
  in *Drosophila* fruit fly, 278–81
  mutations and, 459–60 (*see also* Mutations)
  produced by crossing over, 278, 279f, 280f
  produced by independent assortment of
     chromosomes, 278
Genetics, **238**. *See also* Gene(s); Gene expression;
     Genome
  of bacteria (prokaryotes), 334, 346–52
  of behavior, 1109–13
  chromosomes and (*see* Chromosomal basis of
     inheritance)
  of development (*see* Development)
  environmental factors combined with, effects on
     behavior, 1113–18
  of eukaryotes (*see* Eukaryotic genome)
  genetic variation (*see* Genetic variation)
  inheritance of genes and, 239
  E. Lander on research in, 236–37
  meiosis, sexual life cycle, and, 240–47
  Mendelian (*see* Mendelian inheritance)
  molecular (*see* Molecular basis of inheritance)
  of populations (*see* Population genetics)
  sexual and asexual reproduction and, 239
  of viruses, 334–46
Genetics problems
  laws of probability used for solving, 259–60
  Punnett square for solving, 254, 255f
Genetic testing
  carrier recognition, 269
  fetal testing, 269, 270f
  newborn screening, 269–70
Genetic variation, 238, 247–49, 462–64
  benefits of, to human welfare, 1211–12
  biodiversity crisis and loss of, 1210
  independent assortment of chromosomes as
     source of, 247, 248f, 278
  crossing over as source of, 248, 249f
  evolutionary significance of, in populations,
     248–49, 459–60
  measuring, 463
  mutation as source of, 459–60
  natural selection and role of, 462–64
  between populations, 463–64
  preservation of, by diploidy and balanced
     polymorphism, 466–68
  random fertilization as source of, 248
  sexual recombination as source of, 460
Genome, 8, **219**. *See also* Gene(s)
  analysis of, 392–94
  of *Arabidopsis*, 729f
  comparing, of different species, 399t, 400–402
  determining gene function in, 400
  eukaryotic (*see* Eukaryotic genome)
  evolutionary history of organisms found in, 504–6
  evolution of, 378–81, 505–6
  future studies in, 402
  human (*see* Human genome)
  identifying protein-coding genes in DNA
     sequences, 399
  mapping of, at DNA level, 394–98
  prokaryotic (*see* Prokaryotic genome)

relationship between composition of, and organismal complexity, 374–75

size of, and estimated number of genes in select, 399t

studying expression of interacting gene groups, 400, 401f

viral, 335

Genome mapping, **279**, 394–98

cytogenetic map as, 281, 396f

DNA sequencing as, 396–98

linkage map, 279–81, 396

partial, of *Drosophila* chromosome, 281f

physical, 396

whole-genome shotgun approach to, 398f

Genomic equivalence, 415–18

animal stem cells and, 418

nuclear transplantation in animals and, 415–17

totipotency in plants and, 415f

Genomic imprinting, **288–89**, 364

of mouse *Igf2* gene, 289f

Genomic library, **388**, 389f

Genomics, **398–402**

animal phylogeny based on molecular data and, 635f

comparing genomes, 399t, 400–402

determining gene function, 400

future directions in, 402

genome mapping, 394–98

identifying protein-coding genes in DNA sequences, 399

E. Lander on evolution and, 237

studying expression of gene groups, 400

Genotype, **256**

Hardy-Weinberg theorem and calculating frequencies of, 457–58

norm of reaction, 264, 1109

phenotype versus, 256f

Genus (taxonomy), **496**

Geographic barriers, speciation with and without, 476–82

Geographic distribution of species, 1083

abiotic factors and, 1086–87

behavior and habitat selection and, 1085

biotic factors and, 1085–86

climate and, 1087–92

dispersal and distribution factors, 1084–85

factors limiting, 1084f

Geographic variation, **463–64**

in mice populations, 463f

in yarrow plants, 464f

Geologic record, **518**, 519t

Geometric isomers, 62f

Geospiza fortis, 1161f

Geospiza fuliginosa, 1161f

Geospiza magnirostris (large ground finch), 443f

Geospiza scandens (cactus ground finch), 443f

Germination, 779, 780f

dormancy and, 779–80, 798, 799f

gibberellins and, 798f

light-induced, 803f

phytochromes and, 803–4

stages of, 780

two types of, 780f

Germ layers, **631**, 994

adult derivatives of embryonic, 999t

gastrulation of zygote and formation of, 994–97

Gestation, **978–79**. See also Pregnancy

Ghost crabs (Ocypode), 664f, 829f

Ghrelin hormone, 847f

Giant panda, 160

Giardia intestinalis, 552, 553f

Gibberellins, **797–98**

fruit growth and, 797f

seed germination and, 798f

stem elongation and, 309, 797

Gibbons, 701f

Gibbs, J. Willard, 145

GIFT (gamete intrafallopian transfer), 984

Gigantism, 952

Gill(s), **884**, 885f

gas exchange and, 884–85

fish, 886f

invertebrate, 650f, 652, 885f

Gill circulation, **871**

Ginkgo biloba, 593, 594f

Giraffe, blood pressure in, 876

Giurfa, Martin, 1117

GLABRA-2 homeotic gene, 732, 733f

Glaciers, 588

ecological succession following retreat of, 1174f, 1175f

Glands. See Endocrine glands

Glandular epithelia, **823**

Glans penis, **972**

Gleason, H. A., 1179

Glia cells, **1014–15**

Global warming, 1079, 1204–5

Globigerina, 563f

Globin genes and proteins

evolution of α-globin and β-globin gene families, 379f

multigene families encoding of, 377f, 378

similarity of amino acid sequence in human, 379f

Glomeromycetes (Glomeromycota), 615

Glomerulus, **931**, 932f

Glomus mosseae, 615f

Glucagon, **955**

maintenance of glucose homeostasis by insulin and, 955f, 956

Glucocorticoids, **958**

Glucose, 70

α and β ring forms of, 72, 73f

ATP yield from, in cellular respiration, 173f, 174

blood levels of, homeostatic regulation of, 846

cellular respiration and degradation of, 161, 162, 164f, 165–74

control of blood levels of, 846f, 955f, 956

conversion of carbon dioxide to, in Calvin cycle, 193–95

disaccharide synthesis from, 71f

gene regulation in bacterial metabolism of, 356f

hydrolysis of sucrose to fructose and, 150, 151f

linear and ring forms of, 71f

oxidation of, during glycolysis, 165–67

synthesis of, from muscle proteins, 958

transport of, in blood, 130

Glutamate

light reception, vision, and, 1061

receptors for, and long-term potentiation in vertebrate brain, 1036, 1037f

receptors for, and schizophrenia, 1039–40

taste reception and, 1055

Glutamic acid, 149

Glutamine, synthesis of, 149

Glyceraldehyde-3-phosphate (G3P), **194**

Glycerol phosphate, **65**f

Glycine, 65f

Glycogen, **72**

blood glucose homeostasis and role of, 846

breakdown of, by epinephrine, 204–5, 213f, 946

storage of, in animal, 72f

Glycolipids, **129**

Glycolysis, **164**, 165–67

connection of, to other metabolic pathways, 176–78

energy input and output of, 165f

evolutionary significance of, 176

fermentation and, 174, 175

junction between citric acid cycle and, 168f

steps of, 166–67f

Glycoproteins, **105**, 119, 129. See also Collagen

in viral envelopes, 336, 340

Glycosidic linkage, **70**, 71f

Glyoxysomes, 111

Gnathostomes, **679–84**

chondrichthyans as, 680–82

derived characters of, 679–80

early, 680f

evolution of vertebrate jaws and, 680f

fossil, 680

osteichthyans (ray-finned and lobe-finned fish) as, 682–84

tetrapods as, 684–86 (see also Tetrapods)

Gnetophytes (Gnetophyta), 593, 594f, 600

Gnetum, 594f

Gnom mutant, and axial polarity of plants, 732f

Goiter, 33f, 954

Golden algae (Chrysophyta), **560**

Golgi apparatus, **105**, 106f, 107

cis and trans face of, 105, 106f

cisternae of, 105, 106f

origins of, 525

Gonadotropin-releasing hormone (GnRH), 976, 977

Gonadotropins, **952**. See also Follicle-stimulating hormone (FSH); Luteinizing hormone (LH)

Gonads, 241, **968**

female, 958–59

hormones produced by, 949t, 958–59

male, 958

Goodman, Corey, 1037–38

Gorillas, 701f

Gorter, E., 125

Gould, Stephen Jay, 481

G protein, **206**

acetylcholine, cardiac muscle and, 1024

human olfaction and, 1056

inhibitory, 211

ras gene and Ras, 371, 372f

receptor proteins linked to, 206f

G-protein-linked receptor, **206**f

cAMP as second messenger in pathway of, 210, 211f

Grackle, great-tailed, distribution of, 1084, 1085f

Grade, animal phylogenetic trees and, **630**

Graded potentials, **1018**

action potential and, in neurons, 1018f

Gradualism, **440**

Gradualism model for speciation tempo, 482f

Grafting, vegetative reproduction of plants by, 782

Graft versus host reaction, **916**

Graham, Linda, on evolution of land plants, 510–11

Gram, Hans Christian, 535

Gram-negative bacteria, **535**f, 541

Gram-positive bacteria, **535**f, 543f

Gram stain, **535**f

Grana (granum), **110**, 111f

Grand Canyon

allopatric speciation at, 477f

fossils from strata of sedimentary rock in, 440f

Grand Teton National Park, Wyoming, biotic and legal boundaries of, 1222, 1223f

Granzymes, 911f

Grape, effect of gibberellin on, 797f

Grasshopper

anatomy of, 660f

digestive tract in, 854f

muscle and skeleton interaction in, 1066f

open circulatory system in, 869f

tracheal system, 887f

Grasslands

temperate, 1102f

wildfire in, 1099

Grave's disease, 953f

Gravitropism, **809**

Gravity

blood pressure and, 876

free energy and motion of, 146f

invertebrate detection of, 1050

plant responses to, 809f

Gray crescent, 1005

Gray matter, nervous system, **1026**

Greater prairie chicken (*Tympanuchus cupido*), extinction vortex and case study of, 1216

Great Lakes food web, biological magnification of PCBs in, 1202f

Green algae, 550f, **567–69**

colonial and multicellular, 568f

evolution of green plants from, 573–74

life cycle of *Chlamydomonas*, 569*f*
lichens and, 621–22
Greenhouse effect and global warming, **1204–5**
Green warbler finch (*Certhidea olivacea*), 443*f*
Green world hypothesis, **1193–94**
Grendel, F., 125
Grizzly bear
extinction vortex and case study of, 1217–18
nature reserves and, 1222, 1223*f*
Gross primary productivity (GPP), **1187**
Groth, James, 1149
Ground tissue system, **717**
Growth
allometric, 484*f*
cancer and faulty cell, 232–33
disorders of, in humans, 952
in plants (*see* Plant growth)
as property of life, 3*f*
Growth cone, **1038**
Growth factor, **231**, 948
activation of specific gene by, 213*f*
bone morphogenetic protein BMP-4, 1006
as local regulator, 202–3
regulation of cell cycle and cell division by, 231*f*
Sonic hedgehog, 1008
Growth hormones (GH), **952**
Growth regulators, 203
GTP (guanosine triphosphate), energy for polypeptide synthesis provided by, 323
Guanine (G), 88
DNA structure and, 296*f*, 297*f*
Guanosine triphosphate. *See* GTP (guanosine triphosphate)
Guard cells, **724**
control of transpiration by opening and closing of stomata by, 750*f*, 751
Guppy (*Poecilia reticulata*)
differential predation and natural selection in populations of, 446, 447*f*
mate choice copying, 1131*f*
Gurdon, John, 416
Gustation, **1055**
Guttation, 746*f*
Gymnamoebas, 564*f*
Gymnosperms, **579**
evolution of, 596
four phyla of extant, 593, 594–95*f*
pine life cycle, 596, 597*f*
seed, 593, 596, 597*f*

Habitat
behavior and selection of, 1085
biodiversity crisis and loss/fragmentation of, 1212–13
corridors between, 1221*f*–22
differentiation of, and speciation of cichlids, 479, 480*f*
edges between, 1220–21
isolation of, as prezygotic reproductive barrier, 474*f*
of protists, 550
of red-cockaded woodpecker, 1218, 1219*f*
Habitat selection, species dispersal and, 1085
Habituation as learning, **1115**
Hacker, Sally, 1170
Hagfishes (Myxini), 641*f*, 676–77
Haikouella and *Haikouichthys* fossils, 676, 677*f*
Hair, mammalian, 694
Hair cell, mechanoreception by, **1046**, 1047*f*, 1052, 1053*f*
Haldane, J. B. S., 455, 513, 1130
Hales, Stephen, 756
Half-life of radioactive isotopes, **517**
Halophiles, extreme, 541, 544*f*
Hamilton, William, 1129, 1130
Hamilton's rule, kin selection and, 1129, **1130**
Hantavirus, 344
Haploid cell, **241**. *See also* Gametes
reduction of chromosome from diploid cell to, 242, 243–47

Haploid-diploid system of sex determination, 282*f*
Hardy-Weinberg equation, 457
Hardy-Weinberg equilibrium, 457*f*, 458
conditions for, 458
Hardy-Weinberg theorem, **456–58**
Hare, population cycles of lynx and snowshoe, 1151, 1152*f*
Harper, John, 1148
Harris, William, 1116
Haustoria, **610**
Hawaiian Islands
evolution and adaptive radiation on, 436, 480, 481*f*
evolution of fruit fly *Drosophila* on, 436–37
Hawkmoth larva, mimicry in, 1162*f*
Health, human. *See also* Diseases and disorders; Genetic disorders
benefits of exercise to, 883
risks of anabolic steroids to, 959*f*
Health of organisms, population density and, 1149
Health science. *See* Medicine
Hearing
human ear, 1051*f*
in mammals, 1050–52
pitch distinguished by cochlea, 1052*f*
sound detection in invertebrates and, 1050
Heart, **868**, 871–74
cardiac cycle of, 872, 873*f*
cardiac muscle of, 1024
craniate, 676
maintaining rhythm of, 873, 874*f*
structure of mammalian, 872*f*
Heart attack, **883**
Heart murmur, **873**
Heart rate, 873
Heartwood, **727**
Heat, 49, **142**
activation energy supplied by, 151
exchanges of, between organisms and environment, 834, 835*f*
plant response to excessive, 812
protein denaturation caused by, 85
specific, 49
thermoregulation and (*see* Thermoregulation)
Heat of vaporization, **50**
Heat-shock proteins, 812, **840**
Heavy chains, B cell receptors, **903**, 904*f*
Hedgehog gene, phylogram comparing, 499*f*
Hedrick, Ann, 1119–20
Heinrich, Bernd, 1117
Helicase, **303**, 304*t*
Helicobacter pylori, 542*f*, 858*f*
Helium, models of, 34*f*
Helper T cells, **909**
effect of HIV virus on, 918, 919*f*
interaction of, with MHC molecules, 905*f*
role of, in humoral and cell-mediated immunity, 909, 910*f*
Heme, 83
Heme group, 170
Hemichordates (acorn worm), 641*f*
Hemizygous organisms, 283
Hemocyanin, **892**
Hemocytes, 902
Hemoglobin, 170, **880–81**
comparison of amino acid sequence of, in humans and select animals, 89, 449, 450*f*
evolution of α- and β-globin gene families, 379*f*
heterozygote advantage in, 466
loading and unloading of oxygen by, 892*f*
mRNA degradation in, and eukaryotic gene expression, 368, 369*f*
multigene familes in α- and β-globin, 377*f*
oxygen dissociation curves for, 892*f*
point mutations in, 329*f*
quaternary structure of protein in, 83*f*
as respiratory pigment, 892
sickle-cell disease and, 84*f* (*see also* Sickle-cell disease)

Hemolymph, 657, **868**, 869*f*
Hemophilia, 284, 403, **882**
Hemophilus influenzae, genome mapping of, 398
Hemorrhagic fevers, 344
Henry, Charles, 1112
Henslow, John, 441
Hepatic portal vein, **861**, 869–70
Hepatophyta (liverworts), 580, 582*f*
Herbaceous plants, **720**
Herbicide, auxin as, 795–96
Herbivores, 844
digestion and dentition in, 863*f*
green world hypothesis regarding checks on, and, 1194
plant defenses against, 813, 1163
Herbivory, **1163**
Hercules scarab beetle (*Dynastes hercules*), 1080*f*
Heredity, **238–39**. *See also* Genetics; Inheritance
blending hypothesis of, 251
C. Darwin's theory of evolution and, 438, 443–51
DNA and (*see* Molecular basis of inheritance)
genes, chromosomes, and, 238–39, 274–77 (*see also* Chromosomal basis of inheritance; Mendelian inheritance)
information conveyed by, 7*f*, 27*f*
J. B. Lamarck's theory of, 440–41
Hermaphrodites, **642**, **966**
bluehead wrasse as, 966*f*
sequential, 966
sponges as, 642
Herpesvirus, 340
Hershey, Alfred, experiments on genetic material by, 294, 295*f*, 296
Hesiolyra bergi, 655*f*
Heterochromatin, **360**
Heterochrony, **484–85**
Heterocysts, nitrogen fixation by, 539*f*
Heterokaryon, 611
Heteromorphic generations, **562**
Heterosporous plants, **586**
among seed plants, 592
Heterotrophs, **181**, 538, 539*t*
fungi as, 608–10
prokaryotes as, 538–39
protists as, 550
Heterozygote advantage, **466**
Heterozygotes, **255–56**
average, 463
Hexapods (insects), **658**, 660–64
Hexose sugars, 70*f*
Hfr cell, 349, 350*f*
H+ gradients and pump, 171, 172*f*, 173, 521–22, 739–40, 794
Hibernation, **840**
High-density lipoproteins (HDLs), 883
High-throughput technology, **11**
Hindbrain, **1028**
Hinge joint, 1065*f*
Hippocampus, 1034, 1035*f*
Hippocrates, 605
Hirudinea (leeches), 655*f*, 1012*f*
Histamine, immune response and release of, **901**, 916–17
Histone(s), 360
association of DNA and, in nucleosomes, 360, 361*f*
modifications of, as regulation of eukaryotic gene expression, 363*f*, 364
Histone acetylation, 363*f*, 364
Histone code hypothesis, 364
HIV (human immunodeficiency virus), 337, **341**, 344, 918–19
detection of, 403
drug resistance in, 447, 448*f*
infection by, 918–19
molecular clock used to date origin of, 507
mutation rates of, 459–60
reproductive cycle, 342*f*
transmission, 919
Hoatzin, 863

Hoiland, Wade, 1149
Holdfast, **560**, 561*f*
Holoblastic cleavage, **994**
Holothuroidea (sea cucumbers), 666t, 667*f*
Holsinger, Kent, 1112
Homeobox, **431–32**
Homeodomains, 431–32
Homeostasis, **832**
    animal nutrition and mechanisms of, 844–48
    in body temperature (thermoregulation), 833–41
    calcium, 954*f*, 955
    endocrine system, hormones, and, 953
    excretory system and maintenance of, 927–42
    as feedback system, 832–33
    of glucose blood levels, 845*f*, 955*f*, 956
    of glucose synthesis from proteins, 958
    kidney function, 936, 937*f*, 938
    osmoregulation (water balance/waste disposal),
        922–27
    peripheral nervous system and maintenance of, 1028
    regulating versus conforming and, 832
Homeotherm, 833–34
Homeotic genes, **425, 485**. See also Hox genes
    conservation of, in animals, 431*f*–32
    identity of body parts and, 425
    in plants, 430, 431*f*, 732*f*, 733*f*, 734, 735*f*
    spatial patterns of body parts and, 485–86
Hominids, **702–3**
    timeline for species of, 702*f*
Hominoids, **700**, 701*f*
Homo erectus, 706
Homo floresiensis, 706
Homo ergaster, 704, 705*f*
Homo habilis, 704
Homo heidelbergensis, 705
Homologous chromosomes, **240**
    nondisjunction of, 285*f*
    separation of, in meiosis, 243*f*, 244*f*, 247, 274
Homologous genes, two types of, 505*f*
Homologous structures, **448**
Homology, **448**
    analogy versus, 493–94, 504*f*
    anatomical, 448, 449*f*
    embryological, 448, 449*f*
    evidence for natural selection in, 448–49
    molecular, 449, 492–95
    phylogenies based on evidence of, 492–95
    tree of life and, 449, 450*f*
Homo neanderthalensis, 705
Homoplasies, **494**
    molecular, 495*f*
Homo sapiens, 703, 705–7. See also Human(s)
Homosporous plants, **586**
Homozygotes, **255**, 456
Homunculus, 987*f*
Honey mushrooms (*Armillaria ostoyae*), 608
Hooke, Robert, 95
Horizons, soil, **759**, 760*f*
Horizontal cells, 1061*f*, **1062**
Horizontal transmission of viruses in plants, 345
Hormonal control pathways, 944, 945*f*
Hormones, **203, 791, 943–63**
    animal (human) reproduction and regulation by,
        973–78
    appetite-regulating, 847*f*
    binding of, to receptors, 945–48
    cell signaling by, 203*f*
    cell-surface receptors for water-soluble, 946
    control pathways of, and feedback loops, 944, 945*f*
    digestion and role of, 860*f*
    endocrine system and, 943–44, 948–59
    endocrine glands and secretions of, 949t
    insect, 960*f*
    insulin (see Insulin)
    intracellular receptors for lipid-soluble, 947
    invertebrate, 959–61
    kidney function regulated by, 936, 937*f*, 938
    mechanisms of signaling by, 946*f*
    nervous system chemical signals and, 943, 944

nonpituitary, 953–59
paracrine signaling and, 947–48
pituitary, 948–52
plant (see Plant hormones)
sex (see Sex hormones)
steroid, 205*f*, 947, 959*f*
Hornworts (Anthocerophyta), **580**, 582*f*
Horse, 604
    evolution of, 486, 487*f*
Horseshoe crabs (*Limulus polyphemus*), 658*f*
Horsetails, 587*f*, 588
Horvitz, H. Robert, 429
Host, **545**
    of parasites, **1163**
    symbiotic, 545
Host range of viruses, **337**
Hox genes, 629
    animal development and, 432*f*, 485–86, 627
    evolution of tetrapod limbs and, 485*f*
    expression of, in crustaceans and insects, 432*f*
    vertebrate brain and, 675*f*
    vertebrate origins and, 486*f*
HTLV (human T-cell leukemia virus), 370
Hubbard Brook Experimental Forest, New Hampshire
    acid precipitation and, 1199
    G. Likens on research studies at, 1078–79
    vegetation and nutrient cycling in, 1198, 1199*f*
Hudson Bay, limiting nutrient in salt marsh of, 1191*f*
Hughes, Kimberly, 1120
Human(s)
    biodiversity linked to welfare of, 1211–12
    chromosome number in (see Chromosome num-
        ber in humans)
    circadian rhythms and biological clocks in, 1030–31
    cloning of, 417
    consciousness in, 1036–37
    derived characters of, 701–2
    diseases of (see Diseases and disorders)
    embryo (see Human embryo)
    emotions of, 1034–35
    energy budget for, 830, 831*f*
    environmental impact of (see Human environmen-
        tal impact)
    evolution of (see Human evolution)
    genetic disorders of (see Genetic disorders)
    genome of chimpanzees and, 702
    family tree of tulips, mushrooms, and, 491*f*, 501*f*
    language and speech in, 706, 1011*f*, 1034
    life cycle of, 241*f*
    memory and learning in, 1035–36
    Mendelian inheritance patterns in, 265–70
    sex determination in, 282*f*
    sexes (see Females, human; Males, human)
Human body
    automatic control of breathing by, 890*f*
    basal metabolic rate (BMR) in, 829
    blood (see Blood groups, human)
    brain (see Human brain)
    circulatory and cardiovascular system, 871–83
    digestive system, 855*f*–62
    ear, and hearing, 1051*f*
    elements in, 33t
    endocrine system, 949t, 950t, 951–59 (see also
        Endocrine system)
    excretory system and kidney of, 931–38
    eye, and vision, 1058, 1059*f*, 1060*f*
    gas exchange in, 886–95
    genome (see Human genome)
    growth disorders in, 952
    growth rates in, 484*f*
    hemoglobin, 83*f*, 84*f* (see also Hemoglobin)
    hormones and development of, 952, 953 (see also
        Hormones)
    immune system, 899
    joints of, 1065*f*
    lymphatic system of, 878–79, 901*f*
    metabolic rate, 834
    muscles, 1066*f*–72
    nutrition (see Human nutrition)

reproductive system (see Human reproduction)
respiratory system, 888*f*, 890
sex characteristics in, 283
skeleton, 1065*f*
stabilizing selection and infant size, 466
taste and smell in, 1056*f*, 1057*f*
thermoregulation in, 50, 839*f*
water balance and osmoregulation in, 925*f*
Human brain
    adult, 1028*f*
    arousal and sleep in, 1029–30
    auditory and visual systems of, 1029
    brainstem, 1029–30
    cerebellum, 1030
    cerebral cortex, 1029, 1031, 1032–37
    cerebrum, 1031–32
    circadian rhythms and, 1030–31
    consciousness, 1036–37
    diencephalons, 1030–31
    embryonic development of, 1028*f*, 1029
    emotions and, 1034–35
    information processing in, 1032–33
    language and speech processing in, 706, 1011*f*,
        1034
    lateralization of function in, 1033–34
    memory and learning in, 1035–36
    mechanism of long-term potentiation in, 1037*f*
    primary motor and somatosensory cortices of,
        1033*f*
    thalamus and hypothalamus of, 1030
Human chorionic gonadotropin (HCG), **978**, 982
Human culture, 1131
Human embryo, 987*f*
    development of, 978, 979*f*, 980*f*, 987*f*, 991, 999,
        1000*f*, 1001
    homologous structures in chick and, 449*f*
Human environmental impact, 1200–1206
    acid precipitation as, 55–56, 1201–2
    on aquatic biomes, 1200–1201
    climate change as, 1204–5
    disruption of chemical cycling as, 1200–1201
    disturbances in communities as, 1204
    human population growth and, 1155–56
    rising levels of atmospheric carbon dioxide as,
        1203–4
    on terrestrial biomes, 1200
    toxin in environment, 1202–3
Human evolution, 701–7
    Australopiths and, 703, 704*f*
    bipedalism and, 703–4
    derived characters of humans, 701–2
    earliest hominids and, 702*f*, 703
    early *Homo* genus, 704–5
    Homo sapiens and, 705–7
    Neanderthals and, 705
    tool use and, 704
Human gene, cloning in bacterial plasmid, 387*f*, 388
Human genome, 359, 505
    E. Lander on, 237
    mapping, 394, 398 (see also Human Genome
        Project)
    number of genes in, 374
    types of DNA sequences in, 375*f*
Human Genome Project, 9*f*, 11, 319, **394**, 398
    E. Lander on, 236–37
Human growth hormone, DNA technology and, 404
Human health
    disease and (see Diseases and disorders)
    genetically modified organisms and, 784–85
    human population density, pathogens, and, 1149
Human immunodeficiency virus (HIV), **918**. See also
    HIV (human immunodeficiency virus)
Human life cycle, behavior of chromosome sets in,
    241–42
Human nutrition
    caloric imbalance, 846–48
    digestive system and, 855–62
    nutritional deficiencies in, 33*f*, 34, 849–52
    plant biotechnology and, 784–86

Human population, 1136, 1152–56
  age structure of, 1154–55
  carrying capacity of Earth and, 1155–56
  demographic transition and regional patterns of
    change in, 1153–54
  effects of, on environment (see Human
    environmental impact)
  global exponential growth of, 1152, 1153f
  infant mortality and life expectancy in, 1155
  T. Malthus on, 445
Human reproduction, 969–84
  conception, embryonic development, and birth,
    978–82
  contraception and abortion, 982–83
  female reproductive anatomy, 969–71
  female reproductive cycle, hormonal regulation of,
    973–77
  hormone regulation and gametogenesis, 973,
    974f, 975f, 976–78
  male reproductive anatomy, 971–72
  male reproductive system, hormonal regulation of,
    977–78
  pregnancy and fetal development, 915–16
  sexual response, 972–73
  spermatogenesis and oogenesis in, 974f, 975f
  technologies applied to problems of, 984
Human skull
  allometric growth in, 484f
  comparison to chimpanzee, 484f, 494
Humoral immune response, 899f, 908, 909, 910–14
  antibody classes in, 912f, 913
  antibody-mediated disposal of antigens, 913f, 914
  B cell response in, 910, 911f, 912–14
  overview of, 909f, 911f
  role of helper T lymphocytes in, 909, 910f
  T-dependent and T-independent antigens in, 912
Humus, soil, 759, 760
Hundred Heartbeat Club, 1211
Hunger, plant biotechnology and reduction of
  human, 784
Huntington's disease, 268, 403, 623
Hutchinson Cancer Research Center, 558
Hutton, James, 440
Hybridization, 253
  nucleic acid, 388, 389f
  plant, 252–53
Hybrids
  breakdown of, 475f
  reduced viability and fertility of as reproductive
    barrier, 475f
Hydra sp., 639f
  asexual reproduction in, 239f
  cnidocyte of, 643f
  digestion in, 854f
  environmental exchange and body structure of, 821f
  hormonal regulation in, 959–60
  nervous system of, 1012f
Hydration shell, 51
Hydrocarbons, 61–62
  fats and, 61f
Hydrochloric acid (HCl), 53, 54
Hydroelectric system, closed and open, 147f
Hydrogen
  covalent bonding in, 39f, 40f
  H+ gradients and pump, 171, 172f, 173, 521–22,
    739–40, 794
  valence for, 60f
Hydrogen bond, 42f
  RNA and, 327
  between water molecules, 47, 48f
Hydrogen ion, 53
Hydrolysis, 69
  of polymers, 69f
Hydrophilic substances, 52
Hydrophobic interactions, 83
Hydrophobic substances, 52
Hydroponic culture, 757
  identifying essential plant nutrients using, 757f
Hydrostatic skeleton, 1063–64

Hydrothermal vents, deep-sea, 514f, 541, 1097f
Hydroxide ion, 53
Hydroxyl functional group, 64f
Hydrozoans (Hydrozoa), 644t, 645f
Hymen, 970
Hypercholesterolemia, 137
Hyperpolarization, membrane potential and, 1018f
Hypersensitivity response (HR) in plants, 814, 815f
Hypertension, 883
Hyperthyroidism, 953
Hypertonic solution, 132, 133f
Hyphae, fungal, 609f
  adaptions for trapping and killing prey, 610f
  specialized haustoria, 610f
Hypoblast, 994, 1000
Hypocotyl, 778
Hypodermis, animal, 835f
Hypothalamus, 948, 949t, 950, 1030
  neurosecretory cells of, 944
  relationship between pituitary gland and, 950–51
  secretion of thyroid hormones and role of, 953
  thermoregulation and role of, 839f
Hypothesis, 20
  scientific inquiry and, 20, 21
Hypothyroidism, 954
Hypotonic solution, 132, 133f
Hyracotherium, 486, 487f

I band, muscle, 1066, 1067f
Ice
  insulation of bodies of water by floating, 50–51
  structure of, 51f
Iguana
  desert (Dipsosaurus dorsalis), 939f
  marine, 438f
Imbibition, 780
Immigration, population density and influence of, 1137
Immune system, 343, 898–921
  acquired immunity, 898, 903–14
  active and passive immunization, 914
  diseases caused by abnormal function of, 916–19
  humoral and cell-mediated immunity, 908–14
  innate immunity, 898–903
  in invertebrates, 902–3
  lymphocytes and function of (see Lymphocytes)
  pregnancy and, 915–16, 982
  self-nonself recognition by, 915–16
  suppression of, by glucocorticoids, 958
Immunization, 914
  vaccines and, 343, 914
Immunodeficiency disease, 917–19
  acquired (secondary), 917, 918–19
  inborn (primary), 917, 918
  HIV virus and AIDS as, 918–19
  stress and, 918
Immunoglobulins (Igs), 880, 904
  classes of, 906f
  gene rearrangement in, 906f, 907
  IgA, 912f, 914
  IgD, 912f
  IgE, 912f, 916, 917f
  IgG, 912f, 914
  IgM, 912f, 913
Immunological memory, 903, 908f
Imperfect fungi, 612
Imprinting, 1108–9
  of graylag geese, 1109f
  sexual selection influenced by, in zebra finch, 1126f
  of whooping crane mating and migration, 1109f
Imprinting stimulus, 1108
Inclusive fitness, altruism and, 1129–31
Incomplete dominance, 260, 261f
Incomplete flowers, 773
Incomplete metamorphosis, 661
Incus, 1051
Independent assortment of alleles to gametes,
  256–58, 274, 275f, 278
Indeterminate cleavage, 632
Indeterminate growth, 720

Index fossils, 517f
India, birth rate and population growth in, 1154f
Indian pipe (Monotropa uniflora), 768f
Indirect synaptic transmission, 1023–24
Individualistic hypothesis of community structure,
  1179
Individual variation, natural selection and, 16
Indoleacetic acid (IAA), 793. See also Auxin
Induced fit, enzyme-substrate, 152, 153f
Inducer, 355
Inducible enzymes, 354, 355
  lac operon and regulated synthesis of, 355f
Induction, 420, 1003
  cell signaling and, in cell differentiation and
    development, 420, 421f, 426, 427f
  developmental fate of cells and role of, 1003,
    1006–8
Inductive reasoning, 20
Infant, passive immunity in, 914
Infant mortality, 1155
  in Costa Rica, 1229f
Infection. See Diseases and conditions; Pathogens
Infection thread, 765
Inflammatory response, 901, 948
  major events of, 902f
Inflorescences, 773
Influenza virus, 344
  structure of, 336f
Information flow in cells
  DNA → RNA → protein, 86f, 87
  heritable, in cells, 7–8
Information processing in nervous system, 1013f
  brain and, 1032–33
Ingestion (eating), 853
Ingroup, 498
Inheritance. See also Genetics
  chromosomal basis of, 274–92
  extranuclear genes and exceptions to standard,
    289–90
  of genes, 238–39
  genome and (see Genome)
  Mendelian, 251–73
  molecular basis of, 293–308
  sex-linked, 282–84
Inherited disorders. See Genetic disorders
Inhibitory G protein, 211
Inhibitory postsynaptic potential (IPSP), 1022
Initials, plant cell, 721
Initiation factors, polypeptide synthesis, 323
Injuries, brain, 1035, 1037–41
Innate behavior, 1110–13
  animal signals as, 1111–12
  directed movements as, 1110–11
  mating, parental behavior and, 1112–13
Innate immunity, 898–903
  acquired immunity versus, 899f
  external defenses as, 899
  internal cellular and chemical defenses,
    899–902
  in invertebrates, 902–3
Inner cell mass, 1000
Inner ear, 1051
  equilibrium and, 1052, 1053f
  hearing and, 1051f, 1052, 1053f
Inositol triphosphate (IP3), role in signaling pathways,
  212f
Inquiry, 19
  abiotic synthesis of organic compounds, 59f
  bacterial acquisition of genes from another
    bacterium, 347f
  body color and wing size in Drosophila (parental
    and recombinant types), 279f
  cadherins and formation of blastula, 1003f
  case study of scientific, 21–24
  cell cycle regulation by cytoplasmic signals, 228f
  cell migration and role of fibronectin, 1002f
  competition and niches of barnacles, 1160f
  determining reasons for decline of Illinois greater
    prairie chicken, 1216f

development of differentiated plant cell into
  whole plant, 415*f*
development of floral organs in plants, 430*f*
diet and mate choice in *Drosophila* fruit fly, 1113*f*,
  1114
digger wasp nest-locating behavior, 1115*f*
DNA replication models, 300*f*
dorsal lip of blastopore and cell fate, 1006*f*
egg fertilization and effect of sperm binding on
  Ca^{2+} distribution, 990*f*
eye color in *Drosophila* (wild and mutant
  phenotype), 277*f*
flower color in crosses of true-breeding plants, 253*f*
formation of organic molecules in reducing
  atmosphere, 513*f*
gene specification of enzymes in arginine
  biosynthesis, 311*f*
genetic component to geographic variation in
  yarrow plants, 464*f*
genetic control of lacewing courtship songs, 1112*f*
genetic material in bacteriophages, 295*f*
gray crescent distribution and, cellular potency,
  1005*f*
hydroponic culture and essential plant nutrients,
  757*f*
hypothesis-based scientific, 20–21
kinetochore microtubules during mitotic
  anaphase, 225*f*
limiting nutrient in Hudson Bay salt marsh, 1191*f*
moose population size on Isle Royale, Michigan,
  1150*f*
movement in membrane proteins, 127*f*
nuclear transplantion and development of
  organisms, 416*f*
nutrients limiting phytoplankton production off
  Long Island shore, 1189*f*
parental caregiving by European kestrels and offspring survival, 1142*f*
phloem sap flow from source to sink, 753*f*
photoperiodism in plants and flowering, 807*f*
photosynthesis and light wavelengths, 187*f*
phototropism in plants, 792*f*, 793*f*, 803*f*
platelet-derived growth factor and stimulation of
  human fibroblast cells, 231*f*
polar transport of auxin, 795*f*
predation and natural selection in guppy
  populations, 447*f*
predation and mimicry of warning coloration in
  snakes, 23*f*
relationship of species richness to area, 1178*f*
on reproductive isolation in divergent *Drosophila*
  populations, 477*f*
role of fur in camel water conservation, 926*f*
scientific, as biological theme, 27*f*
seaweed distribution and feeding by sea urchins
  and limpets, 1086*f*
seed color and shape and independent assortment
  of alleles, 257*f*
transfer of genetic material between bacteria, 295*f*
triple response to stress in plants, 799*f*
Insects, 641*f*
  ants (*see* Ants)
  bees (*see* Bees)
  butterflies (*see* Butterflies)
  camouflage in, 446*f*
  chemoreceptors in, 1048, 1049*f*
  compound eyes in, 1058*f*
  development in, hormonal regulation of, 960*f*
  digestive tract in, 854*f*
  as disease vectors, 554*f*, 555, 664
  digger wasp nest-locating behavior, 1115*f*
  ears of, and mechanoreceptors in, 1050*f*
  flight in, 660–61
  as fluid feeders, 845*f*
  fossils, 660
  fruit flies (*see* Fruit flies (*Drosophila* sp.))
  gas exchange in tracheal system of, 886, 887*f*
  genetic control of lacewing courtship song, 1112*f*
  grasshopper, 660*f*, 663*f*

hormonal regulation of development in, 960*f*
Hox gene expression in, 432*f*
kinesis in, 1110*f*
major orders of, 662–63*f*
Malpighian tubules (excretory system) of, 930*f*, 931
metamorphosis in, 661*f*, 943*f*
nervous system, 1012*f*
parasitoid wasp, 813*f*
pheromones in, 437, 1048, 1409*f*
reproduction in, 661, 968, 969*f*
substrate feeding by, 845*f*
taste detection in, 1055*f*
thermoregulation in, 836, 837*f*, 838*f*, 839*f*
Insel, Thomas R., 1112–13
Insertions, nucleotide, as point mutation, 329, 330*f*
Insertion sequences as transposable elements, 351, 352*f*
Institute of Ecosystem Studies (IES), New York,
  1078
Insulation
  animal body, and thermoregulation, 834, 835*f*
  of bodies of water by floating ice, 50, 51*f*
Insulin, 8, 105, **955**
  amino acid sequence in, 80–81
  diabetes mellitus and deficiency of, 956
  DNA technology and synthesis of, 404
  homeostasis of blood glucose and role of, 846*f*,
    955*f*, 956
  target tissues for, 956
Insulin-like growth factors, 289, **952**
Integral proteins, **128**
Integrated hypothesis of community structure,
  1178–79
Integration of sensory information, 1047–48
Integrins, **119**
Integumentary system, **834–35**. *See also* Skin
Integuments, seed plant, **592**, 593*f*
Interaction networks, biodiversity crisis and disrup-
  tion of, 1214
Intercalated disks, **1072**
Intercellular junctions, 120
  in animal tissue, 120, 121*f*
  membrane proteins and, 128*f*
  in plant tissue, 120*f*
Interdisciplinary research teams, **11**
Interferons (α and β), **900**
Intermediate disturbance hypothesis, **1172**
Intermediate filaments, **113**, 118
  structure and function of, 113*t*
Internal environment, regulation of. *See* Animal regu-
  latory systems
Internal fertilization, **967**
International Union for Conservation of Nature and
  Natural Resources, 1212
Interneurons, **1013**
  axon growth direction, 1038*f*
  structure of, 1014*f*
Internodes, **715**
Interoreceptors, **1046**
Interphase
  cell cycle, 221*f*, 222–23*f*
  meiosis and 244*f*
Intersexual selection, **468**, 1125
Interspecific competition, **1160**. *See also* Competition
Interspecific interactions in communities, **1159–65**
  coevolution and, 1164–65
  commensalism as, 1164
  competition as, 1160–61
  disruption of, 1214
  dominant and keystone species and, 1165–71
  herbivory as, 1163
  mutualism as, 1164
  parasitism as, 1163
  pathogens and disease as, 1163
  predation as, 1161–62
Interstitial fluid, **831**
  capillary exchange between blood and, 875, 879*f*
  lymphatic system and, 901*f*
Intertidal zone, 1093*f*, **1096*f***
  keystone predator in, 1168*f*, 1169*f*

Intracellular digestion, **853**
Intracellular receptors, 205
  for lipid-soluble hormones, 947
  steroid hormone interaction with, 205*f*, 947
Intracellular recording for measurement of membrane
  potential, 1016*f*
Intrasexual selection, **468**, 1125
  male competition for mates and, 1126–27
Intrinsic rate of increase in populations (r_{max}), 1144*f*
Introduced species, **1213**
  as threat to biodiversity, 1213–14
Introns, **318**. *See also* Noncoding DNA sequences
  crossing over facilitated by, 319
  functional and evolutionary importance of, 319
Invagination, **995**
Invasive species, 437, **1168**
Inversion, chromosomal, **286*f***, 287
Invertebrates, **638–68**
  animal phyla including, 668*f*
  animal phylogeny and, 638*f*
  annelids (Annelida), 653–55
  arthropods (Arthropoda), 656–65
  bilateral symmetry in, 646
  cephalochordates (Cephalochordata), 674, 675*f*
  chordates (Chordata) as, 667
  circulatory system in, 868, 869*f*, 870
  cnidarians (Cnidaria), 643–46
  diversity of, 639–41*f*
  echinoderms (Echinodermata), 665–66
  eyes of, 1057*f*, 1058*f*
  flatworms (Platyhelminthes), 646–48
  gas exchange in, 884, 885*f*
  gastrovascular cavities of, 868
  gills of, 650*f*, 652, 885*f*
  gravity and sound sensors in, 1050
  immune system of, 902–3
  insects (*see* Insect)
  lophophorates (ectoprocts, phoronids,
    brachiopods), 649
  molluscs (Mollusca), 650–53
  muscles of, 1072
  nematodes (Nematoda), 655–56
  nemerteans (Nemertea), 649–50
  nervous system, 1012*f*, 1020
  osmoregulation in, 924
  parental care among, 968*f*
  regulatory systems of, 959–61
  rotifers (Rotifera), 648–49
  sponges (Porifera), 642–43
  thermoregulation in, 833, 836, 837*f*, 838*f*, 839*f*
  vision in, 1057*f*, 1058
In vitro fertilization (IVF), **984**
In vitro mutagenesis, **400**
Involution, **995**
Iodine deficiency, 33*f*, 34, 954
Ion(s), **41**
  calcium, 211*f*, 212*f*
  electrical charge and, 42
  hydrogen, 53
  as second messengers, 210–12
Ion channels, **133**
  gated, in nervous system, 1017
  ligand-gated, 208*f*, 1017, 1022–25
  membrane potential and, 134–36
  stretch-gated, 1017
  voltage-gated, 1017
  voltage-gated, role in neural action potential,
    1018, 1019*f*
Ionic bonds, **41–42**
  electron transfer and, 41*f*
Ionic compounds (salts), **41**
Ion pumps
  membrane potential maintained by, 134–36
IP_3 (inositol triphosphate), role in signaling pathways,
  212*f*
Iris, of the eye, **1058**, 1059*f*
Irish famine of 19th century, and potato blight, 558
Iron as limiting nutrient in ecosystems, 1189
Irrigation, 762

Island
    adaptive radiation on chains of, 436, 480, 481*f*
    biogeography and species richness on, 1177*f*, 1178*f*
Island equilibrium model, 1177–78
Islets of Langerhans, **955**
Isoetes gunnii quillwort, 587*f*
Isoleucine, feedback inhibition in synthesis of, 157*f*
Isomers, 62–63
    three types of, 62*f*
Isomorphic generations, **562**
Isopods, 664
Isotonic solution, **132**, 133*f*
Isotopes, **35**
    half-life of radioactive, 517
    radioactive, 35–36
Italy, population age structure of, 1154*f*
Iteroparity, **1141**
Ivanowsky, Dimitri, 335

Janzen, Daniel, 1223
Japan
    infant mortality in, 1155
    restoration project in coastal, 1228*f*
Jarvis, Erich, on genetics of songbird behaviors,
        818–19
Jasmonic acid, **813**
Javan rhinoceros, 1211*f*
Jawfish, paternal care by, 1125*f*
Jawless vertebrates, 678–79
Jaws
    evolution of mammalian, 695*f*
    vertebrate, 679, 680*f*, 682–84
Jellies (jellyfish), 639*f*, 644*f*
    internal transport in, 868*f*
Jenner, Edward, 914
Joints, 1065*f*
Joule (J), 49
J-shaped curve of exponential population growth, 1144
Jukes, Thomas, 506
Juvenile hormone, **960**
Juxtaglomerular apparatus (JGA), **937**
Juxtamedullary nephrons, **931**, 936

Kamil, Alan, 467*f*, 1116
Kandel, Eric, 1036
Kaneshiro, Kenneth, 480
    on evolution and mating behavior in *Drosophila*,
        436–37
Kaneshiro Hypothesis, 437
Kangaroo (marsupials), 695
    distribution and abundance of red, in Australia,
        1081*f*
    locomotion in, 1073*f*
Kangaroo rats, 925*f*, 939*f*
Karyogamy, **611**
Karyotype, **240**
    geographic variation in mice populations, 463*f*
    preparation of, 240*f*
    of trisomy 21, 287*f*
Kelp (*Macrocystis*), 561*f*
Keratins, 688
Ketones, 64*f*
Ketoses, 70*f*
Keystone species, **1168–69**
    disruption of interaction networks involving,
        1214
Kidneys
    adaptations of, to diverse habitats, 938, 939*f*
    blood filtration and urine production by, 931–32,
        933*f*, 934
    hormonal regulation of, 936, 937*f*, 938
    nephron and associated structures, anatomy and
        function, 931–34
    urine concentration by (two-solute model), 935*f*
    water conservation by, 934–38
Kilocalorie (kcal), **49**
Kinesis, **1110**
Kinetic energy, **49**, 50, 142
    transformations between potential energy and, 142*f*

Kinetochore, **221**, 224, 225*f*
Kinetoplast, 553
Kinetoplastids, 553, 554*f*
King, Thomas, 416, 506
Kingdom(s) (taxonomy), **496**
    five-kingdom system, 529*f*, 530
    three-domain system and, 14*f*, 530–31*f*, 532
Kinorhyncha, 639*f*
Kin selection, **1130**
    altruism and, in Belding's ground squirrel, 1130*f*
    Hamilton's rule and, 1129–30
Kipukas, in Hawaii, 436
Kissimmee River, Florida, restoration project in, 1227*f*
Klinefelter syndrome, 287
Knee-jerk reflex, 1013*f*
KNOTTED-1 homeotic gene, 732*f*
Koala, 695
    digestive tract of, 863*f*
Kohler, Steven, 1149
Kolbe, Hermann, 59
Komodo dragon, 689*f*
Korarchaeota, 544
Korpi, Nichole, 1116, 11117
Krebs, Han, 168
Krebs cycle. *See* Citric acid cycle
Krill, 664*f*
Kruger National Park, South Africa, elephant popula-
        tions in, 1144*f*
K-selected (density-dependent) populations, **1147**
Kudzu as introduced species, 1213*f*
Kurosawa, Ewiti, 797
Kwashiorkor, 849*f*, 850

Labia majora, **970**
Labia minora, **970**
Labor, **981**
    model for induction of, 981*f*
    stages of childbirth and, 981*f*
LacA gene, 355*f*
Lacewing (*Chrysoperla* sp.), genetic control of
        courtship song in, 1112*f*
LacI gene, 355*f*
Lac operon
    positive control of, by catabolite activator protein,
        356*f*
    regulated synthesis of inducible enzymes and,
        354, 355*f*
α-Lactalbumin, 380
Lactate, 175
    muscle fatigue and accumulation of, 1070–71
Lactation, 380, **981**
    in marsupials, 695, 696*f*
Lacteal, 860
Lactic acid fermentation, **175**
Lactose, 70
    regulation of metabolism of, in bacteria, 354, 355*f*
LacY gene, 355*f*
LacZ gene, 355*f*, 387*f*, 388
Lagging strand, DNA replication, **302***f*, 303*f*
    proteins and functions related to, 304*t*
Lakes, 1094*f*
    biomanipulation and restoration of, 1171
    eutrophication of, 1190, 1201
    evaporative cooling and temperature stability in, 50
    experimental eutrophication of, 1190*f*
    human impact on, 1201
    oligotrophic, 1094
    seasonal temperature and turnover in, 1090, 1091*f*
    zonation in, 1093*f*, 1094
Lamarck, Jean Baptiste, evolutionary views of, 440–41
Laminaria sp., 561
    life cycle of, 562*f*
Lampreys (Cephalaspidomorphi), 678*f*
Lamp shells (brachiopods), 640*f*, 649*f*
Lancelets (Cephalochordata), 498, 641*f*, 674, 675*f*
Land. *See also* Landscape(s); Terrestrial biomes
    colonization of, by animals 527
    colonization of, by fungi, 527, 612
    colonization of, by plants, 527, 573, 574, 575–79

locomotion on, 1073–74
osmoregulation in animals living on, 925–26
role of skeleton in physical support of animal
        body on, 1064–65
Lander, Eric, on genetics research, 236–37
Landmarks, **1115**
Landscape(s)
    biophilia concept and, 1230
    corridors connecting habitat fragments in, 1221–22
    fragmentation and edges of, 1220–21
    nature reserves as protected areas of, 1222–24
    restoring degraded, 1224–28
    sustainable development and conservation of,
        1229–30
Landscape ecology, **1082**, **1220**
Language, human brain and, 706, 1011*f*, 1034*f*
Large ground finch (*Geospiza magnirostris*), 443*f*
Large intestine, **861–62**
Larva, **627**
    amphibian, 686
    insect, 1152*f*
    trochophore, 635
    tunicate, 673, 674*f*
Larynx, **887**
Lascaux, France, Paleolithic art, 1230*f*
Lateral geniculate nuclei, **1063**
Lateral inhibition, **1062**
Lateralization, brain, **1033–34**
Lateral line system, **680**, **1054**
Lateral meristems, **720**
    secondary growth and, 720*f*, 721, 725–28
Lateral roots, **713**
Latitude, global climate and Earth's, 1088*f*
Law of continuity, 875
Law of independent assortment, 256, 257, **258**, 274,
        275*f*
Law of segregation, 253–56, 274, 275*f*
    statement of, **254**
L-dopa, 62, 63*f*, 1040
Leading strand, DNA replication, **302***f*
    proteins and functions related to, 304*t*
Leaf (leaves), **585**, **715**
    abscission of, 800, 801*f*
    anatomy of, 725*f*
    apoptosis in, 800
    in C_4 plants, 196*f*
    effects of transpiration on temperature of, 749
    evolution of, 585, 586*f*
    extranuclear genes and color of, 289, 290*f*
    green color of, 186*f*
    guttation in, 746
    modified, 716*f*
    overexpression of homeotic gene in formation of,
        732*f*
    peroxisomes in, 111*f*
    simple versus compound, 716*f*
    as site of photosynthesis, 183*f* (*see also*
        Chloroplasts)
    tissue organization of, 724, 725*f*
    transpirational pull in, 747*f*
    xerophyte, 751*f*
Leaf primordia, **723***f*
Leaf traces, **724**
Learning, **1114–18**
    associative, 1116–17
    of bird songs, 1118
    cellular mechanisms of, 1036, 1037*f*
    cognition, problem solving and, 1117–18
    cognitive maps and, 1116
    genetic and environmental interactions in, 1118
    habituation as, 1115
    imprinting as, 1108, 1109*f*
    memory and, 1035–36
    sensitization as simple, 1036*f*
    spatial, 1115–16
Leeches (Hirudinea), 655*f*
    nervous system, 1012*f*
Leeuwenhoek, Anton van, 549
Leg, size of animal, and skeletal support, 1065

Legal boundary versus biotic boundary of reserves, 1222, 1223*f*
Legionnaire's disease, 542*f*
Legumes, symbiotic nitrogen fixation between bacteria and, 764, 765*f*, 766
Lemurs, 468, 697*f*
Lens, of the eye, **1059**
 regulation of gene expression in cells of, 367*f*, 419
Lenski, Richard, 538
Lenticels, **728**
Leopold, Aldo, 1083
Lepidosaurs, **689**, 690, 691*f*
Lepidoptera (butterflies, moths). *See* Butterflies
Leptin, obesity and defective gene for, 847–48
Lettuce seed, response of, to red light, 803*f*
Leukemia, 288, 370, 404, 882
Leukocytes, 825*f*, 880*f*, **881**. *See also* White blood cells (leukocytes)
Lewis, Edward, 423, 425
Leydig cells, **971**
Lichens, 621–22
Life, introduction to the study of, 2–29
 biology and study of, 2–8
 biological diversity of (*see* Biodiversity)
 cells as basic units of, 6–8
 chemical context of (*see* Chemistry)
 classification of, (*see also* Systematics; Taxonomy)
 continuum of, on Earth, 512
 ecosystems and, 6
 elements required by, 33–34
 evolution of, 15–19 (*see also* Evolution)
 extraterrestrial sources of, 514
 grouping into species and domains, 12–14
 order as characteristic of, 144*f*
 properties and processes of, 3*f*
 protobionts and origins of, 515
 scientific inquiry into, 19–26
 systems concept applied to, 9–12
 themes connecting biological study of, 26, 27*t*
 tree of (*see* Tree of life)
 unity underlying all, 14, 15*f*
Life cycle, **240**. *See also* Sexual life cycle
 of angiosperm, 600*f*, 772*f*
 of apicomplexan *Plasmodium* sp.,556*f*
 of ascomycete *Neurospora crassa*, 617*f*
 of basidiomycete, 619*f*
 of cellular slime mold, 566*f*
 of chlorophyte *Chlamydomonas*, 569*f*
 of *Drosophila* fruit fly, 421, 422*f*, 423
 of fern, 585*f*
 of fungi, 611*f*, 614*f*
 of hydrozoan *Obelia*, 645*f*
 of moss *Polytrichum*, 581*f*
 of pine (gymnosperm), 596, 597*f*
 of plants, 576, 581*f*, 585*f*, 597*f*, 600*f*
 of plasmodial slime mold, 565*f*
 of protist *Laminaria*, 562*f*
 of trematode blood fluke, 647*f*
 of water mold, 559*f*
Life expectancy, **1155**
 in Costa Rica, 1229
Life history, **1141–43**
 diversity of, 1141–42
 logistic population growth model and, 1147
 reproduction versus survival trade-offs in, 1142–43
Life history traits, natural selection and production of, 1141–43
Life tables, population, **1139**
 of Belding's ground squirrel, 1139*t*
Ligaments, **825***f*
Ligand, **137**, **205**
Ligand-gated ion channels, **208**, **1017**
 chemical synapse and, 1022*f*, 1022–25
 as membrane receptors, 208*f*
Light. *See also* Sunlight
 as abiotic factor, 1087
 animal breeding and, 1107
 animal hibernation and estivation related to, 840, 841

characteristics of, 186
circadian rhythms and, 1030, 1031*f*
conversion of energy in, into chemical energy, 182–85
energy levels of electrons and, 36–37
as limiting factor for ecosystem productivity, 1188
sensory receptors for (*see* Photoreceptors)
vision and (*see* Vision)
Light, plant responses to, 788*f*, 802–8
 biological clocks and circadian rhythms associated with, 805
 blue-light photoreceptors and, 750, 802
 greening of plants in response to, 789*f*, 790*f*, 791
 harvesting of, in thylakoid membrane, 189–92
 interaction of chloroplasts with, 110–11
 opening/closing of leaf stomata and, 750
 photoperiodism as, 806–8
 phytochromes and reception of, 789–91, 802–5
 phototropism as, 792–93, 803*f*
 red light and, 803*f*, 806, 807*f*
Light chain, B cell receptors, **903**, 904*f*
Light-harvesting complexes, **189***f*, 190
Light microscopes and light micrographs (LMs), 95
 types of, 96*f*
Light reactions, photosynthesis, **184–85**, 186–93, 198*f*
 chemiosmosis in chloroplasts, compared to mitochondria, 192–93
 cooperation between Calvin cycle and, 185*f*
 cyclic electron flow during, 191*f*–92
 excitation of chlorophyll by light and, 188, 189*f*
 mechanical analogy for, 191*f*
 nature of sunlight and, 186, 187*f*
 noncyclic electron flow during, 190*f*–91
 organization of thylakoid membrane and, 193*f*
 photosynthetic pigments as light receptors and, 186–88
 photosystems of, 189–90
Lignin, **584**
Likens, Gene, 1081, 1083, 1199
 on ecological studies of Hubbard Brook Experimental Forest, 1078–79
Lilac (*Syringa*) leaf, 725*f*
Limb
 homologous structures, 448, 449*f*
 Hox gene and evolution of tetrapod, 485*f*
 pattern formation during development of vertebrate, 1006, 1007*f*, 1008*f*
Limb bud, 1007*f*, 1008*f*
Limbic system, emotions and, **1034**, 1035*f*
Limiting nutrients, **1188–90**
Limnetic zone, lake, 1093*f*, **1094**
Limpet, seaweed distribution and feeding by, 1086*f*
Lindstedt, Stan, 894
Linkage map, 279–81, **396**
 construction of, 281*f*
 of *Drosophila* genes, 281*f*
Linked genes, **277–82**
 evidence for inheritance and, in *Drosophila*, 277–78
 genetic recombination (crossing over) of, 278–79, 280*f*
 linkage map, 279–80, 281*f*
Linker DNA, 360
Linnaeus, Carolus, as founder of taxonomy, 439, 444
Lion, African (*Panthera leo*), hierarchical classification of, 496*f*
Lipase, 861*f*
Lipid(s), **74–77**
 fats, 75–76
 hydrophobic behavior of, 75
 phospholipids, 76–77
 steroids, 77
Lipid-soluble hormones, intracellular receptors for, 947
Littoral zone, lake, 1093*f*, **1094**
Lively, Curt, 1127–28
Liver, **855**
 blood circulation in, 861, 869–70
 digestive function, 858
 regulation of gene expression in cells of, 367*f*, 419

Liverworts (Hepatophyta), **580**, 582*f*
 gametangia of, 577*f*
Lizards (Squamata), 690
 game theory applied to mating success of side-blotched, 1127–28
 parthenogenic reproduction in, 965, 966*f*
 resource partitioning among *Anolis*, 1161*f*
Loams, **759**
Lobe-fins (Sarcopterygii), **683–84**
Lobotomy, frontal, 1035
Lobsters, 664
 anatomy of, 657*f*
Local regulators, chemical signals as, **202**, 203*f*, 947–48
Locomotion, **1073–74**. *See also* Movement
 energy costs of, 1074*f*
 flying, 1074 (*see also* Flight)
 on land, 1073–74
 muscles and, 1066–72
 pseudopodia and, 563
 skeleton, role of, 1064–65
 swimming, 821*f*
Locus, gene, **239**
 mapping of, using recombination data, 279–81
Logistic population growth model, **1145–46**
 applied to real populations, 1146, 1147*f*
 carrying capacity and, 1145
 hypothetical example of, 1145*t*
 life histories and, 1147
 logistic growth equation and, 1145
 population growth predicted by, 1146*f*
Long-day plants, **806**
Long-distance cell signaling, 203*f*
Long Island, New York, nutrients limiting phytoplankton production off shore of, 1189*f*
Long-term memory, **1035**
Long-term potentiation (LTP), **1036**, 1037*f*
Looped domains, DNA and chromatin packing in, 360, 361*f*
Loop of Henle, **931**, 932*f*
 descending and ascending limbs, 934
Loose connective tissue, **825***f*
Lophophorates, 649*f*
Lophophore, **635**
Lophotrochozoans, **634**, 635
 characteristics of, 635*f*
Lorenz, Konrad, 1108–9
Loriciferans, 640*f*
Low-density lipoproteins (LDLs), 137, **883**
Luciferase, 805
"Lucy" (*Australopithecus afarensis*), 703, 704*f*
Lugo, Ariel, 1226
Lungs, **886**
 breathing and ventilation of, 888–90
 evolution of, 682
 gas exchange and, 886–87, 888*f*
 mammalian, 887, 888*f*
Lupine inflorescence, 773*f*
Luteal phase of, ovarian cycle, **977**
Luteinizing hormone (LH), **952**, 959
 female reproductive cycle and, 976, 977
Lycophytes, **578**, 586, 587*f*
Lyell, Charles, 440, 443
Lyme disease, 543*f*, 545*f*, 546
Lymph, **878**
Lymphatic system, **878**
 defense against infection and, 878–79, 901
 human, 878, 879*f*, 901*f*
Lymph nodes, **878**, 901*f*
Lymphocytes, 880*f*, 881, **898**
 antigen recognition by, 903–5
 B cells, 903–4 (*see also* B lymphocytes (B cells))
 clonal selection of, 907*f*, 908
 development of, 905–8
 gene rearrangement in, 906*f*, 907
 self and nonself recognition and, 915–16
 T cell, 904–5 (*see also* T lymphocytes (T cells))
 testing and removal of self-reactive, 907

Index

Lynx, population cycles of snowshoe hare and, 1151, 1152f
Lyon, Mary, 284
Lysergic acid (LSD), 622
Lysine, 783
Lysogenic cycle, **338**, 339f
Lysosomes, 102, **107–8**
  digestion of materials by, 107f
Lysozyme, 380, **899**
  conformation of, 81f
Lytic cycle, **337**, 338f

M, N, and MN blood groups, 260
MAC (membrane attack complex), **914**
MacArthur, Robert, on island biogeography, 1177–78
Macaques, 700f

Macroclimate, **1087**
Macroevolution, **472**, 482–88
  evolution of genes controlling development, 484–85
  origin of evolutionary novelty and, 482–83
  speciation and (see Speciation)
Macromolecules, **68–91**
  carbohydrates as, 69–74
  classes of, 68
  digestion and enzymatic hydrolysis of, 853
  Golgi apparatus and production of, 106
  lipids as, 74–77
  nucleic acids as, 86–89
  as polymers, 68–69
  proteins as, 77–86
Macronutrients, plant, **757**, 758t
Macrophage, **823**, **900**
  coordinated activity of, 121f
  ingestion of yeast cell by, 898f
  phagocytosis by, 107f
Mad cow disease, 345
Mads-box genes, 433
Magnetic field, reception of Earth's, 1049f
Magnetic resonance imaging (MRI), 1011f
Magnetic reversals, **518**
Magnification, of microscopes, 95
Magnolia (Magnolia grandiflora), 602f
Magnoliids, 602f
Maiden veil fungus (Dictyphora), 618f
Maize (Zea mays)
  artificial selection and, 783f
  germination of, 780f
  B. McClintock's research on genetics of kernel color in, 375f
  mineral deficiencies in, 33f, 759f
  as monoecious species, 773f
  parasitoid wasp defense of, 813f
  phototropism in, 803f
  root response to oxygen deprivation, 811f
  seed, 778f
Major depression, **1040**
Major histocompatibility complex (MHC), **904**
  rejection of tissue grafts and organ transplants and, 916
  T cell interactions with, 904, 905f
Makhubu, Lydia, 32
  on chemistry and medicine, 30–31
Malaria
  heterozygote advantage in hemoglobin and, 466f
  mosquitos as vector for, 555, 664, 1085
  Plasmodium life history and, 555, 556f
  sickle-cell disease and, 267, 466f
Males, human
  contraception for, 982f, 983
  erectile dysfunction in, 211, 948
  hormonal regulation of reproductive system in, 977, 978f
  reproductive anatomy of human, 971f
  sex hormones of, 63f, 958–59, 977–78
  sexual dimorphism and, 468
  sexual response in, 948
  spermatogenesis in, 975f

Malheur National Forest, Oregon, 608
Malignant tumor, **232**
Mallards, 693f
Malleus, **1051**
Malnourishment, **849**, 1156
  diseases caused by, 849f
  reducing human, 784
Malpighian tubules, 930f, 931
Malthus, Thomas, 445
Maltose, dehydration synthesis of, 70, 71f
Mammals (Mammalia), **694–701**
  biological clocks in, 1030, 1031f
  breathing in, 888–89
  circulatory and cardiovascular system of, 870f, 871–83
  countercurrent heat exchange in, 836f
  digestive system of, 855–62
  ear of, hearing and equilibrium in, 1050–53
  early embryonic development in, 999–1001
  eutherian (placental), 697–701, 967
  evolution of, 694–95
  excretory system and kidney of, 931–38
  eye of, 1058–60
  fertilization of eggs in, 990, 991f
  hearing and equilibrium in, 1050–53
  integumentary system, 835f
  jaw and earbones of, 695f
  kidney adaptations by, 939f
  marsupials, 695, 696f, 697, 967
  monotremes, 695, 696f
  nitrogenous wastes of, 927f, 928
  orders of, 699f
  phylogenic relationships of, 698f
  primates, 697, 700f, 701f
  reproduction in, 967, 969–84
  reproductive cloning of, 416, 417f
  respiratory adaptations of endurance runners and deep-diving, 894–95
  respiratory system and gas exchange in, 887–95
  resting potential in neurons of, 1016f
  taste and smell in, 1054–56
  thermoregulation in, 834, 835f, 836f, 837, 839f
Mammary glands, **970**
  lactation and, 380, 695, 696f, **981**
Mandibles, myriapod, **659**
Mangold, Hilde, 1006
Mangrove, 811
Mantid, camouflage in, 446f
Mantle, mollusc, **650**, 1064
Mantle cavity, mollusc, **650**
Map butterflies (Araschnia levana), 462f
Map units, **280**
Marchantia liverwort
  archegonia and antheridia of, 577f
  embryo and placental transfer cell of, 577f
  sporophyte of, 582f
Margulis, Lynn, 522f
Marine animals
  coral reefs, 1097
  at deep-sea vent communities, 514f, 541, **1097**f
  invertebrates (see Invertebrates)
  kidney adaptations in bony fishes, 939f
  osmoregulation in, 923f, 924–25
  respiratory adaptations of diving mammals, 894–95
  salt excretion in birds, 926f
  thermoregulation in, 834f, 835, 836f, 837f
Marine benthic zone, **1097**
Marine biomes
  animals of (see Marine animals)
  benthic zone, 1097f
  coral reefs, 1097f
  estuaries, 1095f
  intertidal zone, 1095f
  nature reserves in, 1224
  oceanic pelagic biome, 1095f
  zonation in, 1093f
Marine ecosystems
  food chains in, 1166f
  food web in, 1166f

habitat loss in, 1213
primary productivity in, 1187f, 1188–90
Marine worms, 640f, 649, 655f
  gills, 885f
Markow, Therese, 1114
Mark-recapture method, estimating wildlife populations using, **1137**
Marler, Catherine, 1114
Mars, 514
Marsupials, **695**, 696f, 697
  biogeography and evolution of, 450f, 528
  convergent evolution of eutherians and, 450, 494f, 495
  reproduction in, 967
Martinez, Lucia, 1112
Mass and weight, terms, 32
Mass extinctions, 518–21
Mass number, **34–35**
Mast cells, **901**
Mate choice. See also Mating; Sexual selection
  copying, 1131f
  diet and, in Drosophila, 1113f, 1114
  by females, 1125–26
  male competition for mates and, 1126–27
Mate choice copying, **1131**
Maternal effect gene, **424**
Mating. See also Sexual selection
  of close relatives, and genetic disorders, 267
  courtship behaviors and, in Drosophila, 436–37
  genetic influences on, 1112–13
  human sexual response and, 972–73
  mate choice, 1123–25
  populations with no random, 458
  random, as source of genetic variation, 248
Mating bridge, conjugation, 349
Matsuzawa, Tetsuro, 1117–1118
Matter, **32**
  chemical bonding and molecule formation, 39–42
  chemical reactions and rearrangement of, 44–46
  elements and compounds making up, 32–34
  laws of thermodynamics and, 143–44
  transformation of, by metabolic processes, 141–44
Maximum likelihood, **501**
Maximum parsimony, **501**
  analogy-versus-homology pitfall and, 504f
  applied to molecular systematics problem, 502–3f
Mayer, Alfred, 334–35
Mayr, Ernst, 455, 473
McClintock, Barbara, genetics research on transposons by, 375f
Meadowlark, similarity between two species of, 473f
Measles virus, 337
Mechanical isolation as prezygotic reproductive barrier, 474f
Mechanical stimuli, plant response to, 809–10
Mechanical stress, plant response to, 799–80
Mechanical work, cellular, 148
  driven by ATP, 149f
Mechanoreceptors, **1048**, 1050–54
  for equilibrium in mammals, 1046, 1047f, 1052–53
  for equilibrium in nonmammals, 1053–54
  for gravity and sound in invertebrates, 1050f
  for hearing in mammals, 1050–52
  for hearing in nonmammals, 1053–54
  lateral line system as, 1054f
  for muscle stretching, 1047f
  for touch, 1048
Mediator protein, 365
Medicines
  chitin used in, 74f
  derived from plants, 594f, 595f, 605t
  DNA technology applications in, 402–4
  Hirudinea (leeches) used in, 655f
  L. Makhubu on, 30–31
  radioactive isotopes used in diagnostic, 36
  stem cells and, 418

neural control of tension in, 1069–71
rate of stimulation in, 1071
relaxed and contracted, 1067f
types of, 1071, 1072t
Muscle spindles, **1048**
Muscle tissue, **823**
Muscularis tissue layer, of stomach, **827**f
Mushrooms, 608, 618–19
Mustard, vegetables artificially selected from wild, 445f
Mutagens, **329**–30
Mutant phenotype, 276
fruit fly eye color, 277f
Mutations, **328**, **459**
in bacteria, 344–48
base-pair substitutions as, 328, 329f
cancer and, 370
as cause of microevolution in populations, 459–60
chromosomal, 285–88, 463–64
deletions, 329, 330f
duplications, 459
as embryonic lethals, 423
frameshifts, 329
gene number and sequence alterations as, 459
genetic variation in populations caused by, 459–60
genomic evolution and role of, 378–81
insertions, 329, 330f
missense, 328, 329f
nonsense, 328, 329f
point, 328–30
populations lacking, 458
proto-oncogenes transformed into oncogenes by, 371f
rates of, 459–60
translocations, **286**f, 287, **288**f, 459
Mutualism, 545, **1164**
roots and mycorrhizal fungi, 620
Myasthenia gravis, 1069
Mycelium, fungal, **609**
Mycetozoans (slime molds), 564–66
Mycoplasmas, 98, 543f
Mycorrhizae, **610**, **744**, **766**–67
agricultural importance of, 620
arbuscular, 615f
symbiotic relationship of root nodules to, 620
two types of, 766, 767f
water absorption in plants and role of, 744, 745f
Mycosis, **622**
Myelencephalon, 1028
Myelin sheath, **1014**
conduction of action potentials and, 1020–21
multiple sclerosis and destruction of, 917
Schwann cells and, 1015f
Myoblasts, 419f, 420
MyoD gene, 419f, 420
Myofibrils, **1066**, 1067f
Myofilaments, **1066**, 1067f
Myogenic heart, **873**
Myoglobin, **895**, **1071**
in oxidative muscle fibers, 1071, 1072f
Myosin, **117**
cell motility, actin filaments and, 117f
cytokinesis and, 226
muscle contraction and, 117f, 1068f, 1069f
Myotonia, **972**
Myriapods (Myriapoda), **658**t, **659**f–60f

NAD+ (nicotinamide adenine dinucleotide), **162**
fermentation and, 174–75
as oxidizing agent and electron shuttle during cellular respiration, 162, 163f, 170, 175
NADH
citric acid cycle and, 168f, 169f, 170
fermentation and, 174, 175f
glycolysis and, 165f, 166f
as source of electrons for electron transport chain, 170, 171f
NADP+ (nicotinamide adenine dinucleotide phosphate), photosynthetic light reactions and role of, 184, 185f, 193f

NADPH
Calvin cycle and conversion of carbon dioxide to sugar using, 193–95
photosynthetic light reactions, and conversion of solar energy to, 185, 190, 191, 193f
Naked mole rat (*Heterocephalus glaber*), altruism in, 1128, 1129f
Nash, John, 1127
National parks
in Costa Rica, 1223f, 1224
Grand Canyon, 440f, 477f
Grand Teton, 1222, 1223f
Yellowstone, 544, 1172, 1173f, 1217f, 1218, 1220f, 1222, 1223f
Native Americans, genome of, 505
Natural family planning, **982**
Natural killer (NK) cells, **902**, 910
Natural selection, 16, 17f, **438**, 444–46, 460, 462–70
artificial selection versus, 445
behavioral traits evolving from, 1118–28
C. Darwin's theory of, 444–46
directional, disruptive, and stabilizing modes of, 465f–66
effects of differential predation on, 446, 447f
evolutionary fitness and, 464–65
evolution in populations due to, 460, 462–70
evolution of drug-resistant HIV as example of, 447, 448f
evolution of sex and sexual reproduction, 469
in finch populations, 443f
frequency-dependent, 467–68
genetic variation and, 462–64
perfection not created by, 469–70
populations with no, 458
preservation of genetic variation despite effects of, 466–68
RNA, protobionts, and dawn of, 515–16
sexual selection and, 468
summary of, 445–46
survival/reproductive success increased by behaviors favored by, 1121–28
Nature reserves, 1222–24
philosophy of, 1222–23
zoned, 1223–24
Nealson, Kenneth, 522f
Neanderthals, 705
Negative feedback, 11f, 832, **944**
kidney regulation by, 937f
as mechanism of homeostasis, 832f
Negative pressure breathing, **888**, 889f
Nematocysts, **644**
Nematodes (roundworms), 640f, 655–56. *See also Caenorhabditis elegans* (nematode)
hydrostatic skeleton in, 1063
as model organism, 412f
as pseudocoelomate, 631f
Trichinella spiralis, 656f
Nemerteans (proboscis worms/ribbon worms), 639f, 649f, 650
Neocortex, **1031**, 1035
Neon, electron orbitals of, 38f
Neoproterozoic era, 628
Nephron, **931**, 932f
blood vessels associated with, 933
production of urine from blood filtrate in, 933f, 934
regional functions of transport epithelium and, 933f
structure and function of, 931–33
Neritic zone, 1093f, **1097**
Nernst equation, 1016–17
Nerve(s), 627, **1012**. *See also* Neuron(s)
cranial, 1026f
development of, 1037–38
herpesvirus in, 340
spinal, 1026f
Nerve cord, dorsal and hollow, in chordates, 673
Nerve net, **1012**
Nervous system, 1011–44
action potentials in, production and conduction, 1017–21

adrenal gland and, 957
central nervous system and brain, 1012, 1026f, 1028–37
central nervous system injuries and diseases, 1037–41
as command and control center, 1011–12
endocrine system overlap with, 943–44
human brain (*see* Human brain)
information processing by, 1013f
invertebrate, 1012f
maintenance of resting potential in neurons by ion pumps and ion channels of, 1015–17
membrane potentials in, 1015
neuron communication at synapses in, 1021–25
neuron structure in, 1013, 1014f
nerve signals (impulses) in, 203
organization of, 1012f, 1013
peripheral nervous system, 1012, 1026f, 1027f, 1028
senses and (*see* Sensory reception)
supporting cells (glia) of, 1014–15
vertebrate, 1026–32
Nervous tissue in animals, **823**. *See also* Nervous system; Neuron(s)
Nest, digger wasps and behaviors for locating, 1115f
Net primary productivity (NPP), **1187**
idealized pyramid of, 1192f
Neural crest, **676**, **998**
as embryonic source of vertebrate characters, 676f
Neural stem cells, 1038–39
Neural tube, **998**
Neuroendocrine pathway, 945f
Neurofibrillary tangles, 1040f
Neurogenic heart, **873**
Neurohormone, 944
Neurohormone pathway, 945f
Neurohypophysis, **950**
Neuromasts, 1054
Neurons, 826f, 943–44, **1011**
action potentials of, 1017–21
development of, 1037–38
gated ion channels of, 1017
interneurons, 1013f, 1014f
ion pumps/ion channels and, 1015–17
membrane potential of, 1015–16
motor, 1013f, 1014f (*see also* Motor neurons)
production of new, in adults, 1038–39
resting potential of, 1016–17
sensory, 1013, 1014f
structure of, 1013, 1014f
supporting cells for, 1014–15
synapses and, 1021–25
Neuropeptides as neurotransmitters, **1025**
Neurosecretory cells, **944**
Neurospora crassa (bread mold)
G. Beadle and E. Tatum experiment on gene-enzyme relationships in, 310, 311f
life cycle of, 616, 617f
Neurotransmitters, **1014**, 1024–25
acetylcholine as, 1024t
amino acids and peptides as, 1024t, 1025
biogenic amines as, 1024t, 1025
as intracellular messenger at neural synapses, 1022, 1024–25
as local regulators, 947–48
major, 1024t
migration of vesicles containing, 112f
Neutral theory, **506**
Neutral variations in populations, **468**
Neutrons, **34**
mass number and, 34–35
Neutrophils, 880f, 881, **900**
Newborns, screening for genetic disorders, 269–70
New World monkeys, 697, 700f
New Zealand, 690
Nicolson, G., 125
Nicotine, 1024, 1163
Night, plant photoperiodism and length of, 806, 807f

9 + 2 structural microtubule pattern in flagella and cilia, 114, 115f, 525
Nirenberg, Marshall, 313
Nitric oxide (NO), 205, **948**
   effects on male sexual function, 948
   as local regulator, 948
   as neurotransmitter, 205, 1025
Nitrogen
   improving protein yield in crops and, 764
   as limiting nutrient in ecosystems, 1188–89
   plant requirement for, and deficiencies of, 33f, 759f, 761
   prokaryotic metabolism and, 539
   soil bacteria and fixing of, for plant use, 763f, 764–66
   valences of, 60f
Nitrogenase, **764**
Nitrogen cycle in ecosystems, 1197f
   critical load and, 1200–1201
   human disturbance of, 1200–1201
Nitrogen fixation, **539**, **764**
   by bacteria, 539, 763f, 764–66
Nitrogen-fixing bacteria, **764**
Nitrogenous bases
   base-pair insertions and deletions, 329, 330f
   base-pair substitutions, 328, 329f
   Chargaff's rules on pairing of, 296, 298, 313f
   genetic code and triplets of, 312–14
   nucleic acid structure and, 87f, 88
   pairing of, and DNA replication, 87–88
   pairing of, and DNA structure, 87f, 296, 297f, 298f
   pyrimidine and purine families of, 88, 298
   sequences (see DNA sequences)
   structure of DNA strand and, 296f
   wobble in pairing of, 322
Nitrogenous wastes, animal phylogeny correlated with form of, 927–28
Nitrosomonas, 542f
NMDA receptors, 1036, 1037f
Nociceptors, **1049**
Nodes, of stem, **715**
Nodes of Ranvier, 1015f, 1021f
Nod genes, 766
Nodules, root, **764**, 765f
   molecular biology of formation of, 766
Noncoding DNA sequences, 374–78
   restriction fragment length polymorphisms and, 394
Noncompetitive enzyme inhibitors, 155f
Noncyclic electron flow, photosynthesis, **190f**, 191
Nondisjunction of chromosomes, **285**
   genetic disorders associated with, 285f, 286
Nonequilibrium model of communities, **1172**
Nonhomologous chromosomes, independent assortment of, 258, 274, 275f
Nonpolar covalent bond, **40**
Nonsense mutations, **328**, 329f
Nonshivering thermogenesis (NST), **838**
Nontemplate DNA strand, 313
Nontropic hormones, 952
Norepinephrine, **956**, **1025**
   stress and secretion of, 957f
Norm of reaction, **264**
   behavior and, 1109
North America
   acid precipitation in, 55–56, 1201f
   climograph for terrestrial biomes of, 1098f
   plate tectonics of, 527, 528f
   species richness of birds in, 1177f
   species richness of trees and vertebrates in, 1177f
Northern fur seal (*Callorhinus ursinus*), 1136f
Notochord, **498**, **673**, **997**
   chordate, 673
   organogenesis and formation of, 997f, 998
Nottebohm, Fernando, 818
N-P-K ratio, 761
NTS (nonshivering thermogenesis), **838**
Nuclear DNA, 109

Nuclear envelope, 102, 103f
Nuclear lamina, 102, 103f
Nuclear magnetic resonance (NMR), 85
Nuclear matrix, 102
Nuclear pore, 102, 103f
Nuclear transplantation in animals, 415–17
Nucleases, **305**
Nucleic acid(s), 86–89. *See also* DNA (deoxyribonucleic acid); RNA (ribonucleic acid)
   components of, 87f
   digestion of, 859f
   hereditary information transmitted by, 293
   as polymer of nucleotides, 87–88 (see also Nucleotide(s))
   roles of, 86–87
   structure of, 87f, 88
Nucleic acid hybridization, **388**, 389f
Nucleic acid probe, **388**, 389f
Nucleoid, 98f, **346**
Nucleoid region, 537
Nucleolus, **102**, 103f
Nucleomorph, 551
Nucleoside, structure of, 87f
Nucleoside triphosphate, DNA strand elongation and, 301, 302f
Nucleosomes, **360**, 361f
Nucleotide(s), 7–8, **87**. *See* also DNA sequences
   amino acids specified by triplets of, 312–14
   base pairing of, in DNA strands, 89, 296 (see also Nitrogenous bases)
   as component of nucleic acid, 87f, 88
   excision repair of DNA damage by, 305f
   incorporation of, into 3' end of DNA strand, 302f
   mapping sequences of, 396–98
   point mutations in, 328–29
   repairing mismatched and damaged, 305f, 306
   restriction fragment analysis of, 392–94, 395f
   structure, 87f
   triplet code of, 312, 313f
Nucleotide excision repair, **305**f
Nucleus, eukaryotic cell, 98, **102**
   chemical signaling and responses in, 213f, 214
   division of (see Mitosis)
   structure of, 102, 103f
   transplantation of, 415–17
Nudibranch, 651f
Numbers, pyramid of, 1193f
Nüsslein-Volhard, Christiane, 423
Nutrient cycling in ecosystems. *See also* Chemical cycling in ecosystems
   general model of, 1195f
   vegetation and, 1198, 1199f
Nutrients
   absorption of, in small intestine, 859–61
   essential animal, 849–52
   essential plant, 756–59
   as limiting factor in ecosystems, 1188–90
   plant root absorption of, 744–46
   translocation of, in plant phloem tissue, 751–53
Nutrition. *See also* Diet; Food
   absorptive, in fungi, 608–10
   animal (see Animal nutrition)
   fiber, 74
   in plants (see Plant nutrition)
   in prokaryotes, 538, 539t

Obelia, life cycle, 645f
Obesity, 847–48
   evolution and, 848
Obligate aerobes, **539**
Obligate anaerobes, **539**
Occam's Razor, 501
Ocean
   benthic zone, 1097f
   as biome (see Marine biomes)
   coral reefs, 1097f
   El Niño Southern Oscillation in, 1170, 1171f
   global warming and increased sea level, 1205
   pelagic zone, 1096f

   primary production and nutrients in, 1188, 1189t, 1190
   upwelling, 1190
   zones of, 1093f
Oceanic pelagic biome, **1096**
Oceanic zone, 1093f
Ocellus, 1057f–1058
Octopuses, 639f, 653f
Odling-Smee, Lucy, 1115–16
Odum, Eugene, 1160
Oil spills, bioremediation of, 406, 546f
Okazaki fragments of DNA lagging strands, 302f, 303f, 305
Old World monkeys, 697, 700f
Oleander (*Nerium oleander*), 751f
Olfaction, **1055**
   in humans, 1034, 1035f, 1056, 1057f
Olfactory bulb, 1034, 1035f, 1057f
Olfactory receptors, 1055
Olfactory receptors, genes for, 459, 505
Oligochaeta (segmented worms), 654f. *See also* Earthworms
Oligodendrocytes, **1015**
Oligosaccharins in plants, **814**
Oligotrophic lakes, **1094**
Ommatidia, **1058**f
Omnivores, **844**
   dentition in, 863f
Oncogenes, **371**
   conversion of proto-oncogenes into, 371f
One gene–one enzyme hypothesis, 310, 311f
One gene–one polypeptide hypothesis, **310**, 330
One gene–one protein hypothesis, 310
On the Origin of Species (Darwin), 15, 438, 439, 443–46, 455
Onychophorans (velvet worms), 641f
Oogenesis, **973**, 974f
Oogonia, 974
Oomycetes, **558**, 559f
Opaque-2 mutant, 783
Oparin, A. I., 513
Open circulatory system, **657**, **868**, 869f
Open system, 143
   equilibrium and work in, 147f
Operant conditioning, **1117**f
Operator, **353**
Operculum, **682**
Operons, 353–54
   positive control of *lac*, 356f
   regulated synthesis of inducible enzymes by *lac*, 355f
   regulated synthesis of repressible enzymes by *trp*, 354f
   repressible versus inducible, 354–56
   repressor protein and regulatory gene control of, 353
Ophiuroidea (brittle star), 666t, 667f
Opiates as mimics of endorphins, 43, 81, 1025
Opisthokonts, **612**
Opossums, 695, 696f
Opposable thumb, **697**
Opsin, **1060**
Opsonization, 913
Optic chiasm, **1063**
Optimal foraging theory, **1122**
Oral cavity, digestion and, **856**
Orangutans, 701f
Orbitals, electron, **38f**–39
   hybridization of, 43f
Orchid
   bilateral symmetry in flower of, 773f
   unity and diversity in family of, 16f
Order
   evolution of biological, 144
   as properties of life, 3f
Orders (taxonomy), **496**
   mammalian, 699f
Organ, 5f, **712**
Organ, animal, **827**. *See also* Organ systems, animal
   digestive, 855–62
   reproductive, 969–73

tissues of, **823**
transplants of, and immune response, 916
vestigial, 448
Organ, plant. *See* Leaf (leaves); Root system; Shoot system
Organelles, 5*f*, **95**
of endomembrane system, 104–9
inheritance of genes located in, and genetic disorders, 289–90
isolating, by cell fractionation, 97
microscopy and views of, 95–97
mitochondria and chloroplasts, 109–11, 192–93
peroxisomes, 109, 110–11
relationship among endomembrane system, 109*f*
structural order in metabolism and, 157*f*
Organic chemistry, **58–59**
Organic compounds
abiotic synthesis of, 59*f*
carbon atoms as basis of, 59–61
carbon skeleton variations and diversity of, 61–63
in Earth's early atmosphere, 59*f*, 513–14
extraterrestrial sources of, 514
functional groups of, 63–66
shapes of three simple, 60*f*
Organic phosphates, 65*f*
Organ identity gene, **430, 734**
ABC hypothesis for flower formation and, 734, 735*f*
Organisms, 4*f*. *See also* Species
anatomy and physiology of, 820
binomial nomenclature for naming, 496
classification of (*see* Systematics; Taxonomy)
colonies of, and origin of multicellular, 526*f*
communities of (*see* Community(ies))
complexity of, related to genomic composition, 374–75
as conformers and as regulators, 832
development of individual (*see* Development)
evolutionary history of (*see* Phylogeny)
genetically modified, 407–8
homeostasis in (*see* Homeostasis)
interactions between environment and, 27*f*, 1080–83 (*see also* Ecology)
life cycles of (*see* Life cycle)
life history, 1141–43, 1147
model, for research studies, 412–13*f*
overproduction of, 445*f*
populations of (*see* Population(s); Population ecology)
thermoregulation in, 833–41
transgenic, 406, 782, 783, 784–86
Organismal ecology, **1082**
Organizer (gastrula organizer), 1006
Organogenesis, **979, 997**
in bird embryo, 998*f*
in frog embryo, 997*f*
from three germ layers, 997–98, 999*t*
Organ systems, **827**
animal, 827*t*
animal reproductive, 969–73
Orgasm, 972–73
Origins of replication (DNA), **226,** 227*f*
in eukaryotes, 301*f*
Orrorin tugenensis, 703*f*
Orthologous genes, **505**
Osculum, 642
Osmoconformers, **923**
Osmolarity, **923**
Osmoregulation, **132,** 922–27
kidneys and, 936, 937*f*, 938
osmosis and, 922–23
role of transport epithelia in, 926–27
two strategies for challenges of, 923–26
water balance and, 131, 132*f*, 133
Osmoregulators, **923**
Osmosis, **132, 740**
water balance 131, 132*f*, 133
water conservation, kidneys, and role of, 936
Osmotic potential, **741**
Osteichthyans, **682–84**

Osteoblasts, 825*f*
Osteons, 825*f*
Ostia, 868
Ostracoderms, 679
Otoliths, 1052
Outer ear, **1051**
Outgroup, 498
Ova. *See* Ovum
Oval window, **1051**
Ovarian cycle, **973**
hormonal regulation of, 976*f*, 977
Ovaries, animal (human), 241, **969**
Ovary, plant, **598, 772,** 774*f*, 775
fruit development from, 778, 779*f*
variation in locations of, 773*f*
Overexploitation of species, 1214
Overnourishment, 846–48
Overproduction, natural selection and, **16**
Oviduct, **969**
Oviparous species, **681**
Oviraptor, 690*f*
Ovoviviparous species, **681**
Ovulation, 969, 977
Ovule, **592, 772,** 774
fertilization and development of seed from, 592, 593*f*, 777*f*–78
Ovum, **964.** *See also* Egg
development of human, 973, 974*f*
plant, 592, 593*f*, 772*f*
Oxidation, **161–62**
beta, 177
NAD$^+$ as agent of, 162–63
peroxisomes and, 110–11
Oxidative phosphorylation, **164**
ATP synthesis during, 164, 165, 170–74
photophosphorylation compared to, 192
Oxidizing agent, **161**
Oxygen
covalent bonding of, 40*f*
deep-diving mammals and storage of, 894–95
dissociation curves of, for hemoglobin, 892*f*
loading/unloading of, by hemoglobin, 892*f*
myoglobin and storage of, 895
origins of, in Earth's atmosphere, 522–23
photosynthesis and production of, 183, 184*f*, 522–23
prokaryotic metabolism and, 539
respiratory pigments and transport of, 892*f*, 893
valences of, 60*f*
Oxytocin, **951**
human pregnancy and childbirth and role of, 981
secretion of, by posterior pituitary, 950*f*, 951
Ozone, depletion of atmospheric, 1205–6

p53 gene, **373**
cancer development and faulty, 373
P 680 Photosystem II, 190
P 700 Photosystem I, 190
Pace, Norman, 541
Pacemaker, heart, **873**
Pacific yew (*Taxa brevifolia*), 595*f*
Paedomorphosis, **485,** 685
Pain
endorphins and reduction of, 43, 81, 952
prostaglandins and sensation of, 948, 1049
sensory receptors for, 1049
Paine, Robert, 1169
Pain receptors (nociceptors), **1049**
Pair-rule genes, 425
Paleoanthropology, **702**
Paleontological species concept, **476**
Paleontology, **440**
Paleozoic era, 519*t*, 520, 521*f*, 527, 596, 629
Palisade mesophyll, **724**
Panama, 1080*f*
Pancreas, **855, 955**
digestive function, 858, 859*f*
glucose homeostasis and role of, 846*f*, 955–56
hormones secretions by, 949*t*, 955*f*, 956

Pangaea, 527, 529*f*, 696
Papaya, genetically engineered, 784*f*
Papillae, 1055
Papilloma virus, 370
Parabasalids (trichomonads), **553**
Parabronchi, **889**
Paracerceis sculpta, mating behavior and male polymorphism in, 1126, 1127*f*
Paracrine signaling, 203*f*, 947–48
Paralogous genes, **505**
Paramecium sp., 556
cilia of, 15*f*
conjugation and reproduction in, 557*f*, 558
interspecific competition between species of, 1160
logistic population growth model applied to, 1147*f*
structure and function of, 557*f*
water balance and role of contractile vacuole in, 132, 133*f*
Paramyosin, 1072
Paraphyletic grouping, **498***f*
Parareptiles, **689**
Parasites, 545, **1163**
blood flukes as, 647*f*
brown-headed cowbird as, 1221
flowers as, 771
leeches as, 655
nematodes as, 656*f*
plants as, 767, 768*f*
tapeworms as, 648*f*
viruses as (*see* Viruses)
Parasitism, **545, 1163**
Parasitoidism, **1163**
Parasitoid wasp, 813*f*
Parasympathetic division of autonomic nervous system, 1027*f*, **1028**
Parathion pesticide, 155
Parathyroid glands, **954**
hormones secreted by, 949*t*, 954–55
Parathyroid hormone (PTH), **954**
Parazoan organization, **633**
Parenchyma cells, **718,** 722*f*
Parental behavior
care of offspring, 690*f*, 967, 968*f*, 1124, 1125*f*, 1142*f*, 1143
genetic influences on, 1112–13
Parental types, **278**
Parietal cells, 857*f*
Parker, John, 93
Parkinson's disease, 623, **1041**
E. Jarvis on, 819
lack of dopamine and, 1025
L-dopa and treatment of, 62, 63*f*
Parsimony, principle of maximum, 501
analogy-versus-homology pitfall and, 504*f*
applied to problem in molecular systematics, 502–3*f*
Parthenogenesis, **648, 965**
in rotifers, 648–49
in whiptail lizards, 965, 966*f*
Partial pressure, loading/unloading of respiratory gases and, 891*f*
Parturition, **981**
Passive immunity, **914**
Passive transport, 130–34, **738**
active transport compared to, 135*f*
defined, **131**
diffusion as, 130
facilitated diffusion as, 133–34
osmosis as, 131–33
Patchiness, environmental, **1082,** 1172, 1173*f*
Paternity
certainty of, 1124–25
DNA technology and establishment of, 405
Pathogens, **1163**
agglutination of, 913
bacteria as, 295*f*, 339, 460, 545–46
B and T lymphocytes response to, 910–14
drug-resistant, 447, 448*f*

fungi as, 622–23
immunity to (see Immune system)
insects as vectors for, 554f, 555, 556f, 664
parasites as (see Parasite(s))
plant (see Plant disease)
plant defenses against, 813–15
population density of hosts and, 1149
prokaryotes as, 545–46
protists as, 552, 553f, 554f, 555, 556f, 564
viruses as, 337, 339, 343–45
Pattern formation, 421–31, 731, 1007
   cell fate determination and, by inductive signals,
      1006–8
   cell signaling and, in C. elegans, 425–27
   cell signaling and transcriptional regulation in
      plants, 429–30
   gene-activation cascade and, in Drosophila,
      421–25
   homeobox sequences and, 431–32
   homeotic genes and, 425
   positional information and, 421, 731, 732–33
   in plant cell development, 730–32
   programmed cell death (apoptosis) in, 427–29
   during vertebrate limb development, 1006–8
Pauling, Linus, 296
PCBs (polychlorinated biphenyls), biological magnifi-
      cation of, in food web, 1202f
Peacocks, sexual dimorphism in, 468f
Pea plants, 603f
   fruit development in, 779f
   gibberellin and stem elongation in, 797
   Mendel's studies on inheritance in, 251–58, 309
   Rhizobium bacteria and nitrogen fixation in, 765f
   triple response to stress in seedlings of, 799f
Peat, 583
Peat bogs, L. Graham on ecological function of, 511
Pectin, 106
Pediastrum, 526f
Pedigree, Mendelian inheritance patterns in humans
      revealed in analysis of, 265–66
Pelagic zone, 1093f
Penguins, 693, 821f
   energy budget for, 830, 831f
   nutritional requirements during molting, 850f
   population dispersion patterns of, 1138f
Penicillin, 155, 611f, 623f
Penicillium sp., 611f, 623f
Penis, 972
   erectile dysfunction in, 211, 948, 1025
Pentose sugars, 70f
PEP carboxylase, 196
Pepsin, 857
Pepsinogen, 857
Peptides, as neurotransmitters, 1024t, 1025
Peptide bond, 80
Peptidoglycan, 535
Perception, sensory input and, 1046. See also Sensory
      mechanisms
Pereira, Sofia, 1120
Perennials, plant, 720
Pericarp, 598
Pericycle, 723
Periderm, 717, 814
   cork cambia and production of, 728
Periodic table of elements, 37
Peripheral nervous system (PNS), 1012, 1026f
   enteric division of, 1028
   functional hierarchy of, 1027f
   homeostasis and, 1028
   parasympathetic divisions of, 1027f, 1028
   role of, in homeostasis, 1028
   Schwann cells of, 1015f
   sympathetic division of, 1027f
Peripheral proteins, 128
Peripheral resistance, 876
Peristalsis, 855, 1064
   in digestive tract, 855
   esophageal, 856f
   movement by, in annelids, 1064

Peristome, 581
Peritubular capillaries, 933
Perivitelline space, 989
Permian period, 596
   mass extinctions in, 518f, 520
Peroxisome, 109, 110, 111f
Peroxisome enzymes, 574
Pert, Candace, 1025
Pertussis (whooping cough), 206f
Petals, flower, 429f, 430, 598, 772
Petiole, 715
Petrels, excessive weight in chicks of, 848f
PET scans, 36f
Pettit, Robert, 643
Pfenning, David and Karin, inquiry into mimicry of
      warning coloration in snakes, 22, 23f, 24
Pfiesteria shumwayae, 555f
P generation, 253
   incomplete dominance and, 261f
   law of segregation and, 253f, 255f, 257f, 275f
pH, 54
   acids,bases,and, 53–54
   buffers, 55
   enzyme activity and effects of, 154f
   pH scale, 53, 54f, 55
Phaeophyta (brown algae), 560–62
Phage(s), 294, 336. See also Bacteriophage (phage)
Phage λ, lytic and lysogenic cycles of, 338, 339f
Phagocytes (phagocytic cells), 899–900
Phagocytosis, 107, 137, 138f, 881, 899, 900f
   antibody-mediated disposal of antigens and, 913f
   lysosomes and, 107f
   four leukocytes capable of, 900
Pharmaceutical products. See also Drug(s); Medicine
   biodiversity and development of new, 1211–12
   derived from plants, 30–31, 594f, 595f, 605t,
      1211, 1212f
   DNA technology and development of, 404
   enantiomers and, 62, 63f
   G-protein pathways and, 206
"Pharm" animals, 406f
Pharyngeal clefts, 673, 676
Pharyngeal slits, 673
Pharyngolepis, 679f
Pharynx, 856
Phase changes, 733
Phase-contrast microscopy, 96f
Phelloderm, 728
Phenotype, 256
   effects of natural selection on, 462–70
   genotype versus, 256f
   impact of environment on, 264, 462
   multiple effects in (pleiotropy), 262
   mutant, 276, 277f
   norm of reaction in, 264
   relationship of, to allele dominance, 261
   wild type, 276f, 277f
Phenotypic polymorphism, 463
Phenylalanine, 313, 320
Phenylketonuria (PKU), 269–70, 458
Pheromones, 610, 945, 967, 1111
   in insects, 437, 1048, 1409f
Philadelphia chromosome, 288
Philippine eagle, 1211f
Phloem, 584, 717, 751–53
   loading and unloading of, 752f
   pressure flow of sap in, 753f
   in roots, 722f
   sieve-tube members and companion cells of, 719
   transport (translocation) of sap through, 584,
      751–53
Phoronids (marine worms), 640f, 649
Phoronis hippocrepia, 649f
Phosphate bonds, high-energy, 148–49
Phosphate functional group, 65f
Phosphofructokinase, stimulation of, 177f
Phospholipids, 76–77
   bilayer structure formed by self-assembly of, in
      aqueous environments, 77f

   membrane models and, 125
   steroids as, 77
   structure of, 76f
Phospholipid bilayer, 125f
   permeability of, 126, 130
Phosphorus as plant nutrient, 761
   deficiency of, 759f, 761f
Phosphorylation, 149
   ATP hydrolysis and, 149–50
   cascade, 209f
   oxidative, 164
   photophosphorylation, 185
   of proteins, as mechanism of signal transduction,
      209–10
   substrate-level, 165f
Photic zone, 1093
Photoautotrophs, 181, 182f
   prokaryotes as, 538, 539f
   protists as, 550
Photoexcitation of chlorophyll, 188, 189f
Photoheterotrophs, 539t
Photomorphogenesis, 802
Photons, light, 186
   photoexcitation of chlorophyll and absorption of,
      188, 189f
Photoperiodism, 806
   flowering and, 806–8
   meristem transition and, 808
Photophosphorylation, 185, 189–92
   oxidative phosphorylation compared to, 192
Photoprotection, 188
Photopsins, 1061
Photoreceptors, 1048
   blue-light, in plants, 750, 802
   brain processing of visual information and,
      1061–63
   for infrared light, 1049f
   in invertebrates, 1057–58
   phototropism in plants and, 792–93
   phytochromes as plant, 789–91, 802–5
   in vertebrate eye, 1057–63
Photorespiration, 195–96
Photosynthesis, 181–200
   absorption and action spectra for, 187f, 188
   alternative mechanisms of, for hot and arid
      climates, 195–98
   Calvin cycle and conversion of CO_2 to sugar in,
      184, 185f, 193–95
   chemical equation for, 44, 183
   chloroplasts as site of, 109, 111f, 182–83
   conversion of light energy into chemical energy
      in, 182–85
   importance of, 197, 198f
   light reactions in, 184, 185f, 186–93
   origins of, 522–23
   overview of two stages of, 184, 185f
   role of, in biosphere, 181, 182f
   splitting of water and redox reactions of, 184
   tracking atoms through, 183, 184f
Photosystem I (PSI), 190, 191f
Photosystem II (PSII), 190, 191f
Photosystems, photosynthetic, 189–90
   light harvesting by, 189f
Phototrophs, 538–39
Phototropin, 802
Phototropism, 792
   early studies of, and discovery of plant hormones,
      792–93
   light wavelengths and, 803f
Phragmoplasts, 574
pH scale, 53, 54f, 55
   soil pH, 762
Phyla (taxonomy), 496
Phylogenetic species concept, 476
Phylogenetic trees, 496, 497–504
   of amniotes, 687f
   of angiosperms, 602f
   of animals, 633, 634f, 635f, 638f
   of biological diversity, 530–31f

of chordates, 672f
cladograms, cladistics, and, 497–99
of eukaryotes, 552f
of fungi, 613f
of Galapagos finches, 18f
as hypotheses, 501–4
mammalian, 698f
maximum parsimony, maximum likelihood, and, 501, 502–3f
of plants, 579f
of prokaryotes, 540f
timing, chronologies, and, 499–500
Phylogeny, **491–95**
of amniotes, 697f
animal, 633–36, 638f
chordate, 671, 672f, 673
circulatory system as reflection of, 867–71
connection between classification and, 496, 497f
continental drift and biogeographical basis of, 528
of eukaryotes, 552f
fossil record as evidence for, 492
of fungi, 612, 613f
genome and, 504–6
mammals, 698–99f
morphological and molecular homologies and, 492–95
phylogenetic trees (see Phylogenetic trees)
plants, 575–59
of prokaryotes, 540–44
systematics (see Systematics)
taxonomic classification and (see Taxonomy)
tree of life and, 491, 507
Phylogram, 499f, 500
Physarum polycephalum, 564f
Physical map, DNA fragments, **396**
Physiology, **820**. See also Animal anatomy and physiology
Phytoalexins, **814**
Phytochemicals, 188
Phytochromes, **802**
as molecular switching mechanism, 804f
as photoreceptors, in plants, 789, 790f, 802–5
structure of, 804f
Phytolacca dodecandra, medicinal properties of, 30
Phytophthora infestans, 558
Phytophthora ramorum (sudden oak death disease), 1163
Phytoplankton, 550
nutrients for, and ecosystem productivity, 1189f
turnover time for, 1192
Phytoremediation, **763**
Pigmentation, skin, 952
Pigments
carotenoids, 188, 189
chlorophyll (see Chlorophyll(s))
photosynthetic, 186–88
respiratory, 892–94
Pili (pilus), 349, **536**
Pilobolus, 614, 615f
Pine, life cycle of, 596, 597f
Pineal gland, hormone produced by, 949t, **959**
Pin flower type, 775f
Pinocytosis, 137, **138**f
Pinyon jays (*Gymnorhinus cyanocephalus*), 1116
Pisonia, seed dispersal in, 480f
Pistil, **598**, 772
Pitch (sound), detection of, **1052**
Pitcher plant, 768f
Pith, plant tissue, **717**, 722
Pittsburgh Compound-B (PIB), 1041
Pituitary gland, 948, **950**
hormones of anterior, 949t, 951f, 952, 976f
hormones of posterior, 949t, 950f, 951
production and release of hormones by, 950f
relationship of, to hypothalamus, 950–51
Pivot joint, 1065f
PKU (phenylketonuria), 269–70, 458
Placenta, **695**, 915, **979**
circulation in fetus and, 980f

Placental mammals. See Eutherian (placental) mammals
Placental transfer cells, **577**
Placoderms, **680**
Placozoa, 639f
Plagiochila deltoidea liverwort, 582f
Plague, 546
Planarians, 639f, **646**
anatomy of, 647f
ocelli and orientation behavior of, 1057f
nervous system, 1012f
protonephridium (flame-bulb) of, 929f, 930
Plankton, 550
Plants, 573–90
adaptations of, for life on land, 573, 574, 575–79
alternation of generations in, 242, 576f
angiosperms and evolution of fruits and flowers (see Angiosperms)
in arid and hot climates, 195–98
artificial selection and selective breeding of, 783–84
biotechnology applied to, 783–86
bryophytes, 580–83
carnivorous, 767, 768f
cells of (see Plant cell)
colonization of land by, 527
crop (see Crop plants)
defenses of, against predators, 813
derived traits of, 575, 576–77f
development of (see Development; Plant development)
diseases in (see Plant disease)
epiphytes, 768f
evolution of, from charophyceans (green algae), 573–74
evolution of, highlights, 579f
extranuclear genes and leaf color in, 289, 290f
genetic engineering in, 406–7, 784–86
L. Graham on evolution of terrestrial, 510–11
greening of (de-etiolation), 789f, 790f, 791
growth in (see Plant growth)
gymnosperms (see Gymnosperms)
hybridization of, 252–53
kudzu as introduced species of, 1213f
medicines derived from, 594f, 595f, 605t
movements in, 805f, 810f
nutrition in (see Plant nutrition)
origin and diversification of, 575–79
parasitic, 768f
photosynthesis in (see Photosynthesis)
phyla of extant, 578t
polyploidy in, 285
reproduction in (see Plant reproduction)
responses of, to signals (see Plant responses)
seedless vascular plants, 584–88
seed vascular plants (see Seed plants)
self-recognition and self-incompatibility in, 775–76
sexual life cycle in, 242f
structure (see Plant structure)
sympatric speciation and evolution of, 478f, 479f
temperature moderation in, 50
threats to, 606
totipotency in, 415
transgenic, 406–7, 782, 783, 784–86
transport (see Transport in vascular plants)
vascular (see Vascular plants)
vascular tissues (see Phloem; Xylem)
water transport in, 48f
Plantae (kingdom), 575f. See also Plant(s)
Plantain, seed production and population density of, 1149f
Plant anatomy. See Plant cell; Plant structure
Plant cells, 717, 718–19f
abscisic acid effects on, 798–99
auxin and elongation of, 794, 795f
brassinosteroid effects on, 798
cell plate of, 225f, **226**
cell walls of, 118, 119f, 743f
central vacuole of, 108f

chloroplasts in (see Chloroplasts)
collenchyma cells, 718f
companion cells, 719f
compartments of, and short-distance transport, 743f
cytokinesis and cell plate formation in, 225f, 226
cytokinin and division/differentiation of, 796
cytoplasmic streaming in, 117f, 118
ethylene effects on, 799–801
expansion of, orientation, 730, 731f
flaccid and turgid, 132–33, 750f
gibberellin effects on, 309, 797
location and fate of, 732–33
mitosis in, 226f
orientation of expansion of, 730, 731f
parenchyma, 718f
pattern formation and development of, 730–32
plane and symmetry of division and growth of, 729f, 730f
plasmodesmata of, 120f
positional information and development of, 731, 732–33
protoplast of, 782f
sclerenchyma cells, 718f
sieve-tube members, 719f
storage of starch in, 71, 72f
structure of generalized, 101f
tracheids, 719f
vacuoles of, 108f
vessel elements, 719f
water balance in, 132, 133f
water relations in, 742f
Plant control systems. See Plant responses
Plant development, 728–35. See also Plant growth
apical meristems and, 576f
animal development compared to, 433
cell division and cell expansion in, 729f, 730f, 796
cell location and developmental fate of cells in, 732–33
cell signaling, induction and, 420, 421f
cell signaling, transcriptional regulation, and, 429–30
embryo development, 777f, 778
gene expression and control of cell differentiation in, 732, 733f
mechanisms of, 429
model organism *Arabidopsis* for study of, 413f, 728, 729f
molecular biology and study of, 728–29
organ-identity genes in, 430, 431f
pattern formation and, 730–32
pattern formation in flowers and, 429f, 430f, 431f
phase changes and shifts in, 733–34
totipotency, 415
Plant disease
chestnut blight, 1168
fungi as cause of, 622, 797
plant defenses against pathogens, 813–15
protistan, 1163
viral, 334, 335f, 345
white rusts and downy mildew, 558
Plant growth, 720–32. See also Plant development
apical meristems and primary, 576f, 720f, 721–25
auxin and, 793f, 794, 795f
cell division, cell expansion, and, 729f, 730
determinate, 720
indeterminate, 720
inhibitors of, 793
lateral meristems and secondary, 720f, 721, 725–28
morphogenesis, differentiation, and, 728–35
pattern formation and, 730–32
Plant hormones, 791–802
abscisic acid, 794t, 798–99
auxin, 794t–97
brassinosteroids, 791, 794t, 798
cytokinins, 794t, 796–97
discovery of, 792–93

ethylene, 794t, 799–801
gibberellins, 309, 794t, 797–98
survey of, 793, 794t
systems biology and interactions of, 801–2
Plant morphology. See Plant structure
Plant nutrition, 756–70
  adaptations of, involving relationships with other
       organisms, 764–67, 768f
  mycorrhizae and, 620, 766–67
  nitrogen as essential in, 33f, 759f, 763–64
  nutritional requirements, 756–59
  soil quality/characteristics, and, 759–63
  "smart plants" and, 762f
  uptake of nutrients, 757f (see also Transport in
       vascular plants)
Plant reproduction
  alternation of generations and, 242f, 576f
  in angiosperms, 598–601, 771–80
  asexual, 781–83
  biotechnology and, 783–86
  in bryophytes, 580–83
  double fertilization, 599, 600f, 776–77
  embryophyte and, 575f, 577f
  flowers and, 598f, 772f, 773f, 775f
  fruit development and, 598, 599f, 778, 779f
  gametophyte, 576, 772, 774f–75
  in gymnosperms, 596, 597f
  pollen and sperm production in seed plants, 592,
       593f, 774f, 775
  pollination, 592, 771–76
  prevention of self-fertilization in, 775–76
  seed, evolutionary advantage of, 593
  seed development, 593f, 777–78
  seed germination, 779, 780f
  in seedless vascular plants, 585f, 586
  sexual, 576, 580, 581f, 585f, 586, 592–93, 596,
       597f, 599, 600f, 601, 771–80
  sporophyte, 576, 771–72
Plant responses, 788–817
  as defense against pathogens and herbivores,
       812–15
  to environmental stimuli other than light, 808–12
  to light, 788f, 802–8
  plant hormones and, 791–802
  signal-transduction pathways involved in, 788–91
Plant structure, 712–19
  cell division and cell expansion affecting, 729–30
  cell types of, 717–19 (see also Plant cell)
  developmental fate of cells affecting, 732–33
  gene expression and cell differentiation affecting,
      732, 733f
  growth and (see Plant growth)
  monocot and dicot, 603f
  overview, 713f
  pattern formation and, 730–32
  phase changes and, 633–34
  plasticity of, 712
  roots, stems, and leaves of, 713–16
  tissue systems, 717
Plasma, blood, 879, 880t
Plasma cells, 908
Plasma membrane, 98, 99, 124–40
  active transport across, 134–36
  cell-cell recognition and carbohydrates of, 129
  cotransport across, 136
  exocytosis, endocytosis,and bulk transport across,
      137, 138f
  fluidity of, 126f–27
  ionic gradients across neuron, 1016f
  membrane potentials of, 1015–21
  models of, 125
  osmosis and transport of water across, 131–33
  passive transport across, 130–34
  phospholipid bilayer of, 125f
  protein facilitation of transport across (see also
      Membrane proteins)
  receptor proteins in, 205, 206–8f
  selective permeability of, 124, 130
  structure of, 99f, 130

synthesis and sidedness of, 129f
voltage across (membrane potential), 134–35
water balance and, 131–33
Plasmids, 343, 349, 537
  cloning genes using, 385f–89
  as cloning vector, 386, 387f, 388, 389f
  F, and bacterial conjugation, 349, 350f
  genetic recombination in bacteria and, 349–51
  in prokaryotic cells, 349–51, 537
  R, and antibiotic resistance, 351
  Ti, 406, 407f
  in yeasts, 390
Plasmodesmata, 120f
Plasmodial slime molds, 564
  life cycle of, 565f
Plasmodium (apicomplexan), 555, 556f. See also Malaria
Plasmodium (slime mold), 564
Plasmogamy, 610, 614f
Plasmolysis, 133
Plasmolyzed cell, 742
Plasticity, 712
Plastids, 110. See also Chloroplasts; Statoliths
  apicoplast, 555
  origins of, 523–25, 550–51
  secondary endosymbiosis and diversity of eukary-
      otes, 551f
  starch storage in, 71, 72f
Platelet, in blood, 880, 881
  blood clotting and, 880f, 882f
  effect of prostaglandins on, 948
Platelet-derived growth factor (PDGF), cell division
    and, 231f
Plate tectonics, 527–29
Platyhelminthes (flatworms), 631f, 639f, 646–48
Pleiotropy, 262
Plomin, Robert, 1133
Pluripotent stem cells, 418
  replacement of cellular elements in blood and, 881f
Pneumatophores, 714f
Pneumonia, 295f, 348
Poikilotherms, 833–34
Point mutations, 328–30
  mutagens causing, 329–30
  proto-oncogene transformed into oncogene by, 371
  as source of genetic variation, 459–60
  types and consequences of, 328–29
Poisons. See also Toxins
  enzyme inhibitors as, 155
  in food, 460
  smooth endoplasmic reticulum and detoxification
    of, 104
  snake, 690, 1162
Poison arrow frog, aposematic coloration in, 1162f
Polar bears (Ursus maritimus), agonistic behavior in,
    1127f
Polar covalent bond, 40, 41f
Polarity in plants, 731
Polar molecule, water as, 47–48
Polar transport of auxin, 794, 795f
Polio virus, 337, 343
Pollen grains, 592, 774–75
  development of, 592–93, 774f
Pollen tube, growth of, 776f
Pollination, 592, 771–76
  cross-, 599
  floral variations and, 773f
  flower structure and, 772f
  gametophyte development and, 774f, 775
  self-incompatibility mechanisms, 775–76
Pollinators, relationship of angiosperms to, 604f
Polyandry, 1124, 1125f
Poly-A tail of mRNA, 317
Polychaetes (marine worms), 655f
Polygamous mating, 1123, 1124f
Polygenic inheritance, 263
Polygyny, 1123
Polymers, 68
  abiotic synthesis of, 514–15
  amino acid, 80

condensation and hydrolysis of, 68, 69f
diversity of, 69
nucleotide, 88
synthesis and breakdown of, 68, 69f
Polymerase chain reaction (PCR), 391f, 392
  medical applications, 403
Polymorphism, 463
  balanced, 466–68
  phenotypic and genetic, 463
Polynucleotides, 87
  assembly of, by RNA polymerases in transcription,
    315f
  as component of nucleic acids, 87f
Polyp (cnidarian), 643
Polypeptides, 78–81. See also Amino acid(s);
    Protein(s)
  amino acid monomers and, 78, 79f, 80
  amino acid polymers and, 80
  determining amino acid sequence of, 80–81
  forming chains of, 80f, 323–24
  one gene-directed production of one, 310
  post-translational modifications to, 324–25, 791
  translation and synthesis of, 320–26
Polyphyletic grouping, 498f
Polyplacophora (chitons), 651f
Polyploidy, 285, 478
  genomic evolution and, 378
  sympatric speciation by, 478f, 479f
Polyribosomes (polysomes), 324, 325f, 326
Polysaccharides, 71–74
  storage, 71, 72f
  structural, 72–74 (see also Cellulose; Chitin)
Polyspermy, fast and slow blocks to, 989
Polytrichum commune moss, 582f
Ponds. See also Lakes
  protists in water of, 549
  turnover in, 1091f
Pons (brain), 1029
  breathing controlled in medulla oblongata and, 1029
Populations, 4f, 454–70, 1082, 1136
  biotic and abiotic influences on, 1148–52
  communities of (see Community(ies))
  conservation of species using approach of small,
    1215–18
  conservation of species using approach of
    declining, 1218–19
  cycles in, 1151–52
  defined, 455
  demographic studies of changes in, over time,
    1139–41
  density, and dispersion patterns in, 1137–39
  density-dependent and density-independent,
    1148–50
  dynamics of, 1150–51
  evolution of, 454 (see also Population genetics)
  human (see Human population)
  life histories of organisms in, 1141–43
  life tables and survivorship curves in, 1139–40
  models of growth in, 1143–47
  reproductive rates in, 1140–41
  species in (see Organisms; Species)
  studying natural selection in virtual, 467f
  variation within and between, 444, 445f
Population cycles, 1151–52
Population density, 1137–38
  density-dependent birth/death rates, 1148–50
  density-independent birth/death rates, 1148
  determining equilibrium for, 1148f
  dispersion patterns and, 1137–39
  population change and, 1148
Population dynamics, 1137f, 1150–51
Population ecology, 1082, 1136–58
  biotic and abiotic influences on populations,
    1148–52
  carry capacity of environment and, 1145
  exponential model of growth in, 1143–45
  human population growth and, 1136, 1152–56
  life history traits as product of natural selection
    and, 1141–43

Index

Mediterranean climate, 1090
Medulla, **1029**
  control center for breathing in, 890*f*
Medulla oblongata, **1029**
  functions controlled by, 1029
Medusa (cnidarian), **643**
Megapascals, **740**
Megaphylls, **585**, 586*f*
Megasporangium, 592, 593*f*
Megaspores, **586**, **775**
  in seed plants, 592, 593*f*
Meiosis, **220**, **238**, **241**, **242**
  alternation of fertilization and, in sexual life cycle, 242*f*, 243
  in human life cycle, 241*f*
  mitosis compared to, 246*f*, 247
  nondisjunction of chromosomes in, 285*f*
  overview of, 243*f*
  reduction of chromosome number during, 242, 243–47
  stages of, 243, 244–45*f*
Meiosis I, **243**, 244*f*
Meiosis II, **243**, 245*f*
Melanocyte-stimulating hormone (MSH), 946, **952**
Melatonin, **959**, 1030
Mello, Claudio, 819
Membranes, biological. *See also* Plasma membrane
  extraembryonic, 688, 999
  fluidity of, 126*f*
  models of, 125
  nuclear envelope as, 102, 103*f*
  structure of, 99
  transport across, 126–27
Membrane antibodies (membrane immunoglobulins), 904
Membrane attack complex (MAC), **914**
Membrane potentials, **135**, **739**, **1015–17**
  basis of, 134–35
  cation uptake and, in transport in plants, 740*f*
  intracellular recording for measurement of, 1016*f*
  maintenance of, by ion pumps, 134–36
  resting, 1016–17
Membrane proteins
  functions of, 127, 128*f*, 129
  movement in, 127*f*
Memory
  human brain, learning, and, 1035–36
  immunological, 903, 908*f*
  short-term and long-term, 1035
Memory cells, **907**
Mendel, Gregor Johann, 249, 251*f*–53, 293. *See also* Mendelian inheritance
Mendelian inheritance, 251–73
  basis of, in chromosomal behavior, 274, 275*f*, 276–77
  genetic variation preserved by, 456*f*
  genetic testing and counseling based on, 268–70
  genotype and phenotype relationship, 256*f*
  in humans, 265–70
  inheritance patterns more complex than explained by, 260–64
  integrating, 264
  law of independent assortment and, 256–58, 274, 275*f*
  law of segregation, 253–56, 274, 275*f*
  laws of probability governing, 258–60
  Mendel's research approach, 251–53
  modern synthesis of Darwinism and, 455
Menopause, **977**
Menstrual cycle, **973**
Menstrual flow phase, of menstrual cycle, **977**
Menstruation, **973**
Mercury, biological magnification of, 1203
Meristems, **720**
  apical, and plant primary growth, 576*f*, 720*f*, 721–25
  flower development and, 429*f*
  lateral, and secondary growth, 720*f*, 725–28
  transition of, and flowering, 808

Meristem identity genes, **734**
Meroblastic cleavage, **994**
Meselson, Matthew
  models of DNA replication by F. Stahl and, 299–300
  research on parthenogenic reproduction in rotifers, 649
Mesencephalon, 1028
Mesenchyme cells, 994–95
Mesenteries, **827**
Mesoderm, **631**, **994**
  gastrulation and formation of, 994
  organs and tissues formed from, 999*t*
Mesohyl, **642**
Mesophyll, **182**, **724**
Mesophyll cells, **196***f*
  loading sucrose into phloem from, 752*f*
Mesozoic era, 519*t*, 520, 521*f*, 527–28, 596, 629
Messenger RNA (mRNA), 86*f*, 87, 102, **311**, 327*t*
  codons of, 313, 314*f*
  degradation of, and regulation of gene expression, 368, 369*f*
  DNA library, 390
  transcription of, 311, 315–17, 790–91
  translation of polypeptides under direction of, 320–26
Metabolic defects, evidence for gene-directed protein synthesis from, 309–10
Metabolic pathways, **141–42**
Metabolic rate, **828**
  activity and, 829–30
  adjustment of, for thermoregulation, 838
  animal bioenergetic strategies and, 829
  animal body size and, 829
  basal, 829
  calculating, 829*f*
  cardiovascular system and, 870
  human, 834
  maximum, over select time spans, 830*f*
  standard, 829
Metabolism, **141–59**
  allosteric regulation of enzymes and controls on, 156*f*, 157
  anabolic pathways in, 142 (*see also* Protein synthesis)
  ATP in, 148–50, 828 (*see also* ATP (adenosine triphosphate))
  catabolic pathways in, 142 (*see also* Cellular respiration)
  energy transformations (laws of thermodynamics), 143–44
  enzymes and, 150–55
  enzymes, regulation of, and controls on, 156–57
  forms of energy and, 142–43
  free energy and, 145–48
  gene expression and adjustments of, in bacteria, 352–56
  metabolic pathways in, 141–42
  organelles and structural order in, 157*f*
  in prokaryotes, 352–56, 539–40
  protobionts and simple, 515
  regulation of, 352–56
  thermoregulation and changes in, 838
  transformation of matter and energy in, 141–44
Metamorphosis, **627**
  in frogs, 686*f*
  in insects, 661*f*, 943*f*
Metanephridia, **930***f*
Metaphase
  meiosis, 244*f*, 245*f*
  mitosis, 221, 223*f*, 224*f*, 226*f*
Metaphase plate, **224***f*
  tetrads on, 247
Metapopulations, **1151**
Metastasis, **233**
Metencephalon, 1028
Methane
  combustion of, as redox reaction, 161, 162*f*
  covalent bonding in, 40*f*
  as greenhouse gas, 540

molecular shape of, 43*f*, 60*f*
  production of, by methanogens, 544
Methanogens, **544**
Methionine, 313, 323
Methylation, DNA, 284
  genomic imprinting and, 289, 364
  regulation of eukaryotic gene expression and, 364
Methylation, histone, 363
Mexico, demographic transition in, 1153*f*
MHC. *See* Major histocompatibility complex (MHC)
Microclimate, **1087**, 1091
Microevolution, **454**, **472**
  gene flow as cause of, 462
  genetic drift as cause of, 460–62
  mutations as cause of, 459–60
  natural selection as cause of, 460, 462–70
  sexual recombination and, 460
Microfibrils in plant cellulose, 72, 73*f*
Microfilaments, **113***t*, **116–18**
  actin and, 116, 226, 1068*f*
  cell motility and, 117*f*
  cytoplasmic streaming and, 117*f*, 118
  structural role of, 117*f*
  structure and function, 113*t*
Micronutrients, plant, **757**, 758*t*
Microphylls, **585**, 586*f*
Micropyle, **599**
MicroRNA (miRNA), 327*t*, **368**
  regulation of gene expression by, 369*f*
Microscopy, 94–97
Microsporangia, 774*f*, 775
Microspores, **586**, 774*f*–75
Microsporidia, 615*f*
Microtubule-organizing center, 221, 222*f*, 223*f*
Microtubules, **113***t*, **114–16**
  cell motility and, 112–18
  centrosomes and centrioles, 114*f*
  cilia and flagella and, 114, 115*f*, 116
  kinetochore, 221, 224, 225*f*
  of mitotic spindle, and chromosome movement, 224
  9 + 2 pattern of, 114, 115*f*, 525
  plant growth and cytoplasmic, 730, 731*f*
  polar, 224
  structure and function, 113*t*
Microvilli, **860**
Midbrain, **1028**, 1029
Middle ear, **1051**
Middle lamella, **118**, 119*f*
Migration
  bird, 1106, 1109*f*, 1110–11
  morphogenesis and cell, 1001–2
Migratory restlessness, 1110–11, 1121
Milk, 694
  α-lactalbumin and production of mammalian, 380
  passive immunity provided by, 914
  prolactin and production of, 952, 981
Miller, Carlos O., 796
Miller, Stanley, 59*f*, 513*f*, 514
Millipedes (Diplopoda), 659*f*
Mimicry
  H. Bates hypothesis regarding, 22
  case study of, in snake populations, 21–24
Mimosa pudica (sensitive plant), rapid turgor movements in, 810*f*
Mimulus sp., 474*f*, 481
Minerals, **851**
  absorption of, by plant roots, 744–46
  availability of soil, to plants, 761–62
  deficiencies of, in plants, 758, 759*f*
  as essential nutritional requirement, 851, 852*t*
  as plant nutrients, 756–59
Mineral nutrients, **756**
Mineralocorticoids, **958**
Minichromosomes, 340
Minimum viable population size (MVP), **1216**
Mining industry, use of prokaryotes in, 405, 546–47
miRNA (microRNA), 327*t*, 368, 369*f*
Mismatch repair of DNA, **305**
Missense mutations, **328**, 329*f*

Mistletoe (*Phoradendron*), 768f
Mitchell, Charles, 1149
Mites, 659f
Mitochondria, 109–11
    chemical energy conversion in, 109–10
    chemiosmosis in, versus in chloroplasts, 109, 173, 192–93
    endosymbiosis and origins of, 523–25
    as site of cellular respiration, 109, 110f, 164–65, 168–74
    structure, 110f
Mitochondrial DNA (mtDNA), human genetic disorders and, 290
Mitochondrial matrix, 110
    ATP synthase as molecular mill in, 171f
    citric acid cycle enzymes in, 169f
Mitochondrial myopathy, 290
Mitosis, 220
    in animal cells, 222–23f
    chromosome duplication and distribution during, 219–20
    cytokinesis and, 224–26
    evolution of, 227f, 228
    meiosis compared to, 246f, 247
    mitotic spindle in, 221, 224f
    phases of, 221, 222–23f
    in plant cells, 226f
Mitotic (M) phase of cell cycle, 221f
Mitotic spindle, 221, 222f, 223f
Mixotricha paradoxa, symbiotic relationships of, 525
Mixotrophs, 550
Model-building in science, 24, 25f
Model organisms, study of development using, 412–13f
Model system, microbial, 334
Modern synthesis of evolutionary theory, 455
Molarity, 53
Molar mass, 52
Molds, 611f
    black bread mold (*Rhizopus stolonifer*), 614f
    bread (*Neurospora crassa*), 616f, 617f
    as pathogens, 622–23
Mole (mol), 52–53
Mole(s), convergent evolution of analogous burrowing characteristics in Australian and North American, 494f, 495
Molecular basis of inheritance, 293–308
    DNA as genetic material, evidence for, 293–98
    DNA proofreading and repair, 305–6
    DNA replication, base pairing to template strands in, 299f, 300f
    DNA replication, models of, 299f, 300f
    DNA replication, proteins assisting in, 303, 304t
    DNA replication, steps in, 300–305
    DNA replication, summary of bacterial, 304f
    DNA structural model, scientific process of building, 296–98
    replicating ends of DNA molecules, 306–7
Molecular clocks, 506–7
    applying, to origin of HIV, 507
    difficulties with, 506–7
    of multicellular eukaryotes, 526
    neutral theory and, 506
    of plants, 578
Molecular formula, 40
Molecular genealogy, 89
Molecular homologies, 449
Molecular mass, 52
Molecular systematics, 491
    animal phylogeny based on, 635f
    applying parsimony to problem of, 502–3f
    prokaryotic phylogeny and lessons of, 540–41
Molecules, 5f, 39–43. *See also* Macromolecules
    amphipathic, 124
    chemical bonds and formation of, 39–42
    defined, 40
    shape and function of, 42–43
    small, as second messengers, 210–12
Mole rats, naked (*Heterocephalus glaber*), altruistic behavior in, 1128, 1129f

Molluscs (Mollusca), 639f, 650–53
    basic body plan, 650f
    Bivalvia (clams, oysters), 652
    Cephalopoda (cephalopods), 652–53f
    exoskeleton of, 650, 1064
    Gastropoda (snails, slugs), 651f–52
    hormonal regulation in, 960
    major classes of, 651t
    nervous system of, 1012f
    Polyplacophora (chitons), 651f
Molting, 657
    nutritional requirements during, 850f
Monkey flower (*Mimulus*), 474f, 481
Monkeys
    Old World, and New World, 697, 700f
    social learning of alarm calls in vervet, 1131–32
Monoclonal antibodies, 913
Monocots (Monocotyledones), 602, 603f
    dicots compared to, 603f
    germination and cotyledons of, 780f
    stem tissue in, 724f
Monocytes, 880f, 881, 900
Monoecious plants, 773
Monogamous mating, 1123, 1124f
Monogeneans, 646t, 647
Monohybrid, 256–57
Monohybrid cross, 256
    multiplication and addition rules applied to, 258, 259f
Monomers, 68
    amino acid, 78–80
    nucleotide, 87f, 88
    polymers built from, 68, 69f
Mononucleosis, 370
Monophyletic grouping, 498f
Monosaccharides, 70–71. *See also* Glucose
    disaccharide synthesis from, 70, 71f
    structure and classification of, 70f
Monosomic cells, 285
Monotremes, 695, 696f
Montreal Protocol, 1206
Moose, stability and fluctuation of population size on Isle Royale, Michigan, 1150f
Moray eel, fine-spotted (*Gymnothorax dovii*), 683f
Morchella esculenta, 616f
Morgan, Thomas Hunt
    experimental evidence for chromosome-gene association from, 276–77, 293
    experimental evidence for linked genes from, 277–78, 279f
Morganucodon, jaw and ear bones of, 695f
Morphogen(s), 424
Morphogenesis, development and, 413, 987
    in animals, 987, 1001–3
    in plants, 728–35
Morphological species concept, 476
Morphology
    animal phylogeny based on, 634f
    phylogeny and evidence of, 492–93
    plant, 712
Morton, Martin, 1138, 1139
Morula, 992
Mosaic evolution, 703
Mosquitos
    as disease vector, 555, 556f, 664, 1085, 1163
    as fluid feeders, 845f
    habitat and distribution of, 1085
    mechanoreceptors in, 1050
Mosses (Bryophyta), 580, 582f, 586, 587f
    life cycle of *Polytrichum*, 581f
    sporophytes of, 577f
Moths
    bat predation of, 1045f
    chemoreceptors in, 1049f
    predator-prey relationship with blue jays, 467f
    sphinx, 820f
    thermoregulation in, 837f, 839f
Motility. *See* Movement
Motor mechanisms, 1063–74

Motor neurons, 1013f
    axon growth direction, 1038f
    muscle contraction stimulated by, 1069–71
    recruitment of, 1070
    structure of, 1014f
Motor output, nervous system function and, 1013f. *See also* Locomotion; Movement
Motor proteins, 78t, 112f, 114
    mechanical work in cells and, 149f
Motor unit of vertebrate muscle, 1070, 1071f
Mountain, effects of, on climate, 1090f
Mountain lion (*Puma concolor*), 1123
Mouse (*Mus musculus*)
    apoptosis and paw formation in, 428, 429f
    effect of social environment on aggressive behavior in California, 1114t
    energy budget for deer, 830, 831f
    genome, 394, 401
    genomic imprinting of *Igf2* gene, 289f
    geographic variation of chromosomal mutations in, 463f, 464
    homeotic genes in, 431f
    lack of V_{1a} receptor in male wild-type, 1113
    as model organism, 413f
    obesity in, 848f
Movement. *See also* Locomotion
    cell crawling during morphogenesis, 1001–2
    cell motility, 112–18
    in plants, 810f
    prokaryotic cell, 536f, 537
    in protists, 117f, 118
Movement corridor, 1221
MPF (maturation promoting factor), 230f
Mucin, 856
Mucosa tissue layer, of stomach, 827f
Mucous membranes, 823
    as body defense mechanism, 899f
Mucus, 899
Mule, as hybrid between horse and donkey, 475f
Mule deer (*Odocoileus hemionus*), foraging and risk of predation, 1123f
Muller, Hermann, 329
Müllerian mimicry, 1162
Multicellularity, origins of, 525–28
Multifactorial characters, 264
    as genetic disorders, 268
Multigene family, 377–78
Multiple alleles, 262
Multiple fruit, 779
Multiple sclerosis, 917, 1015
Multiplication rule and Mendelian inheritance, 258, 259f
Muscle(s)
    cardiac, 826f, 1024, 1072
    contraction (*see* Muscle contraction)
    effects of anabolic steroids on, 959f
    fatigue in, and accumulation of lactate, 1070–71
    interaction between skeleton and, 1066f
    locomotion and contraction of, 1066f
    neural control of tension in, 1069–71
    skeletal, 1066f–72
    smooth, 1072
    stretch receptors for, 1047f
    structure, 1066, 1067f
Muscle cell, 130, 627
    determination and cell differentiation of, 419f, 420
    microfilaments and motility in, 116, 117f
    lactic acid fermentation in, 175
Muscle contraction
    myosin and actin interactions and, 116, 117f, 1068f
    neural controls and, 1069–71
    role of calcium and regulatory proteins in, 1068, 1069f
    role of sarcoplasmic reticulum and T tubules in, 1069f
    sliding-filament model of, 1067f, 1068f
Muscle fiber
    contraction of (*see* Muscle contraction)
    fast, and slow, 1071, 1072t

logistic growth model of, 1145–47
population density, dispersion and demography, 1136–41
Population genetics, **455**, 1136
gene flow and, 462
gene pools and allele frequencies, 455–56
genetic drift and, 460–62
genetic variation due to mutation in, 459–60
genetic variation due to sexual recombination in, 247–49, 460
Hardy-Weinberg theorem and equilibrium in, 456–58
human health and, 458
microevolution and, 454
modern synthesis of Darwinian and Mendelian ideas and development of, 455
natural selection and, 446, 447f, 454–55, 460, 462–70
Population growth
cycles of, 1151–52
density-dependent and density-independent factors in, 1148–50
exponential model of, 1143–45
human, 1136
logistic model of, and concept of carrying capacity, 1145–47
overproduction of offspring in, 445f
zero, 1144
Population size
change in (ΔN), 1143
declining-population approach to conservation, 1218–19
density-dependent and density-independent regulation of, 1148–50
estimating effective, 1216–17
minimum viable, 1216
per capita rate of increase in, 1143–44, 1145
small-population approach to conservation, 1215–18
Population viability analysis (PVA), **1216**
Pore complex, 102, 103f
Porifera. See Sponges (Porifera)
Porphyra, 561
Positional information, **421**, **731**, **1007**
plant cell development and, 731, 732–33
vertebrate limbs and, 1007
Positive feedback, **11**, 12f, **833**
as mechanism of homeostasis, 833
Positive pressure breathing, 888
Positron-emission tomography (PET), 36f
Posterior pituitary gland, **950**
hormones of, 949t, 950f, 951
Posterior side of body, **630**
Postsynaptic cell, **1014**
effect of neurotransmitters on, 1022f, 1023
structure of vertebrate neuron and, 1014f
synaptic terminals on, 1021f
Postsynaptic potentials
excitatory, and inhibitory, 1022
summation of, 1023f
Postzygotic barriers, **473**, 475f
Potassium (K$^+$)
deficiency of, in plants, 759f
ligand-gated channels and, 1022f
regulation of blood concentrations of, in kidney, 934
role of, in opening/closing of stomata, 750
selective channels allowing passage of, 739, 740f
selective permeability of neuron membrane to, 1017f
sodium-potassium pump, 134, 135f, 1016–17
voltage-gated channels for, 1018, 1019f, 1020f, 1021
Potassium channels, 739, 740f
Potato, diseases of, 558
Potential energy, **36**, **142**
transformations between kinetic and, 142f
Potential evapotranspiration, 1176
Precautionary principle, **1083**

Prairie voles (*Microtus ochrogaster*), mating behavior, 1112f, 1113
Precapillary sphincters, 877, 878f
Precipitation
effects of mountains on, 1090
global air and wind patterns and, 1089f
of pathogens, 913
Predation, **1161**–62
effects of differential, on guppy evolution, 446, 447f
foraging behavior and risk of, 1122–23
by fungi, 610f
herbivory as, 1163
by parasites and pathogens, 1163
population cycles and, 1151, 1152f
as population limiting factor, 1150
Predators
adaptations of, 1045f
behavioral variation in prey selection by, 1118, 1119f
defenses against, 23f, 32f, 813, 1162, 1163
fungi as, 610f
keystone species as, 1168f, 1169f
mimicry as defense against, 23f, 1162
seed, 1161
Predator-prey relationship
blue jay and moth, 467f
lynx and snowshoe hare, 1151, 1152f
Preformation, development and concept of, 987
Pregnancy, **978**–81
contraception against, 982–83
in humans, 915–16, 978–81
immunology of, 915–16, 982
reproductive technology and, 983–84
Pre-mRNA, 312
Preprophase band, **730**
Prepuce, **972**
Pressure flow, translocation of sap in angiosperms by, 753f
Pressure potential (ψ_P), **741**
Presynaptic cell, **1014**
Prey, defenses of, 1162. See also Predation; Predators
Prezygotic barriers, **473**, 474f
Priapulans, 640f
Primary cell wall, of plants, 118, 119f
Primary consumers, **1185**
Primary electron acceptor, **189**
Primary growth, plants, **720**, 721–25
of roots, 721f, 722f, 723f
of shoots and stems, 723f, 724, 726f
Primary immune response, 908
Primary motor cortex, brain, 1033f
Primary oocytes, **974**
Primary plant body, **721**
Primary producers, **1185**, **1186**
Primary production in ecosystems, 1187–88
in aquatic ecosystems, 1188–90
energy budget and, 1186–87
gross, 1187–88
net, 1187f, 1188
regional annual net, for Earth, 1188f
in terrestrial and wetland ecosystems, 1190–91
Primary somatosensory cortex, brain, 1032, 1033f
Primary structure of protein, **81**, **82**f
sickle-cell disease related to, 84f
Primary succession, ecological, **1173**
Primary transcript, **312**, 327t
Primary visual cortex, 1032, **1063**
Primase, 303, 304t
Primates, 697–701
derived characters of, 697
humans (see Human(s); Human evolution)
living, 697–701
phylogenetic tree of, 700f
Primer, DNA synthesis, **303**
Primitive streak, **996**
Prions, **345**
propagation of, 346f
Probability, Mendelian inheritance and laws of, 258–60, 268–69

Problem solving in animals, 1117–18
Proboscis worms (Nemertea), 639f
Producers, 6
Production, pyramid of, 1192
Production efficiency in ecosystems, **1191**–92
Products of chemical reactions, 44
Progenitor cells, 1039
Progesterone, intracellular receptors for, 947
Progestins, **959**
Programmed cell death (apoptosis), 108, 427–29
ethylene and plant leaf, 800
Progymnosperms, 596f
Prokaryotes, 534–48. See also Archaea; Bacteria
aerobic, and photosynthetic, 537f
bacteria and archaea as as evolutionary branches of, 541–44
chemiosmosis in early, 521–22
ecological roles of, 544–45
evolution of, and changes affecting Earth, 521–23
H$^+$ gradients and ATP synthesis in, 173
internal and genomic organization, 537
major groups of, 542–43f
motility of, 536–37
nutritional and metabolic diversity among, 538–40
as pathogens, 545–46
phylogeny of, 540–44
prevalence of, 534
protein synthesis in eukaryotes versus, 327–28
reproduction and adaptation by, 537–38
in research and technology, 546–47
structure and shapes of, 534, 535f, 536f
Prokaryotic cell, **8**, **98**. See also Archaea; Bacteria
cell wall, 132, 534–36
chromosome of, 537f
DNA replication in, 300–305
eukaryotic cell compared to, 8f, 98–99, 312f
flagella of, 536f
membranes of, 537f
motility in, 536–37
ribosomes of, 322
RNA polymerase of, 315
structure and shapes of, 98f, 534, 535f
transcription in, 311, 312f, 315, 316, 317
translation in, 311, 312f
Prokaryotic genome, 346–56, 537
bacterial replication of, 346, 347f
complexity of, 374
Prolactin (PRL), **952**, 981
Proliferative phase, menstrual cycle, **977**
Prometaphase, mitosis, 221, 222f, 226f
Promiscuous mating, **1123**
Promoter DNA sequence, 315f, 316f
Pronghorn, respiratory system of, 894
Propanal, 64f
Prophage, **339**, 349
Prophase
meiosis, 244f, 245f
mitosis, **221**, 222f, 226f
Prop roots, 714f
Prostaglandins (PGs), **948**
as local regulators, 948
pain reception and, 948, 1049
platelets and, 948f
Prostate gland, **972**
Prosthetic group, 170
Protease activation, 859f
Proteasome, **369**
degradation of protein by, 369, 370f
Protein(s), 77–86
amino acids of, 78, 79f, 80 (see also Amino acid(s))
antimicrobial, 900–901
aquaporins (see Aquaporins)
carrier, 133, 134f
catabolism of, 177f
catalytic (see Enzyme(s))
cell determination/differentiation and production of specific, 419
channel, 133, 134f
chaperone, 85, 325

Index

conformation, structure, and function of, 81–86
denaturation and renaturation of, 84, 85f
defined, 78
digestion of, 859f
DNA replication and repair, and role of, 301–3, 304t
domains of (see Domains, protein)
enzymes as, 77, 78f (see also Enzyme(s))
folding of, 85, 325, 345–46
functions of, linked to structure, 77, 78t
G (see G protein)
heat-shock, 812, 840
improving yield of, in crop plants, 764
infectious (prions), 345, 346f
integral, 128
interactions among, in cell, 10f
membrane, 127–29
motor (see Motor proteins)
as nutritional requirement, 849–50
peripheral, 128
as polypeptide chain, 78 (see also Polypeptides)
posttranslational processing of, as regulation of eu-
    karyotic gene expression, 369, 370f, 791
PR, 814
R, 813, 814f
receptor (see Receptor proteins)
relay, 215
repressor, 353
respiratory pigments, 892–94
scaffolding, 215f
secretory, 105
stress-induced, 840
structural levels of, 81, 82–83f
synthesis of (see Protein synthesis)
tissue-specific, 419
transmembrane, 128f
transport (see Transport proteins)
Protein folding, 85, 325, 345–46
Protein kinase(s), 209
    role in signal transduction pathway, 1024
Protein kinase A, 210, 211f
Protein phosphatases, 210
Protein phosphorylation, 209–10
Protein synthesis, 309–33
    as anabolic pathway, 142
    DNA-directed, 86f
    gene expression as specification of, 309–14
    genetic code and, 312–14
    overview of transcription and translation steps in,
        311–12
    point mutations affecting, 328–30
    in prokaryotes versus in eukaryotes, 327–28
    RNA, multiple roles in, 327
    RNA modification following transcription as
        phase of, 317–19
    summary of, 331f
    transcription and RNA synthesis as phase of,
        311–12, 315–17
    translation and polypeptide synthesis as phase of,
        311–12, 320–26
Proteobacteria, 542f
Proteoglycans, 119
    in extracellular matrix of animal cells, 119f
Proteomics, 402
Proterozoic era, 527
    fossils from, 526f
Protists, 549–73
    alternation of generations in some, 561–62
    alveolates, 555–58
    amoebozoans, 564–66
    animal evolution from, 628f
    cercozoans, 563
    contractile vacuoles of, 108
    diplomonads and parabasalids, 552, 553f
    diversity of, 549–51
    endosymbiosis and, 550–51
    euglenozoans, 553–54
    evolution of fungi from, 612
    exchange with environment and body of, 821f
    gas exchange in, 884

motility of, 117f, 118
multicellularity and,
    as pathogens, 552, 553f, 554f, 555, 556f, 564
    phylogeny of eukaryotes and place of, 552f
    pseudopodia and movement in, 117f
    radiolarians, 563
    red and green algae, 567–69
    sexual life cycle in some, 242f
    stramenopiles, 558–62
Protista (kingdom), 549. See also Protists
Protobionts, 513, 515
Protons, 34
    atomic number and, 34–35
Protonema, 580, 581f
Protonephridium, 929, 930f
Proton-motive force, 173
Proton pump, 136, 739
    plant cell growth in reponse to auxin and,
        794–95
    transport in plants and role of, 739, 740f
Proto-oncogenes, 371
    conversion of, into oncogenes, 371f
Protoplast, 717, 782
Protoplast fusion, 782
Protostomes
    cleavage in, 631–32
    coelom formation in, 632
    deuterostome development verus, 632f
    fate of blastophore in, 632–33
Protostome development mode, 631–33
Protozoan Mixotricha paradoxa, symbiotic
    relationships of, 525
Provirus, 341
Proximal control elements, 364
Proximal tubule, 931, 932f, 933
Proximate causes of behavior, 1106, 1107, 1108f,
    1109f
Proximate questions, 1107
Prozac (drug), 1025, 1040
PR (pathogenesis-related) proteins, 814
Pseudocoelom, 631
Pseudocoelomates, 631f
Pseudogenes, 378, 468
    in globin gene family, 377f, 378
Pseudopodia, 117f, 563, 564f
Pseudostratified ciliated columnar epithelium, 824f
Psilotum nudum whisk fern, 587f
P site, tRNA binding, 322f
Pteraspis, 679f
Pterophytes, 578, 587f, 588
Pterosaurs, 689
Public sanitation, 546
Puffballs, 618f
Pulmocutaneous circuit, 871
Pulmonary circuit, 871
Pulse, heart and, 873
Punctuated equilibrium model for speciation tempo,
    481, 482f
Pundamilia pundamilia and Pundamilia nyererei, specia-
    tion of, 479, 480f
Punnett square, 254, 255f, 263f
Pupil, of eye, 1059
Purines, 88, 298
Pyloric sphincter, 855f, 858
Pyramid of biomass, 1192, 1193f
Pyramid of numbers, 1193
Pyramid of net production, 1192f
Pyrimidines, 88, 298
Pyrococcus furiosus, 541
Pyrolobus fumarii, 541
Pyruvate
    conversion of, to acetyl CoA, 168f
    as key juncture in catabolism, 176f
    oxidation of glucose to, during glycolysis, 164,
        166–67f
Python
    bulk feeding by, 845f
    energy budget in, 830, 831f
PYY hormone, 847f

Quantitative characters, 263, 463
Quaternary structure of protein, 81, 83f
Quillworts, 586, 587f
Quinn, William, 1116

RAAS (renin-angiotensin-aldosterone system), 937, 938
Rabies, 914
Radial cleavage, 632
Radial glia, 1015
Radial symmetry, 630
    in animal body plan, 630f
    in flowers, 773f
Radiation
    heat and, 835
    mutations caused by, 329–30
Radicle, 778, 780
Radioactive isotopes, 35–36
    use in biological research, 35f
    uses and dangers of, 36
Radiolarians, 563f
Radiometric dating of fossils, 517
Radula, of mollusc, 650
Rafflesia arnoldii, 771f
Raikhel, Natasha, 712, 729, 802
    on systems biology and study of Arabidopsis, 710–11
Rainbow trout (Oncorrhynchus mykiss), 939f
Rain shadow, 1090
Random dispersion of populations, 1138f
Random fertilization, genetic variation from, 248
Range of species, 1081f, 1084, 1085f
    climate change and, 1092f
ras gene, 371
    development of cancer and role of, 371, 372f, 373
Rat
    kangaroo, 925f, 939f
    naked mole, 1128, 1129f
    tetraploidy in, 286f
Ratfish, spotted (Hydrolagus colliei), 681f
Ratites (flightless birds), 693
Ray-finned fishes (Actinopterygii), 682, 683f
Ray initials, 727
Rays, 680–82
Reactants in chemical reactions, 44
    key, and chemical work in cells, 149f
Reaction center, photosynthesis, 189
Reading frame, 314
Receptacle, flower, 598, 772
Reception of cell signaling, 204–8
    intracellular, 205
    intracellular, for lipid-soluble hormones, 947
    by plants, 429–30, 789
    in plasma membrane, 205, 206–8f
Receptive field of ganglion cells, 1062
Receptors, 944. See also Receptor proteins
    cell-surface, for water-soluble hormones, 946
    of internal environment, 832
    intracellular, 205
    intracellular, for lipid-soluble hormones, 947
    in plasma membrane, 205, 206–8f
Receptor-ligand model of gene-for-gene plant resist-
    ance to pathogens, 814f
Receptor-mediated endocytosis, 137, 138f
Receptor molecules. See Receptor proteins
Receptor potential, 1046
Receptor proteins, 78t
    G-protein-linked, 206f
    ligand-gated ion channel as, 208f
    in plasma membrane, 205, 206–8f
    receptor tyrosine kinase, 207f, 231
Receptor tyrosine kinase, 207f, 231
Recessive allele, 254
    sex-linked, 283–84
Recessive trait, 253
    attached earlobes as, 265f
    genetic disorders as, 266–67
    sex-linked, 283f–84
Reciprocal altruism, 1130–31
Reclinomonas americana, 525

Recombinant chromosomes, 248, 249f, 278, 279f, 280f
Recombinant DNA, 384. *See also* Genetic recombination
  bacterial conjugation, plasmids, and, 349–51
  production of, overview, 385
  restriction enzymes and production of, 386f
Recombinant frequency, 279–81
Recombinants (recombinant types), 278
Recombinase, 906
Recruitment of motor neurons, 1070
Rectum, 862
Red algae (rhodophytes), 550f, 561f, 567, 575f
Red blood cells (erythrocytes), 825f, 880–82
  carbohydrates on surface of, 129
  glucose transport in, 130
  hemoglobin and (*see* Hemoglobin)
  normal, and sickled, 84f
  plasma membrane of, 99f, 128
  sickle-cell anemia in, 84 (*see also* Sickle-cell disease)
Red-cockaded woodpecker, 1218, 1219f
Red light, plant responses to, 803f, 806, 807f
Redox reactions, 161–64
  energy harvesting via NAD$^+$ and electron transport chain, 162, 163f, 164
  methane combustion as energy-yielding, 161, 162f
  oxidation of organic fuel during cellular respiration, 162
  photosynthesis as, 184
  principle of, 161–62
Red tide, 555
Reducing agent, 161
Reduction, 161
Reductionism, 9–10
Redundancy model of community, 1180
Reflexes, 1013
  knee-jerk, 1013f
Refractory period following action potential, 1020
Regeneration, asexual reproduction by, 965
Regulation
  as biological theme, 27f
  of cell cycle, 228–33
  by feedback, in biological systems, 11–12
  as property of life, 3f
Regulators versus conformers, 832
Regulatory genes, 420
  homeobox sequences and, 431–32, 627
  homeotic genes as, 425 (*see also* Homeotic genes)
  lacI, 355f
  myoD, 419f, 420
  trpR, 353–54
Regulatory proteins, muscle contraction and role of calcium and, 1068, 1069f
Relative abundance of species in communities, 1165
Relative fitness, 464
Relay proteins, 215
Release factor, 324
Renal artery, 931, 932f
Renal cortex, of kidney, 931, 932f
Renal medulla, of kidney, 931, 932f
Renal pelvis, 931, 932f
Renal vein, 931, 932f
Renin-angiotensin-aldosterone system (RAAS), 937, 938
Repeated reproduction, 1141
Repetitive DNA, 375, 376–77
Replication. *See* DNA replication
Replication bubble, 301f
Replication fork, 301f
Repressible enzymes
  inducible enzymes compared with, 355
  trp operon and regulated synthesis of, 353, 354f
Repressor, 353, 365
  control of eukaryotic gene expression and role of, 365
  trp, in bacteria, 353
Reproduction. *See also* Asexual reproduction; Sexual reproduction
  in animals (*see* Animal reproduction)
  in bacteria (prokaryotes), 346–51, 537–38
  of cells (*see* Cell division)

cycles and patterns of, 965–66
  in fungi, 610–12
  in insects, 661, 968, 969f
  parthenogenesis, 648, 965, 966f
  in plants (*see* Plant reproduction)
  as property of life, 3f
  in protists, 242f
  protobionts and simple, 515f
  semelparity versus iteroparity in, 1141
  of viruses, 336–42
Reproductive barriers, 474–75f
Reproductive isolation, 473
  in divergent *Drosophila* populations, 477f
  reproductive barriers and, 474–75f
Reproductive leaves, 716f
Reproductive rates in populations, 1140–41
Reproductive table, 1140
  for Belding's ground squirrel, 1141f
Reptiles, 688–94
  alligators and crocodiles, 691
  birds, 691–94
  characteristics of, 688–89
  circulatory system, 870f, 871
  dinosaurs, archosaurs, pterosaurs, and theropods, 689, 690f
  kidney adaptations in, 939f
  lepidosaurs, 689, 690, 691f
  nitrogenous wastes of, 927f, 928
  origin and evolutionary radiations of, 689–90
  snakes (*see* Snakes (Squamata))
  thermoregulation in, 835f, 836, 838
  turtles, 690, 691f
Research methods
  absorption spectrum, 187f
  cell fractionation, 97f
  cloning human genes in bacterial plasmid, 387f
  dideoxy chain-termination method for sequencing DNA, 397f, 398
  DNA microarray assay, 401f
  electron microscopy, 96f
  freeze-fracture preparation of cells for, 126f
  intracellular recording for measurement of membrane potential, 1016f
  karyotype preparation, 240f
  light microscopy, 96f
  linkage map, 281f
  Mendel's plant breeding, 252f
  parsimony principle applied to molecular systematics, 502–3f
  polymerase chain reaction (PCR), 391f
  radioactive tracers, 35f
  studying natural selection in virtual populations, 467f
  testcross, 256f
  X-ray crystallography, 86f
Residual volume, breathing, 889
Resolution, of microscope, 95
Resource competition, population regulation through, 1148–49
Resource partitioning, 1161
Respiration. *See* Cellular respiration
Respiratory medium, 884
Respiratory pigments and gas transport, 892–95
  carbon dioxide transport, 893–94
  oxygen transport, 892f, 893
  role of partial pressure gradients in, 891f
Respiratory surface, 884
Respiratory system
  breathing and, 888–90
  in elite animal athletes, 894–95
  mammalian, 887, 888f
Response as property of life, 3f
Response to cell signaling, 945–46
  by regulation, or by transcription, 204, 212–15
  by plants, 429–30, 790–91
Resting potential, 1016
Restoration ecology, 1209, 1224–28
  biological augmentation as, 1226
  bioremediation as, 1226

community recovery from disasters and, 1226f
  exploring global projects for, 1226, 1227–28f
Restriction endonucleases, 338
Restriction enzymes, 338, 386
  recombinant DNA produced using, 386f
Restriction fragments, DNA, 386
  analysis of, 392–94
Restriction fragment length polymorphisms (RFLPs), 394
  forensic analysis using, 405
  linkage mapping, 396f
  as markers for disease-causing alleles, 403f
  noncoding DNA and analysis of, 394
Restriction site, 386f
Reticular fibers, 823
Reticular formation, 1029f
Retina, 1059
  celluar organization of vertebrate, 1062f
  rod and cone cells of, 1059, 1060f, 1061f, 1062f
  visual information processing and, 1061–63
Retinal, 1060f
Retinitis pigmentosa, 462
Retrotransposons, 375–76
  copy and movement of, 376f
Retrovirus, 340–41, 370
  retrotransposons and, 376
  as vector for gene therapy, 403f
Reverse transcriptase, 341
Reznick, David, research on guppy evolution by, 446, 447f
Rheotaxis in fish, 1110f
Rheumatoid arthritis, 917f
Rh factor, 915–16
Rhine River, Europe, restoration project in, 1228
Rhizobium sp., 542f
  nitrogen-fixation by, 764, 765f, 766
Rhizoids, 580
Rhizomes, 715f
Rhizopus stolonifer (black bread mold), life cycle of, 614f
Rhodopsin, 1060f
Rhythm method, contraceptive, 982
Ribbon worms (Nemertea), 639f, 649f
Ribonuclease, determining structure of, 86f
Ribonucleic acid. *See* RNA (ribonucleic acid)
Ribose, 88
Ribosomal RNA (rRNA), 102, 322, 327t
  multigene family for, 377f
  small-subunit (SSU-rRNA), 524, 540
Ribosome(s), 98, 102–4, 309f, 311
  anatomy of functioning, 322f
  computer model of, 322f
  free versus bound, 102, 325
  protein synthesis and, 86f, 87, 323–24
  as site of translation, 311
  structure of, 103f
Ribozymes, 318, 515
  as biological catalyst, 318
  RNA replication by, 515, 516f
Rice (*Oryza sativa*), 475f, 802
  diseases of, 797
  transgenic, 784, 785f
Riechert, Susan, 1119–20
Ringworm, 622
Rivera Gonzales, Carlos, 1230f
Riverine wetlands, 1094
Rivers. *See* Streams and rivers
Rivet model of communities, 1180
RNA (ribonucleic acid), 86. *See also* Messenger RNA (mRNA); Ribosomal RNA (rRNA); Transfer RNA (tRNA)
  as earliest form of genetic material, 515–16
  modification of, after transcription, 317–19
  priming DNA synthesis with, 303
  protein synthesis and role of, 86f
  ribozymes and replication of, 515, 516f
  small nuclear RNA (snRNA), 318, 327t
  transcription and synthesis of, in antiparallel direction, 313, 315f, 316f, 317

Index

translation of polypeptides directed by, 320–26
types of, in eukaryotic cell, 327t
as viral genetic material, 340–42
RNA interference (RNAi), **368**, 369, 400
RNA polymerase, **315**
  attachment of, and initiation of transcription, 315f, 316
  control of eukaryotic gene expression and, 364, 365f
RNA processing, **312**, 317–19
  alteration of mRNA ends (addition of 5' cap and poly-A tail), 317f
  intron function and importance in, 319
  regulation of eukaryotic gene expression and, 368
  ribozyme function during, 318
  split genes and RNA splicing during, 318f, 319
RNA splicing, **318**f
  alternative, 319, 368, 399
RNA strands, antiparallel, 321f
RNA viruses, 340–42, 344
  reproductive cycle of enveloped, 341f
Roadrunner (*Geococcyx californianus*), 939f
Rocks
  as abiotic factor, 1087
  fossils in (see Fossil(s))
  magnetic reversals affecting, 518
Rod cells, eye, **1059**
  production of receptor potential in, 1061f
  structure and light absorption by, 1060f
Rodents, biological clocks in, 1030, 1031f
Rod-shaped (bacilli) prokaryotes, 98f, 535f
Rolling DNA replication, 350f
Roots, 577f, **584**, **713**. See also Root system
  adventitious, 713
  auxin and formation of, 795
  evolution of, 584–85
  fibrous, 713
  gravitropism in, 809f
  lateral, 723f
  lateral transport in, 745f
  modified, 714f
  nitrogen-fixing bacterial nodules on, 764, 765f, 766
  primary growth of, 721f, 722f, 723f
  secondary growth of, 725–28
  taproot, 713
  water and mineral absorption by, 744–46
Root cap, **721**
Root hairs, 713f, **714**
  homeotic gene GLABRA-2 and, 732, 733f
  water and nutrient absorption and role of, 744
Root pressure, **746**
  ascent of xylem sap and, 746
Root system, **713–14**. See also Root
  primary growth in, 721–23
  secondary growth in, 725–28
  water and mineral absorption by, 744–46
Root tip, 713f, 721
Rose-shaped complexes for cellulose synthesis, 574
Rosette cellulose-synthesizing complexes, **574**
Rosy periwinkle (*Catharanthus roseus*), 1211, 1212f
Rotifers (Rotifera), 639f, 648–49
Rough ER (endoplasmic reticulum), **104**, 105f
  functions of, 105
  secretory protein synthesis and, 105
Round window, ear, **1052**
Rous, Peyton, 370
R plasmids, **351**
  antibiotic resistance in bacteria and, 351
R proteins and R genes, 813, 814f
R-selection (density-independent) populations, **1147**
RT-PRC, 403
Rubisco (RuBP carboxylase), **194**
Rudner, Rivka, 818
Ruffled grouse (*Bonasa umbellatus*), 1221
Ruminants, digestion in, **864**f
Running, energy cost of, 1074f
Rwanda, 1155

Saccharomyces cerevisiae. See Yeast (*Saccharomyces cerevisiae*)
Saccule, **1052**, 1053f
Sac fungi (Ascomycota), **616–17**
Sagittaria latifolia (common arrowhead), as dioecious species, 773f
Sahelanthropus tchadensis, 702
Salamanders (Urodela), 475f, 685
  genome, 377f
  heterochrony and evolution of feet of, 484f
  nervous system, 1012f
  paedomorphosis in, 485f
Salicylic acid, **815**
Saliva, 856
Salivary amylase, **856**
Salivary glands, **855**
Salmon, Pacific, life history pattern of, 1141–42
Salmonella sp., 542f
Salts. See also Sodium chloride (NaCl)
  dietary, 852
  excessive, in soils, 762
  excretion of, by birds, 926f
  ionic compounds as, 41
  plant response to excessive, 711–12
Saltatory conduction, **1021**
Salt marsh
  black rush as facilitator species in, 1170f
  limiting nutrient in Hudson Bay, 1191f
Sand dollars, 641f
  cleavage in embryo of, 992f
Sanderson, Michael, 578
Sandpipers (*Calidris mauri*), 1110f
Sanger, Frederick, 80, 396
Sapwood, **727**
Sarcomeres, **1066**, 1067f
Sarcoplasmic reticulum (SR), **1069**
Sarcopterygii (lobe-fins), 683–84
Sargasso Sea, nutrient enrichment experiment in, 1188, 1189t
Sarin nerve gas, 155
SARS (severe acute respiratory syndrome), 344
Satellite DNA, 377
Saturated fatty acid, **75**
Savanna, **1101**f
Sawka, Nadia, 1125
Scaffolding proteins, **215**f
Scala naturae (scale of nature), 439
Scales
  fish, 682
  reptile, 688
Scallops (Bivalvia), 652f, 885f
Scanning electron microscopes and micrographs (SEMs), 96f
Scarlet fever, 339
Scarlet king snake, case study on mimicry of warning coloration in, 21–24
Schemske, Douglas, 481
Schindler, David, 1190
Schistosomiasis, blood fluke and, 30, 647f, 1163
Schistosoma mansoni (blood fluke), 30, 1163
  life cycle, 647f
Schizocoelous development, **632**
Schizophrenia, 1039–40
Schwann cells, **1015**
  myelin sheath and, 1015f
Science
  controlled experiments in, 23–24
  culture of, 25
  discovery, 19–20
  hypothesis-based, 20f–21
  inquiry at heart of, 19
  limitations of, 24
  model-building in, 24, 25f
  technology, society, and, 25–26
  theory in, 24
Scientific method, 21. See also Biological methods
Scion, of plant, **782**
Sclera, 1058, 1059f
Sclereids, **718**

Sclerenchyma cells, **718**f
Scolex, 648
Scorpions, 641f, 659f
Scrapie, 345
Scrotum, **971**
Scutellum, **778**
Scyphozoans (jellies, sea nettles), 644t
Sea anemones (*Anthopleura elegantissima*), 644f, 645
  asexual reproduction in, 965f
Sea cucumbers (Holothuroidea), 666, 667f
Sea hare (*Aplysia californica*), cellular basis of learning in, 1036f
Sea horse (*Hippocampus ramulosus*), 683f
Seal, 821f
  blubber, 835
  bottleneck effect in populations of northern elephant, 461f
  circulatory and respiratory adaptions of Weddell, 894–95
  northern fur, 1136f
Sea level, global warming and rising, 1205
Sea lilies (Crinoidea), 666
Sea mat (*Membranipora membranacea*), 649f
Sea palm (*Postelsia*), 561f
Seasons, climate and effects of, 1088f, 1090, 1091f
Sea otters (*Enhydra lutris*) as keystone predator, 1169f, 1214
Sea squirt (tunicate), 673–74
Sea stars (*Pisaster ochraceous*), 641f, 666, 667f
  anatomy, 665f
  gills, 885f
  innate defenses of, 902
  as keystone predator, 1168f, 1169
  nervous system, 1012f
Sea urchins (Echinoidea), 475f, 641f, 666, 667f
  fertilization of eggs in, 988, 989f, 990f
  gastrulation, 995f
  seaweed distribution affected by feeding of, 1085, 1086f
Sea wasp (*Chironex fleckeri*), 644f
Seaweeds
  alternation of generations in life cycle of, 561, 562f
  brown algae as, 560–62
  distribution of, affected by sea urchin feeding, 1085, 1086f
  green algae as, 567–69
  as human food source, 561f
  red algae as, 567
Sebaceous glands, 899
Secondary plant body, **725**
Secondary cell wall, of plant, **118**, 119f
Secondary compounds, 575
Secondary consumers, **1185**
Secondary endosymbiosis, **551**
  plastids produced by, 551f
Secondary growth, plants, **720–21**, 725–28
  auxin as stimulant to, 796
  cork cambia and periderm production, 728
  vascular cambium and, 725, 726f, 727
  wood as, 605, 727
Secondary immune response, **908**
Secondary oocyte, **974**
Secondary plant body, **725**
Secondary production in ecosystems, **1191**
  green world hypothesis and, 1193–93
  production efficiency of, 1191–93
Secondary structure of protein, 81, 82f
Secondary succession, ecological, **1173**
Second law of thermodynamics, 143, **144**
Second messengers, **210**, **790**
  calcium ions and inositol trisphosphate as, 211f, 212f
  cyclic AMP as, 210f, 211f, 1056
  cyclic GMP (cGMP) as, 790
  small molecules and ions as, 210–12
Secretion, excretory system and, **929**
Secretory phase, menstrual cycle, **977**
Secretory proteins, rough endoplasmic reticulum and synthesis of, 105

Sedimentary rocks, fossils in, **439**, 440*f*
Seed, **579**, **593**
    asexual production of (apomixis), 781
    crop size of, 1142*f*
    development of, from ovule, 593*f*
    dispersion of, 480*f*, 599*f*, 1138*f*
    dormancy of, 779–80, 798, 799*f*
    germination of, 779, 780*f*, 798
    of gynosperms, 593, 596, 597*f*
    structure of mature, 778*f*
Seed coat, **778**
Seedless vascular plants, **578***t*, 584–88
    carboniferous, 588*f*, 596
    classification of, 586–88
    diversity of, 587*f*
    ferns, life cycle, 585*f*
    origins of vascular plants, 584–86
    significance of, 588
Seed plants, **578***t*, 591–606
    angiosperms, 579, 598–604
    gymnosperms, 579, 593–97
    importance of, to human welfare, 591, 605–6
    reduced gametophytes and seeds of, 591–93
Seed predators, 1161
Segmentation genes, **423**, **425**
Segment polarity genes, **425**
Segregation of alleles, 254
    fertilization and, as chance events, 259*f*
    law of, 254–55, 274, 275*f*
Selaginella apoda spike moss, 587*f*
Selective permeability of membranes, **124**, 130
Selective reabsorption/secretion of solutes, **929**
Self-nonself recognition
    in animal immune system, 915–16
    human pregnancy and, 915
    in plants, 775–76
Semelparity, **1141**
Semen, **948**, **972**
Semicircular canals, **1051**
Semiconservative model of DNA replication, **299**, 300*f*
Semilunar valves, **873**
Seminal vesicles, **972**
Seminiferous tubules, **971**
Senile plaques, 1040*f*
Sensations, perception of, **1046**. *See also* Sensory
    receptor
Sensilla, 1055
Sensitive period for learning, **1108**–9
    bird song and, 1118
Sensitization as learning, 1036*f*
Sensory adaptation, **1047**
Sensory input, 1013*f*. *See also* Sensory mechanisms
Sensory mechanisms, 1045–63
    functions of sensory receptors, 1046–48
    for gravity and sound in invertebrates, 1050
    for hearing and equilibrium, 1046, 1047*f*, 1050–54
    for magnetism and light, 1048–49, 1057–63
    mechanoreceptors, 1046, 1047*f*, 1050–54
    overview of, 1045
    for pain, 1049
    for taste and smell, 1048, 1054–57
    for temperature, 1049
    types of sensory receptors, 1048–49
    vision, 1057–63
Sensory neurons, **1013***f*
    structure, 1014*f*
Sensory reception, **1046**
    amplification of stimulus energy in, 1046
    general function of, 1046–48
    integration of sensory information, 1047–48
    transduction of signals, 1046
    transmission of action potentials following, 1046–47
    two mechanisms of, 1047*f*
Sensory receptors, **1046**
    chemoreceptors, 1048
    electromagnetic receptors, 1048, 1049*f*
    exteroreceptors, 1046
    functions performed by, 1046–48

interoreceptors, 1046
    mechanoreceptors, 1046, 1047*f*, 1048
    pain receptors, 1049
    photoreceptors, 1057–63
    stretch, 1046, 1047*f*
    thermoreceptors, 1048*f*, 1049
    transduction/transmission of stimulus by, 1046
Sensory transduction, **1046**
    in cochlea of ear, 1052*f*
    in eye, 1060, 1061*f*
    for taste, 1055, 1056*f*
Sepals, flower, 429*f*, 430, **598**, 772
Septa, fungal hyphae, 609*f*
Septic shock, 902
Sequential hermaphroditism, **966**
Sequoia (*Sequoiadendron giganteum*), 595*f*
Sereno, Paul, 15*f*
Serial endosymbiosis, **524**
Serosa tissue layer, of stomach, 827*f*
Serotonin, **1025**
Seta, of moss, **580**
Severe combined immunodeficiency (SCID), 404, 918
Sex, reproductive handicap of, 469*f*. *See also* Sexual
    reproduction
Sex chromosomes, **240**
    aneuploidy of, and human genetic disorders, 287
    sex determination and, 282*f*
    sex-linked genes on, 283–84
Sex determination, chromosomal basis of, 282*f*–83
Sex hormones, 77
    comparison of functional groups of, 63*f*
    female, 63*f*, 958–59
    gonads and secretion of, 958–59
    male, 63*f*, 958–59, 977–78
Sex-linked genes, **283**
    chromosomal basis of sex and, 282–83
    inheritance of, 283*f*, 284
    X-chromosome inactivation and, 284
Sexual dimorphism, **468**
    human evolution and, 704–5
Sexual life cycle, **240**. *See also* Sexual reproduction
    alternation of fertilization and meiosis in, 240–43
    angiosperm, 600*f*, 772*f*
    of conifer (pine), 596, 597*f*
    genetic variation produced by, 247–49
    of humans, 241*f*
    meiosis and, 243–47
    of protists, 550
    varieties of, 242*f*
    of water mold, 559*f*
Sexual recombination, genetic variation and, 247–49, 460
Sexual reproduction, **239**, **627**, **964**. *See also* Sexual
    life cycle
    in animals, 627, 964–86
    in arthropods (insects), 661, 968, 969*f*
    asexual reproduction compared to, 239, 964
    fertilization mechanisms in, 967–68
    in fungi, 610, 611*f*, 614*f*, 617*f*, 619*f*
    gamete production and delivery in, 968–69
    genetic variation produced by, 247–49
    hormonal control of gametogenesis in animal, 973–78
    in invertebrates (earthworms), 964*f*
    natural selection and advantages/disadvantages of, 469
    in plants, 576, 580, 581*f*,, 585*f*, 586, 592–93, 596, 597*f*, 599, 600*f*, 601
    organs of animal, 969–73
    reduction of chromosome numbers via meiosis in, 242, 243–47
    reproductive cycles and patterns, 965–66
Sexual response, human, 972–73
    neurotransmitters and, 1025
Sexual selection, **468**. *See also* Mating
    imprinting and, in zebrafinch, 1126*f*
    mate choice and, 1125–27
    speciation and, in cichlid fishes, 479, 480*f*
Seyfarth, Richard, 1131–32

S-genes in plants, 776
Shade avoidance in plants, 804–5
Shaffer, Mark, 1217
Shared derived characters, **498**
Shared primitive character, **498**
Sharks, 821*f*, 680–82
    osmoregulation in, 924
    reproduction in, 681–82
    senses, 681
    thermoregulation in, 837*f*
Sheep, cloning of, 416
Shelf fungi, 618*f*
Shell
    amniote, 688
    mollusc, 650
Sherman, Paul, 1138, 1139
Shigella, antibiotic resistance in, 351
Shoot, 577*f*
Shoot system, plant, **713**
    cell fate and position in, 733*f*
    effect of phase changes on, 733*f*
    leaves, 725*f*
    primary growth in, 720*f*, 723*f*, 724
    secondary growth in, 720*f*, 725–28
    stems, 715, 724, 725–28
Short-day plant, **806**
Short-term memory, **1035**
Shrimp, 664
Shuster, Stephen M., 1126–27
Sibling, coefficient of relatedness between, 1129*f*
Sickle-cell disease, **267**, 403, 404
    amino-acid substitute in hemoglobin and, 84*f*
    heterozygote advantage, malaria, and, 267, 466*f*
    identifying sickle-cell allele mutation, 392, 393*f*
    point mutation as cause of, 328, 329*f*
    as recessively inherited disorder, 267
Side-blotched lizard (*Uta stansburiana*), game theory
    applied to mating successes of, 1127*f*, 1128
Sieve plates, **719**
Sieve-tube members, **719**
Signal, animal communication by, **1111**–12
Signal peptide, **326**
Signal-recognition particle (SRP), **326**, 327*t*
Signal transduction, 204, 208–12
    in cochlea of ear, 1052*f*
    hormones and, 945, 946*f*, 947*f*
    membrane proteins and, 128*f*
    in plants, 788–91
    protein phosphorylation and dephosporylation in, 209*f*, 210
    sensory reception in animals and, 1046 (*see also* Sensory transduction)
    small molecules and ions as second messengers in, 210–12
Signal transduction pathway, **202**, 204, 208, **946**
    in egg fertilization (cortical reactions), 989*f*, 990*f*
    general model of, 789*f*
    hormonal control, 945*f*, 946*f*
    of long-term potentiation, 1037*f*
    neural synaptic transmissions and, 1024
    in plants, 788–91
    protein phosphorylation/dephosphorylation and, 209*f*, 210
    relay proteins in, 215
    second messengers in, 210–12
Sign stimulus, fixed action patterns and, **1108**
Silencing, control of eukaryotic gene expression and, 365
Silent Spring (Carson), 1083*f*
Silkworm moth (*Bombyx mori*), chemoreceptors in. 1049*f*
Silurian period, 629
Silversword alliance, adaptive radiation and speciation in, 481*f*, 495
Simple epithelium, **823**
Simple fruit, **779**
Simple leaf, 716*f*
Simple sequence DNA, 376–77
Simpson, George Gaylord, 455

Sinervo, Barry, 1127–28
Singer, S. J., 125
Single bond, 40
Single-lens eye, 1058
Single nucleotide polymorphisms (SNPs), 402
Single-strand binding protein, 303, 304t
Sinoatrial (SA) node, 873–74
Sinuses, open circulatory system, 868, 869f
siRNA (small interfering RNA), 327t, 368, 369f
Sister chromatids, 219
    mitosis and, 219, 220f
    separation, in meiosis, 245f
Skeletal muscle, 826f, 1066
Skeleton
    animal, 1063–65
    endoskeleton, 1064
    exoskeleton, 657, 1064
    human, 1065f
    hydrostatic, 1063, 1064f
    locomotion and, 1073–74
    muscles and, 1066–72
    origins of bone in, 679, 680, 682
    support of, and size of animal, 1064–65
Skin
    in aquatic osteichthyans, 682
    as body defense mechanism, 899
    color of, melanocytes and, 946, 952
    color of, and polygenic inheritance, 263f
    role of, in thermoregulation, 835
    sensory receptors in human, 1048f
    ultraviolet damage to, 305f, 306
Skoog, Folke, 796
Skull, comparisons of human and chimpanzee, 484f, 494
Skunk (Spilogale sp.), 474f
Sleep
    biological clocks and human disorders in, 1030–31
    human brain and state of, 1029–30
Sleeping sickness, 401, 554f, 664
Sleep movements in plants, 805f
Sliding-filament model of muscle contraction, 1067f, 1068
Slime molds, 564–66
    cellular, 565–66
    plasmodial, 564–65
Slow block to polyspermy, 989
Slow muscle fibers, 1071, 1072t
Slugs (Gastropoda), 651–52
Small interfering RNA (siRNA), 327t, 368, 369f
Small intestine, 858–61
    absorption of nutrients in, 859–61
    enzymatic digestion in, 858–59
    structure of, 860f
    villi in, 859–60
Small nuclear ribonucleoproteins (snRNPs), role in RNA splicing, 318, 319f
Small nuclear RNA (snRNA), 318, 327t
Small nucleolar RNA (snoRNA), 327t
Small-population approach to conservation biology, 1215–18
    case study of greater prairie chicken, 1216
    case study of grizzly bear, 1217–18
    effective population size and, 1216–17
    extinction vortex and, 1215–16
    minimum viable population size and, 1216
Smallpox, 914
Small subunit ribosomal RNA (SSU-rRNA), 540
    origins of mitochondria and plastids, and, 524
Smell, human sense of, 1056, 1057f
    olfactory bulb, 1034, 1035f, 1057f
Smooth ER (endoplasmic reticulum), 104, 105f
    functions of, 104–5
Smooth muscle, 826f, 1072
Snails, 639f, 651–52
    Cuban tree, 454f
Snakes (Squamata), 690, 691f
    brown, as introduced species into Guam, 1213f
    bulk-feeding by, 845f

    energy budget in, 830, 831f
    fangs, 862
    garter (Thamnophis), 474f, 1118, 1119f
    infrared receptors in, 1049f
    poisonous, 690
    predation by, 1161–62
    python, 830, 831f, 845f
    scientific inquiry into mimicry in populations of, 21–24
snoRNA (small nucleolar RNA), 327t
Snowball Earth hypothesis, 526
SnRNA (small nuclear RNA), 318, 327t
SnRNPs (small nuclear ribonucleoproteins), 318, 319f
Snyder, Solomon, 1025
Social behavior, 1128–33
    altruistic, and inclusive fitness, 1128–31
    competitive, 1160–61
    cooperative, 1164
    evolution, human culture and, 1132–33
    mating, 1123–28
    social learning and, 1131–32
Social environment, aggressive behavior and influence of, 1114
Social learning, 1131–32
    of alarm calls, 1131–32
    mate choice copying, 1131f
Sociobiology, 1132–33. See also Social behavior
Sociobiology: The New Synthesis (Wilson), 1132
Sodium (Na+)
    ligand-gated channels and, 1022f
    selective permeability of neuron membrane to, 1017f
    voltage-gated channels for, 1018, 1019f, 1020f, 1021
Sodium chloride (NaCl), 33f. See also Salt(s)
    dissolving, in water, 51f
    ionic bonds in crystals of, 41f
Sodium hydroxide (NaOH), 54
Sodium-potassium pump, 134
    active transport by way of, 134, 135f
    neuron resting potential and, 1016–17
Soil, 759–63
    as abiotic factor, 1087
    agricultural impact on, 1200f
    ammonifying bacteria in, 763f, 764
    availability of water and minerals in, 761f
    erosion of, 762
    fertilizers for, 761–62
    horizons, 760f
    irrigation of, 762
    nitrogen fixation by bacteria in, 764–66
    pH of, 762
    reclamation of, 763
    saline, 762, 811
    sustainable agriculture and conservation of, 761–63
    texture and composition of, 759–60
    topsoil and humus in, 759–60
Soil conservation, 761–63
Sokolowski, Marla, 1120
Solar radiation. See Sunlight
Solute, 51
    active transport of, 134–36
    concentration of, in aqueous solutions, 52–53
    concentration of, and water conservation in mammalians, 935–36
    cotransport of, 136, 740f
    diffusion of, 131f
    osmoregulation and balance of water and, 922–27
    passive transport of, across membranes, 130–34
    pressure and concentration of, effects on water potential, 740–41
    proton pumps and transport of, 739f
    transport of, in plant cells, 740f
Solute potential (ψ_s), 741
Solution, 51
    hyperosmotic and hypoosmotic, 923
    hypertonic, hypotonic, and isotonic, 132, 133f
    isoosmotic, 923, 936
    pH of select aqueous, 54f, 55

Solvent, 51
    water as most significant, 51–53
Somatic cells, chromosomal number in, 219, 240
    division of (see Cell division)
    totipotency in differentiated, 415f
Somatic nervous system, 1026
Somites, 674, 998
Sonar, 1045
Songbirds. See Bird songs
Song sparrow
    immigration and populations of, on Mandarte Island, 1151f
    logistic model of population growth applied to, 1146, 1147f
    resource competition and population of, 1149f
Sonic hedgehog growth factor, 1008
Soredia, 621
Sori, 586
Sound, volume and pitch, 1052
Sound detection, mammalian, 1050–52
South Africa
    elephant populations in Kruger National Park, 1144f
    Succulent Karoo restoration project in, 1228f
Southern blotting, restriction fragment analysis using, 394, 395f, 405
Soybeans, bacteroids and nitrogen fixation in, 765f
Spatial heterogeneity, 1086
Spatial learning, 1115–16
Spatial summation, 1023
Specialized transduction, 349
Speciation, 472–90
    adaptive radiation and, 480–81
    allopatric, 476f, 477, 480
    biological diversity linked to, 472
    biological species concept and, 473–76
    continental drift and, 528
    genetics and, 481
    macroevolution and, 472, 482–88
    patterns of evolutionary change and (anagenesis and cladogenesis), 472f
    sympatric, 476f, 478–80
    tempo of, two models, 481–82f
Species, 12, 473
    benefits of diversity in, to human welfare, 1211–12
    biodiversity crisis and loss of, 1165–66
    biological species concept, 473–76
    biome composition of, 1099
    classifying (see Taxonomy)
    in communities (see Community (communities))
    comparing genomes of, 399t, 400–402
    conservation of (see Conservation biology)
    distribution of, 1083–92
    diversity of (see Biodiversity)
    dominant, 1168
    endangered and threatened, 1210–11
    endemic, 450
    extinctions of (see Extinction of species)
    introduced (exotic), 1213–14
    invasive, 1168
    keystone, 1168f, 1169f
    morphological concept of, 476
    origin of new (see Speciation)
    paleontological concept of, 476
    phylogenetic concept of, 476
    populations of (see Populations)
    range of, 1081f, 1084, 1085f
    reproductive barriers separating, 474–75f
    richness and relative abundance of, 1165, 1176–78
    sibling, 476
    as transplants, 1084–85
Species-area curve, 1176, 1177f
Species diversity, 1165–66, 1210–11. See also Biodiversity
Species richness, 1165. See also Biodiversity
    area effects on, 1176–77
    energy, water, and, 1176f
    equatorial-polar gradients of, 1176
    on islands, 1177–78
Species selection, 486

Specific epithet (taxonomy), **496**
Specific heat, **49**
Spectrophotometer, **186**
  determining absorption spectra with, 187*f*
Spectrum of dominance of alleles, 260–62
Speech, human brain, language, and, 706, 1011*f*, 1034*f*
Spemann, Hans, 1005, 1006
Spemann's organizer, 1006
Sperm, **964**
  development of human, 973, 975*f*
  fertilization of ovum by, 988–91
  flagellated plant and charophycean, **574**
  flagellate motion in, 115*f*
  plant, 592, 593*f*
Spermatheca, **968**
Spermatogenesis, **973**
Spermatogonia, **975**
Sphagnum moss, 511, 577*f*, 583*f*
S phase of cell cycle, **221***f*, 228
Sphincters
  digestive tract, **855**
  pyloric, 855*f*, 858
  precapillary, 877, 878*f*
Sphinx moth (*Xanthopan morgani*), 820*f*
Sphygomanometer, 877*f*
Spider monkeys, 700*f*
Spiders, 658–59
  anatomy, 659*f*
  feeding and aggressive behavior in funnel web, 1119*f*, 1120
Spider silk, 82*f*, 658–59
Spiderwort (*Tradescantia*) leaf, 725*f*
Spike moss, 586, 587*f*
Spinal cord, 1026*f*
Spinal nerves, **1026**
Spindle poles, 221
Spines, 498, 716*f*
Spiral cleavage, 631–32
Spiral-shaped prokaryotes, 535*f*
Spiral valve, **681**
Spines, 498, 716*f*
Spirochetes (bacteria), 543*f*
Spirogyra, 550*f*, 569
Spliceosome, **318**, 319*f*
Sponges (Porifera), 633, 639*f*, 642–43, 903
  anatomy, 642*f*
  food digestion in, 853
  origins of, 526–27
Spongocoel, **642**
Spongy mesophyll, **724**
Spontaneous change, free energy and, 146*f*
Spontaneous mutations, 329
Sporangium (sporangia), **577**, 774
  in fungi, 614, 615*f*
  walled spores produced in, 577*f*
Spores, **242**, **576**
  fossilized plant, 578*f*
  homosporous, and heterosporous, 586
  of plants, 576, 577*f*
Sporocytes, **577**
Sporophylls, **586**
Sporophyte, **242**, **576**
  in bryophytes, 580, 581*f*
  as diploid stage in life cycle, 242
  fossilized, 578*f*
  relationship of gametophyte to, 592*f*, 772
  in seedless vascular plants, 584, 585*f*
  in seed plants (angiosperms), 592, 592*f*, 593*f*, 771, 772*f*
  self-incompatibility in, 776
Sporopollenin, **574**, 557*f*
Sporozoites, **555**
Squamous epithelial cells, **823**, 824*f*
Squids, 639*f*, 652, 653*f*
  nervous system, 1012*f*
Squirrels
  allopatric speciation of antelope, 477*f*
  hibernation of Belding's ground, 840*f*
  immigration of Belding's ground, 1138, 1151

flying, 450
  influence of light on biological clocks of, 1030, 1031*f*
  life table of Belding's ground, 1139*t*
  reproductive table for Belding's, 1141*t*
  survivorship curve for Belding's, 1140*f*
SSU-rRNA sequences, 524, 540
Stability, relationship of free energy to, 145, 146*f*
Stabilizing selection, 465*f*, **466**
Staghorn fern (*Platycerium*), 768*f*
Stahl, Franklin, models of DNA replication by M. Meselson and, 299–300
Stalk-eyed flies, mate selection in, 1125, 1126*f*
Stamens, flower, 429*f*, 430, **598**, **772**
Standard metabolic rate (SMR), **829**
Standing crop biomass, 1187, 1194*f*
  pyramid of, 1193*f*
Stanley, Steven, 486
Stanley, Wendell, 335
Stapes, **1051**
Staphylococcus sp., 543*f*
Star anise (*Illicium floridanum*), 602*f*
Starch, **71**
  amylose and amylopectin forms of, 71
  storage of, in plants, 71, 72*f*
  structure of, compared to cellulose, 73*f*
Starlings as introduced species, 1214
Start (initiation) codon, 313, 314*f*
Statocysts, **1050***f*
Statoliths, **809**, **1050**
Stebbins, G. Ledyard, 455
Stele, plant tissue, **717**, 722
Stem, plant, **715**
  gibberellins and elongation of, 309, 797
  modified, 715*f*
  primary growth in, 723–24, 726*f*
  secondary growth in, 725–28
  terminal, 715
  tissue organization of, 724*f*
Stem cells, **418**, **881–82**
  embryonic, 418*f*, *1039*
  neural, 1038–39
  pluripotent, 418
  replacement of blood cellular elements and, 881*f*, 882
  therapeutic cloning and, 418
Stenohaline animals, **923**
Stentor, 550*f*
Steroid hormones, 77
  anabolic, 959*f*
  intracellular receptors and, 205*f*, 947
Steroids, **77**
Stethoscope, 877*f*
Stickle-back fish
  sign stimuli in fixed action pattern in, 1108*f*
  spatial learning and use of landmarks by, 1115–16
  territorial behavior in, 1108*f*
Sticky ends, DNA, 386*f*
Stigma, flower, **598**, **772**
Stingray, southern (*Dasyatis americana*), 681*f*
Stipe, **560**, 561*f*
Stock, plant, **782**
Stolons, 715*f*
Stomach, **857–58**
  defenses of, 899
  evolutionary adaptations of, 863*f*
  interior surface of, 857*f*
  secretion of gastric juice in, 857
  tissue layers of, 827*f*
  ulcers in, 858*f*
Stomata (stoma), **182**, 183*f*, **581**, **724**
  evolution of, 581, 583
  guard cells and opening/closing of, 750*f*, 751
  rate of transpiration regulated by, 749–51
Stop codon, 313, 314*f*, 324
Storage leaves, 716*f*
Storage polysaccharides, 71, 72*f*
Storage roots, 714*f*

Stramenopiles, 558–62
  brown algae, 560–62
  diatoms, 559–60
  flagella, 558*f*
  golden algae, 560
  oomycetes, 558, 559*f*
"Strangling" aerial roots, 714*f*
Stratified epithelium, **823**, 824*f*
Strawberry, guttation in leaf of, 746*f*
Streams and rivers, **1095***f*
  restoration projects in, 1227*f*, 1228*f*
Streptococcus sp., 543*f*, 643
  capsule of, 536*f*
  pneumoniae, genetic transformation of, by DNA, 295*f*, 348
Streptomycin, 322
Streptophyta (kingdom), 575*f*
Stress
  adrenal gland secretions as response to, 957*f*
  effects of, on immune system, 918
  plant response to environmental, 799–800, 811
Stress-induced proteins, **840**
Stretch-gated ion channels, **1017**
Stretch receptors, 1047*f*
Striated muscle, 826*f*
Strobili, **586**
Stroke, **883**
Stroke volume, heart, **873**
Stroma, **110**, 111*f*, **182**, 183*f*, 185*f*
Stromatolites, **521**, 522*f*
Structural formula, **40**
Structural isomers, *62f*
Structural polysaccharides, 72–74. *See also* Cellulose; Chitin
Structure and function, biological organization and correlation of, 27*f*
Strychonos toxifera, 1163
Sturna magna (eastern meadowlark), 473*f*
Sturnella neglecta (western meadowlark), 473*f*
Sturtevant, Alfred H., 279–81
Style, flower, **598**, **772**
Subatomic particles, 34
Suberin, 728
Submucosa tissue layer, of stomach, 827*f*
Substance P, **1025**
Substitutions, point mutations and nucleotide base-pair, 328, 329*f*
Substrate, 81, **152**
  catalysis in active site of enzyme and, 152–54
  induced fit of enzyme and, 153*f*
Substrate feeders, 845*f*
Substrate-level phosphorylation, **165***f*
Sucrase, 152
  hydrolysis of sucrose by, 150, 151*f*
Sucrose
  dehydration synthesis of, 70, 71*f*
  hydrolysis of, by enzyme sucrase, 150, 151*f*
  loading/unloading of, in plant phloem, 752*f*
  molecular mass of, 52
Sugars
  as component of nucleic acids, 87*f*, 88
  conduction of, in phloem tissue, 719*f*, 752
  conversion of carbon dioxide to, in Calvin cycle, 193–95
  disaccharides, 70, 71*f*
  monosaccharides, 70*f* (*see also* Glucose)
  polysaccharides, 71–74
Sugar glider, 450
Sugar sink, **752**
Sugar source, **752**
Sulfhydryl functional group, 65*f*
Sulfolbus archaea, 541
Sulfur dioxide emissions, 1202
Sulston, John E., 429
Summation of muscle cell contractions, 1071*f*
Summation of postsynaptic potential, temporal and spatial, 1023
Sundews (*Drosera*), 768*f*
Sunflower inflorescence, 773*f*

Sunlight
    as abiotic factor, 1087
    characteristics of, 186
    Earth latitudes and, 1088f
    global energy budget and, 1186–87
    as limiting factor in ecosystems, 1188
    plant response to (see Light, plant responses to)
Suprachiasmatic nuclei (SCN), 959, **1030**
Surface tension, **49**
Surface-to-volume ratio
    animal body structure and, 821–22
    of cells, 99f
Survivorship curves, **1139–40**
    idealized, 1140f
Suspension feeders, **642**, **681**, **845**f
Sustainable agriculture, 761, **762**, 763
Sustainable Biosphere Initiative, 1229
Sustainable development, **1229–30**
Sutherland, Earl W., 203
Sutton, Walter S., 274
Swallowing reflex, 856f
Swaziland, traditional and modern medicine in, 30–31
Sweat glands
    as immune response, 899
    thermoregulation and, 837
    X-chromosome mutation and, 284
Sweden, demographic transition in, 1153f
Sweet taste, sensory transduction for reception of,
        1056f
Swim bladder, **682**
Swimming, 1073
    body shape and fast, 821f
    energy cost of, 1074f
Symbion pandora (Cycliophoran), 641f
Symbiont, **545**
Symbiosis, **545**
    between algae and fungus (lichens), 621f
    between animals and fungus, 620
    commensalism as, 545
    herbivores and bacteria, 863–64
    mutualism as, 1164
    parasitism as, 1163
    between plant roots and fungi, 620
    between protozoan and bacteria, 525f
Sympathetic division of autonomic nervous system,
        1027f
    adrenal gland regulation by, 957
Sympatric speciation, **478–80**
Symplast, **743**
Synapses, **1014**
    chemical, 1021, 1022f, 1023–25
    electrical, 1021
    between rod cells and bipolar cells, 1061f
Synapsids, **694**
Synapsis, **247**
Synaptic cleft, **1022**
Synaptic signaling, 203f
Synaptic terminals, **1014**, 1021f
Synaptic vesicles, **1021**
    neurotransmitters in, 1021 (see also
        Neurotransmitters)
Synaptonemal complex, 247
α-Synuclein, 1041
Syphilis (*Treponema pallidum*), 543f
System(s), **9–12**
    emergent properties of, 9
    feedback regulation in biological systems, 11–12
    power and limitations of reductionism in, 9–10
    systems biology, 10–11, 400
Systematics, **491**
    animal phylogeny and, 633–36
    classification and phylogenetic, 495–97
    evolutionary history in genomes and, 504–6
    molecular, 491, 502–3f
    molecular clocks and, 506–7
    phylogenetic trees and, 496, 497–504 (see also
        Phylogenetic trees)
    taxonomy, classification, and, 529–32 (see also
        Taxonomy)

Systemic acquired resistance (SAR), 814, 815f
Systemic circuit, **871**
Systemic lupus erythematosus (lupus), 917
Systems biology, 10–11, 400
    feedback regulation in, 11–12
    plant hormones and, 801–2
    plant morphogenesis and, 729
Systole, cardiac cycle, **872**
Systolic pressure, **876**

T2 phage, infection of E. coli by, 294, 295f
T4 phage
    infection of E. coli by, 334f
    lytic cycle of, 338f
    structure, 336f
Table salt. See Sodium chloride (NaCL)
Table sugar. See Sucrose
Tadpole, frog, 686f
Taiga, 1102
Tail, muscular and postanal, in chordates, 673f
Tapeworms, 639f, 646t
    anatomy, 648f
Taproot system, **713**
Tardigrades (water bears), 641f
    anhydrobiosis in, 925
Tardive dyskinesia, 1040
Taste, receptors for, 1054–56
    in insects, 1055f
Taste buds, **1055**
TATA box, **316**, 364
Tatum, Edward, one gene–one enzyme hypothesis of
        G. Beadle and, 310, 311f
Taxis, 536–37, **1110**
Taxon (taxonomy), **496**
Taxonomy, **439**, **495**. See also Systematics
    of animals, 13f
    binomial nomenclature of, 496
    connection between phylogeny and classification
        of, 496–97
    continuing development of, 531–32
    domains, 13, 14f
    hierarchical classification system of, 496f
    Linnaeus on, 439, 495
    older systems of, 529–30
    of plants, 578t
    of seedless vascular plants, 586, 587f, 588
    three-domain system, 14f, 530–31f, 532
Tay-Sachs disease, **261**
    dominant allele, phenotype, and, 261
    as recessive trait, 266
T cell receptors, **904**
    for antigens, and role of MHC, 904, 905f
T cells. See T lymphocytes (T cells)
Technology, **25–26**. See also DNA technology
    ethics and, 26
    high-throughput, 11
    human carrying capacity and, 1156
Teeth
    biofilm on surface of, 539f, 540
    mammalian, 694
    origins of, 679
Telencephalon, 1028
Telomerase, **307**, 373
Telomeres, 306f, 307
Telophase
    meiosis, 245f
    mitosis, 221, 223f, 226f
Temperate broadleaf forest, **1103**
Temperate grasslands, 1102f
Temperate phage, **338**, 349
Temperature, **49**
    as abiotic factor, 1086
    cold, and plant flowering, 807
    enzyme activity, and effects of, 154f
    maintenance of body (see Thermoregulation)
    membrane fluidity responsive to, 126f
    moderating effect of water on, 49–50
    negative feedback and control of, 832f
    plant responses to excessive, 195–97, 749

Template strand, DNA, **313**
Temporal heterogeneity, 1086
Temporal isolation as prezygotic reproductive barrier,
        474f
Temporal summation, **1023**
Tendons, 825f
Tendrils, 716f
Terminal bud, **715**
Termination
    of transcription, 317
    of translation, 324, 325f
Terminator DNA sequence, **315**f
Terrestrial biomes, 1098–1104
    chaparral, 1101f
    climate and, 1098
    coniferous forest, 1102f
    desert, 1100f
    distribution of major, 1099f
    general features of, 1098–99
    savanna, 1101f
    temperate broadleaf forest, 1103f
    temperate grassland, 1102f
    tropical forest, 1100f
    tundra, 1103f
Terrestrial ecosystems
    food chain in, 1166f
    primary productivity of, 1187f, 1190–91
Territoriality, **1138**
    chemical markers of territories, 1149
    in fish, 1107f, 1108f
    population regulation and, 1149
Tertiary consumers, **1185**
Tertiary structure of protein, 81, **83**f
Tessier-Lavigne, Marc, 1037–38
Testcross, **256**f
Testes, 241, **971**
    hormonal control of, 978f
    hormone synthesis by, 958
Testosterone, 63f, **958**
    as chemical messenger, 205
Tetanus, muscle, **1071**
Tetany, 954
Tetracycline, 322, 537
Tetrad, chromatid, **247**
Tetrahymena, 318
Tetraploidy, 285, 286f
Tetrapods, **684–86**
    amniotic egg in, 687–94
    amphibians, 685–86
    derived characters of, 684
    homologies among, 449
    humans as, 701–7
    limb evolution in, 485f
    mammals, 694–701
    origin of, 527, 684, 685f
    origin of lungs in, 682
    reptiles, 688–94
Tetravalence, 60
Thalamus, **1030**, 1032
Thallus, **560**, 561f
Theory, scientific, **24**
Therapeutic cloning, 418
Thermal energy, **142**. See also Heat
Thermocline, 1091f, **1093**
Thermodynamics, energy transformations and laws
        of, 143–44
Thermogenesis, 838
Thermophiles, extreme, 534f, 541
Thermoreceptors, **1049**
    in skin, 1048f
Thermoregulation, **833–41**
    acclimatization and, 839
    adjustment to changing temperatures, 839–40
    adjustment to metabolic heat production, 838
    in amphibians and reptiles, 835f
    balancing heat loss and gain, 834–38
    behavior responses for, 837–38A
    circulatory adaptations for, 835, 836f, 837f
    ectothermic, 829, 833–34

endothermic, 829, 833–34
evaporative cooling and, 50, 837
feedback mechanisms in, 838–39
in fishes, 834f, 837f
in humans, 839f
insulation as adaptation for, 834
in invertebrates, 833–34, 836, 837f, 838f, 839f
in mammals and birds, 834f, 836f, 837f
modes of heat exchange and, 834, 835f
thermoreceptors and, 1048f, 1049
torpor and energy conservation, 840–41
Theropods, **689**
flight and, 692–93
Thick filaments, myofilaments, **1066**, 1067f
Thigmomorphogenesis, **809**
Thigmotropism, **810**
Thimann, Kenneth, 793
Thin filaments, myofilaments, **1066**, 1067f
Thiols, 65f
Thiomargarita namibiensis, 434
Third World Organization for Women in Science
    (TWOWS), 31
Thoracic cavity, **827**
Thorny-headed worms (acanthocephalans), 640f
Threatened species, **1210–11**
Three-domain system of taxonomy, 14f, 530f, **531**,
    532
Threshold, **1018**
Thrombus, **882**, 883
Thrum flower type, 775f
Thylakoids, **110**, 111f, **182**, 183f
    light reactions in, 184, 185f, 193f
    photosystems as light-harvesting complexes in,
        189–90
    in prokaryotes, 537f
Thylakoid space, 182, 183f
Thymine (T), 88
    DNA structure and, 296f, 297f, 298f
    repair of DNA damage from dimers of, 306
Thyroid gland, **953**
    hormones secreted by, 949t, 953–54
    iodine deficiency and, 33f, 34, 954
Thyroid-stimulating hormone (TSH), **952**, 953f
Thyroxine (T₄), 947, **953**
Tidal volume, breathing, **889**
Tight junctions, 120, **121f**, 627
Tilapia (*Tilapia mossambica*), 923f
Tilman, David, 1149
Time, using molecular clocks to measure absolute,
    506–7
Tinbergen, Niko
    questions on behavior formulated by, 1107
    on spatial learning in digger wasps, 1115
Ti plasmid, **406**, 407f
Tissue, 5f, **712**, **823**
    connective, 823, 825f
    epithelial, 823, 824f
    muscle, 823, 826f
    nervous, 823, 826f
Tissue plasminogen activator (TPA), 380, 404
Tissues, animal
    body plan and organization of, 630–31
    connective, 823, 825f
    embryonic, 994–97
    epithelial, 823
    grafts/transplants of, and immune response, 916
    muscle, 1066–72 (see also Muscles)
    nervous, 823 (see also Neurons)
    organ systems and, 827
Tissue-specific proteins, 419
Tissue systems, plant, **717f**
    in stems, 724f
    transport in, 717 (see also Vascular tissue system)
Tit-for-tat strategy, reciprocal altruism and, 1130–31
T lymphocytes (T cells), 881, **903**
    development of, 905f
    as receptors for antigens, and role of MHC, 904–5
Tobacco mosaic disease (TMV), 334, 335f
    structure, 336f

Tobacco plant, firefly gene and light energy in, 314f
Tomato, *aurea* mutant, and greening of, 789
Tongue, taste receptors on, 1056
Tonicity, **132**
Tonoplast, **108**, 743
Toolson, Eric, 1114
Tool use, human evolution and, 704
Top-down model of community structure, **1170**, 1171f
Topoisomerase, **303**, 304t
Topsoil, **759**
Torpor, **840–41**
Torsion in gastropods, **651**
Totipotency
    in animal cells, 1005
    in plant cells, **415**
Totipotent zygote, **1005**
Touch
    detection of, by mechanoreceptors, 1048
    turgor movements in plants in response to, 810f
Toxic substances
    as human-caused environmental problem, 1202–3
    as population-limiting factor, 1150
Toxins. *See also* Poison(s)
    bacterial (prokaryotes), 339, 535
    biological magnification of, 1202–3
    botulism, 1069
    as defense against predation, 1163
    from dinoflagellates, 555
    enzyme inhibitors as, 155
    in food webs, 1202f
    fungal, 622
    G proteins modified by, 211
    phytoremediation of, 763
Trace elements, **33**
Trachea (windpipe), **887**, 899f
Tracheal systems, insect, **886**, 887f
Tracheids, **584**, 719f, 727
    water conduction by, 719, 746
Trait, genetic, **252**. *See also* Character, genetic
    dominant, 253, 265f
    pedigrees for tracing, 265–66
    recessive, 253, 265f, 283–84
Transacetylase, 355f
Transcription, **311**, 315–17
    activator of, 356
    basic principles of, 311–12f
    cell-type specific, 367f
    initiation of, and regulation of eukaryotic gene ex-
        pression, 364–67
    initiation of, RNA polymerase binding and, 316f
    modification of RNA after, in eukaryotic cells,
        317–19
    molecular components of, 315–16
    of operon genes, 353, 354f
    post-transcriptional gene regulation, 368–70
    in prokaryotic versus eukaryotic cells, 312f, 537
    regulation of eukaryotic gene expression at, 362–70
    regulation of gene expression during development
        at, 418–20
    RNA strand elongation, 315f, 316
    synthesis of RNA transcript, 316–17
    stages of, 315f
    summary of, in eukaryotic cell, 331f
    termination of, 317
Transcription factors, **316**, **364**
    cell response to cell signaling and, 205, 213
    Dlx gene family as, 678
    general, 364
    role of, in control of eukaryotic gene expression,
        316f, 364–66
    specific, and enhancers, 364, 365f
Transcription initiation complex, **316f**
Transcription unit, **315**
Transduction (signal-transduction pathway), 204,
    208–12. *See also* Signal transduction
    in animals, sensory reception, 1046
    in plants, 789–90
    protein phosphorylation and dephosporylation in,
        209f, 210

signal-transduction pathways in, 208
    small molecules and ions as second messengers
        in, 210–12
Transduction in bacteria, 348f–49
Transfer cells, **752**
Transfer RNA (tRNA), **320**, 327t
    binding of specific amino acid to, 321f
    structure and function of, 320, 321f. 322
Transformation
    cancerous, **232**
    genetic, of bacteria, **294**, **348**
Transgenes, 406
    plants, 784–86
Transgenic animal, **406**
Transgenic plant, 406–7f, **782**, 783, 784–86
Transition state, activation of chemical reactions and,
    151
Transitional endoplasmic reticulum, 105
Transitional fossil, 451f
Translation, **311**, 320–26
    basic principles of, 311–12f, 320f
    initiation of, 323f
    initiation of, regulation of eukaryotic gene expres-
        sion at, 369
    molecular components of, 320–23
    polypeptide synthesis in, 323–24
    polyribosomes formed during, 324, 325f
    in prokaryotes versus eukaryotes, 312f, 537
    ribosome function in, 322f, 323
    role of aminoacyl-tRNA synthetase in joining
        tRNA to amino acid during, 321f
    summary of, in eukaryotic cell, 331f
    targeting polypeptides to specific locations, 325–26f
    termination of, 324, 325f
    transfer RNA (tRNA) structure and function in,
        320, 321f, 322
    transformation of polypeptides to functional pro-
        teins following, 324, 325
Translocation
    chromosomal, **286f**, 287, 288f
    of phloem sap, **752**, 751–53
Transmembrane proteins, structure of, 128f
Transmission of sensory receptor potential, 1046–47
Transmission electron microscope (TEM), **96f**
Transpiration, **746**
    ascent of xylem sap dependent on, 747f
    effects of, on wilting and leaf temperature, 749
    stomata and regulation of, 749f, 750f–51
    xerophyte adaptations for reducing, 751
Transpirational pull, 747f
Transpiration-cohesion-tension mechanism, 746–48
Transplanted species, 1084–85
Transplants, tissue and organ, 916
Transport across membranes, 126–27
Transport epithelium
    kidney nephron and role of, 933f
    osmoregulation and, **926**
    salt excretion in marine birds and, 926f, 927
Transport in animals. *See* Circulatory system
Transport in vascular plants, 584, 738–58. *See also*
    Plant nutrition
    absorption of water and nutrients through roots
        as, 744–46
    aquaporins and water, 742
    ascension of water and minerals through xylem,
        746–49
    bulk flow functions in long-distance, 743–44
    overview of, 739f
    physical forces driving, 48f, 738–44
    proton pumps, role of, 739–40
    plant cell compartments and short-distance, 743f
    stomata and regulation of transpiration rates,
        749–51
    symplast and apoplast function in, 743
    translocation of nutrients through phloem, 751–53
    water potential differences and, 740–42
Transport proteins, 78t, **130**, 739
    carrier proteins as, 130, 134f
    channel proteins as, 130, 134f

cotransporter as, 136f
 as electrogenic pump and proton pump, 136f
 facilitated diffusion and role of, 133, 134f
 mechanical work in cells and, 149f
 role of, in membranes, 128f, 130
 role of, in plant transport, 739, 740f
Transport vesicles, 105, 107
Transport work, cellular, 148
 driven by ATP, 149f
Transposable elements, 351–52, 371, 375–76
 genome evolution and, 380–81
 insertion sequences as, 351, 352f
 movement of eukaryotic, 376f
 repetitive DNA as, 375, 376–77
 sequences related to, 376
 transposons as, 343, 352, 375–76)
Transposase, 351, 352f
Transposons, 343, 352, 375–76
 cut-and-paste method of copying, 376f
Transthyretin, 82, 83
Transverse (T) tubules, 1069
Tree(s). See also Forest ·
 American chestnut, 1168
 anatomy of trunk of, 727f
 aspen, 781f
 bonsai, 441f
 effect of climate change on American beech, 1092f
 effect of winds on, 1087f
 energy, water, and species richness of North
  American, 1176f
 individualist hypothesis of communities applied
  to, 1179f
 mutalism between ants and acacia, 1164f
 wood and, 605, 727
Tree of life, 17–19, 491, 507, 512–33. See also
  Biodiversity
 continuum of life on earth and, 512
 early Earth conditions and origins of life, 513–16
 evolution of prokaryotes and, 521–23
 fossil record as chronicle of life, 517–21
 homology and, 449, 450f
 new information and understanding of, 529–32
 origin of eukaryotes, 523–25
Trematodes (flukes), 646t, 647
 life cycle of blood fluke (Schistosoma), 647f
Triacylglycerol, 75
Tricarboxylic acid cycle, 168
Trichinella spiralis (trichinosis), 656f
Trichomonas vaginalis, 553f
Trichoplax adhaerens, 639f
Triglyceride, 75
Triiodothyronine (T₃), 953
Trilobites (Trilobita), 656, 657f
Trimesters of pregnancy, 978–81
Trimethylamine oxide (TMAO), 924
Triose sugars, 70f
Triple response of plants to mechanical stress, 799–80
Triplet code (DNA), 312
Triploblastic animals, 631
 body plans of, 631f
Triploidy, 285
Trisomic cells, 285
Trisomy 21, 287
Tristan da Cunha, 462
Trochophore, molluscs, 650
Trochophore larva, 635
Trophic cascade model, 1170
Trophic efficiency, ecological pyramids and, 1192,
  1193f
Trophic levels in ecosystems, 1185
 decomposition and, 1185–86
 energy transfer between, 1191–94
 food energy available to humans at different, 1193f
Trophic structure in communities, 1166–68
 bottom-up and top-down controls and, 1170–71
 food chains, 1166
 food chains, limits on length of, 1167–68
 food webs and, 1166–67
Trophoblast, 979, 982, 1000

Tropical forests, 1100f
 deforestation of, 1209f, 1212, 1221f
 productivity of, 1187
Tropic hormones, 951, 952
Tropisms, 792
 gravitropism, 809
 phototropism, 792–93, 803f
 thigmotropism, 810
Tropomyosin, 1068
Troponin complex, 1068
Trout
 anatomy of, 682f
 rainbow (Oncorhynchus mykiss), 939f
Trp operon, regulated synthesis of repressible enzymes
 and, 353, 354f
Truckee River, Nevada, restoration project in, 1227f
True-breeding plants, 252–53
Trumpeter swans, mating behaviors, 1124f
Trypanosoma (trypanosomes), 554f. See also Sleeping
  sickness
Tryptophan, 783
 genetic recombination of bacteria capable of
  synthesizing, 347f
 levels of, and gene expression in bacteria, 352–56
Tsetse fly (Glossina palpalis), 554
 genome, 401
Tuataras (Sphenodon punctatus), 690, 691f
Tubal ligation, 983
Tube cell, 599
Tube feet, echinoderms, 665
Tuberculosis (Mycobacterium tuberculosis), 545, 1149,
  1155
Tuber melanosporum, 616f
Tubers, 715f
Tulips, 491f, 501f
Tumor, 232–33. See also Cancer
Tumor-suppressor genes, 371
 faulty and development of cancer, 371, 373
Tumor viruses, 370
Tuna, 821f
 northern bluefin (Thunnus thynnus), 939f, 1214f
 thermoregulation in, 837f
 yellowfin (Thunnus albacares), 683f
Tundra, 1103f
Tunicates (Urochordata), 641f, 673, 674f
 fate map of cells in, 1004f
 larva, 674, 674f
Turbellarians (Turbellaria), 646–47
Turgid plant cell, 132, 742, 750f
Turgor movements in plants, 810f
Turgor pressure, 741
 opening/closing of stomata and, 750f
Turnover in lakes and ponds, 1091f
Turnover time, phytoplankton, 1192
Turtles, 690, 691f
Tympanic membrane
 human, 1051f
 insect, 1050f
Type I diabetes mellitus, 956
Type II diabetes mellitus, 956

Ubiquinone, 170
Ubiquitin, 370f
Ultimate causes of behavior, 1106, 1107, 1108f,
  1109f
Ultimate questions, 1107
Ultracentrifuge, 97
Ultrametric tree, 500f
Ultrasound imaging, fetal testing by, 269, 984f
Ultraviolet (UV) light
 atmospheric ozone depletion and increased, 1206
 as mutagen, 330
 skin damage caused by, 305f, 306
Ulva (sea lettuce), 568f, 569
Umami taste, 1055
Undernourishment, 846
Unequal reproductive success, natural selection and, 16
Unger, Christian, 252
Uniformitarianism, 440

Uniform pattern of population dispersion, 1138f
United States
 acid precipitation in, 55–56, 1202f
 age structure of population in, 1154f, 1155
 aquatic biomes in, 1094f, 1095f, 1096f
 populations of great-tailed grackles in, 1085f
 range of American beech tree in, 1092f
 terrestrial biomes in, 1100f, 1101f, 1102f, 1103f
Unity underlying life's diversity, 14, 15f
 as biological theme, 27f
Unsaturated fatty acid, 75–76
Uracil (U), 88
Urea, 59, 60–61, 928. See also Urine
 as nitrogenous waste, 927f, 928
Ureter, 931, 932f
Urethra, 931, 972
Urey, Harold, 513f, 514
Uric acid as nitrogenous waste, 927f, 928
Urinary bladder, 931
Urination, 936–37
Urine
 filtration of blood by kidneys and production of,
  931–34
 kidney concentration of (two-solute model), 935f
Urodeles. See Salamanders (Urodela)
Use and disuse idea, 441
Uterine cycle, 973
 hormonal regulation of, 976f, 977
Uterus, 959, 969
Utricle, 1052, 1053

V₁ₐ receptor, 1113
Vaccination, 914
Vaccines, 343
 DNA technology and production of, 404
Vacuolar membrane, 743
Vacuoles, 108
 contractile, 108
 food, 107, 108
 in plant cell, 108f, 743
Vagina, 970
Valence, atom, 40
Valence electrons, 38
Valence shell, 38
Vampire bat (Desmodus rotundas), 938f
Van der Waals interactions, 42
 in tertiary structure of proteins, 83f
Van Helmont, Jan Baptista, 756
Van Niel, C. B., 184
Van Overbeek, Johannes, 796
Vaporization, heat of, 50
Variable (V) regions, lymphocytes, 904
Variation, genetic, 238. See also Genetic variation
Vasa recta, 933, 936
Vascular bundles, 717
Vascular cambium, 720
 production of secondary vascular tissue by, 725–27
Vascular cylinder, 717
Vascular plants, 578t
 origin and traits of, 584–86
 seed (see Seed plants)
 seedless, 586–88
 structure of (see Plant structure)
 transport in, 738–58
Vascular tissue system, 578, 717
 phloem, 584, 717, 719, 722f, 751–53
 vascular cambium and secondary, 725–27
 xylem, 584, 717, 722f, 724f, 746–49
Vas deferens, 971
Vasectomy, 983
Vasocongestion, 972
Vasoconstriction, 835
Vasodilation, 835
Vectors. See Cloning vectors; Disease vectors
Vegetal plate, 995
Vegetal pole, 992
Vegetation, regulation of chemical cycling by, 1198,
  1199f
Vegetative reproduction in plants, 781–83

Veins, **715, 869**
  blood flow velocity, 875*f*
  countercurrent heat exchanger in, 836*f*
  structure and function of, 874, 875*f*
Velvet worms, 641*f*
Ventilation, **885**
Ventral side, body, **630**
Ventricles of brain, **1026*f***
Ventricles of heart, **869**
Venules, **869**, 874*f*
Venus flytrap (*Dionaea muscipula*), 768*f*, 810
Vernalization, **807**
Vertebrae, 671
Vertebrates, 629, **671**, 678–708
  amniotes and development of land-adapted egg, 687–94
  amphibians, 685–86
  apoptosis in, 428, 429*f*
  birds, 691–94
  bones and teeth in, origins of, 679
  brain (*see* Brain)
  circulatory and cardiovascular system of, 869–71
  chondrichthyans (sharks, rays), 680–82
  chordates and origin of, 671–77
  comparison of amino acid sequence in select, 449, 450*f*
  clade Deuterostomia and, 633
  craniates and development of head in, 675–77
  derived characteristics of, 678
  development in (*see* Animal development)
  digestive system, evolutionary adaptations of, 862–64
  endocrine system of, 943–59
  evapotranspiration and species richness of North American, 1176*f*
  fossils of early, 678, 679*f*
  gas exchange in, 886–95
  gnathostomes and development of jaws in, 679–84
  hagfishes, 676, 677*f*
  homologous structures in embryos of, 448, 449*f*
  hormone action in (*see* Hormones)
  Hox genes and evolution of, 486*f*
  humans as, 701–7 (*see also* Human(s))
  kidneys and excretory system of, 934–38
  lampreys, 678
  lancelets as, 674, 675*f*
  long-term potentiation in, 1036, 1037*f*
  mammals as, 694–701 (*see also* Mammals)
  nervous system of, 1012–13, 1020–21, 1026–41
  pattern formation during limb development in, 1006–8
  ray-finned and lobe-finned fishes, 682–84
  reproduction in (*see* Animal reproduction)
  reptiles, 688–94
  skeleton of, 1064, 1065*f*
  tetrapods and development of limbs and feet in, 684–86
  tunicates as, 673, 674*f*
  vision in, 1058–63
Vertical transmission of viruses in plants, 345
Vervet monkeys (*Cercopithecus aethiops*), social learning of alarm calls in, 1131, 1132*f*
Vesicles, **104**
  migration of, 112*f*
Vessel, **719**
Vessel elements, **719**, 727
  water conduction by, 719*f*, 746
Vestibule, **970**, 1053
Vestigial organs, **448**
Viagra (drug), 201, 211, 948, 1025
Villi in small intestine, **859**, 860*f*
Viral envelopes, **336*f***
  of animal viruses, 340, 341*f*
Viral neutralization, 913
Virchow, Rudolf, 218
Viridiplantae (Kingdom), 567, 575*f*
Viroids, 345–46
Virulent pathogens, **813**
Virulent phage, **338**

Viruses, 334–43
  in bacteria (*see* Bacteriophage (phage))
  cancer-causing, 370, 374
  capsids and envelopes of, 335–36
  classes of animal, 340*t*
  discovery of, 334–35
  emerging, 344
  evolution of, 342–43
  genome of, 335
  Hershey-Chase experiment on infection of *E. coli* by, 294, 295*f*, 296
  infection of bacteria by, 295*f*
  lytic and lysogenic cycles, 337, 338*f*, 339*f*
  as pathogens, 337, 343–45
  reproduction of, general features, 336, 337*f*
  reproductive cycle, 337–39
  reproductive cycle of animal viruses, 339–42
  size of, 335*f*
  structure of, 335–36*f*
  viroids and prions, 345–46
Visceral mass, mollusc, **650**
Visible light, **186**
Vision, 1057–63
  color, 1059–60, 1061
  geometric isomers and biochemistry of, 62
  in invertebrates, 1057–58
  neural pathways for, 1062*f*
  processing visual information, 1061–63
  sensory transduction in, 1060–61
  vertebrate eye and, 1058, 1059*f*, 1060
Vital capacity, **889**
Vitalism, 59
Vitamins, **850**
  essential nutritional requirements, 850, 851*t*
  vitamin D, **954**
Vitelline layer, 988
Vitreous humor, **1059**
Viviparous species, **682**, 689
Vocal chords, **887**
Vogt, W., 1004
Voltage, cell, 134–35
  membrane potential and, 1015–17
Voltage-gated ion channels, **1017**
  chemical synapse and, 1022*f*
  production/conduction of action potentials and role of, 1018, 1019*f*, 1020*f*, 1021
Volvox sp., 568*f*
Volume (loudness) of sound, 1052
Von Frisch, Karl, 1107
Von Humboldt, Alexander, 1176
Vulva, **970**

Wade, Michael, 1127
Wagler's pit viper (*Tropidolaemus wagleri*), 691
Walker, Brian, 1180
Wallace, Alfred, evolutionary theory of, 443, 1175
Water
  as abiotic factor, 1086
  availability of soil, to plants, 761*f*
  balance of (*see* Water balance)
  climate and effect of bodies of, 1087, 1090*f*
  cohesion and adhesion of, 48–49
  contaminated drinking, 552
  covalent bonds in, 40*f*
  freshwater biomes (*see* Freshwater biomes)
  human ecological footprint and overuse of, 1156
  hydrogen bonding and polarity of, 47–48
  hydrogen bonds of, 48*f*
  insulation of bodies of, by floating ice, 50, 51*f*
  as key to all life, 47
  marine biomes (*see* Marine biomes)
  molecular dissociation of, and acid/base conditions, 53–56
  molecular shape of, 43*f*
  as solvent of life, 51–53
  species richness, energy, and, 1176*f*
  specific heat of, 49–50
  splitting of, during photosynthesis, 183, 184*f*

temperature moderation by, 49–50
  transport of, in plants (*see* Transport in vascular plants)
Water balance, 131–33, 922–27
  in animals living in temporary waters, 925
  in cells with walls, 132, 133*f*
  in cells without walls, 132, 133*f*
  environment and adaptations for,
  in freshwater animals, 924–25
  in kangaroo rat versus in humans, 925*f*
  in land animals, 925–26
  in marine animals, 924, 926*f*
  osmoconformers and osmoregulators as response to challenge of, 923–26
  osmosis and, 131–33, 922–23
  transport epithelia and, 926–27
Water bears (tardigrades), 641*f*, 925
Water buffalo, commensalisms between cattle egrets and, 1164*f*
Water channel proteins, 93
Water conduction in plant tissues, 719*f*
Water conservation, 862
  in camels, 926*f*
  mammalian kidney as terrestrial adaptation, 934–38
Water cycle in ecosystems, 1196*f*
Water flea (*Daphnia* sp.), logistic population growth model applied to, 1146, 1147*f*
Water lily (*Nymphaea* "Rene Gerard"), 602*f*
Watermelon snow (*Chlamydomonas nivalis*), 568*f*
Water molds (Oomycotes), 558, 559*f*
Water pollution, acid precipitation and, 55–56
Water potential (ψ), **740–42**
  aquaporin proteins, water transport in plants, and, 742
  effect of solutes and pressure on, 740–41
  model of water movement and, 741*f*
  quantitative analysis of, 741–42
Water potential equation, 740
Water soluble hormones, cell-surface receptors for, 946
Water strider, 49*f*
Water vascular system, echinoderms, **665**
Watkinson, Andrew, 1148
Watson, James, 9
  on DNA replication, 299
  modeling of DNA structure by F. Crick and, 88–89, 293*f*
Wavelength of light, **186*f***
  photosynthetically important, 187*f*
  phototropism and, 803*f*
Weak chemical bonds, 42
Weapons, 546
Weberian apparatus, 1054
Weddell seal, circulatory and respiratory adaptions of, 894–95
Weight and mass, terms, 32 *n*.
Welwitschia mirabilis, 594*f*
Went, Frits, discovery of auxin by, 792, 793*f*
Wernicke, Karl, 1034
Wernicke's area, brain, 1034, 1035
West Nile virus, 337, 344, 1163
Wetlands, **1094*f***
  primary production in, 1190–91
Wexler, Nancy, 268*f*
Whales
  blubber, 835
  body plan of, 822
  electromagnetic reception in beluga, 1049*f*
  size of blue, 671
  suspension-feeding in, 845*f*
Wheat (*Triticum aestivum*), 478
Whiptail lizards (*Cnemidophorus uniparens*), 965, 966*f*
Whisk fern, 587*f*, 588
White blood cells (leukocytes), 825*f*, **880**, 881
  apoptosis and development of, 428*f*
  body's defense system and, 878, 900
  lymphocytes (*see* Lymphocytes)

lysosomes of, 107, 108
phagocytic, 900
White matter, nervous system, **1026**
White rot (*Phanerochaete chrysoporium*), 623
White rusts (oomycota), 558
Whittaker, Robert H., 529–30, 1179f
Whooping cranes, imprinting in, 1109f
Widow's peak as dominant trait, 265f
Wieschaus, Eric, 423
Wildlife
    effects of acid precipitation on, 686
    mark-recapture method of estimating population
        size of, 1137
Wild type phenotype, **276**f
    fruit fly eye color and, 276, 277f
Wilkins, Maurice, 296, 297
William of Occam, 501
Wilson, E. O.
    on biophilia, 1230
    on endangered species, 1211
    on island biogeography, 1177–78
    on sociobiology, 1132–33
Wilson's phalaropes, mating behavior in, 1124f
Wilt in plant leaves, **742**f
    effects of transpiration on, 749
Wind
    effect of, on trees, 1087f
    global patterns of, 1089f
Wings,
    bird, 692f
    insect, 661
Wisenden, Brian, 1116, 1117
Wiskott-Aldrich syndrome (WAS), 215
Witte, Klaudia, 1125
Wobble, base pair-rule relaxation, **322**
Woese, Carol, 525, 540–41
Wöhler, Friedrich, 59
Wolf, population dispersion patterns, 1138
Wollemia pine (*Wollemia nobilis*), 595f
Wood, 605
    heartwood and sapwood, 727
    production of, by vascular cambium, 727
Work
    ATP as energy source for cellular, 148–50
    equilibrium and, in closed and open systems, 147f

stability, spontaneous change, and capacity for, 146f
Worms
    acorn, 641f
    flatworms, 639f, 646–48, 968f
    marine, 640f
    proboscis/ribbon worms, 639f
    roundworms, 641f
    segmented (annelids), 640f (*see also* Earthworms)
    tapeworm, 639f, 646t, 648f
    thorny-headed, 640f
    velvet, 641f
Wright, Sewall, 455

X chromosome, 240, 282f
    fruit fly eye color and, 276, 277f
    inactivation of, in females, 284f
    sex-linked genes on, 282–84
Xerophytes, **751**
    reduction of transpiration in, 751f
X-O system of sex determination, 282f
X-ray crystallography, **85**, 86f
X-rays as mutagens, 329
X-Y system of sex determination, 282f
Xylem, **584**, **717**
    secondary (*see* Wood)
    in roots, 722f
    in stems, 724f
    transport in, 584, 746–49
    water conduction by vessel elements and
        tracheids of, 719f

Yarrow plants (*Achillea*), geographic variation and ge-
    netics in, 464f
Y chromosome, 240, 282f
    fruit fly eye color and, 276, 277f
    sex-linked genes on, 282–84
Yeast (*Saccharomyces cerevisiae*), 505–6, **611**
    alcohol and bread production and, 175, 623
    budding by, 611f
    cell signaling mechanisms in, 201, 202f
    gene cloning and, 390
    genome, 394, 400
    ingestion of, by macrophage, 898f
Yeast artificial chromosomes (YACs), **390**, 396
Yellow jacket wasp, 1162f

Yellowstone National Park, Wyoming
    archaea in hot springs of, 544
    fires in, 1172, 1173f
    grizzly bear populations in, 1217f, 1218, 1223f
    legal and biotic boundaries of, 1222, 1223f
    natural edges in ecosystem of, 1220f
Yolk, egg, **992**
Yolk plug, **995**
Yolk sac, **1000**

Zach, Reto, 1122
Zeatin, 796
Zeaxanthin, 802
Zebrafinches
    E. Jarvis on genetics of song in, 819
    mate selection in, 1125, 1226f
Zebrafish (*Danio rerio*)
    associative learning in, 1116, 1117f
    as model organism, 413f
Zero population growth (ZPG), **1144**
    age structure and, 1155
    demographic transition and, 1153–54
ZIFT (zygote intrafallopian transfer), 984
Z lines, **1066**, 1067f
Zona pellucida, **991**f
Zonation
    in lakes, 1093f
    in marine communities, 1093f
Zoned reserves, **1223**f, **1224**
Zone of cell division, plant, **722**
Zone of elongation, **722**
Zone of maturation, **722**
Zone of polarizing activity (ZPA), **1007**f
    limb pattern formation and role of, 1008f
Zoospores, 562, **613**f
Z-W system of sex determination, 282f
Zygomycetes (Zygomycota), 613–15
    life cycle, 614f
Zygosporangium, **614**, 615
Zygote, **241**, **964**
    animal, 627, 978–79, 987–1001
    cleavage in, 627f, 992–94 (*see also* Cleavage)
    human, 979f
    plant, 732f, 777–78
    totipotency of, 1005